EXCITING NEW FEATURES FOR 1995

MERRILL PHYSICAL SCIENCE

AN ACTIVE, REAL-LIFE APPROACH THAT CONNECTS SCIENCE TO THE EVERYDAY WORLD

An Educational Program from

GLENCOE

Students experience the principles of physical science each and every day. The simple act of walking involves gravity, which holds them to Earth, friction between the soles of their shoes and the ground, which enables them to overcome inertia, accelerate forward, make turns, and even stop. The new **Merrill Physical Science** makes students aware that everything they see, hear, touch, and smell involves physical science principles.

The **Merrill Physical Science** comprehensive learning and teaching program makes the study of physical science an **active learning experience.** Your students will learn through:

- **Solid concept development,** thematically structured to focus on the principle ideas of physical science.
- **Hands-on activities** that actively involve students in the subject matter.
- **Strong skill development** that leads to success in science and the real world.
- **Fascinating, real-world applictions** that will make the study of physical science come alive in your classroom.

As for teachers' classroom support, the new **Merrill Physical Science** provides a wealth of resource materials in the **Teacher Wraparound Edition** and **Teacher Classroom Resources.** Teaching suggestions, applications, extension activities, plus all new assessment options, and Mr. Wizard's **Science and Technology Videodisc Series** components provide you with all the valuable tools to help you enrich your program and reduce your preparation time.

STUDENTS LEARN BY OBSERVING, EXPERIMENTING, AND ASKING QUESTIONS

Understanding physical science is more than memorizing facts. It's learning to adapt the basic principles of physical science to everyday applications. The new **Merrill Physical Science** offers numerous activities that give students the chance to further explore and investigate the scientific topics covered in the textbook. This not only helps students relate physical science to their everyday world, it also helps to build skills that will make them responsible decision makers and critical thinkers.

New open-ended activities provide students with options to design their own experiments in every chapter.

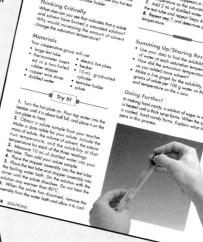

ACTIVITY 15-1 DESIGNING AN EXPERIMENT
Saturation Situation

Two major factors to consider when you are dissolving a solute in water are temperature and the ratio of solute to solvent.

Getting Started
In this activity you will find out at what temperature the saturation point is reached. **CAUTION:** Avoid touching hot materials. Handle any hot test tubes by using the testtube holder.

Thinking Critically
What clue can you see that indicates that a solute and solvent have formed a saturated solution? Why would increasing the amount of solute change the saturation temperature?

Materials
Your cooperative group will use:
- large test tube
- thermometer insert-
  ed in a two-holed
  rubber stopper
- copper wire stirrer
- distilled water
- electric hot plate
- beaker
- 10-ml graduated
  cylinder
- test-tube holder
- solute

Try It!

1. Turn the hot plate on. Pour tap water into the beaker until it is about half full, and place it on the hot plate to heat.
2. Obtain a solute sample from your teacher. Make a data table for your solute. Include the mass of solute, the volume of solvent, the saturation temperature, and the solubility at that temperature for each of the three readings.
3. Measure 10 ml of distilled water into your test tube. Then add your solute sample.
4. Place the stopper assembly into the test tube.
5. Place the test tube and stopper assembly into the boiling water bath. Stir the solution with the stirrer until the solute dissolves. Do not heat the solution any warmer than 80°C.
6. When the solute has dissolved, remove the assembly from the water bath and allow it to cool.

As soon as solute reappears in the solution, record the temperature as the saturation point.
7. Add 2 ml of distilled water to the solution in the test tube and repeat Steps 4-6.
8. Repeat step 7, and determine a third saturation temperature.

Summing Up/Sharing Results
- Use your data to find the solubility in 100 g of water at each saturation point.
- How did the saturation temperature change as you added more solvent?
- Make a line graph for the solubility, placing grams of solute per 100 g water on the y-axis and temperature on the x-axis.

Going Further!
In making hard candy, a solution of sugar in water is heated until a thick syrup forms. When the syrup is cooled, hard candy forms. Explain what happens in this process.

394 SOLUTIONS

Gearing Up
Previewing this Chapter
Use this outline to help you focus on important ideas in this chapter.

...e clothes you wear can make
...eel warmer or cooler. They
...t the amount of thermal ener-
...hat reaches and leaves your
...y. How else can the movement
...thermal energy be affected?

FIND OUT!
Do this simple activity to find out how you can affect the movement of thermal energy.
Turn on a lamp with a bare light bulb. *Being careful not to touch the bulb*, put your hand near it. Do you feel warmth from the bulb? How is thermal energy getting to your hand? What happens if you move your hand nearer to the bulb or farther away? What happens if you put a book between your hand and the lamp? Suppose you use only a piece of paper instead of a whole book. Find some other things that you can put between your hand and the light bulb. Do some seem to block heat better than others? Feel the objects after they've been near the light bulb. Do some feel warmer than others? How can you explain the differences?

Section 6-1 Moving Thermal Energy
  ▶ Conduction
  ▶ Convection
  ▶ Radiation
  ▶ Reducing Movement of Thermal Energy
Section 6-2 Heating Systems
  ▶ Conventional Heating Systems
  ▶ Solar Heating
Section 6-3 Science and Society
Thermal Pollution
  ▶ Not So Hot!
Section 6-4 Using Heat to Do Work
  ▶ Heat Engines
  ▶ Heat Movers

Previewing Science Skills
- In the Skill Builders, you will use variables, constants, and controls, make and use tables, and map concepts.
- In the Activities, you will observe, collect and organize data, sequence, analyze, and infer.
- In the MINI-Lab, you will observe and hypothesize.

What's next?
You have discovered that you can exert some control over the movement of thermal energy. Now you will learn about how thermal energy moves and how that movement can be put to useful purposes.

132

133

MINI-Lab
How can a graph help you observe change?
Place a thermometer in a plastic foam cup of hot water. Measure and record the temperature every 30 seconds for 5 minutes. Make a line graph of the changing temperature showing time on the x-axis and temperature on the y-axis. Repeat the experiment, starting with freshly heated water. This time, cover the cup with a plastic lid. Plot the curve on the same grid as before. List all the information this graph tells you about the two cups.

Chapter Openers offer fun, interesting ways to get your students excited about the upcoming lessons.
- A unique **Find Out** activity entices students to make observations and raise questions about upcoming content.
- **Gearing Up** previews key concepts and skills.
- **What's Next** provides an intriguing transition into the chapter's main ideas.

Mini-Labs are quick hands-on activities that give your students additional opportunities to practice important process skills. Great for in-class instruction or take-home exercises.

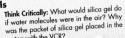

PROBLEM SOLVING

The Packet of Mystery Crystals

When a new video cassette recorder (VCR) was delivered to Peter's home, he was eager to start using it to tape programs. So he asked for and got the job of unpacking the VCR. When he lifted the instrument from the carton, a small flat packet fell out. A label on the packet read "Contains silica gel. Do not eat."

Peter was curious about the contents of the packet, so he looked up "silica gel" in a reference book. There he read that silica gel is the anhydrous form of silica, a mineral that consists mainly of silicon(IV) oxide, SiO_2.

Think Critically: What would silica gel do if water molecules were in the air? Why was the packet of silica gel placed in the carton with the VCR?

SECTION REVIEW

1. Name the following: NaI, FeI_3, K_2SO_4, NH_4Br.
2. Write formulas for compounds composed of (a) lithium and sulfur, (b) calcium and the acetate ion, and (c) barium and oxygen.
3. Write formulas for the following: (a) the anhydrous form of $CoCl_2 \cdot 6H_2O$ and (b) calcium sulfate dihydrate.
4. **Apply:** The label on a package of plant food lists potassium nitrate as one ingredient. What is the formula for this compound?

Skill Builder ☑ **Using Variables, Constants, and Controls**

Design an experiment to distinguish between crystals that are hydrates and those that are not. Include crystals of iron(II) chloride, copper(I) nitrate, and crystals of sucrose. If you need help, refer to Using Variables, Constants, and Controls in the **Skill Handbook** on page 682.

288 CHEMICAL BONDS

Problem Solving features are real-life stories about kids. A critical thinking question engages the student in solving an everyday problem linked to the chapter content.

Flex Your Brain blends critical thinking and problem solving. Students use a step-by-step method to explore a topic while they learn to develop good problem solving skills.

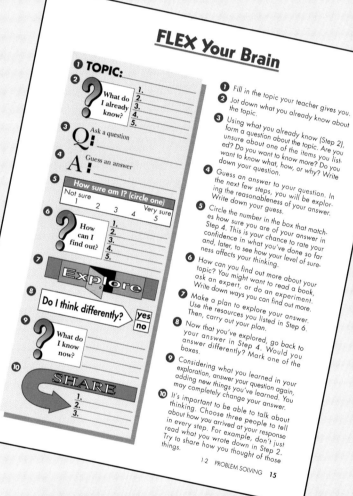

FLEX Your Brain

❶ TOPIC: _____

❷ ❓ **What do I already know?**
1. _____
2. _____
3. _____
4. _____
5. _____

❸ **Q:** Ask a question _____

❹ **A:** Guess an answer _____

❺ **How sure am I? (circle one)**
Not sure 1 2 3 4 5 Very sure

❻ ❓ **How can I find out?**
1. _____
2. _____
3. _____
4. _____
5. _____

❼ **Explore**

❽ **Do I think differently?** yes no

❾ ❓ **What do I know now?** _____

❿ **SHARE**
1. _____
2. _____
3. _____

❶ Fill in the topic your teacher gives you.
❷ Jot down what you already know about the topic.
❸ Using what you already know (Step 2), form a question about the topic. Are you unsure about one of the items you listed? Do you want to know more? Do you want to know what, how, or why? Write down your question.
❹ Guess an answer to your question. In the next few steps, you will be exploring the reasonableness of your answer. Write down your guess.
❺ Circle the number in the box that matches how sure you are of your answer in Step 4. This is your chance to rate your confidence in what you've done so far and, later, to see how your level of sureness affects your thinking.
❻ How can you find out more about your topic? You might want to read a book, ask an expert, or do an experiment. Write down ways you can find out more.
❼ Make a plan to explore your answer. Use the resources you listed in Step 6. Then, carry out your plan.
❽ Now that you've explored, go back to your answer in Step 4. Would you answer differently? Mark one of the boxes.
❾ Considering what you learned in your exploration, answer your question again, adding new things you've learned. You may completely change your answer.
❿ It's important to be able to talk about thinking. Choose three people to tell about how you arrived at your response in every step. For example, don't just read what you wrote down in Step 2. Try to share how you thought of those things.

1-2 PROBLEM SOLVING 15

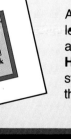

In Your JOURNAL

In your Journal, make a list of examples of noise pollution you have observed in the last week. Write a paragraph describing which were most annoying. Did you create any of these situations?

In Your Journal features help students assess their progress and keep records of their learning.

Skill Builder ☑ **Making and Using Tables**

Organize information about the six kinds of simple machines into a table. Include the type of machine, an example of each type, and a brief description of how it works. You may include other information if you wish. If you need help, refer to Making and Using Tables in the **Skill Handbook** on page 686.

170 MACHINES

A **Skill Builder,** at the end of each section, challenges students to use basic process skills. The activity also directs the students to the **Skill Handbook,** located at the back of the text, for a step-by-step overview on how to accomplish that particular skill.

STUDENTS DISCOVER HOW PHYSICAL SCIENCE IMPACTS PEOPLE AND PLACES AROUND THE WORLD

To recognize and prevent pollution. To understand machinery. To become a broadcast engineer or computer programmer. The all new **Merrill Physical Science** contains a variety of special features to give students an appreciation of physical science and the variety of ways it impacts people and places around the world. All of the features on these pages show the kind of real world application your students will get with the new **Merrill Physical Science.** And they are what make this program more enriching than any other physical science program currently available.

Connect to... features in every chapter integrate physical science with life and earth science.

The **Science and Society** lesson in each chapter challenges students to make decisions and formulate their own viewpoints about issues facing them and their community.

Connect to...
Chemistry

Floppy disks are coated with materials having strong magnetic properties. Elements with these properties such as iron, cobalt, and nickel, are called ferromagnetic. Find out what the prefix *ferro-* means.

Two **Careers** are featured in every unit to expose students to the interesting and wide range of career choices available for those with a knowledge of science.

Noise Pollution

18-3 SCIENCE & SOCIETY

Objectives
▶ Analyze the role of noise as one type of pollution.
▶ Suggest three ways noise pollution can be reduced.

New Science Words
noise pollution

What Is Noise Pollution?

Are you aware that you can be fined for littering on a highway or in a public place? Littering is one of the most obvious types of pollution. There are other types of pollution which may not seem so obvious. One of these is noise pollution. Noise pollution includes sounds that are loud, annoying, or harmful to the ear. These sounds can come from sources such as a jackhammer, a jet engine, or highly amplified music. Noise pollution is becoming a problem that sometimes requires legal intervention because it can be harmful in several ways. Recall the way in which sound waves transfer energy through compressions and rarefactions. If the intensity of the sound waves is high enough, the energy carried can actually shatter windows and crack plaster. However, most laws that govern sound levels were created because loud sounds can damage the human ear.

When sound waves reach the human ear, the vibrations pass through its various parts. Extremely intense vibrations can rupture the eardrum, but loudness-related hearing loss usually develops gradually. Your brain perceives sound when the auditory nerve carries a nerve impulse to the brain. This nerve is composed of many tiny nerve fibers surrounded by a fluid inside your ear. Hearing loss can occur when intense compressional waves traveling through the fluid destroy these nerve fibers. Loud sounds in the frequency range of 4000 to 20 000 Hz cause most of the damage to these nerve fibers. Amplified music, motorcycles, and machinery are sources of sound in this frequency range that often cause hearing loss.

In Your JOURNAL

In your Journal, make a list of examples of noise pollution you have observed in the last week. Write a paragraph describing which were most annoying. Did you create any of these situations?

Connect to... Chemistry

Have you noticed any sound insulating materials in use in your school or community? Describe the properties these materials are likely to have.

18-3 NOISE POLLUTION 471

Can you suggest how the amount of noise pollution could be decreased? One way would be to reduce the intensities of the sound waves from sources that cause noise pollution. Some scientists and engineers work on making quieter machinery and cars. Another way to reduce noise exposure is to insulate the loud areas with sound barriers. Giant walls are built along the sides of highways to keep some of the sound from reaching residential areas. You can also put the sound barriers over your own ears by wearing ear protection.

Think about the other kinds of pollution you are familiar with, such as littering, water pollution, and thermal pollution. Rank your list from the most serious pollution problem to the least serious problem. Where does noise pollution rank? Can you explain your reasoning?

SECTION REVIEW

1. What is noise pollution?
2. How can loud sounds damage your hearing?
3. List at least two things that can be done to reduce the harmful effects of noise pollution.
4. **Connect to Earth Science:** Traffic noise is a major source of noise pollution. How could automobiles be designed to reduce this noise?

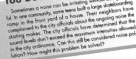

SCIENCE & SOCIETY

You Decide!

Sometimes a noise can be irritating without being harmful. In one community, some teens built a large skateboarding ramp in the front yard of a house. Their neighbors have complained to the city officials about the ongoing noise the skating makes. The city officials have determined that the sound levels don't exceed the maximum intensities allowed in the city ordinance. Can this still be considered noise pollution? How might this problem be solved?

472 WAVES AND SOUND

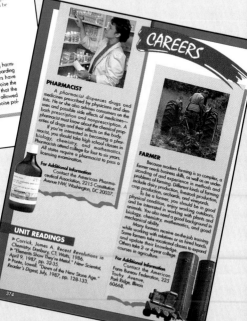

CAREERS

PHARMACIST

A pharmacist dispenses drugs and medicines prescribed by physicians and dentists. He or she also advises consumers on the uses and possible side effects of medicines— both prescription and nonprescription. A pharmacist must know about the chemical properties of drugs and their effects on the body.

If you're interested in becoming a pharmacist, you should take high school classes in biology, chemistry, and mathematics. Pharmacists attend college for four to six years. All states require a pharmacist to pass a licensing examination.

For Additional Information
Contact the American Pharmaceutical Association, 2215 Constitution Avenue NW, Washington, DC 20037.

FARMER

Because modern farming is so complex, a farmer needs business skills, as well as an understanding of and experience in solving problems of farming. Different kinds of farming include dairy production, livestock production, crop production, orchards, and vineyards.

To be a farmer, you should be in good physical condition, enjoy working outdoors, and be interested in working with plants and animals. You also need a good background in biology, chemistry, mathematics, and mechanical skills.

Many farmers receive on-the-job training while working with relatives or as hired hands. Some farmers take vocational classes to expand and update their knowledge. Others take 2- or 4-year college courses in agriculture.

For Additional Information
Contact the American Farm Bureau Federation, 225 Touhy Avenue, Park Ridge, Illinois 60068.

UNIT READINGS
▶ Corrick, James A. *Recent Revolutions in Chemistry.* Danbury, CT: Watts, 1986.
▶ "Elements Show They're Metal." *New Scientist,* April 9, 1987, pp. 32-35.
▶ Ponte, Lowell. "Dawn of the New Stone Age." *Reader's Digest,* July, 1987, pp. 128-133.

374

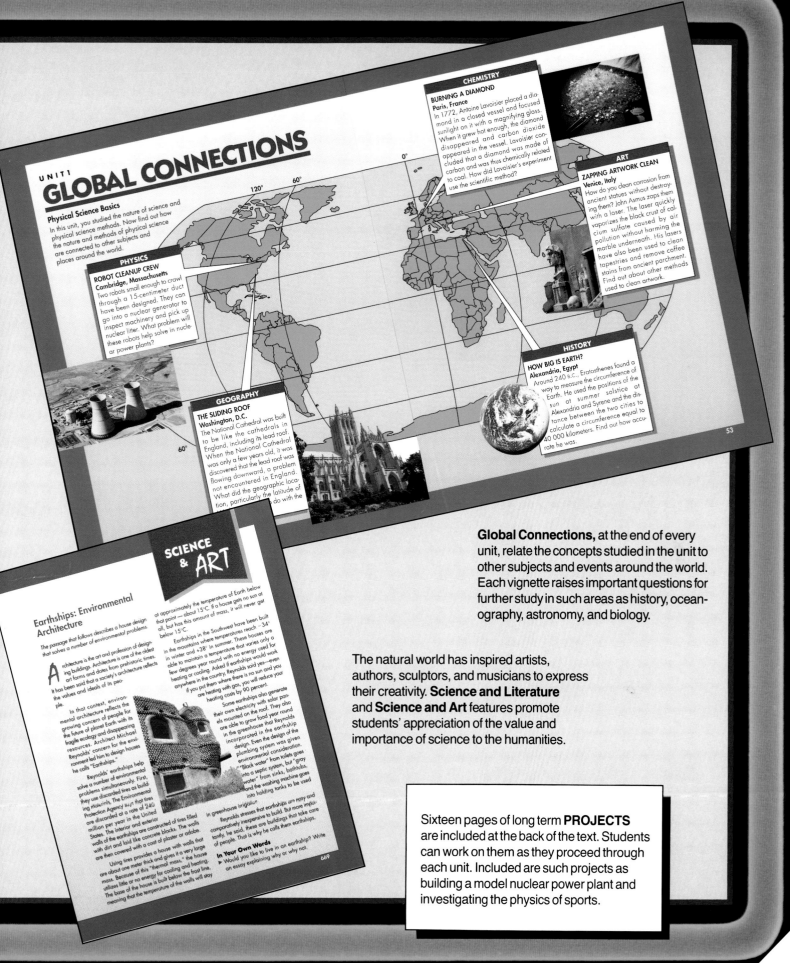

UNIT 1
GLOBAL CONNECTIONS

Physical Science Basics

In this unit, you studied the nature of science and physical science methods. Now find out how the nature and methods of physical science are connected to other subjects and places around the world.

PHYSICS
ROBOT CLEANUP CREW
Cambridge, Massachusetts
Two robots small enough to crawl through a 15-centimeter duct have been designed. They can go into a nuclear generator to inspect machinery and pick up nuclear litter. What problem will these robots help solve in nuclear power plants?

GEOGRAPHY
THE SLIDING ROOF
Washington, D.C.
The National Cathedral was built to be like the cathedrals in England, including its lead roof. When the National Cathedral was only a few years old, it was discovered that the lead roof was flowing downward, a problem not encountered in England. What did the geographic location, particularly the latitude of ... do with the

CHEMISTRY
BURNING A DIAMOND
Paris, France
In 1772, Antoine Lavoisier placed a diamond in a closed vessel and focused sunlight on it with a magnifying glass. When it grew hot enough, the diamond disappeared and carbon dioxide appeared in the vessel. Lavoisier concluded that a diamond was made of carbon and was thus chemically related to coal. How did Lavoisier's experiment use the scientific method?

ART
ZAPPING ARTWORK CLEAN
Venice, Italy
How do you clean corrosion from ancient statues without destroying them? John Asmus zaps them with a laser. The laser quickly vaporizes the black crust of calcium sulfate caused by air pollution without harming the marble underneath. His lasers have also been used to clean tapestries and remove coffee stains from ancient parchment. Find out about other methods used to clean artwork.

HISTORY
HOW BIG IS EARTH?
Alexandria, Egypt
Around 240 B.C., Eratosthenes found a way to measure the circumference of Earth. He used the positions of the sun at summer solstice at Alexandria and Syrene and the distance between the two cities to calculate a circumference equal to 40 000 kilometers. Find out how accurate he was.

53

SCIENCE & ART

Earthships: Environmental Architecture

The passage that follows describes a house design that solves a number of environmental problems.

Architecture is the art and profession of designing buildings. Architecture is one of the oldest art forms and dates from prehistoric times. It has been said that a society's architecture reflects the values and ideals of its people.

In that context, environmental architecture reflects the growing concern of people for the future of planet Earth with its fragile ecology and disappearing resources. Architect Michael Reynolds' concern for the environment led him to design houses he calls "Earthships."

Reynolds' earthships help solve a number of environmental problems simultaneously. First, they use discarded tires as building materials. The Environmental Protection Agency says that tires are discarded at a rate of 240 million per year in the United States. The interior and exterior walls of the earthships are constructed of tires filled with dirt and laid like concrete blocks. The walls are then covered with a coat of plaster or adobe.

Using tires provides a house with walls that are about one meter thick and gives it a very large mass. Because of this "thermal mass," the house utilizes little or no energy for cooling and heating. The base of the house is built below the frost line, meaning that the temperature of the walls will stay at approximately the temperature of Earth below that point — about 15°C. If a house gets no sun at all, but has this amount of mass, it will never get below 15°C.

Earthships in the Southwest have been built in the mountains where temperatures reach –34° in winter and +38° in summer. These houses are able to maintain a temperature that varies only a few degrees year round with no energy used for heating or cooling. Asked if earthships would work anywhere in the country, Reynolds said yes—even if you put them where there is no sun and you are heating with gas, you will reduce your heating costs by 90 percent.

Some earthships also generate their own electricity with solar panels mounted on the roof. They also are able to grow food year round in the greenhouse that Reynolds incorporated in the earthship design. Even the design of the plumbing system was given environmental consideration. "Black water" from toilets goes into a septic system, but "gray water" from sinks, bathtubs, and the washing machine goes into holding tanks to be used in greenhouse irrigation.

Reynolds stresses that earthships are not comparatively inexpensive to build. But more importantly, he said, these are buildings that take care of people. That is why he calls them earthships.

In Your Own Words
► Would you like to live in an earthship? Write an essay explaining why or why not.

669

Global Connections, at the end of every unit, relate the concepts studied in the unit to other subjects and events around the world. Each vignette raises important questions for further study in such areas as history, oceanography, astronomy, and biology.

The natural world has inspired artists, authors, sculptors, and musicians to express their creativity. **Science and Literature** and **Science and Art** features promote students' appreciation of the value and importance of science to the humanities.

Sixteen pages of long term **PROJECTS** are included at the back of the text. Students can work on them as they proceed through each unit. Included are such projects as building a model nuclear power plant and investigating the physics of sports.

STRATEGIES AND RESOURCES
ARE RIGHT AT YOUR FINGERTIPS

As a teacher, you will thoroughly enjoy all the valuable information **Merrill Physical Science** provides in our **Teacher Wraparound Edition.** Everything is well organized, highly visible and positioned, at the point of instruction, to give you the most teaching value.

The **Three-Step Teaching Cycle** includes **Motivate, Teach,** and **Close.** It provides various strategies for developing your individual lesson plans, and also highlights optional activities and program resources for enhancing your presentation.

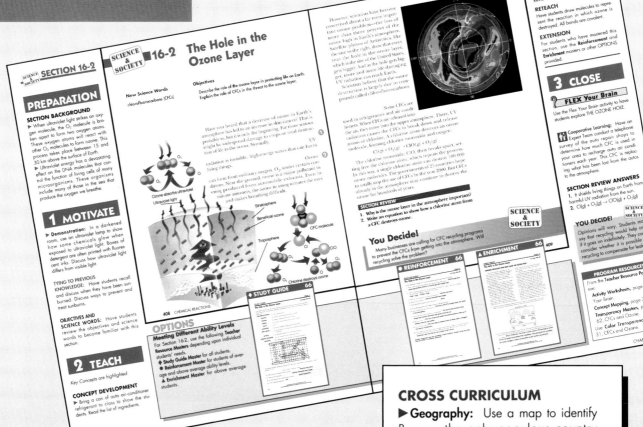

Preceding each chapter is a two-page **Planning Guide** that gives you quick access to chapter content, features, activities, skill exercises, and all other program components.

CROSS CURRICULUM

▶ **Geography:** Use a map to identify Burma, the only populous country besides the United States that does not use the metric system.

Cross Curriculum strategies provide unique ways to connect physical science to other sciences and other disciplines such as math, reading, writing, fine arts, and health.

Student masters designed to help you address different levels of learning abilities are shown in reduced form in the bottom margins. They include **Study Guide, Reinforcement,** and **Enrichment** worksheets. More strategies are suggested in **For Your Gifted Students** and **For Your Mainstreamed Students.**

Meeting Different Ability Levels

For Section 2-4, use the following **Teacher Resource Masters** depending upon individual students' needs.

◆ **Study Guide Master** for all students.

● **Reinforcement Master** for students of average and above average ability levels.

▲ **Enrichment Master** for above average students.

◆ STUDY GUIDE   12

STUDY GUIDE

Metrics for All?

You Decide!

Should the United States switch to using SI measurements exclusively? If so, how could the switch be accomplished?

● REINFORCEMENT   12

▲ ENRICHMENT   12   47

SCIENCE & SOCIETY

CHAPTER 2   47

Multicultural Awareness

Pickling, a process of food preservation that depends upon the chemical process of fermentation and the prohibition of bacterial growth in a highly acidic solution, is found in the cuisine of many cultures. Have students research different pickling processes and prepare lists of how and what products are pickled in different cultures. You may want to enlist the aid of the cafeteria director to assemble pickled foods from various cultures for a tasting.

Multicultural Awareness features highlight the contributions of individuals and societies from diverse cultures.

STUDENT TEXT QUESTIONS

▶Page 47, paragraph 1: **How many feet are in each?** A nautical mile is equal to 6067 feet; a statue mile is equal to 5280 feet. **How many yards?** 2025.3 yards and 1760 yards, respectively. **How many square feet make up an acre?** There are 43 560 square feet in 1 acre.

CROSS CURRICULUM

▶**Geography:** Use a map to identify Burma, the only populous country besides the United States that does not use the metric system.

CHECK FOR UNDERSTANDING

Ask questions 1-2 in the Section Review.

RETEACH

Have students classify examples using three types of conversions: HARD—which changes the size of a product to new metric dimensions; SOFT—where the size is not affected, only how it is measured; and NONE—in which there would be no conversion.

EXTENSION

For students who have mastered this section, use the **Reinforcement** and **Enrichment** masters or other OPTIONS provided.

3 CLOSE

▶Ask students to consider how the conversion to the metric system will be affected by the United States becoming less industrialized and a more technological nation.

SECTION REVIEW ANSWERS

1. Student responses should include inch, foot, yard, and mile. Students should conclude that converting in SI is easier than in the English system.
2. Student essays should give reasons for either support or rejection of SI adoption in the United States.

YOU DECIDE!   SCIENCE & SOCIETY

Answers will vary from total conversion mandated by the government to individual choice.

Numerous alternate assessment strategies are embedded in every chapter. Some of these are highlighted in the **Assessment Options** at the beginning of the chapter. Performance, portfolio, content, and group assessment strategies are included.

ASSESSMENT OPTIONS

PORTFOLIO
Refer to page 447 for suggested items that students might select for their portfolios.

PERFORMANCE ASSESSMENT
See page 447 for additional Performance Assessment options.
Process
Skill Builders, pp. 433, 436, 445
MINI-Lab, p. 428
Activities 17-1, p. 437; 17-2, p. 446
Using Lab Skills, p. 448

CONTENT ASSESSMENT
Assessment—Oral, pp. 432, 442
Section Reviews, pp. 433, 436, 439, 445
Chapter Review, pp. 447-449
Mini Quizzes, pp. 429, 432, 435, 443, 444

GROUP ASSESSMENT
Opportunities for group assessment occur with Cooperative Learning Strategies and Flex Your Brain Activities.

A FULL RANGE OF SUPPORT MATERIALS TO MEET ALL YOUR NEEDS AND THOSE OF YOUR STUDENTS.

HANDS-ON LEARNING

Laboratory Manual contains at least two hands-on laboratory activities for each chapter. Students get more chances to acquire scientific knowledge while you get more opportunities to reinforce and apply chapter concepts.

Activity Worksheets include worksheets for every Mini-Lab and full-page Activity in the chapters.

Science Integration Activities are laboratory activities that relate earth science and life science to specific physical science chapters.

REVIEW & REINFORCEMENT

Study Guide Worksheets are tailored to the needs of students who need a little extra help. They reinforce understanding of the topics and vocabulary found in each chapter.

Reinforcement Worksheets provide a variety of interesting activities to help students of average ability levels retain the important points in every chapter.

Concept Mapping masters reinforce learning by having students complete a concept map for each chapter.

Chapter Review Software presents chapter-end review questions in random order and provides feedback for incorrectly answered questions by noting the textbook page where the answer is found.

Chapter Review masters are two-page review worksheets consisting of 25 questions for each chapter. Ideal for test preparation, alternative tests, and vocabulary review.

ENRICHMENT AND APPLICATION

Enrichment Worksheets challenge your students of above average ability to design, interpret, and research scientific topics based on the text in each lesson.

Critical Thinking/Problem Solving helps your students develop important critical thinking and problem solving skills as they work through additional problems related to chapter topics.

Cross-Curriculum Connections are interdisciplinary worksheets. They emphasize learning by doing and provide valuable insight into the connection earth science has with other disciplines.

Science And Society worksheets encourage further involvement with Science and Society lessons in the student text.

Technology masters explore recent developments in science and technology or explain how familiar machines, tools, or systems work.

ASSESSMENT

Chapter Test masters provide comprehensive tests for each chapter.

Computer Test Bank Package, available in Apple, IBM, and Macintosh versions, provides a convenient tool for creating your own chapter test. The software allows you to add your own problems or edit the existing questions.

Alternate Assessment in the Science Classroom explains the need for nontraditional methods of assessment such as performance assessments and portfolios. In addition to strategies it provides samples of questions, report forms, and a scoring rubric.

Performance Assessment provides specially designed assessments including eight unit summative performance tasks and 24 chapter-related skill assessments.

Performance Assessment in Middle School Science (PAMSS) includes the philosophy and strategies for assessing both the processes and products of science. The booklet contains practical performance assessment task lists and rubrics that you can use immediately to help you evaluate your students' performance.

Color Transparency Package includes 50 full-color transparencies, some with overlays, in a three-ring binder with a resource book of blackline masters and student worksheets for each transparency. Excellent for direct instruction, reteaching, and review.

Transparency Masters include blackline reproductions and student worksheets for each of the program's full-color transparencies.

Spanish Resources provides Spanish translations of chapter objectives, glossary terms, and definitions. Ideal for bilingual classrooms.

Lesson Plan Book is a complete lesson planning resource for teachers. It is a correlation of lessons, objectives, features, and program resources.

Teacher Resource Guide contains a program planning guide, lab design and equipment, safety instruction, a media worksheet, and a Flex Your Brain worksheet in one convenient booklet.

English-Spanish Audiocassettes allow students with reading difficulties, students who absorb concepts better in an auditory way, or students for whom English is a second language to listen to chapters from the text in English and/or Spanish.

Cooperative Learning in the Science Classroom contains background information, strategies, and practical tips for using cooperative learning techniques whenever you do activities.

Lab and Safety Skills in the Science Classroom presents an overview of lab skills and safety skills related to lab activities. The booklet also contains lab and safety skills assessments for evaluating students' understanding of lab and safety skills.

Videodisc Correlation for Optical Data laserdisc program allows you to use this resource with the sweep of a light pen.

Science and Technology Videodisc Series, which features 7 discs containing over 280 videoreports produced and narrated by TV's "Mister Wizard," lets students catch a glimpse of real scientists exploring current problems and technological developments so they can discover the influence of science in day-to-day living. Videodisc Teacher Guides include bar code directories plus teaching strategies, research updates, and complete narration for each videoreport.

Lab Partner Software is a spreadsheet and graphing program that allows you and your students to record, collect, and graph data from laboratory activities simply and effectively. A **User Guide** is also available to assist students through the programs.

Infinite Voyage Video Series (videodiscs/VHS tapes) bring the amazing live action and animated sequences of this award-winning PBS series to your science classroom.

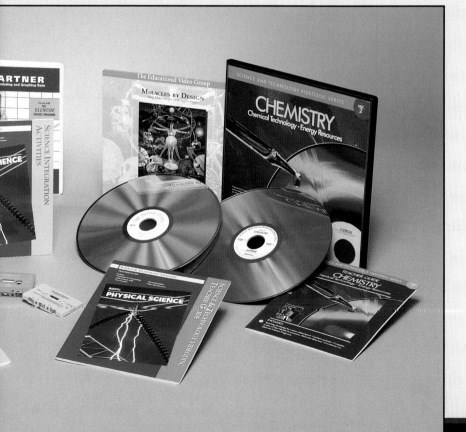

MERRILL

PHYSICAL SCIENCE

TEACHER WRAPAROUND EDITION

GLENCOE
McGraw-Hill

New York, New York   Columbus, Ohio   Mission Hills, California   Peoria, Illinois

MERRILL PHYSICAL SCIENCE

Student Edition
Teacher Wraparound Edition
Teacher Classroom Resources
Study Guide, Student Edition
Study Guide, Teacher Edition
Reinforcement, Student Edition
Reinforcement, Teacher Edition
Enrichment, Student Edition
Enrichment, Teacher Edition
Concept Mapping
Science Activity Worksheets
Chapter and Unit Tests
Chapter Review
Critical Thinking/Problem Solving
Cross-Curriculum Connections
Science and Society
Technology
Teacher Resource Guide

Transparency Package
Laboratory Manual
Laboratory Manual, Teacher Annotated Edition
Spanish Resources
Chapter Review Software (IBM, Apple, Macintosh)
Computer Test Bank (IBM, Apple, Macintosh)
Videodisc Correlation (Optical Data)
Science and Technology Videodisc Series (STVS)
Science and Technology Videodisc Series
  Teacher Guide
Lesson Plan Book
Science Integration Activities
Alternate Assessment in the
  Science Classroom
Performance Assessment
Cooperative Learning in the Science Classroom
Performance Assessment in Middle School Science
  (PAMSS)
Lab Partner Software (IBM, Apple)
Infinite Voyage Series (VHS, Videodiscs)

AUTHORS

Marilyn Thompson
Charles W. McLaughlin
Richard G. Smith

Send all inquiries to:
Glencoe/McGraw-Hill
936 Eastwind Drive
Westerville, Ohio 43081

Printed in the United States of America.

ISBN 0-02-826953-5 (Student's Edition)

3 4 5 6 7 8 9 VH/MC 02 01 00 99 98 97 96 95

ISBN 0-02-826954-3 (Teacher's Edition)

3 4 5 6 7 8 9 VH/MC 02 01 00 99 98 97 96 95

Table of Contents

Teacher Guide

Student Edition

Merrill Physical Science
Goals and Philosophy

*The goal of **Merrill Physical Science** is to help students develop an understanding of the world around them through sound content and the practice of skills that will help them reach that understanding.*

Science educators daily face the task of helping students with different abilities and backgrounds to learn about the living world and to acquire skills that will increase their ability to evaluate that world. **Merrill Physical Science** is dedicated and designed to help both students and teachers meet these goals.

In recent years, scientists and educators have collaborated in an effort to find a clear path toward better science education. Of all the reform-oriented proposals, **Science for All Americans,** a Project 2061 report on literacy goals in science, mathematics, and technology, sponsored by the American Association for the Advancement of Science, and **Scope, Sequence, and Coordination,** sponsored by the National Science Teachers Association, have attained national prominence. Both programs suggest major changes in what, when, and how science is taught. Both programs strongly suggest a more constructivist approach whereby the student, rather than the teacher, becomes the individual who identifies problems, proposes solutions, and then tests those proposals.

In response to the goals of science curriculum reform, **Merrill Physical Science** promotes:

- solid, accurate content,
- a thematic orientation,
- hands-on activities that promote a constructivist approach through more student-planned activities,
- frequent practice of science process skills,
- integration of science concepts across the curriculum,
- numerous opportunities for authentic assessment, and
- decision making and problem solving.

Themes

Themes help students see how separate physical science concepts are related.

The themes of science are broad, unifying ideas that integrate the major concepts of many disciplines. They are an important part of any teaching strategy because they help students see the importance of truly understanding concepts rather than simply memorizing isolated facts. Themes help students see connections between physical science and other science courses.

Merrill Physical Science is a study of matter and energy. The approach of this text emphasizes everday applications of physical laws. As students progress through the course, they soon realize that most of the technological advances they have taken for granted are merely applications of basic physical science principles.

Several unifying themes pervade **Merrill Physical Science.** These themes serve as a conceptual framework for a physical science course and provide a rationale for the sequence of topics in the text. Major themes in the text are

- energy
- stability
- patterns of change
- scale and structure
- systems and interactions

Constructivism in Science

Merrill Physical Science provides a wide range of experiences that help students develop and apply thinking process skills.

Constructivism in Science

Strategies suggested in **Merrill Physical Science** support a constructivist approach to science education. The role of the teacher is to provide an atmosphere where students design and direct activities. To develop the idea that science investigation is not made up of closed-end questions, the teacher should ask guiding questions and be prepared to help his or her students draw meaningful conclusions when their results do not match predictions. Through the numerous activities, cooperative learning opportunities, and a variety of critical thinking exercises in *Merrill Physical Science,* you can feel comfortable taking a constructivist approach to science in your classroom.

Activities

A constructivist approach to science is rooted in an activities-based plan. Students must be provided with sensory motor experiences as a base for developing abstract ideas. *Merrill Physical Science* utilizes a variety of "learning by doing" opportunities. **Find Out** activities that open each chapter allow students to generate questions about the concepts to come, make observations, and share prior knowledge.

MINI-Labs and **Activities** involve students in learning and applying scientific methods to practice thinking skills and construct science concepts. They provide an engaging, diverse, active program. MINI-Labs require a minimum of equipment, and students may take responsibility for organization and execution.

Activities develop and reinforce or restructure concepts as well as develop the ability to use process skills. **Activity** formats are structured to guide students to make their own discoveries. Students collect real evidence and are encouraged through open-ended questions to reflect and reformulate their ideas based on this evidence.

In each chapter, there is one open-ended **Activity** called **"Designing an Experiment,"** that gives students a broad topic to explore and guides them with leading questions to the point where they can determine the direction of the investigation themselves. Students are asked to brainstorm hypotheses, make a decision to investigate one that can be tested, plan procedures, and in the end, think about why their hypotheses were supported or not.

Cooperative Learning

Cooperative Learning adds the element of social interaction to science learning. Group learning allows students to verbalize ideas, and encourages the reflection that leads to active construction of concepts. It allows students to recognize the inconsistencies in their own perspectives and the strengths of others. By presenting the idea that there is no one, "ready-made" answer, all students may gain the courage to try to find a viable solution. Cooperative Learning strategies appear in the *Teacher Wraparound Edition* margins whenever appropriate.

And More...

FLEX Your Brain, a self-directed critical-thinking matrix, is introduced in Chapter 1. This activity, referenced wherever appropriate in the *Teacher Wraparound Edition* margins, assists students in identifying what they already know about a subject, then in developing independent strategies to investigate further. **Revealing Misconceptions** suggests strategies the teacher may use to evaluate students' current perspectives.

Students are encouraged to discover the pleasure of solving a problem through a variety of features. **Apply** questions that require higher-level, divergent thinking appear in **Section Reviews**. The **Problem Solving, Technology,** and **Science and Society** features in each chapter invite students to confront real-life problems. **Think Critically** and **You Decide!** questions encourage students to reflect on issues related to technology and society. The **Skill Handbook** gives specific examples to guide students through the steps of acquiring thinking and process skills. As students complete each numbered section, a **Skill Builder** gives them a chance to assess and reinforce the concepts just learned through practice. **Think and Write Critically, Apply,** and **More Skill Builders** sections of the Chapter Review allow the teacher to assess and reward successful thinking skills.

Science, Technology, and Society

Merrill Physical Science provides a curriculum that helps prepare students for the relationships and responsibilities attendent to the interactions of science, technology, and society.

Science involves the search for knowledge. Technology involves the application of this knowledge to human cultures. As society becomes more technologically complex, people increasingly rely upon it to satisfy their needs and solve their problems. Technology also increasingly impacts the environment and society, causing new challenges. Science literacy, then, is an important goal for all students so that they can use technology productively and be informed decision-makers. The *Merrill Physical Science* curriculum incorporates strategies to develop critical and creative thinking for developing informed decision-making skills.

Critical thinking is characterized by:
- a search for clarity and accuracy,
- open-mindedness,
- taking and defending a position, and
- sensitivity to others' knowledge and feelings

Creative thinking is characterized by:
- engaging in tasks when answers are not apparent,
- pushing the limits of one's knowledge and abilities,
- generating and following one's own standard of evaluation, and
- generating new ways of viewing situations.

Merrill Physical Science provides a curriculum that focuses on the interaction of science, technology, and society.

Student Edition

The Student Edition contains **Technology** features, **Science and Society** articles, and unit-ending **Global Connections** features.

- **Technology** features introduce students to applications of chapter concepts. *Think Critically* questions invite indepth responses.
- **Science and Society** articles focus on the interaction of science and the impact of technology on culture. *You Decide!* questions call for informed decision-making.
- **Global Connections** features encourage awareness of science, technology, and society as a global responsibility.

Teacher Classroom Resources

As part of the *Teacher Classroom Resources*, there is a *Science and Society* booklet with readings and activities that relate science, technology, and society topics to chapter content. These one-page articles are different from the Science and Society features in the textbook. The *Science and Society* booklet articles present students with questions that are large societal life science issues to which there may be no easy answers, but about which students may face difficult decisions as they reach adulthood. There is one article per chapter. Teaching strategies are given.

In the *Technology* booklet, students are introduced to eight life-science related technological questions or advances. Based on overall unit topics, a teacher guide is provided with background information, teaching tips, and references.

Less controversial, but grounded in current scientific research, *Mr. Wizard's Science and Technology Videodisc Series* presents a series of full-motion videoreports designed to make the real world of research and technology real to students. The **Merrill Physical Science** *Science and Technology Videodisc Teacher Guide* provides helpful extensions and alternate uses to help make students aware of their changing world and what roles they might eventually play in it.

Integrating Physical Science Across the Curriculum

Merrill Physical Science includes many opportunities to relate physical science to other sciences and other disciplines across the curriculum.

No subject exists in isolation. At appropriate points in **Merrill Physical Science,** attention is called to other sciences and other disciplines across the curriculum in the *Student Edition,* the *Teacher Wraparound Edition,* and in the *Teacher Classroom Resources.*

Student Edition

- **Connect to ...**—margin features that relate basic questions in other sciences to a physical science
- **Global Connections**—a cross-curricular unit-end feature with a global perspective
- **Science and Literature/Science and Art**—a one-page feature on either art or literature related to the unit topic at the close of each unit

Teacher Wraparound Edition

- **Connect to ...**—suggested answers to the questions about other sciences that are asked in the *Student Edition* margin features.
- **Global Connections/Science and Literature/Science and Art**—provide teaching tips for these unit-end features
- **Cross Curriculum**—relates physical science to health, history, language, math, and other disciplines

Teacher Classroom Resources

- **Science Integration Activities**—full-page activities related to other science fields
- **Cross-Curricular Connections**—relate physical science to home economics, social studies, architecture, and other disciplines

Multicultural Awareness

"Multicultural education is an idea stating that all students, regardless of the groups to which they belong, such as those related to gender, ethnicity, race, culture, social class, religion or exceptionality, should experience education equality in the schools."—James Banks

American classrooms reflect the rich and diverse cultural heritages of the American people. Students come from different ethnic backgrounds and different cultural experiences into a common classroom that must assist all of them to learn. The diversity itself is an important focus of learning experience.

Diversity can be repressed, creating a hostile environment; ignored, creating an indifferent environment; or appreciated, creating a receptive and productive environment. Responding to diversity and approaching it as part of every curriculum is challenging to a teacher, experienced or not. The goal of science is understanding. The goal of multicultural education is to promote the understanding of how people from different cultures approach and solve the basic problems all humans have in living and learning. *Merrill Physical Science* addresses this issue. In the Multicultural Awareness strategies in the *Teacher Wraparound Edition,* students are encouraged to become aware of how cultures around the world deal with topics related to physical science. Also, in each chapter in the

Teacher Wraparound Edition are features called *Multicultural Perspectives* that describe how a science topic relates to people of different cultures. The intent is to build awareness and appreciation for the global community in which we all live.

Two books that provide additional valuable information on multicultural education are:

Banks, James A. (with Cherry A. Mcgee Banks). *Multicultural Education: Issues and Perspectives.* Boston: Allyn and Bacon, 1989.

Banks, James A. (with others). Curriculum Guidelines for Multiethnic Education. Washington, D.C.: National Council for the Social Studies, 1977.

Student Text Features

Chapter Organization

Chapter Introduction

Merrill Physical Science chapter openers give students a hands-on way to explore a concept they'll learn more about in the chapter.

Each chapter of **Merrill Physical Science** opens with a striking full-page photograph illustrating a concept introduced in the chapter. The chapter introductory paragraph establishes a relationship between the photo and the chapter.

FIND OUT!, an inquiry activity, is featured at each chapter's beginning. Designed to give students an opportunity to make observations and raise questions about upcoming chapter content, these brief activities require few materials. **FIND OUT!** provides a hands-on introduction to chapter content.

Gearing Up, an outline of the chapter sections, assists students in previewing the chapter and focusing on its most important ideas.

What's Next? leads students into the body of the chapter.

Benefits
- Students will confidently approach the chapter content with its friendly, real-life opening.
- Students are focused on and ready to learn the chapter concepts after the opening inquiry activity.

Lessons

Numbered lessons divide chapter content into amounts that are manageable for the students.

Each chapter is divided into three to five sections, with student objectives listed at the beginning of each. When appropriate, major sections are divided into subsections.

Objectives provide the framework for the review questions, chapter review, review worksheets (in the *Teacher Classroom Resources*), and chapter tests.

New Science Words are listed at the beginning of each lesson to help students preview the vocabulary words they will learn in that section.

Benefits
- Students can more easily understand the relationships between topics and the frameworks of different areas of physical science.
- Students gain confidence as they see they can progress section by section to gain a full understanding of the chapter content.

Activities

Activities allow students to become fully engaged in the "doing" of science.

Each chapter of **Merrill Physical Science** has two full-page laboratory activities that can be done in one laboratory period, along with shorter MINI-Labs, and Flex Your Brain activities.

Activities provide students with opportunities to learn by doing and to actively engage in learning concepts by using scientific methods. Many of the activities include a problem statement, materials list, step-by-step procedures. They also offer questions to help students review their observations, form hypotheses, design plans to test their hypotheses, and then analyze and draw conclusions about their investigations.

Designing an Experiment Activities are open-ended, student-directed activities. Students are guided to form hypotheses, design plans to test their hypotheses, and then analyze and draw conclusions about their investigations.

MINI-Labs, provide another opportunity to practice science process skills while using scientific methods. These hands-on activities can be completed in a short amount of time, and require simple, common materials.

Flex Your Brain is a self-directed activity students use while investigating content areas. It occurs as a one-page activity in Chapter 1, accompanying a text section discussing critical thinking and problem solving. The Teacher Resource Guide of the *Teacher Classroom Resources* provides a master with spaces for students to write their responses. See page 19T of this teacher guide for more information about **Flex Your Brain**.

Benefits
- The activities allow students to practice the thinking process skills in widely different contexts; this makes them better problem solvers for life.
- The different types of activities meet the diverse needs of students and teachers.

Section Review

The Section Review provides content assessment of chapter concepts.

Following each numbered section are three to five Section Review questions that may include an Apply question that demands a higher level of thinking to answer. A science integration question connects physical science to physics, chemistry, life, or earth science.

Special Text Features

Special text features engage students as they make connections across the curriculum, and practice problem solving and decision making.

Connect to Other Sciences

Most numbered sections have a **Connect to Physics, Connect to Earth Science, Connect to Life Science** or **Connect to Chemistry** feature. These features integrate particular physical science concepts to related concepts in other science disciplines.

Benefits

- Students see the natural interconnectedness of the sciences, giving them a broader and more in-depth understanding of science concepts.

Science and Society

Each chapter has a **Science and Society** section integrated into the chapters, featuring important science-related topics that affect society. At the conclusion of these sections is a **You Decide** feature that provides students an opportunity to practice critical-thinking and problem-solving skills as they formulate opinions on the issue discussed.

Benefits

- Students maintain high interest in science class as they see the relevance to society and their own lives.
- Students practice reasoning, critical thinking, decision making, and communicating their ideas after studying the issues.

Technology

Technology features in each chapter show "real-life" applications of the science concepts. A critical-thinking question at the end of the feature gives students an opportunity to interact with the feature.

Benefits

- This feature makes science concepts interesting and relevant to students.
- Understanding technology will enable students to better handle their future challenges in terms of decisions about the environment and their careers.

Problem Solving

Problem Solving in each chapter feature stories about how people confront a problem linked to the chapter content. The feature's real-life application question engages students in the solving of the problem.

Benefits

- Students will benefit by learning problem-solving skills in a relevant and interesting way.

Margin Features

In Your Journal features encourage students to write creatively, record data, plan experiments, write letters, and state opinions on topics that relate to physical science.

Science and Reading and **Science and Math** are features that provide problems or projects that require reading or math calculations to further explore science concepts. This reinforces and integrates reading and math skills in the science curriculum.

Periodic **Did You Know?** features present students with interesting facts related to the content being developed.

Eco Tips are simple for ways to have a positive effect on the environment. Eco Tips extend the environmental concepts of the book and increase students' sense that their actions have an effect in the world.

Periodic **Student notes** are blue margin questions about main ideas; they can serve as a study guide for students.

Chapter End

Chapter-end materials review, reinforce, and extend concepts.

The three-page chapter-end material begins with a Summary that concisely reviews the major concepts and principles of the chapter. Each summary statement is numbered to correspond to a section objective.

- **Key Science Words** list the chapter vocabulary terms in order of occurrence.
- **Understanding Vocabulary** is an exercise in matching definitions to key terms.
- **Checking Concepts** provides multiple-choice recall questions.
- **Using Lab Skills** provides assessment of various chapter activities.
- **Think and Write Critically** provides higher-level thinking questions.
- **Apply** questions require application of chapter concepts.
- **More Skill Builders** require students to use process skills as they answer content-related questions.
- **Projects** provide ideas for researching, creating, or investigating topics based on chapter concepts.

Answers to all chapter-end questions are provided in the margin of the *Teacher Wraparound Edition*.

Unit Introductions

What's Happening Here? photographs and text combine for an inquiry strategy to introduce each unit. The photos portray a puzzling situation, or an intriguing relationship related to the content of the upcoming unit.

End of Unit Features

Units close with four-page features that include:

Global Connections feature a two-page world map with inter-disciplinary features from around the world. These features provide integration of sciences, strengthen geography knowledge and provide strong multicultural perspective.

Careers are features in which students use real-world applications of science knowledge acquired in the unit. Students can see a range of careers available to people with a variety of educational backgrounds. **Readings** provide several books or magazine articles related to the unit content.

Science and Literature or **Science and Art** features integrate science concepts to literature or art. Included may be fiction or nonfiction book excerpts, paintings, sculpture, photos, or music related to the unit.
Students are actively engaged at the close of the feature as they respond to application or critical-thinking questions.

Skill Reinforcement

Skills are reinforced throughout *Merrill Physical Science.* Each section ends with a **Skill Builder** feature that challenges students to practice basic process skills on a specific science concept. The skill to be learned or practiced is explained in the **Skill Handbook,** a 15-page illustrated reference in the back of the student text. Specific examples are used to guide students through the steps of acquiring skills. **More Skill Builders** in the **Chapter Review** material also reference the **Skill Handbook.**

Appendices

There are three appendices that may be used to expand student learning or application of concepts. **Appendix A** shows SI units and English/Metric and temperature conversions. It provides a table for quick reference to SI base units and derived units. **Appendix B** includes procedures students should practice to ensure lab safety. A chart of safety symbols that are used throughout the text activities alerts students to possible laboratory hazards. **Appendix C,** the periodic table, is available for reference throughout the course.

Projects

Seven long-term projects are designed to be worked on during the course of individual units. Each project lends itself to having students work cooperatively in groups or individually.

Glossaries and Index

The English and Spanish Glossaries provide students with a quick reference to key terms and their pronunciations within the text. Page references are provided for all New Science Words from each chapter so students can easily locate the page on which a word is defined. Because it is complete and cross-referenced, the **Index** allows text material to be found quickly and easily.

Teacher Wraparound Edition

The *Merrill Physical Science* Teacher Wraparound Edition makes teaching life science EASY.

Merrill Physical Science Teacher Wraparound Edition has been designed and arranged to provide you with maximum support for maximum results. Support materials and strategies are there for activities, for curriculum integration, for alternate assessment, for planning, and for meeting the diverse needs of all your students.

Support for Activities

The Teacher Wraparound Edition provides you with information to make your science labs fun and productive.

In the margins of the *Teacher Wraparound Edition,* you will find:
- Materials and Teaching Tips for **Find Out!** activities;
- Objectives, Process Skills, Teaching Tips, and Answers for full-page activities;
- Objectives, Preparation, Materials, Teaching Tips, Guidance, and Answers for Designing an Experiment activities; and
- Materials and Suggested Outcomes for MINI-Labs.

Support for Integration

Cross-curricular connections in the *Teacher Wraparound Edition* save you research time. Look for **Cross Curriculum** teaching tips in the *Teacher Wraparound Edition* margins. Through the explicit integration of physical science with other science and non-science disciplines, students will come to appreciate that physical science is connected to almost everything they do.

Global Connections features connect physical science to other sciences as well as literature, art, history, and geography. Teacher background is provided for the teacher who is unfamiliar with that area. Help is provided in terms of lesson objectives, motivating ideas, teaching strategies, background, and extension strategies.

Teacher support for the **Connect to Earth Science, Connect to Physics, Connect to Life Science** and **Connect to Chemistry** features includes suggested answers to questions. **In Your Journal, Science and Math,** and **Science and Reading** features are supported with suggested responses to questions.

Support for Assessment

Use alternate assessments to confirm your students' grasp of content and skills.

Implementation of science reforms and the coming national science standards require that teachers use alternate forms of assessment to meet the changing curriculum. New assessment forms emphasize the processes of science as well as the products of science learning. Students are frequently challenged to solve complex problems or discover the many options of an open-ended activity. Assessment can be made as students create,

produce, or perform; as they use critical-thinking and problem-solving skills; and as they perform tasks with real-world applications.

In the *Teacher Wraparound Edition,* every chapter opener lists assessment options for that chapter. **Assessment Options** are categorized in one of four areas:
- Portfolio suggestions,
- Performance-assessment items,
- Content-assessment features, and
- Group-assessment opportunities.

Portfolio suggestions are listed on the first page of the Chapter Review. Assessment in the form of modifications to activities are suggested in the teacher margin. Oral-assessment options are provided where appropriate so that teachers can quickly determine if students have internalized concepts and are ready to proceed. See an extended discussion of assessment on pages 22T through 24T in this guide.

Planning/Preparation/Background

All the resources and references you'll need to do your short-term planning are in one place—the *Teacher Wraparound Edition.* Use the two-page chapter planner at the beginning of each chapter to:
- Overview objectives,
- Plan content development,
- Select activities and materials, and
- Select from a wide assortment of program resources in the *Teacher Classroom Resources.*

For assistance in long-term planning, use the Planning Guide on page 16T. As the Planning Guide shows, the program has the flexibility to be used for full-year or semester courses with physical science.

Meets Needs of ALL Students

The *Teacher Wraparound Edition* helps you meet the diverse needs of your students. *Merrill Physical Science* Teacher Wraparound Edition provides you with a wide array of features and options designed to make science learning a successful experience for all your students.

To assist you in meeting the needs of all of your students, the *Teacher Wraparound Edition* provides:
- suggestions for using three types of ability-level worksheets for each section,
- strategies for gifted and mainstreamed students,
- guidelines for meeting the needs of challenged students,
- reteaching and extension strategies,
- cooperative learning strategies for activities, and
- multicultural awareness activities and topics for discussion.

Teacher Classroom Resources

An Effective Teaching Model

The *Merrill Physical Science* Teacher Wraparound Edition delivers the collective teaching experience of its authors, consultants, and reviewers. By furnishing you with an effective teaching model, it saves you preparation time and energy. You, in turn, are free to spend that time and energy on your most important responsibility—your students.

As a professional, you will be pleased to find that this program provides you with readily available activities that will engage your students for the entire class period. Each major section of every chapter may be considered an individual lesson that includes a preparation section followed by a comprehensive three-part teaching cycle that, when utilized consistently, will result in better cognitive transfer for your students.

Theme Development begins each chapter, describing how one or all of the themes of the book are incorporated into the chapter.

Chapter Overview, following Theme Development, lists and decribes the material in each of the sections of the chapter.

Chapter Vocabulary is then listed for you in the order in which the words occur in the chapter.

FIND OUT! activities open the chapter. These activities help you focus the students' attention on the chapter and get them into the material immediately. Everything you will need to help the students complete the FIND OUT! is given alongside the student page. Any advanced preparation or materials are listed for you.

Cooperative Learning strategies are suggested and teaching tips are given to help you conduct the FIND OUT! activities.

The **OPTIONS** section of the chapter openers include activity-based strategies to help you with gifted or mainstreamed students you may have in your class.

PREPARATION

Preparation is an extremely important part of teaching any lesson. The **PREPARATION** section contains **SECTION BACKGROUND** that provides you with science content relevant to the section. Also provided for you in **PREPLANNING** is a list of things you may wish to do to prepare for the section in advance. The **PREPARATION** section will give you the foundation for keeping your lesson instructionally sound.

1 MOTIVATE

The first step to teaching any lesson is to motivate the students. A **Motivate** idea is provided for each section. The ideas may include demonstrations, cooperative learning techniques, audiovisuals, brainstorming, or other ideas that help motivate and focus the class so the lesson can begin. One unique way to get students interested in the section content is by using the FLEX YOUR BRAIN activity. This activity will give students confidence to begin learning section content by helping them find out what they already know and don't know about a certain topic.

Another important way to help motivate students is by connecting the current lesson with previous lessons or to common knowledge possessed by most students. The **Tying to Previous Knowledge** sections help you do this. Research has shown that connecting ideas provides for greater concept retention among students.

2 TEACH

The primary aim of the *Merrill Physical Science* Teacher Wraparound Edition is to give you the tools to accomplish the task of getting concepts of physical science across to your students. Many teaching suggestions are given to you under a series of clearly defined headings. Each section contains, under the **CONCEPT DEVELOPMENT** heading, ways for you to develop the content of the section. This may include a series of questions for you to ask students followed by possible student responses. These questions are a tool for you to use to develop the concepts in the section. Demonstration ideas also appear in Concept Development when they can help you develop student interest in the concepts to be taught.

To help you monitor and adjust your teaching to what students are learning, a **CHECK FOR UNDERSTANDING** idea is provided for you in each section at a point where it seems most appropriate. For students who are having trouble, a **RETEACH** suggestion immediately follows the CHECK FOR UNDERSTANDING hint. The RETEACH tip is a way to teach the same concepts or facts differently to adjust to students' individual learning styles. For those students in the class who do not need additional help understanding the lesson, there are suggestions for **ENRICHMENT** to allow these students to go on while others are reviewing the section. These ENRICHMENT ideas are provided for you in the **OPTIONS** boxes at the bottom of the *Teacher Wraparound Edition* pages.

The **TEACH** step of the *Teacher Wraparound Edition* provides many other strategies to help you teach the content of the section. A section may have a way to connect physical science to another discipline in the **CROSS CURRICULUM** teaching tip. **MINI QUIZZES** assess students' mastery of the material. These can also be used as CHECK FOR UNDERSTANDING activities. An annotation key is provided with each MINI QUIZ to help you refer students to the page on which the answer is found.

The **REVEALING MISCONCEPTIONS** teaching tip suggests questions you may ask to elicit student misconceptions about section content or provide you with a possible misconception that is held by students and a method of correcting that misconception.

TEACHER F.Y.I. tips give you additional information to help you teach the section. These may be everyday applications or connections to other disciplines. Answers are given in the margin to any text questions to be answered by students. Also, for your convenience, we have highlighted the key concepts.

COOPERATIVE LEARNING suggestions are given in various locations of the *Teacher Wraparound Edition*. They are found in the FIND OUT activities, in the lab activities, and when appropriate within the Teach section. In each COOPERATIVE LEARNING tip, a specific cooperative grouping strategy is given to help you make the most of these activities.

You are also provided with information needed to teach each of the special features of the Student Edition such as: MINI-Labs, Science and..., TECHNOLOGY, PROBLEM SOLVING, ACTIVITIES, and Connect to... features.

And There's More

Our special *Teacher Wraparound Edition* has been designed to provide you with the most meaningful teacher information in the most convenient way.

The **OPTIONS** box, located at the bottom of most pages, contains a variety of items. The OPTIONS Box on the Chapter Opener pages provides you with ideas to help you teach the gifted students and the mainstreamed students in your class. Both of these groups pose a challenge to any teacher, and these tips are designed to help you teach the content of the chapter to these exceptional students.

In every classroom there are students with a variety of different ability levels. The OPTIONS box on the first two pages of each section shows you reduced copies of pages in the *Teacher Classroom Resources* to help you deal with all of the different ability levels. The Study Guide Master can be used by all students to review the basic content of the section. The Reinforcement Master will allow average students to go beyond the basic concepts of the chapter while reinforcing them. The Enrichment Master will provide those students who quickly

master section content with an additional challenge to explore the ideas in the section more fully.

On the pages in the chapter, the OPTIONS Boxes provide you with Inquiry Questions and oral assessment questions to use with all students. These are suggested questions you may ask that require critical thinking on the part of the students. The questions relate specifically to the content of the page on which they are located.

With the materials present in the TEACH step of the teacher edition, your efficiency and productivity as a teacher will increase. The TEACH section brings together the major elements that form a sound teaching approach.

3 CLOSE

Closing the lesson is the last but one of the most important steps of teaching any lesson. This step is the complement in many ways to the MOTIVATE step. While the motivate step helps students become involved in the lesson, the Close step helps students bring things together in their minds to make sense of what went on in the lesson. The *Merrill Physical Science* Teacher Wraparound Edition gives you a variety of ways to provide effective closure to a lesson. The Close options help summarize the section, bridge to the next lesson, or provide an application of the lesson.

As you review the *Merrill Physical Science* Teacher Wraparound Edition, you will discover that you and your students are considered very important. With the enormous number of teaching strategies provided by the teacher edition, you should be able to accomplish the goals of your curriculum. The materials allow adaptability and flexibility so that student needs and curricular needs can be met.

The components of the Teacher Classroom Resources *for* ***Merrill Physical Science*** *provide background information and comprehensive teaching material to aid in the effective teaching of physical science.*

In addition to the wide array of instructional options provided in the Student and Teacher Wraparound Editions, ***Merrill Physical Science*** also offers an extensive list of support materials and program resources. Some of these materials offer alternative ways of enriching or extending your physical science program, others provide tools for reinforcing and assessing student learning, while still others will help you directly in delivering instruction.

For your convenience, appropriate resources are called to your attention in PROGRAM RESOURCES boxes and VideoDisc reference throughout the *Teacher Wraparound Edition.*

Hands-On Activities

Activity Masters provide a worksheet for every text Activity and MINI-Lab. This worksheet reproduces the complete text for the Activity or MINI-Lab, provides any needed table for data, and illustrates procedures.

The **Laboratory Manual** is a learning-through-doing program of activities. Based on the philosophy that scientific knowledge is acquired through individual activity and experimentation, the manual consists of many varied laboratory activities designed to reinforce concepts presented in ***Merrill Physical Science***. Laboratory investigations for each Student Edition chapter require students to work through a problem by observing, analyzing, and drawing conclusions. Some of the chemistry labs are microlabs, which make your lab program more efficient and cost effective by reducing the amounts of materials needed. The **Laboratory Manual, Teacher Annotated Edition**, consists of the Student Edition pages with teacher answers on reduced pages in the back. The reduced pages may include suggestions for alternate materials, teaching tips, and sample data, as appropriate, plus answers to all student questions.

The **Lab Partner Software Package** enables students to use an Apple or IBM computer to graph any quantitative data from any of the text Activities or laboratories.

Reinforcement Resources

The **Study Guide** worksheets are suitable for all students; they are closely tied to the student text and require recall of text content.

Reinforcement worksheets are for students of average and above-average ability; a variety of formats are used to reinforce each text lesson.

Concept Mapping masters challenge students to construct a visual representation of relationships among particular chapter concepts. This booklet is developmental in its approach; early concept maps are nearly complete; later ones provide only a skeleton and linking words.

Chapter Review masters are two-page review worksheets consisting of 25 questions for each chapter. They can be used to prepare for tests, as alternate tests, and as vocabulary review.

Chapter Review Software provides chapter-end review questions for student use. Based on the review questions found in the student text at the end of the chapter, the software presents questions in random order. Feedback for incorrectly answered questions provides the page in the student text where the answer is found.

Enrichment Resources

Enrichment worksheets are tailored for students with above-average ability; a wide range of formats allows students to design, interpret, research, and create based on the text of each lesson.

Cross-Curricular Connections masters are interdisciplinary worksheets that relate science to other disciplines. There is one worksheet per chapter; the emphasis is on *doing* the related discipline whenever possible.

Science and Society worksheets show the impact of science on current societal issues and problems. There is one worksheet for each chapter; each ends with a question requiring students to draw conclusions and/or make decisions.

Critical Thinking/Problem Solving worksheets consist of a reading selection related to a chapter topic and questions that help to develop critical-thinking skills while applying concepts learned in the classroom to new situations.

Technology masters explain how something works and/or integrates the sciences. The topics are tied to the student text.

The seven-disc **Science and Technology Videodisc Series (STVS)** contains more than 280 full-motion videoreports on a broad spectrum of topics relating to current research in various science fields, innovations in technology, and science and society issues. In addition to reinforcing science concepts, the videoreports are ideal for illustrating science methods, laboratory techniques, and careers in science. Each disc is centered on a particular science topic.

- Disc 1: PHYSICS
- Disc 2: CHEMISTRY
- Disc 3: EARTH AND SPACE
- Disc 4: PLANTS AND SIMPLE ORGANISMS
- Disc 5: ANIMALS
- Disc 6: ECOLOGY
- Disc 7: HUMAN BIOLOGY

The **Videodisc Correlation** book contains the complete correlation with bar codes of OPTICAL DATA's Videodisc images to the content of *Merrill Physical Science*.

Science Integration Activities broaden the students' understanding of physical science by introducing masters with activities that relate to another science. There is one activity per chapter, each chosen for its relationship to the physical science chapter content.

Assessment Resources

Alternate Assessment in the Science Classroom is a resource book that provides a rationale and strategies to use for authentically assessing student progress during your science course.

Performance Assessment contains seven unit-based performance-assessment activities that students can plan and perform as well as teaching strategies. It also contains one Skill Assessment for each chapter, each with teaching strategies.

Performance Assessment in Middle School Science (PAMSS) provides specific strategies for assessment, emphasizing use of the Performance Task Assessment Lists and rubrics that are included.

Chapter and Unit Tests includes one four-page test for each chapter and one two-page test for each unit. Questions range from simple recall to higher-order thinking process.

Computer Test Banks, available in Apple, IBM, and Macintosh versions, provide the ultimate flexibility in designing and creating your own test instruments. Select test items from two different levels of difficulty, or write and edit your own.

Additional Resources

The **Lesson Plan** booklet contains complete lesson plans for every lesson in the student text. Also included are references to all program components of *Merrill Physical Science*.

The **Spanish Resources** book provides Spanish translations of Objectives, Summary statements, and Key Terms and their definitions for every chapter. Also included is a complete English/Spanish glossary to *Merrill Physical Science*.

The **Color Transparency Package** contains 50 full-color transparencies, as well as the **Transparency Masters**, blackline versions of the transparencies. Also included are a student worksheet for each transparency and instructions for using the transparencies. These materials are conveniently packaged in a three-ring binder.

Planning for Emphasis

The purpose of a Planning Guide is to aid the teacher in developing a course that will offer the best possible program for students.

Merrill Physical Science provides flexibility in the selection of topics and content, which allows teachers to adapt the text to the needs of individual students and classes. In this regard, the teacher is in the best position to decide what topics are to be presented, the pace at which the content is covered, and what material should be given the most emphasis. To assist the teacher in planning the course, a Planning Guide has been provided.

Two Semester Course

Merrill Physical Science may be used in a full-year course of two semesters covering the text activities and chapter-end materials. It is assumed that a year-long course in physical science will have 180 periods of approximately 45 minutes each. In the Planning Guide, each chapter is listed along with the number of class sessions recommended for teaching the chapter. Use the Planning Guide to gauge the amount of time you will spend on each topic.

One Semester Course

Through the selection of specific units, chapters, and sections, **Merrill Physical Science** also may be used in a one-semester course that conforms to a local curriculum emphasis. Alternatives are also presented in the Planning Guide for one-semester, 90-day courses in basic physics (PH) and Chemistry (CH). Columns in the Planning Guide list the number of class sessions suggested for the study of the chapter sections in each of the one-semester alternatives.

Flexibility

Please remember that the Planning Guide is provided as an aid in planning the best course for your students. You should use the Planning Guide in relation to your curriculum and the ability levels of the classes you teach, the materials available for activities, and the time allotted for teaching. You may decide to extend the scope and time devoted to certain topics through the use of enrichment activities and *Teacher Classroom Resources* materials. These materials are listed in the teacher margins and on the interleaf pages preceding each chapter. The Planning Guide will assist you in developing and following a schedule that will enable you to complete your goals for the school year or semester.

Planning Guide

	CLASS SESSIONS			
Chapter	Full-Year Course	Semester Science	Semester PH	CH
1	5	2	3	5
2	9	5	6	9
3	7	4	7	
4	7	4	7	
5	7	4	7	
6	7	3	5	
7	7	3	5	
8	10	4	8	6
9	7	4		7
10	9	5		9
11	9	5		8
12	8	4		8
13	8	3		6
14	3	2		3
15	7	4		7
16	8	4		8
17	9	5		9
18	6	4	6	
19	6	4	6	
20	6	3	6	
21	8	4	8	
22	9	4	8	
23	5	3	4	
24	7	3	4	5
25	6			
TOTALS	**180**	**90**	**90**	**90**

Concept Maps

In science, concept maps make abstract information concrete and useful, improve retention of information, and show students that thought has shape.

Concept maps are visual representations or graphic organizers of relationships among particular concepts. Concept maps can be generated by individual students, small groups, or an entire class. **Merrill Physical Science** develops and reinforces three types of concept maps—the **network tree, events chain,** and **cycle concept map**—that are most applicable to studying science. Examples of the three types and their applications are shown on this page.

Students can learn how to construct each of these types of concept maps by referring to pages 684 and 685 of the **Skill Handbook.** Throughout the course, students will have many opportunities to practice their concept mapping skills, as there is at least one concept mapping Skill Builder per chapter.

Network Tree

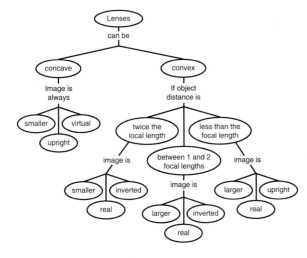

Applications:
- shows causal information
- a hierarchy
- branching procedures

Events Chain

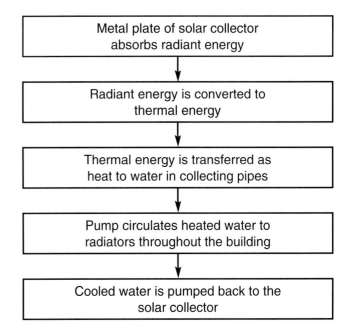

Applications:
- describes the stages of process
- the steps in a linear procedure
- a sequence of events

Cycle Concept Map

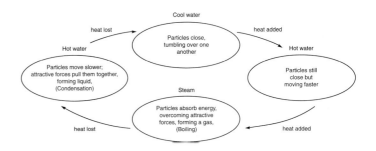

Application: shows how a series of events interact to produce a set of results again and again

Skill Builders/More Skill Builders

The section-ending **Skill Builders** and the **More Skill Builders** section of **Chapter Reviews** in early chapters direct students to make a specific type of concept map, and in most cases concept terms to be used are provided. In later chapters, in a developmental approach, students are given only general guidelines. For example, concept terms to be used may be provided and students are required to select the appropriate model to apply or vice versa. Finally, students may be asked to provide both the terms and type of concept map to explain relationships among concepts. When students are given this flexibility, it is important for you to recognize that, while sample answers are provided, student responses may vary. Look for the conceptual strength of student responses, not absolute accuracy. You'll notice that most network tree maps provide connecting words that explain the relationships among concepts. We recommend that you not require all students to supply these words, but many students may be challenged by this aspect.

More Skill Builders in the **Chapter Reviews** that ask students to make a concept map often provide the concept map format and specific concept terms to use. This will ensure more consistent student responses, and make assessment easier, than when students are asked to make their own concept map style.

Concept Mapping Booklet

The **Concept Mapping** book of the *Teacher Classroom Resources,* too, provides a developmental approach for students to practice concept mapping.

As a teaching strategy, generating concept maps can be used to preview a chapter's content by visually relating the concepts to be learned and allowing the students to read with purpose. Using concept maps for previewing is especially useful when there are many new key science terms for students to learn. As a review strategy, constructing concept maps reinforces main ideas and clarifies their relationships. Construction of concept maps using cooperative learning strategies as described in this Teacher Guide will allow students to practice both interpersonal and process skills.

Flex Your Brain

What is FLEX YOUR BRAIN?

Flex Your Brain is a self-directed activity intended to assist students in developing critical-thinking skills while investigating content areas.

A key element in the coverage of problem-solving and critical-thinking skills in **Merrill Physical Science** is a critical-thinking matrix called **Flex Your Brain.**

Flex Your Brain provides students with an opportunity to explore a topic in an organized, self-checking way, and then identify how they arrived at their responses during each step of their investigation. The activity incorporates many of the skills of critical thinking. It helps students to think about their own thinking and learn about thinking from their peers.

In a step-by-step approach, **Flex Your Brain** leads students to:

- **focus** on a single topic;
- **consider** their prior knowledge of the topic;
- **pose questions** regarding the topic;
- **hypothesize** answers to their questions;
- **evaluate** their **confidence** in their answer;
- **identify** ways to investigate the topic to prove, disprove, or amend their responses;
- **follow through** with their investigation;
- **evaluate** their **responses** to their questions, checking for their own misconceptions or lack of understanding;
- **reconsider** their question responses; incorporate new knowledge gained; and
- **review and share** the thinking processes that they used during the activity.

Where is FLEX YOUR BRAIN found?

In Chapter 1, on page 15 of the student text, is an introduction to the topics of critical thinking and problem solving. **Flex Your Brain** accompanies the text section as a one-page activity in Chapter 1. Brief student instructions are given, along with the matrix itself. A two-page version of **Flex Your Brain** appears as a worksheet on page 5 in the *Activity Worksheets* book of the *Teacher Classroom Resources*. This version provides spaces for students to write in their responses.

In the *Teacher Wraparound Edition*, suggested topics are given in each chapter for the use of **Flex Your Brain.** You can either refer students to Chapter 1 for the procedure or photocopy the worksheet master from the *Teacher Resource Guide.*

Use of **Flex Your Brain** is certainly not restricted to those topics suggested in the *Teacher Wraparound Edition.* Feel free to use it for practice in critical thinking about any concept or topic.

When to Use FLEX YOUR BRAIN

Flex Your Brain can be used as a whole-class activity or in cooperative groups, but is primarily designed to be used by individual students within the class. There are three basic steps.

1. Teachers assign a class topic to be investigated using **Flex Your Brain**.
2. Students use **Flex Your Brain** to guide them in their individual explorations of the topic.
3. After students have completed their explorations, teachers guide them in a discussion of their experiences with **Flex Your Brain,** bridging content and thinking processes.

Flex Your Brain can be used at many different points in the lesson plan.

▶**Introduction:** Ideal for introducing a topic, **Flex Your Brain** elicits students' prior knowledge and identifies misconceptions, enabling the teacher to formulate plans specific to student needs.

▶**Development:** **Flex Your Brain** leads students to find out more about a topic on their own, and develops their research skills while increasing their knowledge. Students actually pose their own questions to explore, making their investigations relevant to their personal interests and concerns.

▶**Review and Extension:** **Flex Your Brain** allows teachers to check student understanding while allowing students to explore aspects of the topic that go beyond the material presented in class.

How to Use FLEX YOUR BRAIN

To assist teachers in using **Flex Your Brain,** an annotated version of the directions appearing on the student page is given below.

1 **Fill in the topic your teacher gives you.**

Focus students by providing a topic that you need to introduce, develop, or review. Topics should be fairly broad and stated in only a few words; for example, "simple machines" or "solutions." Later, when students are familiar with Flex Your Brain, you may want students to select the topic.

2 **Jot down what you already know about the topic. If you know more than five things, write them on another sheet of paper.**

As a class or cooperative group, this could be a brainstorming process. Otherwise, students should recall individually what they know about the topic. Set a reasonable time limit for this step.

As you track student progress through this step, look for evidence of misconceptions. Encourage students to draw knowledge from their own experiences as well as from academic sources.

3 **Using what you already know (Step 2), form a question about the topic. Are you unsure about one of the items listed? Do you want to know more about anything? Do you want to know what, how, or why? Write down your question.**

Students can pose their own questions about the topic and pursue their answers independently; or as a class or group, they can generate several questions. Groups may choose one of these questions to investigate, or the entire class can select one question for all to research.

4 **Guess an answer to your question. In the next few steps, you will be exploring the reasonableness of your answer. Write down your guess.**

The significance of this step is to get students to think, not just know the right answer. Based on what they already know about the topic, students should form hypotheses about the questions asked in Step 3. The correctness of their answers at this point is not as important as the means by which they arrive at them.

Guessing is not a poor means to arrive at an answer if students first consider the facts they know about the topic. Still, students may hesitate to write down answers that they aren't sure of. Encourage students to provide a "best guess."

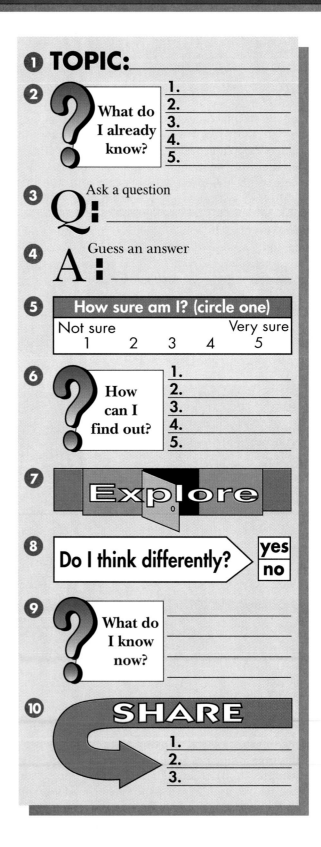

5 **Circle the number in the box that matches how sure you are of your answer in Step 4. This is your chance to rate your confidence in what you've done so far and, later, to see how your level of sureness affects your thinking.**

Students should evaluate their feelings at this point and begin to recognize the extent to which they are confident of their answers. Self-evaluation is critical to successful problem solving. This step becomes especially important when students review their thinking process in Step 10. Make sure students know that emotions and intuition are important aspects of problem solving.

6 **How can you find out more about your topic? You might want to read a book, ask an expert, or do an experiment. Write down ways you can find out more.**

The first time through this activity, you may want to have the class brainstorm ways to explore topics. Discuss the usefulness and appropriateness of the different means of investigation.

Evaluating the appropriateness of sources is an important skill to emphasize at this step. Encourage students to gain knowledge from the world at large, not just from expert sources. Be sure to bring out in your discussion that checking with a friend may be appropriate in some situations, but not in others.

7 **Make a plan to explore your answer. Use the resources you listed in Step 6. Then, carry out your plan.**

Students should use at least three resources before drawing conclusions. Encourage them to consider and use resources that might provide different perspectives on the topic in question.

Experimenting should be encouraged as a means of exploration. Review the scientific method when introducing this step and emphasize the science process skills.

8 **Now that you've explored, go back to your answer in Step 4. Would you answer differently? Mark one of the boxes.**

Students should consider whether they want to change their original answers. If their original answers require modifying in any way, they should mark the "yes" box.

At this step, students should begin to recognize their original misconceptions regarding the topic.

9 **Considering what you learned in your exploration, answer your question again. You may want to add new things you've learned or completely change your answer.**

If students' original answers were correct, request that they restate their answers incorporating new knowledge gained from their explorations. Otherwise, students should correct or modify their answers as needed.

This step leads students to draw conclusions. Help students to recognize how even a wrong answer in Step 4 contributed to the new answer by giving them a basis for exploration. Wrong answers are an important part of the scientific process.

10 **It's important to be able to talk about thinking. Choose three people to tell about how you arrived at your response in every step. For example, don't just read what you wrote in Step 2. Try to share how you thought of those things.**

The process of sharing ensures that students will reflect on what they have done. Encourage students to review each preceding step to determine how they arrived at their responses. Make sure students know that this is not an easy task and that they may struggle to put their process into words.

Verbalizing is important. When students put their own process into their own words, meaningful, internalized learning occurs. Discourage students from ridiculing other students during the sharing process.

The primary goal of **Flex Your Brain** is to improve students' ability to think effectively. Until their thought processes are somehow made clear to them, this will never occur. Step 10 achieves this by engaging students in metacognition, or the process of thinking about thinking.

Metacognition makes the process of thinking conscious and thus allows the process to be examined and improved. It is important to emphasize the importance of sharing and give adequate time to complete this step.

FLEX YOUR BRAIN is flexible.

Flex Your Brain was designed to be flexible in approaching critical thinking and problem solving. These directions are suggestions for one possible use of **Flex Your Brain,** but certainly not the only use. Teachers should feel free to adapt the activity to best suit their own needs and the needs of the diverse classes and students they teach.

Assessment

*What criteria do you use to assess your students as they progress through a course? Do you rely on formal tests and quizzes? To assess students' achievement in science, you need to measure not only their knowledge of the subject matter, but also their ability to handle apparatus, to organize, predict, record, and interpret data, to design experiments, and to communicate orally and in writing. The program presented by **Merrill Physical Science** has been designed to provide you with a variety of assessment tools, both formal and informal, to help you develop a clearer picture of your students' progress.*

Merrill Physical Science presents a wealth of opportunities for performance portfolio development. Each chapter in the student text contains projects, laboratory explorations, enrichment activities, skill builders, library research opportunities, and connections with life, society, and literature. Each of the student activities results in products. A mixture of these products can be used to document student growth during a grading period. At the beginning of each chapter in the **Merrill Physical Science** Teacher Wraparound Edition you will find ASSESSMENT OPTIONS, a useful menu of assessment opportunities available in that particular chapter. These options are classified into performance, group, content, and portfolio suggestions.

PERFORMANCE ASSESSMENT

If we want students to be good problem solvers, then tests of problem-solving competency must logically assess performance on problem-solving tasks. No paper-and-pencil test that grades an answer right or wrong can evaluate performance. Think about a musician, artist, basketball player, or writer. Their work is judged by a performance in a concert, a work of art, a game, or a book. These people do not take paper-and-pencil tests to demonstrate what they know—they perform!

Performance assessments are becoming more common in today's schools. Science curriculums are being revised to prepare students to cope with change and with features that will depend on their abilities to think, learn, and solve problems. Although learning fundamental concepts will always be important in the science curriculum, the concepts alone are no longer sufficient in a student's scientific education. Performance assessments is a way of teaching and learning that involves both process and product. Teachers, as well as the students involved in these activities, will rate the performance and/or the products that result.

Performance Assessment in Middle School Science (PAMSS) and **Alternate Assessment in the Science Classroom**, two of Glencoe's professional handbooks, provide background information, specific examples, and details methods of evaluating performance assessments.

Merrill Physical Science provides opportunities to observe student behavior both in informal and formal setting within the student text.

- Full-page activities contain suggestions for discussion or demonstration that will enable you to assess students' understanding of how the lab relates to the concepts presented in the text.
- MINI-Lab investigations present questions and other opportunities for students to demonstrate or practice skills related to content.
- Using Lab Skills, a section in the Chapter Review, allows students to practice skills by changing a variable in one of the Chapter Activities and MINI-Labs or by repeating the same exercise with entirely different materials.

Activity Worksheets booklet found in *Teacher Classroom Resources* provides formal assessment of student products. These sheets provide space for recording data and observations as students conduct Activities and MINI-Labs.

Merrill Physical Science Teacher Wraparound Edition provides numerous alternate assessment ideas in the margins that will give you ideas for assessing mastery of skills and content Activities, MINI-Labs, and Skillbuilders.

Merrill Physical Performance Assessment **booklet** supplies another approach for assessing student mastery of concepts and skills in the laboratory. This booklet features twenty-five one-page skill assessments and seven performance assessment tasks. These exercises give you additional opportunities to evaluate students' skills in handling laboratory equipment and students's knowledge of science processes. Rubrics and performance task assessment lists for assessing these products can be found in Glencoe's **Performance Assessment in Middle School Science (PAMSS).**

GROUP PERFORMANCE ASSESSMENT

The use of extended projects for the study of science and as an assessment tool to determine what students understand about science can be enhanced by having students work together in cooperative groups.

Recent research has shown that cooperative learning structures produce student learning outcomes for students of all ability levels. **Merrill Physical Science** provides many opportunities for cooperative learning and, as a result, many opportunities to observe group work processes and products. Look for these opportunities in full-page Activities and periodically throughout the chapter.

Cooperative Group Assessment All members of the group contribute to the work process and the products it produces. For example, if a mixed ability, four-member laboratory work group conducts an activity, you can use a rating scale or checklist to assess the quality of both group interaction and work skills. An example, along with information about evaluating cooperative work, is provided in the booklet *Alternate Assessment in the Science Classroom*. All four members of the group are expected to review and agree on the data sheet produced by the group. You can require each member to certify the group results by signing the data sheet or lab report. Research shows that cooperative group assessment is as valid as individual assessment. The booklet *Performance Assessment in Middle School Science (PAMSS)* deals with evaluation of group work and the individual.

STUDENTS' SELF-ASSESSMENT

An important life skill is the ability to self-assess and plan for improvement.

Students often complete their assignments expecting the teacher to grade and return it. Students should learn to thoughtfully study their own work and identify what they have done well and where they need to improve. The booklet *Performance Assessment in Middle School Science (PAMSS)* provides instructional materials to help students objectively assess their work.

ASSESSMENT RESOURCE BOOKS

Glencoe's **Alternate Assessment in the Science Classroom**
Glencoe's **Performance Assessment in Middle School Science (PAMSS)**
Merrill Physical Science Performance Assessment

JOURNALS

Keeping a journal encourages a more thoughtful attitude toward written work and helps students learn more science.

Merrill Physical Science strongly recommends the use of student journals. Journal entries are conducive to thinking about why something has been done. They can be used to note questions, insights, successes, and frustrations. The use of a journal can provide a history of a student's independent work that illuminates the growth of problem-solving or thinking skills. The importance of this is emphasized in that a special feature, **In Your Journal,** appears at least once in each chapter. Students may be asked to use their journals to write creatively or to answer specific questions, such as those in *Section Reviews* or *Chapter Reviews*.

Students are also encouraged to record data and observations, descriptions, and reflections in their journals. They may include diagrams and drawings. Excerpts from the student journals can be included in an individual or group portfolio.

PORTFOLIOS, PUTTING IT ALL TOGETHER

In portfolio assessment, the teacher must keep in mind that the pieces of work in the portfolio have been chosen by the students as representations of their best efforts.

The purpose of a student or cooperative group portfolio is to present examples of the individual or group's work in a "nontesting" environment. The performance portfolio is *not* intended to be a complete collection of all worksheets and other assignments for a grading period. At its best, the portfolio should include integrated performance products that show growth in concept attainment and skill development.

Merrill Physical Science presents a wealth of opportunities for performance portfolio development. Each chapter in the student text contains projects, inquiry questions, enrichment activities, problem solving, skill builders, library research opportunities, and connections with other sciences, society, and literature. Each of the student activities results in a product. A mixture of these products can be used to document student growth during the grading period. The **Merrill Physical Science** *Performance Assessments*, with skills and unit-related performance assessment exercises, provides additional materials that can be included in a portfolio submission. **Merrill Physical Science** strongly suggests including excerpts from student journals in the individual or group portfolio. The booklet *Performance Assessment in Middle School Science (PAMSS)* provides additional background information and specific methods of handling portfolios within the classroom.

CONTENT ASSESSMENT

While new and exciting performance skills assessments are emerging, paper-and-pencil test are still a mainstay of student evaluation. Students must learn to conceptualize, process, and prepare for traditional content assessments. Presently and in the foreseeable future, students will still be required to pass pencil-and-paper tests to exit high school, and to enter college, trade schools, and other training programs.

Merrill Physical Science contains numerous strategies and formative checkpoints for evaluating student progress toward mastery of science concepts. Traditional content assessment forms such as matching, multiple choice, and short essay items are effective in sampling contents.

- *Section Review* questions and application tasks are presented throughout the chapters in the student text. This spaced review process helps build learning bridges that allow all students to confidently progress from one lesson to the next.
- A *Summary* section is located on the first page of the three-page *Chapter Review*. After instruction for the chapter is complete, a summation of the major concepts is presented. The *Summary* enables students to check and reinforce their understanding of the content and concepts presented in the chapter.

- The *Chapter Review* also includes a formal review process for the written content assessment. Individual students or cooperative groups of three to five students can respond to *Chapter Review* questions to check their understanding of science terms, concepts, lab and critical-thinking skills, and problem-solving techniques. By evaluating the student responses to this extensive review, you can determine if any substantial reteaching is needed.

The **Teacher Classroom Resources** contains formal content assessment, including a two-page *Chapter Review*, a four-page *Chapter Test* for each chapter in the student text, and eight two-page unit tests.

- The *Review* can be used to help you determine the students' grasp of the concepts and supporting facts presented in the chapter. Using the review in a whole class session, you can correct any misperceptions and provide closure for a chapter.
- The *Chapter Test* enables students to document their mastery of the concepts developed in the chapter. The test includes multiple choice type items that test knowledge, skill questions, and numerous short answer and essay items that require students to apply and relate concepts.
- *Computer Test Banks* allow you to easily customize tests to fulfill individual assessment plans.

Cooperative Learning in Science

Cooperative Learning fosters academic, personal, and social success for all students.

What is Cooperative Learning?

In cooperative learning, students work together in small groups to learn academic material and interpersonal skills. Group members are responsible for the *group's* accomplishing an assigned task as well as for learning the material themselves. When compared to competitive or individual learning situations in which students work either against each other or alone, cooperative learning fosters academic, personal, and social success for all students. Research shows that successful cooperative learning results in:

- development of positive attitudes toward science;
- choosing to take more science courses as electives;
- positive attitudes toward science carrying over to positive attitudes toward school;
- lower drop-out rates for at-risk students;
- building respect for others regardless of race, ethnic origin, or sex;
- increased awareness of diverse perspectives;
- increased capability for problem solving in sciences;
- increased realization of potential for girls in science classes; and
- development of kindness, sensitivity, and tolerance.

The Teacher's Role

Decide Objectives

Before teaching the lesson, the teacher must decide the academic task and interpersonal skills students will learn or practice in groups. Students can learn most any academic objective in cooperative groups.

The teacher can also specify what interpersonal behaviors are necessary for a group to work cooperatively. When first starting out, it is wise to list and discuss with students basic interpersonal skills needed for people to work together. Basic interpersonal skills you might discuss include being responsible for your own actions, staying on task, listening while others are speaking, and respecting other people and their ideas. Students can learn and practice other interpersonal skills such as using quiet voices, encouraging other group members to participate, summarizing, checking for understanding, disagreeing constructively, reaching a group consensus, and criticizing ideas rather than people.

Select Groups

Cooperative groups usually contain from two to six students. If students are not experienced at working in groups, start with small groups. Consider grouping students in pairs and then joining pairs later to form groups of four or six.

Generally, it is best to assign students to heterogeneous groups. Be certain that each heterogeneous group contains a mixture of abilities, genders, and ethnicity. The use of heterogeneous groups exposes students to ideas different from their own and helps them learn how to work with persons different from themselves.

Change Groups

Initially, cooperative learning groups should work together for only a day or two. After the students are more experienced, they can do group work for longer periods of time. Some teachers change groups every week, while others keep groups of students together during the study of a unit or chapter. Keep groups together long enough for each group to experience success, and change groups often enough that students have the opportunity to work with others.

Structure Tasks

You can structure the learning task to promote the participation of each group member by the arrangement of your classroom and the provision of materials. Limiting the materials needed to accomplish the assigned task causes students to share them. Also, consider assigning students roles that contribute to accomplishing the group task. Student roles should be rotated so each group member has the opportunity to perform each role.

Group Assessment

Finally, decide on how you will assess the learning task and how well the students worked together. Because students are responsible for themselves and other group members learning the material, you can assess group performance during a lesson by frequently asking questions of group members picked at random. It is important that, although each student will be assessed as a group member, group grades are not given. Group grades may result in unequal sharing of responsibilities by group members. Individual learning can be assessed by traditional tests and quizzes.

To assess the learning of interpersonal skills, you can observe their use during the lesson. Groups can assess themselves by rating themselves on a scale from one to ten; they then list ways group members used interpersonal skills and ways to improve group performance.

Teaching the Lesson

Before the Group Task

▶ **Academic Task:** Prepare students for the academic task by teaching any material they might need to know and by giving specific instructions for the task.

▶ **Criteria for Success:** Instruct students that they are responsible for their own learning as well as the learning of other members of the group. Explain the sharing of materials and assuming of roles. Explain your criteria for evaluating group and individual learning.

▶ **Interpersonal Skills:** Specify the interpersonal skills students will be working on, and list what behaviors look and sound like. Explain how you will assess interpersonal skills.

▶ **Group Formation:** Divide the class into groups. Assign roles or divide materials.

During the Group Task

▶ **Provide Assistance with the Academic Task:** Make certain each student can see and hear all other group members. When students are having trouble with the task, answer questions, clarify the assignment, reteach, or provide background as needed. When answering questions, make certain that no students in the group can answer the question before you reply.

▶ **Monitor Student Behavior:** Spend most of your time monitoring the functioning of groups. Praise group cooperation and good use of interpersonal skills.

▶ **Intervene to Teach Interpersonal Skills:** Whenever possible, allow groups to work out their own problems. When groups are having problems, ask group members to figure out how the group can function more effectively. Record your observations of the use of interpersonal skills; share your observations with the groups.

After the Group Task

▶ **Provide Closure to the Lesson:** Reinforce student learning by having groups share their products or summarize the assignment. Answer any questions about the lesson.

▶ **Assess Group and Individual Learning:** Use the criteria discussed before the lesson began to assess and give feedback on how well the academic task was mastered by the groups. Assess individual learning by your traditional methods.

▶ **Assess How Well Groups Functioned:** Have students analyze how well their groups functioned and how well they used interpersonal skills. Groups can list what they did well and what they could do to improve. Have groups share their assessments with the class, and summarize the assessments of the whole class.

Using Cooperative Learning in *Merrill Physical Science*

In *Merrill Physical Science* Teacher Wraparound Edition, Activities, FIND OUTs, and Chapter Reviews suggest using Cooperative Learning. In addition, cooperative learning groups can be used with Section Reviews, Problem Solving, Concept Mapping, and Skill Builder features. The following cooperative learning strategies are referenced in the *Teacher Wraparound Edition.*

Paired Partners

Assign each student a partner, and ask a question or present a problem for them to solve. Each student composes an answer or solution; the pair then shares answers with each other. If partners disagree, they explain and discuss the issues until they agree. When both agree and can explain the answer, partners raise their hands to signify both agree and can explain the answer. After determining if groups have the correct answer, some teachers use thumbs up to indicate "correct" and thumbs down to indicate "incorrect." Paired Partners can be used for Problem Solving, Concept Mapping, and Skill Builder features.

Expert Teams

Give each group member a different part of an assignment to study and master. Send group members with the same part of the assignment from the different teams to work together to become experts on their parts. Bring the experts back to their original groups. Each group member teaches his or her part of the assignment to other members of the original group until everyone has mastered all the material. Expert Teams can be used for Section and Chapter Reviews.

Study Buddies

Study Buddies work together to help one another study for tests or to create concept maps. Group students in fours. After a chapter is completed, give students one class period to work in groups on the Chapter Review before a chapter test. If you wish, Study Buddies can be divided into Expert Teams to study and then teach the material. For concept maps, give each group member a different colored pen. Group members pass the concept map around the table adding to the map on each pass with their colored pens.

Numbered Heads Together

Form groups of three to five and have students number off. Then, ask a question or give an assignment. Have students in each group either agree on a group answer or, for higher- level thinking skills, name an example, make a prediction, or state an application. When students have agreed on an answer, call a number at random. Students with that number raise their hands and wait to be called on. Select one student to provide an answer. Determine if other students with that number have the correct answer by indicating thumbs up or down or by having them write their responses on index cards or on the chalkboard. Numbered Heads Together can be used for Section and Chapter Reviews, Problem Solving, Concept Mapping, and Skill Builders.

Problem-Solving Team

Form groups of four students, and assign roles. The reader reads the problem; the clarifier restates it; the solver suggests answers. If the group agrees on answers, the recorder writes the answers on a paper that all members sign. Review the answers and discuss the problem by calling on any group member. Use thumbs up or down, or write responses on response cards or the chalkboard to determine if all groups have the same answers. This strategy can be used for Problem Solving and Skill Builder features.

Science Investigation

Science Investigation group members work together to perform hands-on science investigations. The Science Investigation strategy is used for Activities, MINI-Labs, and FIND OUT features. In Science Investigation, each group member has a different role and duties to perform for the investigation. Some roles are working roles to accomplish the investigation, while others are interpersonal skill roles that help the group function effectively. Following are possible roles for Science Investigation groups.

Working Roles

Reader: reads any directions out loud
Materials Handler: obtains, dispenses, and returns all materials
Safety Officer: informs group of safety precautions; ensures group handles equipment safely
Recorder: records data collected during the activity; writes answers to questions; has all group members sign data collection and answer sheets
Reporter: reports data collected and answers to questions
Timekeeper: keeps group on task and manages the group's time
Calculator: performs calculations and measurements

Interpersonal Skill Roles

Monitor: ensures that each group member participates and encourages participation
Praiser: compliments group members on fulfilling their assigned tasks; compliments group members on use of interpersonal skills

Checker: checks on learning of group members; ensures that each group member can summarize the results of the activity and answer questions

Resources

Adams, D.M., and M.E. Hamm. *Cooperative Learning, Critical Thinking, and Collaboration Across the Curriculum.* Springfield, IL: Charles C. Thomas Publisher, 1990.

Association for Supervision and Curriculum Development. *Educational Leadership,* Volume 47, Number 4. December 1989–January 1990.

Foot, H.C., M.J. Morgan, and R.H. Shute. *Children Helping Children.* New York: John Wiley & Sons, 1990.

Johnson, D.W., and R.T. Johnson. *Learning Together and Alone: Cooperative, Competitive, and Individualistic Learning.* Englewood Cliffs, NJ: Prentice-Hall, 1987.

Johnson, D.W., and R.T. Johnson., E.J. Holubec, and P. Roy. *Circles of Learning: Cooperation in the Classroom.* Alexandria, VA: Association for Supervision and Curriculum Development, 1984.

Kagan, S. *Cooperative Learning: Resources for Teachers.* Riverside, CA: University of California, 1988.

Shlomo, S. *Cooperative Learning Theory and Research.* Westport, CT: Praeger, 1990.

Slavin, R. *Cooperative Learning Theory, Research, and Practice.* Englewood Cliffs, NJ: Prentice Hall, 1990.

Slavin, R. *Using Student Team Learning.* Baltimore, MD: The John Hopkins Team Learning Project, 1986.

Meeting Individual Needs

With careful planning, the needs of all students can be met in the science classroom.

	DESCRIPTION	SOURCES OF HELP/INFORMATION
Learning Disabled	All learning disabled students have a problem in one or more areas, such as academic learning, language, perception, social-emotional adjustment, memory, or attention.	*Journal of Learning Disabilities* *Learning Disability Quarterly*
Behaviorally Disordered	Children with behavior disorders deviate from standards or expectations of behavior and impair the functioning of others and themselves. These children may also be gifted or learning disabled.	*Exceptional Children* *Journal of Special Education*
Physically Challenged	Children who are physically disabled fall into two categories—those with orthopedic impairments and those with other health impairments. Orthopedically impaired children have the use of one or more limbs severely restricted, so the use of wheelchairs, crutches, or braces may be necessary. Children with other health impairments may require the use of respirators or have other medical equipment.	Batshaw, M.L. and M.Y. Perset. *Children with Handicaps: A Medical Primer.* Baltimore: Paul H. Brooks, 1981. Hale, G. (Ed.). *The Source Book for the Disabled.* NY: Holt, Rinehart & Winston, 1982. *Teaching Exceptional Children*
Visually Impaired	Children who are visually disabled have partial or total loss of sight. Individuals with visual impairments are not significantly different from their sighted peers in ability range or personality. However, blindness may affect cognitive, motor, and social development, especially if early intervention is lacking.	*Journal of Visual Impairment and Blindness* *Education of Visually Handicapped* American Foundation for the Blind
Hearing Impaired	Children who are hearing impaired have partial or total loss of hearing. Individuals with hearing impairments are not significantly different from their hearing peers in ability range or personality. However, the chronic condition of deafness may affect cognitive, motor, and social development if early intervention is lacking. Speech development also is often affected.	*American Annals of the Deaf* *Journal of Speech and Hearing Research* *Sign Language Studies*
Limited English Proficiency	Multicultural and/or bilingual children often speak English as a second language or not at all. Customs and behavior of people in the majority culture may be confusing for some of these students. Cultural values may inhibit some of these students from full participation.	*Teaching English as a Second Language Reporter* R.L. Jones, ed., *Mainstreaming and the Minority Child.* Reston, VA: Council for Exceptional Children, 1976.
Gifted	Although no formal definition exists, these students can be described as having above-average ability, task commitment, and creativity. Gifted students rank in the top 5% of their class. They usually finish work more quickly than other students, and are capable of divergent thinking.	*Journal for the Education of the Gifted* *Gifted Child Quarterly* *Gifted Creative/Talented*

TIPS FOR INSTRUCTION

1. Provide support and structure; clearly specify rules, assignments, and duties.
2. Establish situations that lead to success.
3. Practice skills frequently—use games and drills to help maintain student interest.
4. Allow students to record answers on tape and allow extra time to complete tests and assignments.
5. Provide outlines or tape lecture material.
6. Pair students with peer helpers, and provide class time for pair interaction.

---

1. Provide a clearly structured environment with regard to scheduling, rules, room arrangement, and safety.
2. Clearly outline objectives and how you will help students obtain objectives. Seek input from them about their strengths, weaknesses, and goals.
3. Reinforce appropriate behavior and model it for students.
4. Do not expect immediate success. Instead, work for long-term improvement.
5. Balance individual needs with group requirements.

---

1. Openly discuss with students any uncertainties you have about when to offer aid.
2. Ask parents or therapists and students what special devices or procedures are needed, and if any special safety precautions need to be taken.
3. Allow physically disabled students to do everything their peers do, including participating in field trips, special events, and projects.
4. Help nondisabled students and adults understand physically disabled students.

---

1. As with all students, help the student become independent. Some assignments may need to be modified.
2. Teach classmates how to serve as guides.
3. Limit unnecessary noise in the classroom.
4. Encourage students to use their sense of touch. Provide tactile models whenever possible.
5. Describe people and events as they occur in the classroom.
6. Provide taped lectures and reading assignments.
7. Team the student with a sighted peer for laboratory work.

---

1. Seat students where they can see your lip movements easily, and avoid visual distractions.
2. Avoid standing with your back to the window or light source.
3. Using an overhead projector allows you to maintain eye contact while writing.
4. Seat students where they can see speakers.
5. Write all assignments on the chalkboard, or hand out written instructions.
6. If the student has a manual interpreter, allow both student and interpreter to select the most favorable seating arrangements.

---

1. Remember that students' ability to speak English does not reflect their academic ability.
2. Try to incorporate the students' cultural experience into your instruction. The help of a bilingual aide may be effective.
3. Include information about different cultures in your curriculum to aid students' self-image—avoid cultural stereotypes.
4. Encourage students to share their cultures in the classroom.
5. Incorporate a variety of teaching strategies in your classroom to accommodate different learning styles.

---

1. Make arrangements for students to take selected subjects early and to work on independent projects.
2. Make public services available through a catalog of resources, such as agencies providing free and inexpensive materials, community services and programs, and people in the community with specific expertise.
3. Ask "what if" questions to develop high-level thinking skills; establish an environment safe for risk taking.
4. Emphasize concepts, theories, ideas, relationships, and generalizations.

Student Bibliography

GENERAL SCIENCE CONTENT

Barr, George. *Science Tricks and Magic for Young People.* New York: Dover Publications, Inc., 1987.

Cash, Terry. *175 More Science Experiments to Amuse and Amaze Your Friends: Experiments! Tricks! Things to Make!* New York: Random House, 1991.

Churchill, E. Richard. *Amazing Science Experiments with Everyday Materials.* New York: Sterling Publishing Co., Inc., 1991.

Gold, Carol. *Science Express,* "50 Scientific Stunts for the Ontario Science Centre." New York: Addison-Wesley, 1991.

Herbert, Don. *Mr. Wizard's Supermarket Science.* New York: Random House, 1980.

Lewis, James. *Hocus Pocus Stir and Cook, The Kitchen Science-Magic Book.* New York: Meadowbrook Press, Division of Simon and Shuster, Inc., 1991.

Mandell, Muriel, *Simple Science Experiments with Everyday Materials.* New York: Sterling Publishing Co., Inc., 1989.

Roberts, Royston. *Serendipity: Accidental Discoveries in Science.* New York: John Wiley and Sons, Inc., 1989.

Schultz, Robert F. *Selected Experiments and Projects.* Washington, DC: Thomas Alva Edison Foundation, 1988.

Strongin, Herb. *Science on a Shoestring.* Menlo Park, CA: Addison-Wesley Publishing Co., 1985.

Townsley, B.J. *Famous Scientists.* Los Angeles, CA: Enrich Education Division of Price Stern Sloan Inc., 1987.

PHYSICS

Aronson, Billy. "Water Ride Designers Are Making Waves." *3-2-1 Contact,* August, 1991, pp. 14-16.

Asimov, Isaac. *How Did We Find Out the Speed of Light?* New York: Walker, 1986.

Berger, Melvin. *Light, Lenses, and Lasers.* New York: Putnam, 1987.

Cash, Terry. *Sound.* New York: Warwick Press, 1989.

Catherall, Ed. *Exploring Sound.* Austin, TX: Steck-Vaughn Library, 1989.

Heiligman, Deborah. "There's a Lot More to Color Than Meets the Eye." *3-2-1 Contact,* November, 1991, pp. 16-20.

McGrath, Susan. *Fun with Physics.* Washington, DC: National Geographic Society, 1986.

Myles, Douglas. *The Great Waves.* New York: McGraw-Hill Book Company, 1985.

Taylor, Barbara. *Light and Color.* New York: Franklin Watts, 1990.

Taylor, Barbara. *Sound and Music.* New York: Warwick Press, 1990.

Ward, Allen. *Experimenting with Batteries, Bulbs, and Wires.* New York: Chelsea House, 1991.

Ward, Alan. *Experimenting with Sound.* New York: Chelsea Juniors, 1991.

Wood, Nicholas. *Listen . . . What Do You Hear?* Mahwah, NJ: Troll Associates, 1991.

CHEMISTRY

Barber, Jacqueline. *Of Cabbage and Chemistry.* Washington, DC: Lawrence Hall of Science, NSTA, 1989.

Barber, Jacqueline. *Chemical Reactions.* Washington, DC: Lawrence Hall of Science, NSTA, 1986.

Benrey, Ronald. *Alternative Energy Sources: Experiments You Can Do . . . from Edison.* Washington, DC: Thomas Alva Edison Foundation, Edison Electric Institute, 1988.

Cornell, John. *Experiments with Mixtures.* New York: John Wiley and Sons, Inc., 1990.

Matsubara, T. *The Structure and Properties of Matter.* New York: Springer-Verlag New York Inc., 1982.

Zubrewski, Bernie. *Messing Around with Baking Chemistry: A Children's Museum Activity Book.* Boston, MA: Little Brown and Co., 1981.

LIFE SCIENCE

Dewey, Jennifer Owings. *A Day and Night in the Desert.* Boston, MA: Little Brown, 1991.

Johnson, Cathy. *Local Wilderness.* New York: Prentice Hall, 1987.

Leslie, Clare Walker. *Nature All Year Long.* New York: Greenwillow, 1990.

McGrath, Susan. *The Amazing Things Animals Do.* Washington, DC: National Geographic Society, 1989.

Markmann, Erika. *Grow It! An Indoor/Outdoor Gardening Guide for Kids.* New York: Random House, 1991.

Children's Atlas of the Environment. Chicago, IL: Rand McNally, 1991.

Van Cleave, Janice Pratt. *Biology for Every Kid: 101 Easy Experiments that Really Work.* New York: Wiley, 1990.

EARTH SCIENCE

Ardley, Neil. *The Science Book of Air.* New York: Gulliver Books, Harcourt, Brace, Jovanovich, Publishers, 1991.

Ardley, Neil. *The Science Book of Water.* New York: Gulliver Books, Harcourt, Brace, Jovanovich, Publishers, 1991.

Barrow, Lloyd H. *Adventures with Rocks and Minerals: Geology Experiments for Young People.* Hillsdale, NJ: Enslow, 1991.

Booth, Basil. *Volcanoes and Earthquakes.* Englewood Cliffs, NJ: Silver Burdett Press, 1991.

Javna, John. *50 Simple Things Kids Can Do to Save the Earth.* Kansas City: The Earth Works Group, Andrews and McMeel, a Universal Press Syndicate Co., 1990.

Van Cleave, Janice. *Earth Science for Every Kid.* New York: John Wiley and Sons, Inc., 1991.

Wood, Robert W. *Science for Kids: 39 Easy Geology Activities.* Blue Ridge Summit, PA: Tab Books, 1992.

Teacher Bibliography

CURRICULUM

Aldridge, William G. "Scope, Sequence, and Coordination: A New Synthesis for Improving Science Education." *Journal of Science Education and Technology.*

Banks, James A. "Multicultural Education: For Freedom's Sake." *Educational Leadership,* December 1991/January 1992, pp. 32-35.

Beane, James A. "Middle School, The Natural Home of the Integrated Curriculum." *Educational Leadership,* October 1991, pp. 9-13.

Chemistry of Life: 1988 Curriculum Module, Princeton, NJ: Woodrow Wilson National Fellowship Foundation, 1988.

Driver, R. *The Children's Learning in Science Project, Monographs on Preconceptions in Science.* Center for Studies in Science and Mathematics Education, Department of Education, University of Leeds, 1984-1989.

Hazen, Robert M. and James Trefil. *Science Matter, Achieving Scientific Literacy.* New York: Doubleday, 1991.

Phillips, William. "Earth Science Misconceptions." *The Science Teacher,* October 1991, pp. 21-23.

Piaget, J. *To Understand Is to Invent: The Future of Education.* New York: Grossman Publishers, 1973.

Rutherford, E. James and Andrew Ahlgren. *Science for All Americans.* New York: Oxford University Press, 1990.

TEACHING METHODS

Altshular, Kenneth. "The Interdisciplinary Classroom." *The Physics Teacher,* October 1991, pp. 428-429.

Humphreys, David. *Demonstrating Chemistry.* Ontario, Canada: Chemistry Department, McMaster University Hamilton, 1983.

Johnson, David W., Roger T. Johnson, and Edythe Johnson Holubec. *Circles of Learning.* Edina, MN: Interaction Book Company, 1990.

Johnson, David W., Roger T. Johnson, and Edythe Johnson Holubec. *Cooperation in the Classroom.* Edina, MN: Interaction Book Company, 1991.

Johnson, David W., Roger T. Johnson. *Cooperative Learning: Warm-Ups, Grouping Strategies, and Group Activities.* Edina, MN: Interaction Book Company, 1985.

Novak, Joseph. "Clarify with Concept Maps." *The Science Teacher,* October 1991, pp. 44-49.

Penick, John. "Where's the Science?" *The Science Teacher,* May 1991, pp. 27-29.

CONTENT AREA BOOKS

Physics

Arons, A. B. *A Guide to Introductory Physics Teaching.* New York: John Wiley and Sons, 1990.

Berman, Paul. *Light and Sound.* New York: Marshall Cavendish, 1988.

Gardner, Robert. *Experimenting with Light.* New York: Franklin Watts, 1991.

Urone, Paul Peter. *Physics with Health Science Applications.* New York: Harper and Row Publishers, 1986.

Walpole, Brenda. *175 Science Experiments to Amuse and Amaze Your Friends.* New York: Random House, 1988.

Chemistry

Element of the Week. Batavia, IL: Flinn Scientific, Inc., 1990.

Ground to Grits: Scientific Concepts in Nutrition/Agriculture. Columbia, SC: South Carolina Department of Education, 1982.

Joesten, Melvin. *World of Chemistry.* Philadelphia, PA: Saunders College Publishing, 1991.

Mitchell, Sharon and Frederick Juergens. *Laboratory Solutions for the Science Classroom.* Batavia, IL: Flinn Scientific, Inc., 1991.

Solomon, Sally. "Qualitative Analysis of Eleven Household Compounds." *Journal of Chemical Education,* April 1991, pp. 328-329.

Life Science

Hancock, Judith M. *Variety of Life: A Biology Teacher's Sourcebook.* Portland, OR: J. Weston Walch, 1987.

Middleton, James I. "Student-Generated Analogies in Biology." *American Biology Teacher,* January 1991, pp. 42-46.

Vogel, Steven. *Life's Devices: The Physical World of Plants and Animals.* Princeton, NJ: Princeton University Press, 1989.

Earth Science

Callister, Jeffrey C., Lenny Coplestone, Gerald F. Consuegra, Sharon M. Stroud, and Warren E. Yasso. *Earthquakes.* Washington, DC: NSTA/FEMA, 1988.

Lasca, Norman P. "Build Me a River." *Earth,* January 1991, pp. 59-65.

Little, Jane Braxton. "California Town Unites to Save a Stream." *The Christian Science Monitor,* February 28, 1991.

Sae, Andy S. W. "Dynamic Demos." *The Science Teacher,* October 1991, pp. 23-25.

Laboratory Safety

Managing Activities

Hands-on activities provide another opportunity for students to learn to work together. Decisions and plans made by cooperative groups reflect the real world.

Preplanning and organization are important for successful use of hands-on activities in the classroom. Make copies of specific Activity worksheets ahead of time, from the **Activity Worksheets** booklet. Store materials for each activity in a box with a list of contents on the end. The boxes may be color-coded according to the unit of study. Place materials for each group of students in a plastic bag and label the bag with its contents. Students can be responsible for distributing the materials and checking the bag for its contents. Cleaning up and putting materials in their proper place is an essential part of the laboratory experience.

The materials used in **Merrill Physical Science** are easily accessible. If the budget in your school is limited, have students bring in simple, inexpensive materials such as sugar, baking soda, and so on. Parents may also be willing to donate materials and their time to help organize the materials. Many parents genuinely want to help.

It is important to remember that there is no such thing as failure in science activities. If the experiment does not illustrate what you had intended, turn it into a question and hypothesis activity. Students evaluate their results and form hypotheses on how to alter the experiment. Students then test their hypotheses and draw conclusions. Activities can also end with a question or extension to encourage further exploration of concepts.

Laboratory Safety

Safety is of prime importance in every classroom. However, the need for safety is even greater when science is taught. Outlined on the next page are some considerations on laboratory safety.

The activities in **Merrill Physical Science** are designed to minimize dangers in the laboratory. Even so, there are no guarantees against accidents. However, careful planning and preparation as well as being aware of hazards can keep accidents from happening. Numerous books and pamphlets are available on laboratory safety, with detailed instruction on preventing accidents. However, much of what they present can be summarized in the phrase: *Be prepared!* Know the rules and what common violations occur. Know the Safety Symbols used in this book (see p. 34T). Know where emergency equipment is stored and how to use it. Practice good laboratory housekeeping and management by observing these guidelines:

Classroom/Laboratory

1. Store chemicals properly. (see page 36T)
   a. Separate chemicals by reaction type.
   b. Label all chemical containers. Include purchase date, special precautions, and expiration date.
   c. Discard chemicals when outdated, according to appropriate disposal methods.
   d. Do not store chemicals above eye level.
   e. Wood shelving is preferable to metal. All shelving should be firmly attached to walls. Anti-roll lips should be placed on all shelves.
   f. Store only those chemicals that you plan to use.
   g. Flammable and toxic chemicals require special storage containers.
2. Store equipment properly.
   a. Clean and dry all equipment before storing.
   b. Protect electronic equipment and microscopes from dust, humidity, and extreme temperatures.
   c. Label and organize equipment so that it is accessible.
3. Provide adequate workspace.
4. Provide adequate room ventilation.
5. Post safety and evacuation guidelines.
6. Be sure safety equipment is accessible and works.
7. Provide containers for disposing of chemicals, waste products, and biological specimens. Disposal methods must meet local guidelines.
8. Use hot plates whenever possible as a heat source. If burners are used, a central shut-off valve for the gas supply should be available to the teacher. Never use open flames when a flammable solvent is in the same room.

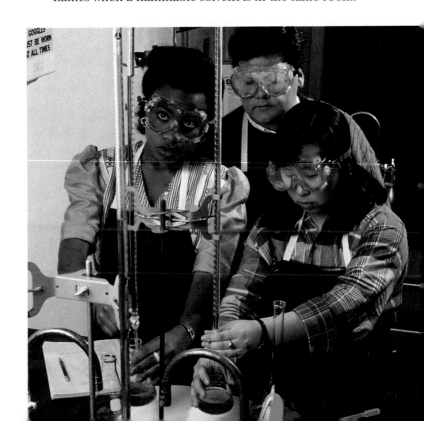

First Day of Class/Labs (with students)

1. Distribute and discuss safety rules, safety symbols, first aid guidelines, and safety contract found in the *Teacher Resource Guide*. Have students refer to Appendix C on pages 673-674, to review safety symbols and guidelines.
2. Review safe use of equipment and chemicals.
3. Review use and location of safety equipment.
4. Discuss safe disposal of materials and laboratory clean-up policy.
5. Discuss proper laboratory attitude and conduct.
6. Document students' understanding of above points.
   a. Have students sign the safety contract and return it.
   b. Administer the safety assessment found on pages 29-31 in the *Teacher Resource Guide*. Reteach those points that students do not understand.

Before Each Investigation

1. Perform each investigation yourself before assigning it.
2. Arrange the lab in such a way that equipment and supplies are clearly labeled and easily accessible.
3. Have available only equipment and supplies needed to complete the assigned investigation.
4. Review the procedure with students, emphasizing any caution statements or safety symbols that appear.
5. Be sure all students know proper procedures to follow if an accident should occur.

During the Investigation

1. Make sure the lab is kept clean and free of clutter.
2. Insist that students wear safety goggles and aprons, if needed.
3. Never allow a student to work alone in the lab.
4. Never allow students to use a cutting device with more than one edge.
5. Students should not point the open end of a heated test tube toward anyone.
6. Remove broken glassware or frayed cords from use. Also clean up any spills immediately. Dilute solutions with water before removing.
7. Be sure all glassware that is to be heated is of a heat-treated type that will not shatter.
8. Remind students that hot glassware looks cool.
9. Prohibit eating and drinking in the lab.
10. Never stir with a thermometer.

After the Investigation

1. Be sure that the lab is clean.
2. Be certain that students have returned all equipment and disposed of broken glassware and chemicals properly.
3. Be sure all hot plates and electrical connections are off.
4. Insist that each student wash his or her hands when lab work is completed.

The *Merrill Physical Science* program uses safety symbols to alert you and your students to possible laboratory dangers. These symbols are explained on the following page. Be sure your students understand each symbol before they begin any activity.

Safety Symbols

Safety symbols alert you and your students to cautions within activities.

	DISPOSAL ALERT This symbol appears when care must be taken to dispose of materials properly.		**ANIMAL SAFETY** This symbol appears whenever live animals are studied and the safety of the animals and the students must be ensured.
	BIOLOGICAL HAZARD This symbol appears when there is danger involving bacteria, fungi, or protists.		**RADIOACTIVE SAFETY** This symbol appears when radioactive materials are used.
	OPEN FLAME ALERT This symbol appears when use of an open flame could cause a fire or an explosion.		**CLOTHING PROTECTION SAFETY** This symbol appears when substances used could stain or burn clothing.
	THERMAL SAFETY This symbol appears as a reminder to use caution when handling hot objects.		**FIRE SAFETY** This symbol appears when care should be taken around open flames.
	SHARP OBJECT SAFETY This symbol appears when a danger of cuts or punctures caused by the use of sharp objects exists.		**EXPLOSION SAFETY** This symbol appears when the misuse of chemicals could cause an explosion.
	FUME SAFETY This symbol appears when chemicals or chemical reactions could cause dangerous fumes.		**EYE SAFETY** This symbol appears when a danger to the eyes exists. Safety goggles should be worn when this symbol appears.
	ELECTRICAL SAFETY This symbol appears when care should be taken when using electrical equipment.		**POISON SAFETY** This symbol appears when poisonous substances are used.
	PLANT SAFETY This symbol appears when poisonous plants or plants with thorns are handled.		**CHEMICAL SAFETY** This symbol appears when chemicals used can cause burns or are poisonous if absorbed through the skin.

Preparation of Solutions

The following text gives some general hints on solution preparation and some safety tips to keep in mind.

For best results, the preparation of each solution is tailored to the requirements of the Activity, MINI-Lab, or FIND OUT activity in which it is used. It is not recommended that solutions be made far in advance. Rather, they should be prepared fresh as needed.

Unless otherwise specified, solutions are prepared by adding the solid to a small amount of water and then diluting with water to the volume listed. Use distilled water for the preparation of solutions. For example, to make a $0.1M$ solution of aluminum sulfate, dissolve 34.2 g of $Al_2(SO_4)_3$ in a small amount of distilled water and dilute to a liter with water. If you use a hydrate that is different from the one specified in a particular preparation, you will need to adjust the amount of the hydrate to obtain the required concentration.

It is most important to use safe laboratory techniques when handling all chemicals. Many substances may appear harmless but are, in fact, toxic, corrosive, or very reactive. Always check the hazard information on the reagent bottle. If in doubt, check with the manufacturer or with Flinn Scientific Inc., (708) 879-6900. Chemicals should never be ingested. Be sure to use proper techniques to smell solutions or other reagents. Always wear safety goggles and an apron. The following general cautions should be used.

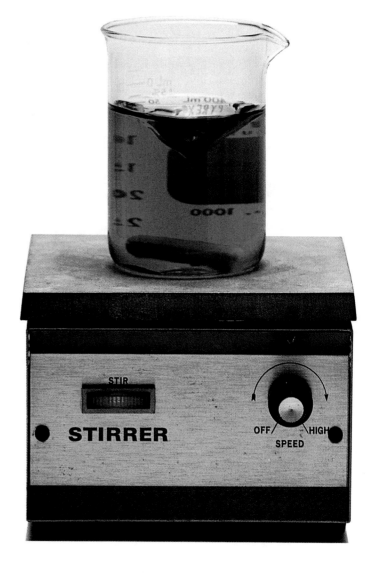

1. *Liquid and/or vapor poisonous/corrosive. Use in the fume hood.*

acetic acid	hydrochloric acid
ammonium hydroxide	nitric acid

2. *Poisonous and corrosive to eyes, lungs, and skin.*

acids	limewater	iron(III) chloride
bases	silver nitrate	potassium permanganate
iodine		

3. *Poisonous if swallowed, inhaled, or absorbed through the skin.*

acetic acid, glacial	copper compounds
barium chloride	lead compounds
chromium compounds	lithium compounds
cobalt(II) chloride	silver compounds

4. *Always add acids to water, never the reverse.*

5. *When either sulfuric acid or sodium hydroxide is added to water, a large amount of thermal energy is released. Sodium metal reacts violently with water. Use extra care if handling any of these substances.*

Chemical Storage and Disposal

General Guidelines

Be sure to store all chemicals properly. The following are guidelines commonly used. Your school, city, county, or state may have additional requirements for handling chemicals. It is the responsibility of each teacher to become informed as to what rules or guidelines are in effect in his or her area.

1. Separate chemicals by reaction type. Strong acids should be stored together. Likewise, strong bases should be stored together and should be separated from acids. Oxidants should be stored away from easily oxidized materials and so on.

2. Be sure all chemicals are stored in labeled containers indicating contents, concentration, source, date purchased (or prepared), any precautions for handling and storage, and expiration date.

3. Dispose of any outdated or waste chemicals properly according to accepted disposal procedures.

4. Do not store chemicals above eye level.

5. Wood shelving is preferable to metal. All shelving should be firmly attached to all walls and have anti-roll edges.

6. Store only those chemicals that you plan to use.

7. Hazardous chemicals require special storage containers and conditions. Be sure to know what those chemicals are and the accepted practices for your area.

8. When working with chemicals or preparing solutions, observe the same general safety precautions that you would expect from students. These include wearing an apron and goggles. Wear gloves and use the fume hood when necessary. Students will want to do as you do whether they admit it or not.

9. If you are a new teacher in a particular laboratory, it is your responsibility to survey the chemicals stored there and to be sure they are stored properly or disposed of. Consult the rules and laws in your area concerning what chemicals can be kept in your classroom. For disposal, consult up-to-date disposal information from the state and federal governments.

Disposal of Chemicals

Local, state, and federal laws regulate the proper disposal of chemicals. These laws should be consulted before chemical disposal is attempted. Although most substances encountered in school laboratories can be flushed down the drain with plenty of water, it is not safe to assume that is always true. It is recommended that teachers who use chemicals consult the following books from the National Research Council.

Prudent Practices for Handling Hazardous Chemicals in Laboratories. Washington, DC: National Academy Press, 1981.

Prudent Practices for Disposal of Chemicals from Laboratories. Washington, DC: National Academy Press, 1983.

These books are useful and still in print, although they are several years old. Current laws in your area would, of course, supersede the information in these books.

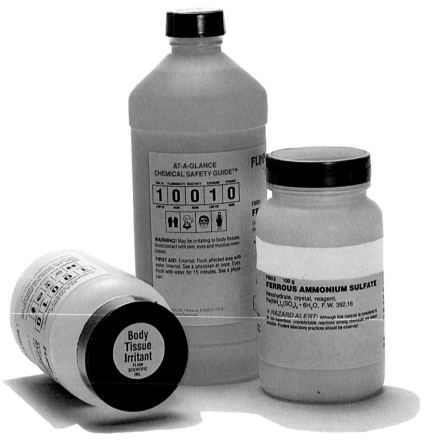

Physical Science Materials List

NONCONSUMABLES			
ITEM	**ACTIVITY**	**MINI LAB**	**FIND OUT**
Aluminum foil,	9-1, 25-1	144, 548	
		646	
heavy duty	14-2		
pieces (2)		523	
strips		567	
Apron	8-1, 13-1		
Bags, plastic, sealable	10-2		
Balance	2-2, 3-2	40, 177	425
	5-2, 7-2	405, 646	
Ball, soccer			189
Balloons, of different shapes			83
medium, round (2)	8-2		
Battery, 6-volt (4)	22-1, 22-2		
	23-1		
6 or 9 volt	21-2		
Beaker,	3-2, 8-2, 14-2,	301	267
	15-1, 16-2	383, 646	
100-mL (7)	25-1		
250-mL (5)	6-1, 15-2, 21-1		
small			299
Board, approximately 100 cm	7-1	66	
long inclined plane		177	
Books,	7-1	87	157
box full (5+)			109
Bottle,		405	
soda pop			457
soda pop, plastic, 2-liter		210	
Bowl, plastic		520	
Box, clear	19-2		
Brick,	7-1		
building (2)	4-2		
Bucket	8-2		
Burner, gas	11-2, 15-2	287, 301	299, 327
Calculator, pocket-sized		609	
Can, coffee, large, with lid			157
Candle		646	
Car			643
Cardboard,	12-2		
thick, (22 cm × 28 cm)	17-1		
Cards		412	
Charcoal briquettes, crushed			
into powder (1 or 2)			379
Clamp, utility		577	
Clay, green, balls (6)	24-2		
modeling	19-2, 25-1		241
white, balls (6)	24-2		
Cloth, or yarn; small piece	6-2		
cotton		548	
wool		631	
Coat hangers, wire		144	
Coins, (3)	7-2		
Compass, magnetic	22-1		

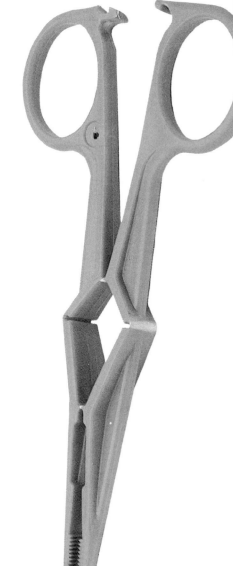

NONCONSUMABLES

ITEM	ACTIVITY	MINI LAB	FIND OUT
Conductivity tester		428	
Construction supplies, misc.	25-2		
Container, plastic, 1 quart	2-2		
Copper foil	9-1		
Corks (10)	4-1		
CRT		605	
Cups,			
clear plastic			379
foam	5-2	42, 490	
foam, with lid		118	
measuring	2-2, 14-2		
paper	8-1, 22-1		219
paper or foam			379
plastic	3-2		
Diffraction grating	19-1		
Diode,	23-1		
Dish, per group (1)			403
Dropper,	8-1	201, 210	
medicine (4)	17-1, 17-2	405	403
Dynamics carts (2)	4-2		
Egg carton, modified	11-1		
Electroscope		631	
Evaporating dish, small (3)	9-2, 14-1		
Extension cord			133
Filter paper			425
Film, undeveloped, or photo-			
graphic film badge		621	
Flask, 250-mL	6-2		
Forceps	25-1		
Freezer bag, plastic	9-1		
Funnel, plastic	21-1		425
Gauge, air pressure			189
Glass, large, clear		7	
Glove, heat proof	8-2		
Glue		144	
Goggles, safety	8-1, 8-2		
	9-2, 11-2		
	12-1, 13-1		
	25-1		
Graduated cylinder,	2-2, 5-2,	40, 646	
	8-1, 15-1,		
	16-1,16-2,		
	17-1, 17-2		
10-cm³	9-2		
Granite, piece of	9-1		
Gravel, fine			219, 379
Greeting cards, musical			595
Hair curlers, electric	5-2		
Hammer	14-2		
Hand lens	9-2		
Heat lamp, or portable hair dryer			425
Hot plate, electric	2-2, 9-2,		
	14-1, 15-1,		
	16-2		
Inflation needle			189
Iron wire, thin pieces of,			
such as hairpins		301	
Jars, small, or beakers		428	619
Knife, or scissors	22-2		
Lamp, with bare bulb			133

NONCONSUMABLES

ITEM	ACTIVITY	MINI LAB	FIND OUT
LEDs, different colors (2)	23-1		
Lid, with straw hole		42	
Light, fluorescent		490	
incandescent		490, 523	
low voltage	22-2		
source	19-2, 20-2		
with socket (3)	21-2		
Magnet,		577	
disk (12)	23-2		
small		605	
Magnetic board, 20 cm × 27 cm	10-1		
Magnetic strip	10-1		
Magnet wire, 22 ga	22-1		
32 ga	22-1		
Marble chips			425
Marbles,	11-1	66	157
or other small, uniformly			
shaped objects			619
Markers	10-1	412	
Mass, 20-g		73	
Matches,	6-2	631	
large wooden	12-1		
Metersticks,	3-1, 4-1,	66, 177	
	4-2, 8-2,		59
	21-1		
(2)	5-1		
Microscopes			643
Milliammeter		567	
Mirrors, plane (2)	20-1		
Nail,	22-1		
large	22-2		
Needle		523, 577	
Newspaper	3-2		
Note cards, colored	13-2		
Nuts, bolts, washers; various			
small			241
Objects, metal		466	
small		520	
with flat, hard surfaces	20-2		
Pads, heavy		476	
Paper,	19-2	87	573
cardstock, thin strip and			
sheets (2)	23-2		
graph	5-2, 24-1	42	
poster, large sheet	25-2		
red, plain, circles,			
1-cm wide	3-1		
selection of strips	3-2		
sheet, 22 cm × 28 cm	7-2		
sheets of various types,			
weights, sizes	3-1		
tissue			545
typing, 22 cm × 28 cm,			
marked with rectangles	17-1		
white, plain,		73, 287	327
circles, 4-cm wide	10-1		
Paper clips	3-1, 13-2,		299
	20-1, 21-2,		
	22-2		
Paper towel	14-2		403

NONCONSUMABLES

ITEM	ACTIVITY	MINI LAB	FIND OUT
Pencils,	7-1	40, 257	573
colored	19-1		
round	19-2		157
Penny, copper	14-1	629	
darkened (2)			403
Pens,		257	
felt-tip	4-1		
colored, set of	25-2		
marking	8-2		
Pinch clamps (2)	6-2		
Pipe, plastic	18-2		
Plaster of paris	14-2		
Plastic food wrap	25-1	490, 520	403
		548	
Polarizing filters (2)	20-2		
Polystyrene sheets	12-2		
Poster board		144	
Pot, cooking	2-2		
Power supply, AC, low voltage	22-2, 23-1		
with rheostat	19-1		
Protractor	20-1		
Pulley	7-1		
Punch, paper		548	
Pump, inflation			189
Radio		476	
Resistor, 1000 ohm	23-1		
Ring stand,	15-2	577, 646	
(2)	1-1		
and ring	3-2, 5-1	646	
	7-1, 21-1		
Red, plastic		631	
Rubber bands, (4)	18-2, 25-1		
long	4-2		
Rubber tubing, 1 m	21-1		
pieces, (3)	6-2		
Rulers,	6-1		157, 545
metric	1-1, 7-2,		
	18-2, 23-2		
Sand	3-2, 16-2	118	219, 379
Sand paper,	22-1		
coarse		73	
Scissors	1-1, 2-1,	87	
	3-2, 12-2,		
	17-1, 21-2		
Slides, microscope			643
Slinky	18-1		
Soda straw,	22-1	7	
cut to length of nail	22-2		
Solder, piece of	9-1		
Splint, wooden	16-1, 16-2		
Spoons, metal			511
small, plastic	16-2		
Stapler	3-1		
Steel wool			267
Stick or dowel, slightly more			
than 2 m long	4-1		
wooden	8-1		
Stirring rod, (3)	6-1	383	
glass		287	

NONCONSUMABLES

ITEM	ACTIVITY	MINI LAB	FIND OUT
Stopper, 2-hole	15-1		
2-hole rubber, medium	5-1		
2-hole rubber with glass			
tubing	6-2		
Stopwatches,	1-1, 18-1	66	
or clock	21-1		
or timer with second hand	3-1	177	
String	1-1, 2-1,	144, 466	
	3-1, 3-2		
	4-1, 5-1		
	7-1, 8-2		
or lightweight cord		463	
Support rod, 30-cm	5-1		
Support rod clamp, right angle	5-1		
Syringe, large, plastic	6-2		
"T," glass or plastic	6-2		
Table, large surface		257	
Tablespoon, measuring	2-2		
Tape,	22-1	520, 577	
magnetic	10-1		
masking	2-1, 3-2		133
	4-2, 20-1		
transparent	3-1, 20-1		
	21-2, 23-2		
or rubber bands		567	
Teaspoon, measuring	2-2		
Test tubes, (7)	11-2, 16-1		327
	17-1, 17-2		
large	12-1, 15-1		
medium-sized (3)	16-2		
same size (2)			267
and stopper	13-1		
Test-tube holders, wire	11-2, 15-1,		
	16-1, 16-2		
Thermometers	5-2, 6-1	42, 118	
	8-2, 15-1	490, 646	
	15-2		
Thread, 1 m		577	
Thumbtacks (10)	4-1		
Timer, with second hand	11-2, 17-1	42	
Tongs	6-1, 8-2	301	299, 643
	14-1		
Toothpicks		330	241
Toy, car, wind-up	12-2	177	
electric, with battery		567	
Twist ties (2)	25-1		
Weights, identical (3)	1-1		
small	1-1		
Wire gauze		646	
Wires, copper, bare, 16 ga	15-1, 22-1		
hook up	23-1		
insulated, 32 ga	22-2		
with small alligator			
clips (3)		567	

CONSUMABLES			
ITEM	ACTIVITY	MINI LAB	FIND OUT
Bread, white			327
Candy-coated chocolates, (2 red, 3 green)	10-2		
Candy-coated peanuts, (4 red, 3 green)	10-2		
Carbonated beverage, colorless	17-2		
Gumdrops	12-2	330	
Hot dogs		144	
Ice, crushed	11-2		
Ice cubes, colored	6-1		
Munchie ingredients	2-2		
Orange juice		428	
Raisins		330	
Salt	6-1, 9-1 11-2, 15-2	403	
Spaghetti, thin	12-2		
Sugar,	11-2		
cubes (4)		383	
Sugar water	9-1		

CHEMICAL SUPPLIES

ITEM	ACTIVITY	MINI LAB	FIND OUT
Acetic acid, dilute	17-1		
Baking soda	9-2		
Beta radiation, source		631	
Bleach, liquid laundry, 5% sodium hypochlorite	12-1		
Borax solution, 4%	8-1		
Calcium carbonate tablets, crushed, (10 g)	9-1		219
Cleaner, containing ammonia		428	
Cobalt(II) chloride (0.5 g)	12-1		
solution, dilute		287	
Copper, small piece	16-1		
Copper(II) sulfate			299
Detergent, dishwashing		7	
Food coloring	8-1		
Ethyl alcohol	13-1		
Hydrochloric acid, 4M	9-2		
dilute	16-1, 17-1		
Hydrogen peroxide solution, 3%	16-2		
Iron(III) chloride solution, dilute, FeCl3		405	
Magnesium, small piece	16-1		
Manganese dioxide	16-2		
Nitric acid, dilute	14-1		
Petroleum jelly			643
Phenolphthalein indicator, 1%	17-2, 25-1		
pH paper	17-1		
Polyvinyl alcohol (PVA), 4% solution	8-1		
Potassium bromide, or other solute	15-1		
Potassium permanganate (0.01M)	13-1		
Radioactive source, weak		621	
Rubbing alcohol		201	
Soap		405	
Sodium chloride			299
Sodium hydroxide solution, (6M)	13-1, 14-1	405	
dilute	17-2		
4 pellets	25-1		
Solids, selection, includes iron and pure nickel		577	
Strontium chloride			299
Vinegar			403
Water, distilled	15-1, 15-2		299
soda			425
Zinc, 30 mesh	14-1		
small piece	16-1		

Supplier Addresses

Addresses and phone numbers throughout this book were accurate at the time of publication and are subject to change.

EQUIPMENT SUPPLIERS

Central Scientific Company
11222 Melrose Avenue
Franklin Park, IL 60131

Edmund Scientific Company
101 Gloucester Pike
Barrington, NJ 08007

Fisher Scientific Company
4901 W. LeMoyne Avenue
Chicago, IL 60651

Flinn Scientific Inc.
P.O. Box 219
Batavia, IL 60510

LaPine Scientific Company
13636 Western Avenue
Blue Island, IL 60406-0780

McKilligan Supply Corporation
435 Main Street
Johnson City, NY 13790

Nasco
901 Janesville Avenue
Fort Atkinson, WI 53538

Sargent-Welch Scientific Co.
911 Commerce Ct.
Buffalo Grove, IL 60089

Science Kit and Boreal Labs
777 E. Park Drive
Tonawanda, NY 14150

VWR of Canada, Ltd.
77 Enterprise N
London, Ontario,
Canada N6N IA5

Ward's Natural Science
Establishment, Inc.
P.O. Box 92912
Henrietta, NY 14692

AUDIOVISUAL DISTRIBUTORS

Agency for Instructional
Technology (AIT)
Box A
Bloomington, IN 47402

Aims Media
9710 Desoto Avenue
Chatsworth, CA 91311-4409

Churchill Films
12210 Nebraska Avenue
Los Angeles, CA 90025

Coronet/MTI Film and Video
Distributors of LCA
108 Wilmot Road
Deerfield, IL 60015

CRM Films
2215 Faraday Avenue
Carlsbad, CA 92008

Educational Materials and
Equipment Co. (EME)
P.O. Box 2805
Danbury, CT 06813-2805

Encyclopaedia Britannica
Educational Corp. (EBEC)
310 S. Michigan Avenue
Chicago, IL 60604

Focus Media, Inc.
485 S. Broadway
Suite 12
Hicksville, NY 11801

Guidance Associates
Box 1000
90 S. Bedford Road
Mount Kisco, NY 10549

Handel Film Corporation
8730 Sunset Blvd.
Los Angeles, CA 90069

Hawkill Associates, Inc.
125 E. Gilman Street
Madison, WI 53703

Image Entertainment
9333 Oso Avenue
Chatsworth, CA 91311

JCE: Software
Department of Chemistry
University of Wisconsin,
Madison
1101 University Avenue
Madison, WI 53706

Journal Films, Inc.
1560 Sherman Avenue
Suite 100
Evanston, IL 60201

Learning Arts
Box 179
Wichita, KS 67201

Macmillan/McGraw-Hill
School Division
4635 Hilton Corporate Drive
Columbus, OH 43232

Modern Talking Picture Service
5000 Park Street N.
Saint Petersburg, FL 33709

National Geographic Society
Educational Services
17th and "M" Streets, NW
Washington, DC 20036

Phoenix Learning Group, Inc.
2349 Chaffee Dr.
St. Louis, MO 63146-3306

PBS Video
1320 Braddock Place
Alexandria, VA 22314-1698

Singer Media Corporation
Seaview Business Park
1030 Calle Cordillera
Unit 106
San Clemente, CA 92673

Society for Visual
Education Inc. (SVE)
1345 Diversey Parkway
Chicago, IL 60614-1299

Sunburst Communication
101 Castleton St.
Pleasantville, NY 10570

Time-Life Videos
Time and Life Building
1271 Avenue of the Americas
New York, NY 10020

SOFTWARE DISTRIBUTORS

Agency for Instructional
Technology, (AIT)
Box A
Bloomington, IN 47402-0120

American Chemical Society
Computer Courses
1155 16th Street NW
Washington, DC 20036

Bergwall Productions, Inc.
540 Baltimore Pike
P.O. Box 2400
Chadds Ford, PA 19317

Carolina Biological Supply Co.
2700 York Road
Burlington, NC 27215

Cross Educational Software
P.O. Box 1536
504 E. Kentucky Avenue
Ruston, LA 71270

Educational Materials and
Equipment Company (EME)
P.O. Box 2805
Danbury, CT 06813-2805

Focus Media, Inc.
485 S. Broadway
Suite 12
Hicksville, NY 11801

IBM Educational Systems
Department PC
4111 Northside Parkway
Atlanta, GA 30327

J and S Software
14 Maple Street
Port Washington, NY 11050

Merlan Scientific, Ltd.
247 Armstrong Avenue
Georgetown, Ontario,
Canada L7G 4X6

Micro-ED, Inc.
P.O. Box 24750
Edina, MN 55424

Microphys
12 Bridal Way
Sparta, NJ 07871

Minnesota Educational
Computing Corporation (MECC)
6160 Summit Drive
Minneapolis, MN 55430

Queue, Inc.
338 Commerce
Fairfield, CT 06430

Scott, Foresman, and Company
1900 E. Lake Avenue
Glenview, IL 60025

Wm. K. Bradford Publishing Co.
310 School Street
Acton, MA 01720

Ventura Educational Systems
910 Ramona Avenue
Suite E
Grover Beach, CA 93433

Photo Credits

We want your opinions!

We at Glencoe Publishing feel that with this edition of *Merrill Physical Science,* we have produced a quality textbook program—but the final proof of that rests with you, the teachers who have had the opportunity to put our materials to use in your classrooms. That's why we would appreciate it if you would take the time to respond to any part of this questionnaire that is appropriate for you. In doing so, you will be letting us know how good a job we've done and where we can work to improve.

Please note: (1) you need not have used all of the program components to respond to this questionnaire; and (2) we encourage you to give us your honest and most candid opinions.

Student Text

Excellent				Poor	
5	4	3	2	1	Organization
5	4	3	2	1	Narrative style
5	4	3	2	1	Readability
5	4	3	2	1	Visual impact
5	4	3	2	1	Usable Table of Contents
5	4	3	2	1	Accuracy of content
5	4	3	2	1	Coverage of science principles
5	4	3	2	1	Reduced number of bold-face terms
5	4	3	2	1	Skill builder questions
5	4	3	2	1	Skill Handbook
5	4	3	2	1	MINI-Labs/Activities
5	4	3	2	1	Margin features
5	4	3	2	1	Using Lab Skills
5	4	3	2	1	Problem Solving features
5	4	3	2	1	Technology features
5	4	3	2	1	Science & Society Sections
5	4	3	2	1	Glossary and Index
5	4	3	2	1	Appendices
5	4	3	2	1	Projects
5	4	3	2	1	Global Connections features
5	4	3	2	1	Unit End features

Teacher Edition

Excellent				Poor	
5	4	3	2	1	Teachability
5	4	3	2	1	Planning charts
5	4	3	2	1	Organization of teaching cycle
5	4	3	2	1	Performance objectives
5	4	3	2	1	Assessment Options

Supplements

5	4	3	2	1	Teacher Classroom Resources
5	4	3	2	1	Laboratory Manual
5	4	3	2	1	Science Integration Activities
5	4	3	2	1	Color Transparency Package
5	4	3	2	1	Test Bank
5	4	3	2	1	Chapter Review Software
5	4	3	2	1	Science and Technology Videodisc Series
5	4	3	2	1	Alternate Assessment in the Science Classroom
5	4	3	2	1	Performance Assessment in Middle School Science
5	4	3	2	1	Performance Assessment

Comments (general or specific):

School Information

1. What is the grade level of the students you teach?   6   7   8   9
2. Total number of students in that grade?   1-50   51-100   101-200   200+
3. Average class size?   25 or fewer   26-30   31-40   41 or more
4. Total school enrollment?   1-200   201-500   501-1000   1000+
5. Ability level of your average class?   Basic   Average   Advanced
6. How appropriate is this text for your class?   Too easy   On level   Too difficult
7. How many years have you used this text?   1   2   3   4   5
8. What text were you using *before* you adopted this program?
   (Title/Publisher/copyright year) _____

Fold

Name _____ Date _____

School _____

Street _____

City _____ State _____ Zip _____

Fold

MERRILL

PHYSICAL SCIENCE

GLENCOE

McGraw-Hill

New York, New York   Columbus, Ohio   Mission Hills, California   Peoria, Illinois

A GLENCOE PROGRAM

MERRILL PHYSICAL SCIENCE

Student Edition
Teacher Wraparound Edition
Teacher Classroom Resources
Study Guide, Student Edition
Reinforcement, Student Edition
Enrichment, Student Edition
Transparency Package

Laboratory Manual
Laboratory Manual,
    Teacher Annotated Edition
Spanish Resources
Chapter Review Software
Computer Test Bank
Videodisc Correlation

REVIEWERS

Sam Barrett, Ph.D.
Harlingen High School
Harlingen, Texas

Richard A. Boolootian, Ph.D.
Mirman School
Los Angeles, California

Theodore L. Boydston, III
Dade County Public Schools
  Region V
Miami, Florida

Karen Brown
Humble High School
Humble, Texas

Robert C. Cambric
St. Francis Academy
Joliet, Illinois

Kathleen Carmona
Alamo Junior High School
Midland, Texas

Stephen A. Clark
Elbert County Comprehensive
  High School
Elberton, Georgia

Billie R. Easley
Thackerville High School
Thackerville, Oklahoma

Lorena Farrar
Westwood Junior High School
Dallas, Texas

Elder Harrison Jr.
Chicago Public Schools
Chicago, Illinois

Mathew Keller
Rancho Cotate High School
Rohnert Park, California

Lillie B. Kelly
Shades Mountain Christian School
Birmingham, Alabama

Sr. Mary Ita O'Donnell
St. Joseph High School
Brooklyn, New York

Sandra McMillen Pace
Southeast High School
Maco, Georgia

Dominic Salinas
Parkway High School
Bossier City, Louisiana

Cover Photograph: Lightning Hits Power Cable by Roger Ressmeyer—Starlight

Send all inquiries to:
Glencoe/McGraw-Hill
936 Eastwind Drive
Westerville, OH 43081

ISBN 0-02-826953-5

Printed in the United States of America.

3 4 5 6 7 8 9 VH/MC 02 01 00 99 98 97 96 95

AUTHORS

Marilyn Thompson teaches physics, chemistry, and physical science at Center Senior High School in Kansas City, Missouri. Ms. Thompson holds a B.A. degree in chemistry with an emphasis in physics and education from Carleton College, Northfield, Minnesota. She is a member of the American Association of Physics Teachers and the National Science Teachers Association.

Charles W. McLaughlin has over 20 years of experience as a high school chemistry teacher and is currently the coordinator of science education for the St. Joseph, Missouri, school district. He holds as Ph.D. in chemistry from the University of Nebraska. The National Science Teachers Association has presented Dr. McLaughlin with three national awards for innovative science education and he received a Presidential Award for Science Teaching.

Richard G. Smith has been teaching chemistry at Bexley High School in Bexley, Ohio, for 28 years. He received a regional outstanding teacher award from the American Chemical Society and has participated in NSF summer institutes in chemistry. Mr. Smith graduated Phi Beta Kappa with a B.S. degree in Education from Ohio University and earned his M.A.T. in Chemistry from Indiana University. He is a member of the American Chemical Society and the National Science Teachers Association as well as other national professional organizations.

CONSULTANTS

Senior Consultant, Physics:
John D. McGervey, Ph.D.
Professor of Physics
Case Western Reserve University
Cleveland, Ohio

Physics:
Patrick Hamill, Ph.D.
Professor of Physics
San Jose State University
San Jose, California

Senior Consultant, Chemistry:
Teresa Anne McCowen
Visiting Assistant Professor of Chemistry
Butler University
Indianapolis, Indiana

Chemistry:
Robert C. Smoot, M.S.
Chemistry Teacher and Rollins Fellow in Science
McDonogh School
McDonogh, Maryland

Reading:
Barbara Pettegrew, Ph.D.
Director of Reading/Study Center
Assistant Professor of Education
Otterbein College
Westerville, Ohio

Special Features:
Stephen C. Blume
Elementary Science Specialist
St. Tammany Public School System
Slidell, Louisiana

John R. Grube
High School Science Coordinator (former)
Eastside Union High School District
San Jose, California

Safety:
Robert Tatz, Ph.D.
Instructional Lab Supervisor
Department of Chemistry
The Ohio State University
Columbus, Ohio

Gifted and Mainstreamed:
Barbara Murdock
Elementary Consultant For Instruction
Gahanna-Jefferson Public Schools
Gahanna, Ohio

Judy Ratzenberger
Middle School Science Instructor
Gahanna Middle School West
Gahanna, Ohio

III

CONTENTS

UNIT 3   THE NATURE OF MATTER   186

Acrylic Latex Gloss
ENAMEL

14

6
C
Carbon
12.011

14
Si
Silicon
28.0855

32
Ge
Germanium
72.59

50
Sn
Tin
118.710

82
Pb
Lead
207.2

ACTIVITIES

MINI-Labs

PROBLEM SOLVING

TECHNOLOGY

SKILL BUILDERS

ORGANIZING INFORMATION
Sequencing: 32, 131, 155, 217, 265, 509, 533, 665

Outlining: 17, 74, 181, 423, 491, 509, 537, 661

THINKING CRITICALLY
Observing and Inferring: 8, 77, 81, 107, 217, 235, 291, 325, 367, 412, 423, 449, 481, 505, 509, 537, 549, 632, 641

Comparing and Contrasting: 27, 51, 89, 116, 131, 239, 265, 291, 325, 349, 371, 385, 401, 433, 449, 462, 581, 593, 611, 617, 623, 647

Recognizing Cause and Effect: 107, 155, 161, 217, 239, 325, 349, 371, 407, 423, 449, 478, 516, 537, 593, 617, 665

EXPERIMENTATION SKILLS
Measuring in SI: 51, 81, 131, 181, 214, 371, 401

Hypothesizing: 27, 51, 131, 207, 291, 349, 401, 415, 481, 525, 537, 563, 577, 593

Using Variables, Constants, and Controls: 27, 140, 155, 239, 288, 571

Interpreting Data: 107, 127, 155, 217, 239, 265, 371, 401, 423, 445, 449, 571, 617

GRAPHIC ORGANIZERS
Concept Mapping: 23, 41, 63, 103, 121, 131, 151, 155, 178, 203, 224, 246, 265, 280, 291, 321, 325, 345, 358, 371, 397, 419, 423, 436, 470, 496, 509, 521, 537, 568, 571, 587, 593, 605, 635, 641, 652

Making and Using Tables: 81, 94, 145, 170, 196, 239, 253, 265, 272, 325, 401, 449, 481, 509, 558, 617, 641, 665

Making and Using Graphs: 45, 51, 67, 81, 107, 181, 217, 262, 314, 333, 349, 393, 481, 571, 641

Interpreting Scientific Illustrations: 27, 181, 291, 307, 336, 349, 481, 601, 628

GLOBAL CONNECTIONS

CAREERS

SCIENCE AND LITERATURE/ART

USING MERRILL PHYSICAL SCIENCE

Physical Science is an everyday experience. It's a subject you're familiar with because every part of your day is based upon physical science principles…the simple act of walking involves gravity, which holds you to Earth, friction between the soles of your shoes and the ground, which allows you to overcome inertia, accelerate forward, make turns, and even stop. Depending on temperature, the morning drizzle may have left a puddle or an icy spot for you to cross. What you see, hear, touch, and smell along your walk all involve physical science principles. **Merrill Physical Science** will help you understand science principles and recognize their applications to everyday life.

a quick tour of your textbook

What's happening here? Have you ever considered what allows gum to be stretched? Each unit begins with thought-provoking photographs that will make you wonder. The unit introduction then explains what is happening in the photographs and how the two relate to each other and to the content of the unit. What allows gum to be stretched? Read the opener to Unit 4 to find out.

It's clearly organized to get you started and keep you going.

As you begin each new chapter, use the **Gearing Up** to preview what topics are covered and how they are organized. You will also preview the skills you will use in this chapter.

After you've performed the **FIND OUT** activity and previewed the chapter, you're ready to further explore the topics ahead. Read **What's next** to see what's ahead.

Chapters are organized into three to five numbered sections. The **Objectives** at the beginning of the numbered section tell you what major topics you'll be covering and what you should expect to learn about them. The **New Science Words** are also listed in the order in which they appear in the section.

Experience science by observing, experimenting, and asking questions.

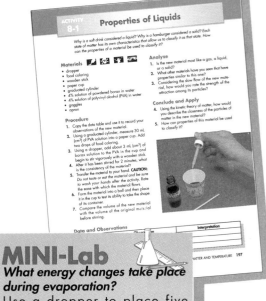

MINI-Lab

What energy changes take place during evaporation?

Use a dropper to place five drops of rubbing alcohol on the back of your hand. Wait for two minutes. What sensations did you feel? What change of state did you *observe*? Is energy entering or leaving your hand? Where does the energy for this process come from?

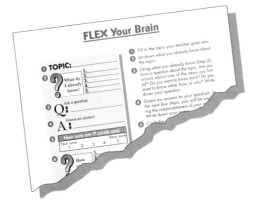

Flex Your Brain is a unique activity you can use to sharpen your critical thinking skills. Starting from what you already know about a science topic, you will apply a simple ten-step procedure to extend your knowledge about the topic from a perspective that interests you.

Science is more than words in a book. The two Activities and the MINI-Labs in each chapter give you the chance to further explore and investigate the science topics covered in your textbook.

In the **Activities,** you'll use household items and laboratory equipment in a hands-on approach to science. In some of the activities, you'll follow easy, step-by-step procedures. In others, you'll design your own experiments. At the end of each Activity are questions that ask you to analyze what you've done.

Most **MINI-Labs** are designed so you can do them on your own or with friends outside of the science classroom using materials you find around the house. Doing a MINI-Lab is an easy and fun way to further your knowledge about the topics you're studying.

Each **Problem Solving** feature gives you a chance to solve a real-world problem or understand a science principle.

PROBLEM SOLVING

Ivan's Isotopes

After carrying out many medical tests, the doctor found a tumor in Ivan's thyroid gland. The doctor decided to treat the tumor with iodine-131, an isotope of iodine. Ivan asked her how the treatment would work. She explained that atoms of some isotopes, like iodine-131, are unstable. One of these atoms has too many neutrons for the number of protons. The nucleus in an unstable isotope rearranges itself spontaneously, resulting in the release of energy called radiation.

The thyroid gland absorbs iodine because the gland needs iodine to function properly. The doctor told Ivan the tumor cells in his thyroid are more sensitive to radiation than the healthy thyroid cells. A controlled dose of radiation from the iodine-131 would kill the tumor cells but would not affect the healthy cells.

Think Critically: Why is iodine-131 unstable? Why is the number of neutrons in an atom important in the field of medicine?

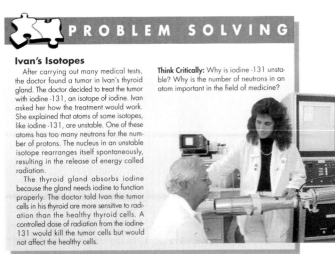

Explore news-making issues, concerns about the environment, and how science shapes your world through technology.

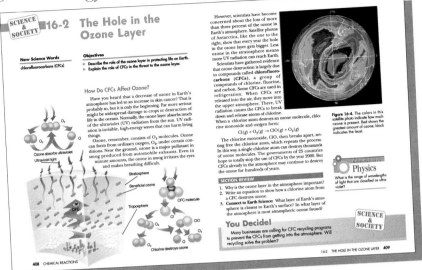

The impact of science on society directly affects you. In the **Science and Society** section in each chapter, you'll learn about an issue that's affecting the world around you. The topics you'll read about are controversial, and you'll explore them from several sides. Then, you'll have a chance to express your opinion in the You Decide feature that follows.

In the **Technology** feature in each chapter, you'll read about recent discoveries, newly developed instruments, and applications of technology that have shaped our world and furthered our knowledge.

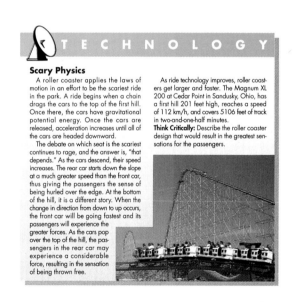

TECHNOLOGY

Scary Physics

A roller coaster applies the laws of motion in an effort to be the scariest ride in the park. A ride begins when a chain drags the cars to the top of the first hill. Once there, the cars have gravitational potential energy. Once the cars are released, acceleration increases until all of the cars are headed downward.

The debate on which seat is the scariest continues to rage, and the answer is, "that depends." As the cars descend, their speed increases. The rear car starts down the slope at a much greater speed than the front car, thus giving the passengers the sense of being hurled over the edge. At the bottom of the hill, it is a different story. When the change in direction from down to up occurs, the front car will be going fastest and its passengers will experience the greater forces. As the cars pop over the top of the hill, the passengers in the rear car may experience a considerable force, resulting in the sensation of being thrown free.

As ride technology improves, roller coasters get larger and faster. The Magnum XL 200 at Cedar Point in Sandusky, Ohio, has a first hill 201 feet high, reaches a speed of 112 km/h, and covers 5106 feet of track in two-and-one-half minutes.

Think Critically: Describe the roller coaster design that would result in the greatest sensations for the passengers.

Connect to...
Life Science

Whales are capable of making sounds that can be detected for miles. Explain which wave properties might help these sounds travel through the ocean so efficiently.

All sciences are related. **Connect to …** features allow you to relate the physical science topics you are studying to other sciences. Use basic library references to find the answer to these questions.

Discover that you can apply what you've learned as you answer questions and practice your science skills.

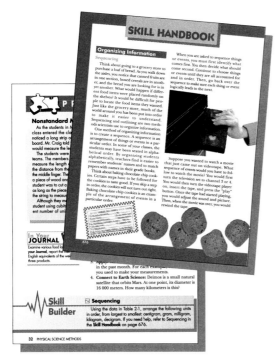

At the end of each section are several Section Review questions that help you test your knowledge. The last two questions challenge you to think critically and **Apply** and **Connect to ...** what you've learned.

The **Skill Builder** feature lets you sharpen your science skills using only paper and pencil. If you need help with these skills, refer to the **Skill Handbook** at the back of the book. Here, you can find complete information about each type of skill covered in the Skill Builders.

A balanced chemical equation tells the story of a chemical reaction. **In your Journal,** write the story of the chemical equation shown in Figure 16-3.

In Your Journal features enable you to write expressively about physical science topics you are studying. It includes writing creatively, giving reports, writing letters, and forming opinions. You may also keep lab notes and responses to Chapter Review questions in your Journal.

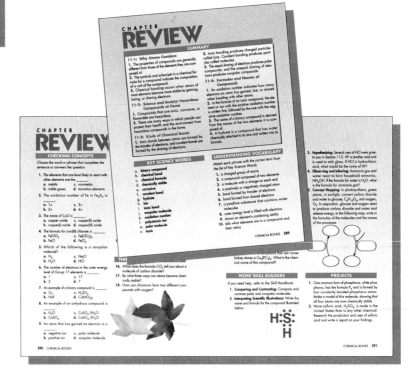

The **Chapter Review** starts with a summary so you can review the major concepts from each section. Then, you'll apply your knowledge and practice thinking skills as you answer the questions that follow.

Discover how physical science topics relate to people and places all over the world.

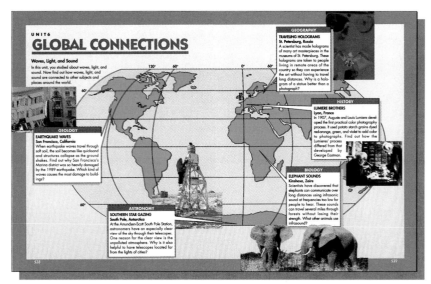

Global Connections help you to see how physical science is related to other sciences as well as social studies, history and health.

Also at the end of each unit you will find two **Careers** that relate to the material in the unit you just read. What jobs may be related to waves, light, and sound? Read the careers at the end of Unit 6 to find out.

What do physical science and literature have in common? A lot, as you'll discover when you read the unit close to Unit 1. Each unit is closed with a reading from literature or an example of art that makes a connection with physical science.

1

PHYSICAL SCIENCE BASICS

In Unit 1, students briefly explore the content of physical science. Students are also introduced to the important role of problem solving as an activity of science. The identification of problems and the choice of strategies to solve them are related to scientific method and experimental design. The unit closes with a discussion on the importance of measurements in science, SI measurements, and graphing as a useful means of displaying and interpreting data.

CONTENTS

ADVANCE PREPARATION

Audiovisuals
Show one or more of the following videos.

▶*Interpreting Data, Testing Hypotheses,* Journal Films.
▶ *Scientific Methods and Values,* Hawkhill.
▶ *Why I Should Stay Awake in Science Class,* Modern.

Field Trips and Speakers
▶ Arrange for a speaker from your local dental or medical association to visit your class to discuss important applications to physical science.
▶ Arrange a field trip to an elementary school classroom to allow students to explain problem solving to younger students.

UNIT

1 PHYSICAL SCIENCE BASICS

2

OPTIONS

Cross Curriculum
▶ In their journals, have students keep logs of types of measurements, measuring instruments, and units of measurements used in other classes.
▶ Have students keep logs of types of problems that arise in other classes and strategies used to solve them. Have the students compare and contrast these strategies to those presented in the unit.

Science at Home
▶ Have students keep a log of the types of measurements, measuring instruments, and units of measurement that they use at home or that they observe being used in various occupations. After one week, have students present their finding to the class.

What's Happening Here?

Does the large photograph belong in a science lab or in an art exhibit? It was shot by a physical scientist. A physical scientist is curious about the way matter behaves and how energy interacts with matter. Because of this curiosity, the scientist has learned how glass and water can bend and reflect light and how chemicals act on film to give these beautiful results. What does it take to be a scientist? Only curiosity and a desire to investigate the world around you. If you are curious, you too can be a scientist.

UNIT CONTENTS

INTRODUCING THE UNIT

What's Happening Here?
▶ Have students look at the photos and read the text. Ask them to tell you what's happening here. Point out to students that in this unit they will be studying the relationship between problem solving and physical science. They will also learn how curiosity, careful observations, hunches, and accurate measurements are used to solve problems.
▶ **Background:** The photograph consists of four images of the same subject each taken with a different colored flash of light. The flashes were provided by a strobe light with colored filters. The images were recorded by a multi-image camera that has four apertures, allowing four independent images to be recorded on the film.

Previewing the Chapters
▶ Name and locate a margin feature in the unit that tells what the inventor of dynamite did with his fortune (Did You Know? page 23); is an activity about bubbles you can do by yourself (MINI-Lab, page 7); outlines Chapter 2 (Gearing Up, page 29); lists kelvin as a section vocabulary word (New Science Words, page 34); tells you how much water is used in a typical home (EcoTip, page 45); and suggests researching physical science and careers (Science and Reading, page 8).

Tying to Previous Knowledge
▶ Have students brainstorm lists of different types of measuring devices and units they have used. Urge them to think of situations, such as buying shoes, clothing, and groceries, in which consumers purchase materials that have been premeasured or sized and packaged.
▶ Use the questions in the OPTIONS box to discuss science and observations.

Multicultural Awareness
Many early cultures used observations and measurements of the sun, planets, and the night sky to navigate over sea and land. Have interested students list specific techniques and inventions used by various cultures.

Inquiry Questions
Use the following questions to focus a discussion of observations and physical science.
▶ **What are the names of the laboratory glassware shown in the large photograph?** *beaker, petri dish*
▶ **In the smaller photo, what observations and measurements do you think the student is making? What question do you think the student may be trying to answer?** *Accept all reasonable answers.*

1 The Nature of Science

CHAPTER SECTION	OBJECTIVES	ACTIVITIES
1-1 Physical Science and You (1 day)	1. **Compare** and **contrast** "pure" science and technology. 2. **Define** physical science. 3. **Discuss** some of the topics covered in physical science.	**MINI-Lab:** *How can patterns help explain complicated systems? p. 7*
1-2 Problem Solving (2 days)	1. **Distinguish** between problems and exercises. 2. **Evaluate** approaches to solving problems. 3. **Compare** and **contrast** hypothesis, theory, and scientific law.	
1-3 Problems? What Problems? Science & Society (1 day)	1. **Describe** some of the environmental issues presently being studied by scientists. 2. **Examine** how scientific controversies arise.	
1-4 Exploring Science (2 days)	1. **Appreciate** the importance of following guidelines in doing experiments. 2. **Define** constant, independent variable, and dependent variable. 3. **Understand** laboratory safety rules.	**Activity 1-1:** *Identifying and Controlling Variables, p. 24*
Chapter Review		

ACTIVITY MATERIALS

FIND OUT	ACTIVITIES	MINI-LABS
Page 5 none	**1-1 Identifying and Controlling Variables, p. 24** string, 1.5 m 3 identical weights 1 smaller weight metric ruler 2 ring stands scissors stopwatch	**How can patterns help explain complicated systems? p. 7** large, clear glass water dishwashing detergent soda straw

CHAPTER FEATURES	TEACHER RESOURCE PACKAGE	OTHER RESOURCES
Skill Builder: *Observing and Inferring,* p. 8	**Ability Level Worksheets** ◆ **Study Guide,** p. 5 ● **Reinforcement,** p. 5 ▲ **Enrichment,** p. 5 **Activity Worksheets,** p. 11	**STVS:** Disc 1, Side 1
Technology: *Driving Smart,* p. 13 **Skill Builder:** *Outlining,* p. 17	**Ability Level Worksheets** ◆ **Study Guide,** p. 6 ● **Reinforcement,** p. 6 ▲ **Enrichment,** p. 6 **Critical Thinking/Problem Solving,** p. 7 **Transparency Masters,** pp. 1, 2 **Activity Worksheets,** p. 5	**Color Transparency 1,** Flex Your Brain
You Decide! p. 19	**Ability Level Worksheets** ◆ **Study Guide,** p. 7 ● **Reinforcement,** p. 7 ▲ **Enrichment,** p. 7 **Concept Mapping,** pp. 7, 8	**STVS:** Disc 6, Side 2
Problem Solving: *Lauren's Experiment,* p. 22 **Skill Builder:** *Concept Mapping,* p. 23	**Ability Level Worksheets** ◆ **Study Guide,** p. 8 ● **Reinforcement,** p. 8 ▲ **Enrichment,** p. 8 **Activity Worksheets,** pp. 7, 8 **Cross-Curricular Connections,** p. 5 **Science and Society,** p. 5 **Transparency Masters,** pp. 3, 4	**Color Transparency 2,** Safety Symbols **Laboratory Manual 1,** No Need To Count Your Pennies **STVS:** Disc 2, Side 1 Disc 1, Side 2 **Science Integration Activity 1**
	ASSESSMENT RESOURCES **Chapter Review,** pp. 5, 6 **Chapter Test,** pp. 5-8 **Performance Assessment** in Middle School Science	**Chapter Review Software** **Test Bank** **Alternate Assessment** **Performance Assessment**

◆ **Basic** ● **Average** ▲ **Advanced**

ADDITIONAL MATERIALS		
SOFTWARE	**AUDIOVISUAL**	**BOOKS/MAGAZINES**
Discovery Lab, MECC. *GTV: Planetary Manager,* EduQuest. *Science Inquiry Collection,* MECC. *Tribbles Revisited: An Introduction to the Scientific Method,* Conduit.	*Becoming Successful Problem Solvers,* Videos, HRM Video. *The Brunel Experience,* Video, Films Incorporated. *Conducting an Experiment,* Video, Journal Films. *Destination: Science,* Video, Coronet. *Hands On! Scientific Inquiry and Problem Solving,* Video Kit, HRM Video.	Carr, Joseph J. *The Art of Science: A Practical Guide to Experiments, Observations, and Handling Data.* San Diego: HighText, 1992. Duden, Jane. *The Ozone Layer.* NY: Crestwood House, 1990. Gutnik, Martin J. *Experiments that Explore: The Greenhouse Effect.* Brookfield, CT: Millbrook Press, 1991.

THEME DEVELOPMENT: This chapter presents the scientific method as an example of problem solving. The systematic approach to identifying, formulating, and solving problems should be used to link the sections within the chapter.

CHAPTER OVERVIEW

▶ **Section 1-1:** In this section the relationship between science and technology is discussed. The scope of topics studied in the physical sciences is presented.

▶ **Section 1-2:** This section continues the theme of problem solving by discussing what a problem is. Four problem-solving strategies are presented and developed.

▶ **Section 1-3: Science and Society:** Three topics—global warming, depletion of the ozone layer, and acid rain—are used as examples to discuss how to define and solve environmental problems.

▶ **Section 1-4:** This section discusses experimentation by introducing the concepts of experimental controls and variables. Five steps that aid in organizing a scientific experiment are outlined. The section concludes with a discussion of the importance of safety in the science classroom.

CHAPTER VOCABULARY

technology	ozone layer
physical science	experiment
model	control
critical thinking	constant
observation	independent
hypothesis	variable
theory	dependent
scientific law	variable
greenhouse	
effect	

4

OPTIONS

For Your Gifted Students

Have students develop cartoon characters that can be used throughout the year. Ask students to pick a concept that is illustrated in the text, such as lab safety. They can use the cartoon characters to illustrate the points in a humorous way. This cartoon strip can help record their year in science.

For Your Mainstreamed Students

Have students make a chart showing the major safety rules that should be followed while conducting a lab. Their charts should illustrate the rules and be displayed all year in the classroom.

Isn't it frustrating when something doesn't work the way you'd like it to? Sometimes that feeling of frustration can lead to ideas for improvements or new inventions.

FIND OUT!

Do this exercise to explore some ways of solving problems.

Working with a partner, think of something in your school that doesn't work as well as it could. You may choose a device, like a pencil sharpener, or a system, such as the cafeteria line.

Without showing each other your work, you and your partner each make a list of ways you could improve the device or system you chose. After *collecting and organizing your data,* write down the steps you would go through to make these improvements.

Now show each other your lists. How are they different? Why do you think you and your partner came up with different approaches to the same problem? Would your answers have been different if you had worked together? Is there any way to find out whether one approach would work better?

Gearing Up
Previewing the Chapter

Use this outline to help you focus on important ideas in the chapter.

Previewing Science Skills

▶ In the **Skill Builders,** you will observe and infer, outline, and make a concept map.
▶ In the **Activity,** you will observe, predict, and control variables.
▶ In the **MINI-Lab,** you will observe and infer.

What's next?

You have identified a problem and attempted to work out a solution to the problem. Now find out how your approach to problem solving compares with the approach used by scientists.

5

INTRODUCING THE CHAPTER

Use the Find Out activity to introduce students to the importance of problem solving as a major activity in science.

FIND OUT!

Cooperative Learning: Have Paired Partners share solutions and determine a single course of action. Allow students to discuss how the "two brains are better than one" approach clarified or enriched their individual thinking about solving the problem. Take time to discuss cooperative learning in general.
Teaching Tips
▶ Emphasize that a long cafeteria line may be a "problem," but the problem that must be tackled by the students is determining the *method* to reduce the cafeteria line.
▶ Point out that "Why are hand-thrown pizzas always round?" is a question. The problem is how to find a method to answer the question.
▶ To avoid "quick-fix" solutions, have students consider whether their improvements have any detrimental short-term or long-term effects.

Gearing Up

Have students study the Gearing Up feature to familiarize themselves with the chapter. Discuss the relationships of the topics in the outline.

What's Next?

Before beginning the first section, make sure students understand the connection between the Find Out activity and the topics to follow.

ASSESSMENT OPTIONS

PORTFOLIO
Refer to page 25 for suggested items that students might select for their portfolios.

PERFORMANCE ASSESSMENT
See page 25 for additional Performance Assessment options.
Process
Skill Builder, pp. 17, 23
MINI-Lab, p. 7
Activity, 1-1, p. 24
Using Lab Skills, p. 26

CONTENT ASSESSMENT
Assessment—Oral, p. 16
Skill Builder, p. 8
Section Reviews, pp. 8, 17, 19, 23
Chapter Review, pp. 25-27
Mini Quizzes, pp. 12, 16, 22

GROUP ASSESSMENT
Opportunities for group assessment occur with Cooperative Learning Strategies and Flex Your Brain Activities.

PREPARATION

SECTION BACKGROUND
▶ Science and technology are sometimes classified as R&D, research and development. Advances in one depend upon the other.

PREPLANNING
▶ Obtain a pair of toddler's sneakers with laces and a pair with Velcro fasteners for the Motivation activity; dishwashing detergent and straws for the MINI-Lab.

1 MOTIVATE

▶ Have students bring in examples of packaging that show technological improvements such as twist-off bottles, tab-open cans, twist-tie and self-sealing food storage bags, and plastic foam containers. Have them compare the benefits and possible drawbacks of such new products.

2 TEACH

Key Concepts are highlighted.

CONCEPT DEVELOPMENT
▶ Ask students which is more important—science or technology. Most students will choose technology. Keep this prejudice in mind as you discuss the importance and interrelationships of both.

VideoDisc
STVS: Wind Engineering, Disc 1, Side 2

1-1 Physical Science and You

New Science Words

technology
physical science

Objectives

▶ Compare and contrast "pure" science and technology.
▶ Define *physical science.*
▶ Discuss some of the topics covered in physical science.

Applying Science

How are scientific discoveries made? Do scientists, with a specific goal in mind, conduct experiments until they reach that goal? The answer is "Sometimes, but not always." Read the brief true accounts that follow.

A scientist forgot to rinse out a flask. It was later discovered that a coating left on the inside of the flask kept the flask from shattering when dropped. This discovery led to the invention of safety glass, similar to that used in automobile windshields.

While studying data from a radio telescope, an astronomy student noticed that a particular star seemed to be emitting short, regular pulses of energy. Her observation led to the discovery of pulsars, stars that are as massive as the sun, but are only the size of a large mountain.

As these accounts show, the path to scientific discovery is not always a direct one. But the processes of science are always the same—observing, questioning, exploring, and seeking answers. Scientists are always trying to understand the world around them—from processes in their own bodies to reactions in the laboratory; from the burning of paper to the explosion of a star.

Figure 1-1. Scientists seek to learn more about Earth by studying the stars.

6 THE NATURE OF SCIENCE

OPTIONS

Meeting Different Ability Levels

For Section 1-1, use the following **Teacher Resource Masters** depending upon individual students' needs.

◆ **Study Guide Master** for all students.

● **Reinforcement Master** for students of average and above average ability levels.

▲ **Enrichment Master** for above average students.

Additional Teacher Resource Package masters are listed in any **PROGRAM RESOURCES** boxes that are in the section. The additional masters are appropriate for all students.

◆ STUDY GUIDE   **5**

STUDY GUIDE   Chapter 1

Physical Science and You   Text Pages 6-8

Read each group of terms. Circle the two terms that are most related. In the spaces provided, explain how the terms are related. Write your answers in complete sentences.

1. matter, animals, energy
   Physical science is the study of matter and energy.

2. knowledge, pure science, technology
   Pure science is the study of something for the advancement of knowledge.

3. pure science, technology, applied science
   Technology is applied science.

4. sunlight, matter, energy
   Sunlight is a form of energy.

5. rocks, matter, energy
   Rocks are an example of matter.

6. electricity, sunlight, matter
   Electricity and sunlight are forms of energy.

7. hardness, observing, questioning
   Observing and questioning are processes of science.

For each term listed, write a definition using your own words.

8. technology: Technology is the application of scientific knowledge to improve the quality of human life.

9. physical science: Physical science is the study of matter and energy.

Answer the following question with complete sentences on the lines provided.

10. How does "pure" science differ from technology?
   Pure science involves the study of a subject for the advancement of knowledge. Technology involves the application of scientific knowledge ("pure" science) to improve the quality of life.

Copyright Glencoe Division of Macmillan/McGraw-Hill
Users of Merrill Physical Science have the publisher's permission to reproduce this page.   5

In their search for knowledge, scientists often make surprising discoveries. Not every discovery will have common, everyday applications. For example, the discovery of pulsars did not lead to the development of any consumer products. However, it did open up a whole new field of investigation. Scientists have learned about how matter behaves under the special condition that exists inside the very dense stars. Someday this information may help them to learn more about matter here on Earth.

Other scientific discoveries, such as the shatterproof glass flask, lead directly to practical and useful everyday applications. The application of scientific knowledge to improve the quality of human life is called **technology.**

There is no sharp boundary between science and technology. Scientific discoveries lead to technological inventions. Inventions, in turn, may lead to further discoveries. Science includes both "pure" science, for the advancement of knowledge, and "applied" science, or technology.

Physical Science

Physical science is the study of matter and energy. Every measurable thing in the universe is either matter or energy. Plants and animals, rocks and clouds, eggs and elephants are all examples of matter. And lightning, thunder, heat, and sunlight are all examples of energy.

In Your JOURNAL
Find a magazine or newspaper article that reports new technology. **In your Journal,** describe the pure science that led to the development of the technology mentioned in the article.

Figure 1-2. By applying their scientific knowledge, scientists and engineers develop products that make our lives easier.

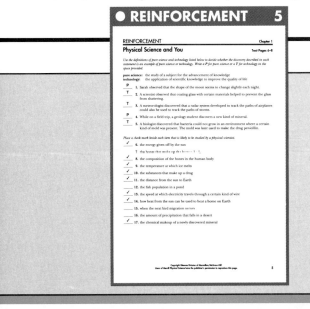

Connect to...
Life Science

Answer: Life on Earth is said to be carbon based because carbon makes up much of all plants and animals.

3 CLOSE

▶ Invite a dentist to your class to discuss technological advances in dentistry.

SECTION REVIEW ANSWERS

1. Science is a study solely for the advancement of knowledge. Technology is the application of scientific knowledge to improve the quality of life. The study of the electrical nature of matter is science, whereas the development of an electric generator is technology.

2. the study of matter and energy

3. Apply: Student responses will vary. Examples: (1) What causes tides? (2) How fast does sound travel in air? (3) Why might fuses be used in an electrical circuit?

4. Connect to Life Science: iron

Skill Builder

Articles collected by students will vary. Make sure that students correctly identify the content as a scientific discovery or as a technological development.

Skill Builder
ASSESSMENT

Oral: Show students a ballpoint pen. Ask selected students to name one scientific discovery and one technological development that led to the manufacturing of these pens.

Figure 1-3. In the laboratory, scientists test their own ideas and check the work of other scientists.

Science and READING

Look through the table of contents for this book to find out what subjects a physical scientist studies. Then find a book in the library that lists such careers, such as *The Occupational Outlook Handbook*. Select a career that relates to physical science and describe it in a brief oral report to your class.

Connect to...
Life Science

Life on this planet is often said to be based on carbon. Find out why carbon is so important to life on Earth.

Physical science deals with the composition and properties of matter. Composition has to do with what matter is made up of. Properties have to do with what matter is like and how it behaves. You're already familiar with some properties of different kinds of matter. Hardness and taste are two examples of properties of matter.

In physical science, you'll learn how matter and energy are related. You'll discover how energy is transferred through matter, as when the sound from a stereo reaches your ears. You'll find out how refrigerators stay cold and why an insulated jacket keeps you warm.

As you learn about electricity, sound, heat, and light, you'll discover how energy is used to do work. In the study of force and motion, you'll learn why acorns fall to Earth while satellites remain in orbit.

As you study physical science, observe how things and ideas are organized into systems, and how different parts of a system interact. Your observations will lead you to ask questions. The rest of this chapter will help you find out how to go about answering those questions.

SECTION REVIEW

1. What is the difference between science and technology? Give an example of each.
2. Define *physical science*.
3. **Apply:** Pose three questions that you think could be answered by the activities of physical science.
4. **Connect to Life Science:** Find out what material enables animal hemoglobin to carry oxygen.

Skill Builder ☑ **Observing and Inferring**

Bring in a newspaper or magazine article related to physical science. Summarize the article and explain whether it deals with a scientific discovery or a technological development. If you need help, refer to Observing and Inferring in the **Skill Handbook** on page 678.

8 THE NATURE OF SCIENCE

OPTIONS

Problem Solving 1-2

Objectives

▶ Distinguish between problems and exercises.
▶ Evaluate approaches to solving problems.
▶ Compare and contrast hypothesis, theory, and scientific law.

New Science Words

model
critical thinking
observation
hypothesis
theory
scientific law

What Is a Problem?

How can astronauts be kept safe and healthy on long space missions? Is Earth's climate warming up? What's the best way to make recorded music sound like the real thing? Each of these questions suggests a problem that can be approached scientifically. They are considered problems because their solutions are not obvious. Some important information is missing.

Solving a problem involves finding missing information, but sometimes it's not clear at first what kind of information is needed. For example, to find out whether the temperature of Earth's atmosphere is increasing, where should temperature readings be made? Many weather stations throughout the world are in or near cities, but temperatures in cities generally are higher than temperatures in unpopulated areas. Scientists must decide whether temperature readings from cities should be included in their data. They also must decide how many years back they should go. Should they check temperatures starting in 1950? 1900? or even further back? As you can see, there are a lot of "problems" in deciding how to go about solving a problem.

What do all problems have in common?

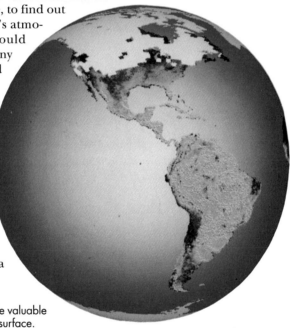

Figure 1-4. Infrared satellite images provide valuable information about temperatures at Earth's surface.

PREPARATION

SECTION BACKGROUND

▶ Problem solving is an important skill. The techniques used are the same as those used to develop and test hypotheses by scientific experimentation.

▶ A scientific law is a description of how two physical quantities that describe a phenomenon are related. A theory is a series of assumptions that, when taken together, offer an explanation or a model for observed phenomena. A theory must comply with past and present appropriate observations and scientific laws as well as predict new hypotheses.

1 MOTIVATE

▶ Develop a set of elementary math exercises, such as addition or subtraction problems, and have students do them. Then ask a volunteer to perform a few knee-bends or jumping-jacks. Discuss why they are both called exercises.

TYING TO PREVIOUS
KNOWLEDGE: Have students recall how they solved the problem of finding different classrooms when they first started school in this building. Point out that they will learn other methods of problem solving in this section.

PROGRAM RESOURCES

From the **Teacher Resource Package** use:
Critical Thinking/Problem Solving, page 7, Fish Kill.

Key Concepts are highlighted.

CONCEPT DEVELOPMENT

Cooperative Learning: Using a Numbered Heads Together strategy, have each team of students select a sport, board game, or video game and explain how it poses a problem to be solved. Have teams discuss how the various game moves can be used as strategies to solve the problem posed by the game.

CROSS CURRICULUM

▶ **Earth Science:** The *troposphere* is the lowest layer of the atmosphere and extends from the surface of Earth to an altitude of about 10-16 km.

In Your JOURNAL

Students may describe how to set an alarm clock. Encourage them to give a detailed account of the process. This becomes a simple exercise—possibly, just pushing a preset button—once they have mastered the technique. Emphasize the difference between problem solving and performing an exercise.

In Your JOURNAL

In your Journal, describe exactly how you could solve the problem of making sure you are awake at a certain time each day. Then describe how this problem can become an exercise.

Figure 1-5. Thomas Edison was an inventor who perfected the technique of applying scientific discoveries to develop and improve hundreds of products.

Figure 1-6. Maps and street signs can help a stranger find an address.

Solving problems always involves uncertainty. So, it's not surprising that scientists sometimes make false starts or end up on dead-end paths before they arrive at solutions. Solving problems often involves trial-and-error and the ability to learn from mistakes. For example, in the process of inventing the light bulb, Thomas Edison tried more than 100 materials before he found one that would work as the filament of the bulb.

A problem for one person may not be a problem for someone else. For a stranger, finding a certain building downtown is a problem that requires using a map and reading street signs. For someone who passes the building on the way to work every day, finding the building is not a problem.

There's a difference between a problem and an exercise. In an exercise, the steps required to find the solution are usually obvious. For example, finding the average weight of five classmates is an exercise if you know how to calculate averages. If you don't know how to find averages, you are faced with a problem.

Problem-Solving Strategies

Before you can solve a problem, you need to understand exactly what the problem is. That may sound obvious, but people often have trouble solving problems because they don't know where to start. Sometimes that's because they haven't defined the problem clearly enough.

OPTIONS

Meeting Different Ability Levels

For Section 1-2, use the following **Teacher Resource Masters** depending upon individual students' needs.

◆ **Study Guide Master** for all students.
● **Reinforcement Master** for students of average and above average ability levels.
▲ **Enrichment Master** for above average students.

Additional Teacher Resource Package masters are listed in any PROGRAM RESOURCES boxes that are in the section. The additional masters are appropriate for all students.

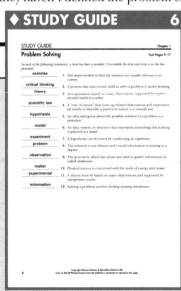

◆ STUDY GUIDE   6

Suppose a friend asks you to help fix a broken bicycle. How will you proceed? Maybe you'll look over the bike and ask your friend a lot of questions. Is something wrong with a tire? Is there a problem with the gears? Does the bicycle rattle? Your questions and observations will help you pinpoint the specific problem. You'll progress from knowing only that the bicycle is broken to knowing, for example, that the gears don't shift properly. The more precisely you can define the problem, the less time you'll spend looking for solutions.

Once you've defined the problem, there's no single "right" way to start looking for answers. The important thing is to be systematic. Proceed in logical steps from what you know to what you don't know. Keep track of your steps, so that if something doesn't work, you can move on to something else instead of trying the same thing over again.

Here are some ways to try solving problems:

• Use what you know about the problem to predict a solution and try it. If your effort fails, think about why it didn't work. Then make another prediction and try that. Keep eliminating possibilities until you find the one that works. You've probably used this method to search for something you've lost. You think about when you last saw the item, and where you've been since then. This helps you to direct your search. Then you consider where you may have left the item, and you look there. If you don't find it, you look in the next logical place.

What is the first step in solving a problem?

❷

● REINFORCEMENT   6

REINFORCEMENT   Chapter 1
Problem Solving   Text Pages 9–17

Complete the following.

1. How does a problem differ from an exercise?   **In an exercise, the steps required to**
find a solution usually are obvious. In a problem, the steps needed to find a
solution may not be obvious.

Identify the sense you could use to make each of the following observations.

sight	2. the distance between two points
hearing	3. the loudness of a stereo system
taste	4. the saltiness of a stew
sight	5. the number of students in a classroom
touch	6. determining whether bathwater was too hot or too cold
taste or smell	7. determining whether milk in a container has soured
taste	8. the spiciness of a dinner

Identify the sense that each object listed is designed to help.

hearing	9. hearing aid
sight	10. microscope
touch	11. thermometer
sight	12. ruler
hearing	13. stereo headphones
sight	14. telescope
hearing	15. stethoscope

Place the following terms in logical order by writing the numbers 1 through 4 in the space provided.

3   16. theory
4   17. scientific law
2   18. hypothesis
1   19. problem

20. What is an experiment?   **a test of a hypothesis**

6   Copyright Glencoe Division of Macmillan/McGraw-Hill
Users of Merrill Physical Science have the publisher's permission to reproduce this page.

▲ ENRICHMENT   6

11

ENRICHMENT   Chapter 1
Problem Solving   Text Pages 9–17

SOLVING A MEASUREMENT PROBLEM

One type of problem solving that we often encounter is determining the size of something. When this type of problem occurs, we do not always have the appropriate measuring tools available. For example, you may be out shopping and need to know if a large box will fit in the trunk of your parents' car. If you could find the dimensions of the box and the trunk, you could determine if the box will fit before you spend time and energy lifting the box up to the trunk.

In this activity you will use paper clips as your measuring device. You will find the height and width of your textbook with a large paper clip. Then you will use this information and other data to find the height and length of your textbook using a small paper clip.

Procedure
1. Measure the height and width of the figure below using a large paper clip. Record these values in the table.

2. Measure the height and width of the figure using the small paper clip. Record these values in the table.
3. Measure the height and width of your textbook using the large paper clip. Record these values in the table.
4. Predict the height and width of your textbook in small paper clips. Record your prediction in the table.

Data	Sample data	
	Large paper clip	Small paper clip
Figure height	1	1.5
Figure width	3.5	5.2
Textbook height	5.2	7.8
Textbook width	3.8	5.7

Analyze and Conclude
1. How can you find the height and width of your textbook in small paper clips, without measuring it with a small paper clip?   **Multiply the measurement in large paper clips by**
1.5. Example: 5.2 ×1.5 = 7.8

2. Measure your textbook with a small paper clip and record your measurements in the table.   **Answers will vary.**
Compare your prediction with the actual measurements.

6   Copyright Glencoe Division of Macmillan/McGraw-Hill
Users of Merrill Physical Science have the publisher's permission to reproduce this page.

CONCEPT DEVELOPMENT
▶ Continue the discussion of exercises begun in the Motivation by having students identify differences between solving problems and completing exercises. Point out that some tasks that at first require problem-solving skills, such as riding a bike, roller-skating, and tying shoelaces, eventually become simply exercises.

MULTICULTURAL PERSPECTIVES

High-Tech Folk Remedies

The basic principles of science have been used by people everywhere in solving the problems of living, or in this case healing. Large drug corporations may use computers to screen thousands of plants a year, but find only a few with medical potential. Shaman Pharmaceuticals Inc., a small company, can only screen around 75 plants a year, but finds about half of these show some medical potential. How can they achieve a comparable success ratio to the larger companies without having giant robotic systems? Shamans, or traditional healers, have learned about the healing properties of various plants through observation, trial and error, and experimentation conducted over many centuries. Shaman Pharmaceuticals sends scientists to talk with these practicing shamans, and to learn how various illnesses and symptoms are treated. The scientists concentrate on these cures when looking for substances to screen.

This type of research, known as ethnobotany, also benefits the shamans' communities. Shaman Pharmaceuticals, Inc. employs local people to harvest the plants it tests and has set up a foundation that puts money back into the cultures that supply the company's drug leads. Most of these communities are in the rain forests of Latin America. Ethnobotany may not only provide drugs to heal the illnesses of others, but may help to heal the illnesses of poverty and habitat destruction that many of the shamans' cultures face.

▶ **Mathematics:** Point out that patterns can be used to solve sequence problems. Have students discuss patterns in the following sequences and predict the missing integer.

0, 1, 2, 3, 4, ... (5)
0, 1, 4, 9, 16, ... (25)
0, 1, 1, 2, 3, 5, 8, ... (13)

▶ **Earth Science:** Have students identify and discuss patterns that occur in the earth sciences. These patterns may include crystal structures or cycles, such as days, lunar months, years, tides, and phases of the moon. Ask students how these patterns can be used to identify materials or predict events.

▶ **Life Science:** Have students discuss patterns of change, such as life cycles, that take place in living organisms.

MINI QUIZ

Use the Mini Quiz to check students' recall of chapter content.

1 **Which of the following situations are problems and which are exercises for an average student in your class?**
  a. making change
  b. riding a bike
  c. rewiring a lamp
  d. distinguishing a planet in the night sky
  Problems: c, d; exercises: a, b

2 **What are four problem-solving strategies?** *Use past knowledge to make a guess; look for patterns on which to make predictions; develop a model; break the problem into smaller, simpler problems.*

What is a model?

Figure 1-7. The wind tunnel is used to test the effects of wind on the airplane model.

• Look for patterns that will help you make predictions about the problem. Suppose you occasionally break out in a rash. If you pay attention to what you eat, touch, and wear every day, you may find a pattern that helps you discover what's causing the rash. Putting information into a table or graph or making a drawing sometimes can help you find patterns.

• Develop a model. When your problem deals with something complicated or difficult to see, it may help to develop a model. A **model** is an idea, system, or structure that represents whatever you're trying to explain. The model is never exactly like the thing being explained, but it is similar enough to allow comparisons.

To find out how the shape of an airplane can affect performance, scientists and engineers make model airplanes of different shapes. These models are based on theories that describe how moving air behaves. They then test the different models under various conditions to find out which shape works best. They might also create different computer models, which are programs that predict the outcomes of different designs under various conditions.

OPTIONS

ENRICHMENT
▶ Have interested students research the life and inventions of Thomas Edison and present their findings to the class.
▶ Arrange to have students visit an elementary school classroom to observe how small children use problem-solving skills.
▶ Have interested students research the tangram, an ancient Chinese design puzzle, and demonstrate several of its solutions to the class with a poster.

TECHNOLOGY

Driving Smart

The time spent sitting in traffic is expected to increase fourfold by the year 2000. In an effort to improve safety and traffic flow, scientists and engineers are working on systems that use traffic monitoring, navigation equipment, and radio links. Early efforts are directed at helping motorists avoid traffic jams. Traffic sensors embedded in the road transmit data about traffic volume and speed to a central computer. This computer analyzes the data to predict the locations of traffic jams. This information is then transmitted by radio to an onboard computer in an individual car. The location of pending traffic jams and possible alternate routes are then projected on the car's video screen to help the driver choose the best route.

Another line of research involves vision-enhancement systems originally developed for the military. These systems could be linked to vehicle control to provide automatic speed control and emergency braking. Improvement of the sensory apparatus of a car would enable more vehicles to travel closer together, safely, at high speeds.

Think Critically: What problems exist with a system that provides drivers alternate routes around a traffic jam?

• Break the problem down into smaller, simpler problems. Sometimes it's hard to see what needs to be done when the problem is complicated. Look for ways to solve it step-by-step.

If one problem-solving approach doesn't work, try another. As you search for solutions, keep thinking about what you first knew about the problem and what you've learned from each problem-solving attempt. When you find a solution, think again about the problem and ask yourself if your solution makes sense.

Connect to... Earth Science

The famous stone slabs in England called Stonehenge may represent an ancient calendar. Find out how scientists used the four problem-solving strategies to decide possible meanings of Stonehenge.

TECHNOLOGY

▶ Have students collect articles about the latest technological improvements in the automobile industry. Help students differentiate between those improvements that deal with the operation of the automobile and those that improve the overall safety of the automobile.

▶ For more information on driving safety, see "Smart Highways" by Dan McCosh, *Popular Science*, November 1989, pp. 76-79.

Think Critically: Student responses may vary, but could include the idea that the switch to alternate routes could produce traffic congestion in other locations.

Connect to... Earth Science

Answer:
1. Use past knowledge to make a guess; other formations seemed to coincide with season changes and the sun's changes and sun's position.
2. Look for patterns; Stonehenge slabs, when viewed at certain angles, lined up with the sun's position on winter solstice and spring equinox.
3. Develop a model; some ancient societies, called Druids, in England followed rituals based on Earth and sun positions.
4. Break the problem into smaller problems; the scientists examined various portions of the Stonehenge formations and used aerial views to see the overall formations.

CONCEPT DEVELOPMENT

▶ Discuss inductive and deductive reasoning aspects in determining why the chili discussed in the text tasted bland. In the process of inductive reasoning, one generalizes from many experiences. Having eaten many bowls of chili, one can generalize on the attributes of chili, such as (a personal choice of) color, texture, and taste. Having made many bowls of chili, one can generalize on the methods of making it, such as cooking time and temperature. Having reached a general idea of what "good" chili is, *both* from making and eating a lot of it, one can evaluate a particular batch.

▶ From generalizing about the cooking times and temperatures of many batches of chili, one can eliminate these as factors in making this batch bland, unless it was uncooked or burned. This elimination is an example of deductive reasoning, or evaluating from a generalization.

Critical Thinking

What is critical thinking?

Imagine that you have just made a batch of chili, and it just doesn't taste right. It tastes bland. What could have gone wrong? Did you follow the recipe? Did you cook it at the right temperature for the proper length of time? After thinking about it, you decide that you may have left out an essential ingredient—chili powder. How did you arrive at this conclusion? Without being aware of it, you probably used some aspect of critical thinking.

Critical thinking is a process that uses certain skills to solve a problem. Let's see how you may have used critical thinking to solve the "great chili problem." First you identified the problem—the bland taste—by mentally comparing the taste of your chili with that of other batches of chili you've eaten. Next you may have separated important information from unimportant information by deciding that the temperature and cooking time of the chili had little to do with its flavor. Finally, you examined your assumption that you had followed the recipe correctly. This seemed like the best bet. You looked at the recipe again and concluded that you had left out the chili powder.

You probably went one step further and analyzed your conclusion. You asked if leaving the chili powder out would make the chili bland. If the answer was "yes," then you may have solved the problem.

"Flex Your Brain," as seen on the next page, is an activity that can be used throughout this book. This activity will help you to think about and examine your thinking. "Flex Your Brain" is a way to keep your thinking on track when you are investigating a topic. Each activity takes you through a series of steps, starting with what you already know about a topic and leading to new conclusions and awareness. Then, it encourages you to review and discuss the steps you took.

The "Flex Your Brain" activities, and other features of this book, are designed to help you improve your critical-thinking skills. You'll become a better problem solver, and your next batch of chili will taste great.

OPTIONS

ENRICHMENT

▶ Have students interview their parents to see how they use problem solving in their lives.

FLEX Your Brain

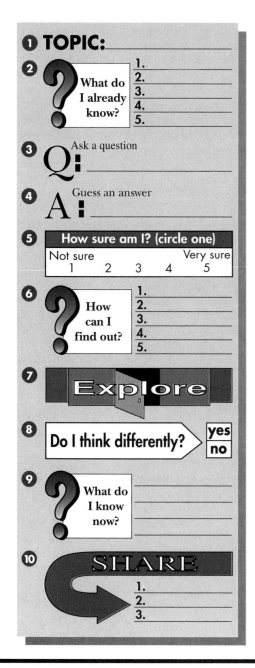

① TOPIC: _____

② ❓ What do I already know?
1. _____
2. _____
3. _____
4. _____
5. _____

③ **Q:** Ask a question _____

④ **A:** Guess an answer _____

⑤
How sure am I? (circle one)	
Not sure	Very sure
1 2 3	4 5

⑥ ❓ How can I find out?
1. _____
2. _____
3. _____
4. _____
5. _____

⑦ **Explore**

⑧ Do I think differently? ▶ yes / no

⑨ ❓ What do I know now?
_____
_____
_____

⑩ **SHARE**
1. _____
2. _____
3. _____

❶ Fill in the topic your teacher gives you.

❷ Jot down what you already know about the topic.

❸ Using what you already know (Step 2), form a question about the topic. Are you unsure about one of the items you listed? Do you want to know more? Do you want to know what, how, or why? Write down your question.

❹ Guess an answer to your question. In the next few steps, you will be exploring the reasonableness of your answer. Write down your guess.

❺ Circle the number in the box that matches how sure you are of your answer in Step 4. This is your chance to rate your confidence in what you've done so far and, later, to see how your level of sureness affects your thinking.

❻ How can you find out more about your topic? You might want to read a book, ask an expert, or do an experiment. Write down ways you can find out more.

❼ Make a plan to explore your answer. Use the resources you listed in Step 6. Then, carry out your plan.

❽ Now that you've explored, go back to your answer in Step 4. Would you answer differently? Mark one of the boxes.

❾ Considering what you learned in your exploration, answer your question again, adding new things you've learned. You may completely change your answer.

❿ It's important to be able to talk about thinking. Choose three people to tell about how you arrived at your response in every step. For example, don't just read what you wrote down in Step 2. Try to share how you thought of those things.

1-2 PROBLEM SOLVING **15**

CONCEPT DEVELOPMENT

▶ To acquaint students with this strategy, divide the class into small groups and have them explore a topic using the Flex Your Brain worksheet. Students should have some familiarity with the topic chosen. Possible topics might include cacti, volcanoes, and robots, or topics from a list the class brainstorms. See pages 19T-21T for a more detailed description of the Flex Your Brain process.

TEACHER F.Y.I.

▶ A reproducible version of the Flex Your Brain activity with space for students to write in their responses can be found in the **Activity Worksheets** booklet in the Teacher Resource Package. See the Program Resources box below.

► Students often fail to conceptualize the difference between a scientific law and a theory. Use the following demonstration to initiate a discussion.

► **Demonstration:** Fill one 1-L beaker with hot water and another with cold water. Have students feel each. Ask the students to predict what the mixture of the two would feel like. Pour the hot and cold water into a 2-L beaker and have students verify their predictions by feeling the temperature of the mixture. Ask them why they were so sure of their predictions. Most will discuss past experience and make a rudimentary statement of heat flowing from hot to cold materials. Inform them that they were making their predictions based on scientific law, which describes what will happen. Point out that a law doesn't explain why—that is the function of a theory. Tell the students that the "why" will be discussed in later chapters.

MINI QUIZ

Use the Mini Quiz to check students' recall of chapter content.

3 A(n) _____ is an educated guess about the answer to a problem. *hypothesis*

4 A(n) _____ is an explanation based on many observations supported by experimental results. *theory*

5 A(n) _____ is a "rule of nature." *scientific law*

CHECK FOR UNDERSTANDING

Ask questions 1-2 and the **Apply** and **Connect to Earth Science** questions in the Section Review.

RETEACH

Cooperative Learning: Using a Numbered Heads Together strategy, have each team of students propose a method of teaching a group of small children a task by using one or more problem-solving methods.

EXTENSION

For students who have mastered this section, use the **Reinforcement** and **Enrichment** masters or other OPTIONS provided.

Figure 1-8. Observations of the simple cocklebur led to the idea for the zipperless fastener.

What is a hypothesis?

Problem Solving in Science

The steps to solving a scientific problem are similar to those you use to solve any problem. The first step, **observation**, is using your senses to gather information. In science, tools such as microscopes, rulers, and clocks can help make your observations more precise.

Good observations lead to testable predictions about how to solve a problem or explain how something works. In science, a testable prediction is called a **hypothesis.** **3**

How do you find out if a hypothesis is right? A hypothesis can be tested by conducting experiments and making further observations. In a later section of this chapter, you'll find out more about experiments. If one hypothesis turns out to be wrong, another one can be proposed and tested. It's never possible to prove that a hypothesis is absolutely right. However, you can keep ruling out possibilities until you settle on one you think is most likely to be right. It may take many experiments and many different kinds of data to thoroughly test a hypothesis. The more results you obtain that support the hypothesis, the more confident you can be that it's correct.

Scientists use the information they gather during experimentation to form a theory. A **theory** **4** is an explanation based on many observations supported by experimental results. A theory is the most logical explanation of why things work the way they do. Theories may lead the way to more experiments. As new information is collected, a theory may need to be revised or discarded and replaced with another theory.

Over many years, scientists have observed that matter is never created nor destroyed in chemical changes. It is stated as the law of conservation of mass. A **scientific law** is a "rule of nature" that sums up related observations and experimental results to describe a pattern in nature. Generally, laws can be used to predict what will happen in a given situation, but don't explain why. Theories can serve as explanations of laws. Like theories, laws can be changed or discarded if new observations show them to be incorrect. **5**

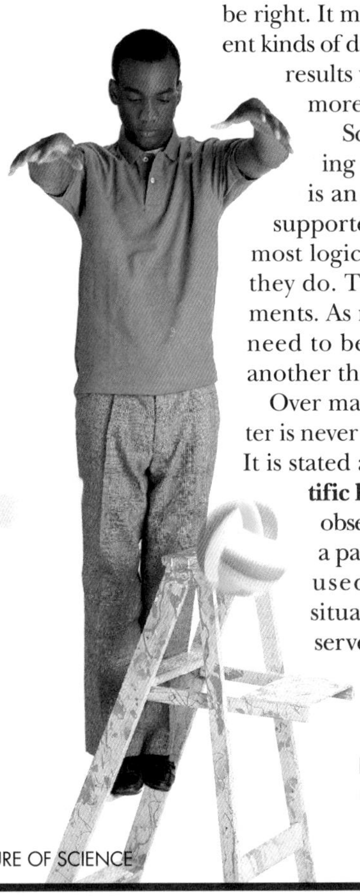

Figure 1-9. You can learn something about gravity by observing how different objects fall.

16 THE NATURE OF SCIENCE

OPTIONS

Figure 1-10. A simple event, such as the falling of an apple, inspired Isaac Newton to investigate gravity. This study eventually led to the development of an entirely new field of physics.

Whether you're puzzling over a physical science mystery in the classroom or just trying to figure out where you left your homework, you can use what you've learned about problem solving to lead you to a solution.

SECTION REVIEW

1. Explain the difference between an exercise and a problem. Give an example of each.
2. Compare and contrast these terms: *hypothesis, theory, scientific law.*
3. **Apply:** Develop a model to describe how you decide what to wear to school every day. Could someone who doesn't know you use the model to predict what you'll wear tomorrow?
4. **Connect to Earth Science:** Describe how the moon's phases, which are apparent changes in the moon's appearance, form a pattern that is useful for humans.

☑ Outlining

Think of a problem you solved or tried to solve recently. Outline the steps you followed in searching for the solution. If you need help, refer to Outlining in the **Skill Handbook** on page 677.

Skill Builder

---

3 CLOSE

▶ Write several traffic regulations pertaining to bicycles on the chalkboard. Have students discuss how these regulations allow car drivers, bike riders, and pedestrians to make probable predictions about what will happen at an intersection. Compare these regulations to scientific laws.

SECTION REVIEW ANSWERS

1. With an exercise, the method for reaching the solution is known; solving a crossword puzzle. With a problem the method of solution must be developed; fixing a flat tire.

2. A hypothesis is an educated guess, based on the best available knowledge. A theory is an explanation based on observations supported by test results. A scientific law is a rule of nature that sums up related observations and experimental results.

3. Apply: Student responses will vary, but could include such considerations as weather conditions, school dress codes, and current fashion trends. A stranger should be able to use a well-conceived model to make fairly accurate predictions.

4. Connect to Earth Science: This pattern allows seasonal, time, and planetary motion predictions.

Skill Builder
Student responses should outline the steps followed in solving a problem.

Skill Builder
ASSESSMENT
Performance: To determine if students can effectively use problem-solving strategies, present a new problem, such as the classroom door would not unlock this morning, for them to solve.

PREPARATION

SECTION BACKGROUND

▶ Global warming, ozone depletion, and acid rain are results of physical processes that take place in the atmosphere. The extent and effects of these processes are discussed.

1 MOTIVATE

▶ Ask students to describe the environment of a greenhouse. Discuss similar environments, such as solariums, that demonstrate solar energy being absorbed and converted to heat.

TYING TO PREVIOUS KNOWLEDGE:
Have students recall the distinctive smell of ozone in the air after an electrical storm.

2 TEACH

Key Concepts are highlighted.

CONCEPT DEVELOPMENT

▶ Ozone depletion takes place when a chlorofluorocarbon, such as CCl_2F_2, is decomposed by ultraviolet radiation and free chlorine reacts with ozone.

$$Cl + O_3 \rightarrow ClO \text{ and } O_2$$

V i d e o D i s c

STVS: Acid Rain and Plants, Disc 6, Side 2

CHECK FOR UNDERSTANDING

Ask questions 1-2 and the **Connect to Life Science** question in the Section Review.

SCIENCE & SOCIETY | **1-3**

Problems? What Problems?

New Science Words	Objectives
greenhouse effect ozone layer	▶ Describe some of the environmental issues presently being studied by scientists. ▶ Examine how scientific controversies arise.

Research or Action?

Is Earth's environment being changed? You may have heard about global warming, ozone depletion, and acid rain. But did you know that scientists disagree about the extent to which these occurrences may be problems and what should be done about them?

The **greenhouse effect,** heating Earth by the atmosphere's trapping the sun's energy, is necessary to provide an environment in which life as we know it can exist. But the burning of fossil fuels adds increased amounts of carbon dioxide to the atmosphere, and this heating may be happening at a faster-than-usual rate, causing global warming.

What is the greenhouse effect?

In the 1970s, scientists began to worry about damage to the **ozone layer,** a part of the atmosphere that protects life on Earth from the damaging effects of ultraviolet radiation from the sun. Scientists suggested that continued use of chlorofluorocarbons (KLOR uh floor uh kar bunz) (CFCs), chemicals used in refrigeration and in manufacturing plastic foam products, would destroy the ozone layer.

Around the same time, other scientists warned that sulfur and nitrogen oxides released when fossil fuels burn were making precipitation very acidic. This precipitation, usually called acid rain, was harmful to trees, crops, and aquatic life.

18 THE NATURE OF SCIENCE

OPTIONS

Meeting Different Ability Levels

For Section 1-3, use the following **Teacher Resource Masters** depending upon individual students' needs.

◆ **Study Guide Master** for all students.

● **Reinforcement Master** for students of average and above average ability levels.

▲ **Enrichment Master** for above average students.

Since these predictions were made, scientists have gathered data. Some scientists say their data show that the problems are serious and need immediate action. Others say that more research is needed before drastic action is taken to solve problems that could be minor. Just about everyone agrees that changes in the atmosphere today may have harmful effects far beyond what is presently suspected. At the very least, we must reduce those activities that continue to add acids, CFCs, and carbon dioxide to the atmosphere.

Figure 1-11. The trees in this forest show the effects of acid rain.

SECTION REVIEW

1. Think of a topic on which you think more scientific research needs to be done. How would you decide what kind of research should be done next?
2. Does it ever make sense to start trying to solve a problem before you've learned everything you can about it?
3. **Connect to Life Science:** Why might changing the temperature of Earth's atmosphere by a small amount be harmful to plant and animal life?

Connect to...
Life Science

Describe how ultraviolet rays from the sun can be harmful to life on Earth.

You Decide!

If you were a scientist studying global warming, ozone depletion, or acid rain, how would you decide when enough research had been done and when action should be taken? How would you know what action to take? Who should make these decisions, scientists doing the research, government, or the public? Would your answers be the same if you were considering a smaller scientific problem that would not affect the health of a whole planet and its inhabitants?

SCIENCE & SOCIETY

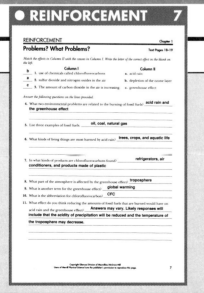

19

Connect to...
Life Science

Answer: Overexposure to UV rays can cause skin cancers and other mutations.

3 CLOSE

Cooperative Learning: Have Problem Solving Teams collect data detailing carbon dioxide levels and emissions over the past few years. They should then discuss whether there are correlations to global warming.

SECTION REVIEW ANSWERS

1. Responses will vary. An example topic is gasoline alternatives. Its research is needed due to depletion of gasoline supplies.

2. No; you should always learn as much about a problem as possible before attempting to find a solution.

3. Connect to Life Science: Habitats and migration routes could change. Polar ice melting would change water levels worldwide.

YOU DECIDE! **SCIENCE & SOCIETY**

Student responses will vary, but should indicate that the amount of information available, the critical nature of the problem, and the need for a speedy solution will play a part in any decision about when action should be taken.

1-4 Exploring Science

SECTION BACKGROUND

▶ Galileo is credited with establishing the scientific method, in which explanations of phenomena are verified by controlled observations.

1 MOTIVATE

▶ Have students discuss the following situation. The coach heard Jeff and Juan bragging that each could hit a ball harder than the other. Coach asks you to set up and referee a contest between Jeff and Juan. What would you do to make sure the contest is fair?

TYING TO PREVIOUS
KNOWLEDGE: Have students recall the meaning of the term *hypothesis.* Point out that in this section they will learn a standard method that is used to confirm a hypothesis.

In Your JOURNAL

Students' lists will contain a variety of controlled conditions. Some common answers include age of the balls and dropping from the same height.

VideoDisc

STVS: Drugs from Snake Venom, Disc 2, Side 1

STVS: Computerized Apple, Disc 1, Side 2

PROGRAM RESOURCES

From the **Teacher Resource Package** use:

Science Integration Activity 1

Use **Laboratory Manual 1,** No Need to Count Your Pennies.

New Science Words

experiment
control
constant
independent variable
dependent variable

In Your JOURNAL

In your Journal, list conditions that you, as a consumer, would have to control to test the bouncing characteristics of two brands of tennis balls.

Objectives

▶ Appreciate the importance of following guidelines in doing experiments.
▶ Define *constant, independent variable,* and *dependent variable.*
▶ Understand laboratory safety rules.

Experimentation

You've learned that problem solving in science involves making observations, forming a hypothesis, and testing the hypothesis with experiments. Now you'll learn just how to conduct an experiment.

An **experiment** is an organized procedure for testing a hypothesis. When scientists conduct experiments, they usually are seeking new information. Classroom experiments often demonstrate and verify information that already is known but may be new to you.

When doing an experiment, it is important to follow certain guidelines to reduce the chance of reaching wrong conclusions. Suppose you want to know whether storing microwave popcorn in a freezer will make it pop better. You store a package of popcorn in the freezer for a day or two, pop the corn, and count the unpopped kernels. Could you draw a meaningful conclusion from this "experiment?" No, because you don't have anything to compare your results with. Maybe you'd get the same number of unpopped kernels with corn stored at room temperature. But you don't know, because you didn't test any unfrozen popcorn.

To draw a conclusion, you need a control—a standard for comparison. In an experiment, a **control** shows that your result is related to the condition you're testing and not to some other condition.

To find out if storing popcorn in the freezer makes a difference, you need to test popcorn stored at room temperature as a control. All other conditions should be the

OPTIONS

Meeting Different Ability Levels

For Section 1-4, use the following **Teacher Resource Masters** depending upon individual students' needs.

◆ **Study Guide Master** for all students.
● **Reinforcement Master** for students of average and above average ability levels.
▲ **Enrichment Master** for above average students.

Additional Teacher Resource Package masters are listed in any **PROGRAM RESOURCES** boxes that are in the section. The additional masters are appropriate for all students.

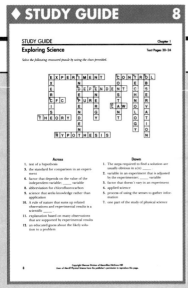

same for both batches of popcorn. The popcorn should be the same brand, equally fresh, stored for the same period of time, and popped in the same microwave oven, at the same power, for the same length of time. Only one condition, the place of storage, should differ between the two batches. All of the other factors are constants. A **constant** is a factor that doesn't vary in an experiment.

Can you be confident in conclusions based on the results of popping just one bag of popcorn stored each way? What if one of the bags happened to be defective? To be sure of your conclusions, you should repeat the experiment several times with different bags of popcorn, storing half of the bags in the freezer and half at room temperature.

If your experiment shows that storing microwave popcorn in the freezer makes it pop better, you may want to do another experiment to find out if the length of time the popcorn is stored makes a difference. You could store different batches of popcorn for different lengths of time. ③ Length of time stored would be the **independent variable,** the factor adjusted by the experimenter. The measure of popping success—the number of unpopped kernels— would be the dependent variable. A **dependent variable** depends on the value of the independent variable. What factors would be constants?

Keeping an orderly procedure for an experiment will help you to draw conclusions and decide what to do next in your investigation. It will also allow others to duplicate your investigation. Although scientists agree that there is no one way to solve a problem, their scientific methods often include the following steps:

Determine the problem. What do you want to find out?

Make a hypothesis. What prediction do you want to test?

Test your hypothesis. What steps can you take to reach a conclusion about your hypothesis? What measurements should you record?

Analyze the results. What happens during your experiment?

Draw conclusions. Do your observations and data suggest that your hypothesis is correct? If not, do you think your hypothesis is wrong, or do you need to change your experimental procedure?

EcoTip

Design an experiment to test for smog outside your house. HINT: Rubber bands left outside in a very polluted area will break easily in a few weeks.

What are dependent and independent variables?

Connect to...
Chemistry

Stomach antacids often describe how much stomach acid they can neutralize. What independent and dependent variables would you have to identify in order to compare such claims?

Figure 1-12. Keeping accurate records is an important part of scientific experimentation.

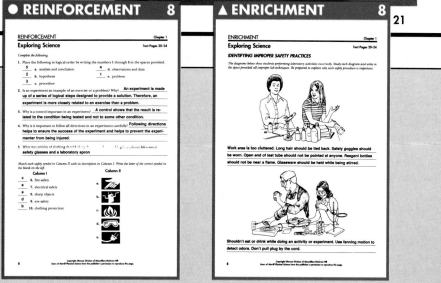
Key Concepts are highlighted.

CONCEPT DEVELOPMENT

▶ Point out that experiments are conducted to confirm a hypothesis or to confirm a *null* hypothesis, that is, the hypothesis that the independent variable in the experiment does not affect the dependent variable.

Cooperative Learning: Have students generate a list of factors, such as temperature, moisture, and sunlight, that might be factors when rubber bands are used to test for smog as described in the EcoTip. Assign factors to individual Problem Solving Teams and have them generate hypotheses and devise experiments to eliminate these factors.

STUDENT TEXT QUESTION

▶ Page 21, paragraph 3: **What factors would be constants?** *The constants are the same as before with the addition of similar storage conditions.*

CROSS CURRICULUM

▶ **Language Arts:** Have students look up the word *experiment* in a dictionary. Students should find that it is related to the Latin root *experiri* (to try). Have students explain how the meaning of the word reflects its root.

Connect to...
Chemistry

Answer: Independent variable is the amount of antacid material. Dependent variable is the amount of stomach acid neutralized.

1 **What is an experiment?** *an organized procedure for testing a hypothesis*

2 **In an experiment a(n) _____ is used as a standard for comparison.** *control*

3 **The _____ is the factor that is adjusted by the experimenter.** *independent variable*

PROBLEM SOLVING

To operate the tape player, the carbon dry cells cost 16.2 cents per hour and the alkaline dry cells cost 12.6 cents per hour. The alkaline dry cells are the better buy, even though their initial cost is more than that of the carbon dry cells.

Thinking Critically: Lauren solved the problem by stating a hypothesis; testing the hypothesis by comparing the efficiency of the two types of dry cells while keeping all other factors constant; collecting and analyzing data; and drawing a conclusion.

CROSS CURRICULUM

▶ **Art:** Safety symbols are icons—images that convey information. Have students design an icon to alert students to the laboratory safety hazards of long hair, clothing with floppy sleeves, or jewelry.

CHECK FOR UNDERSTANDING

Ask questions 1-2 and the **Apply** and **Connect to Chemistry** questions in the Section Review.

RETEACH

Cooperative Learning: Using a Numbered Heads Together strategy, divide the class into teams. Give each team a large index card on which to write a problem for an experiment. Have teams exchange their cards. Each team now generates a hypothesis for the question they now hold and writes it on the card. Again, they exchange the cards. Ask each team to devise an experiment based on the question and hypothesis on the card that it now has.

Safety

When working in the physical science laboratory, you'll handle glass, hot objects, sharp objects, and chemicals. A few rules will help you carry out experiments and activities safely.

PROBLEM SOLVING

Lauren's Experiment

Lauren walked for about 40 minutes every morning before school. During her walk, she used headphones to listen to a tape player attached to her belt.

Lauren found that she had to replace the carbon dry cell batteries in the tape player about every two and one-half weeks. So, she decided to conduct an experiment to find out whether alkaline dry cells, which cost more, would be less expensive to use than carbon dry cells. She hypothesized that, over a period of time, using alkaline dry cells would save her money.

She purchased two alkaline dry cells for $2.04 and two carbon dry cells for $1.38. She tested the dry cells on her morning walks, keeping track of the amount of time the tape player was in operation using each pair of dry cells. To keep the test fair, she played the same tape and kept the volume of the player constant throughout the experiment.

Two alkaline dry cells lasted 16 hours and 15 minutes, whereas two carbon dry cells lasted only eight and one-half hours. Lauren then divided the cost of the dry cells by the number of hours to determine which dry cells were less expensive to use. Which dry cells were the better buy?

Think Critically: What problem-solving methods did Lauren use in the experiment?

OPTIONS

INQUIRY QUESTIONS

▶ **What good is knowing that a null hypothesis is true?** *It eliminates the need to keep the null independent variable constant in any future experiments.*

▶ **What are placebos and how are they used in experiments?** *Placebos are materials that are known to have no medical effects on humans. They are used as controls in the experimental testing of medicines and drugs. Because they have no effects they are given to one group of people in place of the experimental medications given to another group.*

ENRICHMENT

▶ Have students research safety icons used in the construction industry, on medicines and household goods, in buildings, and along streets and highways. Have students draw samples of the icons and quiz the class on their meanings.

First, know what you're supposed to do before you begin. Read and follow all directions carefully and pay close attention to any caution statements.

Dress appropriately to reduce the chance of accidents. Avoid clothing with large, floppy sleeves. Remove dangling jewelry and tie back or cover long hair.

Think about what you're doing. Handle glass carefully, and don't touch hot objects with your bare hands. To be on the safe side, treat all equipment as if it were hot. Wear safety glasses and a protective apron.

Be sure you understand the safety symbols explained in Appendix B on page 674. They will be used throughout the textbook to alert you to possible laboratory dangers.

Your workspace should contain only materials needed. Keep other objects out of the way. Arrange your equipment so that you won't have to reach over burners or across equipment that could be knocked over.

Watch closely when your teacher demonstrates how to handle equipment, how to dispose of materials, how to clean up spills, and any other safety practices.

Make sure you know the location and proper operation of safety equipment, such as fire extinguishers.

SECTION REVIEW

1. What is the function of a control in an experiment?
2. You are doing an experiment to find out how the temperature of water affects the rate at which sugar dissolves. What factors should remain constant? What factors will vary?
3. **Apply:** Design an experiment to determine the fastest route from your home to school.
4. **Connect to Chemistry:** A chemist made some observations about a new type of plastic that may biodegrade in acid soil. State a possible hypothesis about these findings. How would your hypothesis be tested?

☑ Concept Mapping

Arrange these steps in organizing a scientific experiment to make an events chain concept map: *draw conclusions, make a hypothesis, determine the problem, analyze the results, test your hypothesis.* If you need help, refer to Concept Mapping in the **Skill Handbook** on pages 684 and 685.

Skill Builder

Did You Know?

Alfred Nobel, the man who left his fortune to fund the Nobel prizes, was the inventor of dynamite.

EXTENSION

For students who have mastered this section, use the **Reinforcement** and **Enrichment** masters or other OPTIONS provided.

3 CLOSE

▶ Have students review the microwave popcorn experiments discussed in the text and identify the instruments they would use to measure the controls, constants, and variables mentioned in the text.

SECTION REVIEW ANSWERS

1. A control is used as a basis for comparing data collected during an experiment.

2. Constants: quantity of water, quantity of sugar; variable: temperature of water

3. Apply: Student responses will vary, but should include at least one constant—mode of transportation—and one variable—routes taken.

4. Connect to Chemistry: Possible hypothesis: The plastic material will degrade faster as the soil it is in becomes more acidic. Testing: Bury equal-sized pieces of plastic the same depth in the same soil under measured variable acid conditions. After a constant time, examine the plastic for signs of decay.

Skill Builder
ASSESSMENT

Performance: Have the five described steps written on pieces of poster board. Give five students each one of the poster board pieces. Go back to the popcorn experiment, or some other example, and have the students hold up their poster board pieces in the proper sequence to describe the best way to do the experiment.

Skill Builder

Initiating Event

Determine the problem.

↓

Make a hypothesis.

↓

Test your hypothesis.

↓

Analyze the results.

↓

Draw conclusions.

OBJECTIVE: **Identify** and **manipulate** variables in a controlled experiment.

PROCESS SKILLS applied in this activity:
▶ **Observing** in Procedure Steps 4 and 5.
▶ **Predicting** in Procedure Step 7.
▶ **Controlling variables** in Procedure Step 6.

COOPERATIVE LEARNING
Divide the class into Science Investigation Teams of three.

TEACHING THE ACTIVITY
Troubleshooting: Advise students to securely tie the weights. Use twine that is heavy enough to untie easily.
▶ Objects in the 2- to 5-gram range are suitable for weights. The smaller weight should be about half the mass of the heavier weights.
▶ When one weight swings, its motion is transferred to the other weight and then back again. The pattern is obvious and changes in the pattern are easily recognized. Adding a third weight produces a much more complex pattern.
▶ Focus the lesson on investigating cause and effect by controlling variables.

PROGRAM RESOURCES
From the **Teacher Resource Package** use:

Transparency Masters, pages 3-4, Safety Symbols.

Activity Worksheets, pages 7-8, Activity 1-1: Identifying and Controlling Variables.

Use **Color Transparency** number 2, Safety Symbols.

ACTIVITY 1-1 Identifying and Controlling Variables

You have seen that science can be used to solve problems. In solving problems, variables and constants are important. How can variables help solve problems?

Materials
• string, 1.5 meters
• identical weights (3)
• smaller weight (1)
• metric ruler
• ring stands (2)
• scissors
• stopwatch

CAUTION: *Refer to page 674 in Appendix B for an explanation of safety symbols.*

Procedure
1. Cut the string into one 60-cm length and three 30-cm lengths.
2. Tie one 30-cm string to each of the identical weights.
3. Using knots that can be easily untied, tie the long string between the two ring stands and attach two short strings as shown.
4. Swing one of the weights and *observe* what happens to the other weight. *Measure* distances and times as precisely as possible. *Record* this information.
5. Make a list of variables, such as length of string and amount of weight, that may affect the movements of the weights.
6. Adjust the identified variables one at a time. *Measure* and *record* the response of the swinging weights.
7. When all variables have been tested, *predict* the effect of adding a third string and weight. Test your prediction.

Analyze
1. How do the two swinging weights affect each other?
2. What variables did you identify?
3. Which variable has the greatest effect and which has the least?

Conclude and Apply
4. Why is it important to change only one variable at a time?
5. Is adding the third weight the same as changing one variable, or does it involve changing more than one? Explain.

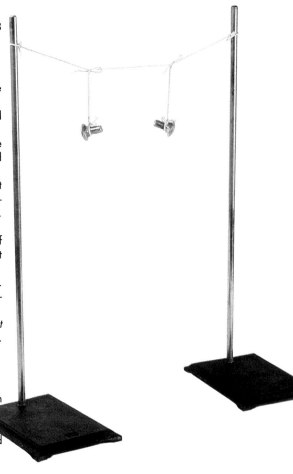

ANSWERS TO QUESTIONS
1. Energy is transferred through the horizontal string. When one weight loses all of its energy to the other, it stops moving.
2. Variables include: the distance between the weights, the length of the string, differences in the lengths of the string tied to weights, and differences in the weights.
3. Unequal string length has the greatest effect. Distance between weights has the least effect.

4. to identify the response for which the variable is responsible
5. The third weight can transfer energy to either one or two weights. Also, it changes the tension of the horizontal string. Adding this weight introduces at least three variables.

Activity
ASSESSMENT
Performance: To further assess students' understanding of variables, see USING LAB Skills, Question 12, on page 26.

SUMMARY

1-1: Physical Science and You

1. Science includes both "pure" science, which is study for the purpose of advancing human knowledge, and technology, which is applying science to improve the quality of human life.
2. Physical science is the study of matter and energy.
3. Some physical science topics include the composition of matter, the types of energy, and the interactions of matter and energy.

1-2: Problem Solving

1. A problem and an exercise both involve finding missing information. With an exercise, the method for finding the information is known. With a problem, the method must be developed as the solution is sought.
2. In solving a problem, a systematic series of steps should be followed, always leading from known information to unknown information.
3. A hypothesis is a testable prediction. A theory is an explanation based on many observations supported by experimental results. A scientific law describes a pattern in nature.

1-3: Science and Society: Problems? What Problems?

1. Some environmental issues being studied by scientists include global warming, ozone depletion, and acid rain.
2. Different interpretations of the same observations often lead to different conclusions.

1-4: Exploring Science

1. In conducting a scientific experiment, certain guidelines should be followed to ensure that the purpose of the experiment is met and the results of the experiment are valid.
2. All experiments involve certain variables. An independent variable is determined by the experimenter. A dependent variable depends on the value of the independent variable.
3. Certain safety rules and procedures must be followed in the science laboratory at all times.

KEY SCIENCE WORDS

a. **constant**
b. **control**
c. **critical thinking**
d. **dependent variable**
e. **experiment**
f. **greenhouse effect**
g. **hypothesis**
h. **independent variable**
i. **model**
j. **observation**
k. **ozone layer**
l. **physical science**
m. **scientific law**
n. **technology**
o. **theory**

UNDERSTANDING VOCABULARY

Match each phrase with the correct term from the list of Key Science Words.

1. the study of matter and energy
2. applying science to improve quality of life
3. an idea, system, or structure that can be used to solve a problem
4. a testable prediction
5. the use of human senses to gather information
6. an organized method of testing a hypothesis
7. describes but doesn't explain a pattern in nature
8. a factor that doesn't change in an experiment
9. warming Earth's atmosphere by trapping energy from the sun
10. factor in an experiment that is adjusted by the experimenter

THE NATURE OF SCIENCE **25**

SUMMARY

Have students read the summary statements to review the major concepts of the chapter.

UNDERSTANDING VOCABULARY

1. l	**6.** e
2. n	**7.** m
3. i	**8.** a
4. g	**9.** f
5. j	**10.** h

ASSESSMENT
Portfolio

Encourage students to place in their portfolios one or two items of what they consider to be their best work. For each item, ask students to explain why that item was chosen and what they learned from it. Items might be selected from the following.
• Skill Builder article and summary, p. 8
• Enrichment interview, p. 14
• Cross Curriculum icons, p. 23

Performance

Additional performance assessments may be found in *Performance Assessment* and *Science Integration Activities* that accompany **Merrill Physical Science**. Performance Task Assessment Lists and rubrics for evaluating these activities and other products generated throughout the chapter can be found in Glencoe's *Performance Assessment in Middle School Science*.

OPTIONS

ASSESSMENT

To assess student understanding of material in this chapter, use the resources listed.

COOPERATIVE LEARNING
Consider using cooperative learning in the THINK AND WRITE CRITICALLY, APPLY, and MORE SKILL BUILDERS sections of the Chapter Review.

PROGRAM RESOURCES

From the **Teacher Resource Package** use:

Cross-Curricular Connections, page 5, Using Analogies to Develop Thinking Skills.

Science and Society, page 5, Consumer Product Testing.

Chapter Review, pages 5-6.

Chapter and Unit Tests, pages 5-8, Chapter Test.

REVIEW

CHAPTER

REVIEW

CHECKING CONCEPTS

1.	b	**6.**	c
2.	c	**7.**	d
3.	a	**8.**	b
4.	b	**9.**	b
5.	d	**10.**	a

USING LAB SKILLS

ASSESSMENT

Use these alternate lab exercises to assess students' understanding of skills used in this chapter.

11. One pattern is a separation by compact discs and cassette tapes. Another pattern is by the type of music, such as rock or classical. Accept all reasonable answers.

12. Controlled variables could include identical means of holding the pens, identical supplying of a writing surface, identical pressure applied during writing, and identical absorbancy of the paper.

THINK AND WRITE CRITICALLY

13. With an exercise, you know exactly what you are trying to solve and the method to use to reach the solution. Solving a crossword puzzle is an example of an exercise. A problem involves a great deal of uncertainty. A problem is often not well defined, and the best method for solving it is not known. A crossword puzzle would be a problem if the clues were not numbered.

14. A hypothesis, a theory, and a scientific law are similar in that they all deal with using information to answer a question or solve a problem. A hypothesis is an educated guess based on the best information available, a testable prediction. A theory is an explanation that has been tested and supported by results. A scientific law is a statement that describes a pattern in nature.

CHECKING CONCEPTS

Choose the word or phrase that completes the sentence or answers the question.

1. Study of science for the sole purpose of advancing our knowledge is called _____ science.
  a. experimental
  b. pure
  c. hypothetical
  d. technological

2. Physical science would involve the study of all of the following except _____.
  a. the melting point of wax
  b. the composition of wax
  c. the behavior of bees producing wax
  d. energy released by burning wax

3. A(n) _____ is used as a standard for comparison in an experiment.
  a. control
  b. theory
  c. independent variable
  d. constant

4. A _____ is an explanation supported by experimental results.
  a. conclusion
  b. theory
  c. scientific law
  d. model

5. It is believed that chlorofluorocarbons are responsible for _____.
  a. the greenhouse effect
  b. acid rain
  c. global warming
  d. ozone depletion

6. Which of these is not a safety rule to be followed in every laboratory?
  a. Follow all directions carefully.
  b. Clean up all spills immediately.
  c. Wear rubber-soled shoes at all times.
  d. Know the location of the fire extinguisher.

7. _____ shields Earth from the damaging effects of ultraviolet radiation.
  a. The atmosphere
  b. Carbon dioxide
  c. Nitrogen oxide
  d. Ozone

8. The _____ describes the steps followed in conducting an experiment.
  a. problem
  b. procedure
  c. conclusion
  d. data

9. A scientific _____ is sometimes called a "rule of nature."
  a. theory
  b. law
  c. model
  d. hypothesis

10. Which is the final step in an experiment?
  a. Reach a conclusion.
  b. State the problem.
  c. Set up a procedure.
  d. Record data.

USING LAB SKILLS

11. In the MINI-Lab on page 7, you examined a larger system by looking for patterns within smaller units. When you enter a store that sells recorded music, what patterns can you see that help the overall organization of the music in the store?

12. In Activity 1-1 on page 24, you carefully controlled and identified variables to solve a problem. Assume you are testing two different ink pens to see which one would write for the longer time. What would be some important controls to consider?

THINK AND WRITE CRITICALLY

Answer the following questions in your Journal using complete sentences.

13. Why is it usually easier to find the solution to an exercise than it is to find the solution to a problem? Include examples in your answer.

14. Describe how a hypothesis, a theory, and a scientific law are related.
15. Discuss the importance of recording all observations and data when conducting a science experiment.
16. Describe four safety precautions to be followed in the science laboratory.
17. Describe one current environmental issue that is controversial and explain why scientists disagree on the issue.

APPLY

18. In a study of the sun, what questions might a pure scientist ask? What questions might an applied scientist ask? How might the two sets of questions be related?
19. What aspects of the following items would a physical scientist be interested in?
    a. an electric guitar   **b.** a piece of coal
20. Which problem-solving approach would you use to solve the following problems? Explain your choice in each case.
    a. solving a complex word problem in math
    b. figuring out a secret code
    c. predicting how a skyscraper would be affected by an earthquake
21. Design an experiment to determine how the temperature of water affects the time it takes sugar to dissolve in it. Identify the variables, constants, and control, if any.
22. Explain this statement: Scientists often learn as much from an incorrect hypothesis as they do from one that is correct.

MORE SKILL BUILDERS

If you need help, refer to the Skill Handbook.

1. **Comparing and Contrasting:** Compare and

contrast the methods used to complete an exercise and to solve a problem.
2. **Hypothesizing:** Propose a hypothesis to explain why a balloon filled with air weighs more than a deflated balloon.
3. **Interpreting Scientific Illustrations:** The following are safety symbols used in two different experiments. Using Table B-2 on page 674 in Appendix B, write out what safety precaution is indicated by each symbol.

a.
b.

4. **Using Variables, Constants, and Controls:** Do some objects fall faster than others? Design an experiment to find out. State your hypothesis and describe your procedure for testing it. Identify your controls, constants, and variables.

PROJECTS

1. Make a poster illustrating laboratory safety techniques.
2. Make a scrapbook of recent newspaper or magazine articles dealing with the scientific debate surrounding global warming, the ozone layer, and/or acid rain. Read the articles carefully and include at the end of your scrapbook a short essay explaining your position on the problem.

15. A written record of observations and data allows another person to duplicate the experiment exactly and to compare the results with those of the original experiment.
16. Student responses may vary, but should include four of the safety precautions included in the chapter.
17. Student responses may vary, but will probably include one of the three issues discussed in this chapter—global warming, ozone depletion, or acid rain.

APPLY

18. A pure scientist might ask about the sun's size, composition, age, temperature, movements, and methods of energy production. An applied scientist might ask how the sun's energy can be harnessed for use on Earth. Both sets of questions deal with the sun. Also, before the applied scientist can answer questions, he or she must use some of the pure scientist's findings.
19. Student responses may vary. Examples could include the following:
a. how the length and thickness of the strings or the shape, composition, and structure of the guitar body affect the sound
b. the chemical composition of the coal, its hardness and color, how hot it must be before it burns
20. **a.** Word Problem: Break it down into simpler problems.
b. Code: Look for patterns.
c. Predicting: Create and study models.
21. Constants: volume of water, mass of sugar
    Control: water at same temperature
    Independent variable: water temperature
    Dependent variable: time required for sugar to dissolve
22. A scientist is able to eliminate an incorrect hypothesis as a possible solution to a problem.

MORE SKILL BUILDERS

1. **Comparing and Contrasting:** The methods used to solve a problem are developed as the solution to the problem is sought. The methods used to complete an exercise have already been tested and are found to produce the desired results.

2. **Hypothesizing:** Student responses may vary, but should include the idea that the inflated balloon contains something that the deflated balloon does not—air—and it has weight.
3. **Interpreting Scientific Illustrations: a.** The first symbol indicates an open flame; the second indicates safety goggles should be worn; the third indicates that the chemicals used are poisonous; the fourth that the chemicals are caustic to the skin.
b. The first symbol indicates a possible electric hazard; the second symbol indicates that the equipment being used is quite hot; the

third symbol indicates that safety goggles should be worn; the fourth symbol indicates that the chemicals used are potentially explosive.
4. **Using Variables, Constants, and Controls:** Students should describe an experiment in which they measure the time it takes for objects having different physical characteristics (mass, shape, size) to fall the same distance. The distance will be constant. Variables will consist of the differences in the objects tested.

Physical Science Methods

CHAPTER SECTION	OBJECTIVES	ACTIVITIES
2-1 Standards of Measurement (2 days)	1. **Define** standard of measurement. 2. **Recognize** the need for standards of measurement. 3. **Name** the prefixes used in SI and tell what multiple of ten each represents.	**Activity 2-1:** *Characteristics of Systems of Measurement, p. 33*
2-2 Using SI Units (2 days)	1. **Identify** SI units and symbols for length, volume, mass, density, time, and temperature. 2. **Define** derived unit. 3. **Demonstrate** an ability to convert related SI units.	**MINI-Lab:** *What is the density of a pencil? p. 40*
2-3 Graphing (1 day)	1. **Identify** three types of graphs and explain the correct use of each type. 2. **Distinguish** between dependent and independent variables. 3. **Interpret** graphs.	**MINI-Lab:** *How can a graph help you observe change? p. 42*
2-4 Metrics for All? Science & Society (1 day)	1. **Analyze** the benefits and drawbacks of universal use of SI measurements. 2. **Give examples** of SI units used in the United States.	**Activity 2-2:** *Metric Munchies, p. 48*
Chapter Review		

ACTIVITY MATERIALS				
FIND OUT	**ACTIVITIES**		**MINI-LABS**	
Page 29 classroom objects	**2-1 Characteristics of Systems of Measurement, p. 33** string, 1 m long scissors masking tape	**2-2 Metric Munchies, p. 48** balance 100-mL graduated cylinder munchie ingredients measuring cup measuring teaspoon measuring tablespoon 1-quart plastic container cooking pot hot plate	**What is the density of a pencil? p. 40** balance pencil 100-mL graduated cylinder	**How can a graph help you observe change? p. 42** thermometer plastic foam cup lid with straw hole graph paper timer with second hand

CHAPTER FEATURES	TEACHER RESOURCE PACKAGE	OTHER RESOURCES
Problem Solving: *Nonstandard Measurement Units,* p. 32 **Skill Builder:** *Sequencing,* p. 32	**Ability Level Worksheets** ◆ **Study Guide,** p. 9 ● **Reinforcement,** p. 9 ▲ **Enrichment,** p. 9 **Activity Worksheets,** pp. 13, 14 **Transparency Masters,** pp. 5, 6	**Color Transparency 3,** *SI Units and Prefixes* **STVS:** *Disk 3, Side 2*
Technology: *Space Spheres,* p. 37 **Skill Builder:** *Concept Mapping,* p. 41	**Ability Level Worksheets** ◆ **Study Guide,** p. 10 ● **Reinforcement,** p. 10 ▲ **Enrichment,** p. 10 **Activity Worksheets,** pp. 5, 19 **Concept Mapping,** pp. 9, 10 **Cross-Curricular Connections,** p. 6 **Technology,** pp. 7, 8	**Laboratory Manual 2,** *Relationships* **Laboratory Manual 3,** *Viscosity* **Science Integration Activity 2**
Skill Builder: *Making and Using Graphs,* p. 45	**Ability Level Worksheets** ◆ **Study Guide,** p. 11 ● **Reinforcement,** p. 11 ▲ **Enrichment,** p. 11 **Activity Worksheets,** p. 20 **Critical Thinking/Problem Solving,** p. 8 **Science and Society,** p. 6 **Transparency Masters,** pp. 7, 8	**Color Transparency 4,** *Types of Graphs* **STVS:** *Disk 1, Side 2*
You Decide! p. 47	**Ability Level Worksheets** ◆ **Study Guide,** p. 12 ● **Reinforcement,** p. 12 ▲ **Enrichment,** p. 12 **Activity Worksheets,** pp. 15, 16	
Summary Think & Write Critically Key Science Words Apply Understanding Vocabulary More Skill Builders Checking Concepts Projects Using Lab Skills	**ASSESSMENT RESOURCES** **Chapter Review,** pp. 7, 8 **Chapter Test,** pp. 9–12 **Unit Test,** pp. 13, 14 **Performance Assessment in Middle School Science**	**Chapter Review Software** **Test Bank** **Alternate Assessment** **Performance Assessment** **STVS:** Disc 3, Side 2

◆ Basic   ● Average   ▲ Advanced

ADDITIONAL MATERIALS

SOFTWARE	AUDIOVISUAL	BOOKS/MAGAZINES
Interpreting Graphs, Sunburst. *Introduction to General Chemistry: The Metric System,* EduQuest. *Measurement Process: Distance and Area,* EduQuest. *The Metric System,* Queue. *The Properties of Matter,* Queue. *Quantities and Measurements,* Queue. *SI/Metric Literacy,* EME Corp.	*How Low Can You Go? (Part 1),* Video, Insight Media. *It's Chemical Series,* Videos and Laserdisc, HRM Video. *It's Chemical Series: Density in Gases, Density in Liquids, Density in Solids,* Videos, Modern. *Mass and Density: Investigating Matter,* Laserdisc, AIMS Media. *Matter and Its Measures,* Video, Lucerne Media. *Observing, Recording, Mapping, and Graphing,* Video, Journal Films.	Asimov, Isaac. *The Measure of the Universe.* New York, NY: Harper and Row, 1983. Lamon, William E. *Metric System of Measurement: A Handbook for Teachers.* Portland, OR: Continuing Ed. Pr., 1981. Taylor, Barbara. *Weight and Balance.* NY: Watts, 1990.

THEME DEVELOPMENT: This chapter introduces the SI system of measurement and graphing as two methods of gaining and interpreting information. In developing the SI system, stress how base units are related to each other and how the same set of prefixes is used for all units.

CHAPTER OVERVIEW

▶ **Section 2-1:** This section introduces the SI system as a standardized decimal system of measurement that is being used by the scientific community and by most countries.

▶ **Section 2-2:** The SI prefixes and base units for length, mass, time, and temperature are introduced in this section. The relationships among length, volume, mass, and density are discussed.

▶ **Section 2-3:** Three types of graphs and their specific uses are presented as ways of displaying information.

▶ **Section 2-4: Science and Society:** Students are asked to evaluate the impact of converting the United States to SI.

CHAPTER VOCABULARY

standard	kilogram
SI	density
meter	time
volume	second
derived units	kelvin
liter	graph
mass	

VideoDisc

STVS: Charting Air Space, Disc 3, Side 2

CHAPTER

2 Physical Science Methods

28

OPTIONS

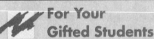

For Your Gifted Students

▶ Have students research the standardization of currency. When did it occur? Why? They can compare the need for standard units of measurement discussed in the chapter to the need for standard currency.

▶ Students can use centimeter-graph paper to draw a scaled floor plan of their classroom, home, or school.

For Your Mainstreamed Students

▶ Using a paper clip as a unit of measure for 1 gram, have students use a double-pan balance to weigh several items (pencil, tennis ball, crayon, etc.).

▶ Have students estimate the Celsius temperature for the classroom, normal body temperature, a summer day at the beach, and a winter day skiing. Compare with classmates' estimates and discuss.

Look around your classroom. In order to build the room and produce all the things inside it, such as the desks, chairs, shelves, and chalkboards, many measurements had to be made. Think about some of the things that were measured and the tools used to measure them.

FIND OUT!

Do this simple activity to find out how measurements are made.

Imagine that measuring tools have not been invented. Pick something in your classroom to use as a tool for *measuring* length. It can be an object from your desk; a hand, foot, or arm; or anything else that can easily be used.

Working with a partner, *measure* a distance in the room with your measuring device. Now have your partner *measure* the same distance, first using his or her own measuring device, then using yours. Which measurements can you compare? How similar are they? How could you improve your measuring devices?

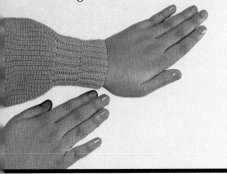

Gearing Up
Previewing the Chapter

Use this outline to help you focus on important ideas in this chapter.

Previewing Science Skills

► In the Skill Builders, you will sequence, make a concept map, and make and use graphs.
► In the Activities, you will observe, collect and organize data, and measure in SI.
► In the MINI-Labs, you will measure in SI, make inferences, and make and use graphs.

What's next?

Now that you have compared measurements made with your own measuring devices, find out what a measurement standard is. Once you know why standards are so important in making measurements, learn to use the system of measurement that is used by scientists throughout the world.

29

INTRODUCING THE CHAPTER
Use the Find Out activity to introduce students to the inherent difficulties of measuring without standardized units.

FIND OUT!
Materials: ordinary classroom objects
Cooperative Learning: Select a measuring device at random from those chosen by the class and assign Problem Solving Teams to devise ways of using the device to measure the length of a paper clip, the length of the school building, the diameter of the wire in a paper clip, and the diameter of a tree.
Teaching Tips
► Have all the students measure at least two common objects, such as the length of the chalk tray and the width of a student desk, for comparisons.
► Students should discuss the measurements they made. Focus the discussion on the conceptualization of the unit, the measuring device and its relationship to the unit, how the device is used in making the measurement, and the value of the measurement.
► Have the students discuss the limitations of the measurements they made.

Gearing Up
Have students study the Gearing Up section to familiarize themselves with the chapter. Discuss the relationships of the topics in the outline.

What's Next?
Before beginning the first section, make sure students understand the connection between the Find Out activity and the topics to follow.

ASSESSMENT OPTIONS

PORTFOLIO
Refer to page 49 for suggested items that students might select for their portfolios.

PERFORMANCE ASSESSMENT
See page 49 for additional Performance Assessment options.
Process
Skill Builders, pp. 41, 45
MINI-Lab, pp. 40, 42
Activities 2-1, p. 33; 2-2, p. 48
Using Lab Skills, p. 50

CONTENT ASSESSMENT
Assessment—Oral, pp. 36, 44
Skill Builder, p. 32
Section Reviews, pp. 32, 41, 45, 47
Chapter Review, pp. 49–51
Mini Quizzes, pp. 31, 39, 44

GROUP ASSESSMENT
Opportunities for group assessment occur with Cooperative Learning Strategies and Flex Your Brain Activities.

PREPARATION

SECTION BACKGROUND

▶ One major reason that science has progressed is because of its reliance on quantitative observations. The SI system is used by the scientific community to collect and communicate these observations.

1 MOTIVATE

Cooperative Learning: Using the Numbered Heads Together strategy, have students suggest solutions to the following paradox: A pound of feathers will balance a pound of gold, but it is possible that an ounce of feathers will not balance an ounce of gold. There are two standard ounces: the avoirdupois ounce, of which 16 constitute a pound; and the troy ounce, of which 12 constitute a pound.

▶ Have students recall standard sizes of products such as batteries (AAA, AA, B, C, D) and light bulbs (75 W, 100 W). Ask them why these products must be standardized and conjecture how manufacturers make sure their products meet these standards.

TYING TO PREVIOUS KNOWLEDGE:
Have students recall the relationships among pennies, dimes, and dollars. Point out that their knowledge of the relationships being based upon ten will be important in their understanding of the metric system.

2 TEACH

Key Concepts are highlighted.

CONCEPT DEVELOPMENT

▶ Make sure students understand that the term *exact quantity* indicates that people have agreed how to define, reproduce, and use the quantity.

New Science Words

standard
SI

Objectives

▶ Define standard of measurement.
▶ Recognize the need for standards of measurement.
▶ Name the prefixes used in SI and tell what multiple of ten each represents.

Units and Standards

How wide is your desk? At what temperature does ice cream start to melt? How fast does sugar dissolve? In order to answer any of these questions, some measurement must be made.

Measuring is an important skill. It is especially important in science. In order for a measurement to be useful, a measurement standard must be used. A **standard** is an exact quantity that people agree to use for comparison. 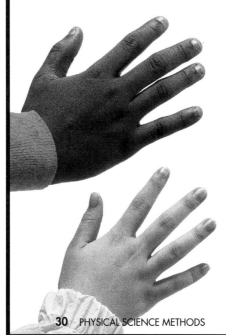 When all measurements are made using the same standard, the measurements can be compared to each other.

Suppose you and a friend want to make some measurements to find out if a desk will fit through a doorway. You have no ruler, so you decide to use your hands as measuring tools. Using the width of his or her hands, your friend measures the doorway and says it is 8 "hands" wide. Using the width of your hands, you measure the desk and find it is 7-3/4 "hands" wide. Will the desk fit through the doorway? You can't be sure. What if your hands are wider than your friend's hands? Then the distance equal to 7-3/4 of your hands might be greater than the distance equal to 8 of your friend's hands.

What mistake did you make? Even though you both used your hands to measure, you didn't check to see if your hands were the same width as your friend's hands. In other words, you didn't use a measurement standard, so you can't compare measurements.

30 PHYSICAL SCIENCE METHODS

OPTIONS

Meeting Different Ability Levels

For Section 2-1, use the following **Teacher Resource Masters** depending upon individual students' needs.

◆ **Study Guide Master** for all students.
● **Reinforcement Master** for students of average and above average ability levels.
▲ **Enrichment Master** for above average students.

Additional Teacher Resource Package masters are listed in any PROGRAM RESOURCES boxes that are in the section. The additional masters are appropriate for all students.

◆ **STUDY GUIDE** 9

STUDY GUIDE   Chapter 2
Standards of Measurement   Text Pages 30–33

Some prefixes used in SI are listed in the table below. Use the information in the table to answer questions 1–5.

SI Prefix	Meaning
kilo-	thousand (1000)
hecto-	hundred (100)
deka-	ten (10)
deci-	tenth (0.10)
centi-	hundredth (0.01)
milli-	thousandth (0.001)

1. How many meters are in one kilometer? **1000 m**
2. What part of a liter is one milliliter? **0.001 m or one thousandth meter**
3. How many grams are in two dekagrams? **20 g**
4. If one gram of water has a volume of one milliliter, what would the mass of one liter of water be in kilograms? **one kilogram**
5. What part of a meter is a decimeter? **0.10 m or one tenth meter**

In the blank at the left, write the term that correctly completes each statement. Choose from the terms listed below.

| metric | SI | standard |
| ten | prefixes | tenth |

standard 6. An exact quantity that people agree to use for comparison is a ____.
SI 7. The system of measurement used worldwide in science is ____.
ten 8. SI is based on units of ____.
metric 9. The first system of measurement that was based on units of ten was the ____ system.
prefixes 10. In SI, ____ are used with the names of the base unit to indicate the multiple of ten that is being used with the base unit.
tenth 11. The prefix deci- means ____.

Copyright Glencoe Division of Macmillan/McGraw-Hill
Users of Merrill Physical Science have the publisher's permission to reproduce this page.   9

International System of Units

Suppose the label on a ball of string indicates that the length of the string in the ball is "150." Can you tell how much string is in the ball? No. It could be 150 feet, 150 meters, or 150 of some unit you've never heard of. In order for a measurement to make sense, it must include a number and a unit.

Your family probably buys lumber by the foot, milk by the gallon, and potatoes by the pound. These measurement units are part of the English system of measurement, which is most commonly used in the United States. Most other nations use a system of measurement based on multiples of ten. The first such system of measurement, called the metric system, was devised by a group of scientists in the late 1700s. The system was based on a set of standards established and agreed to by the scientists.

In 1960 an improved version of the metric system was devised. Known as the International System of Units, this system is often abbreviated SI, from the French *Le Système Internationale d'Unités*. **SI is the standard system of measurement used worldwide.** All SI standards are universally accepted and understood by scientists.

In SI, each type of measurement has a base unit, such as the meter, which is the base unit of length. In the next section, you will learn the units used to measure length, mass, time, temperature, volume, and density.

The system is easy to use because it is based on multiples of ten. Prefixes are used with the names of the base units to indicate what multiple of ten should be used with the base unit. For example, the prefix *kilo-* means 1000. So a *kilometer* is 1000 meters. The most frequently used prefixes are shown in Table 2-1. Based on information from the table, how would you express a centimeter in meter units?

What system of measurement is used in the U.S.?

Figure 2-1. The standard kilogram mass, composed of a platinum-iridium alloy, is kept at the International Bureau of Weights and Measures in Sevres, France.

Table 2-1

IMPORTANT SI PREFIXES		
Prefixes	Symbol	Multiplying factor
kilo-	k	1000
deci-	d	0.1
centi-	c	0.01
milli-	m	0.001
micro-	µ	0.000 001
nano-	n	0.000 000 001

Connect to... Earth Science

Astronomers have developed a non-SI unit that is convenient for their measurements. The standard is the distance from Earth to the sun and is called the astronomical unit, or AU. Find out what one AU would equal in an SI unit.

31

PROBLEM SOLVING

The students measuring with string had a measurement standard, whereas those measuring in cubits did not.

Think Critically: Measurement standards are necessary in order that different measurements of the same quantity can be compared.

3 CLOSE

▶ Have students identify several Olympic track and swimming events such as the 100-m dash and the 200-m free-style. Ask them to explain why these events are measured in SI units.

SECTION REVIEW ANSWERS

1. Student responses may include that SI is based on ten and that the same prefixes are used for all measurements.
2. 0.1 meter = one decimeter; 1000 meters = one kilometer
3. Apply: Student responses will vary. Accept all reasonable responses.
4. Connect to Earth Science: 16 km

Skill Builder

kilogram, gram, decigram, centi-gram, milligram

Skill Builder
ASSESSMENT
Performance: Ask students which has more mass, a 1-g vitamin pill or a 1-mg pill?

In Your JOURNAL

Accept all reasonable examples, such as 12 fluid oz and 355 mL for a soft drink.

PROGRAM RESOURCES

From the **Teacher Resource Package** use:

Transparency Masters, pages 5-6, SI Units and Prefixes.

Use **Color Transparency** number 3, SI Units and Prefixes.

PROBLEM SOLVING

Nonstandard Measurement Units

As the students in Mr. Craig's science class entered the classroom, everyone noticed a long strip of tape on the chalkboard. Mr. Craig told the students that they would measure the length of the tape.

The students were divided up into two teams. The members of one team were to measure the length of the tape in cubits, the distance from the elbow to the end of the middle finger. The other team was given a piece of wood and a ball of string. Each student was to cut a piece of string exactly as long as the piece of wood, and then use the string to measure the tape.

Although they measured carefully, each student using cubits came up with a different number of units for the length of the

tape. The students using pieces of string all came up with the same number of units.

Why were measurements in cubits different but those made with string the same?
Think Critically: Why is it important that measurement be based on standard units?

In Your JOURNAL

Examine various food labels and, **in your Journal**, report the metric and English equivalents of the weights of three products.

SECTION REVIEW

1. What are some advantages of using SI over the English system of measurement?
2. In SI, the base unit of length is the meter. What would you call 0.1 meter? 1000 meters?
3. **Apply:** Make a list of measuring tools you have used in the past month. For each example, tell what units you used to make your measurements.
4. **Connect to Earth Science:** Deimos is a small natural satellite that orbits Mars. At one point, its diameter is 16 000 meters. How many kilometers is this?

Skill Builder

☑ **Sequencing**

Using the data in Table 2-1, arrange the following units in order, from largest to smallest: centigram, gram, milligram, kilogram, decigram. If you need help, refer to Sequencing in the **Skill Handbook** on page 676.

32 PHYSICAL SCIENCE METHODS

OPTIONS

INQUIRY QUESTIONS

▶ **What specialized units are used to measure the size of printing type?** *point or pica* **the weight of gems?** *carat* **the height of horses?** *hand* **nautical speed?** *knot* **the diameter of wire?** *mil (1/1000 inch)* **speed of playing music?** *m.m. (metronome marking)* **an amount of wood?** *cord or rack* **corrective lenses?** *diopter* **small concentrations?** *ppm (parts per million)* **recording speeds?** *RPM (revolutions per minute)* **cross-stitch fabric?** *threads per inch* **loudness?** *bel or decibel*

▶ **The price of gasoline is 112.9 cents. How many millidollars is that?** *1129 millidollars* **Where else is the value of something estimated in millidollars?** *The tax rate of real estate is expressed as millidollars per dollar of valuation.*

DESIGNING AN EXPERIMENT
Characteristics of Systems of Measurement

To develop the International System, people had to agree on set standards and basic definitions of scale. If you had to develop a new measurement system, you, too, would have to have people agree with the new standards and definitions. In this activity your team will have the opportunity to use string to design and test your own SI (String International) measurement system.

Getting Started

Before you design your measurement system, remember the requirements of all measurement systems. What will be the standard in your system? Into what divisions will you divide the string length base unit?

Thinking Critically

What problems are you going to have to solve to develop a useful system of measurement using string?

Materials

- string, 1 m long
- scissors
- masking tape

Try It!

1. Within your group, choose an object in the classroom that will serve as your standard. Keep in mind that it should be similar in size to what you will *measure*.

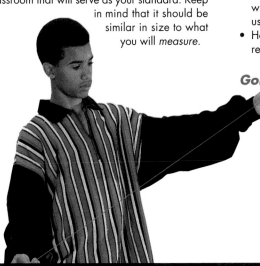

2. Decide how you could use tape to mark the scale divisions on your string. Use different pieces of string to try different-sized scale divisions of the base unit.
3. *Design a data table* to organize and report your measurements. Be sure to include what was used for your standard, what objects were measured, their lengths, and the scale divisions used with string.
4. Use the marked, scaled strings to *measure* various objects. Be sure to include objects longer and shorter than your string.

Summing Up/Sharing Results

- Which of your string scale systems will provide the most accurate measurement of small objects? Explain your answer.
- Are any of your scale divisions easy to report as decimal numbers?
- When sharing your results with other groups, why is it important for them to know what you used as a standard?
- How is it possible for different numbers to represent the same length of an object?

Going Further!

If you were to design a new measurement system for mass, what parts of your design would be the same as they were for the string and length system? What parts would be different?

2-1 STANDARDS OF MEASUREMENT **33**

OBJECTIVE: Design and carry out an experiment to show the necessary components of an acceptable measurement system.
Time: One class period to brainstorm, and one-half to one class period to complete the activity and summarize results.

PROCESS SKILLS applied in this activity are **measuring, modeling,** and **collecting** and **organizing data.**

PREPARATION: Have various colors of string available, if possible.
Cooperative Learning: Divide the class into Science Investigation Teams.

THINKING CRITICALLY

Student responses will vary. Problems may include that the string may stretch and the tightness of the string while measuring may depend on who does the measuring. Let students share problems and suggest solutions.

TEACHING THE ACTIVITY

*Refer to the **Activity Worksheets** for additional information and teaching strategies.*
▶ Use heavy string to make handling easy.
▶ Do not make metersticks or any other measuring devices available to students.
▶ Encourage students to use common classroom objects as standards.

SUMMING UP/SHARING RESULTS

▶ Accuracy increases for measurement of small objects when smaller scale divisions are used.
▶ If a group divided their string into 10 parts, it would be easy to express measurements as decimal numbers.
▶ The measurements must have a label, or unit, reflecting what the standard is or the measurements cannot be used by others.

GOING FURTHER!

Answers may include that this system must also be based on a standard, but the means of measurement would be different.

Activity
ASSESSMENT

Performance: To further assess students' understanding of measurement systems, see USING LAB SKILLS, Question 11, on page 50.

PREPARATION

SECTION BACKGROUND
▶ The SI system defines seven base units. In this section four base units, those that measure length, mass, time, and temperature, are introduced. These units are necessary to describe motion and energy, the subjects of the next six chapters.

PREPLANNING
▶ To prepare for the MINI-Lab, obtain several 100-mL graduated cylinders.

1 MOTIVATE

▶ **Demonstration:** Using three identical opaque plastic bottles, fill one with sand, the second with water, and leave the third empty. Stopper each. Have students close their eyes as you rearrange the bottles. After they have opened their eyes, ask if they can determine the contents of each bottle by sight. Now pass the bottles around the classroom and have students determine their contents without opening the bottles. Ask how they made their determinations.

TYING TO PREVIOUS KNOWLEDGE:
Have students use Tables A-1 through A-5 on page 670 to associate familiar metric units with products or uses such as milligrams (vitamin pills), watt (light bulb), liter (soda bottles), and volt (batteries). Point out that these units are associated with the metric system of measurement that students will be learning more about in this section.

2-2 Using SI Units

New Science Words

meter
volume
derived units
liter
mass
kilogram
density
time
second
kelvin

Objectives

▶ Identify SI units and symbols for length, volume, mass, density, time, and temperature.
▶ Define *derived unit*.
▶ Demonstrate an ability to convert related SI units.

SI Units and Symbols

Every type of quantity measured in SI has a base unit and a symbol for that unit. These names and symbols are shown in Table 2-2. All other SI units can be derived from these seven base units.

Table 2-2

SI BASE UNITS		
Quantity Measured	Unit	Symbol
Length	Meter	m
Mass	Kilogram	kg
Time	Second	s
Electric current	Ampere	A
Temperature	Kelvin	K
Amount of substance	Mole	mol
Intensity of light	Candela	cd

Length

The word *length* is used in many different ways. For example, the length of a novel is the number of pages or words it contains.

In scientific measurement, length is the distance between two points. That distance may be the diameter of a period on this page or the distance from Earth to the moon. The SI unit of length is the **meter** (m). A baseball bat is about 1 meter long. Metric rulers and metersticks are used to measure length.

What is the SI unit of length?

OPTIONS

Meeting Different Ability Levels
For Section 2-2, use the following **Teacher Resource Masters** depending upon individual students' needs.
◆ **Study Guide Master** for all students.
● **Reinforcement Master** for students of average and above average ability levels.
▲ **Enrichment Master** for above average students.
Additional Teacher Resource Package masters are listed in any **PROGRAM RESOURCES** boxes that are in the section. The additional masters are appropriate for all students.

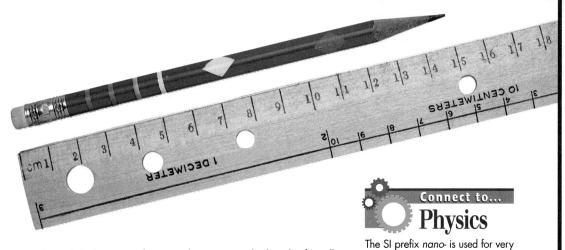

Figure 2-2. A metric ruler is used to measure the length of small objects, such as a pencil.

Recall that measurement in SI is based on multiples of ten. The prefix *deci-* means 1/10, so a decimeter is one-tenth of a meter. Similarly, a centimeter (cm) is one-hundredth of a meter. The diameter of a shirt button is about 1 cm.

$$100 \text{ cm} = 10 \text{ dm} = 1 \text{ m}$$

How many centimeters are in 1 decimeter?

Centimeters can be divided into smaller units called millimeters (mm). A millimeter is 1/1000 of a meter. One tooth along the edge of a postage stamp is about 1 mm long.

The size of the unit you select to make a measurement will depend on the size of the item being measured. For example, you would probably use the centimeter to measure the length of your pencil and the meter to measure the length of your classroom. What unit would you use to measure the distance from your home to school? You would probably want to use a unit larger than a meter. The kilometer (km), which is 1000 meters, is used to measure long distances. One kilometer is about ten football fields long.

Suppose you know the length of something in meters and want to change, or *convert*, the measurement to centimeters. Because 1 m = 100 cm, you can convert from

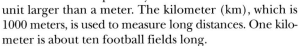

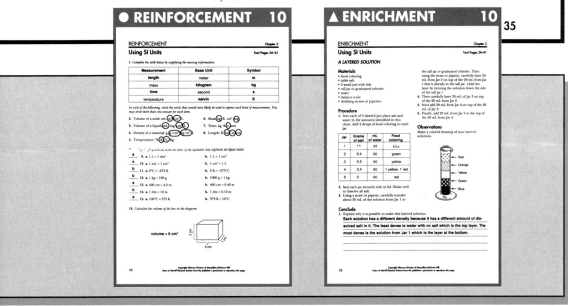

2 TEACH

Key Concepts are highlighted.

CONCEPT DEVELOPMENT

▶ Distribute metric rulers and have students identify the millimeter, centimeter, and decimeter markings on the ruler. Have them measure common objects. As they are measuring, have each of them choose an object that best represents a centimeter. Allow them to make estimations and use their rulers to check their estimations.

Connect to...
Physics

Answer: The prefix *nano-* means one-billionth. The red light would be 710 billionths of a meter.

MULTICULTURAL PERSPECTIVES
Social Time

• The passage of time may be subject to accurate measurement by a variety of instruments, but social time varies a great deal from region to region, and culture to culture.

People's ideas of punctuality vary from culture to culture. Americans are concerned even with anticipated lateness, calling ahead to apologize because they think they are going to be late. In other cultures, such as many Latin American or Arab cultures, one may be an hour or more late without an apology being made or expected.

The pace of life varies too. A study that compared accuracy of bank clocks and the average walking speed in six societies found that the U.S. came in second in time preoccupation in both measures of social time. Japan, it appears, is even more time conscious, with all clocks measured shown to be accurate within 30 seconds of the official time. Indonesia came in sixth in both categories, with clocks varying by more than three minutes off the officially measured time.

The SI prefix *nano-* is used for very small measurements. The wavelength of red light in a compact disc player may be 710 nanometers. Find out what *nano-* means and find the wavelength of the red light in meters.

CONCEPT DEVELOPMENT

▶ Review the Example and Practice Problems using the factor label method.

$$1.98 \text{ m} \times \frac{100 \text{ cm}}{1 \text{ m}}$$
$$= (1.98 \times 100) \text{ cm} = 198 \text{ cm}$$

$$253.8 \text{ km} \times \frac{1000 \text{ m}}{1 \text{ km}} \times \frac{100 \text{ cm}}{1 \text{ m}}$$
$$= (253.8 \times 1000 \times 100) \text{ cm}$$
$$= 25\ 380\ 000$$

$$75 \text{ cm} \times \frac{1 \text{ dm}}{10 \text{ cm}} = (75 \div 10) \text{ dm}$$
$$= 7.5 \text{ dm}$$

$$75 \text{ cm} \times \frac{1 \text{ m}}{100 \text{ cm}} = (75 \div 100) \text{ m}$$
$$= 0.75 \text{ m}$$

▶ In SI measurements that have values greater than 9999 or less than 0.999, groups of three integers to the left and to the right of the decimal point are separated by spaces, not commas, because a comma is used to represent the decimal point in some European countries. Thus 12345.6789 cm is expressed 12 345.678 9 cm. Numbers of only four digits have neither a comma nor a space.

TEACHER F.Y.I.

▶ There are prefixes that represent 10 and 100, namely *deka-* and *hecto-*. However, they are rarely used.

REVEALING MISCONCEPTIONS

▶ Students may believe that the SI system is more precise than the English system because it is used by scientists. Point out that both systems can yield equally precise measurements. For instance, a micrometer used by machinists can measure the diameters of bolts to the nearest 0.0001 inch. Scientists use SI because it is *easier to use* than the English system.

PRACTICE PROBLEM ANSWERS

1.   1 km = 100 000 cm
    253.8 km = 25 380 000 cm
2.   1 cm = 0.1 dm
    75 cm = 7.5 dm
    1 cm = 0.01 m
    75 cm = 0.75 m

meters to centimeters simply by multiplying by 100. Because SI is based on multiples of ten, any unit can be converted to a related unit by multiplying or dividing it by the appropriate multiple of ten.

If you follow these "rules," conversion will be easy:

- A measurement consists of two parts, a number and a unit label.
- To convert from larger to smaller units, multiply.
- To convert from smaller to larger units, divide.

For example, to convert 532 cm to meters, you divide because you're converting from smaller (cm) to larger (m) units. Because 100 cm = 1 m, divide 532 by 100. So, 532 cm = 5.32 m.

Another way to convert units is to multiply by a ratio that equals one. For example, 1 meter = 100 centimeters. Therefore,

$$\frac{1 \text{ meter}}{100 \text{ centimeters}} = \frac{100 \text{ centimeters}}{100 \text{ centimeters}} = 1$$

To convert 532 cm to meters, write

$$532 \text{ cm} \times \frac{1 \text{ m}}{100 \text{ cm}} = \frac{532 \text{ m}}{100} = 5.32 \text{ m}$$

The cm label is cancelled, because it appears in both the numerator and the denominator.

EXAMPLE PROBLEM

Problem Statement: How many centimeters are in 1.98 meters?

Known Information: 1 m = 100 cm
<u>Strategy Hint:</u> Think about which unit is larger. When converting from larger to smaller units, multiply. Because 1 m = 100 cm, multiply 1.98 by 100.

Solution: 1.98 m = 198 cm

PRACTICE PROBLEMS

<u>Strategy Hint:</u> First change kilometers to meters; then change meters to centimeters.

1. How many centimeters are in 253.8 kilometers?

<u>Strategy Hint:</u> Remember the meanings of the prefixes.

2. A bookshelf is 75 cm wide. How many decimeters is this? How many meters would this be?

OPTIONS

ASSESSMENT—ORAL

▶ How many millimeters are there in 2.5 meters? *2500 millimeters*
▶ How many meters are there in 650 millimeters? *0.65 meter*
▶ How many centimeters are there in 0.464 meter? *46.4 centimeters*
▶ How many centimeters are there in a decimeter? *10 cm* How many cubic centimeters are there in a cubic decimeter? *1000 cm³* A cubic decimeter is the same as a liter. How many cubic centimeters are there in a liter? *1000 cm³*

▶ A bottle of orange juice contains 1.2 liters. How many cubic centimeters is this? *1200 cm³* How many glasses of 200 cm³ each can be filled with this bottle of juice? *six*
▶ How many square centimeters are there in a square meter? *One m² is 1 m × 1 m = 100 cm × 100 cm = 10 000 cm².*

TECHNOLOGY

Space Spheres

The space shuttle *Challenger* served as the manufacturing site for one of the latest reference materials produced by the National Bureau of Standards. The reference material is a polystyrene sphere that measures 10 micrometers across. The head of a pin could hold 18 000 of these spheres. The spheres will be packaged in a 5-mL vial containing about 30 million spheres in water. These spheres can be used as a reference for manufacturers and researchers who need to calibrate instruments to check particle size in products such as cosmetics, paint pigments, flour, toner used in photocopiers, and so on. The spheres can also be used to improve microscopic measurements made in areas such as medicine and electronics.

The *Challenger* was chosen as the manufacturing site because of its reduced-gravity environment. Spheres produced by conventional processes on Earth tend to float or sink during their formation. This results in spheres with a variation in diameter that is too great for use as a standard. The reduced gravity of space allows the production of spheres that are very uniform in size and shape.

Think Critically: Why is particle size important in the common products listed?

As you move ahead in this section, you will learn about several different types of measurements. Keep in mind that the conversion "rules" you have used here can be used with any base unit in SI, because the system is based on multiples of ten. The prefixes remain the same, no matter what base unit you may be using.

Volume

The amount of space occupied by an object is called its **volume.** If you wanted to know the volume of a solid object, such as a building brick, you would measure its length, width, and height, and multiply the three figures together. For the brick, your measurements would be in centimeters, and the volume would be expressed in cubic centimeters (cm^3). For a larger object, such as a truck, your measurements would be in meters and the volume in cubic meters (m^3).

②

TECHNOLOGY

Think Critically: All products mentioned need a uniform small particle size for consistent performance or application.

CONCEPT DEVELOPMENT

▶ Discuss the uncertainty in measurements that come from (a) measuring with an improper instrument, such as a warped or chipped meterstick; (b) using and reading the instrument incorrectly, such as not holding a meterstick parallel to the dimension of the object being measured; and (c) recording the measurement improperly.

▶ **Demonstration:** Have students use metersticks to measure the sizes of their waists or heads, or the circumference of a round wastebasket or a tree. Have them repeat the measurements with a metric tape measure. Ask them to explain why the measurements made with the tape measure are more accurate.

INQUIRY QUESTIONS

▶A vitamin capsule contains 200 milligrams of vitamin C. How many capsules could be made from 1.0 kilogram of vitamin C? Hint: Convert 1.0 kilogram to milligrams. *1.0 kilogram = 1000 grams = 1 000 000 milligrams. Therefore, 1 000 000 milligrams × 1 capsule/200 milligrams = 5000 capsules.*

▶What is the area of a rectangular tabletop that measures 150 centimeters by 200 centimeters? *30 000 cm²* What is the area of the table in square meters? *30 000 cm² =*

$$30\ 000\ cm^2 \times \frac{1\ m^2}{10\ 000\ cm^2} = 3\ m^2$$

▶A medical procedure requires a solution containing 2 milligrams of antibiotic dissolved in 5 cubic centimeters of sterile salt solution. If you have a bottle containing 650 cm³ of sterile salt solution, how many 5-cm³ doses could be prepared from the bottle? *130 doses of 5 cm³ each* How much antibiotic would you have to dissolve in the bottle to get the correct solution? *260 milligrams*

CHAPTER 2 **37**

▶ A measurement is *accurate* if its value compares well to the values of other measurements made of the object by other people or by using different instruments.

▶ *Precision* indicates how well the instrument is calibrated; that is, how well its smallest measurement unit is marked. For instance, a metal ruler that has markings indicating millimeters is more precise than a plastic ruler that has only centimeter markings. As a result, the same measurement, when repeated, will give the same value.

▶ The following diagrams indicate that measurements should have both accuracy and precision.

not precise/   precise/   precise/
not accurate   not accurate   accurate

CONCEPT DEVELOPMENT

▶ Review the Example Problem using the factor-label method.

$$538 \text{ cm}^3 \times \frac{1 \text{ mL}}{1 \text{ cm}^3} \times \frac{1 \text{ L}}{1000 \text{ mL}}$$

$$= (538 \div 1000) \text{ L} = 0.538 \text{ L}$$

In Your JOURNAL

$$\frac{\$0.60}{1 \text{ L}} \times \frac{4 \text{ L}}{1 \text{ gal}} = \$2.40/\text{gal}$$

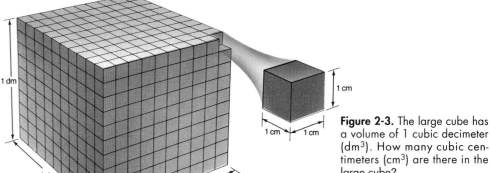

Figure 2-3. The large cube has a volume of 1 cubic decimeter (dm³). How many cubic centimeters (cm³) are there in the large cube?

What is a derived unit?

In Your JOURNAL

In many countries, gasoline is sold in units of liters. If one liter is approximately the same volume as one quart, find the approximate cost of one gallon of gasoline if it costs 60 cents per liter. Show your calculations **in your Journal**.

There is no simple tool that can be used to measure the volume of an object directly. Volume units are obtained by combining SI units of length. Units obtained this way are called **derived units.**

How do you measure the volume of a liquid? A liquid has no "sides" to measure. In measuring a liquid's volume, you indicate the capacity of a container that holds that amount of liquid. Liquid volumes are sometimes expressed in cubic centimeters, as in doses of medicine. The most common units for expressing liquid volumes are liters and milliliters. A **liter** occupies the same volume as a cubic decimeter (dm³). That is, a liter is the same volume as a cube that is 1 dm (10 cm) on each side. A liter is slightly larger than a quart. The liter is not an SI unit, but it is used with that system.

One liter (L) is equal to 1000 milliliters (mL). A cubic decimeter (dm³) is equal to 1000 cubic centimeters (cm³). So, because 1 L = 1 dm³, 1 mL = 1 cm³.

Suppose you wanted to convert a measurement in liters to cubic centimeters. The same "rules" you used for converting length can be used for any SI unit.

EXAMPLE PROBLEM

Problem Statement: How many liters of gasoline are in 538 cm³?

Known Information:
1 cm³ = 1 mL
Strategy Hint: 1 L = 1000 cm³.   1 L = 1000 mL; therefore, 1 L = 1000 cm³.
Change cm³ to mL.   Because you are converting from smaller to larger units, you divide 538 by 1000.

Solution: 538 cm³ = 0.538 L

OPTIONS

INQUIRY QUESTIONS

▶ **What is the curved surface of a liquid contained in a graduated cylinder called?** *meniscus*

▶ **What is the mass of the sun?** *about 2 000 000 000 000 000 000 000 000 000 000 kg (about two million-trillion-trillion kg)*

▶ **A commercial brand of low-sodium table salt (crystals of sodium chloride) advertises 50 percent less sodium per teaspoon than regular table salt. The label indicates that 100 g of this product and 100 g of regular table salt contain the same amount of sodium. How can this be?** *The volume of the sodium chloride crystals in this product is twice as large as the volume of the sodium chloride crystals in regular table salt. This would indicate that the two products have relied on two different crystallization techniques. The 50 percent less sodium brand produced a lower-density product.*

To measure volume in the laboratory, you will use a slender glass container called a graduated cylinder. The volumes are marked on a scale along the cylinder, as shown in Figure 2-4.

Mass

A table tennis ball and a golf ball have about the same volume. But if you pick them up, you notice a difference. The golf ball has more mass. **Mass** is the amount of matter in an object. The SI unit of mass is the **kilogram** (kg). For measuring objects of small mass, the gram (g) is used. How many grams are there in 1 kilogram?

In the laboratory, mass is measured with a balance. There are several different types of balances, but they all operate on the same principle. You use something of known mass to balance something else of unknown mass.

Density

If you were to take a cube of polished aluminum and a cube of silver the same size, they would look quite similar. And they would have the same volume. But the cube of silver would have more mass. The mass and volume of an object can be used to find the density of the material it is made of. **Density** is the mass per unit volume of a material.

Like volume, density is a derived unit. You can find the density of an object by dividing its mass by its volume. For example, the density of an object having a

Figure 2-4. To read the volume of a liquid, look along the bottom of the curved surface of the liquid.

Science and MATH

You probably know how much you weigh in pounds. Find your mass in kilograms. HINT: 1 pound has a mass of 0.45 kg.

Figure 2-5. Although the two balls are about the same size, the ball on the left has more mass.

Did You Know?

The mass of the Milky Way galaxy is more than 100 million times that of the sun.

2-2 USING SI UNITS **39**

Table 2-3

MINI-Lab

Materials: balance, pencil, 100-mL graduated cylinder

Teaching Tips

▶ The mass measurement must be made before the pencil is wet.

Answers to Questions: The mass in grams of the pencil and the mL change in the volume of water to float the pencil should be in close agreement.

MINI-Lab
ASSESSMENT

Performance: Have students come up to the teacher's desk to read the volumes of several liquids in graduated cylinders.

CHECK FOR UNDERSTANDING

Ask questions 1-2 and the **Apply** and **Connect to Chemistry** questions in the Section Review.

RETEACH

Use the following diagram to illustrate the mechanics of converting decimal units.

k– - - [h–] - [dk–] - (base) - - d– - - - c– - - - m–
| | | | | | |
k– - - [h–] - [dk–] - (base) - - d– - - - c– - - - m–

Locate the original unit on the top line and draw an arrow from it to the desired unit on the bottom line. For example, to convert 3.46 m to centimeters, locate *m* on the top line and draw an arrow to *cm* on the bottom line.

km - [hm] - [dkm] - - m - - -dm - - -cm - - -mm
| | | | | | |
km - [hm] - [dkm] - - m - - -dm - - -cm - - -mm

To convert, move the decimal point *two* places to the *right*. Thus, 3.46 m = 346 cm.

To express 350 g as kilograms, locate *g* on the top line and connect it by an arrow to *kg* on the line below.

kg - [hg] - [dkg] - - g - - - dg - - - cg - - - mg
| | | | | | |
kg - [hg] - [dkg] - - g - - - dg - - - cg - - - mg

The diagram indicates that the decimal point must be moved *three* places to the *left*. Thus, 350 g = 0.350 kg.

MINI-Lab

What is the density of a pencil?
Use a balance to *measure* the mass of a pencil in grams. Then put 90.0 mL of water into a 100-mL graduated cylinder. Lower the pencil, eraser end down, into the cylinder until the pencil floats. Read the new volume number at the water's surface. How many mL did the water level rise? How does this compare with the mass of the pencil? Continue to push the pencil point down until it is completely underwater. Read the new volume. *Calculate* the pencil's density by dividing its mass by the change in volume of the water level when the pencil is completely underwater.

Table 2-3

Material	Density (g/cm³)	Material	Density (g/cm³)
Hydrogen	0.000 09	Quartz	2.6
Oxygen	0.0013	Aluminum	2.7
Cork	0.24	Iron	7.9
Water	1.0	Copper	8.9
Glue	1.27	Lead	11.3
Sugar	1.6	Mercury	13.6
Table salt	2.2	Gold	19.3

mass of 10 g and a volume of 2 cm³ is 5 g/cm³. This value is expressed as 5 grams per cubic centimeter. Notice that both the mass and volume units are used to express density.

Sometimes the density of an object can help you to identify the material it's made of. Table 2-3 lists the densities of some familiar materials.

Time and Temperature

When working in the laboratory, it is often necessary to keep track of how long it takes for something to happen, or whether something heats up or cools down. These measurements involve time and temperature.

Time is the interval between two events. The SI unit for time is the **second.** In the laboratory, you will use a stopwatch or a clock with a second hand to measure time.

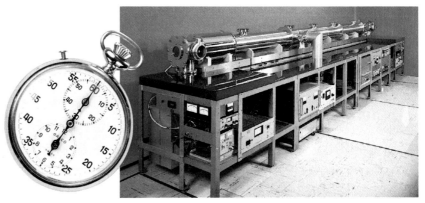

Figure 2-6. The stopwatch (left) and the atomic clock (above) both measure the same thing—time.

OPTIONS

ENRICHMENT

▶ Have students research supercooling and its role in superconductivity.

▶ Interested students can research the difference between mass and weight.

▶ Have students devise a way to measure the thickness of a postage stamp or its mass.

PROGRAM RESOURCES

From the **Teacher Resource Package** use:

Concept Mapping, pages 9-10.

Cross-Curricular Connections, page 6, Measuring Angles.

Activity Worksheets, page 19, MINI-Lab: What is the density of a pencil?

Technology, pages 7-8, Electric Thermometers.

Science Integration Activity 2

Use **Laboratory Manual 3,** Viscosity.

You will learn the scientific meaning of temperature in a later chapter. For now you can think of temperature as a measure of how "hot" or how "cold" something is. The temperature of a material is measured with a thermometer.

Figure 2-7. A Celsius Thermometer

For most scientific work, temperature is measured on the Celsius (C) scale. On this scale, the freezing point of water is zero degrees (0°C), and the boiling point of water is one hundred degrees (100°C). Between these points, the scale is divided into 100 equal divisions. Each one represents 1 Celsius degree. On the Celsius scale, average human body temperature is 37°C and a typical room temperature may be between 20°C and 25°C.

The SI unit of temperature is the **kelvin** (K). Zero on the Kelvin scale (0 K) is the coldest possible temperature, also known as absolute zero. That is −273°C, 273 degrees below the freezing point of water!

Most laboratory thermometers are marked only with the Celsius scale. Because the divisions on the two scales are the same size, the Kelvin temperature can be found by adding 273 to the Celsius reading. So, on the Kelvin scale, water freezes at 273 K and boils at 373 K. Notice that degree symbols are not used with the Kelvin scale.

SECTION REVIEW

1. Make the following conversions.
   a. 100 cm to meters   c. 27°C to K
   b. 2.3 dm³ to liters
2. Explain why density is a derived unit.
3. **Apply:** How many examples of the use of SI units can you find? Observe road signs and outside thermometers and check labels of products in your home.
4. **Connect to Chemistry:** Chemists sometimes use density to identify a sample. What is the density of an unknown liquid that has a mass of 42.0 g and a volume of 55.0 mL?

☒ Concept Mapping

Make a network tree concept map to show the SI base units used to measure length, mass, time, and temperature. If you need help, refer to Concept Mapping in the **Skill Handbook** on pages 684 and 685.

Skill Builder ∿

EXTENSION

For students who have mastered this section, use the **Reinforcement** and **Enrichment** masters or other OPTIONS provided.

CROSS CURRICULUM

▶**History:** The Celsius and Kelvin temperature scales were named in honor of Anders Celsius and William Thomson, Lord Kelvin, two scientists who made many contributions to the study of heat.

3 CLOSE

Cooperative Learning: Use the following demonstration and the Numbered Heads Together strategy to have students explain how SI mass units are related to SI volume units for water.

▶**Demonstration:** Fill a 10-mL graduated cylinder with water and place it on one pan of a balanced double-pan balance. On the other pan, place an empty, identical 10-mL graduate and a 10-g mass.

SECTION REVIEW ANSWERS

1. a. 1 cm = 0.01 m; 100 cm = 1 m
   b. 1 dm³ = 1 L; 2.3 dm³ = 2.3 L
   c. 27°C + 273 = 300 K
2. Density units are obtained by dividing the SI base unit for mass by the SI derived unit for volume.
3. **Apply:** Student responses will vary.
4. **Connect to Chemistry:**
42.0 g /55.0 mL = 0.764 g/mL.

Skill Builder
ASSESSMENT
Performance: Use the network tree to assess the student's ability to organize information in the format of a concept map.

Skill Builder ∿

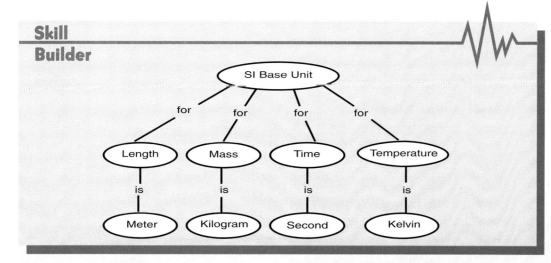

PREPARATION

SECTION BACKGROUND

▶Graphs are important means of displaying information to be compared. Line graphs are the most important type of graph in science because some can be analyzed to provide equations that relate the information being displayed.

MINI-Lab

Materials: plastic foam cup, lid with straw hole, thermometer, graph paper, timer with second hand

Teaching Tips

▶ Use the activity to teach students to read the Celsius thermometer.

▶ Have students insert the thermometer through the straw hole in the lid.

Answer to Question: The graph will show that the rate of temperature reduction is most rapid when the temperature is highest. It will also show that adding a lid significantly reduces the rate at which temperature decreases.

MINI-Lab
ASSESSMENT

Content: Examine the students' graphs to determine how they labeled the intervals on the axes. Make sure that the intervals consistently represent the same amount of change.

1 MOTIVATE

Cooperative Learning: Assign students to cut graphs from newspapers and magazines and bring them to class. Using the Numbered Heads Together strategy, have each group devise a classification system for the graphs.

2-3 Graphing

New Science Words

graph

Objectives

▶ Identify three types of graphs and explain the correct use of each type.
▶ Distinguish between dependent and independent variables.
▶ Interpret graphs.

MINI-Lab

How can a graph help you observe change?
Place a thermometer in a plastic foam cup of hot water. *Measure* and record the temperature every 30 seconds for 5 minutes. *Make a line graph* of the changing temperature showing time on the *x*-axis and temperature on the *y*-axis. Repeat the experiment, starting with freshly heated water. This time, cover the cup with a plastic lid. Plot the curve on the same grid as before. List all the information this graph tells you about the two cups.

Using Graphs

What happens when heat is applied to an ice cube? Did you answer, "The ice cube melts"? Most people would. However, suppose this were a scientific investigation. You would measure and record mass, temperature, temperature changes, changes in state, and the time intervals involved. At the end of the investigation, you would describe the procedure and results in both words and numbers.

Often it is helpful to be able to show what happens during the course of an investigation. This can be done with a graph. A **graph** is a visual display of information or data. A graph of the ice cube investigation would look something like Figure 2-8.

Graphs are not only used in science. They are useful for displaying information in business, sports, and many everyday situations. Different kinds of graphs are appropriate for displaying different types of information. It is important to use the correct kind of graph for the data you are presenting.

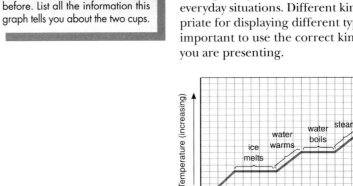

Figure 2-8. The graph represents what happens when water is heated over a period of time.

OPTIONS

Meeting Different Ability Levels

For Section 2-3, use the following **Teacher Resource Masters** depending upon individual students' needs.

◆ **Study Guide Master** for all students.
● **Reinforcement Master** for students of average and above average ability levels.
▲ **Enrichment Master** for above average students.

Additional Teacher Resource Package masters are listed in any **PROGRAM RESOURCES** boxes that are in the section. The additional masters are appropriate for all students.

◆ STUDY GUIDE 11

STUDY GUIDE   Chapter 2
Graphing   Text Pages 42-45

Choose the term from the word list that best completes each statement. Write the term in the blank at the left of each statement.

graph	vertical	dependent	line graph
horizontal	independent	bar graph	x-axis
hatch marks	pie graph	y-axis	percentages

graph 1. A visual display of data or information is a _____.

bar graph 2. Information that is collected by counting can best be displayed on a _____.

vertical 3. In a line graph, the _____ axis is called the y-axis.

vertical or y-axis 4. In a line graph, the dependent variable is plotted on the _____.

pie graph 5. A graph that shows information as parts of a circle is a _____.

line graph 6. The type of graph that is useful for showing trends or continuous change is a _____.

percentages 7. Information in a pie graph is often shown as _____.

independent 8. Information that remains constant and does not depend on changes in the value of another variable is called the _____ variable.

horizontal or x-axis 9. In a line graph, the independent variable is plotted on the _____ axis.

hatch marks 10. Numbers that are left off a graph to save space can be shown using lines called _____.

dependent 11. A variable that changes as a result of the other variable is called a _____ variable.

x-axis 12. In a line graph, the horizontal axis is also called the _____.

Three of the most commonly used kinds of graphs are line graphs, bar graphs, and pie graphs. The section on Making and Using Graphs, on page 687 in the **Skill Handbook**, is a step-by-step guide to constructing each of these kinds of graphs. Study this material when you have finished reading this section.

Line Graphs

Line graphs are used to show trends or continuous change. Suppose you want to show how the temperature of a room changes after you switch on the heat one chilly morning. Taking temperature readings in the room every five minutes, you might collect information that looks like that shown in Table 2-4. If you look closely at the data, you can see how temperature changed over time. But the relationship is easier to see in the graphs shown in Figure 2-9. Both graphs show that temperature increased for the first 15 minutes, then stayed constant. Do the graphs tell you anything about what made the temperature change?

In this example, two things are changing, or varying—time and temperature. Time is the independent variable. Its value does not depend on changes in the value of the other variable, temperature. Temperature is the dependent variable. Its value depends on changes in the time. In a line graph, the dependent variable always is plotted on the vertical *y*-axis, and the independent variable is plotted on the horizontal *x*-axis.

Both graphs in Figure 2-9 show the same information. Notice, however, that the temperature scales along the vertical axes are different. In the graph on the left, each square represents 1°C. What does each square represent in the graph on the right? The hatch marks on the

Table 2-4

ROOM TEMPERATURE	
Time (minutes after turning on heat)	Temperature (°C)
0	16
5	17
10	19
15	20
20	20
25	20

Figure 2-9. Two Graphs of the Same Room Temperature Data

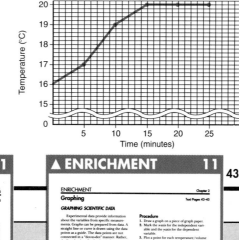

STUDENT TEXT QUESTIONS

▶ Page 43, paragraph 2: **Do the graphs tell you anything about what made the temperature change?** *No; the graphs do not give any information about the cause of the temperature changes.*

▶ Page 43, paragraph 4: **What does each square represent in the graph on the right?** *One square represents 0.2°C.*

2 TEACH

Key Concepts are highlighted.

CONCEPT DEVELOPMENT

▶ Make sure students can read graphs by citing various times from the graph shown in Figure 2-8 and having students respond with the appropriate temperatures.

▶ Ask students to discuss what assumptions they are making when they connect two data points by a line. Are they sure about all or any of the points on the line? Point out that the values at the beginning and end of the interval were measured. However, those in-between were not. The students are assuming that the line would represent these measurements.

PROGRAM RESOURCES

From the **Teacher Resource Package** use:

Activity Worksheets, page 20, MINI-Lab: How can a graph help you observe change?

● **REINFORCEMENT 11**

▲ **ENRICHMENT 11**

43

▶ **Language Arts:** Have students write paragraphs describing how ice melts by using Figure 2-8. Allow students to share their paragraphs with the class.

▶ **Social Studies:** Have students identify graphs in their social studies textbooks. Have a volunteer cite a page in the text. Instruct the class to turn to this page and follow along as the volunteer describes what the graph represents. Allow time for several students to respond.

MINI QUIZ

Use the Mini Quiz to check students' recall of chapter content.

1 In a line graph, the _____ variable is plotted on the vertical, *y*-axis. *dependent*

2 _____ graphs are useful for showing information collected by counting. *Bar*

3 The "slices" of a pie graph usually are represented as _____ of the total. *percentages*

VideoDisc

STVS: Computer Graphics, Disc 1, Side 2

In Your JOURNAL

For line graphs, the written explanations should focus on relationships between the variables. For pie or bar graphs, students should focus on patterns revealed by the graph.

Connect to...
Earth Science

---

vertical axis between the 0 and the 15 mean that numbers between 0 and 15 have been left out to save space. Compare the two graphs in Figure 2-9. Which graph shows a bigger temperature change over the same time period? Be careful! The two graphs show exactly the same information, but because there is more space between the numbers on the vertical axis in the graph on the right, the change looks larger.

Bar Graphs

A bar graph is useful for showing information collected by counting. For example, suppose you measured the temperature in every classroom in your school and organized your data in a table like Table 2-5. You could show these data in a bar graph like the one shown in Figure 2-10. The height of each bar corresponds to the number of rooms at a particular temperature.

In a line graph, adjacent points are connected with a straight or curving line. In a bar graph, the bars are not connected. Do you see why? If the bars corresponding to 20°C and 21°C were connected, for example, the graph would suggest that a number of rooms had temperatures between 20°C and 21°C, when actually, no rooms had such temperatures.

Table 2-5

TEMPERATURE OF CLASSROOMS	
Temperature (°C)	Number of Classrooms
16	1
17	3
18	3
19	2
20	3
21	5
22	5
23	3

In Your JOURNAL

To a scientist, a graph is like an efficiently written short story. Find a graph in a newspaper or magazine. **In your Journal,** write about the trend shown or the pattern revealed in the graph.

Figure 2-10. A typical bar graph shows comparisons, but is not used to indicate trends.

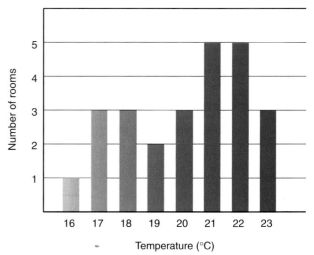

OPTIONS

ASSESSMENT—ORAL

▶ **What would the graph shown in Figure 2-8 display if the time axis were reversed?** *It would show what happens to a small amount of water as it freezes.*

▶ **What do you think the flat line to the left in the graph on Figure 2-8 indicates?** *the time interval during which the ice is turning from a solid into a liquid at 0°C*

▶ **What *time* is displayed in the graphs shown in Figure 2-9?** *the time that has gone by since the heater was turned on*

PROGRAM RESOURCES

From the **Teacher Resource Package** use:

Transparency Masters, pages 7-8, Types of Graphs.

Critical Thinking/Problem Solving, page 8, Sports Performance.

Science and Society, page 6, The Move to Metric.

Use **Color Transparency** number 4, Types of Graphs.

Pie Graphs

A pie graph is used to show how some fixed quantity is broken down into parts. The circular "pie" represents the total. The "slices" represent the parts and usually are represented as percentages of the total.

Figure 2-11 shows how a pie graph could be used to show the percentage of buildings in a neighborhood using each of a number of heating fuels. You can easily see that more buildings use gas heat than any other kind of system. What else does the graph tell you?

When you use graphs, think carefully about the conclusions you can draw from them. Can you infer cause and effect from looking at a graph? How might the scale of the graph affect your conclusions? Is any information missing or improperly connected?

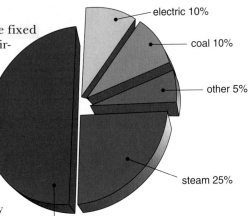

Figure 2-11. A pie graph shows the different parts of a whole quantity.

SECTION REVIEW

1. Your class does an experiment to show how the volume of a gas changes with changes in temperature. You are asked to make a line graph of the results. What are the dependent and independent variables?
2. Explain why points are connected in a line graph, but not in a bar graph.
3. **Apply:** A survey shows that, in your neighborhood, 75 people ride the bus; 45 drive their own cars; 15 carpool; 9 walk, ride bikes, or ride motorcycles; and 6 use different methods on different days to get to work. What kind of graph would be best for displaying these results at a neighborhood meeting?
4. **Connect to Earth Science:** Using a newspaper or other resources, obtain the temperature highs for a week. Plot a line graph of your findings.

Connect to... Earth Science

Care must be taken that rivers, lakes, and oceans are not polluted by water that contains possibly harmful substances. The following percentages show water usage in a typical U.S. home: Toilet flushing, 33%; laundry, 26%; bathing, 20%; dishwashing, 3%; miscellaneous, 18%. Express these percentages in a pie graph.

☑ Making and Using Graphs

Find a graph in a newspaper or magazine. Tell what kind of graph you found and write an explanation of what the graph shows. If you need help, refer to Making and Using Graphs in the **Skill Handbook** on page 687.

Skill Builder

Ask questions 1-2 and the **Apply** and **Connect to Earth Science** questions in the Section Review.

RETEACH

Demonstration: Stick 10 birthday cake candles in holders in a long piece of plastic foam. Light the second candle and let it burn for only 5 seconds. Light the remaining candles in turn, letting the third candle burn for 10 seconds, the fourth for 15 seconds, etc. Remove the candles from the holders, clip their wicks, and place them side by side, bases aligned, on an overhead projector. Ask students to discuss what the silhouette displays.

EXTENSION

For students who have mastered this section, use the **Reinforcement** and **Enrichment** masters or other OPTIONS provided.

3 CLOSE

▶ Have students explain how to find out how large a slice of a pie graph is to be if percentages are known.

SECTION REVIEW ANSWERS

1. Independent variable is temperature; dependent variable is volume.
2. Line graphs show trends, and the spaces between measured points have meaning. Bar graphs show information collected by counting, and the spaces between bars do not represent any information.
3. **Apply:** This information would best be represented by either a bar graph or a pie graph.
4. **Connect to Earth Science:** Accept various results, but look for temperature on the vertical axis and time on the horizontal axis.

Skill Builder

Student responses will vary according to the graph they select. Accept all reasonable responses.

Skill Builder
ASSESSMENT

Oral: If students found line graphs, have them identify the dependent and independent variables. For pie graphs, have them check to see that the percentages total 100 percent. For bar graphs, have them explain why the bars are not connected.

 **2-4 Metrics for All?**

PREPARATION

SECTION BACKGROUND
▶Other SI units are defined by adding prefixes to these base units or are derived from base units.

1 MOTIVATE

▶Have students identify products that are now packaged with both metric and English units.

TYING TO PREVIOUS
KNOWLEDGE: Have students recall SI measurements that they are familiar with. Point out that these measurements are also familiar to citizens of most countries of the world.

2 TEACH

Key Concepts are highlighted.

CONCEPT DEVELOPMENT
▶Inform students that the Metric Conversion Act of 1975 outlined a method by which the voluntary metrification of the United States would take place. Lack of funding and public interest have hampered the project.

CROSS CURRICULUM
▶**Geography:** Use a map to identify Burma, the only populous country besides the United States that does not use the metric system.

CHECK FOR UNDERSTANDING
Ask questions 1-2 and the **Connect to Earth Science** question in the Section Review.

Objectives
▶ Analyze the benefits and drawbacks of universal use of SI measurements.
▶ Give examples of SI units used in the United States.

Metrics in the United States

In the United States, athletes compete on courses that are measured in meters, medicine is sold in milligrams and milliliters, and many automobile parts are measured in SI units. But carpenters still buy lumber measured in feet and inches, farmers measure their land in acres and their crops in bushels, fabric is sold by the yard, and highway signs give distances in miles and speed limits in miles per hour.

For nearly 100 years, advocates of the metric system have argued for widespread adoption of the system in the United States. But opponents have argued just as vigorously against it.

Representatives of industry say such a changeover would require them to replace or convert their machinery—a costly process. But people in favor of the change point out that machinery is often replaced anyway, and the cost would be a one-time expense that would produce lasting benefits. Switching to SI units would make trade easier with other countries, most of which use SI. And because SI is based on multiples of ten, it makes calculations and conversions much easier. Using the system might reduce calculation errors and save time.

OPTIONS

Meeting Different Ability Levels
For Section 2-4, use the following **Teacher Resource Masters** depending upon individual students' needs.
◆ **Study Guide Master** for all students.
● **Reinforcement Master** for students of average and above average ability levels.
▲ **Enrichment Master** for above average students.

Many citizens resist the switch to SI units because they have grown up using such units as feet, pounds, and gallons, and they feel more comfortable using them. However, most people do not really know very much about these units, especially how units relate to one another. For example, do you know how many cubic inches there are in a fluid ounce? Do you know how many ounces there are in a pound, or how many inches are in a mile?

These are just a few of the questions that arise in using our present system. Look up the information needed to answer them. Then think about how easy such measurement conversions would be in a system like SI.

SECTION REVIEW

1. Write a list of different units used to measure length in the United States. Then show the calculations necessary to convert from one unit to another. Do the same thing using SI units for length. Which is easier?
2. Write a one-paragraph essay summarizing your position on the adoption of SI in the United States.
3. **Connect to Earth Science:** Copper ore is mined and refined, then the metal is used in common items, such as pennies. How does the metric prefix *centi-* relate to the number of pennies (cents) in one dollar?

In your Journal, explain your opinions about adopting SI in the United States.

Historically, the base units in the English system did not have precise standards. Find the standards that were historically used for two different English units. Explain why these standards are not precise enough to be used in measurements in physics.

You Decide!

If the United States should switch to using SI measurements exclusively, how could the switch be accomplished?

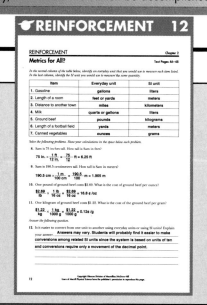

RETEACH

Have students classify English to metric conversion examples into three types of conversions: HARD—those that change the size of a product to new metric dimensions; SOFT—where the size is not affected, only how it is measured; and NONE—in which there would be no conversion.

EXTENSION

For students who have mastered this section, use the **Reinforcement** and **Enrichment** masters or other OPTIONS provided.

Connect to...
Physics

Answer: Student answers may include
  one foot—length of king's foot
  one inch—first thumb knuckle
  one yard—distance from king's nose to outstretched finger.
These standards would vary from person to person or time to time.

3 CLOSE

▶Ask students to consider how the conversion to the metric system will be affected by the United States becoming less industrialized and a more technological nation.

SECTION REVIEW ANSWERS

1. Student responses should include inch, foot, yard, and mile. Students should conclude that converting in SI is easier than converting in the English system.
2. Student essays should give reasons for either support or rejection of SI adoption in the United States.
3. **Connect to Earth Science:** *Centi-* means 1/100. Each cent is 1/100 of a dollar.

YOU DECIDE!

Answers will vary from total conversion mandated by the government to individual choice.

ACTIVITY 2-2
40 minutes

OBJECTIVE: Compare advantages and disadvantages of converting from English to metric measure.

PROCESS SKILLS applied in this activity:
▶**Measuring** in Procedure Steps 2 and 3.
▶**Observing** in Procedure Step 7.

👥 COOPERATIVE LEARNING
Divide the class into Science Investigation Teams with one ingredient assigned to each team. All teams must share data and may share in the experimental product.

TEACHING THE ACTIVITY
Troubleshooting: To cook the Munchies you will need a large saucepan, a large spoon for mixing, a hot plate or burner, a small spoon, and a roll of waxed paper. Allow ample room for students to view the preparation.
▶Provide each team with an assigned ingredient and the appropriate measuring equipment.
▶Prepare a master ingredient list on the overhead or the chalkboard.
▶Have students put the first five ingredients into the pot. Heat slowly to a boil, then boil for four minutes while mixing constantly. Remove from heat and add the rest of the ingredients. Immediately portion onto wax paper using the small spoon. You should have enough for the class.
▶A class discussion is recommended prior to completing Conclude and Apply.

PROGRAM RESOURCES
From the **Teacher Resource Package** use:
Activity Worksheets, pages 15-16, Activity 2-2: Metric Munchies.

Metric Munchies

Look through a recipe book. Are any of the amounts of ingredients given in metric units? Chances are, English measure is used. How could you convert English measurements to metric measurements?

Materials
- balance
- graduated cylinder, 100-mL
- munchie ingredients
- measuring cup
- measuring teaspoon
- measuring tablespoon
- plastic container, 1 quart
- hot plate
- cooking pot

Procedure
1. Copy the data table and the list of munchie ingredients.
2. Use the English measuring cup or spoon to *measure* out the proper amount of munchie ingredient assigned to your team.
3. Use the balance or graduated cylinder to determine the metric value of the measured ingredient. Convert solid measure to grams. Convert liquid measure to milliliters.
4. Write the metric equivalent in your data table. Also write it on the metric ingredients list posted in the classroom.
5. Copy the completed list of metric measures.
6. At the direction of the teacher, place your ingredient in the cooking pot.
7. Watch how the teacher cooks the munchies, then write cooking instructions.

Data and Observations Sample Data

Ingredient	English Measure	Metric
Margarine	1/2 cup	114 g
Sugar	2 cups	432 g
Cocoa	6 tablespoons	39 g
Milk	1/2 cup	118 mL
Rolled oats	3 cups	258 g
Vanilla	1 teaspoon	5 mL
Nuts	1/2 cup	52 g

Analyze
1. The volume ratio of sugar to oats is 2 to 3. What is their mass ratio?
2. Which recipe, English or metric, requires the use of the most measuring devices?
3. Which kind of measure tends to be more accurate, volume or mass?

Conclude and Apply
4. English measured recipes tend to use whole numbers and simple fractions. How could you simplify the metric recipe?
5. How would kitchen equipment change if all recipes were metric?
6. What benefits and problems can you see in changing all recipes to metric?

ANSWERS TO QUESTIONS
1. roughly 2 to 1
2. The English recipe requires at least three. Metric could be done with two.
3. mass
4. Round numbers off to the nearest 5 or 10.
5. A gram scale and volume measure in milliliters would be added.
6. Measuring quantities by mass will simplify many measurements. However, kitchens will need to be equipped with balances capable of measuring grams. Accept other answers dealing with such concerns as publishing new cookbooks and assessing nutritional values in metric serving sizes.

Activity
ASSESSMENT
Performance: To further assess students' understanding of the metric system, see USING LAB SKILLS, Question 12, on page 50.

SUMMARY

2-1: Standards of Measurement
1. A standard of measurement is an exact quantity that people agree to use as a basis of comparison.
2. When a standard of measurement is established, all measurements are compared to the same exact quantity—the standard. Therefore, all measurements can be compared with one another.
3. In SI, prefixes are used to make the base units larger or smaller by multiples of ten. The most common prefixes and their values are: *kilo-* 1000, *deci-* 0.1, *centi-* 0.01, *milli-* 0.001, *micro-* 0.000 001, and *nano-* 0.000 000 001.

2-2: Using SI Units
1. The most commonly used units in SI and their symbols include: length—meter, m; volume—cubic decimeter, dm³; mass—kilogram, kg; density—grams per cubic centimeter, g/cm³; time—second, s; and temperature—kelvin, K. Liter and degree Celsius are also commonly used for volume and temperature, respectively.
2. A derived unit is one that is obtained by combining other SI units. Volume and density units are derived units.
3. Any SI unit can be converted to any other related SI unit by multiplying or dividing by the appropriate multiple of ten.

2-3: Graphing
1. Line graphs show continuous changes between related variables. Bar graphs are used to show data collected by counting. Pie graphs show how a fixed quantity can be broken into parts.
2. In a line graph, the independent variable is always plotted on the horizontal *x*-axis; the dependent variable is always plotted on the vertical *y*-axis.
3. Many different kinds of data can be interpreted from graphs.

2-4: Science and Society: Metrics for All?
1. There are many benefits and drawbacks to the adoption of SI.
2. SI units are already in wide use on consumer goods and distance signs in the United States.

KEY SCIENCE WORDS

a. **density**
b. **derived unit**
c. **graph**
d. **kelvin**
e. **kilogram**
f. **liter**
g. **mass**
h. **meter**
i. **second**
j. **SI**
k. **standard**
l. **time**
m. **volume**

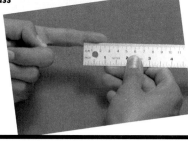

UNDERSTANDING VOCABULARY

Match each phrase with the correct term from the list of Key Science Terms.

1. the modern version of the metric system
2. the amount of space occupied by an object
3. an agreed-upon quantity to be used for comparison
4. the amount of matter in an object
5. obtained by combining SI units
6. a visual display of data
7. the SI unit of mass
8. the SI unit of length
9. a metric unit of volume
10. mass per unit volume

PHYSICAL SCIENCE METHODS **49**

SUMMARY

Have students read the summary statements to review the major concepts of the chapter.

UNDERSTANDING VOCABULARY

1. j		**6.** c	
2. m		**7.** e	
3. k		**8.** h	
4. g		**9.** f	
5. b		**10.** a	

ASSESSMENT
Portfolio
Encourage students to place in their portfolios one or two items of what they consider to be their best work. For each item, ask students to explain why that item was chosen and what they learned from it. Items might be selected from the following.
- Flex Your Brain exploration, p. 39
- MINI-Lab graphs and conclusions, p. 42
- Cross Curriculum paragraphs, p. 44

Performance
Additional performance assessments may be found in *Performance Assessment* and *Science Integration Activities* that accompany **Merrill Physical Science.** Performance Task Assessment Lists and rubrics for evaluating these activities and other products generated throughout the chapter can be found in Glencoe's *Performance Assessment in Middle School Science.*

OPTIONS

ASSESSMENT
To assess student understanding of material in this chapter, use the resources listed.

COOPERATIVE LEARNING
Consider using cooperative learning in the THINK AND WRITE CRITICALLY, APPLY, and MORE SKILL BUILDERS sections of the Chapter Review.

PROGRAM RESOURCES
From the **Teacher Resource Package** use:
Chapter Review, pages 7-8.
Chapter and Unit Tests, pages 9-12, Chapter Test.
Chapter and Unit Tests, pages 13-14, Unit Test.

CHECKING CONCEPTS

1. c	6. a
2. b	7. c
3. a	8. b
4. d	9. b
5. d	10. d

USING LAB SKILLS

ASSESSMENT

Use these alternate lab exercises to assess students' understanding of skills ued in this chapter.

11. Student answers may include that when you tape the scale divisions on the string, decide on a consistent edge or area of the tape to make your exact division mark. Have the entire class agree to use the same marking system.

12. The English system will sometimes produce fractional amounts that are more difficult to measure, particularly if 1/3 is involved.

THINK AND WRITE CRITICALLY

13. SI measurements are used in science classes because they are used throughout the world and allow scientists to compare measurements.

14. Conversion between two different units of length can be made by multiplying or dividing by the proper multiple of ten. All SI measurements, including volume and mass, can be converted in this way.

15. Line graphs consist of data plotted on a grid within a set of axes. Line graphs are best used to show a continuous change in data that involves two variables.

Bar graphs consist of a pair of axes and a series of bars. Bar graphs are best used to show data collected by counting.

Pie graphs consist of a circle divided into segments. Pie graphs are best used to show the different parts that make up a whole quantity.

16. A line graph; time would be the independent variable and temperature would be the dependent variable.

CHECKING CONCEPTS

Choose the word or phrase that completes the sentence or answers the question.

1. A meaningful measurement must have _____.
   - **a.** a number only
   - **b.** a unit only
   - **c.** a number and a unit
   - **d.** a prefix and a unit

2. The _____ is an example of an SI unit.
   - **a.** foot
   - **b.** second
   - **c.** pound
   - **d.** gallon

3. The system of measurement used by scientists around the world is the _____.
   - **a.** SI
   - **b.** Standard system
   - **c.** English system
   - **d.** Kelvin system

4. SI is based on _____.
   - **a.** inches
   - **b.** multiples of five
   - **c.** English units
   - **d.** multiples of ten

5. The SI prefix that means 1/1000 is _____.
   - **a.** *kilo-*
   - **b.** *nano-*
   - **c.** *cent-*
   - **d.** *milli-*

6. The symbol for deciliter is _____.
   - **a.** dL
   - **b.** dcL
   - **c.** dkL
   - **d.** Ld

7. The symbol for _____ is µg.
   - **a.** nanogram
   - **b.** kilogram
   - **c.** microgram
   - **d.** milligram

8. _____ is the distance between two points.
   - **a.** Volume
   - **b.** Length
   - **c.** Mass
   - **d.** Density

9. Which of the following is *not* a derived unit?
   - **a.** cubic decimeter
   - **b.** meter
   - **c.** cubic centimeter
   - **d.** grams per milliliter

10. 1000 mL is equal to all of the following except _____.
    - **a.** 1 L
    - **b.** 100 cL
    - **c.** $1 \ dm^3$
    - **d.** $1 \ cm^3$

USING LAB SKILLS

11. In Activity 2-1 on page 33 you learned the importance of having a reference standard and a clear way to divide a scale in a measurement system. Explain how you could improve the accuracy of the system you used for marking the scale divisions.

12. In Activity 2-2 on page 48 you compared English and metric measurements in a food recipe. Suppose you wanted to make five times that much food. Compare the difficulty of measuring five times the English measure with the same increase in the metric measurements.

THINK AND WRITE CRITICALLY

Answer the following questions in your Journal using complete sentences.

13. Why are SI measurements used in science classes?

14. Explain how to convert from one length measurement in the SI system to another. Can volume and mass measurements be converted in the same way? Why or why not?

15. Describe three different types of graphs and the types of data best displayed by each.

16. Suppose you set a glass of water in direct sunlight for two hours and measure its temperature every ten minutes. What type of graph would you use to display your data? What would the dependent variable be? The independent variable?

17. What are some advantages and disadvantages of adopting the SI system for use in the United States?

---

17. Advantages: SI measurements are based on multiples of ten and the same prefixes are used for all types of measurement, thus making conversion easy; people in most nations measure in SI units. Disadvantages: Conversion would involve considerable expense; people are reluctant to change from a system they are familiar with.

18. Make the following conversions.
    a. 1500 mL to liters   c. 5.8 dg to mg
    b. 2 km to cm   d. 22°C to kelvin
19. Standards of measurement used during the Middle Ages were often based on such things as the length of the king's arm. What arguments would you use to convince people of the need for a different system of standard measurements?
20. List the SI units of length you would use to express the following. Refer to Table 2-1 on page 31.
    a. the diameter of an atom
    b. the width of your classroom
    c. the width of a pencil lead
    d. the length of a sheet of paper
    e. the distance to the moon
21. Determine the density of each of the following objects.
    a. mass = 15 g, volume = 2 cm^3
    b. mass = 200 g, volume = 80 mL
    c. mass = 1.8 kg, volume = 0.2 L
22. Suppose you measure the distance a go-cart travels every five seconds for a 60-second period. What kind of graph would you use to display your data? What would the dependent and independent variables be?

MORE SKILL BUILDERS

If you need help, refer to the Skill Handbook.

1. **Comparing and Contrasting:** Consider the base units and conversion procedures in SI and the English system. Compare and contrast the ease with which conversions can be made between units within each system.
2. **Hypothesizing:** A metal sphere is found to have a density of 5.2 g/cm^3 at 25°C and a density of 5.1 g/cm^3 at 50°C. Propose a

hypothesis to explain this observation. How could you easily test your hypothesis?
3. **Measuring in SI:** Determine the mass, volume, and density of your textbook, a container of milk, and an air-filled balloon. Make your measurements in SI units using the appropriate measuring tool and the quickest, most accurate method possible.
4. **Making and Using Graphs:** Using the data in Table 2-3 on page 40, graph the densities of the following materials: water, sugar, salt, iron, copper, lead, and gold. Use the proper type of graph and let each unit on your graph represent 0.1 g/cm^3. Then, answer the following questions:
    a. Why did you choose this type of graph?
    b. What would be the mass of 5 cm^3 of sugar?
    c. If you had a 1-g sample of each material shown in the graph, which sample would have the greatest volume?
    d. How could your graph be made more accurate?

PROJECTS

1. Devise your own system of measurements. What will be the standard for each type of measurement in your system? How will conversions between units be made?
2. Find the metric equivalent of such things as your weight in pounds, a gallon of milk, and the distance to your school in miles.

18. a. 1.5 L
    b. 200 000 cm
    c. 580 mg
    d. 295 K
19. Student responses should include importance of being able to compare measurements.
20. a. nanometer, nm
    b. meter, m
    c. millimeter, mm
    d. centimeter, cm
    e. kilometer, km
21. a. 7.5 g/cm^3
    b. 2.5 g/mL
    c. 9 kg/L
22. A line graph; time in seconds would be the independent variable and distance would be the dependent variable.

MORE SKILL BUILDERS

1. **Comparing and Contrasting:** Students should name and compare the base units of measurement of length, mass, volume, temperature, and time for the two systems. The fact that SI measurements are based on multiples of ten should be contrasted with the lack of any consistent or logical base in our system. The ease of converting in SI should be contrasted with the difficulty in our system.
2. **Hypothesizing:** Hypothesis: the metal expands when heated. The hypothesis can be tested by measuring the mass and volume of the ball at the two temperatures.
3. **Measuring in SI:** Student answers will vary. Make sure that students used the correct methods to make the required measurements.
4. **Making and Using Graphs:**

a. A bar graph was chosen because the data consist of discrete bits of information that do not involve a relationship between dependent and independent variables and do not make up a whole quantity.

b.   mass = density × volume
        mass of sugar = 1.6 g/cm^3 × 5 cm^3
                      = 8 g

c. water

d. The graph could be made more accurate by using units smaller than 1 g/cm^3.

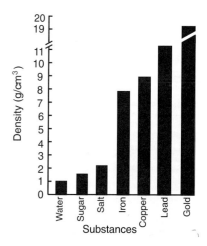

Objective

In this unit ending feature, the unit topic "Physical Science Basics" is extended into other disciplines. Students will see how the basics of physical science are used in events occurring around the planet.

Motivate

Cooperative Learning: Assign one Connection to each group of students. Using the Expert Teams strategy, have each group research to find out more about the geographic location of the Connection—its climate, culture, flora and fauna, and ecological issues.

Teaching Tips

▶ Ask students to identify the problem in each Connection and discuss possible ways that scientists could have found solutions to the problems.

Wrap-Up

Conclude this lesson by presenting students with a problem, such as which freezes faster—equal samples of 5°C water, 50°C water, or 90°C water? Have them identify variables and controls needed to solve the problem. Have them decide how to display their findings in a graph.

PHYSICS

Background: Both robots have miniature video cameras that tilt and rotate. This gives the technician operating the robots a clear view. One of the robots is able to pull itself upright after leaving the ducts and then climb up to inspect the reactor.

Discussion: Discuss other places where similar robots might prove useful. Ask students to describe the kinds of movements a robot would need to make in each situation.

Answer to Question: They allow inspection and cleanup to be done in areas unsafe for human workers.

Extension: Ask students to design a robot for a particular job and label its parts and functions.

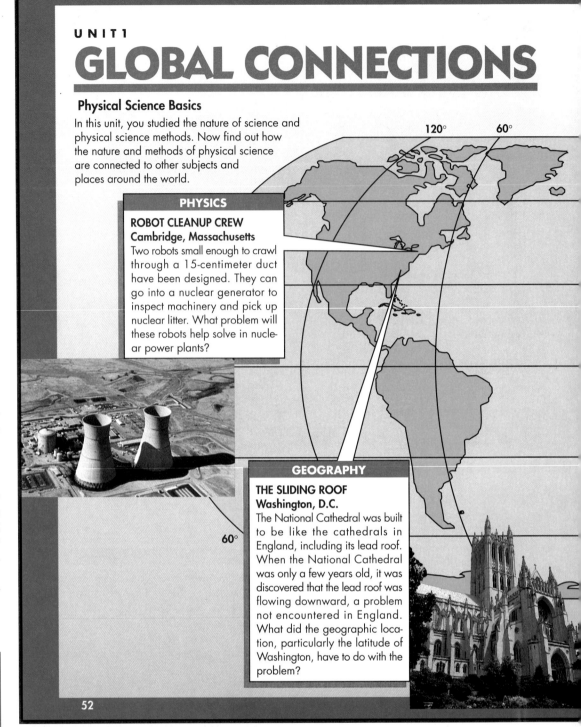

UNIT 1
GLOBAL CONNECTIONS

Physical Science Basics

In this unit, you studied the nature of science and physical science methods. Now find out how the nature and methods of physical science are connected to other subjects and places around the world.

PHYSICS

ROBOT CLEANUP CREW
Cambridge, Massachusetts
Two robots small enough to crawl through a 15-centimeter duct have been designed. They can go into a nuclear generator to inspect machinery and pick up nuclear litter. What problem will these robots help solve in nuclear power plants?

GEOGRAPHY

THE SLIDING ROOF
Washington, D.C.
The National Cathedral was built to be like the cathedrals in England, including its lead roof. When the National Cathedral was only a few years old, it was discovered that the lead roof was flowing downward, a problem not encountered in England. What did the geographic location, particularly the latitude of Washington, have to do with the problem?

52

GEOGRAPHY

Background: Pure lead is soft enough to cut with a fingernail. At about 80°C, the lead would be malleable enough to begin to flow. The roof was remade with a less malleable alloy of 94% lead and 6% antimony.

Discussion: Discuss how geographic location must be taken into account when building.

Answer to Question: When the summer sun in Washington, DC, heated the roof of the cathedral, it got hot enough for the lead to start flowing under its own weight. In England, which is farther north, summer days are not as hot.

Extension: Have students research the properties of lead.

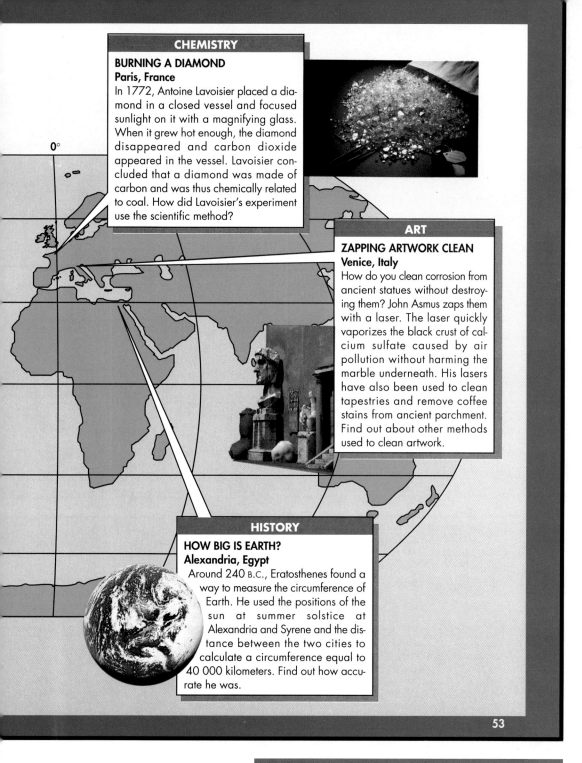

CHEMISTRY
BURNING A DIAMOND
Paris, France
In 1772, Antoine Lavoisier placed a diamond in a closed vessel and focused sunlight on it with a magnifying glass. When it grew hot enough, the diamond disappeared and carbon dioxide appeared in the vessel. Lavoisier concluded that a diamond was made of carbon and was thus chemically related to coal. How did Lavoisier's experiment use the scientific method?

0°

ART
ZAPPING ARTWORK CLEAN
Venice, Italy
How do you clean corrosion from ancient statues without destroying them? John Asmus zaps them with a laser. The laser quickly vaporizes the black crust of calcium sulfate caused by air pollution without harming the marble underneath. His lasers have also been used to clean tapestries and remove coffee stains from ancient parchment. Find out about other methods used to clean artwork.

HISTORY
HOW BIG IS EARTH?
Alexandria, Egypt
Around 240 B.C., Eratosthenes found a way to measure the circumference of Earth. He used the positions of the sun at summer solstice at Alexandria and Syrene and the distance between the two cities to calculate a circumference equal to 40 000 kilometers. Find out how accurate he was.

53

HISTORY
Background: Eratosthenes used as a unit the Greek *stadion*. The Romans reckoned 8 stadia to their mile of 1000 double paces. The Roman mile is equivalent to about 1665 English yards.

Discussion: Tell students that most people of his time thought Eratosthenes' figure was too high. Discuss why people might have preferred to believe Earth was smaller.

Answer to Question: Present measurements give the circumference of Earth as 24 846 miles (39 977 kilometers).

Extension: Have students research ancient units of measurement.

CHEMISTRY
Background: Lavoisier had earlier proved that combustion came about through the combination of a substance with some portion of the air.

Discuss.on: Lavoisier is considered the father of modern chemistry. He was the first scientist to combine experimentation and observation with measurement. Discuss with students the importance of measurement in science.

Answer to Question: Lavoisier identified the problem, gathered experimental data, and made a conclusion.

Extension: Have students prepare a report on the work of Lavoisier.

ART
Background: Asmus was in Venice in 1972 to make laser holograms of art treasures threatened by tides and air pollution when he first used a laser to clean a statue.

Discussion: When Asmus was trying to get funding for projects, the National Endowment for the Arts told him "this is science" and the National Science Foundation told him "this is art." Ask students to discuss this contradiction.

Answer to Question: Other ways involve mechanical methods, such as using a scalpel, or chemical methods, such as dissolving the black crust with solvents.

Extension: Have students research the life-size terra cotta army found in the tomb of Chinese Emperor Qin Shi-huang and plans to restore it.

SURVEYOR

Background: About one third of all surveyors work for federal, state, or local governments. Others work for utility companies, gas and oil companies, or construction, engineering, and architectural firms.

Related Career	Education
Drafter	technical school
Cartographer	college degree
Machinist	high school
Instrument maker	technical school

Career Issue: Laser technology replaces the surveyor's transit and the instrument worker. Using a laser requires additional training on the part of the survey crew and also is more expensive, but lasers are extremely accurate.

What do you think? Lead students in a discussion of their attitudes about using lasers for surveying. Do they think the increased expense and loss of a job on the team is worth the increase in accuracy?

QUALITY-CONTROL INSPECTOR

Background: Although most inspectors work for private industries, they must be knowledgeable about federal and state laws that govern the manufacturing of the products they inspect.

Related Career	Education
Food-processing technician	technical school
Pharmaceutical technician	technical school
Paper pulp tester	high school
Automotive parts inspector	high school

Career Issue: Many companies are working to get all employees, not just quality-control inspectors, involved in quality control. Some people think this would eliminate the need for inspectors.

What do you think? Lead students in a discussion of their own attitudes toward quality control in the manufacture of products.

SURVEYOR

Before any construction project can begin, a *surveyor* must establish land boundaries, collect information from maps, charts, or plats, and measure or locate elevations and land contours.

Surveyors work in parties ranging from 3 to 6 people, consisting of a party chief and assistants. An instrument worker sets up the transit and takes gradings. A rod worker holds a graduated rod that measures elevations. The chain workers work in pairs to measure distances between surveying points.

If you're interested in becoming a surveyor, you should enjoy outdoor work, have good eyesight, and be in good physical condition. You should also enjoy teamwork. High school classes in science, mathematics, and drafting would be helpful.

Technical and community colleges offer 1-, 2-, or 3-year programs in surveying. All states require surveyors to be licensed or registered.

For Additional Information
Contact American Congress on Surveying and Mapping, 5410 Grosvenor Lane, Suite 100, Bethesda, MD 20814.

QUALITY-CONTROL INSPECTOR

Quality-control inspectors oversee a production process to ensure that the quality of a given product meets certain minimum standards. The products they inspect include things as varied as automobiles, chemicals, clothing, pharmaceuticals, food products, computers, and electronics.

If you're interested in becoming a quality-control inspector, you should like the practical aspects of science and mathematics, especially laboratory work. You must pay close attention to details, and your work must be accurate.

Most quality-control inspectors have a college degree with an emphasis on science. An inspector in the food industry, for example, should have a degree in food science or biology, while an inspector in the chemical or pharmaceutical industry should have a degree in chemistry.

For Additional Information
Contact American Society for Quality Control, P.O. Box 3005, Milwaukee, Wisconsin 53201.

UNIT READINGS

▶ Aaseng, Mathan. *Better Mousetraps: Product Improvements That Led to Success.* Minneapolis, MN: Lerner Publications Co., 1990.
▶ Holzinger, Philip R. *The House of Science.* New York, NY: John Wiley & Sons, 1990.

UNIT READINGS

Background
▶ *Better Mousetraps: Product Improvements That Led to Success* focuses on people who have taken a product and improved or adapted it.
▶ *The House of Science* asks students to visualize science as a series of connected rooms. The "house" has rooms for chemistry, physics, biology, geology, and so on.

More Readings
Ansley, David. "Have Laser, Will Travel." *Discover.* December, 1990, pp. 44-48. This article presents a detailed description of laser technology in art restoration.

VideoDisc
STVS: Map Science, Disc 3, Side 2

Asimov on Physics

by Isaac Asimov

The passage that follows is a brief history of the development of the common thermometer.

One applicable physical characteristic, which must have been casually observed by countless people, is the fact that substances expand when warmed and contract when cooled. The first of all those countless people, however, who tried to make use of this fact to measure temperature was the Italian physicist Galileo Galilei. In 1603 he inverted a tube of heated air into a bowl of water. As the air cooled to room temperature, it contracted and the water moved up into the tube. Now Galileo was ready. The water level kept on changing as room temperature changed, being pushed down when it warmed and expanded the trapped air, and being pushed up when it cooled and contracted the trapped air. Galileo had a thermometer (which, in Greek, means "heat measure"). The only trouble was that the basin of water was open to the air and air pressure kept changing. That also shoved the water level up and down, independently of temperature, and skewed the results.

By 1654, the Grand Duke of Tuscany, Ferdinand II, evolved a thermometer that was independent of air pressure. It contained a liquid sealed into a tube, and the contraction and expansion of the liquid itself was used as an indication of temperature change. The volume change in liquids is much smaller than in gases, but by using a sizable reservoir of liquid which was filled so that further expansion could only take place up a very narrow tube, the rise and fall within that tube, for even tiny volume changes, was considerable.

This was the first reasonably accurate thermometer, and was also one of the few occasions on which the nobility contributed to scientific advance.

In 1701, Isaac Newton suggested that the thermometer be thrust into melting ice and that the liquid level so obtained be marked as 0, while the level attained at body temperature be marked off as 12, and the interval divided into twelve equal parts.

In Your Own Words

▶ The measurement of temperature is a fairly recent idea—less than 400 years old. Write an essay on how your life might be different if thermometers had never been invented.

55

Source: Isaac Asimov. *Asimov on Physics.* New York, NY: Doubleday & Co., 1976.

Biography: Isaac Asimov was born in Russia in 1920. When he was 3 years old, his family moved to New York City. He taught biochemistry at Boston University from 1949 to 1958, then left to become a full-time writer. Asimov wrote more than 400 books, mostly nonfiction emphasizing science and technology. He is, however, best known as an author of science fiction.

TEACHING STRATEGY

Have students read through the passage by Isaac Asimov. Then have them respond to the discussion questions below.

Discussion Questions

1. **From the passage given here, what does Asimov think about Newton's temperature scale and the fact that Newton was English?** *He states that a 12-degree scale was a logical choice for Newton, because he was English, and the English seem to have a fondness for things in multiples of 12.*

2. **What is Asimov's opinion of the contributions of European nobility to science?** *He does not think they contributed much at all. He states that the Grand Duke of Tuscany's invention of the first reasonably accurate thermometer was one of "the few occasions on which the nobility contributed to scientific advance."*

Other Works

▶ Other books by Isaac Asimov include: *Asimov's New Guide to Science.* New York, NY: Doubleday & Co., 1984. *X Stands for Unknown.* New York, NY: Doubleday & Co., 1984.

▶ Science fiction books by Isaac Asimov include the Foundation series and the Robot novels. New York, NY: Ballantine Books.

Classics

▶ Asimov, Isaac. *Asimov's Biographical Encyclopedia of Science and Technology.* New York, NY: Doubleday & Co., 1982. Traces the history of science through the careers of people.

▶ Berger, Melvin. *Mad Scientists in Fact and Fiction.* New York, NY: Watts, 1980. Discusses real and fictional scientists who have formed unusual theories.

In Unit 2, students are introduced to kinematics, the study of motion, and dynamics, the study of the causes of motion. Newton's three laws of motion are introduced to encapsulate the relationship between motion and force. From forces, students then move on to the concept of energy, the various types of energy, and the law of conservation of energy.

CONTENTS

ADVANCE PREPARATION

Activities
▶ **Activity 4-2, page 104, and Activity 7-1, page 162,** require building bricks for each activity group.
▶ **Activity 5-2, page 128,** requires a set of heated hair curlers.

UNIT

2 ENERGY AND MOTION

PHOTON

56

OPTIONS

Cross Curriculum
▶ Have students keep logs of how terms, such as *force, energy, work, power,* and *efficiency* are used in other classes. At the end of the unit, have students compare and contrast the usages of the words in these classes and in science class.
▶ Have students note how motion is described in words, music, and pictures in various classes.

Science at Home
▶ Have students monitor TV and newspaper articles on sports events and collect verbs and adjectives used to describe the action.
▶ Have students monitor TV and newspapers to find measurements of motion. Have them categorize the types of motion and the units used to measure motion.

What's Happening Here?

Would you like to have a car that never needs gas? If so, then the car in this picture—built by students competing in the National Collegiate Solar Car Race—is the car for you. It runs on sunshine, or solar energy. Do you run on solar energy? The vegetables and grains that give you energy couldn't grow without the sun. So, in a way, you run on sunshine, too. How is energy changed into motion? Is heat a form of energy? In Unit 2, you'll learn more about energy and motion.

UNIT CONTENTS

57

Multicultural Awareness

Have interested students research ways in which motion in the natural world has been artistically portrayed and interpreted by various cultures. Have students focus their attention on performing arts, such as ceremonial and ritual dancing and chants; visual arts, such as prints, petroglyphs, carvings, and pottery; and in language arts, such as poetry.

Inquiry Questions

Use the following questions to focus a discussion of motion and energy.

▶ **What do the motions of the solar car and the sprinters have in common?** *Accept all reasonable answers. Both can change their speed and direction; both need a supply of energy to move; and the shapes of both affect their efficiency.*

▶ **Why do you think the car has a streamlined shape?** *Accept all reasonable answers. To reduce "wind force" [air resistance].*

INTRODUCING THE UNIT

What's Happening Here?

▶ Have students look at the photos and read the text. Ask them to tell you what's happening here. Point out to students that in this unit they will be studying motion, force, and energy and the relationships among them.

▶ **Background:** The photograph shows a solar-powered car participating in the Tour de Sol, a 210-mile race from Montpelier, Vermont to Cambridge, Massachusetts. The race, sponsored by the Massachusetts Institute of Technology, encourages the development of solar-powered cars for limited-distance commuting. The race started on May 25, 1989, with five entries, and was won five days later by a car entered by the University of Alabama. The cost of the winning car was $3000.

Previewing the Chapters

▶ Have students make a list of the sports, entertainment, and recreational activities depicted by photographs in this unit. Ballet (page 74); baseball (pages 70 and 91); bicycling, (pages 169, 175, and 176); bowling (page 103); diving (page 75); downhill sledding (page 116); drag car racing (page 65); frisbee throwing (page 88); isometric exercises (page 97); pool (page 101); roller coaster riding (page 93); sky-diving, (pages 83 and 89); space walking (page 94); swimming (pages 99 and 124); swinging (pages 60, 92, and 114); tennis (page 158); track (page 61); tug-of-war (page 71); weight training (page 108)

Tying to Previous Knowledge

▶ Have students brainstorm for words that describe different types of motion, such as *swirling, tumbling, gliding.* Have them associate these words with the photographs in the unit.

▶ Use the **inquiry questions** in the OPTIONS box at left to investigate motion with students.

3 Moving Objects

CHAPTER SECTION	OBJECTIVES	ACTIVITIES
3-1 Describing Motion (2 days)	1. **Describe** speed as a rate. 2. **Perform calculations** involving speed, time, and distance. 3. **Interpret** distance-time graphs.	**Activity 3-1:** *Design a Slow Flyer*, p. 64
3-2 Velocity and Acceleration (1 day)	1. **Compare** and **contrast** speed, velocity, and acceleration. 2. **Calculate** acceleration.	**MINI-Lab:** *Does greater velocity require greater acceleration?* p. 66
3-3 Crashing to Save Lives **Science & Society** (1 day)	1. **Evaluate** the effects of wearing seat belts during a car crash. 2. **Form an opinion** about whether laws should make people wear seat belts.	
3-4 Force and Motion (2 days)	1. **Recognize** different kinds of forces. 2. **Identify** cause and effect relationships between force and changes in velocity. 3. **Give examples** of the effects of inertia. 4. **State** Newton's first law of motion.	**MINI-Lab:** *Is friction a force?* p. 73
3-5 Effects of Gravity (2 days)	1. **Give examples** of the effects of gravity. 2. **Examine** how gravitational force is related to mass and distance. 3. **Distinguish** between mass and weight.	**Activity 3-2:** *Balancing Forces Against Gravity*, p. 78
Chapter Review		

ACTIVITY MATERIALS

FIND OUT	ACTIVITIES		MINI-LABS	
Page 59 metersticks	**3-1 Design a Slow Flyer, p. 64** stopwatch or timer with second hand meterstick or metric tape measure string paper sheets of various types, weights, and sizes transparent tape paper clips and stapler	**3-2 Balancing Forces Against Gravity, p. 78** selection of paper strips scissors masking tape plastic cup string 250 mL sand beaker balance ring stand and ring sheets of newspaper	**Does greater velocity require greater acceleration? p. 66** stopwatches metersticks marbles 1/4 inch hardboard (10cm x 50cm to 100 cm)	**Is friction a force? p. 73** 1 sheet plain white paper 20-g mass 1 sheet coarse sandpaper

CHAPTER FEATURES	TEACHER RESOURCE PACKAGE	OTHER RESOURCES
Skill Builder: *Concept Mapping,* p. 63	**Ability Level Worksheets** ◆ **Study Guide,** p. 13 ● **Reinforcement,** p. 13 ▲ **Enrichment,** p. 13 **Critical Thinking/Problem Solving,** p. 9 **Activity Worksheets,** pp. 22, 23 **Transparency Masters,** pp. 9, 10	**Color Transparency 5,** Distance-Time Graph
Skill Builder: *Making and Using Graphs,* p. 67	**Ability Level Worksheets** ◆ **Study Guide,** p. 14 ● **Reinforcement,** p. 14 ▲ **Enrichment,** p. 14 **Activity Worksheets,** p. 28	**Laboratory Manual 4,** Speed and Acceleration **STVS:** Disc 2, Side 1
You Decide! p. 69	**Ability Level Worksheets** ◆ **Study Guide,** p. 15 ● **Reinforcement,** p. 15 ▲ **Enrichment,** p. 15 **Activity Worksheets,** p. 5	
Technology: *Inertia Sponges,* p. 72 **Skill Builder:** *Outlining,* p. 74	**Ability Level Worksheets** ◆ **Study Guide,** p. 16 ● **Reinforcement,** p. 16 ▲ **Enrichment,** p. 16 **Cross-Curricular Connections,** p. 7 **Science and Society,** p. 7 **Activity Worksheets,** p. 29 **Transparency Masters,** pp. 11, 12	**Color Transparency 6,** Newton's First Law **Laboratory Manual 5,** Projectile Motion **STVS:** Disc 1, Side 1
Problem Solving: *An Experiment for the Shuttle,* p. 76 **Skill Builder:** *Observing and Inferring,* p. 77	**Ability Level Worksheets** ◆ **Study Guide,** p. 17 ● **Reinforcement,** p. 17 ▲ **Enrichment,** p. 17 **Concept Mapping,** pp. 11, 12 **Activity Worksheets,** pp. 24, 25	**STVS:** Disc 2, Side 2 **Science Integration Activity 2**
Summary Think & Write Critically Key Science Words Apply Understanding Vocabulary More Skill Builders Checking Concepts Projects Using Lab Skills	**ASSESSMENT RESOURCES** **Chapter Review,** pp. 9, 10 **Chapter Test,** pp. 20-23 **Performance Assessment in** **Middle School Science**	**Chapter Review Software** **Test Bank** **Alternate Assessment** **Performance Assessment**

◆ **Basic**   ● **Average**   ▲ **Advanced**

ADDITIONAL MATERIALS

SOFTWARE	AUDIOVISUAL	BOOKS/MAGAZINES
Fall Guy: Investigation of Falling Objects, Queue. *Laws of Motion,* EME Corp. *Motion: Displacement and Velocity,* Queue. *Motion: Velocity and Acceleration,* Queue. *Motion: Distance, Displacement and Time,* Queue. *Playing With Science: Motion,* Sunburst. *PSL Motion Experiments,* EduQuest. *Wood Car Rally,* MECC.	*Force and Friction,* Laserdisc, Journal Films. *Gravity,* Laserdisc, Journal Films. *Gravity,* Video, AIT. *Gravity: How It Affects Us,* Video, Britannica. *Physics Of Sports,* Laserdisc, Video Discovery. *What If?,* Video, Journal Films.	Friedhoffer, Robert. *Forces, Motion, and Energy.* NY: Watts, 1993. Sauvain, Phillip. *Motion.* NY: Discovery, 1992. Taylor, Barbara. *Force and Movement.* NY: Watts, 1990. Ward, Alan. *Forces and Energy.* NY: Watts, 1992.

3

▪ MOVING OBJECTS

THEME DEVELOPMENT: A theme that emerges in this chapter is that objects change their positions when forces act upon them. A net force acting on an object can be inferred from changes in its motion.

CHAPTER OVERVIEW

▶ **Section 3-1:** This section introduces the concept of an object's speed as the rate of change in its position. Instantaneous speed, constant speed, average speed, and distance-time graphs are discussed.

▶ **Section 3-2:** Velocity and speed are compared. The concept of acceleration is introduced as a rate of uniform change in velocity.

▶ **Section 3-3: Science and Society:** This section describes how seat belts reduce injuries from car crashes and asks students to form an opinion on the mandatory use of seat belts.

▶ **Section 3-4:** The concept of force and the property of inertia are described, followed by a discussion of friction and Newton's first law of motion.

▶ **Section 3-5:** The concept of an object's weight is developed. The operation of scales is explained.

CHAPTER VOCABULARY

speed	balanced
instantaneous	forces
speed	net force
constant speed	inertia
average speed	friction
velocity	gravity
acceleration	weight
force	

CHAPTER
3   Moving Objects

58

OPTIONS

For Your Gifted Students

▶ Have students use a spring scale attached to a block of wood to explore how friction impedes motion. Have them pull the wood over a rough surface such as sandpaper, and record the force needed. Have students think of ways to reduce friction, thus reducing the force needed to move the wood. (For example, put soap, water, a row of pencils, or other materials between the block and the sandpaper to see if the amount of friction is reduced.)

For Your Mainstreamed Students

▶ Roll a marble through a toilet paper tube that is raised 1 cm at one end. Measure the distance the marble rolls. Place different types of material at the bottom end of the tube. Ask students to predict the distance the marble will roll. Test the predictions.

Every day people and things move around you—cars go by, your classmates move about in the halls, leaves blow in the wind. You know these things are moving because you see the motion. Now think about motion that you don't see. A magician makes an object seem to disappear by distracting the audience so they don't see where the object goes. If you don't see motion, how can you tell something has moved?

FIND OUT!

Do the following activity to find out if you can detect movement without seeing motion.

Close your eyes while a classmate moves something in the classroom. Now open your eyes and see if you can *observe* what was moved. Be aware of the clues you're using. Are you using only your eyes, or are other senses helping? If you figure out what was moved, can you tell how far it moved? How do you know?

Gearing Up
Previewing the Chapter
Use this outline to help you focus on important ideas in this chapter.

Section 3-1   Describing Motion
▶ Speed
▶ Calculating Speed
▶ Graphing Speed

Section 3-2   Velocity and Acceleration
▶ Velocity and Speed
▶ Acceleration

Section 3-3   Science and Society
Crashing to Save Lives
▶ Studying Crashes

Section 3-4   Force and Motion
▶ What Is a Force?
▶ Effects of Forces on Objects
▶ Inertia and Mass
▶ Newton's First Law
▶ Friction

Section 3-5   Effects of Gravity
▶ Gravitational Force
▶ Weight
▶ Measuring Forces

Previewing Science Skills
▶ In the Skill Builders, you will make a concept map, graph, outline, and observe and infer.
▶ In the Activities, you will measure, control variables, and experiment.
▶ In the MINI-Labs, you will calculate and observe and interpret.

What's next?

You can tell that something has moved without actually seeing the motion. Now you will learn about how and why things move and how different forces affect motion.

59

INTRODUCING THE CHAPTER
Use the Find Out activity to introduce students to the notion that an object's motion can be inferred from a change in its position.

FIND OUT!
Materials: metersticks

Cooperative Learning: Group students into threes. Have each group fold three pieces of paper into thirds. Label one piece of paper "Motion I can see," the second "Motion I can detect by sound," and the third "Motion I think exists, but can't detect directly." Each student in each group should start with one of these pieces of paper and spend 1–2 minutes listing as many examples of that kind of motion as possible in one column. Then have them switch papers, fold back the used columns, and add to the list on the paper until each student has contributed to each list. Share the results as a class.

Teaching Tips
▶ If students measure how far an object has moved, they will likely measure the distance in a straight line. Ask them if the object could have followed any other path. Ask them if they can determine the true path the object followed.

Gearing Up
Have students study the Gearing Up feature to familiarize themselves with the chapter. Discuss the relationships of the topics in the outline.

What's Next?
Before beginning the first section, make sure students understand the connection between the Find Out activity and the topics to follow.

ASSESSMENT OPTIONS

PORTFOLIO
Refer to page 79 for suggested items that students might select for their portfolios.

PERFORMANCE ASSESSMENT
See page 79 for additional Performance Assessment options.
Process
Skill Builders, pp. 63, 67, 74

CONTENT ASSESSMENT
MINI-Lab Assessment, pp. 66, 73
Skill Builder, p. 77
Section Reviews, pp. 63, 67, 69, 74, 77
Chapter Review, pp. 79–81
Mini Quizzes, pp. 62, 67, 74, 76
Activity 3-1, p. 64,; Activity 3-2, p. 78
Assessment—Oral, pp. 65, 72, 73

GROUP ASSESSMENT
Opportunities for group assessment occur with Cooperative Learning Strategies and Flex Your Brain Activities.

PREPARATION

SECTION BACKGROUND

▶ The back and forth motion of a swing is oscillatory motion, a type of periodic motion.

▶ Since an object's motion is a change in its position, the term *position* must be described. An object's position at any moment is given relative to, or measured from, some arbitrary reference point that is stationary or can be considered stationary.

▶ Average speed is *defined* by the equation

$$v = d/t$$

where *d* represents the distance measured along the path that the object moved, and *t* represents the time during which the object moved.

▶ The *slope* at any point on a distance-time graph is equivalent to the instantaneous speed of the object at that time and location. If a segment of a graph is a straight line, the speed is constant and the slope of the line is the average velocity during the time interval.

PREPLANNING

▶ To prepare for Activity 3-1, obtain the materials listed on page 64.

▶ Obtain a small rubber ball, string, a thumbtack, and several wind-up or battery-operated toy cars.

1 MOTIVATE

▶ **Demonstration:** (1) Roll a rubber ball across a desk. (2) Drop it onto the desk and catch it on the rebound. (3) Attach a piece of string to the ball with a thumbtack and swing the ball back and forth. Ask volunteers to demonstrate other types of motion using the ball. Discuss similarities and differences in these motions.

3-1 Describing Motion

New Science Words

speed
instantaneous speed
constant speed
average speed

Objectives

▶ Describe speed as a rate.
▶ Perform calculations involving speed, time, and distance.
▶ Interpret distance-time graphs.

Speed

When something moves, it changes position. It travels from one place to another, even if in motion for a brief time. Think about someone swinging. If asked to describe the motion of a swing, you would probably say something like "back-and-forth." How would you describe the motion of a rubber ball bouncing on a sidewalk?

You don't always have to see something move to know that motion has taken place. For example, suppose you look out a window and see a mail truck parked next to a mailbox. One minute later, you look out again and see the same truck parked down the street from the mailbox. Although you didn't observe the motion, you know the truck moved. How do you know? Its position relative to the mailbox has changed.

Motion can be described as a change in position. To ① know if the position of something has changed, you need a reference point. In the case of the mail truck, the mailbox was a reference point. You can also use the reference point to get a rough idea of how far the truck moved. But there's one thing you don't know. You don't know how *fast* the truck moved in reaching its new position.

Descriptions of motion often include speed—how *fast* something moves. If you think of motion as a change in position, then speed is an expression of how much time it takes for that change in position to occur. Any change over time is called a rate. **Speed,** then, is the rate of change in position. Speed can also be described as simply a rate of motion.

There are different "kinds" of speed. The speedometer in a car shows instantaneous speed. **Instantaneous speed** is the rate of motion at any given instant. At the moment the picture in Figure 3-2 was taken, the car was

Figure 3-1. Although the swing set does not move from one place to another, the swings are in motion.

EcoTip

When you have to go somewhere, move your muscles. Walk, bike, or skate to the store or to a friend's house instead of riding in a car or bus. It's good for you and for the environment.

OPTIONS

Meeting Different Ability Levels

For Section 3-1, use the following **Teacher Resource Masters** depending upon individual students' needs.

◆ **Study Guide Master** for all students.
● **Reinforcement Master** for students of average and above average ability levels.
▲ **Enrichment Master** for above average students.

Additional Teacher Resource Package masters are listed in any PROGRAM RESOURCES boxes that are in the section. The additional masters are appropriate for all students.

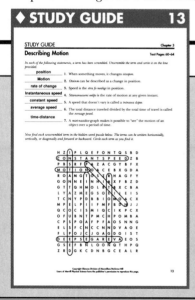

◆ STUDY GUIDE 13

traveling at a speed of 80 km/h. On a highway, a car may travel at the same speed for a fairly long period of time. A speed that does not vary is called a **constant speed.**

Much of the time, the speeds you deal with are not constant. Think about riding your bicycle for a distance of 5 kilometers. As you start out, your speed increases from 0 km/h to, say, 20 km/h. You slow down to 12 km/h as you pedal up a steep hill and speed up to 35 km/h going down the other side of the hill. You stop for a red light, speed up again, and move at a constant speed for a while. As you near the end of the trip, you slow down and then stop. Checking your watch, you find that the trip took 15 minutes, or one-quarter of an hour. How would you express your speed on such a trip? Would you use your fastest speed, your slowest speed, or some speed in-between the two?

In cases where rate of motion varies a great deal, such as this bicycle trip, the best way to describe speed is to use average speed. **Average speed** is total distance traveled divided by total time of travel. On the trip just described, your average speed was 5 kilometers divided by 1/4 hour, or 20 km/h.

Calculating Speed

How could you find out who is the fastest runner in your school? One way would be to get all the students together to run in a giant race. However, this isn't very practical. A better way would be to have each student run a certain distance and to time each runner. The runner with the shortest time is the fastest student. In other words, if you know the distance and time, you can calculate average speed. Knowing these values, you can use this equation:

$$v = \frac{d}{t}$$

Figure 3-2. The speedometer of a car shows how fast the car is moving at any given instant.

Did You Know?

In the finals of the 100-m dash of the 1988 Olympics, Ben Johnson and Carl Lewis each reached a peak speed of 43.37 km/h during one 10-m stretch.

Connect to...
Life Science

Participating in sports is part of living a healthy life. However, some sports, like downhill skiing, have their own risks to health. Downhill skiers have been clocked at speeds up to 200.2 km/h. Convert this speed to miles/h, remembering that 1 mile equals 1.6 km.

61

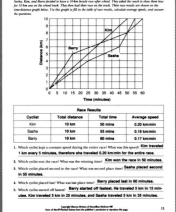

TYING TO PREVIOUS KNOWLEDGE: Ask students to recall that the units marked on a speedometer of a bike or car are miles per hour and kilometers per hour. Have them recall that the quantities that make up these units were introduced in Chapter 2.

2 TEACH

Key Concepts are highlighted.

CONCEPT DEVELOPMENT

▶ Ask students to describe other types of periodic motion, such as the motion of a bee's wing or the post in a cassette recorder.

▶ Students may have difficulty with the term *relative* used in describing an object's position. Explain that the term means "dependent upon" or "with reference to."

▶ Ask each student to secretly choose a classmate and write a description of his or her position in the classroom. Have students exchange and read the descriptions to see if they can identify the persons chosen. Discuss the common characteristics of those descriptions that lead to correct identifications.

▶ Review the concept of *rate* by having students measure their breathing rates. Discuss other time rates, such as heart rate (pulse), growth rates, and interest rates. Discuss the units that describe these rates and point out similarities in the units.

Connect to...
Life Science

Answer:

$$200.2 \, \frac{km}{h} \times \frac{1 \, mile}{1.6 \, km} = 125.1 \, miles/h$$

Answer: 125.1 miles/h

CONCEPT DEVELOPMENT

▶ Show students that time units really do emerge from the equation

$$t = d/v$$

That is,

$$m \div \frac{m}{s} = m \times \frac{s}{m} = s$$

Emphasize that the vertical axis in Figure 3-3 represents the distance each swimmer has swum from the beginning of the workout, and the horizontal axis represents the time that has elapsed since the start of the workout.

REVEALING MISCONCEPTIONS

▶ Students often interpret the height of the graph as its slope. Point out that the steepness of the line of a distance-time graph indicates the average speed; the height of the line indicates the distance the object has traveled.

PRACTICE PROBLEM ANSWERS

1. 9.37 m/s
2. 21.9 s

CHECK FOR UNDERSTANDING

Use the Mini Quiz to check for understanding.

MINI QUIZ

Use the Mini Quiz to check students' recall of chapter content.

1 **What is motion?** *a change in position*

2 **What two quantities do you need to know to calculate average speed?** *distance and time*

3 **What does a flat line on a segment of distance-time graph tell you about the average speed for that time period?** *no change in distance occurs, therefore average speed is zero*

EXAMPLE PROBLEM: Calculating Speed

Problem Statement:	Your neighbor says she can skate at a speed of 1 m/s. To see if you can skate faster, you have her time you as you skate as fast as you can for 100 m. Your time is 67 s. Who skates faster?
Known Information: Strategy Hint: Remember that speed is a rate.	distance, d = 100 m time, t = 67 s
Unknown Information:	speed, v
Equation to Use:	$v = \dfrac{d}{t}$
Solution:	$v = \dfrac{100 \text{ m}}{67 \text{ s}} = 1.5$ m/s You skate faster than your neighbor.

PRACTICE PROBLEM

Strategy Hint: What units will your answer be given in?

1. Florence Griffith Joyner set a world record by running 200 m in 21.34 s. What was her average speed?

EXAMPLE PROBLEM: Calculating Time from Speed

Problem Statement:	Sound travels at a speed of 330 m/s. If a firecracker explodes 3630 m away from you, how long does it take for the sound of the explosion to reach you?
Known Information: Strategy Hint: Rearrange equation to solve for time.	velocity, v = 330 m/s distance, d = 3630 m
Unknown Information:	time, t
Equation to Use:	$v = \dfrac{d}{t}$ Rearranged becomes: $t = \dfrac{d}{v}$
Solution:	$t = \dfrac{d}{v} = \dfrac{3630 \text{ m}}{330 \text{ m/s}} = 11$ s It takes 11 seconds for the sound of the explosion to reach you.

PRACTICE PROBLEM

Strategy Hint: Rearrange the equation.

2. The world's fastest passenger elevator operates at an average speed of about 10 m/s. If the 60th floor is 219 m above the first floor, how long does it take the elevator to go from the first floor to the 60th floor?

OPTIONS

ENRICHMENT

▶ Have students find out how the speedometer on a bike or a car works.
▶ Have students investigate the speeds at which various organisms such as ants, wasps, turtles, horses, leopards, ostriches, and falcons move. Ask them to present the information as a bar graph on a poster.

PROGRAM RESOURCES

From the **Teacher Resource Package** use:
Critical Thinking/Problem Solving, page 9, Radar Detectors and Speeding.
Transparency Masters, pages 9-10, Distance-Time Graph.
Use **Color Transparency** number 5, Distance-Time Graph.

Graphing Speed

A distance-time graph makes it possible to "see" the motion of an object over a period of time. For example, the graphs in Figure 3-3 show how two swimmers performed during a 30-minute workout. The smooth, red line represents the motion of a swimmer who swam 800 m during each 10-minute period. Her speed was constant at 80 m/min.

The blue line represents the motion of a second swimmer, who did not swim at a constant speed. She covered 400 m during the first 10 minutes of her workout. Then she rested for the next 10 minutes. During this time, her speed was 0 m/min. The slope of the graph over the next 10 minutes shows that she swam faster than before and covered 800 m. What total distance did she cover? What was her average speed for the 30-minute period?

SECTION REVIEW

1. What units would you use to describe the speed of a car? Would you use different units for the speeds of runners in a neighborhood race? Explain your answers.
2. In a skateboarding marathon, the winner covered 435 km in 36.75 h. What was the winner's average speed?
3. **Apply:** Make a distance-time graph for a 2-hour car trip. The car covered 50 km in the first 30 minutes, stopped for 30 minutes, and covered 60 km in the final 60 minutes. Note the three graph segments. Which graph segment slopes the most? Which one does not slope? What was the car's average speed?
4. **Connect to Life Science:** Describe the measurements needed to determine the speed at which your hair grows.

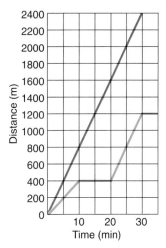

Figure 3-3. Distance-time graphs like the one shown here make it possible to visualize motion over a period of time.

In your Journal, describe the fastest you have ever moved
a) without a vehicle.
b) with a vehicle.
Estimate these speeds in km/h.

☑ Concept Mapping

Make a network tree concept map that shows and defines the three kinds of speed described in this section. If you need help, refer to Concept Mapping in the **Skill Handbook** on pages 684 and 685.

Skill Builder

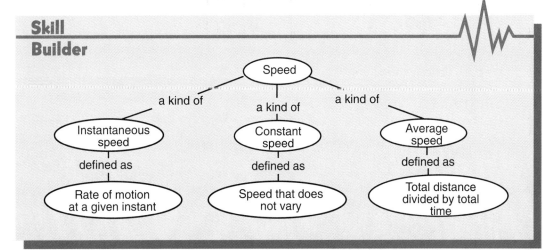

RETEACH
Have students calculate the average speed of a wind-up or battery-operated toy car, using metersticks and a wall clock.

EXTENSION
For students who have mastered this section, use the **Reinforcement** and **Enrichment** masters or other OPTIONS provided.

STUDENT TEXT QUESTION
▶ Page 63, paragraph 2: **What total distance did she cover?** *1200 m* **What was her average speed for the 30-minute period?** *The second swimmer's average speed was 40 m/min.*

3 CLOSE

▶ Repeat the Demonstration described in the Motivation section of this section. Have students identify when the ball appeared to move with constant speed.
▶ Ask the Section Review questions.

SECTION REVIEW ANSWERS
1. km/h; yes, m/s; the neighborhood race would involve short distances and short periods of time
2. 11.8 km/h
3. Apply: The graph segment of the first 30 minutes slopes the most; the segment for the next 30 minutes doesn't slope; the average speed is 55 km/h.
4. Connect to Life Science: Students would need to measure the change in the length of their hair over a period of time, such as four weeks.

$$speed = \frac{length\ change}{time}$$

Fast-growing hair grows at a speed of 0.38 mm/day.

Skill Builder
ASSESSMENT
Performance: Assess students' abilities to organize new information into their concept maps by asking them to add examples of when to use these types of speed measurements.

ACTIVITY 3-1

OBJECTIVE: **Examine** a variety of variables included in the measurement of speed in a glider **designed** to fly as slowly as possible.
Time: one class period

PROCESS SKILLS applied in this activity are **observing, measuring,** and **controlling variables.**

PREPARATION

Cooperative Learning: Science Investigation Teams of 3 or 4

SAFETY: Be sure the flight test area is cleared of people and breakable objects.

THINKING CRITICALLY

The speed can be calculated by dividing the total distance by the time of flight. You would want your glider to have a long flight time, so having a wide surface area and light weight would probably be beneficial.

TEACHING THE ACTIVITY

*Refer to the **Activity Worksheets** for additional information and teaching strategies.*

Cooperative Learning: Each team will design and test a glider to compete with other teams. All teams should contribute in devising a set of rules to make this a fair contest—flight location and distance, launching methods, assignment of judges, etc.
• Guide students to realize that by measuring the linear flight distance and total time, they can calculate average speed.

SUMMING UP/ SHARING RESULTS

Actual speed is likely to change during travel, so calculations show average speed. The curved path distance is greater than a corresponding straight path. The straight path distance measurement will result in a slower average speed. Answers will vary, but weight, balance, shape, and type of paper used can be important factors to experiment with.

How do heavy jet planes fly high above Earth's surface? Their shape, wing design, and high thrust all contribute. Engineers use many physics principles to design flying machines to move very fast, glide, or maneuver quickly. Can you design planes with specific flying behaviors from materials such as paper and tape?

Getting Started
In this activity, you will design a paper glider to fly as slowly as possible. You will *measure* distance and *calculate* your glider's speed.

Safety Notes
Be sure to throw your glider only in a clear path.

Thinking Critically
How can the speed of your glider be determined? What kinds of properties do you want your glider to have if it is to move as slowly as possible?

Materials
• stopwatch or timer with second hand
• meterstick or metric tape measure
• string
• paper sheets of various types
• transparent tape
• paper clips and stapler

Try It!

1. Design a paper glider from the materials.
2. As a class, establish rules for testing the gliders. Consider location, number of trials, necessary measurement, and so forth.
3. Test fly your glider. Record the necessary measurements in a data table and calculate the speed of the flight.
4. Make any adjustments to the glider. Test fly it again and calculate the speed.
5. When you are satisfied with your design, perform a final trial. Compare your results with those of other teams.

64 MOVING OBJECTS

Summing Up/Sharing Results
• In calculating your glider's speeds, did you find its maximum, minimum, or average speed?
• If your glider travels a curved path, which distance measurement will give the slowest speed calculation—along the curved path or along the straight line between the starting and landing point?
• What factors affected your glider's flight? Which were you able to change? How?

Going Further!
Which is more important in determining glider speed—how hard you throw the glider or the design of the glider? How would you change the design of your glider to achieve the fastest possible speed? Create a new airplane and try it.

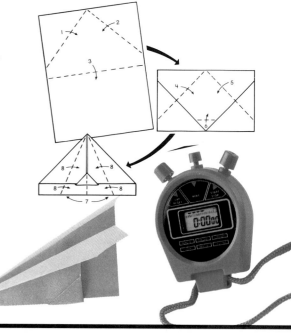

GOING FURTHER!
Glider design is more likely to be the most important variable. A fast glider should probably have a narrower, more pointed design.

ACTIVITY ASSESSMENT
Oral: Ask students to explain why average speed is easier to determine and why the speed varies during flight.

PROGRAM RESOURCES

From the **Teacher Resource Package** use:

Activity Worksheets, pages 22-23, Activity 3-1: Design a Slow Flyer.

Velocity and Acceleration

Objectives

▶ Compare and contrast speed, velocity, and acceleration.
▶ Calculate acceleration.

Velocity and Speed

You turn on the radio and hear the tail end of a news story about a swarm of killer bees. The swarm, moving at a speed of 60 km/h, has just left a town 60 kilometers north of your location. Should you be worried? What should you do? Unfortunately, you don't have enough information. Knowing the speed of the swarm isn't much help. Speed only describes how fast something is moving. You also need to know the direction the swarm is moving. In other words, you need to know the velocity of the swarm. **Velocity** describes both speed and direction.

Picture a motorcycle racing down the highway at 100 km/h. It passes another motorcycle going 100 km/h in the opposite direction. The speeds of the motorcycles are the same, but their velocities are different because the motorcycles are not moving in the same direction.

You learned earlier that speed isn't always constant. Like speed, velocity may also change. Unlike speed, the velocity of an object can change, even if the speed of the object remains constant! How can this be? Read on and you'll find out.

Acceleration

At the starting line of a drag strip, a driver sits, idling the dragster's engine. With the starting signal, the driver presses the gas pedal to the

New Science Words

velocity
acceleration

In Your JOURNAL

In your Journal, explain from a physics perspective why we have speed limits on our streets and highways rather than velocity limits.

OPTIONS

ASSESSMENT—ORAL

▶ How would you convert a car's speedometer to a velocity meter? *Attach a compass to the speedometer panel so that speed and direction could be read simultaneously.*
▶ Using information found in the first paragraph of this section, draw the possible locations from the town after one hour of flight. What velocity of the swarm would worry you? *60 km/h, south* What velocity will put the swarm farthest from the reader? *60 km/h, north*

SECTION BACKGROUND

▶ Velocity and acceleration are both rates of motion. The slope of a velocity-time graph represents acceleration.

PREPLANNING

▶ Obtain boards and marbles for the MINI-Lab. Ask students who have digital wristwatches with stopwatches to wear them the day of the activity.
▶ Obtain several wind-up or battery-operated toy cars.

1 MOTIVATE

▶**Demonstration:** Have students observe as you place a wind-up or battery-operated toy car on the floor and release it first in one direction and then in the opposite. Emphasize the average speed in both directions was the same. Ask them if speed indicates how fast and/or where something is going. Have them explain how they would describe where something is going.

TYING TO PREVIOUS

KNOWLEDGE: Have a student explain the phrase "stepping on the gas." Relate the function of the accelerator and the motion of a car.

VideoDisc

STVS: Sand Blasting with Dry Ice, Disc 2, Side 1

In Your JOURNAL

Speed is only the rate at which we change our position. Velocity includes direction, too. So, going around a curve might violate a velocity limit.

2 TEACH

Key Concepts are highlighted.

CONCEPT DEVELOPMENT
▶ Ask students to give ways of describing direction, such as uphill, downhill, right, left, or compass points.

Connect to...
Earth Science

Answer: Earth speeds up as it approaches the sun, slows down as it moves away, and changes direction as it orbits.

MINI-Lab
Materials: stopwatches, metersticks, marbles, 1/4 inch hardboard (10 cm by 50 cm to 100 cm)
▶ Arrange students in small groups.
▶ Show the students how to make velocity-time graphs. Point out that the slope of the graph indicates acceleration.
▶ **Answer:** The acceleration does not significantly change as long as the ramp is at the same angle, but the velocity increases with time.

MINI-Lab
ASSESSMENT
Oral: Ask students to describe how the results of this MINI-Lab compare to their own experiences with slides.

PROGRAM RESOURCES
From the **Teacher Resource Package** use:

Activity Worksheets, page 28, MINI-Lab: Does greater velocity require greater acceleration?

Use **Laboratory Manual 4,** Speed and Acceleration.

Connect to...
Earth Science

Describe at least two ways Earth accelerates as it moves around the sun.

MINI-Lab
Does greater velocity require greater acceleration?
Make a ramp by propping a board on a textbook. Let a marble roll down the ramp and across a hard, flat surface. Make two time measurements: travel time of the marble down the ramp and travel time of the marble across the flat surface for a distance of 1 m from the bottom of the ramp. *Calculate* the marble's velocity across the flat surface. Change the starting point of the marble on the ramp and repeat the procedure. Does acceleration change? Does velocity change?

---

floor. The car leaps forward and builds up speed, moving faster and faster until it crosses the finish line. Then the driver releases a drag chute, and the car rapidly slows down and comes to a stop. All the while the car gains speed, it is accelerating. Strange as it may seem, the car is also accelerating as it slows down! How is this possible?

Acceleration is the rate of change of velocity. Because velocity includes both speed and direction, if either value changes, velocity will change. So, acceleration is both the rate of change in velocity and the direction of that change. For example, if a car goes around a curve, its direction changes. So even if its speed remains constant, the velocity of the car changes. In other words, acceleration occurs through a change in direction.

If an object travels in a straight line and the directions of acceleration and velocity occur along the same line, as with the dragster, then acceleration is just the rate of change of speed. If the acceleration is in the same direction as the velocity, then the dragster *speeds up*. If they are in opposite directions, then the dragster *slows down*.

The amount of acceleration depends on both the change in velocity and the time interval. The *time interval* is the amount of time that passed while the change in velocity was taking place. The acceleration will be large, if the change in velocity is large. Acceleration will also be large if the change in velocity occurs in a small time interval.

To calculate average acceleration, divide the change in velocity by the time interval. To find the *change in velocity*, subtract the initial velocity (starting velocity) from the final velocity.

$$a = \frac{v_f - v_i}{t} = \frac{\Delta v}{t}$$

The symbol Δ is the Greek letter *delta* and stands for "change in."

When calculating acceleration, be sure to include all proper units and algebraic signs. The unit for velocity is meters/second (m/s) and the unit for time is seconds (s). Thus, the unit for acceleration is

$$\frac{meters/second}{second}.$$

This unit is usually written as m/s^2 and is read as "meters per second squared" or "meters per second per second."

OPTIONS

Meeting Different Ability Levels
For Section 3-2, use the following **Teacher Resource Masters** depending upon individual students' needs.
◆ **Study Guide Master** for all students.
● **Reinforcement Master** for students of average and above average ability levels.
▲ **Enrichment Master** for above average students.
Additional Teacher Resource Package masters are listed in any PROGRAM RESOURCES boxes that are in the section. The additional masters are appropriate for all students.

◆ **STUDY GUIDE** 14

STUDY GUIDE | Chapter 3
Velocity and Acceleration | Text Pages 65–67

Use the terms below to fill in the blanks.

acceleration	direction	meters per second squared (m/s²)	slowing down
$a = \frac{v_f - v_i}{t} = \frac{\Delta v}{t}$	divide	meters per second (m/s)	subtract
	increasing speed	positive	time interval
	negative	seconds(s)	velocity
change			

Speed is the rate of motion of an object. _____**Velocity**_____ describes an object's speed and direction. The velocity of an object can _____**change**_____ even if the speed of the object remain constant. This would occur if the _____**direction**_____ of the object's motion changes.

The rate of change of velocity is called _____**acceleration**_____. The size of an acceleration depends on both the change in velocity and the _____**time interval**_____ of the change.

To calculate acceleration, _____**divide**_____ the change in velocity by the time interval. To find the change in velocity, _____**subtract**_____ the initial velocity (v) from the final velocity (v). The equation for acceleration is $a = \frac{v_f - v_i}{t} = \frac{\Delta v}{t}$. Final velocity will be less than initial velocity if an object is _____**slowing down**_____ and acceleration will have a _____**negative**_____ value. Final velocity will be greater than initial velocity if an object is _____**increasing speed**_____ and acceleration will have a _____**positive**_____ value.

The units for velocity are _____**meters per second (m/s)**_____. The units for time is _____**seconds (s)**_____. Therefore, the units for acceleration are _____**meters per second squared (m/s²)**_____.

Copyright Glencoe Division of Macmillan/McGraw-Hill
Users of Merrill Physical Science have the publisher's permission to reproduce this page.

14

EXAMPLE PROBLEM: Calculating Acceleration

Problem Statement:

A car's velocity changes from 0 m/s to 60 m/s 10 seconds later. Calculate the car's average acceleration.

Known Information:

Strategy Hint: Figure velocity change by subtracting initial velocity from final velocity.

initial velocity, v_i, = 0 m/s
final velocity, v_f, = 60 m/s
time interval, t, = 10 s

Unknown Information:

Acceleration, a

Equation to Use:

$$a = \frac{v_f - v_i}{t}$$

Solution:

$$a = \frac{v_f - v_i}{t} = \frac{60 \text{ m/s} - 0 \text{ m/s}}{10 \text{ s}} = 6 \text{ m/s}^2$$

PRACTICE PROBLEM

Strategy Hint: Find the change in velocity by subtracting initial velocity from final velocity.

1. At the top of its highest hill, a roller coaster's speed is 10 m/s. Three seconds later, it reaches a speed of 32 m/s just before it gets to the bottom. What was its acceleration?

SECTION REVIEW

1. One jet plane is flying east at 880 km/h, and another plane is traveling north at 880 km/h. Do they have the same velocities? The same speeds? Explain your answers.
2. Near the end of a daily swim, a swimmer pushes to swim faster and increases from 1.1 m/s to 1.3 m/s during the last 20 s of his workout. What is his acceleration during this interval?
3. **Apply:** Describe three different ways to change your velocity when you're riding a bicycle.
4. **Connect to Chemistry:** Rates are a way to describe changes during chemical reactions. What is a rate? Compare the equations for speed and acceleration to see what many rates have in common.

☑ Making and Using Graphs

Decide whether you should use a line graph, a bar graph, or a pie graph to show how velocity changes over time. Explain your choice. Show how you would set up the graph. If you need help, refer to Making and Using Graphs in the **Skill Handbook** on page 687.

67

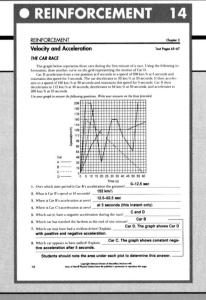

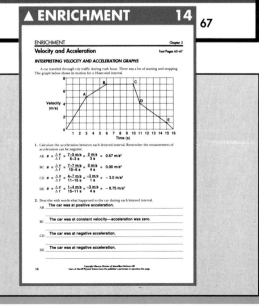

CHECK FOR UNDERSTANDING

Use the Mini Quiz to check for understanding.

MINI QUIZ

Use the Mini Quiz to check students' recall of chapter content.

1 **What is velocity?** *both speed and direction*

2 **What is acceleration?** *rate of change of velocity*

3 **What is the unit of acceleration?** *m/s^2*

RETEACH

Repeat the Demonstration found in the Motivation of Section 3-1.

EXTENSION

For students who have mastered this section, use the **Reinforcement** and **Enrichment** masters or other OPTIONS provided.

3 CLOSE

▶ Ask questions 1-2 and the **Apply** and **Connect to Chemistry** questions in the Section Review.

SECTION REVIEW ANSWERS

1. No, they are traveling in different directions; the speeds are the same; they will travel the same distance in the same amount of time.

2. 0.01 m/s^2

3. Apply: Answers may include: apply brakes, pedal faster, change directions, etc. Accept all reasonable responses.

4. Connect to Chemistry: Both show changes divided by time.

Skill Builder

ASSESSMENT

Performance: Students should select a line graph. Once they have, ask them to describe and then sketch a velocity-time graph for a bicycle ride through a hilly park.

PREPARATION

SECTION BACKGROUND
▶ Inertia is the tendency of an object to resist any change in its motion. It accounts for unbelted car passengers crashing into windshields and backs of seats. This concept will be developed in Section 3-4.

PREPLANNING
▶ Obtain a skateboard, a long ramp, a small piece of clay, several rubber bands, a plastic foam cup, some cotton, paper towels, and four hard-boiled eggs.

1 MOTIVATE

▶ Have students discuss commercials that advocate seat belt use.

2 TEACH

Key Concepts are highlighted.

CONCEPT DEVELOPMENT
▶ Emphasize that wearing seat belts increases the stopping time and spreads the force over a larger area.

Connect to...
Life Science

Answers will vary. Take a class poll and model the calculation of percent.

 **SCIENCE & SOCIETY** **3-3 Crashing to Save Lives**

In Your JOURNAL

In your Journal, make a list of safety features you can identify in a typical modern car. Be sure to look both on the inside and outside of the car.

Connect to...
Life Science

Psychologists use surveys to study behaviors in groups of people. Survey at least 10 people by asking each one "Do you Always, Usually, Seldom, or Never use seat belts?" Find the percent in each category.

Objectives
▶ Evaluate the effects of wearing seat belts during a car crash.
▶ Form an opinion about whether laws should make people wear seat belts.

Studying Crashes

How would you like to develop and perfect something that could save thousands of lives every year and keep hundreds of thousands of other people from being hurt? That's what scientists are trying to do with experiments called crash tests. In crash tests, researchers put lifelike dummies in cars, then crash the cars into each other or into concrete walls. Sometimes the dummies are placed on a sledlike device that runs on tracks. As cameras and other instruments record the process, the sled accelerates, then stops suddenly.

By studying the results of crash tests and real car collisions, scientists have learned what happens to people in accidents and how some injuries and deaths can be prevented.

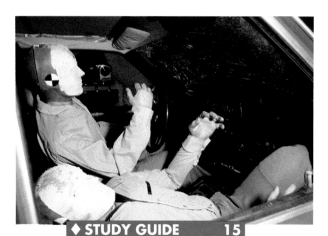

OPTIONS

Meeting Different Ability Levels

For Section 3-3, use the following **Teacher Resource Masters** depending upon individual students' needs.

◆ **Study Guide Master** for all students.
● **Reinforcement Master** for students of average and above average ability levels.
▲ **Enrichment Master** for above average students.

Additional Teacher Resource Package masters are listed in any PROGRAM RESOURCES boxes that are in the section. The additional masters are appropriate for all students.

◆ **STUDY GUIDE** 15

STUDY GUIDE   Chapter 3
Crashing to Save Lives   Text Pages 68-69

Listed below are statements that either agree with the textbook or don't agree with the textbook. If the statement does agree, place a (✓) to the left of the statement. If the statement doesn't agree, rewrite it so it will agree with the textbook. Underline the words you change.

✓ 1. Researchers put lifelike dummies in cars for crash tests.

2. When a car traveling about 50 km/h collides head-on with something solid, the car begins to expand and speed up. **When a car traveling about 50 km/h collides head-on with something solid, the car begins to crumple and slow down.**

3. Within 0.1 second after a car crash, any passenger not wearing a seat belt continues to move forward at the same speed the car was traveling. **Within 0.1 second after a car crash, the car stops but because of inertia, any passenger not wearing a seat belt continues to move forward at the same speed the car was traveling.**

✓ 4. By studying the results of crash tests and real car collisions, scientists have learned what happens to people in auto accidents.

✓ 5. A person in a car wearing a seat belt becomes "part" of the car.

6. The force needed to slow a person down from 50 km/h to zero in 0.1 second is equal to 2 times that person's height. **The force needed to slow a person down from 50 km/h to zero in 0.1 second is equal to 14 times that person's weight.**

7. A seat belt not only holds a person in place, but it also helps deflect and concentrate some of the force of the crash. **A seat belt not only holds a person in place, but it also helps absorb and spread out some of the force of the crash.**

Copyright Glencoe Division of Macmillan/McGraw-Hill
Users of Merrill Physical Science have the publisher's permission to reproduce this page. 15

When a car traveling about 50 km/h collides head-on with something solid, the car crumples, slows down, and stops within 0.1 second. Any passenger not wearing a seat belt continues to move forward at the same speed the car was traveling.

Within 0.02 second (one-fiftieth of a second) after the car stops, the unbelted person slams into the windshield, dashboard, or steering wheel. Backseat passengers slam into the backs of the front seats at a speed of 50 km/h—the same speed they would reach falling from a three-story building.

A person wearing a seat belt becomes "part" of the car and slows down when the car slows down. The force needed to slow a person from 50 km/h to zero in 0.1 second is equal to 14 times that person's weight. The belt not only holds the person in place, it also "gives," increasing the time it takes for the person to come to rest and spreading out the force so it's not concentrated on one part of the body.

SECTION REVIEW

1. Describe what happens to a person who's not wearing a seat belt during a car crash.
2. Describe how seat belts protect passengers and drivers during accidents.
3. **Connect to Life Science:** Even while saving a person's life, the force exerted by a seat belt during a crash can cause serious injuries. What parts of the body are most likely to be injured? Explain.

You Decide!

Safety experts say that about half the people who die in car crashes would survive if they wore seat belts. Most states have passed laws requiring drivers and front seat passengers to wear seat belts. But some resent the laws. They think everyone should be free to decide whether or not to use seat belts. Some feel the same way about laws requiring motorcycle riders to wear helmets. Should laws require people to wear seat belts or helmets?

SCIENCE & SOCIETY

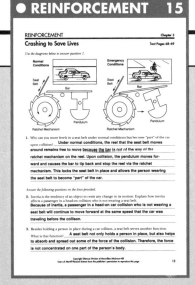

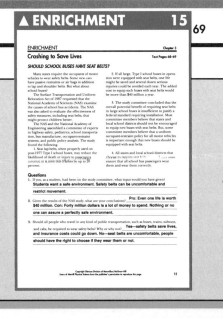

69

● REINFORCEMENT 15   ▲ ENRICHMENT 15

CHECK FOR UNDERSTANDING
▶ Ask questions 1-2 and the **Connect to Life Science** question in the Section Review.

RETEACH

Demonstration: Attach a hard-boiled egg to the middle of a skateboard with a small bit of clay. Starting about 2 m from a wall, thrust the skateboard toward the wall. Attach another hard-boiled egg to the skateboard with several rubber bands and repeat. Have students compare the effects of the crashes on both eggs.

EXTENSION

For students who have mastered this section, use the **Reinforcement** and **Enrichment** masters or other OPTIONS provided.

3 CLOSE

? FLEX Your Brain

Use the Flex Your Brain activity to have students explore REQUIRING SEAT BELTS IN SCHOOL BUSES.

ASSESSMENT

Portfolio: Use the Flex Your Brain activity to reinforce critical-thinking and problem-solving skills. In Step 2, students might list how fast school buses travel, how seats are designed, or how many people are on the bus.

PROGRAM RESOURCES

From the **Teacher Resource Package** use:

Activity Worksheets, page 5, Flex Your Brain.

SECTION REVIEW ANSWERS

1. A person not wearing a seat belt in a crash continues to move forward after the car stops and collides with the inside of the car.
2. The belt stops the wearer with the car.
3. **Connect to Life Science:** Accept all reasonable answers. Often ribs are cracked; and the lungs, the spleen, and the liver can be damaged.

3-4 Force and Motion

PREPARATION

SECTION BACKGROUND

▶ Quantities that require a direction to fully describe them, such as velocity and acceleration, are called *vectors*. Vectors are represented by small arrows.

MULTICULTURAL PERSPECTIVE

Although the law of inertia is called Newton's first law, Galileo is credited for formulating it. However, inertia was described in Chinese literature more than two thousand years ago.

PREPLANNING

▶ If you intend to conduct the Cooperative Learning activity in the Motivation section, obtain two straws and a table tennis ball for each Problem Solving Team.

▶ Obtain two empty, glass soda bottles and some dried beans if conducting the Demonstration on page 73.

1 MOTIVATE

Cooperative Learning: Assign Problem Solving Teams. Give each team two soda straws and a table tennis ball. Have each team select two experimenters who must start the ball moving on the desk top, keep it moving for a minute, and stop it by blowing through straws. Have each team make and record observations of how the motion of the ball changed and what caused the changes. Have teams report and discuss their observations.

▶ Have volunteers describe their experiences with various amusement park rides using the terms *constant velocity*, *acceleration*, and *deceleration*. Ask them if they had more fun when they were moving with constant velocities or with accelerations. Have them recall if the exciting part of the ride was the feeling that they were falling or being pushed or pulled.

3-4 Force and Motion

New Science Words

force
balanced forces
net force
inertia
friction

Objectives

▶ Recognize different kinds of forces.
▶ Identify cause and effect relationships between force and changes in velocity.
▶ Give examples of the effects of inertia.
▶ State Newton's first law of motion.

Figure 3-4. The force exerted by the bat sends the ball flying. How does the force exerted by the ball affect the motion of the bat?

What Is a Force?

Push a door open. Stretch a rubber band. Squeeze a piece of clay. Shove a book across a table. In each case, you are applying a force. A **force** is a push or a pull one body exerts on another. Sometimes the effects of a force are obvious, as when a moving car crashes into a stationary object, such as a tree. Other forces aren't as noticeable. Can you feel the force the floor exerts on your feet?

List all the forces you might exert or encounter in a typical day. Think about pushing, pulling, stretching, squeezing, bending, and falling.

Effects of Forces on Objects

In your list, what happened to the objects that had forces exerted on them? If an object was moving, did the force change the object's velocity? Think of a swinging bat meeting a speeding baseball. The ball's velocity certainly changes.

Force does not always change velocity. Think about a game of tug-of-war with your dog. You plant your feet firmly and lean back to push against the ground, causing the ground to push back on you. Your dog does the same. Now consider the forward and backward forces acting on you. If you don't move forward or backward, the force of the dog pulling you forward must be balancing the force of the ground pushing you back. Forces that are equal in size and opposite in direction are called **balanced forces.**

Now what happens if your feet hit a slippery spot on the ground? Your feet slip, and the ground can't exert as much force back you. The forces of the dog pulling

OPTIONS

Meeting Different Ability Levels

For Section 3-4, use the following **Teacher Resource Masters** depending upon individual students' needs.

◆ **Study Guide Master** for all students.
● **Reinforcement Master** for students of average and above average ability levels.
▲ **Enrichment Master** for above average students.

Additional Teacher Resource Package masters are listed in any PROGRAM RESOURCES boxes that are in the section. The additional masters are appropriate for all students.

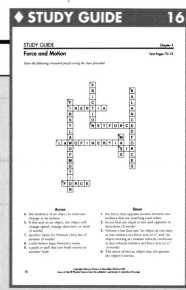

◆ **STUDY GUIDE** 16

STUDY GUIDE · Chapter 3
Force and Motion · Text Pages 70–74

Solve the following crossword puzzle using the clues provided.

Across

4. the tendency of an object to resist any change in its motion
5. If this acts on an object, the object will change speed, change direction, or both. (2 words)
7. another name for Newton's first law of motion (3 words)
8. a title before Isaac Newton's name
9. a push or pull that one body exerts on another body

Down

1. the force that opposes motion between two surfaces that are touching each other
2. forces that are equal in size and opposite in directions (2 words)
3. Newton's law that says "an object at rest stays at rest unless a net force acts on it" and "an object moving at constant velocity continues at that velocity unless a net force acts on it." (4 words)
6. The more of this an object has, the greater the object's inertia.

you forward and the ground pushing you back become unbalanced, and there is a net force on you. A **net force** on an object always changes the velocity of the object. When the dog pulls you forward with more force than the ground pushes you back, you accelerate in the direction of the greater force.

Remember that velocity involves both speed and direction. A net force acting on an object will change its speed, direction, or both. In the tug-of-war, the net force on you causes both your speed and direction to change.

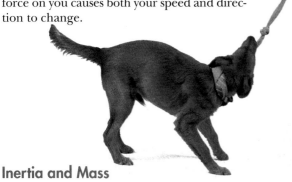

Inertia and Mass

Picture a hockey puck sliding across the ice. Its velocity hardly changes until it hits something, such as the wall, net, or another stick. The velocity of the puck is constant, and its acceleration is zero until it hits something that alters its speed or direction.

The sliding puck demonstrates the property of inertia. **Inertia** (in UR shuh) is the tendency of an object to resist any change in its motion. If an object is moving, it tends to keep moving at the same speed and in the same direction unless a force acts on it. In other words, the velocity of the object remains constant unless a force changes it. If an object is at rest, it tends to remain at rest. Its velocity is zero unless a force makes it move.

Would you expect that a bowling ball would have the same inertia as a table tennis ball? Why would there be a difference? The more mass an object has, the greater its inertia. Recall that mass is the amount of matter in an object, and a bowling ball certainly contains more matter than a table tennis ball. So the bowling ball would have greater inertia than the table tennis ball.

In Your JOURNAL

Inertia plays an important role in most sports. **In your Journal,** write a paragraph describing the role of inertia in your favorite sport.

Science and READING

Before a runner is given credit for a record in track, officials carefully analyze the conditions under which the event was held. What are some of the factors they consider?

OBJECTIVES AND SCIENCE WORDS: Have students review the objectives and science words to become familiar with this section.

2 TEACH

Key Concepts are highlighted.

CONCEPT DEVELOPMENT

▶ Have students classify the forces on their lists into pulls or pushes and have volunteers sketch situations on the chalkboard. Have them label what was being pulled or pushed and what was doing the pulling or pushing.

▶ Introduce visualizing forces as arrows. Sketch two arrows representing the force needed to lift a book and a TV. Explain that the length of the arrow indicates the size of the force. The direction of the arrow indicates the direction of the force. Encourage volunteers to try to sketch arrows to represent the forces in their lists.

▶ Have students make a class list of highway design and traffic features that exist to accommodate inertia (e.g., banked curves, reduced speed limits for curves, guard rails, etc.).

VideoDisc

STVS: Safer Roads, Disc 1, Side 1

For more information on air bags in automobiles, see "Air Bags vs. Seat Belts: Why You Should Care" by Henry, Ed, and Sherri Miller, *Changing Times*, March 1988, pp. 67-70.

Think Critically: An air bag offers little or no protection against a side impact, second impact, or rollover, or if the passengers aren't using seat belts.

TEACHER F.Y.I.

▶ The general study of motion in physics is called *mechanics*. Mechanics is further subdivided into two areas of study. *Kinematics* is the study of the relationships among the quantities which describe motion, such as position, time, velocity, and acceleration. The equations of average speed and acceleration are examples of kinematic equations. *Dynamics* is the quantitative study of the causes of motion.

Connect to...
Earth Science

As Earth rotates, different areas of water are closest to the moon and are pulled more strongly by the moon's gravity. This causes a net force on the ocean's water, and the water flows in that direction.

Inertia Sponges

Seat belts are designed to reduce the effect of inertia in a crash by holding the passengers in place. However, in a high-speed crash, belts provide limited protection to the head and upper body. These parts of the body can be protected by air bags, which provide an instantaneous cushion for the head and upper body at the time of impact.

Air bags are designed to be used in addition to seat belts. An air-bag system consists of one or more crash sensors, an ignitor and gas generator, and an inflatable nylon bag. The nylon bag for the driver is stored in the steering wheel, and the bag for the front-seat passenger is inside the dashboard. If a car hits something with sufficient force (speeds in excess of from 15 to 20 kilometers per hour), impact sensors trigger the flow of electric current to an ignitor. The ignitor causes a chemical reaction to occur, producing harmless nitrogen gas. The nitrogen gas pushes the air bag from its storage compartment just in time to absorb the inertia of the occupants. The bag then immediately deflates so that it will not interfere with the driver.

Think Critically: Under what crash conditions would an air bag offer little or no protection?

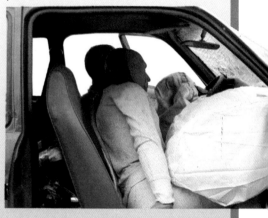

Connect to...
Earth Science

On ocean beaches the water level rises and falls regularly each day. Why doesn't the inertia of the water keep it in the same location? Explain what causes the water to move.

You wouldn't change the velocity of a bowling ball very much by swatting it with a paddle, but you could easily change the velocity of a table tennis ball. Because of its greater inertia, a much greater force would be needed to change the velocity of the bowling ball.

Newton's First Law

Forces change the motion of an object in very specific ways—so specific that Sir Isaac Newton (1642 - 1727) was able to state laws to describe the effects of forces.

Newton's first law of motion says that an object moving at a constant velocity keeps moving at that velocity unless a net force acts on it. If an object is at rest, it stays at rest unless a net force acts on it. Does this sound familiar? It

OPTIONS

ASSESSMENT—ORAL

▶ **What evidence do you have that there is a change in velocity of a ball when you hit it with a bat?** *The speed and direction of the ball both change.*

▶ **What evidence do you have that there is a change in velocity of the bat when you hit a ball?** *The bat slows down a little. You can also feel the change in the motion of the bat.*

PROGRAM RESOURCES

From the **Teacher Resource Package** use:

Cross-Curricular Connections, page 7, Reading Maps.

Science and Society, page 7, Is 65 mph Safe?

is the same as the earlier discussion of inertia. Thus, you'll understand why this law is sometimes called the *law of inertia*. You've probably seen—and felt—this law at work without even knowing it.

Suppose you're pushing a wheelbarrow full of leaves across your yard. Your rake is resting on top of the load. The wheel hits a rock and the wheelbarrow stops suddenly. What would happen to the rake? The rake would probably continue forward and fly out of the wheelbarrow. Why would this happen? No one would have pushed the rake. No net forward force would have acted on it. But because of inertia, the rake would keep moving forward at the same speed. If it wasn't for the rake hitting the ground, it would have kept moving until some other force stopped it.

Friction

You've just learned that inertia causes an object that is moving at constant velocity to keep moving at that velocity unless a net force acts on it. But you know that if you shove a book across a long table, it seems to slow down and stop by itself. You don't see any force acting on the book. Why does it stop?

There is a force between the surfaces of the book and the table. The force is friction. **Friction** is the force that opposes motion between two surfaces that are touching each other. Would you expect more friction between an

Figure 3-5. When the wheelbarrow strikes a rock, it stops suddenly. The rake keeps moving forward at its original speed because of its inertia.

MINI-Lab
Is friction a force?
Place a sheet of plain white paper on a flat surface. Set a 100-g mass on the paper about 7 cm from one end of the paper. Grip the other end of the paper near the edge and give it a quick, smooth yank. What happens to the 100-g mass? Replace the paper with a sheet of coarse sandpaper, rough side up, and repeat the procedure. *Observe* what happens to the 100-g mass. How do you *interpret* the different results? Use Newton's first law to explain your observations.

3-4 FORCE AND MOTION **73**

CHECK FOR UNDERSTANDING

Use the Mini Quiz to check for understanding.

MINI QUIZ

Use the Mini Quiz to check students' recall of chapter content.

1 **What are balanced forces?** *forces equal in size and opposite in direction*

2 **What is inertia?** *the tendency of an object to resist any change in motion*

3 **What is friction?** *the force that opposes motion between two touching surfaces*

RETEACH

Tie a piece of string around a book and suspend it. Cut the string. Point out that before the string was cut, the book was at rest, indicating that there were balanced forces acting on it. After the string was cut, it accelerated, indicating there was a net force acting on it.

EXTENSION

For students who have mastered this section, use the **Reinforcement** and **Enrichment** masters or other OPTIONS.

3 CLOSE

▶ Have students explain why some people may feel they are falling forward when they step off an escalator.

▶ Ask questions 1-2 and the **Apply** and **Connect to Chemistry** questions in the Section Review.

SECTION REVIEW ANSWERS

1. The rosin reduces the chances of the dancer slipping.

2. The jet airplane; inertia is related to mass, not speed.

3. Apply: Some possible answers are catching a football, sliding into a base, diving from a diving board.

4. Connect to Chemistry: The creams and gels reduce the friction as the razor is dragged over the skin.

Skill Builder
ASSESSMENT
Performance: Use this Skill Builder to make sure students can select main topics and support each topic with specific details.

Figure 3-6. How is friction helping this ballerina?

oily floor and a slick, leather shoe sole or between a rough sidewalk and the bottom of a tennis shoe? The amount of friction depends on two factors—the kinds of surfaces and the force pressing the surfaces together.

If there were no friction, your life would be much different. You wouldn't be able to walk or hold things between your fingers. Your shoes would fall off. Friction between the soles of your shoes and the floor makes it possible for you to walk. You can hold something with your fingers because of friction. Shoelaces remain tied because of friction.

As you complete this section, you should be more aware of the importance of force and motion. They are part of everything you do and everything that happens around you. A force—gravity—keeps you on the ground. Muscles in your body exert forces that move your arms and legs and eyes. Friction makes it possible for you to walk and to turn the pages of this book. And these are but a few examples of how force and motion affect your life.

SECTION REVIEW

1. Before dancing on a smooth wooden floor, ballet dancers sometimes put a sticky powder called rosin on their shoe soles. Why? What force are they taking advantage of?
2. Explain which has greater inertia, a speeding car or a jet airplane sitting on a runway.
3. **Apply:** Think of and describe three examples from sports in which a force changes the velocity of an object or a person.
4. **Connect to Chemistry:** Using concepts from this section, explain why shaving gels and creams make shaving more comfortable.

Skill Builder

☑ Outlining

In an outline, organize all of the information you have learned relating to inertia and Newton's first law of motion. If you need help, refer to Outlining in the **Skill Handbook** on page 677.

Skill Builder

I. Inertia
   1. The tendency of an object to resist any change in motion
      a. proportional to mass
      b. proportional to force needed to overcome it

II. Newton's First Law
   1. An object moving at a constant velocity keeps moving at that velocity unless a net force acts upon it.
      a. The force needed to change an object's velocity depends on its inertia.

Effects of Gravity

Objectives

▶ Give examples of the effects of gravity.
▶ Examine how gravitational force is related to mass and distance.
▶ Distinguish between mass and weight.

New Science Words

gravity
weight

Gravitational Force

An Olympic diver is poised high above the water on a diving platform. The diver bounces up in the air and then hurtles toward the water. Did you ever wonder why the diver plunges downward instead of flying off into space? Probably not. Seeing objects fall is a very common experience. You may not have thought about it, but you've been watching the force of gravity at work.

Every object in the universe exerts a force on every other object. That force is **gravity.** Often, the force is too slight to notice. For example, there's a gravitational force of attraction between your hand and your notebook, but when you let go of your notebook, it doesn't stay in your hand. The force is too small.

The amount of gravitational force between objects depends on two things—their masses and the distance between them. The masses of your hand and your notebook are quite small, so the force of attraction between them is weak. The mass of the Earth is very large, so its gravitational force is strong.

The amount of force due to Earth's gravity acting on an orbiting satellite depends on its distance from Earth. The closer it is to Earth, the stronger the pull of gravity. The farther away it is, the less effect gravity has on it.

Weight

The measure of the force of gravity on an object is the object's weight. The term **weight** is most often used in reference to the gravitational force between Earth and a body at Earth's surface. Weight isn't the same as mass, but the

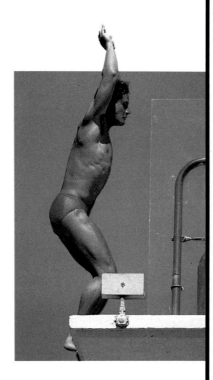

3-5   EFFECTS OF GRAVITY   **75**

SECTION 3-5

PREPARATION

SECTION BACKGROUND

▶ Newton was the first to describe the gravitational force between two objects quantitatively. The force is directly proportional to the product of the two masses and inversely proportional to the square of the distance between their centers. This indicates that if the distance between two objects is doubled, the force between them will fall to one-quarter of the value it was before the objects were moved.

1 MOTIVATE

TYING TO PREVIOUS KNOWLEDGE: Have the students recall balanced and net forces from Section 3-4.

2 TEACH

Key Concepts are highlighted.

CONCEPT DEVELOPMENT

▶ A satellite must travel faster the closer it is to Earth because the gravitational force is stronger. Inertia causes the satellite to move in a straight line, but Earth's gravity causes it to fall away from that line.

VideoDisc

STVS: Losing Weight by Design, Disc 2, Side 2

OPTIONS

INQUIRY QUESTIONS

▶ **Why is the word** *weightless* **often used to describe astronauts in outer space, but never the word** *massless?* *Astronauts in outer space are in free fall. This causes them to feel weightless because they cannot feel a reaction force to their weight. Mass is constant, independent of location.*

▶ **What would a 40-N backpack weigh on the moon?** *About 7 N*

▶ **How much force does your body exert on Earth?** *The value of your weight.*

PROGRAM RESOURCES

From the **Teacher Resource Package** use:
Concept Mapping, pages 11–12,
Science Integration Activity 3

▶ In a falling elevator, you would not feel the reaction force under your feet. So, you would feel weightless. Distinguish between free fall and weightlessness.

▶ Discuss the difference between mass and weight. Point out that an object has mass in and by itself. However, there must be *another* object for it to have weight.

 PROBLEM SOLVING

Its mass would stay the same.
Think Critically: The astronauts' masses could change if they ate more or less than normal or if their activity patterns changed.

CHECK FOR UNDERSTANDING

Use the Mini Quiz to check for understanding.

MINI QUIZ

Use the Mini Quiz to check students' recall of chapter content.

① **What is the force of gravity?** *the force that every object exerts on every other object*
② **What is weight?** *the measure of the force of gravity on an object*
③ **Weight is measured in what units?** *newtons*
④ **What instrument is used to measure weight?** *a scale*

 **Connect to...**
Life Science

Problems may include pooling of blood, atrophy of muscle tissue, or loss of bone strength.

 **PROBLEM SOLVING**

An Experiment for the Shuttle

NASA was having a competition to select several student experiments for scientists to conduct while the shuttle orbited Earth. Ellen decided to enter an experiment about how the time spent on a shuttle flight would affect the masses of the astronauts. The mass of each astronaut would be determined before and after the mission. During the flight, the astronauts would have to list the foods they ate and the liquids they drank and the masses of each. Ellen's experiment required that the masses of the food and liquid packets be measured and labeled to the nearest 0.01 gram.

How would the mass of any material on Earth compare with its mass during the shuttle mission?
Think Critically: What factors could cause changes in the astronauts' masses?

 **Connect to...**
Life Science

Astronauts who spend extended time in reduced gravity may suffer unique health problems. Find out what some of these problems are.

two are related. Recall from Chapter 2 that mass is the amount of matter in an object. The greater an object's mass, the stronger the gravitational force on it. In other words, the more mass an object has, the more it weighs.

Mass is measured in grams (g) and kilograms (kg). Weight, which is a force, is measured in units called newtons (N). A kilogram of mass on Earth's surface weighs 9.8 N. On Earth, a tape cassette weighs about 0.5 N, a backpack full of books weighs about 40 N, you probably weigh 450 to 750 N, and a wide-bodied jumbo jet weighs about 3.4 million N.

The gravitational force an object exerts on other objects is related to its mass. Earth exerts a stronger gravitational force than the moon, because Earth has more mass. Because of the moon's weaker gravitational force, a person weighing about 480 N on Earth would weigh only about 80 N on the moon. Does this mean that the person would have less mass on the moon than on Earth? No. Unlike weight, mass doesn't change with changes in gravity. Because mass remains constant, the person would have the same inertia on the moon as on Earth.

OPTIONS

Meeting Different Ability Levels

For Section 3-5, use the following **Teacher Resource Masters** depending upon individual students' needs.

◆ **Study Guide Master** for all students.
● **Reinforcement Master** for students of average and above average ability levels.
▲ **Enrichment Master** for above average students.

Additional Teacher Resource Package masters are listed in any PROGRAM RESOURCES boxes that are in the section. The additional masters are appropriate for all students.

◆ **STUDY GUIDE** 17

STUDY GUIDE | Chapter 3
Effects of Gravity | Text Pages 75–78

In the blank at the left, write the letter of the term that correctly completes each statement.

b 1. Every object in the universe exerts a force on every other object. This force is called ____.
   a. friction   b. gravity

a 2. The measure of the force of gravity on an object is the object's ____.
   a. weight   b. inertia

a 3. The amount of gravitational force between two objects depends on their ____.
   a. color and density   b. mass and distance

a 4. Weight is measured in units called ____.
   a. Newtons   b. seconds

a 5. The greater an object's ____, the stronger the gravitational force on it.
   a. mass   b. velocity

b 6. Mass is measured in units called ____.
   a. meters and kilometers
   b. grams and kilograms

b 7. A scale uses the principle of ____ to measure how much something weighs.
   a. acceleration   b. balanced forces

b 8. Earth exerts a stronger gravitational force than the moon because ____ has more mass.
   a. the moon   b. Earth

b 9. The masses of your hand and your notebook are quite small, so the force of attraction between them is ____.
   a. strong   b. weak

b 10. An object transported from the surface of Earth to the surface of the moon has its weight ____.
   a. increased   b. decreased

a 11. ____ doesn't change with changes in gravity.
   a. Mass   b. Weight

a 12. The ____ mass an object has, the more that object weighs.
   a. more   b. less

b 13. On Earth gravity exerts a(n) ____ force on your body.
   a. upward   b. downward

Copyright Glencoe Division of Macmillan/McGraw-Hill
Users of *Merrill Physical Science* have the publisher's permission to reproduce this page.   17

Measuring Forces

Scales use the principle of balanced forces to measure how much something weighs. To see the principle work, hang a rubber band from a hook or a nail. Then attach something heavy to the lower end of the rubber band and see how much the band stretches. If you attach something even heavier, will the band stretch more? Yes, because the length of the rubber band is a measure of the force on it. The band stretches until it is exerting an upward force equal to the weight of the object hung.

A scale works something like the rubber band. When you step on a bathroom scale, the force of your body stretches a spring inside the scale. The stretched spring pulls on levers, as shown in Figure 3-7, until the upward force of the scale equals the downward force of your weight. The dial on the scale, which is marked off in units of weight, moves until the spring stops stretching. The number showing on the dial indicates your weight.

Gravity, like friction, is a force we tend to take for granted, even though it affects everything we do. Try to imagine living on a planet where the force of gravity was only half as great as Earth's. How would your life be different?

Figure 3-7. When you step on a bathroom scale, the downward force of gravity—your weight— is balanced by the upward force exerted by the spring.

SECTION REVIEW

1. Arriving on a newly discovered, Earth-sized planet, you find that you weigh one-third as much as on Earth. Is the planet's mass greater or less than Earth's?
2. Why don't you feel the gravitational force between your hand and a pencil? What do you feel?
3. **Apply:** Use Newton's first law and the concept of gravity to explain how a satellite orbits Earth.
4. **Connect to Life Science:** Your weight affects your health. But, is weighing 500 N good or bad for you? Use your weight in pounds to answer that question by converting your weight to Newtons. 1 N = 0.22 pounds.

In Your JOURNAL

In your Journal, write a short story describing what a sporting event or other activity would be like if the gravitational force were half as strong.

☑ Observing and Inferring

Select three objects in the room and, without touching them, try to guess which weighs the most. What clues help you to make your guesses? How can you tell if you guessed right? If you need help, refer to Observing and Inferring in the **Skill Handbook** on page 678.

Skill Builder

RETEACH

Have students find the mass and weight of a book.

EXTENSION

For students who have mastered this section, use the **Reinforcement** and **Enrichment** masters or other OPTIONS provided.

3 CLOSE

▶ Invite someone from the Department of Weights and Measures to discuss the department's responsibilities and to demonstrate how to validate commercial scales.

▶ Ask questions 1-2 and the **Apply** and **Connect to Life Science** questions in the Section Review.

SECTION REVIEW ANSWERS

1. The mass is less.
2. The masses are small and the gravitational forces weak. They feel the gravitational attraction between the pencil and Earth.
3. Apply: Inertia makes the satellite move in a straight line. Gravity acts to pull it toward Earth.
4. Connect to Life Science: Model conversion from pounds to Newtons. Accept all reasonable answers as to whether 500 N is a good weight.

Skill Builder

Students might infer that larger objects are heavier. They might also consider the density of the object. They can find out by weighing each object.

Skill Builder
ASSESSMENT

Oral: Check the understanding of mass and weight by asking students how the mass and weight of the three objects would change on the moon. Mass would not. The weight would be 1/6 of the value on Earth.

OBJECTIVE: Apply knowledge of gravitational force to the investigation of a physical property.

PROCESS SKILLS applied in this activity:
▶ **Measuring** in Procedure Step 4.
▶ **Experimenting** in Conclude and Apply Questions 3 and 4.

COOPERATIVE LEARNING
Use the Science Investigation strategy and divide the class into teams of three students. Provide each team with a different type of paper to start. Conclude the lab by having teams share data and observations.

TEACHING THE ACTIVITY
Troubleshooting: Prior to class, prepare and label paper strips and put handles on cups.
▶ If sand is poured too rapidly, the paper may give way suddenly and cause spills.
▶ When paper starts to tear it will continue without significant addition of force.
▶ The acceleration of gravity number could be rounded off to 10 to make math easier.
▶ Students should be allowed to practice on two or three paper strips.
▶ Teams can be expected to measure the strength of two or three types of paper each.

ACTIVITY 3-2 Balancing Forces Against Gravity

Imagine yourself hanging by your arms from a tree branch. Why do you eventually get tired and climb or jump down? When your arms get tired, they can't exert an upward force on your body to balance the force of gravity pulling your body down (your weight). Can you use this example to help you design a plan for comparing the strength of other materials?

Materials
- selection of different types of paper strips
- masking tape
- string
- beaker
- ring stand and ring
- sheets of newspaper
- scissors
- plastic cup
- sand, 250 mL
- balance

Procedure
1. Prepare a data table with the headings "sample," "mass of sand," and "weight of sand."
2. Place the ring stand as shown. Select a paper strip and record its identity in the data table. Cut the strip as shown. Tape one side of the strip to the ring and tape the other side to the cup as shown.
3. Slowly pour sand into the cup. When the paper strip begins to tear, stop pouring.
4. Use the balance to *measure* the combined mass of the cup and sand. *Record* this measurement and return the sand to its container.
5. Repeat Steps 3, 4, and 5 using different paper strips.
6. Using the formula below, *calculate* the weights of the cup and sand for each paper strip tested. Record these weights.

$$\text{Weight} = \frac{\text{mass of sample in g}}{1000 \text{ g/kg}} \times 9.80 \text{ N/kg}$$

Data and Observations   Sample Data

Sample	Mass of Sand (g)	Weight of Sand (N)
a	85	0.83
b	44	0.43
c	82	0.80

78 MOVING OBJECTS

Analyze
1. The ability of a material to resist tearing is called shear strength. What did this investigation show about the shear strengths of different types of paper?
2. Why would it be incorrect to refer to shear strength in grams or kilograms?

Conclude and Apply
3. This investigation tests the shear strength in one direction only. How could you find out if the shear strength depends on the direction in which the paper is torn?
4. Would this investigation work as well if water were used in place of sand?
5. Why is gravity a good choice of force to use for measuring the strength of different materials?

ANSWERS TO QUESTIONS
1. Each kind of paper has its own shear strength. (Some are several times stronger than others.)
2. Kilogram is a mass measurement. Shear strength is resistance to force.
3. Using samples of the same papers, repeat the investigation, tearing the papers at an angle of 90° to the direction tested the first time.
4. Anything that adds weight will work.
5. Gravity is a uniform force. The experiment is repeatable anywhere on Earth.

Activity
ASSESSMENT
Oral: Ask students to explain why it is harder to hang from a tree by one arm as opposed to two.

SUMMARY

3-1: Describing Motion
1. Motion is a change in position of a body. Speed is the rate at which a body changes position.
2. Average speed is the ratio of distance traveled to time and describes motion, even if speed varies.
3. A distance-time graph represents the motion of an object throughout a travel period.

3-2: Velocity and Acceleration
1. Velocity describes the speed and direction of a moving body. A change in velocity may be a change in speed, direction, or both. Acceleration is the rate of change in the velocity.
2. Acceleration is calculated by dividing change in velocity by the time interval involved.

3-3: Science and Society: Crashing to Save Lives
1. Seat belts reduce injuries by spreading out the force over more of the body and allowing the force to act over a slightly longer period of time.
2. Some people believe that seat belts should be required by law, others don't.

3-4: Force and Motion
1. A force is a push or a pull one body exerts on another body. Balanced forces acting on a body do not change the motion of the body. Unbalanced forces result in a net force, which always changes the motion of a body.
2. A net force in the same direction of the velocity increases speed. A net force in the opposite direction of the velocity decreases speed. If the net force is in a different direction, the direction of the velocity will change.
3. Inertia explains why a massive, fast-moving bowling ball is more difficult to stop than a table tennis ball at the same speed.
4. Newton's first law says an object's motion will not change unless a net force acts on it.

3-5: Effects of Gravity
1. Gravity causes planets to orbit the sun and people to remain on Earth's surface.
2. The larger an object's mass, the larger is the gravitational force on that object. The gravitational force between two objects decreases as the distance between them increases.
3. Mass is the amount of matter in an object. Weight is the force of gravity on that mass.

KEY SCIENCE WORDS

a. **acceleration**
b. **average speed**
c. **balanced forces**
d. **constant speed**
e. **force**
f. **friction**
g. **gravity**
h. **inertia**
i. **instantaneous speed**
j. **net force**
k. **speed**
l. **velocity**
m. **weight**

UNDERSTANDING VOCABULARY

Match each phrase with the correct term from the list of Key Science Words.

1. rate of change in position
2. speed that does not change
3. rate of change in velocity
4. a push or pull exerted on an object
5. type of force that changes the motion of an object
6. tendency of an object to resist change in motion
7. a force that opposes motion between surfaces
8. force exerted by every object in the universe on every other object
9. measure of the force of gravity on an object
10. rate of motion at a given point in time

MOVING OBJECTS **79**

SUMMARY

Have students read the summary statements to review the major concepts of the chapter.

UNDERSTANDING VOCABULARY

1. k		6. h	
2. d		7. f	
3. a		8. g	
4. e		9. m	
5. j		10. i	

ASSESSMENT
Portfolio

Encourage students to place in their portfolios one or two items of what they consider to be their best work. For each item, ask students to explain why that item was chosen and what they learned from it. Items might be selected from the following;
- Skill Builder concept map, p. 63
- Flex Your Brain, p. 69
- In Your Journal paragraph, p. 71

Performance

Additional performance assessments may be found in *Performance Assessment* and *Science Integration Activities* that accompany **Merrill Physical Science.** Performance Task Assessment Lists and rubrics for evaluating these activities and other products generated throughout the chapter can be found in Glencoe's *Performance Assessment in Middle School Science.*

OPTIONS

ASSESSMENT
To assess student understanding of material in this chapter, use the resources listed.

COOPERATIVE LEARNING
Consider using cooperative learning in the THINK AND WRITE CRITICALLY, APPLY, and MORE SKILL BUILDERS sections of the Chapter Review.

PROGRAM RESOURCES
From the **Teacher Resource Package** use:
Chapter Review, pages 9-10.
Chapter and Unit Tests, pages 20-23, Chapter Test.

CHAPTER
REVIEW

CHECKING CONCEPTS

1. a		**6.** a	
2. b		**7.** b	
3. b		**8.** c	
4. b		**9.** b	
5. d		**10.** d	

USING LAB SKILLS

ASSESSMENT

Use these alternate lab exercises to assess students' understanding of the skills used in this chapter.

11. The glider would probably have a long, thin design. Some students might experiment with a paper clip weight for stability.

12. Answers will vary according to the materials used.

THINK AND WRITE CRITICALLY

13. An object has moved if its position relative to a reference point has changed. To calculate its speed, you would need to know the distance it moved and the amount of time it took to move that distance. To determine its velocity, you need to know the direction in which it traveled.

14. Any change in the speed and/or direction of a moving object is accelerated motion. So, if the car changes direction by turning a corner, the car is accelerating, even if its speed does not change.

15. Friction only acts when two surfaces are in contact. Gravity acts over distances. The texture of surfaces affects friction, but not gravity.

16. Weight is a measure of the force of gravity on a body. The more mass a body has, the more it will weigh. Mass and weight differ in that the mass of a body never changes due to its position. The weight of a body is not constant; it varies with location. The weight of a body depends upon the distance of the body from Earth.

17. Inertia resists any change in motion. Because of its inertia, a body at rest tends to remain at rest, and a body in motion tends to keep moving in a straight line at a constant velocity.

CHAPTER
REVIEW

CHECKING CONCEPTS

Choose the word or phrase that completes the sentence or answers the question.

1. The best way to describe the rate of motion of an object that changes speed several times is to calculate the object's _____.
 a. average speed   c. instantaneous speed
 b. constant speed   d. variable speed

2. Which of the following is a force?
 a. inertia   c. acceleration
 b. friction   d. velocity

3. The unit for _____ is m/s^2.
 a. weight   c. inertia
 b. acceleration   d. gravity

4. Which of the following is not used in calculating acceleration?
 a. initial velocity   c. time interval
 b. average speed   d. final velocity

5. A body accelerates if it _____.
 a. speeds up   c. changes direction
 b. slows down   d. all of these

6. The gravitational force between two objects depends on their _____.
 a. masses   c. shapes
 b. velocities   d. volume

7. _____ acts between surfaces that are in contact.
 a. Inertia   c. Gravity
 b. Friction   d. A net force

8. An object's weight is directly related to its _____.
 a. volume   c. mass
 b. velocity   d. shape

9. An object of large mass has _____ than an object of small mass.
 a. less inertia   c. less weight
 b. more inertia   d. greater acceleration

10. A constant velocity means acceleration is _____.
 a. positive   c. increasing
 b. negative   d. zero

80 MOVING OBJECTS

USING LAB SKILLS

11. In Activity 3-1 on page 64, you designed an experiment to find out how slowly you could make a glider fly. Redesign your glider to see how fast you can make it fly. What changes would you make? Try it and calculate its speed.

12. Use the procedure in Activity 3-2 on page 78 to test the shear strength of other materials such as aluminum foil, waxed paper, or human hair. Report your findings in a table.

THINK AND WRITE CRITICALLY

Answer the following questions in your Journal using complete sentences.

13. Can you tell an object has moved if you do not see it? What information would you need to calculate the object's speed? Its velocity?

14. Explain how it is possible for an automobile traveling at constant speed to be accelerating.

15. Friction and gravity are both forces. Describe at least two differences between them.

16. Compare and contrast mass and weight.

17. Describe some common effects of inertia.

APPLY

18. How can an object lose weight without losing mass, yet not lose mass without losing weight?

19. A cyclist must travel 800 kilometers. How many days will the trip take if the cyclist travels at an average speed of 16 km/h?

20. A satellite's velocity is 30 000 m/s. After one minute, it is 15 000 m/s. What is the satellite's acceleration?

21. A cyclist leaves home and rides due east for a distance of 45 kilometers. She returns home on the same bike path. If the entire trip takes 4 hours, what is her average speed?

APPLY

18. An object can lose weight simply by changing location—by moving farther from Earth. The mass of the object is not affected. The only way an object can lose mass is for some matter to be removed from it. When this happens, the object also loses weight, because weight depends on mass.

19. Known information: distance = 800 km; speed = 16 km/h
Unknown information: Time in days
Formula to use: $t = d/v$
Solution: t = 800 km/16 km/h
 = 50 h
 = 2 days, 2 hours

20. Known information:
v_i = 30 000 m/s; v_f = 15 000 m/s
time interval = 1 minute or 60 s
Unknown information: acceleration
Formula to use: $a = (v_f - v_i)/t$
Solution:
 a = (15 000 m/s – 30 000 m/s)/60s
 = –250 m/s^2

21. Known information:
distance = 90 km; time = 4 h
Unknown information: average speed
Formula to use: $v = d/t$
Solution: v = 90 km/4 h = 22.5 km/h

80 CHAPTER 3

22. trip west—2.25 h; trip east—1.75 h
$v = 45$ km/1.75 h = 26 km/h east
$v = 45$ km/2.25 h = 20 km/h west

22. The return trip of the cyclist in Question 21 took 30 minutes longer than her trip east, although her total time was still 4 hours. What was her velocity in each direction?

MORE SKILL BUILDERS

If you need help, refer to the Skill Handbook.

1. **Measuring in SI:** Which of the following represents the greatest speed: 20 m/s, 200 cm/s, or 0.2 km/s? HINT: Express all three in meters/second and then compare them.

2. **Observing and Inferring:** A car sits motionless on a hill. What two major forces are acting on the car? Are the forces balanced or unbalanced? Explain how you inferred your answers.

3. **Making and Using Tables:** The four cars shown in the table were traveling at the same speed and the brakes were applied in all four cars at the same instant.

Car	Mass	Stopping Distance
A	1000 kg	80 m
B	1250 kg	100 m
C	1500 kg	120 m
D	2000 kg	160 m

What is the relationship between the mass of a car and its stopping distance? How do you account for this relationship?

4. **Making and Using Graphs:** The following data were obtained for two runners.

SALLY		ALONZO	
Distance	Time	Distance	Time
2 m	1 s	1 m	1 s
4 m	2 s	2 m	2 s
6 m	3 s	2 m	3 s
8 m	4 s	4 m	4 s

Make a distance-time graph that shows the motion of both runners. What is the average speed of each runner? What is the instantaneous speed of each runner 1 second after they start? Which runner stops briefly? During what time interval do Sally and Alonzo run at the same speed?

5. **Making and Using Graphs:** Study this acceleration graph.

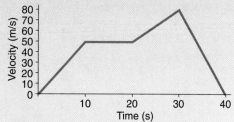

What is the acceleration of the object between 0 seconds and 10 seconds? Between 30 and 40 seconds? When is the object not accelerating? What is its speed during that interval? During what interval does the object have negative acceleration?

PROJECTS

1. Look up the mass of the sun, Earth's moon, and each planet in the solar system. Make a poster to share this information with your classmates. Include some information about conditions on each of the bodies. Speculate what your weight might be on each of the planets if they were the same size as Earth. Discuss how conditions might affect the motion of objects on and near the surface of each planet.

2. Write a letter to your state representative explaining your position on whether or not there should be a law requiring the use of seat belts in cars. Be sure to use scientific facts to support your position.

5. **Making and Using Graphs:** acceleration between 0 s and 10 s =
$$a = \frac{v_f - v_i}{t} = \frac{50 \text{ m/s} - 0 \text{ m/s}}{10 \text{ s}} = \frac{50 \text{ m/s}}{10 \text{ s}}$$
$$= 5 \text{ m/s}^2$$
acceleration between 30 s and 40 s =
$$a = \frac{v_f - v_i}{t} = \frac{0 \text{ m/s} - 80 \text{ m/s}}{10 \text{ s}} = \frac{-80 \text{ m/s}}{10 \text{ s}}$$
$$= -8 \text{ m/s}^2$$

The object is not accelerating between 10 s and 20 s. Its velocity is constant at 50 m/s. The object has negative acceleration between 30 s and 40 s.

MORE SKILL BUILDERS

1. **Measuring in SI:** In meters/second, the three speeds are: 20 m/s, 2 m/s, and 200 m/s. The third speed—0.2 km/s—represents the greatest speed.

2. **Observing and Inferring:** The two major forces acting on the car are gravity and friction. Gravity tends to pull the car down the hill, friction of the hand brake tends to prevent the car from rolling down the hill. Since the car is at rest, there is no net force acting on it. Thus, the logical inference is that the force tending to pull the car down the hill is exactly balanced by the force of friction.

3. **Making and Using Tables:** The greater the mass of the car, the greater its stopping distance. The greater the mass of the car, the greater its inertia, and therefore, the more difficult it will be to change the motion of the car and bring it to rest. Assuming equal braking force is applied to each car, the most massive car, D, will take the greatest amount of time to come to rest, and will therefore travel the greatest distance.

4. **Making and Using Graphs:**

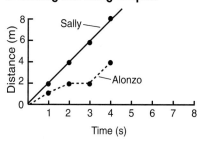

Average speed:
Sally, 8 m/4 s = 2 m/s
Alonzo, 4 m/4 s = 1 m/s
Instantaneous speed:
Sally, 2 m/1 s = 2 m/s
Alonzo, 1 m/1 s = 1 m/s
Alonzo stops briefly after 2 seconds for a 1-s period. Between 3 and 4 seconds the two runners have the same speed, 2 m/s. This can be seen by noting the identical slopes of the graphs during this interval, or it can be calculated by noting the distance traveled by each runner during that period.

4 Acceleration and Momentum

CHAPTER SECTION	OBJECTIVES	ACTIVITIES
4-1 Accelerated Motion (1 day)	1. **Explain** how force, mass, and acceleration are related. 2. **Compare** the rates at which different objects fall. 3. **Observe** the effects of air resistance.	**MINI-Lab:** *How does air resistance affect a falling object?* p. 87
4-2 Projectile and Circular Motion (2 days)	1. **Explain** why things that are thrown or shot follow a curved path. 2. **Compare** motion in a straight line with circular motion. 3. **Define** weightlessness.	**Activity 4-1:** *Projecting Projectile Pathways,* p. 95
4-3 To Boldly—and Safely—Go Science & Society (1 day)	1. **Analyze** the advantages and disadvantages of exposing astronauts to weightlessness. 2. **Draw conclusions** about the safety of space travel.	
4-4 Action and Reaction (2 days)	1. **Analyze** action and reaction forces. 2. **Calculate** momentum. 3. **Explain** conservation and momentum.	**Activity 4-2:** *A Massive Problem,* p. 104
Chapter Review		

ACTIVITY MATERIALS

FIND OUT	ACTIVITIES		MINI-LABS
Page 83 balloons of different shapes	**4-1 Projecting Projectile Pathways, p. 95** stick or dowel, slightly more than 2 m long meterstick string or thread corks (10) thumbtacks (10) felt-tip pen	**4-2 A Massive Problem, p. 104** dynamic carts (2) long rubber band building bricks (2) meterstick masking tape	**How does air resistance affect a falling object? p. 87** old hardcover book paper scissors

CHAPTER FEATURES	TEACHER RESOURCE PACKAGE	OTHER RESOURCES
Skill Builder: *Comparing and Contrasting,* p. 89	**Ability Level Worksheets** ◆ **Study Guide,** p. 18 ● **Reinforcement,** p. 18 ▲ **Enrichment,** p. 18 **Activity Worksheets,** p. 37	
Technology: *Scary Physics,* p. 93 **Skill Builder:** *Making and Using Tables,* p. 94	**Ability Level Worksheets** ◆ **Study Guide,** p. 19 ● **Reinforcement,** p. 19 ▲ **Enrichment,** p. 19 **Activity Worksheets,** pp. 31, 32 **Concept Mapping,** pp. 13, 14 **Transparency Masters,** pp. 13, 14	**Color Transparency 7,** Motion of a Projectile **STVS:** Disc 1, Side 2 **Science Integration Activity 4**
You Decide! p. 97	**Ability Level Worksheets** ◆ **Study Guide,** p. 20 ● **Reinforcement,** p. 20 ▲ **Enrichment,** p. 20 **Activity Worksheets,** p. 5	**STVS:** Disc 4, Side 2
Problem Solving: *The Icy Challenge,* p. 102 **Skill Builder:** *Concept Mapping,* p. 103	**Ability Level Worksheets** ◆ **Study Guide,** p. 21 ● **Reinforcement,** p. 21 ▲ **Enrichment,** p. 21 **Activity Worksheets,** pp. 33, 34 **Critical Thinking/Problem Solving,** p. 10 **Cross-Curricular Connections,** p. 8 **Science and Society,** p. 8 **Transparency Masters,** pp. 15, 16	**Color Transparency 8,** Newton's Third Law **Laboratory Manual 6,** Conservation of Momentum **Laboratory Manual 7,** Velocity and Momentum **STVS:** Disc 1, Side 2
Summary Think & Write Critically Key Science Words Apply Understanding Vocabulary More Skill Builders Checking Concepts Projects Using Lab Skills	**ASSESSMENT RESOURCES** **Chapter Review,** pp. 11, 12 **Chapter Test,** pp. 24–27 **Performance Assessment in** **Middle School Science**	**Chapter Review Software** **Test Bank** **Alternate Assessment** **Performance Assessment**

◆ **Basic**   ● **Average**   ▲ **Advanced**

ADDITIONAL MATERIALS		
SOFTWARE	**AUDIOVISUAL**	**BOOKS/MAGAZINES**
General Physics Series: Volume 3: Motion, Volume 4: Conservation Laws, Volume 5: Circular Motion, Cross Educational Software. *MMV Force and Motion,* Queue. *The Newtonian Sandbox,* Sunburst. *Projectile Motion,* EME Corp. *Rocket Factory,* MECC. *Sir Issac Newton's Games,* Sunburst.	*Circular Motion: Gravitation,* Video, Insight Media. *Gravity: Falling Bodies and Projectile Motion,* Video, Guidance Associates. *Motion,* Video, AIT. *Newton's Laws of Motion: Demonstrations of Mass, Force, and Momentum,* Laserdisc, AIMS Media *Physics at the Indy 500,* Laserdisc, Video Discovery. *Physics of Sports,* Laserdisc, Video Discovery. *Vortex and Rotation,* Video, Films Inc.	Gartrell, Jack E., Jr., and Schafer, Larry E. *Evidence of Energy—An Introduction to Mechanics, Book Two:* NSTA Publications, 1991. Radetsky, Peter. "The Man Who Mastered Motion." *Science 86,* May 1986, pp. 52-60.

THEME DEVELOPMENT: Patterns of change continue as a theme in this chapter. Newton established his three laws of motion by considering common patterns of change in all motion. These laws can be used to analyze and predict changes in the motion of objects. Stress the importance of having only three laws to explain the motion of almost all objects.

CHAPTER OVERVIEW

▶ **Section 4-1:** This section develops Newton's second law of motion. Falling objects and the effect of air resistance on their motion are discussed.

▶ **Section 4-2:** This section develops the concepts of projectile motion and circular motion. Centripetal acceleration and force are introduced, and weightlessness is discussed.

▶ **Section 4-3: Science and Society:** The effects of long periods of weightlessness on astronauts are presented. Students are asked to weigh the advantages and disadvantages of sending humans on long space voyages.

▶ **Section 4-4:** Newton's third law of motion is presented with a discussion of momentum and the law of conservation of momentum.

CHAPTER VOCABULARY

Newton's second law of motion
air resistance
terminal velocity
projectile
centripetal acceleration
centripetal force
isometric exercise
Newton's third law of motion
momentum
law of conservation of momentum

CHAPTER

4 Acceleration and Momentum

82

OPTIONS

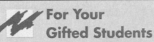 **For Your Gifted Students**

▶ Have students make a projectile by taping a straw to a balloon, feeding fishing line through the straw, and attaching one end of the line to a wall. Inflating the balloon the same amount each time, test the effects of attaching differently shaped cards to the front of the balloon by measuring the distance traveled when air is released from the balloon.

For Your Mainstreamed Students

▶ Students can have a parachute-making contest. Let students experiment with a variety of materials, sizes, and shapes for their parachutes. Have them determine which parachutes will stay aloft the longest and which will support the most weight.

The force of gravity acts on this soap box derby car, causing it to accelerate downhill. A second force acting on the car allows it to change speed and direction. What do you think this second force is?

FIND OUT!

Do this activity to find out what determines how a balloon moves.

Drop an uninflated balloon from shoulder level. What does it do? Now, blow up the balloon, but don't tie it closed. Again, hold the balloon at shoulder level and let it go. What happens to it? Does it fall to the ground right away?

Next, blow up the balloon, tie it closed, and drop it from shoulder level. *Compare* this motion to the motion in the first two trials. If you keep batting the balloon with your hand, can you keep it from touching the floor?

Gearing Up
Previewing the Chapter
Use this outline to help you focus on important ideas in this chapter.

Section 4-1   Accelerated Motion
▶ Newton's Second Law
▶ Falling Objects
▶ Terminal Velocity

Section 4-2   Projectile and Circular Motion
▶ Projectiles
▶ Moving in Circles
▶ Weightlessness in Orbit

Section 4-3   Science and Society
To Boldly—and Safely—Go
▶ Effects of Weightlessness

Section 4-4   Action and Reaction
▶ Newton's Third Law
▶ Rocket Propulsion
▶ Momentum

Previewing Science Skills
▶ In the Skill Builders, you will compare and contrast, make and use tables, and make a concept map.
▶ In the Activities, you will hypothesize, observe, collect and organize data, and analyze.
▶ In the MINI-Lab, you will experiment, observe and infer, and hypothesize.

What's next?

You will find out what changes in conditions can cause the motion of an object to vary. You will also learn how outside forces affect the motion of an object.

83

ASSESSMENT OPTIONS

PORTFOLIO
Refer to page 105 for suggested items that students might select for their portfolios.

PERFORMANCE ASSESSMENT
See page 105 for additional Performance Assessment options.
Process
Skill Builders, pp. 94, 103
MINI-Lab, p. 87
Activities 4-1, p. 95; 4-2, p. 104
Using Lab Skills, p. 106

CONTENT ASSESSMENT
Assessment—Oral, pp. 86, 88
Skill Builder, p. 89
Section Reviews, pp. 89, 94, 97, 103
Chapter Review, pp. 105-107
Mini Quizzes, pp. 85, 93, 102

GROUP ASSESSMENT
Opportunities for group assessment occur with Cooperative Learning Strategies and Flex Your Brain Activities.

INTRODUCING THE CHAPTER
Use the Find Out activity to introduce students to the motion of falling objects. Tell them that as they read this chapter they will learn how objects fall and what all falling objects have in common.

FIND OUT!
Preparation: Obtain one balloon for each student.
Materials: balloons of different shapes
Cooperative Learning: Assign Problem Solving Teams to investigate if the shape of an inflated and tied off balloon affects the way if falls.
Teaching Tips
▶ You may wish to do this activity out of doors or in a hallway to allow students to observe the motions of the balloons more easily.
▶ Have students carefully note the changes in motion when (1) a falling balloon is tapped upward, (2) a falling balloon is tapped downward, (3) a falling balloon is tapped sideways, (4) a rising balloon is tapped upward, (5) a rising balloon is tapped downward, (6) a rising balloon is tapped sideways, and (7) a balloon resting in one hand is tapped sideways.
▶ Allow students to discuss their observations and then compare and contrast the above changes.

Gearing Up
Have students study the Gearing Up feature to familiarize themselves with the chapter. Discuss the relationships of the topics in the outline.

What's Next?
Before beginning the first section, make sure students understand the connection between the Find Out activity and the topics to follow.

PREPARATION

SECTION BACKGROUND

▶ Newton's first law describes the motion of an object on which there were either no forces or balanced forces. Newton's second law describes the effect on an object's motion while there is a net force acting on it. In metric units, the unit of force is a newton and is defined as the force necessary to produce an acceleration of one meter per second per second on an object with a mass of one kilogram. That is, $1 \text{ N} = 1 \text{ kg} \cdot \text{m/s}^2$.

▶ Because of gravitational attraction, an object near Earth's surface falls with an acceleration of about 9.8 m/s^2 in a vacuum. However, the observed acceleration of an object is usually less because of the effects of air resistance.

PREPLANNING

▶ Obtain a table tennis ball for the motivation demonstration below; a soccer ball, a golf ball, and a flexible plastic ruler for the Reteach demonstration on page 85; 7 metal washers and fishing line for the demonstration on page 87; a large bottle of liquid dishwashing soap or shampoo and a marble for the demonstration on page 88.

1 MOTIVATE

▶ **Demonstration:** Make a slingshot using a rubber band and two fingers. Use it to accelerate a table tennis ball across a table top. Ask students to hypothesize how the change in motion of the table tennis ball would be affected by the stretch of the rubber band or how it would be affected if a stiffer, thicker rubber band were used.

TYING TO PREVIOUS
KNOWLEDGE: Have students recall from Section 3-5 the weight of a kilogram on Earth's surface. Tell them that they will learn why this is so in this section.

4-1 Accelerated Motion

New Science Words

Newton's second law of motion
air resistance
terminal velocity

Objectives

▶ Explain how force, mass, and acceleration are related.
▶ Compare the rates at which different objects fall.
▶ Observe the effects of air resistance.

Newton's Second Law

With Newton's first law, you learned how to describe the motion of a speeding sports car or a stationary hockey puck. You also learned that the motion of an object only changes if a net force acts on it, such as the brakes of a car or a fast-moving hockey stick. As you read this chapter, you will find out some reasons things move the ways they do.

Suppose you are a passenger in a car stalled on the tracks at a railroad crossing. You need to push the car off the tracks as soon as possible. Would you rather be riding in a compact car or a stretch limousine? Would you rather the driver be about as strong as you or a weightlifting champion?

Figure 4-1. The two men want to get the car off the tracks as quickly as possible. What two factors will determine how fast they can push the car?

OPTIONS

Meeting Different Ability Levels

For Section 4-1, use the following **Teacher Resource Masters** depending upon individual students' needs.

◆ **Study Guide Master** for all students.
● **Reinforcement Master** for students of average and above average ability levels.
▲ **Enrichment Master** for above average students.

Additional Teacher Resource Package masters are listed in any **PROGRAM RESOURCES** boxes that are in the section. The additional masters are appropriate for all students.

◆ STUDY GUIDE   18

STUDY GUIDE   Chapter 4
Accelerated Motion   Text Pages 84-89

Solve the puzzle below by writing the term in the diagram that best completes each statement. You will find one other term spelled vertically in the black box.

```
1.                      M A S S
2.                    S E C O N D
3.          B A L A N C E D
4.                    N E W T O N
5.                  F A L L I N G
6.                    W E I G H T
7.                  L A R G E R
8.  A I R R E S I S T A N C E
9.          G R A V I T Y
10.            M O T I O N
11.              F O R C E
12.    T E R M I N A L
```

1. Force equals _____ times acceleration.
2. Newton's _____ law of motion states that a net force acting on an object causes the object to accelerate in the direction of the force.
3. The law of inertia states that when the forces acting upon an object are _____, the motion of the object will not change.
4. The unit of force is the _____.
5. Gravity causes _____ objects to accelerate.
6. The force of gravity acting upon the mass of an object is the object's _____.
7. The _____ the force acting on an object, the greater the acceleration of the object.
8. The force air exerts on a moving object is _____ _____. (2 words)
9. Weight is a measure of the force of _____.
10. Any change in an object's position is _____.
11. In the equation $F = m \times a$, F stands for _____.
12. The highest velocity reached by a falling object is its _____ velocity.

Fill in the blank below with the term in the black box.

Force equals ___**acceleration**___ times mass.

18

You may not realize it, but in arriving at your answers to the questions, you used Newton's second law of motion. From experience, you know that mass, force, and acceleration are somehow related. **Newton's second law of motion** says that a net force acting on an object causes the object to accelerate in the direction of the force. The amount of acceleration is affected by the size of the force and the mass of the object. A larger force acting on an object causes a greater acceleration. A larger mass requires a greater force than a smaller mass would require to achieve the same acceleration.

Think about the stalled car. To get the greatest acceleration across the tracks, you'd want to push the smallest mass using the greatest force. So, you would prefer to push the compact car, and you'd want the weightlifter to help you.

Newton's second law can be expressed in equation form as:

$$force = mass \times acceleration$$
$$F = ma$$

Mass is expressed in kilograms and acceleration is expressed in m/s². Thus, force is expressed in units of kg • m/s².

You learned in Chapter 3 that one newton is the standard unit for measuring force. A newton is the amount of force needed to accelerate an object with a mass of 1 kg at an acceleration of 1 m/s². In other words, $1 N = 1 kg • m/s^2$.

Read the following Example Problem, then do the Practice Problems that are found on the next page.

Connect to...
Life Science

Many athletes lift weights to become better discus throwers. Explain how this might help them, using specific terms from Newton's second law.

EXAMPLE PROBLEM: Calculating Force

Problem Statement:	How much force is needed to accelerate a 70-kg rider and her 200-kg motorcycle at 4 m/s²?
Known Information:	mass, $m = 70 kg + 200 kg = 270 kg$
Strategy Hint: Remember to combine the masses of the rider and motorcycle.	acceleration, $a = 4 m/s^2$
Unknown Information:	force (F)
Equation to Use:	$F = m \times a$
Solution:	$F = m \times a = 270 kg \times 4 m/s^2$ = 1080 kg • m/s² = 1080 N

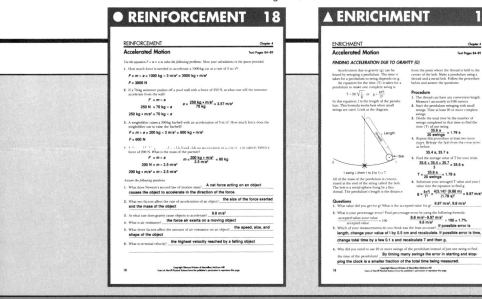

Key Concepts are highlighted.

CONCEPT DEVELOPMENT

▶ Discuss the motivation demonstration using Newton's second law. Have students explain the motion of the dragster's car mentioned on pages 65 and 66 using this law.

▶ **Demonstration:** Show how mass affects acceleration with a constant force. Place a flexed ruler next to a golf ball and release the ruler. Have students observe the motion of the ball. Repeat using a soccer ball.

MINI QUIZ

Use the Mini Quiz to check students' recall of chapter content.

1 **State Newton's second law of motion in words and as an equation.** *A net force acting on an object will cause the object to accelerate in the direction of the force; F = ma.*

2 **Define one newton of force.** *the amount of force needed to give a mass of 1 kg an acceleration of 1 m/s²*

Connect to...
Life Science

Lifting weights strengthens the athletes so they can use more force in throwing the discus. As a result, there is a greater acceleration on the discus, causing a greater velocity and a greater travel distance.

1. $F = m \times a$
   $= (1000 \text{ kg} + 160 \text{ kg}) \times 3 \text{ m/s}^2$
   $= 3480 \text{ N}$

2. $F = m \times a$
   $a = \dfrac{F}{m}$
   $= \dfrac{300 \text{ N}}{63 \text{ kg}} = \dfrac{300 \text{ kg} \cdot \text{m/s}^2}{63 \text{ kg}}$
   $= 4.76 \text{ m/s}^2$

CONCEPT DEVELOPMENT

▶ Make sure students realize that a falling object doesn't fall *fast*, it continually falls *faster*. Have students think of the difference in the feelings they would have in their hands catching a book that fell from a first-floor balcony and one that fell from a twelfth-floor balcony.

▶ The acceleration of gravity varies with location on Earth's surface. Its value increases slightly with latitude (because of Earth's rotation) and decreases with altitude.

▶ **Demonstration:** Securely attach a metal washer at each of the following positions along a 2.0-m length of fishing line: 0 cm, 5 cm, 20 cm, 45 cm, 80 cm, 125 cm, and 180 cm. Hold the string at the 2-m end as high as possible over a metal waste can or a metal cake pan. Have students discuss what they would hear if the string of washers fell at a constant speed. (An increasing interval between the clicks of the washers striking the metal can.) Release the string. Have students discuss why the regular interval between clicks indicated that the string of washers had a constant acceleration. (The constant time interval between the washers striking the can indicates that successive washers were striking the can at higher speeds. They had to fall greater distances in the same time interval. Increasing velocity supports the notion of a constant acceleration.)

PRACTICE PROBLEMS

Strategy Hint: What units combine to make a newton?

Strategy Hint: Rearrange the equation.

1. It takes a force of 3000 N to accelerate an empty 1000-kg car at 3 m/s². If a 160-kg wrestler is inside the car, how much force will be needed to produce the same acceleration?

2. A 63-kg skater pushes off from a wall with a force of 300 N. What is the skater's acceleration?

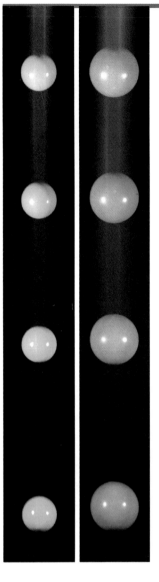

Falling Objects

It is hard to believe, but, if you dropped a bowling ball and a marble from a bridge at the same time, they'd both splash into the water at almost the same instant. (As you read further, you'll find out why they don't hit the water at exactly the same instant.) This means their accelerations would be just about the same. Would you have expected the bowling ball to hit the water sooner because it has more mass? It's true that the force of gravity would be greater on the bowling ball because of its larger mass. But the larger mass also gives the bowling ball more inertia, so more force is needed to change its velocity. The marble has a much smaller mass than the bowling ball, but its inertia also is much less. Figure 4-2 shows the motion of two balls frozen by high-speed photography. The blue ball is more massive than the green one, but you can see that they fall at the same rate.

Near Earth's surface, gravity causes all falling objects to accelerate at 9.8 m/s². Does the number 9.8 seem familiar? When you studied the relationship between mass and weight, you learned that any object with a mass of one kilogram weighs 9.8 newtons on Earth. Now you'll find out why.

Any force can be calculated using the equation $F = m \times a$. The weight of an object W is the force of gravity acting on its mass. So, we can substitute and write $W = m \times a$. Acceleration due to gravity is 9.8 m/s², so $W = m \times 9.8 \text{ m/s}^2$. So a mass of 1 kg weighs 9.8 kg • m/s², or 9.8 newtons. You could calculate your weight in newtons if you knew your mass. For example, a person with a mass of 50 kg would have a weight of 490 newtons.

Figure 4-2. As the photograph shows, the rate of acceleration of a falling body is not affected by the mass of the body.

86 ACCELERATION AND MOMENTUM

OPTIONS

ASSESSMENT—ORAL

▶ **What is the difference in the forces on a bat used to hit a home run and one used to bunt a baseball? How does the baseball react in each situation? How can you explain this phenomenon in terms of Newton's second law of motion?** *The force of the bat on the ball is less in a bunt than in a hit. Thus, the ball undergoes less of an acceleration and it moves away at a slower speed than a ball that is hit.*

Acceleration due to gravity (g) is the same for all objects, regardless of mass. This means that if no force other than gravity is present, all objects accelerate at 9.8 m/s². Think about that for a minute. Does a leaf accelerate as fast as an acorn? Does a feather fall as fast as a penny?

What would happen if you took two identical sheets of paper, crumpled one into a ball, and dropped both sheets at the same time? If your answer is that the crumpled ball would fall faster than the flat sheet, you are correct. But this behavior does not agree with what you've just learned. How can this disagreement be explained?

The only explanation for the behavior of the two sheets of paper is that some force is at work in addition to gravity. Anything that moves in Earth's atmosphere is affected by air resistance. **Air resistance** is the force air exerts on

Figure 4-3. Some force other than gravity must affect the flat sheet of paper, causing it to fall more slowly than the crumpled sheet of paper.

MINI-Lab

How does air resistance affect a falling object?

Obtain an old book. Cut a piece of paper the same size as the cover of the book. *Predict* whether the book or the paper will hit the floor first if you drop them the same way and at the same time. Try dropping them with the greatest surface area facing down. Which object has the greater acceleration? If the acceleration due to gravity is the same for all objects, how can you explain your results? Next, try to devise methods to make the book and paper fall at nearly the same acceleration. Describe your new methods and *analyze* how they work.

TEACHER F.Y.I.

▶ The table below illustrates the relationship between the time during which an object falls, its final speed, and the distance it has fallen from rest.

Time (s)	Final Speed (m/s)	Distance (m)
0.1	1	0.05
0.5	4.9	1.22
1.0	9.8	4.90
2.0	19.6	19.60
3.0	29.4	44.10

If falling from rest, final speed is calculated from the equation $v = gt$, and distance is figured from $d = 1/2\ gt^2$. The variable g represents the acceleration due to gravity, 9.8 m/s².

MINI-Lab

Materials: an old book, a piece of paper, scissors

Teaching Tips

▶ Suggest that the materials be dropped from waist height.

▶ Have extra paper available. Students may wish to crumple it in their experiment.

Answers to Questions

▶ The book appears to have the greater acceleration.

▶ Since it is more massive, the book has greater inertia and resists the upward push of air resistance more effectively than does the flat paper.

▶ Students may place the paper on top of the book or in the book before they drop them. They may crumple the paper into a dense wad. These methods reduce the surface area of the paper that is acted upon by air resistance.

INQUIRY QUESTIONS

▶ A force of 10 N is needed to produce an acceleration of 2.0 m/s² on a 3.0-kg wooden block sliding across a table. What is the force of friction acting on the sliding block? What is its direction? *The net force on the block is 6 N, 3 kg × 2 m/s². The difference between the 10 N acting on the block and the net force of 6 N, must be the force of friction. Thus, the force of friction is 4 N. It is acting in the direction opposite the direction in which the block is moving.*

PROGRAM RESOURCES

From the **Teacher Resource Package** use: **Activity Worksheets,** page 37, MINI-Lab: How does air resistance affect a falling object?

MINI-Lab
ASSESSMENT

Oral: Have students explain and discuss how this experiment would differ if performed on the moon, where there is no air resistance and about one-sixth of the gravity as on Earth's surface. The paper and book would fall with equal acceleration, and the acceleration rate would be less than on Earth.

CONCEPT DEVELOPMENT

▶ Point out that students who parachute out of airplanes are not the only ones who are familiar with terminal velocity. Explain that a scuba diver descending in the ocean also has a terminal velocity.

▶ **Demonstration:** Soak the labels off a bottle of a clear liquid soap, such as a dishwashing detergent or a shampoo. Remove the bottle's cap and drop a marble into the bottle. Have students observe the terminal velocity of the marble falling through the liquid.

TEACHER F.Y.I.

▶ The terminal velocity of a falling object depends upon many factors including the size and shape of the falling object and the viscosity (a measure of the ability of a fluid to flow) of the material it is falling through. A skydiver falling in a horizontal position with a closed parachute reaches a terminal velocity of about 60 m/s (200 km/h), while one falling with an open chute will reach a velocity of about 5 m/s (20 km/h).

CROSS CURRICULUM

▶ **Life Science:** Have students research the terminal velocities achieved by birds, such as falcons, during a dive.

In Your JOURNAL

Accept all reasonable answers. Roller coasters, free-fall rides, jumping out of a tree, and pole vaulting are all examples of activities involving near free-fall situations.

In Your JOURNAL

In your Journal, write a paragraph describing a situation in which you have experienced or observed something close to free-fall. Think about amusement park rides, athletic events, or even movie scenes.

Figure 4-4. The Frisbee is designed to use air resistance to help it soar and maneuver as it moves through the air.

a moving object. This force acts in the opposite direction to that of the object's motion. In the case of a falling object, air resistance pushes up as gravity pulls down.

The amount of air resistance on an object depends on the speed, size, shape, and density of the object. The larger the object, the greater the amount of air resistance on it. This is why feathers, leaves, and sheets of paper fall more slowly than pennies, acorns, and crumpled balls of paper. Recall that the bowling ball and marble dropped from a bridge don't fall at exactly the same rate. Which do you think hits the water first?

Figure 4-5. The snowflakes (left) and the hailstones (right) are both solid forms of water. Yet, because of differences in shape and size, snowflakes tend to drift and blow through the air, while hailstones fall straight to the ground.

OPTIONS

ENRICHMENT

▶ Have students research how streamlining is used to reduce air resistance when designing cars and airplanes.
▶ Have students research how the bodies of animals, such as fish, demonstrate streamlining.

ASSESSMENT—ORAL

▶ **Some small insects can fall hundreds of meters and walk away unharmed after hitting the ground. Can you explain this phenomenon in terms of air resistance and terminal velocity?** *If the insect has a low weight and a relatively large surface area, then air resistance can overcome the force of gravity before the insect reaches a high velocity. This is its terminal velocity—the highest velocity the falling insect will reach. The insect is falling slowly enough when it lands that it won't be harmed.*

Terminal Velocity

As an object falls, air resistance gradually increases until it balances the pull of gravity. According to the law of inertia, when the forces acting on an object are balanced, the motion of the object will not change. So, the falling object will stop accelerating. It will continue to fall, but at a constant, final velocity. This **terminal velocity** is the highest velocity that will be reached by a falling object.

Think about the things you now know about moving objects. You knew that a leaf fell more slowly than an acorn. You also knew that a rock that is dropped from a height of 10 meters is traveling faster when it hits the ground than a rock dropped from one meter. Now you know why. You will learn more about moving things as you continue reading this chapter.

Figure 4-6. Air resistance acts on the parachute, allowing the parachutist to fall at a terminal velocity that is slow enough to allow a safe landing.

SECTION REVIEW

1. A weightlifter raises a 440-kg barbell with an acceleration of 2 m/s². How much force does the weightlifter exert on the barbell?
2. A book falls from the balcony of a 12th-floor apartment. It smashes on the ground 2.5 s later. How fast is it moving just before it hits?
3. **Apply:** Use what you have learned about falling objects, air resistance, and terminal velocity to explain why a person can parachute safely to Earth from a high-flying airplane.
4. **Connect to Chemistry:** Some jet planes combine special fuels with air and burn them in three engines to create hot gases that accelerate the plane forward at 3 m/s². What acceleration would be possible with two engines?

☑ Comparing and Contrasting

Skill Builder

Use a balance to find the masses of an uninflated balloon and a balloon filled with air. Drop the two balloons from the same height at the same time and compare and contrast the rates at which they fall. If you need help, refer to Comparing and Contrasting in the **Skill Handbook** on page 679.

4-1   ACCELERATED MOTION   **89**

Skill Builder

Students should set up an experiment where they can measure the speed at which the balloons fall. Distance should be measured in meters and time in seconds.

3 CLOSE

PREPARATION

SECTION BACKGROUND

▶ The motion of a projectile can be explained by considering its vertical and horizontal motions independently. At any instant during its motion, the projectile has a vertical acceleration downward because of its weight and, therefore, a continuously increasing downward velocity. However, because there are no horizontal forces acting on the moving projectile (assuming air resistance is negligible), it has a constant horizontal velocity. The constant horizontal speed and constantly increasing speed downward cause the projectile to follow a curved path called a parabola.

PREPLANNING

▶ Obtain a flexible plastic ruler, a rubber ball, a plastic ruler with a central groove or a tube from a roll of paper towels, and two large matched marbles or ball bearings for demonstrations.
▶ For Activity 4-1, obtain a 2-m dowel or stick, 10 small corks, and 10 thumbtacks for each activity group.

1 MOTIVATE

▶ **Demonstration:** Place a rubber ball at the edge of a table. Gently strike the ball with a slightly flexed plastic ruler so that it falls off the table. Repeat the demonstration flexing the ruler more each time you repeat the demonstration. Have students describe the shape of the curve that the ball makes and ask them when they have seen similar curves.

4-2 Projectile and Circular Motion

New Science Words

projectile
centripetal acceleration
centripetal force

Objectives

▶ Explain why things that are thrown or shot follow a curved path.
▶ Compare motion in a straight line with circular motion.
▶ Define weightlessness.

Projectiles

Have you noticed anything about the moving objects described in this unit so far? Nearly all have been moving in straight lines. But that's not the only kind of motion you know about. Skateboarders wheel around in circles, cars go around hairpin curves, and rockets shoot into the air and curve back to Earth. How do the laws of motion account for these kinds of motion?

If you've ever played darts, thrown a ball, or shot an arrow from a bow, you have probably noticed that they didn't travel in straight lines. They started off straight, but then curved downward. That's why dart players and archers learn to aim above their targets.

Anything that's thrown or shot through the air is called a **projectile.** Because of Earth's gravitational pull and their own inertia, projectiles follow a curved path. ❶

Here's why. When you throw a ball, the force from your hand makes the ball move forward. It gives the ball *horizontal motion*, that is, motion parallel to Earth's surface. ❷ Once you let go of the ball, no other force accelerates it forward, so its horizontal velocity is constant.

When you let go of the ball, something else happens as well. Gravity starts pulling it downward, giving it *vertical motion*, or motion perpendicular to Earth's surface. Now the ball has constant horizontal velocity, but increasing vertical velocity. Gravity exerts an unbalanced force on the ball, changing the direction of its path from forward

Figure 4-7. A basketball becomes a projectile when it is thrown toward the basket. It follows a curved path that goes above the basket and then down.

OPTIONS

Meeting Different Ability Levels

For Section 4-2, use the following **Teacher Resource Masters** depending upon individual students' needs.

◆ **Study Guide Master** for all students.
● **Reinforcement Master** for students of average and above average ability levels.
▲ **Enrichment Master** for above average students.
Additional Teacher Resource Package masters are listed in any **PROGRAM RESOURCES** boxes that are in the section. The additional masters are appropriate for all students.

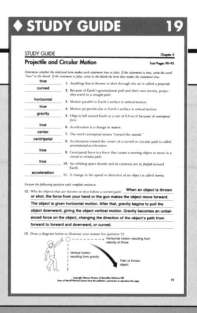

◆ STUDY GUIDE 19

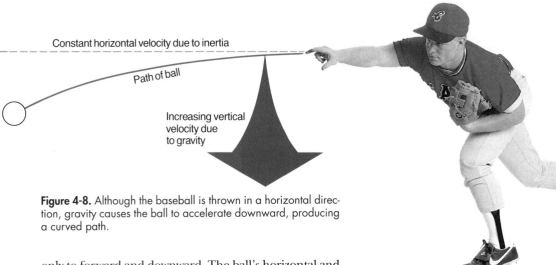

Constant horizontal velocity due to inertia

Path of ball

Increasing vertical velocity due to gravity

Figure 4-8. Although the baseball is thrown in a horizontal direction, gravity causes the ball to accelerate downward, producing a curved path.

only to forward and downward. The ball's horizontal and vertical motions are completely independent of each other.

If you throw a ball horizontally from shoulder height, will it take longer to hit the ground than a ball you simply drop from the same height? Surprisingly, both will hit the ground at the same time. If you have a hard time believing this, Figure 4-9 may help. The two balls have the same acceleration due to gravity, 9.8 m/s^2 downward.

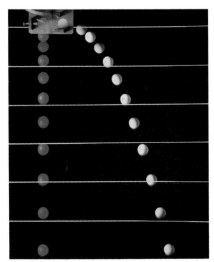

Connect to...
Earth Science

Fighting forest fires involves many different techniques, including using planes to drop fire retardants on the trees to slow the spread of the flames. Approximately where should the plane release the chemicals so they will fall on the fire? Draw a diagram and explain your answer.

Figure 4-9. The two balls in the photograph were released at the same time. Although one ball has horizontal velocity, gravity causes both balls to accelerate downward at the same rate.

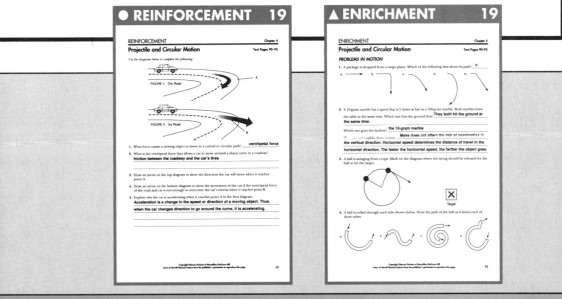

TYING TO PREVIOUS KNOWLEDGE: Have students recall the explanation of the motion of a hockey puck using Newton's first law from Section 3-4 and the motion of a falling ball described in the previous section. Tell them that this lesson will build upon their knowledge to help them explain the motion of an arrow and a pop fly to center field.

2 TEACH

Key Concepts are highlighted.

CONCEPT DEVELOPMENT

▶ **Demonstration:** Rest a marble or steel ball bearing at the edge of a table. Make a ramp from a plastic ruler or from a cardboard tube from a roll of paper towels cut in half lengthwise. Place a second ball in the raised end of the ramp so that as it reaches the end of the ramp, it will strike the first ball and both will fall onto the floor. Have the students observe that both balls hit the floor almost simultaneously.

Connect to...
Earth Science

Answer: The plane should release the chemicals before it is directly over the target area. The chemicals will continue to move forward at the plane's velocity as they fall.

REVEALING MISCONCEPTIONS

▶ Ask students to draw the forces on a ball *immediately after* it is hit by a bat, and have them explain their drawings. Many students will describe three forces: the weight of the ball downward, air resistance opposite to the motion of the ball, and a force causing the ball to move horizontally. Point out that the force causing the ball to move horizontally existed only when the ball was in contact with the bat. Only two forces are acting on the ball.

VideoDisc
STVS: Home-Grown Tornadoes, Disc 1, Side 2

CONCEPT DEVELOPMENT

▶ Make sure students realize that as an object moves in a circle, the *change* in its direction of motion is always toward the center of the circle, while the direction of its motion is always perpendicular to the radius of the circle. To help students understand the difference, have them visualize moving a very heavy brick along a big circle. Each time they move the brick, they must slide it forward just a little and then twist it a bit so it fits along the circle. The twist, which represents the change in direction of the brick, is always toward the center of the circle. The brick itself is always aligned along the circle itself, which means it is always perpendicular to the radius of the circle.

▶ Students may be familiar with the term *centrifugal force*. Point out that this force appears to be acting outward on an object when viewed by someone moving in a circle with the object. Have students think of sunglasses sliding across the dashboard away from the driver as the car makes a sharp left turn. In reality, the apparent motion away from the center is due to a lack of a sufficiently large centripetal force keeping the object moving in a circle.

CROSS CURRICULUM

▶ **Language Arts:** Have students look up *centripetal* in a dictionary. Students should find that it comes from the Latin roots, *centri* (center) and *petere* (to go seek). Ask a volunteer to explain how the word reflects the meaning of its roots.

EcoTip

The faster a car goes, the faster it burns fuel. Every day in the United States, cars traveling over the speed limit waste hundreds of liters of gasoline. Encourage drivers you ride with to obey speed limits.

Moving in Circles

Recall that acceleration is a change in velocity either in speed, in direction, or both. Now picture a bicycle moving at a constant speed along the westbound straightaway of an oval track. Because its speed is constant in a straight line, the bicycle is not accelerating. However, when the bicycle enters a curve, even if its speed does not change, it is accelerating, because its direction is changing. The change in the direction of the velocity is toward the center of the curve. Acceleration toward the center of a curved or circular path is called **centripetal** (sen TRIHP uh tuhl) **acceleration.** The bicycles and their riders shown in the photo experience centripetal acceleration and lean toward the inside of the curve. Their bodies and bicycles have changed from the upright position that they had on the straightaway. The word *centripetal* means "toward the center."

In order for the bicycle to be accelerating, some unbalanced force must be acting on it in a direction toward the center of the curve. That force is a centripetal force. **Centripetal force** is a force that causes a moving object to move in a curved or in a circular path.

When a car rounds a sharp curve on a highway, the centripetal force is the friction between the tires and the road surface. But if the road is icy or wet, and the tires lose their grip, the centripetal force may not be enough to overcome the car's inertia. Then, the car would shoot off in a straight line in the direction it was traveling at the spot where it lost traction.

Weightlessness in Orbit

Maybe you've seen pictures of astronauts floating inside the space shuttle with various pieces of equipment suspended in midair beside them. Any item that is not fastened down in the shuttle will float around and pose a possible hazard for the astronauts and their equipment. The astronauts and their belongings are experiencing weightlessness.

92 ACCELERATION AND MOMENTUM

OPTIONS

INQUIRY QUESTIONS

▶ Suppose the book mentioned in Question 2 of the Section Review on page 89 is thrown sideways with a speed of 1 m/s from the same balcony. How far from the side of the building will the book crash? *2.5 m*

PROGRAM RESOURCES

From the **Teacher Resource Package** use:

Transparency Masters, pages 13-14, Motion of a Projectile.

Concept Mapping, pages 13-14.

Science Integration Activity 4

Use **Color Transparency** number 7, Motion of a Projectile.

Scary Physics

A roller coaster applies the laws of motion in an effort to be the scariest ride in the park. A ride begins when a chain drags the cars to the top of the first hill. Once the cars are released, acceleration increases until all of the cars are headed downward.

The debate on which seat is the scariest continues to rage, and the answer is, "that depends." As the cars descend, their speed increases. The rear car starts down the slope at a much greater speed than the front car, thus giving the passengers the sense of being hurled over the edge. At the bottom of the hill, it is a different story. When the change in direction from down to up occurs, the front car will be going fastest and its passengers will experience the greater forces. As the cars pop over the top of the hill, the passengers in the rear car may experience a considerable force, resulting in the sensation of being thrown free.

As ride technology improves, roller coasters get larger and faster. The Magnum XL 200 at Cedar Point in Sandusky, Ohio, has a first hill 201 feet high, reaches a speed of 112 km/h, and covers 5106 feet of track in two-and-one-half minutes.

Think Critically: Describe the roller coaster design that would result in the greatest sensations for the passengers.

But to be truly weightless, the astronauts would have to be free from the effects of gravity. Orbiting 400 km above Earth, the shuttle and everything inside it still respond to those effects. In fact, gravity keeps the shuttle in orbit.

So what does it really mean to say that something is weightless in orbit? Think about how the weight of an object is measured. When you place an object on a scale, gravity causes the object to push down on the scale. In turn, the scale pushes back on the object with the same force. The dial on the scale measures the amount of upward force needed to offset gravity.

Did You Know?

The pull of gravity differs from place to place on Earth. In the U.S., gravity is greatest in Minot, North Dakota, and smallest in Key West, Florida.

Walker, Jearl. "Thinking about physics while scared to death (on a falling roller coaster)." *Scientific American*, Oct. 1983, pp. 162-169.
▶ Have the students share their scariest roller coaster ride. Have them explain which seat they chose and why.

Think Critically: The first hill should be high and the slope steep, and the remainder of the ride should be low so most of the energy remains kinetic.

CONCEPT DEVELOPMENT

▶ **Demonstration:** Place a small hole in the bottom of a foam plastic cup. While holding the hole shut, fill the cup with colored water. Hold the cup as high as you can and drop it into a bucket placed directly beneath it on the floor. Have students observe that no water ran from the cup as it fell because both the cup and water were in free-fall.

▶ Point out that weightlessness is the sensation felt in free-fall when there is no support force under your body. The word *weightless* also refers to the state of an object so far from any other object that the gravitational force would be negligible.

MINI QUIZ

Use the Mini Quiz to check students' recall of chapter content.

1. **What is a projectile?** *anything thrown or shot through the air*
2. **What is vertical motion and what is horizontal motion?** *Horizontal motion is parallel to Earth's surface and vertical motion is perpendicular to Earth's surface.*
3. **What is centripetal acceleration?** *acceleration toward the center of a curved or circular path*

ENRICHMENT

▶ Have students research applications of centripetal force to explain how the spin cycle of a washing machine removes water from clothing.

RETEACH

Have students place tracing paper over Figure 4-2 and mark the vertical positions of one of the falling balls. Then have them imagine that the ball was also moving sideways with a constant speed. Have them change their drawing to account for this. Ask them to describe the curve showing the motion of the ball.

EXTENSION

For students who have mastered this section, use the **Reinforcement** and **Enrichment** masters or other OPTIONS provided.

3 CLOSE

▶ Ask students to identify the force that causes the centripetal acceleration of the moon.

SECTION REVIEW ANSWERS

1. Refer to Figure 4-8 in the student text. Students' diagrams should show the dart being launched on a slightly upward path, so that the downward curve of the dart caused by gravity brings the dart to the target bull's-eye.
2. The string provides the centripetal force that keeps the yo-yo moving in a circular path. If the string breaks, the yo-yo will fly off in a straight line in the direction it was moving when the string broke.
3. Apply: No; mass is independent of gravity.
4. Connect to Life Science: Motion disturbs the fluid in the semicircular canals in the ears, affecting your balance. Rapid changes in direction can cause dizziness or nausea.

What is free-fall?

Figure 4-11. The space shuttle and everything in it are in free-fall around Earth, thus producing apparent weightlessness.

Now suppose that the scale is falling, being pulled downward by gravity at the same rate as the object being weighed. The scale couldn't push back on the object, so its dial would read zero. The object would seem to be weightless. This is what is happening in a space shuttle orbiting Earth. The shuttle and everything in it, including the astronauts, are all "falling" toward Earth at exactly the same rate of acceleration. When an object is influenced only by gravity, it is said to be in free-fall. An orbiting space shuttle and all its contents are in free-fall around Earth.

SECTION REVIEW

1. Use a diagram similar to Figure 4-8 to show why a dart player has to aim above the target to hit the bull's-eye. In your diagram, show the forces acting on the dart, the dart's path, and the two kinds of motion involved.
2. A child is swinging a yo-yo in a circle. What provides the force to keep the yo-yo going in a circle? What is the force called? What happens if the string breaks?
3. **Apply:** Does the mass of an astronaut change when he or she becomes weightless in orbit?
4. **Connect to Life Science:** The repetitive circular and up-and-down motion on many amusement rides can cause motion sickness. Explain what causes this.

Skill Builder

☑ Making and Using Tables

Make a table showing important characteristics of projectile motion, circular motion, and free-fall. Table headings should include: Kind of Motion, Shape of Path, and Laws or Forces Involved. You may add other headings. If you need help, refer to Making and Using Tables in the **Skill Handbook** on page 686.

Skill Builder

Tables should be set up as shown at right. Accept any correct data students include to complete the table.

Skill Builder
ASSESSMENT
Performance: Have students add a column entitled "Practical Examples."

Important Characteristics of Three Kinds of Motion		
Kind of Motion	Shape of Path	Laws or Forces
Projectile		
Circular		
Free-fall		

DESIGNING AN EXPERIMENT
Predicting Projectile Pathways

Professional baseball players must be able to predict projectile paths. Almost as soon as a fly ball is hit, the outfielders begin moving themselves to where the ball will land. How can they predict this? Ignoring air resistance, the horizontal velocity of the ball will not change and the acceleration due to gravity will be constant, so the path can be predicted.

Getting Started
In this activity, you will construct and use a device to help you *predict* the trajectory of a thrown object. Only throw the object when your teacher instructs.

Thinking Critically
How does the angle at which an object is thrown affect its path? If you throw a ball horizontally at the same time another ball is dropped from the same height, how do their flight times *compare*?

Materials
Your cooperative group will use:
- stick or dowel, slightly longer than 2 m
- meterstick
- thumbtacks (10) or tape
- string or thread
- felt-tip pen
- corks (10)

Try It!

1. Construct the device pictured below after placing marks at 20-cm intervals along the stick.

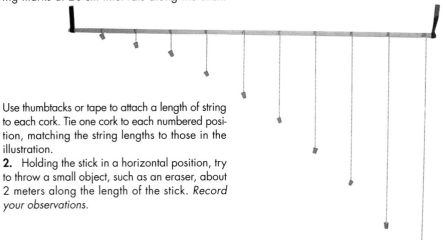

Use thumbtacks or tape to attach a length of string to each cork. Tie one cork to each numbered position, matching the string lengths to those in the illustration.

2. Holding the stick in a horizontal position, try to throw a small object, such as an eraser, about 2 meters along the length of the stick. *Record your observations.*

3. Repeat Step 2 with the stick tilted upward at an angle of about 45°. Try it again with the stick tilted downward at about the same angle. *Record your observations.*

Summing Up/Sharing Results
- *Describe* the paths followed by the objects thrown at all three angles.
- What forces acted on the objects while in flight?
- In this model, what do the progressively increasing lengths of the strings represent?

Going Further!
How could you determine the upward angle at which a thrown object would travel the greatest distance? Is this approximately consistent with your experience of throwing a baseball?

SUMMING UP/SHARING RESULTS
When thrown horizontally, the path curved downward. When thrown upward, the path curved up slightly and was more level. When thrown downward, the path curved down more sharply. Gravity and a small amount of air resistance acted on the object. The string lengths indicate the increasing velocity and fall distance during each interval of time resulting from gravitational acceleration.

GOING FURTHER!
Draw a horizontal line from the "zero" end of the stick. Tilt the stick upward until the last cork touches the line. Yes. You would aim above the target. The greater the distance to the target is, the higher you must aim.

Activity
ASSESSMENT
Oral: To assess the students' understanding of trajectories, discuss the following questions. Does throwing an object at a given speed at a greater upward angle always ensure a greater horizontal distance? (no) Does it ensure a greater time of flight? (yes)

OBJECTIVE: Construct and use a model to predict the trajectory of a thrown object.
Time: one class period

PROCESS SKILLS applied in this activity are **hypothesizing, measuring,** and **collecting** and **organizing data.**

PREPARATION
Cooperative Learning: Divide the class into groups of three or four. Each team can construct a device by dividing the work among team members.

SAFETY
Be sure only small, smooth objects are used as projectiles. Space groups so that throwing the objects is not a hazard.

THINKING CRITICALLY
If thrown above the horizontal, the path will curve up and then down in a parabola. If thrown horizontally or at a downward angle, the path will curve down with increasing steepness. The flight times would be the same.

TEACHING THE ACTIVITY
Refer to the Activity Worksheets for additional information and teaching strategies.
- The best measurement of length is from the lower edge of the stick to the center of the cork. The string can be taped so it hangs from the lower edge of the stick.
- The distances listed are rounded off to the nearest centimeter. The speed of the throw is assumed to be about 4 m/sec. At this speed, the time of travel from one cork to the next is 0.05 sec. The calculation of full distance is based on the formula $d = 1/2 \, gt^2$.

PROGRAM RESOURCES
From the **Teacher Resource Package** use:

Activity Worksheets, pages 31-32, Activity 4-1: Predicting Projectile Pathways

 **4-3** To Boldly—and Safely—Go

PREPARATION

SECTION BACKGROUND

▶ Isometric exercise is a method of strengthening muscles by having them exert forces repetitively against the force exerted by groups of muscles or bones.

1 MOTIVATE

▶ Ask students to explain why leg weights are sometimes worn by athletes in training.

V i d e o D i s c
STVS: Growing Plants in Space, Disc 4, Side 2.

2 TEACH

Key Concepts are highlighted.

CONCEPT DEVELOPMENT

▶ One way to overcome weightlessness in space is to build a large doughnut-shaped ring called a torus. If the torus is set spinning in outer space, the centripetal force on someone standing on the inside of the outer wall of the torus would cause a feeling similar to standing on the floor on Earth. One torus has been proposed that would have a radius of about 500 m and rotate about 5 revolutions per minute.

CHECK FOR UNDERSTANDING

Have students explain why a hand-grip exerciser would be good exercise equipment to have on a spaceflight.

New Science Words

isometric exercises

Objectives

▶ Analyze the advantages and disadvantages of exposing astronauts to weightlessness.
▶ Draw conclusions about the safety of space travel.

Effects of Weightlessness

If you could be the first person to set foot on Mars, would you go? What if you knew the trip would take about nine months and might be bad for your health? No one is sure how astronauts' bodies might react to such long exposure to weightlessness.

When Russian cosmonauts experienced weightlessness for more than 200 consecutive days, they had health problems. Their experiences and other experiments show that long periods of weightlessness weaken the heart and bones. After being in space for nine months, an astronaut might be too weak to perform the

96 ACCELERATION AND MOMENTUM

◆ **STUDY GUIDE** 20

OPTIONS

Meeting Different Ability Levels

For Section 4-3, use the following **Teacher Resource Masters** depending upon individual students' needs.

◆ **Study Guide Master** for all students.
● **Reinforcement Master** for students of average and above average ability levels.
▲ **Enrichment Master** for above average students.

Additional Teacher Resource Package masters are listed in any **PROGRAM RESOURCES** boxes that are in the section. These additional masters are appropriate for all students.

delicate steps involved in landing a spacecraft on Mars.

Some space experts say the problems could be prevented by simulating gravity on the spacecraft. A special exercise program might help, too. Some exercises, like jogging, wouldn't be as effective on Mars as on Earth. But **isometric exercises,** in which muscles push against other muscles could help astronauts stay in shape with or without gravity.

Other space experts argue that it's better not to send people to Mars at all. These experts claim that robots loaded with sensors, instruments, and arms for gathering samples could do the job just as well as humans, if not better.

But could robots explore the planet as thoroughly as humans? And should humans have to miss out on the adventure?

What are isometric exercises?

SECTION REVIEW

1. Why don't scientists know as much as they'd like about the effects of prolonged weightlessness?
2. Do space mission planners need to consider the effects of weightlessness on anything besides astronauts? Explain your answer.
3. **Connect to Earth Science:** Find out how an Earth-like environment, including gravity, could be simulated on a spacecraft or a space colony.

Connect to...

Life Science

Research several isometric exercises and share them with the class.

You Decide!

As a space agency official planning a mission to Mars, would you send instruments to be operated by astronauts or robots? How would you make the decision? Now suppose you're an astronaut. Would you volunteer for the Mars mission?

SCIENCE & SOCIETY

● **REINFORCEMENT** 20

▲ **ENRICHMENT** 20

97

RETEACH
Draw balanced forces on a compressed hand-grip exerciser. Have students identify the forces being exerted by the person exercising.

EXTENSION
For students who have mastered this section, use the **Reinforcement** and **Enrichment** masters or other OPTIONS provided.

3 CLOSE

▶ Ask questions 1-2 and the **Connect to Earth Science** question in the Section Review.

? FLEX Your Brain

Use the Flex Your Brain activity to have students explore the SAFETY OF SPACE TRAVEL.

ASSESSMENT
Portfolio: Use the Flex Your Brain activity to reinforce critical-thinking and problem-solving skills. In Step 2, students might list prolonged exposure to low gravity, living in confined spaces, availability of entertainment or food, boredom, etc.

SECTION REVIEW ANSWERS
1. Weightless conditions on Earth can only be maintained for very short periods of time (less than a minute).
2. They would have to consider the effects of weightlessness on plants and animals and design ways to overcome weightlessness to perform daily activities.
3. Connect to Earth Science: A rotating doughnut-shaped ring could simulate gravity. Sunlight could be directed into the ring using mirrors, and plants could supply food and an atmosphere.

YOU DECIDE!
SCIENCE & SOCIETY

Answers will vary. Students should support their opinions with logical statements and assumptions.

PROGRAM RESOURCES
From the **Teacher Resource Package** use:

Activity Worksheets, page 5, Flex Your Brain.

PREPARATION

SECTION BACKGROUND

▶ Newton's third law states that forces arise in pairs; that is, if one body exerts a force on a second body, the second body exerts an equal and opposite force on the first body. The forces are sometimes called action-reaction pairs.

▶ The momentum of an object is equal to the product of its mass and its instantaneous velocity. The momentum of a system is the sum of all the momenta of the parts of the system.

▶ The law of conservation of momentum states that if there is no external, net force acting on an object or a system, the momentum of the object or system remains the same. Conversely, the change in the value of momentum of an object or system is equal to the product of the external force and the time interval during which the force acts. (See the Teacher F.Y.I. on page 101.)

PREPLANNING

▶ Obtain three large, identical rubber bands, several wire ties from plastic food storage bags, and a small weight for the motivation demonstration; a bathroom scale, preferably metric, for the demonstration on page 100.

PROGRAM RESOURCES

From the **Teacher Resource Package** use:

Transparency Masters, pages 15-16, Newton's Third Law.

Use **Color Transparency** number 8, Newton's Third Law.

4-4 Action and Reaction

New Science Words

Newton's third law of motion
momentum
law of conservation of momentum

Objectives

▶ Analyze action and reaction forces.
▶ Calculate momentum.
▶ Explain conservation of momentum.

Newton's Third Law

A boy blows up a balloon for his sister. He lets the balloon go and it darts away on a zigzag course, making her giggle. A young soldier, firing a rifle for the first time, is startled by the backward "kick" of the rifle. A man leaping from a boat toward land falls in the water when the boat scoots away from the shore. As different as these examples of motion may seem, they all illustrate one point: forces always act in pairs, called action-reaction pairs.

Newton's third law of motion describes action-reaction pairs this way: When one object exerts a force on a second object, the second one exerts a force on the first that is equal in size and opposite in direction. A less formal way of saying the same thing is "to every action there is an equal and opposite reaction."

Let's look at the examples of action-reaction pairs described earlier. The balloon exerts force on the air inside, causing the air to rush out of the neck of the balloon. The air exerts an equal force on the balloon, but in the opposite direction. This reaction force causes the balloon to dart away from the escaping air.

When a soldier fires a rifle, the hot gases from the exploding gunpowder exert a force on the bullet, sending it speeding out of the barrel of the gun. The bullet exerts an equal and opposite force on the trapped gases, causing the rifle to "kick" backward.

In the third example, when the man leaps from the boat, the boat exerts a force on his feet, moving him forward. His feet exert an equal and opposite force on the boat, sending it backward.

State Newton's third law of motion.

1

98 ACCELERATION AND MOMENTUM

OPTIONS

Meeting Different Ability Levels

For Section 4-4, use the following **Teacher Resource Masters** depending upon individual students' needs.

◆ **Study Guide Master** for all students.

● **Reinforcement Master** for students of average and above average ability levels.

▲ **Enrichment Master** for above average students.

Additional Teacher Resource Package masters are listed in any PROGRAM RESOURCES boxes that are in the section. The additional masters are appropriate for all students.

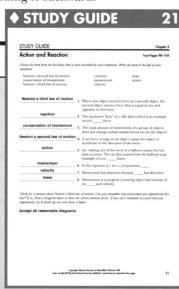

◆ STUDY GUIDE   21

STUDY GUIDE   Chapter 4
Action and Reaction   Text Pages 98-104

Choose the term from the list below that is best described by each statement. Write the term to the left of each statement.

Newton's second law of motion   reaction   mass
conservation of momentum   momentum   action
Newton's third law of motion   velocity

Newton's third law of motion   1. When one object exerts a force on a second object, the second object exerts a force that is equal in size and opposite in direction.

reaction   2. The backward "kick" of a rifle that is fired is an example of a(n) _____ force.

conservation of momentum   3. The total amount of momentum of a group of objects does not change unless outside forces act on the objects.

Newton's second law of motion   4. A net force acting on an object causes the object to accelerate in the direction of the force.

action   5. Air rushing out of the neck of a balloon causes the balloon to move. The air that comes from the balloon is an example of a(n) _____ force.

momentum   6. In the equation p = m × v, p represents _____.

velocity   7. Momentum has direction because _____ has direction.

mass   8. Momentum is a property a moving object has because of its _____ and velocity.

Think for a minute about Newton's third law of motion. Can you remember any event when you experienced this law? If so, draw a diagram below to show the action-reaction forces. If you can't remember an event that you experienced, try to think up one and draw it below.

Accept all reasonable diagrams.

Copyright Glencoe Division of Macmillan/McGraw-Hill
Users of Merrill Physical Science have the publisher's permission to reproduce this page.   21

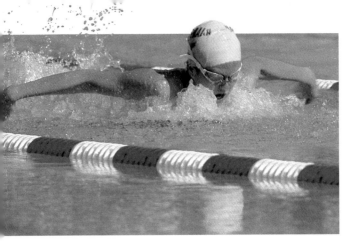

Figure 4-12. As the swimmer's hands and feet push against the water, the water pushes back, moving the swimmer forward.

Newton's third law can be used to explain how a swimmer moves through the water. With each stroke, the swimmer's arm exerts a force on the water. The water pushes back on the swimmer with an equal force in the opposite direction. But if the forces are equal, how can the swimmer move forward? It's possible because the forces are acting on different things. The "action" force acts on the water; the "reaction" force acts on the swimmer. The swimmer, having less mass than the pool full of water, accelerates more than the water.

A very important point to keep in mind when dealing with Newton's third law is that action-reaction forces always act on *different* objects. Thus, even though the forces may be equal, they are not balanced. In the case of the swimmer, one force acts on the swimmer. Thus, a net force, or unbalanced force, acts on the swimmer, and a change in motion can take place.

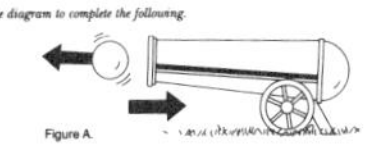

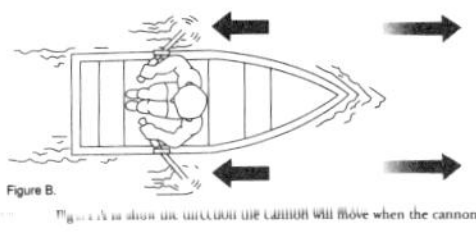

Compare the example of the swimmer with that of two teams in a tug of war. Both teams exert force on the ground with their feet. As long as both teams hold the rope, we can think of the rope and the teams as part of a single object. The net force on this object comes from the forces exerted by the ground on the feet of the contestants. The members of one team lean backward, pushing on the ground, and the ground

Figure 4-13. The action of passing the basketball forward will propel the player backward.

● REINFORCEMENT 21

REINFORCEMENT — Chapter 4

Action and Reaction — Text Pages 98–104

Use the diagram to complete the following.

Figure A.

Figure B.

1. [illegible] Figure A to show the direction the cannon will move when the cannonball is fired.
2. Draw arrows on Figure B to show the direction the oars must move to propel the boat forward.
3. Does the arrow you drew on Figure A represent an action force or a reaction force? **reaction force**
4. Does the arrow you drew on Figure B represent an action force or a reaction force? **an action force**
5. If the force which propels the cannonball forward is 500 N, how much force will move the cannon backward? Explain. **The force will also be 500 N because action-reaction forces are equal and opposite.**

Solve the following.

1. What is the momentum of a 2-kg toy truck that moves at 10 meters per second?
   $p = m \times v = 2\text{ kg} \times 10\text{ m/sec} = 20\text{ kg} \cdot \text{m/s}$
2. What is the momentum of a 2000-kg truck that moves at 10 meters per second?
   $p = m \times v = 2000\text{ kg} \times 10\text{ m/s} = 20\,000\text{ kg} \cdot \text{m/s}$
3. Which truck has more momentum? Why? **the 2000-kg truck because it has a greater mass**

 21

▲ ENRICHMENT 21

ENRICHMENT — Chapter 4

Action and Reaction — Text Pages 98–104

NEWTON'S LAWS IN MOTION

Coach Rogers had 6 positions to fill on his football team. In order to be considered for a particular position, the players had to meet certain physical criteria, Table 1. Coach Rogers had obtained data on each player that he planned to use in assigning players to positions, Table 2. Determine each player's mass from his weight. Assume $a = 9.8\text{ m/s}^2$. Use your knowledge of Newton's laws to assign the players to the positions for which they are best suited.

Table 1

Position	Description/Criteria
line	Stops other players from crossing the scrimmage line. Requires great strength in a short distance.
back	Runs with football. Requires speed and agility.
end	May block as a lineman or act as a pass receiver. Requires both speed and strength.

Table 2

Player	Weight	Mass	Time/[illegible] dash	Speed at finish line
Allen	833 N	**85.0 kg**	4.51 s	16.0 m/s
Terry	735 N	**75.0 kg**	4.40 s	16.4 m/s
Frank	911 N	**93.0 kg**	4.82 s	15.0 m/s
Dave	825 N	**84.2 kg**	4.71 s	15.3 m/s
Bob	1010 N	**103.1 kg**	4.90 s	14.7 m/s
Carlos	931 N	**95.0 kg**	4.60 s	15.7 m/s

Select two players for each position. Assign each player to a position. Explain your selection in terms of Newton's laws.

Position	Player	Reasoning
line	**Frank, Bob**	**great strength**
back	**Allen, Terry**	**small and fast**
end	**Dave, Carlos**	**strong and fast**

Assuming their accelerations remained the same, how many kilograms would Dave have to gain to exert the same force at the finish line as Allen? (Hint: Determine a for each boy using $v = v_o + at$, where $v_o = 0$ because the players started from a rest position. Then use $F = ma$ to solve for m.)

$$m = \frac{302\text{ N} - 274\text{ N}}{3.25\text{ m/s}^2} = 8.6\text{ kg}$$

 21

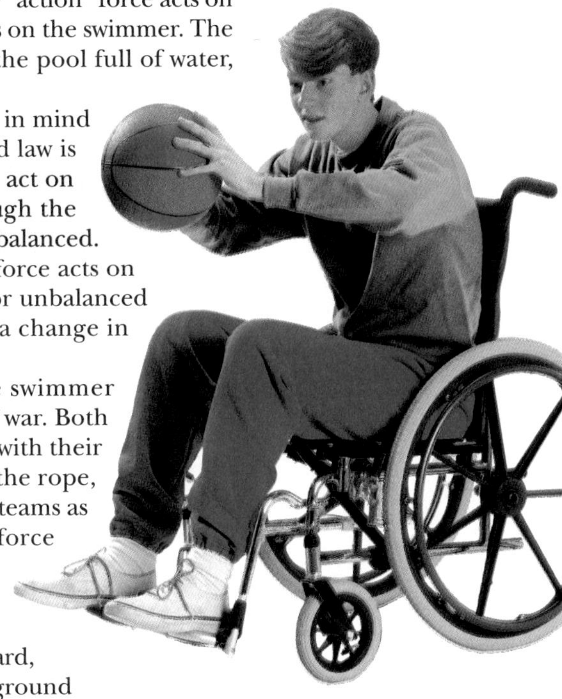

1 MOTIVATE

▶ **Demonstration:** Have a student measure the lengths of three rubber bands. Suspend a weight from one rubber band and have a student measure its new length. Remove and link an identical rubber band to the first with a wire tie from a plastic food storage bag. Ask students to predict by how much each rubber band will elongate if you suspend a weight from the second rubber band. Demonstrate the elongation of each rubber band and have a student measure the length of each rubber band. Have students compare the elongations with the elongation of the single rubber band. Link a third rubber band to the chain in a similar fashion and repeat the questioning and the demonstration. Ask students to summarize their observations.

Cooperative Learning: Have Problem Solving Teams determine if the shape of an inflated balloon rocket affects its motion.

TYING TO PREVIOUS KNOWLEDGE: Have students recall the motion of the untied inflated balloon from the Find Out activity on page 83. Point out that the cause of the motion is much like that which causes a rocket to move. Tell students they will learn more about rocket propulsion in this chapter.

2 TEACH

Key Concepts are highlighted.

CONCEPT DEVELOPMENT

▶ Have students draw arrows representing action-reaction pairs in each situation described on pages 98 and 99. Make sure students identify every force, the source of the forces, and the object on which each force is acting.

VideoDisc

STVS: VTOL Airliners, Disc 1, Side 2

▶ **Demonstration:** Have a student stand on a bathroom scale and another report the scale reading to the class. While bracing the scale with your foot, instruct the first student to carefully jump off the scale while the student observes any changes to the scale reading when the first student jumps. Have the student report the observation to the class. In terms of Newton's third law, discuss the sudden increase in the scale reading as the student jumped. Point out that the new value was the sum of her weight and the force she pushed down on the scale while beginning to jump. The force that the scale exerted upward on the student was equal to this new value but opposite in direction. The difference between the weight of the student and this upward force that the scale exerted on the student resulted in a net upward force on the student. The net force caused the student to accelerate upward, off the scale, as described by Newton's second law.

Answer: A human exerts a force on the sidewalk, and the reaction force of the sidewalk on the person moves the person forward. A fish pushes on the water, and the reaction force of the water propels the fish forward.

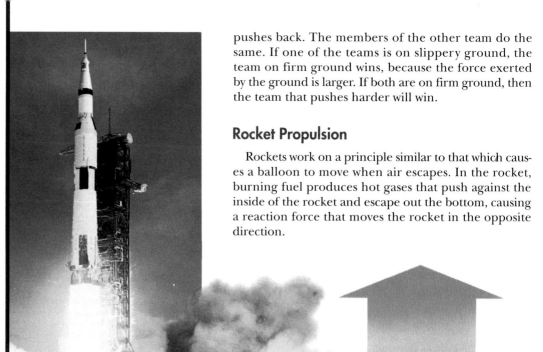

Figure 4-14. The "action force" of the expanding gases rushing out of the rocket results in a "reaction force" being exerted on the rocket, sending the rocket in the opposite direction.

Using Newton's third law, describe the similarities between a human walking on a sidewalk and a fish swimming in the ocean.

pushes back. The members of the other team do the same. If one of the teams is on slippery ground, the team on firm ground wins, because the force exerted by the ground is larger. If both are on firm ground, then the team that pushes harder will win.

Rocket Propulsion

Rockets work on a principle similar to that which causes a balloon to move when air escapes. In the rocket, burning fuel produces hot gases that push against the inside of the rocket and escape out the bottom, causing a reaction force that moves the rocket in the opposite direction.

Momentum

If a toy truck rolls toward you, you can easily stop it with your hand. However, such a tactic would not work with a full-sized truck, even if it were moving at the same speed as the toy truck. It takes more force to stop the full-sized truck because it has more momentum (moh MENT um) than the toy truck has. **Momentum** is a property a moving object has due to its mass and velocity. Momentum can be calculated with this equation, in which p represents momentum:

$$momentum = mass \times velocity$$
$$p = m \times v$$

The unit for momentum is kg · m/s. Notice that momentum has a direction, because velocity has a direction.

OPTIONS

INQUIRY QUESTIONS

▶ **A 70-kg girl jumps off a bathroom scale with an upward acceleration of 0.5 m/s². What is the reading of the scale as she was jumping?** *Her weight 70 kg × 9.8 m/s² + 70 kg × 0.5 m/s² = 721 N.*

▶ **During your dive into a swimming pool, how big a force are you exerting on Earth?** *your weight* **Why doesn't the Earth fall up to you?** *Its mass is so great, about 6 × 10²⁴ kg, that the gravitational force you exert on it produces a negligible acceleration.*

▶ **Explain why you feel an outward force on your hand by the string when you spin a yo-yo above your head.** *You feel an outward force of the string on your hand because you are causing an inward force on the string and the string exerts an equal and opposite force on you.*

Figure 4-15. Because of its much greater mass, the real fire engine has more momentum than the toy engine, even when the two trucks are moving at the same speed.

The two trucks described on the previous page may have the same velocity, but the full-sized truck has more momentum because of its greater mass. A speeding bullet has a large momentum because of its high velocity, even though its mass is small. A lumbering elephant may have a low velocity, but because of its large mass it has a large momentum.

The momentum of an object doesn't change unless its mass, or velocity, or both, change. But momentum can be transferred from one object to another. Think about what happens when a ball rolling across a pool table hits another ball that is standing still. At first, the rolling ball has momentum, and the motionless ball does not. When they collide, the ball that was at rest starts moving. It gains

Figure 4-16. Before the balls collide, the moving ball has all the momentum (left). After the balls collide, all of the balls have momentum (right). The total momentum of the balls is the same in both photographs.

▶ Make sure that students realize that the momentum of an object is the product of two quantities: its mass and its velocity.

▶ Discuss how the change in the momentum of an object is caused by two factors: the size of the net force acting on the object and the time interval during which the net force acts. Have students think about pushing a stalled car. A lot of students pushing for a short time and a few students pushing for a longer time will cause equal changes in the car's momentum.

TEACHER F.Y.I.

▶ The change in momentum is equal to the impulse, which is the product of the net force and the time interval during which it acts. The statement can be written as an equation,

$$Ft = m\Delta v.$$
$$F = ma$$
$$F = m\frac{(v_f - v_i)}{t}$$
$$Ft = m(v_f - v_i) = m\Delta v$$
$$\Delta p = m\Delta v$$

MULTICULTURAL PERSPECTIVE

And the Rocket's Red Glare...

Centuries ago, the Chinese invented gunpowder. This new invention was first used in the fireworks and rockets that were common during celebrations. Gunpowder, however, was quickly adapted to war purposes. By the 14th century, Chinese armies were using two-stage rockets in battles. These rockets would take a warhead over the enemy where the warhead would release arrows.

ENRICHMENT

▶ Allow students who enjoy model rocketry to discuss their hobby and demonstrate a launch to the class.

▶ During one space mission, ground control asked who was piloting the spacecraft. The response was "Newton." Explain this response.

►The action force is Stewart's throwing the skate; the reaction force is the skate exerting an opposite force on Stewart.

Think Critically: When Stewart threw the equipment toward the center of the pond, the effect was Stewart's moving in the opposite direction toward the edge.

CONCEPT DEVELOPMENT

► Discuss shooting a rubber dart gun in terms of conservation of momentum. Make sure students realize that the total momentum of the system (gun and dart) was zero both before and after the dart was fired. Because the dart had forward momentum, the gun had to recoil with an equal momentum in the opposite direction; because the gun had more mass than the dart, its speed was slower than that of the dart.

CROSS CURRICULUM

► **Social Studies:** Have students research the history of rocketry.

STUDENT TEXT QUESTION

Page 102, paragraph 2: **What outside force makes that happen?** *The outside force acting on the pool balls is friction.*

MINI QUIZ

Use the Mini Quiz to check students' recall of chapter content.

1 **How do the sizes and the directions of the forces in action-reaction pairs compare?** *equal in size and opposite in direction*

2 **What two measurements are needed to calculate the momentum of an object?** *mass and velocity*

3 **What is the unit of momentum?** *kg • m/s*

In Your JOURNAL

Students may describe collisions between automobiles, athletes, or other objects.

The Icy Challenge

The winter had been very cold, and the ice on the local pond was thick and smooth—just right for ice hockey. One day Stewart and his friends were walking across the pond, carrying their skates and hockey equipment. A few meters from the edge of the pond, Stewart slipped and fell and landed on his back.

After making sure he wasn't hurt, Stewart's friends challenged him to make it to land without turning over or standing up. Stewart tried pushing against the ice with his hands and feet, but the ice was so slippery that he didn't move. Then he had a brainstorm. He took one of his skates and threw it as hard as he could toward the center of the pond. Stewart continued to throw pieces of his hockey equipment toward the center of the pond until he found himself at the pond's edge.

Think Critically: Describe the forces involved in the throwing of the equipment. Explain what motions took place and why they occurred.

EcoTip

Get in motion! Weed gardens by hand or by hoe instead of using harmful chemicals. You and your garden will benefit from the exercise.

momentum. The first ball slows down and loses momentum. If you were to measure the total momentum of the two balls before and after the collision, it would be the same. The momentum the second ball gains is equal to the momentum that the first ball loses. Total momentum is conserved—it doesn't change.

The **law of conservation of momentum** states that the total amount of momentum of a group of objects does not change unless outside forces act on the objects. After the collision, the balls on the pool table eventually slow down and stop rolling. What outside force makes that happen?

OPTIONS

INQUIRY QUESTIONS

► In a circus, a 50-kg clown is shot out of a cannon at 20 m/s. What is the recoil speed of the cannon if it has a mass of 250 kg? *The momentum of the clown is 50 kg × 20 m/s = 1000 kg • m/s. Because momentum is conserved, the cannon must have an equal momentum in the opposite direction. The cannon recoils with a speed of 4 m/s because 250 kg × 4 m/s = 1000 kg • m/s.*

PROGRAM RESOURCES

From the **Teacher Resource Package** use:

Critical Thinking/Problem Solving, page 10, Tires and Hazardous Weather Conditions.

Cross-Curricular Connections, page 8, A 17th Century Timer.

Science and Society, page 8, Bicycle Helmets.

Use **Laboratory Manual 6,** Conservation of Momentum and Velocity; and **7,** Velocity and Momentum.

With Newton's third law and conservation of momentum, you can explain all sorts of motion that may seem complicated at first. Bouncing on a trampoline, knocking down bowling pins with a ball, and tackling a football player are a few examples. Think about how you would explain these and other examples of motion.

SECTION REVIEW

1. A boater tries to jump a few feet from a boat to land. Instead, he lands in the water. Explain why.
2. Compare the momentums of a 50-kg dolphin swimming 16.4 m/s and a 6300-kg elephant walking 0.11 m/s.
3. **Apply:** Some directors assign larger dancers to perform slow, graceful steps and smaller dancers to perform quick movements. Does this plan make sense?
4. **Connect to Earth Science:** Huge masses of ice called glaciers changed the landscape as they crept across the land. Would a glacier have a large or small momentum? Explain your answer.

☑ Concept Mapping

Make two events chains showing what happens when a rolling ball (Ball One) hits a resting ball (Ball Two). Use the phrases: *gains momentum; rests; rolls more slowly or stops; hits Ball Two; rolls; loses momentum; is hit by Ball One; starts rolling.* If you need help, refer to Concept Mapping in the **Skill Handbook** on pages 684 and 685.

Skill Builder

CHECK FOR UNDERSTANDING

Ask questions 1-2 and the **Apply** and **Connect to Earth Science** questions in the Section Review.

RETEACH

Have students bring in action photographs of various sporting events and identify action-reaction pairs and net forces. Have students explain their choices to the class.

EXTENSION

For students who have mastered this section, use the **Reinforcement** and **Enrichment** masters or other OPTIONS provided.

3 CLOSE

▶ Have students explain the results of the motivation demonstration in terms of Newton's third law.

SECTION REVIEW ANSWERS

1. In reaction to the force of the boater's foot pushing against the boat, the boat moves away from land, causing the boater to land in the water.

2. Dolphin's momentum: 50 kg × 16.4 m/s = 820 kg • m/s; Elephant's momentum: 6300 kg × 0.11 m/s = 693 kg • m/s. The dolphin has greater momentum.

3. Apply: Yes; a large dancer moving quickly would have more momentum than a smaller dancer moving at the same speed making it more difficult to change speed or direction.

4. Connect to Earth Science: With their large masses glaciers have enormous momenta.

Skill Builder

You may wish to provide students with the map forms and initial entries as shown.

Skill Builder
ASSESSMENT
Performance: Have students perform this experiment. Is the momentum still conserved if the balls move off at angles to each other? Ask students how the direction of Ball Two can be controlled.

Ball 1	Ball 2
Rolls	Rests
Hits ball 2	Hit by ball 1
Loses momentum	Gains momentum
Rolls more slowly	Starts rolling

ACTIVITY 4-2

30 minutes

OBJECTIVE: Compare the roles of mass and velocity in the momentum of an object.

PROCESS SKILLS applied in this activity:
▶ **Observing** in Procedure Steps 5, 6, and 7.
▶ **Controlling Variables** in Procedure Steps 6 and 7.
▶ **Defining Operationally** in Analyze Questions 2 and 3 and Conclude and Apply Question 6.

COOPERATIVE LEARNING
The ideal group size is three. But it may be necessary to work in larger teams if lab space and equipment are limited.

TEACHING THE ACTIVITY

Troubleshooting: The lab setup requires about 2 meters of counter or table space.
▶ Keep extra rubber bands handy. If the extra long type is not available, link together several shorter ones.
▶ Lighter carts than those pictured can be used, but may not survive the collisions.
▶ If appropriate, the lab can lead to a discussion of momentum within a stationary or a moving frame of reference. (What is the momentum of the carts if this lab were conducted inside a moving railroad car?)

Activity
ASSESSMENT

Oral: Ask students to discuss the question about the bowling ball in the introductory paragraph.

A Massive Problem

Total momentum in a system is always conserved. All of the velocity of a rolling billiard ball will transfer to a second ball when they collide. What would happen if the ball at rest were a bowling ball? The following activity shows how mass affects momentum.

Materials
- dynamics carts (2)
- long rubber band
- building bricks (2)
- meterstick
- masking tape

Procedure
1. *Prepare a data table* like the one shown.
2. Attach a long rubber band to the two dynamics carts. Move the carts apart until the rubber band is taut, but not stretched.
3. Place a piece of tape on the table to mark the halfway point between the two carts. Lay the meterstick on the table with the 50-cm mark beside the piece of tape.
4. Pull the carts apart until the ends of the rubber band line up with the ends of the meterstick.
5. Release both carts at the same time so that they gain the same momentum. *Observe* and *record* the point along the meterstick where the carts collide. Also *observe* where the carts stop after the collision.
6. Place a brick on cart A and repeat Steps 4 and 5.
7. Add a second brick to cart A and repeat Steps 4 and 5.

Analyze
1. How can you tell from the data which cart was moving faster?
2. How can both carts have the same momentum if they are traveling at different speeds?
3. How does the addition of mass to one cart affect the location of the collision point? How does it affect what happens to the carts after the collision?

Conclude and Apply
4. If one cart were released slightly before the other, how would the momenta of the two carts be affected?
5. If one cart has more momentum than the other, what happens when the carts collide?
6. Suppose momentum is said to be negative (–) in one direction and positive (+) in the opposite direction. If two carts having the same amount of momentum are traveling in opposite directions, what is the total momentum of the two-cart system?

Sample Data

Data and Observations

	Collision Point	Distance Traveled		Location after Collision	
		Cart A	Cart B	Cart A	Cart B
Trial 1	50 cm	50 cm	50 cm	20 cm	80 cm
Trial 2	40 cm	40 cm	60 cm	15 cm	77 cm
Trial 3	20 cm	20 cm	80 cm	12 cm	68 cm

ANSWERS TO QUESTIONS

1. Because both carts traveled for the same period of time, the cart that traveled farther had the higher average velocity.

2. The faster cart has a lower mass.

3. The collision point will be closer to the origin of cart A. Cart A will move less distance from the collision than will cart B.

4. The cart released first will gain the greater momentum.

5. If the cart with the greater momentum also has the greater mass, it will continue to move forward.

6. The sum of the total momentum is zero.

PROGRAM RESOURCES

From the **Teacher Resource Package** use:
Activity Worksheets, pages 33-34, Activity 4-2: A Massive Problem.

SUMMARY

4-1: Accelerated Motion

1. According to Newton's second law, a net force acting on an object causes the object to accelerate in the direction of the force. The size of the acceleration depends on the strength of the force and the mass of the object.

2. Near Earth's surface, gravity causes falling objects to accelerate at a rate of 9.8 m/s². Ignoring air resistance, all objects accelerate at this rate, regardless of mass.

3. Air resistance acts in the opposite direction to that in which the object is moving.

4-2: Projectile and Circular Motion

1. Objects thrown or shot through the air are called projectiles. All projectiles have both horizontal and vertical velocities. The horizontal velocity is constant; the vertical velocity, which is affected by gravity, increases.

2. When an object moves along a circular path, it is accelerated toward the center of the circle.

3. When an object is influenced only by gravity, it is said to be in free-fall. Objects in free-fall

can be considered weightless. To be truly weightless, an object would have to be free from gravity.

4-3: Science and Society: To Boldly— and Safely—Go

1. Health problems have resulted from long exposure to weightlessness. Experimentation has shown some of the problems can be prevented.

2. Space experts argue whether or not robots could explore planets without endangering astronauts.

4-4: Action and Reaction

1. Forces always act in pairs. The forces in an action-reaction pair are always equal in size and opposite in direction.

2. All moving objects have momentum. The momentum of an object is the product of its mass and velocity.

3. The total momentum of a set of objects is conserved unless a net force acts on the set.

KEY SCIENCE WORDS

a. **air resistance**
b. **centripetal acceleration**
c. **centripetal force**
d. **isometric exercise**
e. **law of conservation of momentum**
f. **momentum**
g. **Newton's second law of motion**
h. **Newton's third law of motion**
i. **projectile**
j. **terminal velocity**

UNDERSTANDING VOCABULARY

Match each phrase with the correct term from the list of Key Science Words.

1. deals with action-reaction forces
2. force that opposes the motion of a falling object near Earth's surface.
3. an object that is thrown through the air
4. acceleration toward the center of a circle
5. product of an object's mass and velocity
6. describes the effect of a net force on an object
7. exerting muscles against muscles
8. causes circular motion
9. achieved when acceleration due to gravity is balanced by air resistance
10. unchanging nature of the total momentum of a set of objects

ACCELERATION AND MOMENTUM **105**

OPTIONS

ASSESSMENT

To assess students understanding of material in this chapter use the resources listed.

👥 COOPERATIVE LEARNING

Consider using cooperative learning in the THINK AND WRITE CRITICALLY, APPLY, and MORE SKILL BUILDERS sections of the Chapter Review.

PROGRAM RESOURCES

From the **Teacher Resource Package** use:
Chapter Review, pages 11-12
Chapter and Unit Tests, pages 24-27, Chapter Test.

SUMMARY

Have students read the summary statements to review the major concepts of the chapter.

UNDERSTANDING VOCABULARY

1. h		**6.** g	
2. a		**7.** d	
3. i		**8.** c	
4. b		**9.** j	
5. f		**10.** e	

ASSESSMENT
Portfolio

Encourage students to place in their portfolios one or two items of what they consider to be their best work. For each item, ask students to explain why that item was chosen and what they learned from it. Items might be selected from the following.

• In Your Journal paragraph, p. 88
• Connect to Earth Science answer and diagram, p. 91
• Problem Solving answer, p. 102

Performance

Additional performance assessments may be found in *Performance Assessment* and *Science Integration Activities* that accompany **Merrill Physical Science**. Performance Task Assessment Lists and rubrics for evaluating these activities and other products generated throughout the chapter can be found in Glencoe's *Performance Assessment in Middle School Science*.

CHECKING CONCEPTS

1. b	6. c
2. d	7. a
3. b	8. d
4. c	9. b
5. d	10. a

USING LAB SKILLS

ASSESSMENT

Use these alternate lab exercises to assess students' understanding of the skills used in this chapter.

11. The initial velocity in the vertical direction determines the height reached and the time in the air. Horizontal velocity does not affect the time of flight.

12. They would have the same momentum if cart B had twice the velocity of cart A.

THINK AND WRITE CRITICALLY

13. The weight of an object is the force of gravity acting on its mass. Therefore, the greater the mass of an object, the greater the force of gravity that acts on it and the greater its weight.

14. The rate at which gravity causes a falling object to accelerate is independent of the mass of the object. Although the force of gravity acting on a large mass at the same distance from Earth is greater than for a small mass, the greater inertia of the larger mass requires more force be exerted on it to change its motion.

15. In order for two forces to be balanced, they must act on the same object. The forces in an action-reaction pair act on different objects; therefore, they cannot be balanced by each other.

16. Although the spaceship is kept from flying off into space by Earth's gravity, the spaceship and everything in it are in free-fall around Earth. This condition produces the impression of weightlessness because there is no "upward" force to act against gravity. Because the spaceship does not exert any force against the astronauts, the astronauts feel weightless.

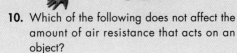

CHECKING CONCEPTS

Choose the word or phrase that completes the sentence or answers the question.

1. A net force acting on a moving object causes the object to _____.
  a. fall **c.** stop
  b. accelerate **d.** curve

2. _____ is the effect of gravity on an object.
  a. Mass **c.** Centripetal force
  b. Momentum **d.** Weight

3. Which of these opposes acceleration due to gravity?
  a. momentum **c.** reaction force
  b. air resistance **d.** terminal velocity

4. According to Newton's second law, _____ equals mass times acceleration.
  a. gravity **c.** force
  b. momentum **d.** weight

5. What force causes a leaf to fall more slowly than a penny?
  a. gravity **c.** inertia
  b. momentum **d.** air resistance

6. Which best illustrates Newton's third law?
  a. projectile motion **c.** rocket propulsion
  b. circular motion **d.** centripetal force

7. The _____ velocity of a projectile is considered to be constant.
  a. horizontal **c.** accelerated
  b. circular **d.** vertical

8. An object in free-fall can be considered _____.
  a. moving horizontally **c.** motionless
  b. heavy **d.** weightless

9. _____ is reached when air resistance and acceleration due to gravity are equal.
  a. Negative acceleration
  b. Terminal velocity
  c. Centripetal acceleration
  d. Weightlessness

10. Which of the following does not affect the amount of air resistance that acts on an object?
  a. mass **c.** shape
  b. size **d.** speed

USING LAB SKILLS

11. In Activity 4-1 on page 95, you studied the motion of projectiles thrown at several angles. Explain what determines the time a pop fly hit in a baseball game will remain in the air.

12. Look back at your results from Activity 4-2 on page 104. Suppose you have cart A carrying a load that makes it twice as massive as cart B. Under what conditions could both carts have the same momentum?

THINK AND WRITE CRITICALLY

Answer the following questions in your Journal using complete sentences.

13. On Earth, why does an object of large mass weigh more than an object of smaller mass?

14. Explain why gravity does not cause a falling object of large mass to accelerate at a faster rate than a falling object of smaller mass.

15. If the forces in an action-reaction pair are equal in size and opposite in direction, why aren't they balanced forces?

16. A spaceship orbiting Earth is held in its orbit by Earth's gravity. Yet, astronauts in the spaceship are said to be weightless. Explain.

17. Explain why a marble moves in a straight line as it rolls across the table, but follows a curved path once it rolls off the table.

17. A ball rolling across a table has no net force acting on it to cause it to change its motion. Once the ball rolls off the edge of the table, gravity is the only force acting on it and the ball becomes a projectile. Because the ball has a constant horizontal velocity and a constant vertical acceleration downward, the path of the ball is curved.

18. What force is exerted on a 1000-kg car accelerating at a rate of 15 m/s²?

19. The motion of a 12-kg object is opposed by a 30-N force of friction. At what rate does friction slow the object down?

20. You are asked to design a winding mountain road. What force must you try to increase in designing this road? How might you do this?

21. A 5-kg object with a velocity of 6 m/s strikes a motionless 10-kg ball. The object stops moving as a result of the collision. What is the velocity of the ball after the collision?

22. The moon has no atmosphere and its gravity is about one-sixth as strong as that of Earth. Considering these factors, how would the motions of objects near the moon be different than the same motions near Earth?

MORE SKILL BUILDERS

If you need help, refer to the Skill Handbook.

1. **Interpreting Data:** The table contains data about four objects dropped to the ground from the same height at the same time.

Object	A	B	C	D
Mass	5.0 g	5.0 g	30.0 g	35.0 g
Time of Fall	2.0 s	1.0 s	0.5 s	1.5 s

a. Which object falls fastest? Slowest?
b. On which object is the force of gravity greatest?
c. Is air resistance stronger on A or B?
d. Which object is probably largest in size? Explain your reasoning.

2. **Observing and Inferring:** A girl weighing 360 N gets on a motionless elevator at the ground floor. She steps onto a scale and remains on the scale while the elevator accelerates, then moves at a constant speed, and finally slows to a stop at the 120th floor. During that time, the readings on the scale range from a high of 365 N to a low of 355 N. Infer what the reading was on the ground floor, on the way up, stopping, and stopped on the 120th floor. Why do these readings change?

3. **Recognizing Cause and Effect:** When using a high-pressure hose, why is it necessary for firefighters to grip the hose strongly and plant their feet firmly?

4. **Making and Using Graphs:** Construct a time-distance graph of the following data for a ball thrown into the air at an angle to the ground.

Height	0	25	40	45	40	25	0
Time	0	1	2	3	4	5	6

Use the graph to answer the following:
a. Does the ball accelerate vertically? How do you know?
b. When is the ball's vertical velocity zero?
c. If the ball has a horizontal velocity of 40 m/s, how far will it travel before it hits the ground?

PROJECTS

1. Make a poster diagram of a rocket engine showing how it works. If possible, build a model rocket. Share the results of the project with your classmates. Use Newton's third law to explain why a rocket lifts off.

2. Research the positive and negative aspects of prolonged space flight. Write an essay stating your position on this topic. Read your essay aloud and have a class debate.

ACCELERATION AND MOMENTUM **107**

18. $F = m \times a$
$= 1000 \text{ kg} \times 15 \text{ m/s}^2$
$= 15\ 000 \text{ N}$

19. $F = m \times a$

$a = \dfrac{F}{m}$

$= \dfrac{30 \text{ N}}{12 \text{ kg}} = \dfrac{30 \text{ kg} \bullet \text{m/s}^2}{12 \text{ kg}}$

$= 2.5 \text{ m/s}^2$

20. The centripetal force acting on any cars moving along the road must be made as large as possible to keep the cars moving in a curved path around the mountain. This force is affected by the force of friction between the road surface and the tires and by the shape of the curves. Therefore, you could use a slightly rougher material for the road surface, to increase friction, and you could avoid making sharp curves. The road surface could also be angled upward in the outside parts of the curves.

21. Momentum must be conserved, so the momentum of the ball must be the same as that of the object that started it in motion.

Momentum of object:

$p = m \times v$
$= 5 \text{ kg} \times 6 \text{ m/s} = 30 \text{ kg} \bullet \text{m/s}$

Velocity of ball:

$v = \dfrac{p}{m} = \dfrac{30 \text{ kg} \bullet \text{m/s}}{10 \text{ kg}} = 3 \text{ m/s}$

22. Because of the moon's smaller force of gravity, the rate of acceleration of a falling object due to gravity would be smaller on the moon than on Earth. However, there would be no air resistance to slow a falling object near the moon, so there would be no terminal velocity. A falling object would continue to accelerate at the same rate until it struck the moon's surface.

The low reading occurs as the elevator slows at the top. The scale must exert a force less than the girl's weight to produce a net downward force, slowing her to a stop. Any time the elevator is not accelerating (stopped or moving at constant velocity) the scale must produce a force equal to the girl's weight.

3. **Recognizing Cause and Effect:** The force of the water may knock them down (Newton's third law).

4. **Graphing:**
a. Yes; the time-distance graph for the ball's vertical motion is not a straight line, indicating that the motion is accelerated.
b. The vertical velocity of the ball is zero at $t = 3$ seconds.

c. $v = \dfrac{d}{t}$ $d = v \times t$
$= 40 \text{ m/s} \times 6 \text{ s} = 240 \text{ m}$

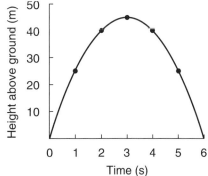

MORE SKILL BUILDERS

1. **Interpreting Data:**
a. Object C falls fastest, object A slowest.
b. Object D   c. Object A
d. Object D, because it has more mass, but falls slowly.

2. **Observing and Inferring:** The high reading occurs as the elevator begins its upward motion. The scale must exert a greater upward force than the weight of the girl to produce a net upward force.

CHAPTER 4   **107**

5 Energy

CHAPTER SECTION	OBJECTIVES	ACTIVITIES
5-1 Energy and Work (2 days)	1. **Distinguish** between kinetic and potential energy. 2. **Recognize** that energy can change from one form to other forms with no loss of total energy. 3. **Compare** the scientific meaning of *work* with its everyday meaning.	**Activity 5-1:** *Conservation Connections,* p. 117
5-2 Temperature and Heat (2 days)	1. **Recognize** the difference between the motion of an object and the motion of the particles that make up the object. 2. **Contrast** heat and temperature. 3. **Explain** what determines the thermal energy of a sample of matter.	**MINI-Lab:** *Can you create energy?* p. 118
5-3 Energy from the Oceans and Earth Science & Society (1 day)	1. **Explain** why ocean waters and subsurface rock may represent possible new sources of thermal energy. 2. **Discuss** the benefits and drawbacks of proceeding with research and development of these new energy sources.	
5-4 Measuring Thermal Energy (2 days)	1. **Define** *specific heat.* 2. **Calculate** changes in thermal energy.	**Activity 5-2:** *A Hot Topic,* p. 128
Chapter Review		

ACTIVITY MATERIALS

FIND OUT	ACTIVITIES		MINI-LABS
Page 109 box full of books (more than 4)	**5-1 Conservation Connections, p. 117** ring stand and ring support rod clamp, right angle support rod, 30 cm metersticks (2) rubber stopper, 2-hole, medium string, 1m masking tape	**5-2 A Hot Topic, p. 128** set of electric hair curlers thermometers, Celsius (2) plastic foam cup graph paper balance graduated cylinder	**Can you create energy? p. 118** sand plastic foam cup with lid Celsius thermometer

CHAPTER FEATURES	TEACHER RESOURCE PACKAGE	OTHER RESOURCES
Skill Builder: *Comparing and Contrasting,* p. 116	**Ability Level Worksheets** ◆ **Study Guide,** p. 22 ● **Reinforcement,** p. 22 ▲ **Enrichment,** p. 22 **Activity Worksheets,** pp. 39, 40 **Cross-Curricular Connections,** p. 9 **Transparency Master,** pp. 17, 18 **Science and Society,** p. 9	**Color Transparency 9,** Kinetic and Potential Energy **Laboratory Manual 8,** The Energy of a Pendulum **Laboratory Manual 9,** Work and Power **STVS:** Disc, Side 2 **Science Integration Activity 5**
Problem Solving: *A Cold Cup of Tea and a Warm Soft Drink,* p. 120 **Skill Builder:** *Concept Mapping,* p. 121	**Ability Level Worksheets** ◆ **Study Guide,** p. 23 ● **Reinforcement,** p. 23 ▲ **Enrichment,** p. 23 **Activity Worksheets,** pp. 5, 45 **Transparency Masters,** pp. 19, 20	**Color Transparency 10,** Cool and Hot Matter **STVS:** Disc 2, Side 2 Disc 2, Side 2
You Decide! p. 123	**Ability Level Worksheets** ◆ **Study Guide,** p. 24 ● **Reinforcement,** p. 24 ▲ **Enrichment,** p. 24 **Science and Society,** p. 9 **Critical Thinking/Problem Solving,** p. 11 **Activity Worksheets,** p. 5	**STVS:** Disc 2, Side 2
Technology: *Infrared Weather Eyes,* p. 125 **Skill Builder:** *Interpreting Data,* p. 127	**Ability Level Worksheets** ◆ **Study Guide,** p. 25 ● **Reinforcement,** p. 25 ▲ **Enrichment,** p. 25 **Activity Worksheets,** pp. 41, 42 **Concept Mapping,** pp. 15, 16	**Laboratory Manual 10,** Heat Transfer
Summary Think & Write Critically Key Science Words Apply Understanding Vocabulary More Skill Builders Checking Concepts Projects Using Lab Skills	**ASSESSMENT RESOURCES** **Chapter Review,** pp. 13, 14 **Chapter Test,** pp. 28-31 **Performance Assessment in** **Middle School Science**	**Chapter Review Software** **Test Bank** **Alternate Assessment** **Performance Assessment**

◆ **Basic**   ● **Average**   ▲ **Advanced**

ADDITIONAL MATERIALS

SOFTWARE	AUDIOVISUAL	BOOKS/MAGAZINES
Energy and Power, Micro Ed. *Heat, Light, and Sound,* Queue. *Heat,* Queue. *Heat, Temperature, and Graphs,* EduQuest. *Heat and Temperature,* Queue. *Heat,* Cross Educational Software. *Learning All About Energy,* Queue.	*Energy at Work,* Laserdisc, Churchill Media. *Energy,* Video, Insight Media. *Energy and Work,* Video, Britannica. *Heat: Molecules In Motion,* Laserdisc, AIMS Media. *Power To Do Work,* Video, AIT. *Thermal Energy,* Video, AIT.	Ardley, Neil. *Heat.* NY: Discovery, 1992. Mellett, Peter, and Jane Rossiter. *Hot and Cold.* NY: Watts, 1993. Stwertka, Albert, and Eve Stwertka. A Chilling Story: *How Things Cool Down.* Englewood Cliffs, NJ: Silver Burdett Press, 1991.

THEME DEVELOPMENT: The theme of this chapter is energy and its use in describing how matter behaves. Energy as the ability to cause a change is introduced and should be emphasized in each section. Mechanical energy is discussed and is used to introduce the concept of thermal energy at the microscopic level.

CHAPTER OVERVIEW

▶ **Section 5-1:** Kinetic and potential energies are discussed qualitatively. Work is introduced as the means of transferring energy through motion. Mechanical energy in a pendulum is used to introduce the law of conservation of energy.

▶ **Section 5-2:** This section presents the relationship between the temperature of a material and the average kinetic energy of its particles. The difference between thermal energy and heat is discussed.

▶ **Section 5-3: Science and Society:** Possible energy resources from the oceans and Earth are presented. Students are asked to analyze the economic and environmental factors of research projects involving these energy resources.

▶ **Section 5-4:** Specific heat is introduced as a means of measuring changes in thermal energy.

PREPLANNING

▶ Motivation demonstration for Section 5-3; piece of granite rock

CHAPTER VOCABULARY

energy	temperature
kinetic energy	thermal
potential energy	energy
work	heat
mechanical energy	magma
law of conservation	specific heat
of energy	

CHAPTER

5 Energy

108

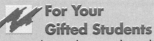

OPTIONS

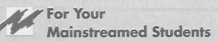

For Your Gifted Students

Have the students make a liquid thermometer. They should devise a way to make their own temperature scale and compare it with the Fahrenheit, Celsius, and Kelvin scales. Have students come up with a formula to convert their scales to one of the scales mentioned.
(See "For Your Mainstreamed Students" for directions on making a liquid thermometer.)

For Your Mainstreamed Students

Students can make a liquid thermometer by filling a milk carton with colored water. Make a hole at the center top of the carton. Insert a plastic straw in the hole and seal it in place. Fill the straw part way with colored water. Record the daily increase or decrease in the water level of the straw. Chart the rise and fall of the thermometer.

How many ways do you use your own energy every day? Do some kinds of work take more effort than others? Is all exertion work?

FIND OUT!

Compare and contrast your experiences performing the following tasks to answer the questions.

Stand and hold your arms out in front of you at waist level with your hands together, palms up. Have a classmate stack two books on your hands. Raise the books to about shoulder level, then lower them. Now try raising them overhead. Are you working harder than you did when you raised them to shoulder level? Lower the books again. Have your classmate put two more books on the pile, so you're holding four books. Try to raise them to shoulder level. Are you using more force than when you were holding only two books?

Hold the four books at shoulder level until your arms get tired. Are you applying force? Can you *conclude* that you're doing work?

Now fill a box of books and try pushing it along the floor. Can you push it farther if a classmate helps?

Gearing Up
Previewing the Chapter
Use this outline to help you focus on important ideas in this chapter.

Previewing Science Skills
► In the Skill Builders, you will compare and contrast, make a concept map, and interpret data.
► In the Activities, you will measure in SI, observe and infer, collect and interpret data, prepare graphs, and hypothesize.
► In the MINI-Lab, you will measure in SI, observe and infer, and hypothesize.

What's next?

You have seen that sometimes things move when you exert force, sometimes they don't. Now find out why this is so. As you move through this chapter, you will learn what energy is and how it's related to work. You will learn to recognize when work is done and when it isn't. And, finally, you will find out some things about heat and temperature that may surprise you, especially if you've always thought they meant the same thing.

109

INTRODUCING THE CHAPTER
Use the Find Out activity to introduce students to the concept of work and energy. Tell them that they will learn more about these concepts and how they are related in this chapter.

FIND OUT!
Preparation: Obtain sets of similar books.
Materials: four books per pair of students

Cooperative Learning: Assign Problem Solving Teams to conduct this activity quantitatively. Have students measure the weight of the books or calculate the weight from mass measurements of the books. Have the team use the measurements from this activity to calculate work as an enrichment for Section 5-1.
Teaching Tips
► **CAUTION:** *Students with health problems should limit their participation in this activity.*
► Have students raise or lower the books each time at a slow, constant speed.
► During this activity, ask students to state when they are doing work and when the work is increased.

Gearing Up
Have students study the Gearing Up feature to familiarize themselves with the chapter. Discuss the relationships of the topics in the outline.

What's Next?
Before beginning the first section, make sure students understand the connection between the Find Out activity and the topics to follow.

ASSESSMENT OPTIONS

PORTFOLIO
Refer to page 129 for suggested items that students might select for their portfolios.

PERFORMANCE ASSESSMENT
See page 129 for additional Performance Assessment options.
Process
Skill Builders, pp. 121, 127
MINI-Lab, p. 119
Activities 5-1, p. 117; 5-2, p. 128
Using Lab Skills, p. 130

CONTENT ASSESSMENT
Assessment—Oral, pp. 115, 120
Skill Builder, p. 116
Section Reviews, pp. 116, 121, 123, 127
Chapter Review, pp. 129-131
Mini Quizzes, pp. 111, 115, 121

GROUP ASSESSMENT
Opportunities for group assessment occur with Cooperative Learning Strategies and Flex Your Brain Activities.

PREPARATION

SECTION BACKGROUND

▶ Energy is defined as the ability of an object or phenomenon to cause a change. A moving baseball has energy because you can see and feel the change in motion of your hand as you catch it. Light is a form of energy because it can change pigments in photographic film and in the retina of the eye and can cause sunburn.

▶ An object can be described as having kinetic energy, a measure of its motion, and potential energy, a measure of its position or condition. Mechanical energy for an object is the sum of its kinetic and potential energies.

PREPLANNING

▶ Obtain a roll of waxed paper for the Motivation demonstration; a small weight and wood block for the Close demonstration.

1 MOTIVATE

▶ **Demonstration:** Attach a 1.0-m piece of waxed paper to several books with thumbtacks to form a track.

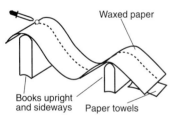

Waxed paper

Books upright and sideways   Paper towels

Using a medicine dropper, place a drop of water at the top of the ramp. Have students observe its motion. Repeat this several times, each time altering the shape of the ramp. Before releasing the drop, have students predict its motion. Afterwards, allow students to explain their reasoning in making their predictions.

▶ Have students discuss where changes of motion occur during a roller coaster ride.

5-1 Energy and Work

New Science Words

energy
kinetic energy
potential energy
work
mechanical energy
law of conservation of energy

Objectives

▶ Distinguish between kinetic and potential energy.
▶ Recognize that energy can change from one form to other forms with no loss of total energy.
▶ Compare the scientific meaning of *work* with its everyday meaning.

Kinetic and Potential Energy

Have you seen any examples of energy in action today? Unless you stayed in bed all day with the covers over your head, the answer to the question is "yes." Just about everything you see or do involves energy.

Energy is a bit mysterious. You can't smell it. In most cases, you can't even see it. Light is one form of energy you can see. Light doesn't seem to do much, but without it, you wouldn't be able to see anything. You can't see electricity, but you can see its effects in a glowing light bulb, and you can feel its effects in the coils of a toaster. You can't see the energy in milk, but you can see and feel its effects when your muscles use that energy to move.

If a baseball flies through the air and shatters a window, it certainly changes the window! When an object is able to change its environment, we say the object has energy. The baseball had energy and did work on the window by causing the window to move. As all of the examples above show, energy involves change.

Scientists have some difficulty defining energy because it exists in so many different forms. Traditionally, energy has been defined as the ability to do work — to cause something to move. But when work is performed, there is always a change. This connection offers a useful general definition. **Energy** is the ability to cause change. ❶

Energy comes in many forms. Some of these forms include radiant, electrical, chemical, thermal and nuclear energy. The basic unit of energy is the joule (JEWL), named ❷ for the British scientist James Prescott Joule. You'll learn more about this unit of measure later in the chapter.

Figure 5-1. A healthful diet, such as the well-balanced breakfast shown here, provides the body with "fuel." Energy stored in food is converted to energy that the body can use.

OPTIONS

Meeting Different Ability Levels

For Section 5-1, use the following **Teacher Resource Masters** depending upon individual students' needs.

◆ **Study Guide Master** for all students.

● **Reinforcement Master** for students of average and above average ability levels.

▲ **Enrichment Master** for above average students.

Additional Teacher Resource Package masters are listed in any **PROGRAM RESOURCES** boxes that are in the section. The additional masters are appropriate for all students.

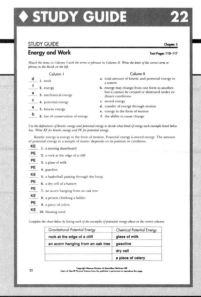

◆ **STUDY GUIDE** 22

STUDY GUIDE   Chapter 5
Energy and Work   Text Pages 110–117

Match the items in Column I with the terms or phrases in Column II. Write the letter of the correct term or phrase in the blank on the left.

	Column I		Column II
d	1. work	a.	total amount of kinetic and potential energy in a system
f	2. energy	b.	energy may change from one form to another, but it cannot be created or destroyed under ordinary conditions
a	3. mechanical energy	c.	stored energy
c	4. potential energy	d.	transfer of energy through motion
e	5. kinetic energy	e.	energy in the form of motion
b	6. law of conservation of energy	f.	the ability to cause change

Use the definitions of kinetic energy and potential energy to decide what kind of energy each example listed below has. Write KE for kinetic energy and PE for potential energy.

Kinetic energy is energy in the form of motion. Potential energy is stored energy. The amount of potential energy in a sample of matter depends on its position or condition.

KE	1. a moving skateboard
PE	2. a rock at the edge of a cliff
PE	3. a glass of milk
PE	4. gasoline
KE	5. a basketball passing through the hoop
PE	6. a dry cell of a battery
PE	7. an acorn hanging from an oak tree
KE	8. a person climbing a ladder
PE	9. a piece of celery
KE	10. blowing wind

Complete the chart below by listing each of the examples of potential energy above in the correct column.

Gravitational Potential Energy	Chemical Potential Energy
rock at the edge of a cliff	glass of milk
an acorn hanging from an oak tree	gasoline
	dry cell
	a piece of celery

22

Usually when you think of energy, you think of action—of some motion taking place. Motion-related energy is called kinetic energy. **Kinetic energy** is energy in the form of motion. A spinning motorcycle wheel, a leaping ballet dancer, and a flying Frisbee all have kinetic energy. How much? That depends on the mass and velocity of the moving object.

The greater the mass of a moving object, the more kinetic energy it has. Similarly, the greater its velocity, the more kinetic energy it has. A truck traveling at 100 km/h has more kinetic energy than a motorcycle traveling at the same speed. However, the motorcycle has more kinetic energy than an identical motorcycle moving at 80 km/h.

Energy doesn't have to involve motion. Even motionless, any sample of matter may have stored energy that gives it the potential to cause change if certain conditions are met. **Potential energy** is stored energy. The amount of potential energy a sample of matter has depends on its position or condition.

A flowerpot sitting on a second-floor windowsill has potential energy due to its position. If something knocks it off the windowsill, gravity will cause it to fall toward the ground. As it falls, its potential energy will change to kinetic energy.

Figure 5-2. This motorcycle is converting energy stored in gasoline into kinetic energy.

Connect to...
Life Science

Hawks and other predatory birds depend on swift descents to capture their prey. Sometimes when they strike, their force breaks the necks of their victims. Explain how they take advantage of potential and kinetic energy to be efficient hunters.

Figure 5-3. The kinetic energy of each vehicle is different because kinetic energy depends on mass and velocity.

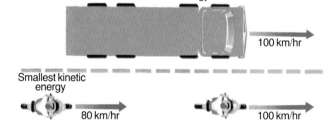

Greatest kinetic energy

100 km/hr

Smallest kinetic energy

80 km/hr   100 km/hr

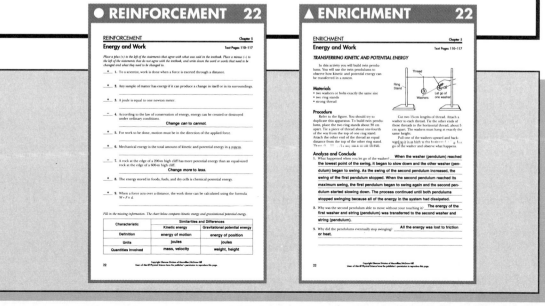

● **REINFORCEMENT** 22

REINFORCEMENT   Chapter 5
Energy and Work   Text Pages 110–117

Place a plus (+) to the left of the statements that agree with what was said in the textbook. Place a minus (−) to the left of the statements that do not agree with the textbook, and write down the word or words that need to be changed and what they need to be changed to.

___ 1. To a scientist, work is done when a force is exerted through a distance.

_+_ 2. Any sample of matter has energy if it can produce a change in itself or in its surroundings.

_+_ 3. A joule is equal to one newton meter.

_−_ 4. According to the law of conservation of energy, energy can be created or destroyed under ordinary conditions.
              Change can to cannot.

_+_ 5. For work to be done, motion must be in the direction of the applied force.

_+_ 6. Mechanical energy is the total amount of kinetic and potential energy in a system.

_−_ 7. A rock at the edge of a 200-m high cliff has more potential energy than an equal-sized rock at the edge of a 600-m high cliff.
              Change more to less.

_+_ 8. The energy stored in foods, fuels, and dry cells is chemical potential energy.

_+_ 9. When a force acts over a distance, the work done can be calculated using the formula $W = F \times d$.

Fill in the missing information. The chart below compares kinetic energy and gravitational potential energy.

Characteristic	Similarities and Differences	
	Kinetic energy	Gravitational potential energy
Definition	energy of motion	energy of position
Units	joules	joules
Quantities involved	mass, velocity	weight, height

22

▲ **ENRICHMENT** 22

ENRICHMENT   Chapter 5
Energy and Work   Text Pages 110–117

TRANSFERRING KINETIC AND POTENTIAL ENERGY

In this activity you will build twin pendulums. You will use the twin pendulums to observe how kinetic and potential energy can be transferred in a system.

Materials
• two washers or bolts exactly the same size
• two ring stands
• strong thread

Procedure
Refer to the figure. You should try to duplicate this apparatus. To build twin pendulums, place the two ring stands about 50 cm apart. Tie a piece of thread about one-fourth of the way from the top of one ring stand. Attach the other end of the thread an equal distance from the top of the other ring stand. Thread the thread any stack on the thread.

Cut two 15-cm lengths of thread. Attach a washer to each thread. Tie the other ends of these threads to the horizontal thread, about 5 cm apart. The washers must hang at exactly the same height.

Pull one of the washers upward and backward so it is as high as the horizontal thread. Let go of the washer and observe what happens.

Analyze and Conclude
1. What happened when you let go of the washer? **When the washer (pendulum) reached the lowest point of the swing, it began to slow down and the other washer (pendulum) began to swing. As the swing of the second pendulum increased, the swing of the first pendulum stopped. When the second pendulum reached its maximum swing, the first pendulum began to swing again and the second pendulum started slowing down. The process continued until both pendulums stopped swinging because all of the energy in the system had dissipated.**

2. Why was the second pendulum able to move without your touching it? **The energy of the first washer and string (pendulum) was transferred to the second washer and string (pendulum).**

3. Why did the pendulums eventually stop swinging? **All the energy was lost to friction or heat.**

22

Copyright Glencoe Division of Macmillan/McGraw-Hill
Users of Merrill Physical Science have the publisher's permission to reproduce this page.

CONCEPT DEVELOPMENT

▶ Familiarize students with the size of a joule. About one joule of energy is needed to lift a glass of milk to your mouth or lift an apple from the floor to the table. About 1500 J of energy is needed for a student to climb a flight of stairs.

TEACHER F.Y.I.

▶ The kinetic energy of an object is defined by the equation $K.E. = 1/2\ mv^2$ where $K.E.$ represents the kinetic energy of an object, m its mass, and v its velocity. The equation indicates that the kinetic energy varies directly with the *mass* of an object and the *square of its velocity*.

▶ The gravitational potential energy of an object is given by the equation

$$P.E. = mgh$$

where P.E. represents the gravitational potential energy of an object, m its mass, g the acceleration of gravity, and h is its height above some arbitrary zero level.

REVEALING MISCONCEPTIONS

▶ Students often confuse energy transformations with changes in matter. For example, ask students how energy is related to the food they eat. Some may state that food is converted into energy in the body. In reality, the chemical energy of the food is converted into mechanical energy of the muscles as food is digested and used as fuel.

▶ Discuss how everyday situations can be described in terms of energy conversions, but not in terms of matter to energy conversions.

CROSS CURRICULUM

▶ **Language Arts:** Have students look up the words *kinetic* and *potential* in the dictionary. Students should find that the former comes from the Greek root *kinein* (to move) and the latter from the Latin root *potere* (to be powerful). Ask a volunteer to state how the words reflect the meaning of their roots. Note that "cinema," which means moving pictures, also comes from the same Greek word as kinetic.

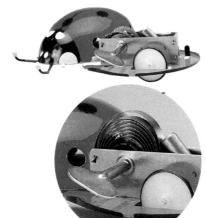

Figure 5-4. The spring in the wound condition has potential energy that can be used to make the toy move. In the enlarged view, the unwound spring has neither potential nor kinetic energy.

Potential energy is related to height above Earth's surface and is sometimes called gravitational potential energy. The greater the height, the greater the potential energy. A flowerpot sitting on a fifth-floor windowsill has more potential energy than one sitting on a lower windowsill.

Think of the spring in a wind-up toy. The tension in the spring is its condition. As the spring is wound, it gains potential energy. When the spring is released, the spring unwinds and makes the toy move. The potential energy of the spring is changed to kinetic energy of the toy.

The energy stored in foods, fuels, and dry cells are examples of chemical potential energy. These and other forms of potential energy will be discussed in later chapters of this book.

Work

To most people, the word *work* means something they do to earn money. Work can be anything from filling fast-food orders, loading trucks, or teaching, to doing office work at a desk. The scientific meaning of work is more specific. **Work** is the transfer of energy through motion. ⑤ In order for work to take place, a force must be exerted through a distance.

Figure 5-5. Work is done on the books when they are being lifted, but no work is done on them when they are being held or carried horizontally.

OPTIONS

ENRICHMENT

▶ Have students research the imaginary inventions of cartoonist, Rube Goldberg. Have them discuss the energy conversions illustrated by his contraptions.

▶ Have students research the concept of entropy found in the thermodynamics section of most high school physics texts. Have students present their research to the class by discussing the answer to the Section Review **Apply** question in terms of entropy.

In which case would you do more work—lifting a pack of gum from the floor to waist level or lifting a pile of books through the same distance? Would more work be done if you lifted the books from the floor to your waist or if you raised them all the way over your head? The amount of work done depends on two things: the amount of force exerted and the distance over which the force is applied.

When a force acts over a distance in the direction of an object's motion, the work done can be calculated as

$$\text{Work} = \text{force} \times \text{distance}$$
$$W = F \times d$$

Work, like energy, is measured in joules. One joule is equal to a newton-meter (N • m), which is the amount of work done when a force of one newton acts through a distance of one meter.

Science and WRITING

Spend a few minutes observing the different forms of energy around you. List all the different forms and describe events that result from one form of energy changing to another.

 6

EXAMPLE PROBLEM: Calculating Work

Problem Statement:	A student's full backpack weighs 10 N. She lifts it from the floor to a shelf 1.5 m high. How much work is done on the pack full of books?
Known Information: Strategy Hint: Remember that weight is a measure of the force of gravity on an object.	force, F = 10 N distance, d = 1.5 m
Unknown Information:	Work (W)

Equation to Use:	$W = F \times d$
	   $= 10\text{ N} \times 1.5\text{ m}$
	   $= 15\text{ N} \bullet \text{m}$

Solution:	$= 15\text{ J}$

PRACTICE PROBLEMS

Strategy Hint: The joule is a derived unit. What other units make it up?

Strategy Hint: Work requires a force to be exerted over a distance.

1. A carpenter lifts a 45-kg beam 1.2 m. How much work is done on the beam?

2. A dancer lifts a 400-N ballerina overhead a distance of 1.4 m and holds her there for several seconds. How much work is done on the ballerina?

CONCEPT DEVELOPMENT

▶ **Demonstration:** Using two thumbtacks, attach opposite ends of a long stretched, rubber band to a board forming a sling shot. Carefully use the sling shot to propel a small toy car along the board. Have students relate the kinetic energy of the car to the elastic potential energy of the rubber band.

▶ Have students realize that the relationship between a joule of energy and a joule of work comes from the definition: *work is the transfer of energy through motion.* When one joule of work is done on an object, one joule of energy has been transferred to the object.

▶ Point out that if friction acts on a moving object, the direction of the force is opposite the direction of motion; the work is negative.

TEACHER F.Y.I.

▶ The joule is equivalent to a newton-meter. If fundamental metric units are substituted for a newton, a newton-meter becomes
$\text{kg} \bullet \text{m/s}^2 \times \text{m} = \text{kg} \bullet \text{m}^2/\text{s}^2$
Likewise, if fundamental metric units are substituted in the equations for potential energy and kinetic energy, identical units emerge.
$\text{kg} \times \text{m/s}^2 \times \text{m} = \text{kg} \bullet \text{m}^2/\text{s}^2$ and
$\text{kg} \times (\text{m/s})^2 = \text{kg} \bullet \text{m}^2/\text{s}^2$

PRACTICE PROBLEM ANSWERS
1. $W = F \times d$
   $= (45\text{ kg} \times 9.8\text{ N/kg}) \times 1.2\text{ m}$
   $= 441\text{ N} \times 1.2\text{ m}$
   $= 529.2\text{ J}$
2. $W = F \times d$
   $= 400\text{ N} \times 1.4\text{ m}$
   $= 560\text{ J}$

VideoDisc
STVS: Hydroelectric Power, Disc 2, Side 2

PROGRAM RESOURCES

From the **Teacher Resource Package** use:
Science and Society, page 9, Energy Efficient Engines.
Science Integration Activity 5
Use **Laboratory Manual 9,** Work and Power.

CONCEPT DEVELOPMENT

▶ It is often difficult for students to understand why they feel tired holding books if they are not doing any work. Point out that in describing work, it is important to identify on what the work is being done. When holding books, the students are not doing work *on their books.* They are doing work *on their muscles.* Discuss that thousands of fibrils which make up muscle tissue can be pictured as small, coiled springs. When a muscle is contracted, these fibrils are constantly contracting, and relaxing. In contracting, work is being done on the fibrils. The students feel tired because they are doing work on their muscles.

TEACHER F.Y.I.

▶ Energy can be considered as a convenient number to describe an object or situation much like an accountant uses numbers in bookkeeping to describe incomes, expenditures, and bankruptcy. The conservation of energy means that the number that describes the total amount of energy does not change.

CONCEPT DEVELOPMENT

▶ **Demonstration:** Clamp each end of a 1-m length of plastic tubing to a ring stand. Adjust the clamps so that both ends of the tubing are the same height above the table forming a shallow, U-shaped ramp. Hold a marble slightly above one end of the tubing and ask students to predict the height that the marble will reach on the opposite side. Have a student mark the predicted positions on the tube using a felt tipped marker. Release the marble and have students observe the height it reaches. Rearrange the tubing to form various shaped ramps and discuss the motion of the marble, stressing the conservation of mechanical energy.

▶ Point out that the conservation of mechanical energy is independent of time. That is, the value of the mechanical energy is constant and does not change from moment to moment. For example, even though the potential and kinetic energies are constantly changing for a swinging pendulum, their sum is constant.

Name two factors to keep in mind when deciding when work is being done.

There are two factors to keep in mind when deciding when work is being done: something has to move, and the motion must be in the direction of the applied force. If you pick up a pile of books from the floor, work is done on the books. They move upward, in the direction of the applied force. If you hold the books in your arms, no work is done. Some upward force is still being applied (to keep the books from falling), but no movement is taking place. Even if you carry the books across the floor at a constant speed, no work is done on the books. The force being applied to the books is still upward, but your motion across the floor is sideward, or horizontal.

Conservation of Energy

Have you ever ridden on the swings in a playground? Try to remember what it was like swinging back and forth, high and low. Now think about the energy changes involved in such a ride.

The ride starts with a push to start you moving—to give you some kinetic energy. As the swing rises, kinetic energy changes to potential energy of position. At the top of each swing, potential energy is greatest. Then, as the swing moves downward, potential energy changes to kinetic energy. At the bottom of each swing, kinetic energy is greatest, and potential energy is at its minimum.

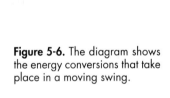

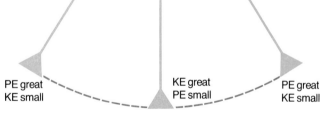

Figure 5-6. The diagram shows the energy conversions that take place in a moving swing.

PE great KE small

KE great PE small

PE great KE small

114 ENERGY

OPTIONS

INQUIRY QUESTIONS

▶ **The kinetic energy of a hockey puck is 20 J as it moves from ice onto the cement surrounding the rink. By how much is its energy decreased if it stops on the cement?** *20 J*

▶ **If the cement causes a frictional force of 10 N on the puck, how far does it slide?** $-10 \text{ N} \cdot d = -20 \text{ N} \cdot m = -20 \text{ J}; d = 2.0 \text{ m}$

▶ **What happens to this energy?** *It is converted into heat.*

MULTICULTURAL PERSPECTIVE

Karate—The Empty Hand

Karate means "empty hand" and was created by Okinawans in the 17th century. But empty hands break concrete blocks. A trained karateka can break a 3.8 cm block by moving his or her hand at 11 m/s to create a force of 3069 N. Amazingly, the bones in the human hand can withstand up to 40 times that force.

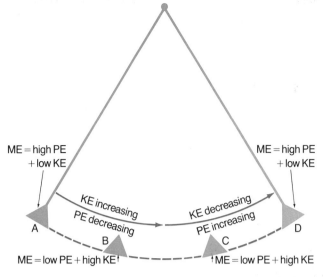

ME = high PE
+ low KE

ME = high PE
+ low KE

KE increasing
PE decreasing

KE decreasing
PE increasing

A

B

C

D

ME = low PE + high KE

ME = low PE + high KE

As the swing continues to move back and forth, energy is converted from kinetic to potential to kinetic, over and over again. At any point along its path, the swing will have both potential energy and kinetic energy. Taken together, potential and kinetic energy of the swing make up its mechanical energy. **Mechanical energy** is the total ⑦ amount of kinetic and potential energy in a system.

Scientists have learned that in any given situation, energy may change from one form to another, but the total amount of energy remains constant. In other words, energy is conserved. This fact is recognized as a law of nature. According to the **law of conservation of energy,** energy may change form but it cannot be created or destroyed under ordinary conditions.

Suppose the law of conservation of energy is applied to the swing. Would you expect the swing to continue moving back and forth forever? You know this doesn't happen. The swing slows down and comes to a stop. Where does the energy go?

If you think about it, friction and air resistance are constantly acting on the swing and rider. These unbalanced forces cause some of the mechanical energy of the swing to change to thermal energy—heat. With every pass of the swing, the temperatures of the swing, the rider, and the air around them go up a little bit. So the mechanical energy of the swing isn't lost, it is converted to thermal energy. Thermal energy is discussed in the next section.

Figure 5-7. The total mechanical energy (K.E. + P.E.) of a moving swing changes very little in one swing back and forth. A small amount of mechanical energy is converted to thermal energy due to friction.

Did You Know?

A person on a bicycle converts chemical energy into kinetic energy ten times more efficiently than does a seagull in flight.

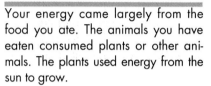

In Your JOURNAL

Your energy came largely from the food you ate. The animals you have eaten consumed plants or other animals. The plants used energy from the sun to grow.

CHECK FOR UNDERSTANDING
▶ Ask questions 1-2 and the **Apply** and **Connect to Life Science** questions in the Section Review.

RETEACH
Repeat the demonstration on page 113, securely attaching the car to the rubber band with a wire tie. Pull on the rubber band indicating that you are doing work on the system. Release the rubber band and discuss how mechanical energy is conserved as the car oscillates. As the oscillations decrease, discuss how friction is doing work on the system.

EXTENSION
For students who have mastered this section, use the **Reinforcement** and **Enrichment** masters or other OPTIONS provided.

ASSESSMENT—ORAL

▶ **Why is the first hill of a roller coaster ride the highest?** *The total mechanical energy of the ride is mostly due to the potential energy of the roller coaster at the top of this hill. The contribution to this total due to kinetic energy is very small at this point. If a later hill were higher, the mechanical energy needed would be larger than the original mechanical energy, and the coaster could not reach the top.*

▶ **Where will a roller coaster be moving fastest: immediately after it comes down the first hill, above ground level, at ground level, or in a valley below ground level?** *The roller coaster will be moving fastest below ground level; its kinetic energy will be a maximum because its gravitational energy will be a minimum.*

Figure 5-8. As the sled moves down the hill, what energy changes are taking place? Is any work being done on the sled?

▶ **Demonstration:** Construct a small pendulum using a small weight and a piece of string. Have students describe how mechanical energy is conserved as it swings back and forth.

SECTION REVIEW ANSWERS

1. When you drop the ball, its potential energy is changing to kinetic energy. When the ball hits the floor and bounces upward, kinetic energy is again changing to potential energy. The potential energy becomes less with each bounce. When the ball stops bouncing, its energy has been transformed into heat, sound, etc.

2. $W = F \times d$

$$F = \frac{W}{d} = \frac{1470 \text{ J}}{20 \text{ m}}$$

$$= 73.5 \text{ N}$$

3. Apply: It is not energy, but the fuels burned to supply our energy that are in short supply.

4. Connect to Life Science

$W = F \times d = 580 \text{ N} \times 3.1 \text{ m}$

$W = 1798 \text{ J}$

It is more work than running because it creates an increase in gravitational potential energy.

The next time you hear someone talking about *energy* or *work*, think about the scientific meanings of those words. Ask yourself what kind of energy is being discussed and whether the work involves a force being applied over a distance.

SECTION REVIEW

1. Imagine you're standing on a stepladder and you drop a basketball. The first bounce will be highest. Each bounce after that will be lower until the ball stops bouncing. Describe the energy changes that take place, starting with dropping the ball.
2. A game-show contestant won a prize by pushing a bowling ball 20 m using his nose. The amount of work done was 1470 J. How much force did the person exert on the ball?
3. **Apply:** A lot of discussion has focused on the need to drive more efficient cars and use less electricity. If the law of conservation of energy is true, why are people worried?
4. **Connect to Life Science:** One of the best aerobic exercises is walking up stairs. For example, if Jenna weighs 580 N, and she climbs a 3.1-m flight of stairs, how might this be more work than running 3.1 m?

Skill Builder

☒ Comparing and Contrasting

Compare and contrast the everyday meaning of *work* with the scientific definition of that term. Give examples of work in the everyday sense that would not be considered work in the scientific sense. If you need help, refer to Comparing and Contrasting in the **Skill Handbook** on page 679.

Skill Builder

The everyday meaning of *work* would include any time effort was given. The scientific meaning of *work* would require a force being exerted through a distance. Examples of work in the everyday sense that would not meet scientific meaning are: Jim worked hard in reading his English assignment, or Jennifer worked in holding the garage door open.

Skill Builder

ASSESSMENT

Oral: Perform several tasks; such as pulling on a locked door, lifting a chair, or dropping a book. Ask the students if work is being done and to explain why or why not.

ACTIVITY 5-1 DESIGNING AN EXPERIMENT
Conservation Connections

Imagine yourself swinging in a swing. What would happen if a friend tried to stop you by grabbing the swing's chain halfway up as you passed the lowest point? Would you come to a complete stop or continue rising to your previous maximum height? Use this activity to model this situation and answer these questions.

Getting Started
In this activity, you will build a pendulum with a length that changes at the bottom of the path. *Investigate* the exchange of potential and kinetic energies in its motion.

Hypothesizing
Examine the pictured apparatus . How is it similar to the situation in the introductory paragraph? **Hypothesize** what will happen to the pendulum's motion and final height if its swing is interrupted by the cross arm? Write down your **hypothesis.**

Materials
Your cooperative group will use:
• ring stand and ring
• support rod clamp, right angle
• support rod, 30 cm
• rubber stopper, 2-hole, medium
• string (1 m)
• metersticks (2)

Try It!

1. Set up the apparatus as shown. Be sure the cross arm intersects with the pendulum string.
2. Devise a way to *measure* the starting and ending heights of the pendulum. *Record* your starting and ending heights in a table.
3. Move the stopper to the same height as the cross arm, with no slack in the string. Release it. Record the height the stopper reaches at the opposite end of its swing.
4. Repeat the experiment several times, starting your swing both above and below the height of the cross arm. *Record your observations.*

Summing Up/Sharing Results
• For a single swing released from the height of the cross arm, is the ending height of the stopper exactly the same as its starting height? Explain why or why not.
• What happens when the starting height is higher than the cross arm?
• At what point along a single swing does the stopper have the greatest kinetic energy? The greatest potential energy?

Going Further!
When are the potential and kinetic energies of the stopper both zero at the same time? What has happened to the energy in this situation?

SUMMING UP/SHARING RESULTS
Air resistance and friction slow the stopper and take some energy out of the system, so it cannot reach the starting height. If released higher than the cross arm, the stopper wraps the string around the cross arm until it stops and falls. The K.E. is greatest at the bottom and lowest at the top. The P.E. is greatest at the top and lowest at the bottom.

GOING FURTHER!
The K.E. and P.E. are both zero when the stopper comes to a rest. Friction and air resistance converted all the mechanical energy to heat.

Activity
ASSESSMENT
Performance: When dropped from the same height, a pendulum without interference from a cross arm will remain in motion longer than a pendulum with one arm. Ask students to discuss and explain this. Some energy transfers into the cross arm.

OBJECTIVE: Construct a pendulum to compare the exchange of potential and kinetic energy.
Time: One class period for setting up lab and devising measurement methods, and one half class period for post-lab discussion.

PROCESS SKILLS applied in this activity are **measuring, collecting** and **organizing data,** and **observing and inferring.**

PREPARATION
Have additional materials available (string, extra ring stands, banner paper, and masking tape).
Cooperative Learning: Use the Science Investigation Team strategy in groups of four. Teams should be encouraged to share ideas with other teams.

HYPOTHESIZING
The shape of the pendulum's path will change, but the maximum height on the opposite end should still be close to the original height because energy will be conserved.

TEACHING THE ACTIVITY
*Refer to the **Activity Worksheets** for additional information and teaching strategies.*
• Students may need some help developing measurement systems. A piece of banner paper could be taped to a wall, with the pendulum placed directly in front of it. One person could view the pendulum at eye level and mark the highest points on the paper. Or tie a piece of string at the height of the cross arm between two ring stands to make the starting and ending heights easier to spot.
• Remind students that changing the release height affects the pendulum's maximum P.E., changing the maximum K.E., too.

PROGRAM RESOURCES
From the **Teacher Resource Package** use:
Activity Worksheets, pages 39-40, Activity 5-1: Conservation Connections.

PREPARATION

SECTION BACKGROUND

▶ The average K.E. of a material is directly related to the absolute temperature of the material.

▶ Comparing the temperatures of two samples of a material, compares the average K.E. of the two samples.

▶ The thermal energy of a material is the total kinetic and potential energies of all of its particles and depends on the amount of material.

▶ Heat is the thermal energy transferred between objects at different temperatures.

1 MOTIVATE

▶ Have students rub their hands together and then touch their cheeks. Ask them to explain if work is being done on their hands. Have them observe how the work changes the thermal energy of their hands. Ask them if they can use a sense other than sight to detect the energy changes.

Cooperative Learning: Have Problem Solving Teams devise several ways of detecting if equal amounts of water in two identical containers are at different temperatures.

Connect to...
Life Science

Answer: Cold-blooded animals (fish, amphibians, and reptiles) do not have regulated internal temperatures. Their temperature depends on the environment. Warm-blooded animals have internally regulated temperatures.

TYING TO PREVIOUS

KNOWLEDGE: Have students recall the definition of *energy* from Section 4-1 and list and discuss situations that indicate heat is a kind of energy. Tell them they will be learning more about heat in this section.

5-2 Temperature and Heat

New Science Words

temperature
thermal energy
heat

Objectives

▶ Recognize the difference between the motion of an object and the motion of the particles that make up the object.
▶ Contrast heat and temperature.
▶ Explain what determines the thermal energy of a sample of matter.

Temperature

What do you know about temperature? When the air temperature outside is high, you probably describe the weather as "hot." Ice cream, which has a low temperature, feels "cold." The words *hot* and *cold* are commonly used to describe the temperature of a material. Although not very scientific, these terms can be useful. Just about everyone understands that "hot" indicates high temperature and "cold" indicates low temperature.

Most people, when they think of temperature, automatically think of heat also. This association makes sense, because heat and temperature are related. But, they are not the same. To understand the relationship between temperature and heat, you need to know about matter.

All matter is made up of particles so small that you can't see them, even with an ordinary microscope. The particles that make up any sample of matter are constantly moving, even if the sample itself is perfectly still. Everything you can think of—the book on your desk, the shoe on your foot, even the foot inside the shoe—is made up of moving particles.

You know that moving things have kinetic energy. Because they are in constant motion, the particles that make up matter have kinetic energy. The faster the particles move, the more kinetic energy they have. **Temperature** is a measure of the average kinetic energy of the particles in a sample of matter. As the temperature of a material increases, the particles move faster and their average kinetic energy becomes greater. Similarly, as the temperature of a material decreases, its particles

Connect to...
Life Science

Animals are classified as warm-blooded or cold-blooded, but a cold-blooded animal may have a higher internal temperature than a warm-blooded one. Find out what these terms mean and give examples of each.

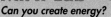
MINI-Lab

Can you create energy?
Pour sand into a plastic foam cup until the cup is full enough to just cover the bulb of a thermometer. *Measure* the temperature of the sand to the nearest tenth of a degree. Remove the thermometer and place a lid on the cup. While holding the lid firmly in place, shake the cup vigorously for several minutes. Stop shaking, remove the lid, and *measure* the temperature of the sand immediately. What effect did shaking have on the temperature of the sand? Was energy "created"? Explain.

OPTIONS

Meeting Different Ability Levels

For Section 5-2, use the following **Teacher Resource Masters** depending upon individual students' needs.

◆ **Study Guide Master** for all students.

● **Reinforcement Master** for students of average and above average ability levels.

▲ **Enrichment Master** for above average students.

Additional Teacher Resource Package masters are listed in any **PROGRAM RESOURCES** boxes that are in the section. The additional masters are appropriate for all students.

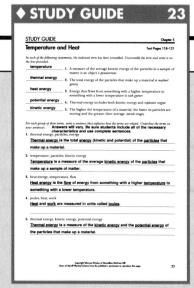

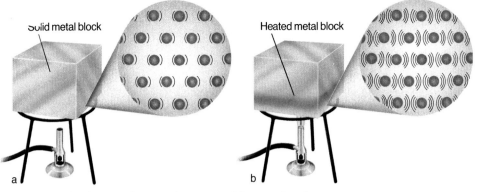

Solid metal block | Heated metal block

Figure 5-9. The drawing illustrates the motion of the particles of a material when the material is cool (a) and when it is hot (b).

move slower and their average kinetic energy decreases. Which particles are moving faster, those in a cup of hot tea or those in the same amount of iced tea?

Thermal Energy

If you place an ice-cold teaspoon on top of a scoop of ice cream, nothing will happen. But suppose you place a hot teaspoon on the ice cream. Now the ice cream under the spoon starts to melt. The hot spoon causes the ice cream to change because it transfers energy to the ice cream. Where does this energy come from? The spoon isn't moving, and its position is the same as that which the cold spoon had. So the energy is not due to the motion or the position of the spoon. Instead, it is related to the temperature of the spoon.

The change in the ice cream is caused by thermal energy. Like temperature, thermal energy is related to the energy of the particles that make up matter. **Thermal energy** is the total energy of the particles in a material. This total includes both kinetic and potential energy. The kinetic energy is due to vibrations and movement within and between particles. The potential energy is determined by forces that act within or between the particles.

Suppose you stack two hot teaspoons at the same temperature on a scoop of ice cream. What will happen? The two spoons will melt more ice cream than the single spoon did in the same amount of time. The stacked spoons have twice as much mass and, therefore, twice as many moving particles. The more mass a material has at the same temperature, the greater its thermal energy.

a

b

c

Figure 5-10. An ice-cold spoon (a) has no effect on ice cream. Two hot spoons (c) have more thermal energy than one hot spoon (b), so they melt more ice cream.

MINI-Lab
Materials: sand, plastic foam cup with lid, thermometer
Teaching Tips
▶ Enough sand should be used to just cover the bulb of the thermometer.
▶ Practice should be given in reading the thermometer and estimating tenths of degrees. Make sure proper precautions are taken with the thermometers.
Answers to Questions
▶ The K.E. of each particle converts to higher *molecular* K.E., raising the temperature. No energy was "created."

MINI-Lab
ASSESSMENT
Content: Ask students to explain where the increase in the average K.E. of the sand came from. Stress conservation of energy. It came from moving their bodies.

PROGRAM RESOURCES

From the **Teacher Resource Package** use:

Activity Worksheets, page 45, MINI-Lab: Can you create energy?

Transparency Masters, pages 19-20, Cool and Hot Matter.

Use **Color Transparency** number 10, Cool and Hot Matter.

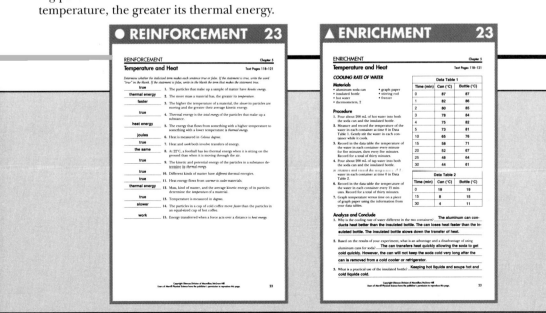

● **REINFORCEMENT** 23

REINFORCEMENT   Chapter 5
Temperature and Heat   Text Pages 118-121

Determine whether the italicized term makes each sentence true or false. If the statement is true, write the word "true" in the blank. If the statement is false, write in the blank the term that makes the statement true.

true	1. The particles that make up a sample of matter have *kinetic energy.*
thermal energy	2. The more mass a material has, the greater its *temperature.*
faster	3. The higher the temperature of a material, the *slower* its particles are moving and the greater their average kinetic energy.
true	4. Thermal energy is the *total energy* of the particles that make up a substance.
heat energy	5. The energy that flows from something with a higher temperature to something with a lower temperature is *thermal energy.*
joules	6. Heat is measured in *Celsius degrees.*
true	7. Heat and *work* both involve transfers of energy.
the same	8. At 22°C, a football has *less* thermal energy when it is sitting on the ground than when it is moving through the air.
true	9. The kinetic and potential energy of the particles in a substance determine its *thermal energy.*
true	10. Different kinds of matter have *different* thermal energies.
true	11. Heat energy flows from *warmer* to *cooler* materials.
thermal energy	12. Mass, kind of matter, and the average kinetic energy of its particles determine the *temperature* of a material.
true	13. Temperature is measured in *degrees.*
slower	14. The particles in a cup of cold coffee move *faster* than the particles in an equal-sized cup of hot coffee.
work	15. Energy transferred when a force acts over a distance is *heat energy.*

Copyright Glencoe Division of Macmillan/McGraw-Hill
Users of Merrill Physical Science have the publisher's permission to reproduce this page.   23

▲ **ENRICHMENT** 23

ENRICHMENT   Chapter 5
Temperature and Heat   Text Pages 118-121

COOLING RATE OF WATER

Materials
• aluminum soda can   • graph paper
• insulated bottle   • stirring rod
• hot water   • freezer
• thermometers, 2

Procedure
1. Pour about 200 mL of hot water into both the soda can and the insulated bottle.
2. Measure and record the temperature of the water in each container at time 0 in Data Table 1. Gently stir the water in each container while it cools.
3. Record in the data table the temperature of the water in each container every minute for five minutes, then every five minutes. Record for a total of thirty minutes.
4. Pour about 200 mL of tap water into both the soda can and the insulated bottle.
5. Measure and record the temperature of the water in each container at time 0 in Data Table 2.
6. Record in the data table the temperature of the water in each container every 15 minutes. Record for a total of thirty minutes.
7. Graph temperature versus time on a piece of graph paper using the information from your data tables.

Data Table 1		
Time (min)	Can (°C)	Bottle (°C)
0	87	87
1	82	86
2	80	85
3	78	84
4	75	82
5	73	81
10	65	76
15	58	71
20	52	67
25	48	64
30	44	61

Data Table 2		
Time (min)	Can (°C)	Bottle (°C)
0	19	19
15	8	15
30	4	11

Analyze and Conclude
1. Why is the cooling rate of water different in the two containers? **The aluminum can conducts heat better than the insulated bottle. The can loses heat faster than the insulated bottle. The insulated bottle slows down the transfer of heat.**

2. Based on the results of your experiment, what is an advantage and a disadvantage of using aluminum cans for soda? **The can transfers heat quickly allowing the soda to get cold quickly. However, the can will not keep the soda cold very long after the can is removed from a cold cooler or refrigerator.**

3. What is a practical use of the insulated bottle? **Keeping hot liquids and soups hot and cold liquids cold.**

Copyright Glencoe Division of Macmillan/McGraw-Hill
Users of Merrill Physical Science have the publisher's permission to reproduce this page.   23

2 TEACH

Key Concepts are highlighted.

CONCEPT DEVELOPMENT

▶ Make sure students realize that heat is the thermal energy that flows *spontaneously* from warmer to cooler materials. Devices, such as refrigerators and air conditioners, can be used to reverse the flow, but require additional sources of energy.

PROBLEM SOLVING

▶ Because both drinks are essentially water, and assuming the same size, the thermal energy of the tea was greater than the thermal energy of the soft drink.
Think Critically: Heat flowed from the tea to the environment, but heat flowed from the environment to the soft drink.

TEACHER F.Y.I.

▶ Temperature is an *intrinsic* quality. It is independent of the amount of substance. Thermal energy is an *extrinsic* quantity; it depends upon the amount of substance.

VideoDisc
STVS: Solar Food Dryer, Disc 2, Side 2
STVS: Solar Tower, Disc 2, Side 2

MINI QUIZ

Use the Mini Quiz to check students' recall of chapter content.

1. **What is thermal energy?** *the total energy of the particles that make up a material*
2. **What is heat?** *energy that flows from something at a higher temperature to something at a lower one*

PROBLEM SOLVING

A Cold Cup of Tea and a Warm Soft Drink

Carol and Alicia were tired after playing a hard game of soccer. Shortly after arriving at Alicia's house and sitting down on the back porch, Alicia's grandmother peeked her head out the door.

"I am making myself a cup of tea," she said. "Would you girls like some?"

"Thanks. That sounds good," replied Carol. "I'm thirsty."

Alicia was thirsty too but didn't want hot tea. She told her grandmother, "No, I'll just have a cold soft drink."

They had just taken a sip of their drinks when Alicia suggested that they listen to a new cassette tape of her favorite group. The girls left their drinks and went to listen to the tape. When they finally returned to finish their drinks, Carol's tea was cold, and Alicia's soft drink was warm. How did the thermal energy of the two drinks compare when the girls first got the drinks?
Think Critically: Explain how heat was transferred in both drinks while the girls were listening to the tape.

EcoTip
Thermal energy must be used to heat water. Take a shower instead of a bath. The average shower uses one-third the amount of hot water a bath does.

Different kinds of matter have different thermal energies, even when mass and temperature are the same. For example, a 5-g sample of sand has a different thermal energy than a 5-g sample of pudding at the same temperature. This difference is due mainly to the ways in which the particles of the materials are arranged.

It is important to remember that the thermal energy of a material depends on the total energy of its particles. The kinetic energy of the object itself has no effect on its thermal energy. For example, at 20°C a golf ball has the same thermal energy whether it's sitting on the ground or speeding through the air.

Heat

On a warm day, what would happen if you pressed your left hand against a cool tile wall? Your hand would feel cooler. Its temperature would have decreased. If you

120 ENERGY

OPTIONS

ASSESSMENT—ORAL
▶ **How can thermal energy be used to explain both hotness and coldness?** *Hotness can be explained as the presence of thermal energy. Coldness can be explained as the relative absence of thermal energy.*
▶ **Are heat and work properties of matter?** *No, heat is thermal energy transferred between matter at two different temperatures. Work represents the energy transferred to matter by motion.*

PROGRAM RESOURCES
From the **Teacher Resource Package** use:
Activity Worksheets, page 5, Flex Your Brain.

then touched the same spot on the wall with your right hand, the spot wouldn't feel as cool as it did. The temperature of the spot would have increased when you touched it with your left hand. Energy flowed from your warm hand to the cool tile. **Heat** is the energy that flows from something with a higher temperature to something with a lower temperature. Remember that heat always flows from warmer to cooler materials—never from cooler to warmer.

Like work, heat is measured in joules and both involve transfers of energy. Heat is energy transferred between objects at different temperatures. Work is energy transferred when a force acts over a distance.

The next time you listen to a weather report, think about the difference between temperature and heat. And when you drop an ice cube into your drink, think about how the cooling occurs. Does the melting ice cause the liquid to cool? Or does heat flowing from the liquid to the ice, cool the drink and cause the ice to melt?

Figure 5-11. Heat flows from hot cocoa to your hand, making your hand feel hot. Heat flows from your hand to an ice cube, making your hand feel cold.

SECTION REVIEW

1. In terms of thermal energy, why does a bottle of soda left in the sun have a higher temperature than one left in an ice chest?
2. Which has more thermal energy, a 5-kg bowling ball that has been resting on a hot driveway for 4 hours on a 35°C day, or the same bowling ball rolling down a lane in an air-conditioned bowling alley?
3. **Apply:** Using your knowledge of heat, explain what happens when you heat a pan of soup on the stove, then put some leftover warm soup in the refrigerator.
4. **Connect to Life Science:** Use physics terms and concepts to explain why you take your temperature by placing a thermometer under your tongue and waiting several minutes.

✉ Concept Mapping

Create a network tree that shows how the following words and phrases are related: *energy, potential energy of particles, energy transfer (higher to lower temperature), heat, kinetic energy of particles,* and *thermal energy.* If you need help, refer to Concept Mapping in the **Skill Handbook** on pages 684 and 685.

Skill Builder

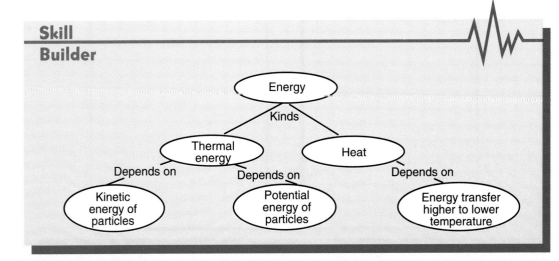

Ask questions 1-2 and the **Apply** and **Connect to Life Science** questions in the Section Review.

RETEACH
Have students repeat the first motivation activity. Discuss and explain their observations using the terms *work, temperature, thermal energy,* and *heat.*

EXTENSION
For students who have mastered this section, use the **Reinforcement** and **Enrichment** masters or other OPTIONS provided.

3 CLOSE

❓ FLEX Your Brain
Use the Flex Your Brain activity to have students explore HEAT.

ASSESSMENT
Portfolio: Use the Flex Your Brain activity to reinforce critical-thinking and problem-solving skills. In Step 2, students might list different ways of controlling heat flow.

SECTION REVIEW ANSWERS
1. The soda left in the sun absorbs more energy, and its average K.E. goes up.
2. The ball that rested in the sun for several hours has more thermal energy.
3. Apply: Energy from the stove burner transfers to the soup. Heat will flow from the warm soup to the air in the refrigerator.
4. Connect to Life Science: It takes several minutes for the thermometer to reach equilibrium with your body.

Skill Builder
ASSESSMENT
Performance: Have students shake hands with students near them. Ask them to use specific terms and phrases from this Skill Builder to explain why some hands feel warm and some feel cold.

 **Energy from the Oceans and Earth**

PREPARATION

SECTION BACKGROUND
▶ Geothermal energy refers to thermal energy found in molten magma beneath Earth's surface. Thermal energy can be used to produce steam for heating and for generating electricity.

PREPLANNING
▶ Obtain a small piece of granite rock, tongs, a medicine dropper, and a gas burner for the Motivation demonstration.

1 MOTIVATE

▶ **Demonstration:** Using tongs, heat a small piece of granite rock over a gas flame. When very hot, carefully place it on a heat-proof pad and let a drop of water fall on it. Have students observe the water vaporizing. Ask them to discuss how rising steam could be used to do work on a turbine and produce electricity.

PROGRAM RESOURCES
From the **Teacher Resource Package** use:

Science and Society, page 9

Critical Thinking/Problem Solving, page 11, Is the Oil Age Ending?

Activity Worksheets, page 5, Flex Your Brain.

V i d e o D i s c
STVS: Geothermal Wells, Disc 2, Side 2

New Science Words
magma

Objectives
▶ Explain why ocean waters and subsurface rock may represent possible new sources of thermal energy.
▶ Discuss the benefits and drawbacks of proceeding with research and development of these new energy sources.

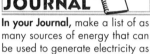

In your Journal, make a list of as many sources of energy that can be used to generate electricity as you can. Put a star beside those that could be used in your area.

Exploring New Energy Resources

Scientists are always searching for new sources of energy and improved methods of using our present energy sources. Two new possibilities being explored involve the harnessing of thermal energy present in oceans waters and in rocks beneath Earth's surface.

In some ocean areas the temperature difference between surface water and deeper water is as much as 15°C. Scientists believe that they can use some of the thermal energy that flows between such regions to produce electricity.

Another possible source of energy is **magma** (MAG muh), the molten rock that lies several kilometers beneath Earth's surface. Scientists are working on drilling deep wells in order to use the thermal energy stored in the magma.

Both of these proposed projects are ambitious and, if successful, could be of tremendous benefit to all peoples of the world. However, possible drawbacks must be considered. Each of these projects will be very expensive and will take many years to produce practical results. It is also possible that they could produce some harmful side effects in the environment.

122 ENERGY

OPTIONS

Meeting Different Ability Levels
For Section 5-3, use the following **Teacher Resource Masters** depending upon individual students' needs.
◆ **Study Guide Master** for all students.
● **Reinforcement Master** for students of average and above average ability levels.
▲ **Enrichment Master** for above average students.
Additional Teacher Resource Package masters are listed in any PROGRAM RESOURCES boxes that are in the section.

◆ **STUDY GUIDE** 24

STUDY GUIDE   Chapter 5
Energy from the Oceans and Earth   Text Pages 122–123

Use the words listed below to fill in the blanks in the paragraphs.

deep	kinetic energy	more
electricity	law of conservation of energy	potential energy
energy	lower	surface
higher	magma	thermal energy

The __law of conservation of energy__ states that energy can change from one form to another, but it cannot be created or destroyed under ordinary conditions. By applying this law, scientists hope to harness some of the __thermal energy__ that lies in rocks beneath Earth's surface and in ocean water.

Molten rock that lies several kilometers beneath Earth's surface is called __magma__. Scientists hope to drill deep wells into Earth to tap the stored, or __potential energy__, in magma. This energy may then be changed into forms of energy that are useful to society.

Heat is one form of __energy__. Temperature is a measure of the average __kinetic energy__ of the particles in a sample of matter. Heat energy flows from regions of __higher__ temperature to regions of __lower__ temperature.

The surface water of the ocean has a higher temperature and __more__ kinetic energy than deeper water. Heat energy flows form the warm __surface__ water to the cooler __deep__ water. Scientists believe that they can harness some of this heat energy and convert it into __electricity__.

24

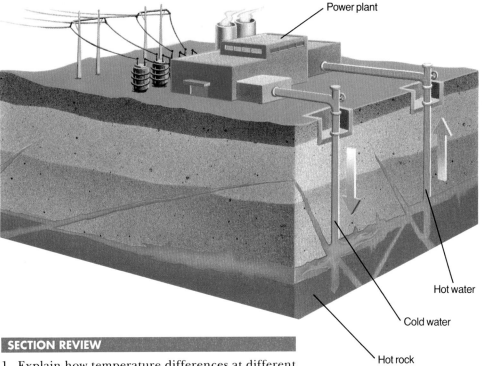

Power plant

Hot water

Cold water

Hot rock

SECTION REVIEW

1. Explain how temperature differences at different depths of the ocean provide a possible energy source.
2. Why do you think projects like the ones mentioned in this section are so expensive and take so long to complete?
3. **Connect to Life Science:** Harnessing the ocean's thermal energy could change the nearby ocean temperature. What effects might this have on the marine ecosystem?

You Decide!

The growing demand for electricity combined with diminishing natural sources of fuel has created a need for new sources of energy to produce electricity. All possible methods of developing new energy sources should be examined and evaluated carefully, including the negative aspects of proceeding with such projects. The most obvious negative aspects include possible harmful effects on the environment and the huge cost in time and money. Should tax dollars be used to support research and development to provide new energy sources? If not, who should foot the bill?

SCIENCE & SOCIETY

123

---

2 TEACH

Key Concepts are highlighted.

CONCEPT DEVELOPMENT
▶ Introduce the word *geothermal*. Have students brainstorm its meaning.

CHECK FOR UNDERSTANDING
Ask questions 1-2 and the **Connect to Earth Science** question in the Section Review.

RETEACH
Cooperative Learning: Assign Numbered Heads Together Groups to sketch methods of producing electricity by thermal energy sources in the oceans or Earth.

EXTENSION
For students who have mastered this section, use the **Reinforcement** and **Enrichment** masters or other OPTIONS provided.

3 CLOSE

? FLEX Your Brain

Use the Flex Your Brain activity to have students explore GEOTHERMAL ENERGY.

ASSESSMENT
Portfolio: Use the Flex Your Brain activity to reinforce critical-thinking and problem-solving skills. In Step 2, students might list how geysers act.

SECTION REVIEW ANSWERS

1. Energy in the form of heat flows from regions of higher to lower temperature. Scientists believe that they can devise methods of using some of this energy to produce electricity.

2. The projects require extensive time and preparation. Scientists must ensure that the projects are safe for the environment.

3. Connect to Earth Science: Changing the pattern of ocean currents or marine temperature could affect the survival of certain marine life. Ocean currents can affect weather, too.

PREPARATION

SECTION BACKGROUND
▶ The specific heat of a material can be used to quantitatively describe a change in its thermal energy. By definition, the specific heat is the amount of energy needed to change the temperature of one kilogram of a material by one Kelvin degree. Its unit is J/(kg • K).

PREPLANNING
▶ Obtain four Pyrex beakers, 50 g of sand, two thermometers, and a gas burner and stand for the Motivation demonstration.

1 MOTIVATE

▶ **Demonstration:** Fill each of two beakers with 50 mL of water at room temperature. Measure their temperatures using two thermometers. Heat 50 mL of water in a beaker and 50 g of sand in a similar beaker to a temperature of 100°C. Carefully pour each, separately, into one of the first two beakers. Have students read the resulting temperatures and calculate the temperature changes. Ask students to conjecture about the reasons for the difference in the temperature changes.

TYING TO PREVIOUS
KNOWLEDGE: Have students recall the metric units and, where appropriate, the instruments used to measure energy, mass, and temperature. Tell students that they will use this knowledge to learn more about changes in thermal energy as something is heated or cooled.

New Science Words
specific heat

Objectives
▶ Define *specific heat*.
▶ Calculate changes in thermal energy.

Specific Heat

Have you ever jumped into a swimming pool or lake on a hot summer day and found the water surprisingly cold? Even though lots of radiant energy has been transferred to the water from the sun, the temperature of the water is still cooler than that of the surroundings.

Different materials need different amounts of heat to produce similar changes in their temperatures. The materials have different specific heats. The **specific heat** (C_p) of a material is the amount of energy it takes to raise the temperature of 1 kg of the material 1 degree Kelvin. Specific heat is measured in joules per kilogram per degree Kelvin [J/(kg • K)]. Table 5-1 shows the specific heats of some familiar materials. How does the specific heat of water compare with the specific heats of the other materials?

Now that you see how high the specific heat of water is compared to other materials, do you understand why jumping into the water on that hot day felt strikingly cold? The materials around the water heat up much faster than the water itself. So the water is cold in comparison with its surroundings. Water, alcohol, and other materials with a high specific heat can absorb a lot of energy with little change in temperature. The specific heats of different substances depend on the chemical makeup of the substances.

Figure 5-12. Because of its high specific heat, water warms up more slowly than its surroundings.

OPTIONS

Meeting Different Ability Levels
For Section 5-4, use the following **Teacher Resource Masters** depending upon individual students' needs.
◆ **Study Guide Master** for all students.
● **Reinforcement Master** for students of average and above average ability levels.
▲ **Enrichment Master** for above average students.
Additional Teacher Resource Package masters are listed in any PROGRAM RESOURCES boxes that are in the section. The additional masters are appropriate for all students.

◆ **STUDY GUIDE** 25

STUDY GUIDE
Measuring Thermal Energy

In the blank, write the term that completes each statement.

1. The amount of energy it takes to raise the temperature of 1 kilogram of a material 1 Celsius degree is called _____ **specific heat**
2. Another term used for specific heat is _____ **heat capacity**
3. Specific heat is measured in _____ **joules** _____ per kilogram per degree Celsius.
4. Specific heat can be used to measure changes in _____ **thermal energy**
5. Thermal energy is the _____ **total** _____ energy of the particles that make up a material.
6. In the equation $Q = m \times \Delta T \times C_p$ the symbol Δ means _____ **change**
7. A measure of the average kinetic energy of the particles in a sample of matter determines the matter's _____ **temperature**
8. The transfer of energy from something at a higher temperature to something at a lower temperature is called _____ **heat**
9. In the equation $Q = m \times \Delta T \times C_p$ the change in thermal energy is shown by _____ **Q**
10. When calculating changes in thermal energy, the change in temperature and the change in thermal energy are always _____ **positive** _____ numbers.
11. Heat always flows from _____ **higher to lower** _____ temperatures.
12. Work and heat both involve _____ **transfers** _____ of energy.

Table 5-1

SPECIFIC HEAT OF SOME COMMON MATERIALS [J/(kg • K)]	
Water 4190	Iron..................................450
Alcohol 2450	Copper 380
Aluminum 920	Silver 235
Carbon (Graphite)............710	
Sand..............................664	

TECHNOLOGY

Infrared Weather Eyes

The satellite picture that you see on your TV weather show is usually an infrared image captured by a GOES satellite. GOES (**G**eostationary **O**perational **E**nvironmental **S**atellite) satellites remain directly above the same point on Earth's surface. Each satellite monitors a circular region of the surface 10 000 kilometers across. Within this circle, clouds appear white and Earth's surface appears gray. A meteorologist can point out a line of clouds that indicates a weather front and run a sequence of images to demonstrate how that front is moving.

The satellite's sensors measure many bands of infrared radiation. One band detects moisture in the air. Dry air appears black and moist air appears in varying shades of gray. Because bad weather often breaks out when dry air intrudes into moist air, these water vapor images can be used to predict storms. Other bands of radiation reveal information about wind speed and direction, rainfall, fog, snow, and ice. Newer satellites, with a "sharper eye," may one day provide data for making accurate global weather forecasts 30 to 90 days in advance.

Think Critically: In addition to weather forecasting, what are some other uses for satellite data from infrared sources?

● **REINFORCEMENT** 25

▲ **ENRICHMENT** 25

2 TEACH

Key Concepts are highlighted.

CONCEPT DEVELOPMENT

► Specific heat can be thought of as the amount of energy absorbed or released by a kilogram of material for each degree of change in temperature. The energy gained or lost per kilogram is expressed in J/kg and the temperature change of one degree is expressed as K. Thus the unit of specific heat is

$(J/kg)/K = J/kg \times 1/K = J/(kg \bullet K)$

► Although the absolute value of the temperature of an object is different on the Celsius and Kelvin scales, the change in thermal energy is the same for 1°C or 1°K. So, specific heat can have °C or K in the denominator interchangeably.

► By comparing the values of the specific heat of different materials, one can compare the amount of energy materials will absorb or lose under similar circumstances. For example, the specific heat of aluminum is almost four times that of silver. Undergoing similar temperature changes, an aluminum spoon will absorb four times as much thermal energy as a silver spoon of the same weight.

TECHNOLOGY

For additional information on weather satellites, see "Ready, Set, GOES: Weather Eyes for the 21st Century," by Joanne Heckman, *Space World*, July 1987, pp. 23-26.

Think Critically: Satellite monitoring of infrared sources could provide information on ocean currents, patterns of thermal pollution, forest fires, volcanic activity, etc.

▶ Historically, the specific heat of water is measured as a calorie (c), which is the amount of energy needed to raise the temperature of one gram of water by one Celsius degree. This is not an SI unit. However, dieticians measure the energy equivalent of foods in kilocalories (C). A kilocalorie equals 4180 joules.

PRACTICE PROBLEMS ANSWERS

1. $Q = \Delta T \times m \times C_p$
   $= (90°C – 12°C) \times 0.23$ kg $\times$
   $\quad$ 4190 J/(kg • K)
   $= 78°C \times 0.23$ kg $\times$
   $\quad$ 4190 J/(kg • K)
   $= 75\ 000$ J

2. $Q = \Delta T \times m \times C_p$
   $C_p = \dfrac{Q}{\Delta T \times m} = \dfrac{180\ 480\ \text{J}}{12°C \times 45\ \text{kg}}$

   $= \dfrac{180\ 480\ \text{J}}{540\ \text{kg} • \text{K}}$

   $= 334$ J/(kg • K)

Connect to...
Chemistry

Answer: If her earlobe remained cooler than the earring, her earlobe must have a higher specific heat.

Figure 5-13. Devices like this simple calorimeter are used to measure thermal energy transfer.

Labels: Thermometer, Stirrer, Cover, Inner chamber, Insulated flask (outer chamber)

Using Specific Heat

Changes in thermal energy cannot be measured directly. No instrument can make such measurements. However, specific heat can be used to measure changes in thermal energy. For example, suppose you take a 3.1-g ball of aluminum foil from a pot of water at a temperature of 30°C and allow it to cool to room temperature, which is 15°C. You now have enough information to find out the change in the thermal energy of the ball of foil using the following equation:

$$\text{Change in thermal energy} = \text{mass} \times \text{Change in temperature} \times \text{specific heat}$$

$$Q = m \times \Delta T \times C_p$$

The symbol Δ (delta) means change, so ΔT is the change in temperature. "Change" is included in Q, which is the variable for energy change.

$$\Delta T = T_{final} - T_{initial}$$

When ΔT is positive, the object has increased in temperature and gained heat. When ΔT is negative the object has decreased in temperature and given off heat.

EXAMPLE PROBLEM: Calculating Changes in Thermal Energy

Problem Statement: A 3.1-g ball of aluminum foil cools from 30°C to 15°C. What is the change in its thermal energy?

Known Information:
Strategy Hint: Make sure you're using the appropriate units. Remember a change of 1°C is equal to a change of 1°K.

Mass = m = 3.1 g = 0.0031 kg
T_{final} = 15.0°C
$T_{initial}$ = 30.0°C
Specific heat (C_p) = 920 J/(kg • K)

Unknown Information: Energy change (Q)

Equation to Use:
$Q = \Delta T \times m \times C_p$
$\Delta T = T_{final} - T_{initial}$

Solution:
$Q = (T_{final} - T_{initial}) \times m \times C_p$
$\quad = (15.0°C - 30.0°C) \times 0.0031$ kg $\times 920$ J/(kg • K)
$\quad = -43$ J

The foil ball loses 43 J of thermal energy as it cools.

OPTIONS

INQUIRY QUESTIONS

▶ **If water takes longer to heat up than its surroundings, why does it take away heat from your body so quickly?** *Although water has a large specific heat, the conductivity of the water is high and thermal energy is quickly spread throughout the water resulting in a longer time for the water to become heated. The conductivity of water is more than that of air, and the heat from your body is transferred to the surrounding water more quickly resulting in a rapid drop in skin temperature.*

▶ **Why do you think the unit of specific heat is J/(kg • K) rather than J/(L • K)?** *The volume of a material depends upon its temperature and therefore, the specific heat would be different at each temperature. However, the mass of a material does not depend upon its temperature.*

PRACTICE PROBLEMS

Strategy Hint: Will your answer be a positive or negative number?

Strategy Hint: What is the unknown information?

1. Calculate the change in thermal energy when 230 g of water warms from 12°C to 90°C.

2. A 45-kg brass sculpture gains 180 480 J of thermal energy as its temperature increases from 28°C to 40°C. What is the approximate specific heat of brass?

The thermal energy characteristics of complex systems depend on the specific heats of the substances involved and the masses and shapes of the systems. For example, as shown in the photo, elephants fan their ears to dissipate heat and lower their body temperature. Without this ability, the large mass, shape, and high specific heat of the materials in an elephant's body would keep its temperature too high.

With your new understanding of specific heat, think about temperature changes you've observed in objects around you. Now you have an idea about why a kettle of water takes so long to boil and why a sandy beach heats up quickly on a sunny day.

SECTION REVIEW

1. A bucket of sand and a bucket of water are side by side in direct sunlight. Which warms faster? Why?
2. Use Table 5-1 on page 125 to calculate the change in thermal energy when a 55-g iron nail cools from 90°C to 25°C.
3. **Apply:** If you wanted to quickly cool a piece of hot metal, would it be smarter to plunge it into a container of water or a container of sand at the same temperature?
4. **Connect to Chemistry:** Water and a liquid called ethylene glycol are used in automobile radiators to keep the engine from overheating. Explain whether you would rather have a coolant with a high or a low specific heat.

✉ Interpreting Data

Equal amounts of iron, water, and sand, all at the same temperature, were placed in an oven and heated briefly. Use the data in Table 5-1 on page 125 to match each final temperature with the appropriate material: 31°C, 5°C, and 46°C. If you need help, refer to Interpreting Data in the **Skill Handbook** on page 683.

Connect to... **Chemistry**

While Karen was blow drying her hair, she noticed her silver earring had become uncomfortably hot. If her earring were about the same mass as her earlobe, which of the two had the higher specific heat?

Skill Builder

ENRICHMENT
▶ Have students research the calorimeter, an instrument used to measure thermal energy released in physical changes and chemical reactions.

PROGRAM RESOURCES
From the **Teacher Resource Package** use:
Concept Mapping, pages 15-16.
Use **Laboratory Manual 10,** Heat Transfer.

Skill Builder
ASSESSMENT
Performance: Two students heated two equal masses of water and alcohol on a hot plate for 10 minutes. Assuming neither one boils, which would have the higher temperature? Why? *The alcohol; because it has a lower specific heat.*

CHECK FOR UNDERSTANDING
Ask questions 1-2 and the **Apply** and **Connect to Chemistry** questions in the Section Review.

RETEACH
Ask students to look at Table 5-1. The values of the specific heats are ranked from high to low. Have the students recall the results of the Motivation demonstration or perform the demonstration now. Relate the results of the demonstration to the specific heats listed on the table. Ask students to predict the results of repeating the demonstration using 50 g of clay instead of sand.

EXTENSION
For students who have mastered this section, use the **Reinforcement** and **Enrichment** masters or other OPTIONS provided.

3 CLOSE

▶ Ask students if they have any evidence that thermal energy is also conserved.

SECTION REVIEW ANSWERS
1. The sand heats more quickly than the water because it has a lower specific heat than water.

2. $Q = \Delta T \times m \times C_p$
$Q = -65°C \times 0.055$ kg $\times$ 450 J/(kg • K)
$= -1609$ J

3. Apply: Plunge the metal into water. With its higher specific heat, water takes more heat from the metal as its temperature rises.

4. Connect to Chemistry: Coolants should have a high specific heat so they can absorb a lot of energy without drastic temperature changes.

CROSS CURRICULUM
▶ **History:** Have students research the experiments conducted by James Prescott Joule quantitatively relating thermal energy and work.

Skill Builder
5°C = water, 31°C = iron, 46°C = sand

ACTIVITY 5-2
40 minutes

OBJECTIVE: Measure the heat delivered by a hair curler over a 5-minute period.

PROCESS SKILLS applied in this activity:
▶ **Measuring** in Procedure Steps 4 and 5.
▶ **Using Numbers** in Analyze Statement 3.
▶ **Interpreting** in Conclude and Apply Question 5.

COOPERATIVE LEARNING
Divide class into Science Investigation Teams of three. Teams will develop conclusions after comparing lab results.

TEACHING THE ACTIVITY
Troubleshooting: Do not allow the water in the cup to overflow into the curler. The water inside the curler provides an even flow of heat to the thermometer.

▶ One set of hair curlers will serve the entire class. The type with a hard plastic outer covering is recommended.

▶ Heat the set of curlers to maximum temperature prior to class. Warn students not to touch metal interiors of the cylinders.

▶ Assign different sized curlers to different teams.

▶ Heat loss to air is ignored in this activity, but could become part of the follow-up discussion. Placing a lid over the cup would control most of the heat loss during the 5-minute procedure.

▶ A class discussion period after completing **Analyze** is recommended.

PROGRAM RESOURCES
From the **Teacher Resource Package** use:

Activity Worksheets, pages 41-42, Activity 5-2: A Hot Topic.

Activity
ASSESSMENT
Content: Ask students to explain why hot water bottles are used to warm people in bed.

A Hot Topic

Have you ever used heat to change the shape of something? If you have ironed clothes or curled your hair you have probably used heat to help you accomplish the task. How much heat is required to do these things? In this activity, you will use your understanding of specific heat to find out how much heat is released from a hot roller.

Materials
- set of electric hair curlers
- thermometers, Celsius (2)
- plastic foam cup
- graph paper
- balance
- graduated cylinder

Procedure
1. *Prepare a data table* like the one shown.
2. *Measure* the mass of the plastic foam cup. Fill the cup about halfway with cool water and measure its mass again. Determine the mass of the water in kilograms.
3. Carefully remove a heated curler from its heating unit. **CAUTION:** *Don't touch any hot metal parts.* Stand the curler, open end up, on the table and pour in 2 mL of cool water.
4. Using two thermometers, *measure* and *record* the temperature of the water in the cup and the temperature of the water in the curler.
5. Carefully lower the curler into the cup of water. *Measure* and *record* the water temperatures every minute for five minutes.
6. *Prepare a time-temperature graph,* with time along the x-axis and temperature along the y-axis. Plot both heating and cooling curves.

Analyze
1. What happened to the water in the cup? Explain in terms of heat.
2. What was the change in temperature of the water in the cup over the 5-minute interval?
3. Using the formula below, find the change in thermal energy (Q), in joules, of the water in the cup.

$$Q = m \times \Delta T \times C_p$$

Data and Observations   Sample Data

Time in Minutes	Water Temperature (°C)	
	in curler	in cup
0	78	21
1	73	24
2	67	26
3	64	28
4	61	30
5	60	31

Conclude and Apply
4. Does the curler still have thermal energy available to continue heating the water after five minutes? How do you know?
5. *Compare* your results with those of your classmates. Do some curlers provide more heat than others? Which curlers provide the most heat?
6. How do the starting temperatures of all the curlers compare?
7. Which statement is more accurate: "Some curlers are hotter than others," or "Some curlers contain more thermal energy than others"? Explain your answer.

ANSWERS TO QUESTIONS

1. The water became hotter; its temperature rose. Heat produced by electricity was transferred to and stored in the curler. The stored heat was transferred to the water in the cup.

2. probably about 10°C

3. Most results will be in the 1000 J to 2000 J range.

4. Yes. The temperature inside the curler is still higher than that of the surrounding water.

5. Yes. The smaller curlers have less heat to deliver.

6. The starting temperatures are all nearly the same.

7. "Hotter" refers to temperature, or average kinetic energy of the particles. "Contain more thermal energy" refers to total energy, both kinetic and potential, and is more accurate.

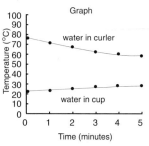

Graph

CHAPTER
REVIEW

SUMMARY

5-1: Energy and Work

1. Energy is the ability to cause change. Energy may be in the form of motion (kinetic energy) or it may be stored (potential energy).

2. Energy exists in many different forms, and it can change from one form to other forms with no loss of total energy.

3. Work is the transfer of energy through motion. Work is done only when force produces motion in the direction of the force.

5-2: Temperature and Heat

1. All matter is made up of tiny particles that are in constant motion. This motion is not related to or dependent on the motion of the object.

2. Heat and temperature are related, but they are not the same. The temperature of a material is a measure of the average kinetic energy of the particles that make up the material. Heat is the energy that flows from a warmer to a cooler material.

3. The thermal energy of a material is the total energy—both kinetic and potential—of the particles that make up the material.

5-3: Science and Society: Energy from the Oceans and Earth

1. Temperature differences between layers of ocean waters and the energy of magma beneath Earth's surface represent two possible new sources of thermal energy.

2. The benefits and drawbacks of projects to develop new energy sources should be thoroughly investigated and evaluated before the projects are allowed to proceed.

5-4: Measuring Thermal Energy

1. Different materials have different heat capacities, or specific heats. Thus, their thermal energies change at different rates.

2. The specific heat of a material can be used to calculate changes in the thermal energy of the material.

KEY SCIENCE WORDS

a. **energy**
b. **heat**
c. **kinetic energy**
d. **law of conservation of energy**
e. **magma**
f. **mechanical energy**
g. **potential energy**
h. **specific heat**
i. **temperature**
j. **thermal energy**
k. **work**

UNDERSTANDING VOCABULARY

Match each phrase with the correct term from the list of Key Science Words.

1. the ability to cause change
2. energy of motion
3. Under normal conditions, energy cannot be created or destroyed.
4. energy required to raise the temperature of 1 kg of a material 1 degree Kelvin
5. total energy of the particles in a material
6. the transfer of energy through motion
7. flows from warmer to cooler materials
8. stored energy
9. measure of the average kinetic energy of the particles in a material
10. the total amount of kinetic and potential energy in a system

ENERGY **129**

SUMMARY

Have students read the summary statements to review the major concepts of the chapter.

UNDERSTANDING VOCABULARY

1. a	**6.** k
2. c	**7.** b
3. d	**8.** g
4. h	**9.** i
5. j	**10.** f

ASSESSMENT
Portfolio

Encourage students to place in their portfolios one or two items of what they consider to be their best work. For each item, ask students to explain why that item was chosen and what they learned from it. Items might be selected from the following.

- Connect to Earth Science answer, p. 111
- Skill Builder concept map, p. 121
- Practice Problems calculations, p. 127

Performance

Additional performance assessments may be found in *Performance Assessment* and *Science Integration Activities* that accompany **Merrill Physical Science.** Performance Task Assessment Lists and rubrics for evaluating these activities and other products generated througout the chapter can be found in Glencoe's *Performance Assessment in Middle School Science.*

OPTIONS

ASSESSMENT

To assess student understanding of material in this chapter, use the resources listed.

👥 COOPERATIVE LEARNING

Consider using cooperative learning in the THINK AND WRITE CRITICALLY, APPLY, and MORE SKILL BUILDERS sections of the Chapter Review.

PROGRAM RESOURCES

From the **Teacher Resource Package** use:
Chapter Review, pages 13-14.
Chapter and Unit Tests, pages 28-31, Chapter Test.

CHAPTER
REVIEW

CHECKING CONCEPTS

1. b	**6.** b
2. a	**7.** a
3. a	**8.** c
4. c	**9.** c
5. c	**10.** b

USING LAB SKILLS

ASSESSMENT

Use these alternate lab exercises to assess students' understanding of the skills used in this chapter.

11. Doubling the mass of the pendulum would double the maximum K.E. and P.E.

12. Students will need to put the rollers in an environment with enough thermal energy to transfer to the rollers. For example, they might boil or bake them.

THINK AND WRITE CRITICALLY

13. Gravitational potential energy is the energy an object has due to its position above Earth's surface. Another type of potential energy is energy of a wound spring. Both of these types of energy are stored; kinetic energy is energy of motion.

14. At the top of a swing, a pendulum's potential energy is maximum; as it falls from this position, potential energy changes to kinetic energy. At the bottom of a swing, kinetic energy of the pendulum is at its greatest. As the pendulum moves up the other side of its swing, kinetic energy changes to potential energy. The total mechanical energy of the pendulum decreases with each swing as it is converted to thermal energy.

15. Thermal energy is the total kinetic and potential energy of all the particles that make up a material. Temperature is a measure of the average kinetic energy of the particles of a material. Heat is the transfer of energy due to a difference in temperature.

CHAPTER
REVIEW

CHECKING CONCEPTS

Choose the word or phrase that completes the sentence or answers the question.

1. The basic SI unit of energy is the _____.
  a. kilogram **c.** newton
  b. joule **d.** Kelvin

2. If the velocity of an object increases, the _____ of the object will also increase.
  a. kinetic energy **c.** specific heat
  b. mass **d.** potential energy

3. Which of these is not used to calculate change in thermal energy?
  a. volume **c.** specific heat
  b. temperature change **d.** mass

4. The _____ of a material is a measure of the average kinetic energy of its particles.
  a. potential energy **c.** temperature
  b. thermal energy **d.** specific heat

5. Which of these does not represent work done on a rock in the scientific sense?
  a. lifting a rock **c.** holding a rock
  b. throwing a rock **d.** moving a rock

6. The total amount of kinetic and potential energy in a closed system is called _____.
  a. specific heat **c.** stored energy
  b. mechanical energy **d.** temperature

7. As the temperature of a material increases, the average _____ of its particles increases.
  a. kinetic energy **c.** specific heat
  b. potential energy **d.** mass

8. Kinetic energy is directly related to _____.
  a. volume **c.** mass
  b. force **d.** position

9. The _____ of an object depends upon its position.
  a. kinetic energy **c.** potential energy
  b. thermal energy **d.** mechanical energy

10. The particles in a material all have _____.
  a. the same mass
  b. kinetic energy
  c. the same temperature
  d. the same velocity

USING LAB SKILLS

11. Review Activity 5-1 on page 117. What would the effect be on the maximum potential and kinetic energies if the stopper were twice as massive?

12. In Activity 5-2 on page 128, you determined the amount of thermal energy stored in a heated hot roller. Design an experiment to reheat the rollers to their original temperature without using the base of the hot roller apparatus.

THINK AND WRITE CRITICALLY

Answer the following questions in your Journal using complete sentences.

13. Describe two types of potential energy. How does this energy differ from kinetic energy?

14. Describe the energy changes in a swinging pendulum. Explain how energy is conserved, even as a pendulum slows down.

15. Compare and contrast heat, temperature, and thermal energy.

16. A copper bowl and a clay bowl of equal mass were heated from 27°C to 100°C. Which required more heat? Explain.

17. Describe some possible benefits and drawbacks of converting the thermal energy of the oceans and magma to useful purposes.

---

16. Because the specific heat of copper is greater than that of clay, more heat was needed to raise the temperature of the copper pot than was needed to produce the same temperature change in the clay pot.

17. The benefits are that both energy sources are inexhaustible and relatively clean, and their use would conserve Earth's dwindling supply of fossil fuels. The drawbacks include the expense involved in research and the possible harmful effects on the environment.

18. While performing a chin-up, Carlos raises himself 0.8 m. How much work does Carlos, who weighs 600 N, accomplish doing a chin-up?

19. A football player picks up a football, runs with it, and then throws it to a teammate. Describe the work done on the ball.

20. Wind has more kinetic energy than does still air. Why does air feel cold on a windy winter day and hot on a calm summer day?

21. How much thermal energy does 420 g of liquid water gain when it is heated from its freezing point to its boiling point?

22. 50 g of water and 50 g of sand each absorb 200 J of solar energy. What will be the temperature change of each material?

MORE SKILL BUILDERS

If you need help, refer to the Skill Handbook.

1. **Comparing and Contrasting:** Compare and contrast heat and work.

2. **Sequencing:** Equal amounts of carbon, silver, alcohol, copper, and aluminum (listed in Table 5-1 on page 125) are placed in the sun for one minute. All start at the same cold temperature. List the materials in descending order of the average kinetic energy of their particles at the end of the interval.

3. **Measuring in SI:** A non-SI unit often used to measure thermal energy is the calorie, which is equal to 4.18 J. The numbers of calories needed to raise the temperature of 1-kg samples of three different materials 1 degree Celsius are given below. Convert each value to joules.

Material	Calories
wood	420
glass	120
mercury	33

4. **Hypothesizing:** Propose a hypothesis to explain why a person with a fever often feels chills, even in a warm room.

5. **Concept Mapping:** Below is a blank concept map of the energy changes of a gymnast bouncing on a trampoline. Complete the map by indicating the type of energy—kinetic, potential, or both—the gymnast has at each of the following stages in his or her path: a. halfway up; b. the highest point; c. halfway down; d. the lowest point, just before hitting the trampoline.

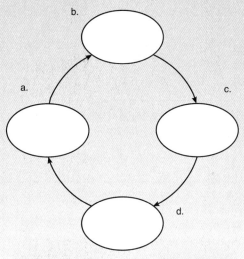

PROJECTS

1. Research and write a paper about the life of Albert Einstein. Describe how he explained the law of conservation of mass and energy.

2. Make a poster showing possible energy sources other than burning fossil fuels. Note the advantages and disadvantages of each and indicate which you think is the best resource to develop further and why.

ENERGY **131**

18. $W = F \times d$
   $= 600 \text{ N} \times 0.8 \text{ m}$
   $= 480 \text{ J}$

19. Work is done on the ball when the player picks it up and when the ball is thrown to a teammate. No work is done on the ball when the player carries it.

20. Cold air feels cold because the particles of air have lower average kinetic energy, regardless of whether the air is moving or not. Warm air feels warm because the particles of air have higher average kinetic energy.

21. $Q = \Delta T \times m \times C_p$
   $= 100°C \times 0.420 \text{ kg} \times$
   $4190 \text{ J/(kg} \cdot \text{K)}$
   $= 175\ 980 \text{ J}$

22. $Q = mC_p \Delta T$; solving for ΔT,
   $\Delta T = Q/(m \cdot C_p)$
   $\Delta T_{water} = \dfrac{(200 \text{ J})}{(0.05 \text{kg}) \cdot [4190 \text{ J/(kg} \cdot \text{K)}]}$
   $\Delta T_{water} = 0.95°C$
   $\Delta T_{sand} = \dfrac{(200 \text{ J})}{(0.05 \text{kg}) \cdot [664 \text{ J/(kg} \cdot \text{K)}]}$
   $\Delta T_{sand} = 6.0°C$

MORE SKILL BUILDERS

1. **Comparing and Contrasting:** Both heat and work involve the transfer of energy, and both are measured in joules. Energy is transferred as heat when two materials are at different temperatures. Energy is transferred as work when a force acts through a distance.

2. **Sequencing:** The order will be from the substance with the lowest specific heat to that with the highest specific heat: silver, copper, carbon, aluminum, and alcohol.

3. **Measuring in SI:** Wood: 420 cal $\times$ 4.18 J/cal = 1756 J
   Glass: 120 cal $\times$ 4.18 J/cal = 502 J
   Mercury: 33 cal $\times$ 4.18 J/cal = 138 J

4. **Hypothesizing:** When a person has a fever, the person perspires because of an elevated body temperature. Heat is carried away from the body as the perspiration evaporates, causing the person to feel cool, a condition known as chills.

5. **Concept Mapping:** See map at left.

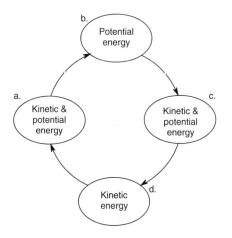

CHAPTER

6 Using Thermal Energy

CHAPTER SECTION	OBJECTIVES	ACTIVITIES
6-1 Moving Thermal Energy (2 days)	1. **Compare** and **contrast** the transfer of thermal energy by conduction, convection, and radiation. 2. **Differentiate** between conductors and insulators. 3. **Explain** how insulation affects the transfer of energy.	**Activity 6-1:** *Creating Convection Currents, p. 141*
6-2 Heating Systems (2 days)	1. **Describe** three types of conventional heating systems. 2. **Explain** how solar energy can be used to heat buildings. 3. **Explain** the differences between passive and active solar heating systems.	**MINI-Lab:** *Can the sun be used to cook food? p. 144*
6-3 Thermal Pollution Science & Society (1 day)	1. **Identify** problems associated with thermal pollution. 2. **Discuss** solutions for thermal pollution problems.	
6-4 Using Heat to Do Work (2 days)	1. **Describe** how internal combustion engines and external combustion engines work. 2. **Explain** how a heat mover can transfer thermal energy in a direction opposite to that of its natural movement.	**Activity 6-2:** *The Four-Stroke Engine, p. 152*
Chapter Review		

ACTIVITY MATERIALS

FIND OUT	ACTIVITIES		MINI-LABS
Page 133 lamp with bare bulb extension cord(s) masking tape	**6-1 Creating Convection Currents, p. 141** colored ice cubes tongs thermometer beaker, 250-mL salt stirring rod ruler	**6-2 The Four-Stroke Engine, p. 152** matches flask, 250-mL glass or plastic "T" pinch clamps (2) large syringe, plastic rubber tubing (3 pcs.) small piece of cloth or yarn rubber stopper, 2-hole, with glass tubing	**Can the sun be used to cook food? p. 144** glue aluminum foil strips of poster board, 30 cm × 1m string wire coat hangers hot dog

CHAPTER FEATURES	TEACHER RESOURCE PACKAGE	OTHER RESOURCES
Problem Solving: *The Warm House*, p. 138 **Skill Builder:** *Using Variables, Constants, and Controls*, p. 140	**Ability Level Worksheets** ◆ **Study Guide**, p. 26 ● **Reinforcement**, p. 26 ▲ **Enrichment**, p. 26 **Activity Worksheets**, pp. 47, 48 **Cross-Curricular Connections**, p. 10	**Laboratory Manual 11,** Conduction of Heat **Laboratory Manual 12,** Specific Heats of Metals **STVS:** Disc 1, Side 1 Disc 2, Side 2
Skill Builder: *Making and Using Tables*, p. 145	**Ability Level Worksheets** ◆ **Study Guide**, p. 27 ● **Reinforcement**, p. 27 ▲ **Enrichment**, p. 27 **Activity Worksheets**, p. 53 **Concept Mapping**, pp. 17, 18 **Science and Society**, p. 10 **Transparency Masters**, pp. 21, 22	**Color Transparency 11,** Heating Systems **STVS:** Disc 2, Side 2 **Science Integration Activity 6**
You Decide! p. 147	**Ability Level Worksheets** ◆ **Study Guide**, p. 28 ● **Reinforcement**, p. 28 ▲ **Enrichment**, p. 28 **Activity Worksheets**, p. 5	**STVS:** Disc 6, Side 2
Technology: *Cooling Crystals*, p. 150 **Skill Builder:** *Concept Mapping*, p. 151	**Ability Level Worksheets** ◆ **Study Guide**, p. 29 ● **Reinforcement**, p. 29 ▲ **Enrichment**, p. 29 **Activity Worksheets**, pp. 49, 50 **Critical Thinking/Problem Solving**, p. 12 **Technology**, pp. 9, 10 **Transparency Masters**, pp. 23, 24	**Color Transparency 12,** Four-Stroke Engine **Laboratory Manual 13,** Thermal Energy from Foods
Summary Think & Write Critically Key Science Words Apply Understanding Vocabulary More Skill Builders Checking Concepts Projects Using Lab Skills	**ASSESSMENT RESOURCES** **Chapter Review**, pp. 15, 16 **Chapter Test**, pp. 32-35 **Performance Assessment in Middle School Science**	**Chapter Review Software** **Test Bank** **Alternate Assessment** **Performance Assessment**

◆ **Basic**   ● **Average**   ▲ **Advanced**

ADDITIONAL MATERIALS

SOFTWARE	AUDIOVISUAL	BOOKS/MAGAZINES
Learning All About Heat and Sound, Queue.	*Furnace In the Sky*, Video, Britannica. *Heat and Energy Transfer*, Video, Coronet. *Keeping Warm*, Laserdisc, Journal Films. *Learning About Heat*, Video, Britannica. *The Secret Life of the Central Heating System*, Video, Lucerne Media.	Garner, Robert. *Experimenting with Energy Conservation.* NY: Watts, 1992.

THEME DEVELOPMENT: The chapter discusses the transfer, production, and uses of thermal energy. Energy conversions and conservation should be stressed in each section.

CHAPTER OVERVIEW

▶ **Section 6-1:** The three types of thermal energy transfer—conduction, convection, and radiation—are discussed in this section. Thermal conductors and insulators are compared and contrasted.

▶ **Section 6-2:** This section discusses the three primary types of home-heating systems in terms of energy conversions and thermal energy transfers. Passive and active solar heating methods are introduced.

▶ **Section 6-3: Science and Society:** The environmental problem of thermal pollution of water systems is discussed. Students are asked to evaluate the advantages and disadvantages associated with building an industrial plant that may produce thermal pollution in a local river.

▶ **Section 6-4:** Heat engines are introduced as devices that change thermal energy into mechanical energy. Internal and external combustion engines, refrigerators, and heat pumps are discussed.

CHAPTER VOCABULARY

conduction	cooling
fluid	towers
convection	heat engines
radiation	combustion
insulators	internal
radiator	combustion
solar energy	engine
solar	external
collectors	combustion
thermal	engine
pollution	heat mover
	heat pump

132

OPTIONS

 **For Your
Gifted Students**

Students can test various metals for their ability to conduct heat. Have them take nails made from different metals (steel, aluminum, brass, and so on) and place a drop of wax on the head of the nail. They should hold the nail with a pair of insulated tongs, heat the unwaxed end with a candle, and record the time it takes for the wax to melt. Have them hypothesize whether the size of the nail will affect the speed of heat transfer, then test the hypothesis.

 **For Your
Mainstreamed Students**

Students can test various brands of polystyrene foam cups from fast food restaurants for their effectiveness. They should place the same amount of the same temperature hot and cold water in the various cups. A thermometer should be placed in the water and the top covered with plastic wrap. Students should record the temperature after 5 and then 10 minutes. The change in heat energy of the various cups can be charted. Results may be shared with the restaurants.

The clothes you wear can make you feel warmer or cooler. They affect the amount of thermal energy that reaches and leaves your body. How else can the movement of thermal energy be affected?

FIND OUT!

Do this simple activity to find out how you can affect the movement of thermal energy.

Turn on a lamp with a bare light bulb. Being careful not to touch the bulb, put your hand near it. Do you feel warmth from the bulb? How is thermal energy getting to your hand? What happens if you move your hand nearer to the bulb or farther away? What happens if you put a book between your hand and the lamp? Suppose you use only a piece of paper instead of a whole book. *Experiment* with other things that you can put between your hand and the light bulb. Do some seem to block heat better than others? Feel the objects after they've been near the light bulb. Do some feel warmer than others? How can you explain the differences?

Gearing Up
Previewing this Chapter
Use this outline to help you focus on important ideas in this chapter.

Previewing Science Skills
▶ In the Skill Builders, you will use variables, constants, and controls; make and use tables; and map concepts.
▶ In the Activities, you will observe, collect and organize data; model; analyze; and infer.
▶ In the MINI-Lab, you will analyze and hypothesize.

What's next?

You have discovered that you can exert some control over the movement of thermal energy. Now you will learn about how thermal energy moves and how that movement can be put to useful purposes.

133

INTRODUCING THE CHAPTER
Use the Find Out activity to introduce students to the concept of heat transfer by convection and radiation.

FIND OUT!
Preparation: If you plan to conduct the activity in the classroom, have students bring in small desk lamps that use incandescent light bulbs. Obtain several electrical extension cords and wide masking tape.
Materials: lamp and bare light bulb for each group of three students, extension cords, and masking tape
Cooperative Learning: Assign Problem Solving Teams.
Teaching Tips
▶ **CAUTION:** *Hot light bulbs are not to be handled. Secure extension cords with masking tape to avoid tripping.*
▶ A string of well-insulated outdoor decoration lights may be used to supply a classroom with light bulbs for individual or small-group investigations. Replace any colored bulbs with clear or frosted bulbs for better results.
▶ Cardboard frames used for overhead transparencies can be used to mount different materials, such as paper, clear plastic wrap, foil wrap, and construction paper. Have students observe how these materials affect the transfer of thermal energy.

Gearing Up
Have students study the Gearing Up feature to familiarize themselves with the chapter. Discuss the relationships of the topics in the outline.

What's Next?
Before beginning the first section, make sure students understand the connection between the Find Out activity and the topics to follow.

ASSESSMENT OPTIONS

PORTFOLIO
Refer to page 153 for suggested items that students might select for their portfolios.

PERFORMANCE ASSESSMENT
See page 153 for additional Performance Assessment options.
Process
Skill Builders, pp. 140, 145
MINI-Lab, p. 144
Activities 6-1, p. 141; 6-2, p. 152
Using Lab Skills, p. 154

CONTENT ASSESSMENT
Assessment-Oral, pp. 136, 144, 150
Skill Builders, p. 151
Section Reviews, pp. 140, 145, 147, 151
Chapter Review, pp. 153-155
Mini Quizzes, pp. 136, 144, 150

GROUP ASSESSMENT
Opportunities for group assessment occur with Cooperative Learning Strategies and Flex Your Brain Activities.

PREPARATION

SECTION BACKGROUND

▶ Thermal energy is spontaneously transferred from a material at a higher temperature to a material at a lower temperature in three ways: conduction, convection, and radiation. Heat is transferred by conduction mostly in solids. Convection is the predominant method of heat transfer in fluids. Thermal energy can also be transferred by radiation.

▶ Materials, such as metals, with many free electrons that easily transport kinetic energy are good thermal conductors. Materials that lack this property are good insulators.

PREPLANNING

▶ To prepare for Activity 6-1, make several trays of ice cubes dyed with food coloring.

▶ To prepare for the first demonstration on page 135, find a long metal utensil used for grilling, some wax, and some thumbtacks.

1 MOTIVATE

▶ **Demonstration:** Cut a spiral from a piece of construction paper and suspend it by a thread above an unlit light bulb. Have students note that the spiral begins to rotate only after the light is turned on. Allow students to conjecture on the possible causes of the spiral's motion.

VideoDisc

STVS: New Skid Control, Disc 1, Side 1

STVS: Images of Heat, Disc 2, Side 2

TYING TO PREVIOUS KNOWLEDGE:

Point out that students already know that heat naturally moves from warmer materials to cooler materials. In this section they will learn three methods of how this occurs.

6-1 Moving Thermal Energy

New Science Words

conduction
fluid
convection
radiation
insulators

Objectives

▶ Compare and contrast the transfer of thermal energy by conduction, convection, and radiation.
▶ Differentiate between conductors and insulators.
▶ Explain how insulation affects the transfer of energy.

Conduction

Thermal energy travels as heat from a material at higher temperature to a material at lower temperature. If you pick up an ice cube, heat from your hand transfers to the ice, causing it to melt. If you pick up a hot spoon, the heat from the spoon moves to your hand, perhaps causing you to drop the spoon. How does the thermal energy move from place to place?

One way is by conduction. **Conduction** is the transfer of energy through matter by direct contact of particles. Recall that all matter is made up of tiny particles that are in constant motion. The temperature of a material is a measure of the average kinetic energy of its particles.

Energy is transferred when particles moving at different speeds bump into each other. When faster-moving particles collide with slower-moving particles, some of the energy of the faster-moving particles is passed along to the slower-moving particles. The faster particles slow down and the slower particles speed up.

Heat may be transferred by conduction through a given material or from one material to another. Think about what happens when one end of a metal spoon is placed in boiling water. Heat from the water is transferred to the spoon. The end of the spoon in the water becomes hotter than the other end of the spoon. But eventually the entire spoon becomes hot as in Figure 6-1.

Conduction can take place in solids, liquids, and gases. Because their particles are packed closer together, solids usually conduct heat better than liquids or gases. However,

What is conduction?

EcoTip

When cooking or baking, leave the tops on the pots and keep the oven door closed. This will prevent energy from escaping and being wasted.

OPTIONS

Meeting Different Ability Levels

For Section 6-1, use the following **Teacher Resource Masters** depending upon individual students' needs.

◆ **Study Guide Master** for all students.

● **Reinforcement Master** for students of average and above average ability levels.

▲ **Enrichment Master** for above average students.

Additional Teacher Resource Package masters are listed in any PROGRAM RESOURCES boxes that are in the section. The additional masters are appropriate for all students.

◆ STUDY GUIDE 26

STUDY GUIDE   Chapter 6
Moving Thermal Energy   Text Pages 134–141

In each of the following statements, a term has been scrambled. Unscramble the term and write it on the line provided.

conduction	1. The transfer of thermal energy through matter by direct contact of particles is called *doenutcon*.
gases	2. Conduction can take place in solids, liquids, and *sags*.
convection	3. The transfer of energy by the movement of matter is called *vceinootnc*.
fluid	4. Any material that can flow is *luifd*.
conductor	5. Any material that allows heat to pass through it easily is a *rtcooundc*.
radiation	6. The type of heat transfer that does not require matter is *radintioa*.
waves	7. Radiation is the transfer of energy in the form of invisible *vawes*.
insulator	8. Any material that does not allow heat to pass through it easily is an *rtnsluaio*.
metals	9. Many conductors, such as silver and copper, are *lemtas*.
radiant energy	10. Energy that travels by radiation is often called *darinta greeny*.
heat	11. Insulators, such as wood and air, are poor conductors of *hea*.
matter	12. The transfer of thermal energy by convection and conduction both require *ettram*.

On the lines provided, explain the differences between conduction, convection, and radiation. Use the information in the exercise above to help you. Write your answers in complete sentences.
Answers will vary. Check to make sure that students' answers are written in complete sentences.

26   Copyright Glencoe Division of Macmillan/McGraw-Hill

Figure 6-1. Part of the spoon is heated by contact with the hot water (left). Heat is transferred through the metal spoon, particle by particle, until the entire spoon is hot (right).

some solids conduct heat better than others. Many metals have loosely held electrons that can move around easily and can transfer kinetic energy to nearby particles more efficiently. Silver, copper, and aluminum are good heat conductors, while wood, plastic, glass, and fiberglass are poor conductors of heat. Why do you think cooking pots are made of metal? What are the handles usually made of?

Convection

Liquids and gases differ from solids because they can flow. Any material that can flow is a **fluid.** The most important way thermal energy is transferred in fluids is by convection. **Convection** is the transfer of energy by the movement of matter. How does this differ from conduction? In conduction, energy moves from particle to particle, but the particles themselves remain in place. In convection, the particles move from one location to another, carrying energy with them.

When heat is added to a fluid, its particles begin to move faster, just as the particles of a solid do. However, the particles of a fluid have more freedom to move. So they move farther apart. The fluid is said to expand. A hot-air balloon is a good example of the expansion of a heated fluid. When the air in the balloon is heated, the particles move faster and farther apart. The air particles striking the sides of the balloon exert force, causing it to inflate.

Figure 6-2. The motion of the sawdust shows that a convection current is present in the liquid.

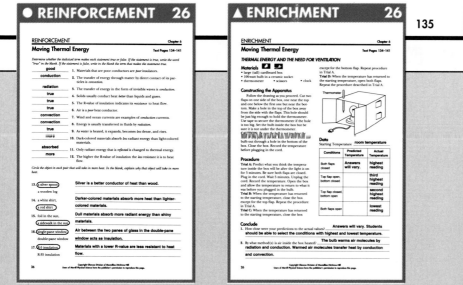

Key Concepts are highlighted.

CONCEPT DEVELOPMENT

▶**Demonstration:** Dip the heads of several small thumbtacks into melted wax and attach them with soft wax at 5-cm intervals along the shaft of a long, metal spatula or fork used for outdoor grilling. Hold the far end of the spatula or fork in the flame of a laboratory burner. Have the students observe the order in which the thumbtacks fall as heat is conducted along the shaft and melts the wax. Repeat the demonstration using a heat-resistant, glass stirring rod of similar dimensions. Have students note the difference in the time intervals between the thumbtacks falling in each demonstration.

▶**Demonstration:** Pour water in a clear plastic shoe box until it is two-thirds full. At one end of the box place an immersion heater and at the other end place a sealed plastic bag of ice cubes against the outside wall. Using a slide projector, cast the shadow of the box on the chalkboard. Have students note the vertical convection currents as the water is heated. Repeat the demonstration on an overhead projector and have students note that the primary convection currents are set up horizontally.

STUDENT TEXT QUESTION

▶Page 135, paragraph 1: **Why do you think cooking pots are made of metal?** *Metals are good conductors of thermal energy.* **What are the handles usually made of?** *plastic or wood (poor thermal energy conductors)*

Cooperative Learning: Assign Numbered Heads Together groups to explain the motion of the spiral in the Motivate demonstration.

▶ **Demonstration:** Ask students to design large scale models of convection and conduction using students to represent the particles of matter. Model conduction in a solid by having students move side to side while standing close together. Convection would have students moving faster and spreading apart in a cyclic pattern, as in Figure 6-2.

CROSS CURRICULUM

▶ **Language Arts:** Have students look up the words *conduction, convection,* and *radiation* in a dictionary. Students should find that the words come from the Latin roots *conducere* (to carry), *convehere* (to bring together), and *radius* (ray), respectively. Ask volunteers to explain how the meaning of each word reflects its root.

MINI QUIZ

Use the Mini Quiz to check students' recall of chapter content.

❶ _____ is the transfer of energy through matter by direct contact of particles. *Conduction*

❷ _____ is the transfer of energy in the form of waves. *Radiation*

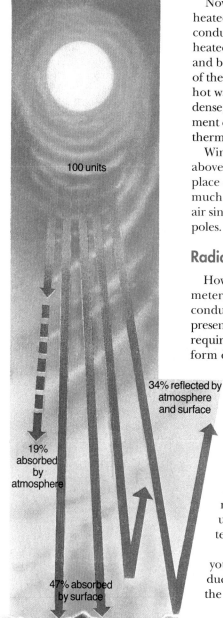

100 units

19% absorbed by atmosphere

47% absorbed by surface

34% reflected by atmosphere and surface

Now think about what happens when a pot of water is heated. The stove burner heats the bottom of the pot by conduction. Water touching the bottom of the pot is also heated by conduction. As this water is heated, it expands and becomes less dense. Cooler, denser water at the top of the pot sinks and pushes the hot water upward. As the hot water rises, it cools by conduction, becomes more dense, and sinks, forcing warmer water to rise. This movement creates convection currents. These currents transfer thermal energy from warmer to cooler parts of the fluid.

Winds are examples of convection currents. The air above the equator is warmer than the air at any other place on Earth, and it rises. Air at the poles, however, is much cooler than it is anywhere else. This cold, dense air sinks and moves along Earth's surface away from the poles. Some ocean currents are also convection currents.

Radiation

How does the sun warm Earth from 150 million kilometers away through mostly empty space? In order for conduction or convection to take place, matter must be present. There is a third type of heat transfer that does not require matter. **Radiation** is the transfer of energy in the ❷ form of waves. Energy that travels by radiation is often called radiant energy. Once radiant energy from the sun reaches Earth, some of it is reflected, or bounced back, toward space, and some is absorbed. Only radiant energy that is absorbed changes to thermal energy.

Different materials absorb radiant energy differently. Shiny materials reflect radiant energy; dull materials absorb it. Dark-colored materials absorb more radiant energy than light-colored materials, which explains why summer clothing is usually made of lighter-colored materials, and winter clothing is darker colored.

If you hold your hand near a lighted electric bulb, your hand feels hot because thermal energy is produced when your hand absorbs radiant energy from the bulb.

Figure 6-3. Only the radiant energy that is absorbed is converted to thermal energy.

OPTIONS

ASSESSMENT—ORAL

▶ Air (oxygen) is necessary for a candle or the wick of a lantern to burn. Why does the flame of a candle or lantern glow more brightly if a glass chimney is placed around it? *Convection currents are formed in the chimney above the flame. These currents cause fresh air to enter at the base of the chimney and aid burning.*

▶ Why won't you get burned if you grab the hot handle of a pan with a dry dishcloth, but you might if you grab the handle with a wet dishcloth? *The tiny spaces among the fibers*

of a dry dishcloth are filled with air, which is a poor conductor of heat. However, the spaces among the fibers of a wet dishcloth are filled with water, which conducts heat more readily.

▶ Why does a nail inserted in a potato decrease the time it takes for the potato to bake in a conventional oven? *The nail conducts heat better to the center of the potato than does the potato itself.*

Reducing Movement of Thermal Energy

When the weather is really cold, doesn't it feel good to wrap yourself up in a thick sweater or curl up under a fluffy quilt? And in hot weather, wouldn't you rather have juice from a bottle that has been inside a picnic cooler than one that has been sitting out on a table?

What do these two situations have in common? In each case, some material is used to reduce the flow of heat by conduction, convection, or radiation. In the first case, the material of the sweater or quilt traps your body heat and keeps it from escaping to the open air. In the second case, the material of the picnic cooler keeps heat from flowing to the juice.

Good conductors are materials that allow heat to move easily through them. Good **insulators** do not allow heat to move easily through them. Some insulators, such as wood, plastic, glass, and fiberglass, have already been identified as being poor conductors.

Gases, such as air, are excellent insulators. Several types of insulating material contain many tiny pockets of trapped air. These pockets restrict the formation of convection currents and the trapped air is a good insulator. Plastic foam is a type of insulation commonly used in beverage cups and picnic coolers. This foam is mostly tiny pockets of trapped air. Down jackets and quilts are stuffed with tiny feathers or fibers that trap air.

Buildings are insulated to keep them warm in winter and cool in summer. In cold weather, heat in a building tends to flow to the colder outside. Insulation reduces the amount of heat lost this way. In the United States, about 10 percent of all energy produced is used to heat buildings, so you can see why it is important to prevent as much heat loss as possible. In warm weather, air conditioners remove heat from building interiors. Insulation reduces the amount of heat that flows into a cool building from the outside, thus keeping the inside of the building cooler.

Building insulation is usually made of some fluffy material, such as fiberglass, cellulose, or treated paper. The insulation, which is packed into outer walls and under roofs, is sometimes covered with shiny aluminum foil. By reflecting radiant energy back toward its source, the foil cuts down on energy transfer due to radiation.

Science and READING

Form a team to design an energy-efficient home. Each member of the team should draw up a house plan, and the team should select the best one. Then each member should research one aspect of the new house for the best energy conservation ideas.

Figure 6-4. Air trapped in its shaggy coat keeps this polar bear warm.

In Your JOURNAL

Think about the building materials in or on the walls, ceilings, or attic space in your home and school. **In your Journal,** identify the kinds of insulators.

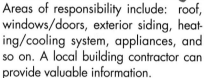

TEACHER F.Y.I.

▶ Thermal energy is radiated from matter as electromagnetic radiation, most commonly in the form of infrared energy. Excited electrons in a material lose energy by emitting photons of electromagnetic energy with wavelengths slightly less than that of visible light, hence the name *infrared,* which means "below red." Like other forms of electromagnetic energy, such as visible light, infrared energy can propagate through a vacuum, reflect from, refract through, and be absorbed by matter.

CONCEPT DEVELOPMENT

▶ Discuss how trapped air in snow, crumpled newspapers, and layered clothing provides good insulation.

Science and READING

Areas of responsibility include: roof, windows/doors, exterior siding, heating/cooling system, appliances, and so on. A local building contractor can provide valuable information.

REVEALING MISCONCEPTIONS

▶ Some students may think that materials are intrinsically cold or hot. For example, ask them why bathroom tiles feel cold to bare feet but a shaggy rug on top of the tiles feels warm. The discussion may reveal that students believe tiles are always cold and rugs are always warm. The feelings that the students experience are correct; however, both materials are at the same temperature. Make sure students are aware that the tile feels cool because it absorbs heat from a bare foot and cools the foot. The trapped air among the fibers of the rug provides insulation that dramatically reduces heat conduction and, therefore, reduces heat loss.

138 CHAPTER 6

 PROBLEM SOLVING

Think Critically: The aluminum backing reduces heat loss due to radiation. The insulation and thermal windows all contain pockets of trapped air. These pockets reduce the transfer of thermal energy because air is a poor conductor of heat.

 **P R O B L E M   S O L V I N G**

The Warm House

Mary and her family lived in a small house near the Canadian border. Because their house had become too small for their needs, the family was having a larger house built nearby.

What does the *R* indicate in R-values?

One day Mary went to the new house with her father to check on a few things. They wanted to make sure that the house was being properly constructed to withstand the cold winters in the area. Mary's father had her check all the exterior walls to see that they were insulated. Mary found that the workers had used foam insulation backed with aluminum foil. Next Mary's father went up to the attic to make sure that rolls of fiberglass insulation had been installed between the rafters. Meanwhile, Mary checked to see that all the windows had stickers indicating that they were double-paned thermal windows. Satisfied that their new house would be nice and warm, Mary and her father returned home.

Think Critically: What was the purpose of the aluminum backing on the exterior wall insulation? What do the foam insulation, the fiberglass insulation, and the thermal windows have in common that helps them to prevent the loss of heat?

To help consumers understand the energy transfer qualities of the many materials used in building construction, a rating system has been established in which each material is given an R-value. The *R* indicates resistance to heat flow. Table 6-1 shows the R-values for some common building materials.

To have a well insulated house, materials with an R-value of at least 19 should be used in the outer walls and those with R-values of 30-44 in the roof or ceilings. Higher R-values are needed for roofs and ceilings because the warmest air inside the house is carried upward by convection currents.

OPTIONS

INQUIRY QUESTIONS

▶ **Both adobe bricks used to build pueblos and ice blocks used to build igloos have very good insulation properties. How do their functions differ?** *The adobe brick conducts little heat from the warmer air outside the pueblo to the cooler air inside during the daytime and vice versa at night. The ice blocks conduct little heat from the warmer air inside the igloo to the colder air outside.*

▶ **Why do birds fluff their feathers and mammals fluff their fur to keep warm?** *The fluffing increases the amount of air trapped in the feathers or fur, which increases their insulating properties.*

▶ **Does blubber have a high or low R-value? Explain.** *Blubber has a high R-value because it acts as an insulator in arctic mammals.*

▶ **Why do the instructions for foods that are heated in a microwave oven sometimes indicate that the container should remain unopened for a few minutes after heating?** *The time is needed for heat to be conducted throughout the food.*

Even though glass is a good insulator, windows do transfer energy. A single pane of glass has an R-rating of only 1, but using double-pane windows reduces heat loss considerably because a thin "sandwich" of air is trapped between two panes of glass. The air is an excellent insulator, and the narrow space restricts the formation of convection currents.

Some double-pane windows have a higher R-value because air is replaced with a harmless, colorless gas that is a better insulator. High R-values help keep buildings cool during hot weather, too.

You may have used a vacuum bottle to carry cold or hot liquids for lunch. This bottle is similar to a double-pane window. It has a double glass wall with a vacuum between the layers. One side of each layer is coated with aluminum to reduce heat transfer by radiation.

Glass

Glass

Dead-air space

Figure 6-5. The air trapped in this double-pane window serves as a layer of insulation.

Table 6-1

R-VALUES OF VARIOUS MATERIALS*

Material	R-Value Ratio
Brick	0.08/cm
Plasterboard (drywall)	0.35/cm
Stucco	0.08/cm
Wood siding	0.60/cm
Air space	1.82-3.56/cm
Fiberglass	1.22/cm
Loose cellulose	1.46/cm
Aluminum siding	0.01/cm
Loose foam	1.89/cm
Loose vermiculite	1.09/cm

*The total R-value is the product of the R-value ratio and the thickness of the layer in cm.

CONCEPT DEVELOPMENT

▶ Students should think of the R-value of a material as a rate of resistance to heat flow for each centimeter-thickness of insulating material. For example, a building brick is about 20 cm × 9 cm × 6 cm. Normally, a brick is placed in a wall with a depth of 9 cm. In this way, its R-value is 0.72 (9 cm × 0.08/cm). However, if the brick is placed in a wall lengthwise, its R-value would be 1.6 (20 cm × 0.08/cm). Why isn't the latter building method normally used? Explain to students that bricks are used to support rather than to insulate. The cost would be prohibitive because more than twice as many bricks would have to be used in the latter method. Other insulation materials are far less expensive.

▶ Students should also be made aware that the R-value of a wall or ceiling made of several layered materials is the sum of the individual R-values for each material. For example, a wall made of 1-cm layers of plasterboard, brick, and wood siding would have an R-value of 1.03 (0.35 + 0.08 + 0.60).

CHECK FOR UNDERSTANDING

Ask questions 1-3 and the **Apply** and **Connect to Chemistry** questions from the Section Review.

RETEACH

Explain how a vacuum bottle insulates any material it contains.

EXTENSION

For students who have mastered this section, use the **Reinforcement** and **Enrichment** masters or other OPTIONS provided.

INQUIRY QUESTIONS

▶ **What is the R-value of a wall made of bricks that are 9 cm thick?** *R-value = 0.72; 9 cm × 0.08/cm = 0.72*

▶ **How thick would a solid brick wall have to be to have an R-value of 19?** *19 ÷ 0.08/cm = 240 cm*

▶ **A house is built with a dead air space between interior and exterior brick walls. Assuming each brick wall is one layer thick, how thick would the entire wall be to have an R-value of 19?** *The two brick layers would have an R-value of 0.72 each, or 1.4. The R-*

value of the air must be 19 – 1.4, or 17.6. 17.6 ÷ 2.5/cm, roughly the average R-value of air, yields 7 cm. The thickness of the wall would be 25 cm, 18 cm for the bricks and 7 cm for the air space.

PROGRAM RESOURCES

From the **Teacher Resource Package** use:

Cross-Curricular Connections, page 10, Asbestos.

Use **Laboratory Manual 11,** Conduction of Heat; **12,** Specific Heats of Metals.

▶ Invite a representative from a local professional builders' association or utility company to discuss insulation.

SECTION REVIEW ANSWERS

1. Conduction transfers thermal energy by direct contact of particles. Convection transfers energy by matter moving from one location to another. Radiation transfers energy in the form of waves.

2. Heat is not transferred easily through a poor conductor, which is the same characteristic of a good insulator.

3. Wood and plastic are poor conductors (good insulators) of heat.

4. Apply: The plastic foam contains hundreds of tiny air bubbles that act as insulation and keep the food warm.

5. Connect to Chemistry

$$\frac{\text{R-value of wood}}{\text{R-value of aluminum}} = \frac{.60/cm}{.01/cm}$$
$$= 60$$

Wood insulates 60 times better than aluminum because wood contains air pockets and has few free electrons.

Connect to...
Earth Science

Accept all reasonable answers.

Skill Builder
ASSESSMENT
Performance: After students complete the experiment, ask them to describe how they would improve the experimental design.

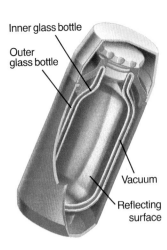

Inner glass bottle
Outer glass bottle

Vacuum
Reflecting surface

Figure 6-6 . This cutaway drawing of a vacuum bottle shows that its construction is similar to that of a double-pane window.

Connect to...
Earth Science

Different climates require different insulating materials and amounts. Call an insulation specialist to find out what materials and R-values are recommended for roofs and ceilings in your area.

Adding insulation and special windows are not the only ways to reduce heat loss from buildings. Many buildings, especially older ones, have cracks and gaps around windows and doors through which heat can escape. These heat leaks should be filled with caulking, putty, or weather stripping to reduce energy loss and fuel bills.

Now that you know more about how thermal energy is transferred, think about things you can do to stay cooler or warmer. You can sit under a shady umbrella or put on a sweater. You can wear light-colored clothing or close a window. You can weatherproof your home by adding insulation and eliminating heat leaks around windows and doors. What other ways can you think of?

SECTION REVIEW

1. Name and describe three methods of thermal energy transfer.
2. Explain why poor conductors of heat are good insulators of heat.
3. Why do many cooking pots and pans have wooden or plastic handles?
4. **Apply:** For many years, many fast food restaurants served their hot sandwiches in plastic foam containers instead of wrapping them in less expensive paper. Why was plastic foam used?
5. **Connect to Chemistry:** Use Table 6-1 on page 139 to determine whether wood siding or aluminum siding is the better insulator. By what factor? Explain your answer.

Skill Builder

☑ Using Variables, Constants, and Controls

Design an experiment to find out which material makes the best insulation: plastic foam pellets, shredded newspaper, or crumpled plastic bags. Remember to state your hypothesis and indicate what factors must be held constant. If you need help, refer to Using Variables, Constants, and Controls in the **Skill Handbook** on page 682.

Skill Builder

Example Experiment
Hypothesize: Different materials do not insulate equally.

Objective: Compare the abilities of plastic foam pellets, shredded newspaper, and crumpled plastic bags to keep an ice cube from melting.

Procedure: Place three similarly sized ice cubes, one each into three plastic sandwich bags. Twist tie the bags. Center each of these bags into identical empty soup cans and pack each with a different insulating material. Place all three cans in direct sunlight. After 30 minutes remove the bags and note the amount of melted ice water in each bag. The best insulator will have the least amount of water.

Controls: size of ice cubes, size of cans, amount of insulating material, time exposed to the sun

DESIGNING AN EXPERIMENT
Creating Convection Currents

What happens when you use some ice cubes to cool a drink? After a while, the drink feels cooler than before you added the ice. What actually happens to the particles that make up the ice cube when it melts? How does convection aid in the cooling of your drink?

Getting Started

In this activity, you will be exploring the changes that occur when a melting ice cube encounters a glass of warm, fresh water and a glass of warm, salt water.

Hypothesizing

Write a **hypothesis** describing what you think will happen when an ice cube melts in a sample of warm, fresh water. What do you think will happen when an ice cube melts in warm, salt water?

Materials

Your cooperative group will use:
- colored ice cubes
- warm fresh water
- tongs
- a ruler
- thermometer
- beaker, 250-mL
- salt
- stirring rod

Try It!

1. *Prepare a data table* for recording the water temperature in salt water and in fresh water at the surface, the bottom, and three measured depths in between.

2. Obtain an ice cube that has been strongly dyed with food coloring. Using tongs, gently place the ice cube in a beaker 3/4 full of warm, fresh water. Keep the beaker and water as still as possible.

3. *Observe* the ice-water mixture for several minutes. Write a detailed description of your observations. Then *measure* the temperature at the surface, at the bottom of the mixture, and at three measured levels in between.

4. Now empty the beaker and fill it to the same level with warm water. Add salt to the water, stirring vigorously as you pour, until no more salt will dissolve.

5. Repeat Steps 2 and 3 using the saltwater solution in place of the fresh water.

Summing Up/Sharing Results

- As the ice melts, what happens to the colored meltwater in the sample of fresh water? In the salt water?
- Do you *observe* convection currents in this activity?
- Of the three liquids involved in this activity, which do you think is the most dense?

Going Further!

Predict what would happen to the coloring and temperature of the liquid if you left the beaker containing fresh water and a colored ice cube untouched for 30 minutes? Test your prediction.

SUMMING UP/SHARING RESULTS

In fresh water, the cold meltwater streams to the bottom and the warm water moves to the top, resulting in a convection current. In salt water, the colored meltwater stays on top. In fresh water, the temperature is lowest at the bottom. In salt water, the temperature is lowest at the top. Salt water is the most dense, because cold meltwater sinks in fresh water but floats in salt water.

GOING FURTHER!

After a while, the temperature throughout the liquid will become nearly the same and the food coloring will be mixed evenly in the solution.

Activity
ASSESSMENT
Performance: To further assess students' understanding of convection, see USING LAB SKILLS, Question 11, on page 154.

OBJECTIVE: Explore relationships between convection currents and fluid density.
Time: One class period for pre-lab discussion and conducting the experiment; one class period for post-lab discussion and Going Further.

PROCESS SKILLS applied in this activity are **observing, collecting and organizing data,** and **inferring.**

PREPARATION

Make several trays of ice cubes colored with food coloring.

Cooperative Learning: Groups of two or three

SAFETY

Caution students to place thermometers far from the edge of their table. Remind them to stir with stirring rods, not thermometers.

HYPOTHESIZING

Students may suggest that as an ice cube melts to create a layer of cold water at the surface, the warmer water beneath it will be less dense and will rise to the surface. The salt water will be more dense than the cold water, so the meltwater will stay on top.

TEACHING THE ACTIVITY

*Refer to the **Activity Worksheets** for additional information and teaching strategies.*
- It is assumed that students understand density and that less dense materials will float on more dense materials.
- Allow two cubes per team.
- Provide about 70 grams of salt to each team. Most or all should dissolve with considerable stirring.
- Students may need help setting up their data table and deciding at what depths to make their measurements.

PROGRAM RESOURCES

From the **Teacher Resource Package** use:

Activity Worksheets, pages 47-48, Activity 6-1: Creating Convection Currents.

PREPARATION

SECTION BACKGROUND
► The most common types of heating systems are hot water, steam, and forced hot air.

► In homes containing passive or active solar heating, it is used primarily in conjunction with conventional heating systems or to supplement heating water for washing and bathing.

1 MOTIVATE

► Have students identify the energy sources and the type of energy used in their home-heating systems. From a class poll, rank the energy sources from most used to least used.

VideoDisc
STVS: Solar House, Disc 2, Side 2

TYING TO PREVIOUS
KNOWLEDGE: Point out that in the last section students learned the three ways in which thermal energy is transferred. In this section they will learn how these methods help warm their homes.

MULTICULTURAL PERSPECTIVE

Central Heating
The Chinese were the first to use central heating for their homes. Instead of building fires inside the house, they would build one outside and heat air to create a convection current that would move into the house. The Eskimos reverse the concept in their igloos. By digging the entranceway lower than the inside of the igloo, they create a natural pressure barrier to keep cold air out. Since cold air sinks to the lowest point, the entranceway fills with cold air from the outside and then the flow stops. The warmer air inside the igloo stays in because it would have to go down through colder air to escape.

6-2 Heating Systems

New Science Words
radiator
solar energy
solar collectors

Objectives
► Describe three types of conventional heating systems.
► Explain how solar energy can be used to heat buildings.
► Explain the differences between passive and active solar heating systems.

Conventional Heating Systems

What is the weather like where you live? Is it cold part of the year or is it warm all year round? Sometimes, even in warm climates, the weather can be cold enough that buildings need to be heated. For this reason, most buildings have some sort of heating system.

All heating systems must have a source of energy, such as fuel or electricity. The simplest type of heating system is one in which fuel is burned right in the area to be heated, such as in a stove or fireplace. The energy released by the burning fuel is transferred to the surrounding air by conduction, convection, and radiation.

Many heating systems use radiators to transfer energy. A **radiator** is a device with a large surface area designed to heat the air near it by conduction. Convection currents then circulate the heat to all parts of the room.

In some heating systems, radiators are heated by electricity. However, most systems are set up so that fuel is

Figure 6-7. The design of this radiator permits large quantities of air to be heated by contact with its surface.

Did You Know?
For every degree you lower your thermostat, your heating costs are lowered by 2-3 percent.

Figure 6-8. In this heating system, water is heated by the furnace. The hot water is pumped to the radiators to heat the rooms of the house.

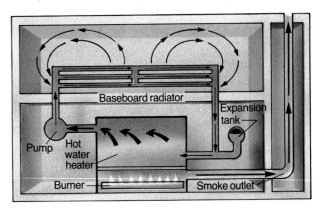

Baseboard radiator
Expansion tank
Pump
Hot water heater
Burner
Smoke outlet

OPTIONS

Meeting Different Ability Levels
For Section 6-2, use the following **Teacher Resource Masters** depending upon individual students' needs.

♦ **Study Guide Master** for all students.

● **Reinforcement Master** for students of average and above average ability levels.

▲ **Enrichment Master** for above average students.

Additional Teacher Resource Package masters are listed in any PROGRAM RESOURCES boxes that are in the section. The additional masters are appropriate for all students.

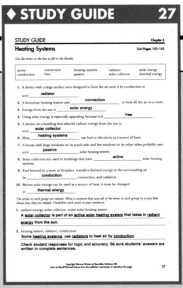

♦ STUDY GUIDE   27

STUDY GUIDE   Chapter 6
Heating Systems   Text Pages 142–145

Use the terms in the box to fill in the blanks.

| active | convection | heating systems | radiator | solar energy |
| conduction | free | passive | solar collector | thermal energy |

1. A device with a large surface area designed to heat the air near it by conduction is a(n) __radiator__

2. A forced-air heating system uses __convection__ to heat the air in a room.

3. Energy from the sun is __solar energy__

4. Using solar energy is especially appealing because it is __free__

5. A device on a building that absorbs radiant energy from the sun is a(n) __solar collector__

6. Most __heating systems__ use fuel or electricity as a source of heat.

7. A house with large windows on its south side and few windows on its other sides probably uses a(n) __passive__ solar heating system.

8. Solar collectors are used in buildings that have __active__ solar heating systems.

9. Fuel burned in a stove or fireplace transfers thermal energy to the surrounding air by __conduction__, convection, and radiation.

10. Before solar energy can be used as a source of heat, it must be changed to __thermal energy__

The terms in each group are related. Write a sentence that uses all of the terms in each group in a way that shows how they are related. Underline each word used in your sentences.

1. radiant energy, solar collector, active solar heating system
A __solar collector__ is part of an __active solar heating system__ that takes in __radiant energy__ from the sun.

2. heating system, radiator, conduction
Some __heating systems__ use __radiators__ to heat air by __conduction__.

Check student responses for logic and accuracy. Be sure students' answers are written in complete sentences.

Copyright Glencoe Division of Macmillan/McGraw-Hill
Users of Merrill Physical Science have the publisher's permission to reproduce this page.   27

burned in a furnace, and the heat is transported to radiators throughout the building. In one such system, the furnace uses the energy to heat water, which is then pumped through the pipes to the radiators. After the water cools, it is returned to the furnace to be heated again.

In a similar type of heating system, the furnace heats water to its boiling point, producing steam. The steam travels through insulated pipes to the radiators. As it cools, the steam condenses to water, which is returned to the furnace. Steam-heating systems need only about one-fiftieth as much water as hot-water systems, but the pipes and furnace need special insulation to keep the steam from condensing before it reaches the radiators.

Another type of heating system is the forced-air system, in which energy released in the furnace is used to heat air. A blower forces the heated air through a system of large pipes, called ducts, to openings, called vents, in each room. In the rooms the warm air circulates by convection. Cooler air passes through other vents and ducts to the furnace to be heated.

Some buildings are heated entirely by electricity. Heating coils are enclosed within floors or ceilings and are heated by electrical energy. Nearby air is heated by conduction, and people and materials in the room are also heated by radiation. Such systems, sometimes called radiant electric heating systems, provide even heating but are usually expensive to operate due to the high cost of electricity.

Connect to... Life Science

People devised many ways to heat their homes before electricity and gas services were available. This allowed them to live in many more places on Earth. What are some of the methods human beings have used to stay warm?

In Your JOURNAL

In your Journal, describe the heating system in your home, apartment, or school. How are conduction, convection, and radiation involved?

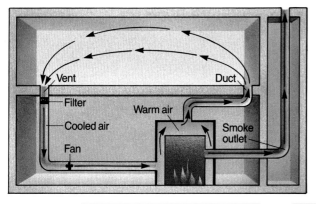

Figure 6-9. In a forced-air heating system, air heated by the furnace is used to heat the rooms of the house.

Vent · **Duct** · **Filter** · **Warm air** · **Cooled air** · **Smoke outlet** · **Fan**

---

2 TEACH

Key Concepts are highlighted.

Cooperative Learning: Assign Numbered Heads Together groups and have them identify and explain energy conversions and thermal energy transfers that take place in the heating systems shown in Figures 6-8 and 6-9.

Connect to... Life Science

Vent systems were built to carry heat from a ground floor fireplace. People used fire to heat water for water bottles and to heat irons to warm their beds.

CONCEPT DEVELOPMENT

▶ Emphasize that the major difference between passive and active solar heating systems is the peripheral equipment. Passive solar heating systems use no mechanical means of transferring energy; active solar heating systems do. Both heat matter by absorbing radiant energy from the sun.

CROSS CURRICULUM

▶ **Earth Science:** Have students explain why the windows of a house in the Northern Hemisphere should face south for maximum sunlight. In which direction should the windows of a house in the Southern Hemisphere face?

PROGRAM RESOURCES

From the **Teacher Resource Package** use:

Transparency Masters, pages 21-22, Heating Systems.

Use **Color Transparency** number 11, Heating Systems.

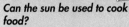

MINI-Lab
Can the sun be used to cook food?
Make a solar cooker by gluing aluminum foil to a large piece of poster board. Bend the board into an arc so that the ends of the board are nearly parallel to one another. Hold the board in this shape with string stretched between its corners. Use wire coat hangers to make a mount that will hold the board with its arc pointed directly at the sun. Using another coat hanger, fashion a device to hold a hot dog. Position the hot dog in the hottest region at the center of the arc. Why is it hot? *Analyze* your design and determine whether it is an active or passive solar energy system.

Figure 6-10. The passive (left) and active (right) solar heating systems change the sun's energy to thermal energy.

Solar Heating

If you have ever gotten into a car that has been sitting in direct sunlight for any length of time, you know that energy from the sun can be changed to thermal energy. Energy from the sun is known as **solar energy.** Because solar energy is free, the idea of using it to heat buildings is especially appealing.

Two basic types of systems are used to capture solar energy and convert it to thermal energy to heat buildings. The first type is passive solar heating. Passive systems use no fans or mechanical devices to transfer heat from one area to another. Some materials in the system absorb radiant energy during the day, convert it to thermal energy, and radiate the thermal energy after dark.

A house with a passive solar heating system usually has a wall of large windows on the south side to receive maximum sunlight. The other exterior walls are heavily insulated and have few windows. During the day, sunlight passes through the windows and is absorbed by some material, such as water or concrete. The radiant energy is converted to thermal energy, which is stored in the absorbing material. Later, when the house begins to cool, the stored energy radiates from the material, warming the rooms.

As you may have guessed, the second type is called an active solar heating system. Most active solar heating systems include **solar collectors,** devices that absorb radiant energy from the sun. The collectors are usually installed on the roof or south side of a building.

OPTIONS

Figure 6-11 shows one type of solar collector. The metal plate absorbs radiant energy from the sun. Why do you think it's painted black? The glass or plastic sheets reduce energy loss due to convection. Water-filled pipes are located just beneath the metal plate. Radiant energy is absorbed and converted to thermal energy to heat the water in the pipes. A pump circulates the heated water to radiators in the system. Cooled water is returned to the collector to be reheated. Some systems have large, insulated tanks for storing heated water to be used as needed.

If you were asked to redesign your building, what type of heating system would you install? What would you use for insulation in your building, and where would you install it? What other steps would you take to keep the people in the building comfortable in all kinds of weather?

Figure 6-11. In an active solar system, the liquid heated in the solar collector is circulated throughout the house.

SECTION REVIEW

1. What are the main differences between electrical, radiator, and forced-air heating systems?
2. Compare and contrast active and passive solar heating systems.
3. **Apply:** Suppose you are an architect from a cold climate who has been asked to design a building for Phoenix, Arizona, where the temperature averages 22°C and can reach 50°C in summer. What do you know about keeping buildings warm that will help a building stay cool in hot weather?
4. **Connect to Earth Science:** Solar energy is free, so why don't most people depend entirely on it for home heating?

✉ Making and Using Tables

In a table, organize information about the kinds of heating systems discussed in this chapter. Include any type of information you think is important. If you need help, refer to Making and Using Tables in the **Skill Handbook** on page 686.

Skill Builder

Ask questions 1-2 and the **Apply** and **Connect to Earth Science** questions in the Section Review.

RETEACH
Have students list the three types of thermal energy transfer that take place in a radiator and rank them from most predominant method to least. Ask them to explain why the term *radiator* does not describe its primary method of heat transfer.

EXTENSION
For students who have mastered this section, use the **Reinforcement** and **Enrichment** masters or other OPTIONS provided.

3 CLOSE

SECTION REVIEW ANSWERS
1. Electrical heating systems have no furnaces, and no fuel is burned in buildings heated by them.
2. In passive systems, solar energy directly heats an area. No devices circulate the energy. In active systems, energy is collected, stored, transferred, and circulated by mechanical devices.
3. Apply: Student responses will vary, but should incorporate ideas about using insulation and solar heating systems. Accept reasonable answers.
4. Connect to Earth Science: Houses must be located in areas with ample sunlight for effective solar heating. Homes usually have standard heating systems to supplement solar heating if there isn't enough sunlight.

PROGRAM RESOURCES
From the **Teacher Resource Package** use:
   Concept Mapping, pages 17-18.
   Science Integration Activity 6

Skill Builder
ASSESSMENT
Performance: Have students use their table to analyze the type of heating system used in at least two buildings other than their home or school.

Skill Builder

Type of Heating System	Specific Name	Heating Method
Conventional	Radiator	Conduction/convection
	Forced-air	Convection
	Radiant electric	Conduction/radiation/convection
Solar	Passive	Radiation
	Active	Radiation/conduction

PREPARATION

SECTION BACKGROUND
▶ Thermal pollution is a detrimental change in the temperature in an environment caused by an artificial source.

1 MOTIVATE

▶**Demonstration:** Moisten a cotton ball with ethanol, wrap it around the bulb of a thermometer, and show that the temperature reading decreases as the alcohol evaporates. Have students hypothesize how evaporation is used to cool materials.

VideoDisc
STVS: Greenhouse Effect, Disc 6, Side 2

2 TEACH

Key Concepts are highlighted.

CONCEPT DEVELOPMENT
▶ Cooling towers cool water in one of two ways. In one method, heated water is exposed directly to the atmosphere. In the second method, hot water in a primary system of pipes is cooled when it heats water in a secondary set of pipes that surround the primary system.

Connect to...
Earth Science

Factories, power plants, and excessive traffic are possible examples.

 **6-3 Thermal Pollution**

New Science Words

thermal pollution
cooling towers

Objectives

▶ Identify problems associated with thermal pollution.
▶ Discuss solutions for thermal pollution problems.

Connect to...
Earth Science

Find out what industries or activities might produce thermal pollution in your community, even on a small scale.

Not So Hot!

Have you ever been in a city on a warm day, surrounded by cars, large buildings, and concrete? If so, you may have noticed that it seems to be hotter there than in the suburbs, where there's less traffic and less activity. Much of the energy used in everyday life—electrical, chemical, mechanical, radiant, or nuclear energy—ends up as waste thermal energy that is given off into the surroundings. The heat removed from air-conditioned buildings and vehicles is released to the outside air, just as heat is released into a kitchen by a refrigerator.

The level of waste thermal energy can reach unhealthy levels. **Thermal pollution** occurs when waste thermal energy significantly changes the temperature of the environment. It is a particular problem in areas where power plants and factories use water to cool their buildings and equipment, warming the water in the process. If the warmed water is dumped into a river, lake, or ocean, the added heat may cause problems for the plants and animals living there.

Fish are especially sensitive to increases in water temperature. Some species will die within hours in water warmer than 25°C.

146 USING THERMAL ENERGY

OPTIONS

Meeting Different Ability Levels
For Section 6-3, use the following **Teacher Resource Masters** depending upon individual students' needs.
◆ **Study Guide Master** for all students.
● **Reinforcement Master** for students of average and above average ability levels.
▲ **Enrichment Master** for above average students.
Additional Teacher Resource Package masters are listed in any PROGRAM RESOURCES boxes that are in the section. The additional masters are appropriate for all students.

◆ **STUDY GUIDE** 28

STUDY GUIDE   Chapter 6
Thermal Pollution   Text Pages 146–147

Write the vocabulary term from this section that best completes each statement in the space provided.

1. The problem caused when waste thermal energy raises the temperature of the environment is _____**thermal pollution**_____.

2. Devices in which water is cooled by fans or evaporation before being released into the environment are _____**cooling towers**_____.

Use the words in the box to fill in the blanks.

temperature	25°C	buildings	pollution	heat	plants
factories	hours	raising	ocean	equipment	fish
animals	lake	increases		thermal	species

Thermal ____**pollution**____ is a problem caused when waste ____**thermal**____ energy raises the ____**temperature**____ of the environment. Power plants and ____**factories**____ use water to cool their ____**buildings**____ and ____**equipment**____. Dumping this water after ____**raising**____ the temperature into a nearby river, ____**lake**____ or ____**ocean**____ adds ____**heat**____ and may cause problems for ____**plants**____ and ____**animals**____. Animals especially sensitive to ____**increases**____ in water temperature are ____**fish**____. Some ____**species**____ of fish will die within ____**hours**____ in water warmer than ____**25°C**____.

28

Thermal pollution can be reduced by releasing small amounts of warm water mixed with plenty of cooler water. Some factories and power plants use **cooling towers,** where water is cooled by fans or by evaporation. Newer structures may build decorative fountains or ponds to cool or store water. Cooled water can be released into the environment without causing harm. Or, the extra thermal energy can be used to heat greenhouses or other buildings.

SECTION REVIEW

1. Thermal pollution may encourage the growth of certain water plants. Why might this be a problem?
2. A company plans to build several greenhouses to get rid of waste heat from cooling water. Suggest reasons why this plan might not be sufficient. What might the company do to improve the plan?
3. **Connect to Earth Science:** Explain how you would design a new power plant to use excess thermal energy creatively and constructively.

You Decide!

A company wants to build a factory by a river that runs through your city, creating new jobs, but also generating waste thermal energy. What steps would you take to find out whether the environment will be damaged? Should the company be allowed to build its factory?

SCIENCE & SOCIETY

CHECK FOR UNDERSTANDING
Ask questions 1-2 and the **Connect to Earth Science** question in the Section Review.

RETEACH

? **FLEX Your Brain**

Use the Flex Your Brain activity to have students explore the THERMAL POLLUTION.

ASSESSMENT
Portfolio: Use the Flex Your Brain activity to reinforce critical-thinking and problem-solving skills. In Step 2, students might list news stories they have read or heard about thermal pollution.

EXTENSION
For students who have mastered this section, use the **Reinforcement** and **Enrichment** masters or other OPTIONS provided.

3 CLOSE

SECTION REVIEW ANSWERS
1. Heavy plant growth might keep light from penetrating a body of water. Decaying plants could use much of the oxygen from the water.
2. Student answers may include that building greenhouses would only use some of the heat. Greenhouses need to be cooled, instead of warmed, in spring and summer. Build auxiliary cooling towers. Allow water to drain slowly into a stream.
3. Connect to Earth Science: Encourage creative designs, such as heating nearby buildings or building fountains or decorative cooling towers.

YOU DECIDE!
SCIENCE & SOCIETY
Accept all reasonable answers.

PROGRAM RESOURCES
From the **Teacher Resource Package** use:

Activity Worksheets, page 5, Flex Your Brain.

6-4 Using Heat to Do Work

PREPARATION

SECTION BACKGROUND

▶ Heat engines convert thermal energy to mechanical energy; this implies that heat can do work. An internal combustion engine converts the chemical potential energy in fuel to thermal energy as the fuel burns. Thermal energy causes gases produced by the burned fuel to expand and do work against a piston. The mechanical energy of the piston produces motion.

▶ By reversing the processes of a heat engine, heat can be transferred from a material at a lower temperature to a material at a higher temperature. Work must be done on a system to reverse the natural flow of heat.

PREPLANNING

▶ Ask to borrow working models of internal combustion engines from the instructor at a local technical high school for demonstrations.

1 MOTIVATE

▶ Ask students to discuss how their lives would be different without the internal combustion engine.

TYING TO PREVIOUS

KNOWLEDGE: Point out to students that just as they have the ability to lift and move objects, heat also can do work.

In Your JOURNAL

Engines get hot when they run because friction produces waste thermal energy. The sound an engine makes also takes energy. Accept other reasonable answers.

6-4 Using Heat to Do Work

New Science Words

heat engines
combustion
internal combustion engine
external combustion engine
heat mover
heat pump

Objectives

▶ Describe how internal combustion engines and external combustion engines work.
▶ Explain how a heat mover can transfer thermal energy in a direction opposite to that of its natural movement.

Heat Engines

① **Heat engines** are devices that convert thermal energy into mechanical energy by burning fuel in a process called **combustion**, which means rapid burning. The two main classes of heat engines are based on where combustion happens—inside the engine or outside the engine.

② In an **internal combustion engine,** fuel burns inside the engine, in chambers called cylinders. Gasoline and diesel engines, such as the ones used in cars and trucks, are examples of internal combustion engines.

Figure 6-12 shows what the cylinders look like inside the gasoline engine of a car. Each cylinder has two openings that open or close with valves. A piston inside each cylinder moves up and down, turning a rod called a crankshaft. The motion of the crankshaft is transferred to the wheels of the car through a series of moving parts. The wheels exert a force on the road, through the tires. The equal and opposite force of the road on the tires accelerates the car forward.

Each movement of the piston up or down is called a stroke. An automobile engine is called a four stroke engine because the piston makes four strokes in each cycle. Follow the steps of the four stroke cycle in Figure 6-12.

1. *Intake stroke.* In another part of the engine called the carburetor (CAR buh ray tur), gasoline is broken up into fine droplets and mixed with air. In the cylinder, the intake valve opens and the piston moves downward, drawing the fuel-air mixture into the cylinder.

OPTIONS

Meeting Different Ability Levels

For Section 6-4, use the following **Teacher Resource Masters** depending upon individual students' needs.

◆ **Study Guide Master** for all students.
● **Reinforcement Master** for students of average and above average ability levels.
▲ **Enrichment Master** for above average students.

Additional Teacher Resource Package masters are listed in any PROGRAM RESOURCES boxes that are in the section. The additional masters are appropriate for all students.

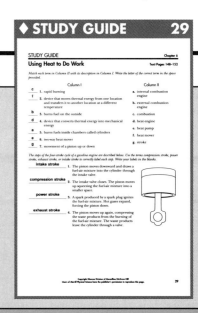

◆ **STUDY GUIDE** 29

STUDY GUIDE   Chapter 6
Using Heat to Do Work   Text Pages 148–152

Match each term in Column II with its description in Column I. Write the letter of the correct term in the space provided.

	Column I	Column II
c	1. rapid burning	a. internal combustion engine
f	2. device that moves thermal energy from one location and transfers it to another location at a different temperature	b. external combustion engine
b	3. burns fuel on the outside	c. combustion
d	4. device that converts thermal energy into mechanical energy	d. heat engine
a	5. burns fuels inside chambers called cylinders	e. heat pump
e	6. two-way heat mover	f. heat mover
g	7. movement of a piston up or down	g. stroke

The steps of the four-stroke cycle of a gasoline engine are described below. Use the terms compression stroke, power stroke, exhaust stroke, or intake stroke to correctly label each step. Write your labels in the blanks.

intake stroke   1. The piston moves downward and draws a fuel-air mixture into the cylinder through the intake valve.

compression stroke   2. The intake valve closes. The piston moves up squeezing the fuel-air mixture into a smaller space.

power stroke   3. A spark produced by a spark plug ignites the fuel-air mixture. Hot gases expand, forcing the piston down.

exhaust stroke   4. The piston moves up again, compressing the waste products from the burning of the fuel-air mixture. The waste products leave the cylinder through a valve.

Copyright Glencoe Division of Macmillan/McGraw-Hill
Users of Merrill Physical Science have the publisher's permission to reproduce this page.   29

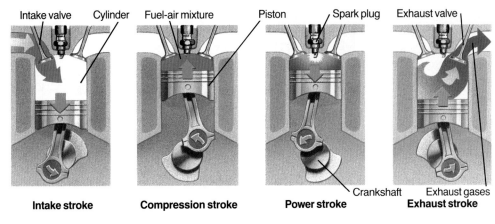

Intake valve · Cylinder · Fuel-air mixture · Piston · Spark plug · Exhaust valve

Intake stroke **Compression stroke** **Power stroke** Crankshaft · Exhaust gases **Exhaust stroke**

2. *Compression stroke.* The intake valve closes, and the piston moves up. The fuel-air mixture is squeezed, or compressed, into a smaller space.

3. *Power stroke.* When the piston is almost at the top of the cylinder, a spark plug produces a hot spark that ignites the fuel-air mixture. As the mixture burns, hot gases expand, forcing the piston down. Energy is transferred from the piston to the wheels of the car through the crankshaft and other moving parts.

4. *Exhaust stroke.* The piston moves up again, compressing the waste products from burning the fuel-air mixture. The exhaust valve opens to let them out.

Some engines have fuel injectors instead of carburetors. In fuel injector engines, only air enters the cylinder during the intake stroke. During the compression stroke, fine droplets of fuel are injected directly into the compressed air in the cylinder. The other steps are the same as in an engine with a carburetor.

In a diesel engine, fuel also is injected into compressed air in the cylinder. But the engine has no spark plugs. The fuel-air mixture is compressed, which causes it to become hot enough to ignite without a spark.

In an internal combustion engine, only part of the thermal energy produced by burning fuel is converted to mechanical energy. The rest is left over as waste thermal energy due to friction and the heating of engine parts. Gasoline engines convert only about 12 percent of the chemical potential energy in the fuel to mechanical energy. Diesel engines convert up to 25 percent of the potential energy to mechanical energy.

Figure 6-12. This drawing shows what takes place during each stroke of a four stroke cycle.

Only a small percentage of the chemical potential energy of gasoline is actually used to move your car. **In your Journal,** list evidence that much of the energy is wasted.

How do fuel injectors operate?

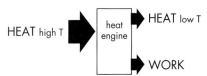
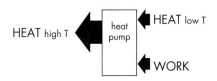
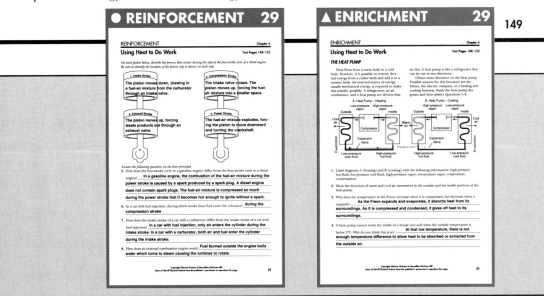

For more information on cooling crystals, see "Magna Fridge" by Jim Schefter, *Popular Science*, March 1989, pp. 93 and 143.

Think Critically: The properties of the refrigerant would determine how cold the refrigerator could get. The substance used would not be effective at temperatures below its boiling point.

MINI QUIZ

Use the Mini Quiz to check students' recall of chapter content.

1 Heat engines are devices that convert _____ energy into _____ energy. *thermal, mechanical*

2 In a(n) _____ , fuel is burned inside the engine. *internal combustion engine*

3 In a(n) _____ , fuel is burned outside the engine. *external combustion engine*

CHECK FOR UNDERSTANDING

Ask questions 1-2 and the **Apply** and **Connect to Chemistry** questions in the Section Review.

RETEACH

Cooperative Learning: Using the Paired Partners strategy, have students make flash cards with the names of the strokes of the four stroke cycle. On the reverse side of each card, describe the stroke. Partners can then test each other by shuffling the cards and sequencing them both by name and description. Students can alter the cards to represent the four stroke cycle of a diesel engine.

Figure 6-13. Turbines are used to convert thermal energy to mechanical energy.

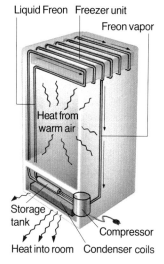

Figure 6-14. In a heat mover, such as a refrigerator, thermal energy is removed from one location and is released in another location.

Liquid Freon   Freezer unit
Freon vapor
Heat from warm air
Storage tank
Compressor
Heat into room   Condenser coils

150 USING THERMAL ENERGY

In an **external combustion engine,** fuel is burned outside the engine. In old-fashioned steam engines, such as those used to power early locomotives, fuel was burned to boil water in a chamber outside the engine. The steam produced passed through a valve in the engine, where it pushed a piston. The motion of the piston was transferred to the wheels of the locomotive.

Modern steam engines, such as those used in electrical power stations, don't have pistons. Instead, steam is directed onto huge, fanlike devices called turbines. The steam pushes against the turbine blades, and the turbine rotates rapidly.

Heat Movers

When you put warm food into the refrigerator, the food gets cooler. Where does the thermal energy in the food go? Feel the back of the refrigerator, and you'll notice that it's warm. But you know that heat always flows from warmer to cooler areas. So how can heat flow from the cool refrigerator to the warm room? It can't unless work is done. The energy to do the work comes from the electricity that powers the refrigerator.

A refrigerator is an example of a heat mover. A **heat mover** is a device that removes thermal energy from one location and transfers it to another location at a different temperature. Refrigerators use the process of evaporation to remove heat from the food inside. A liquid is pumped through coils inside the refrigerator. In most cooling systems, liquid Freon is used because it evaporates at low temperatures. As the liquid evaporates and becomes a gas, it absorbs heat, cooling the inside of the refrigerator. The Freon gas is then pumped to a compressor on the outside of the refrigerator. Compressing the Freon causes its temperature to rise above room temperature. So the Freon loses heat to the air around it and becomes liquid again. The excess heat is transferred into the room, sometimes with the help of fans.

An air conditioner is another kind of heat mover, removing thermal energy from a warm house and transferring it to the even warmer outdoor surroundings.

A **heat pump** is a two-way heat mover. In warm weather, it operates like an air conditioner. But in cold weather, it removes thermal energy from the cool outside air and transfers it to the inside of the house.

OPTIONS

TECHNOLOGY

Cooling Crystals

A conventional refrigerator uses the principle that a liquid absorbs heat when allowed to evaporate and expand. An entirely different approach to refrigeration is being based on the fact that certain crystals give off heat when they are magnetized and absorb heat when demagnetized.

One such crystal is gadolinium gallium garnet. Scientists have mounted crystal wafers of this substance on the outside of a wheel that rotates the wafers in and out of a magnetic field. As they rotate, they alternately absorb and give off heat. This magnetic refrigerator can attain temperatures close to absolute zero.

Possible uses for this include cooling infrared sensors on spacecraft, cooling medical research equipment, and cooling super computers.

Think Critically: What factor would determine how cold a gas-cycle refrigerator could get?

SECTION REVIEW

1. What are the main differences between a diesel engine and a gasoline engine? How are they alike?
2. What happens to the thermal energy converted from chemical energy in a heat engine?
3. **Apply:** Explain whether it is a good idea to cool your house by leaving the refrigerator door open.
4. **Connect to Chemistry:** In which stroke of a four-stroke cycle is chemical potential energy converted to thermal energy? Explain your answer.

Connect to... Earth Science

Freon is a type of chlorofluorocarbon (CFC). What is the main environmental effect that may result when Freon is released in the atmosphere?

☑ Concept Mapping

Make a cycle concept map to show the steps in one cycle of a four stroke internal combustion engine. If you need help, refer to Concept Mapping in the **Skill Handbook** on pages 684 and 685.

Skill Builder

Skill Builder

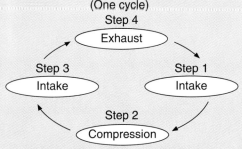

Four-stroke Internal Combustion Engine
(One cycle)

Step 4 — Exhaust
Step 3 — Intake
Step 1 — Intake
Step 2 — Compression

Skill Builder
ASSESSMENT
Oral: Sketch a diagram of one of the strokes. Ask students to use their concept maps to identify which stroke is pictured and what will happen next.

Connect to... Earth Science

Answer: Some CFCs, including Freon, are linked to the destruction of the ozone layer in our atmosphere.

3 CLOSE

▶ Invite a representative from a utilities company to discuss the advantages and disadvantages of heat pump and heating/air-conditioning systems.

SECTION REVIEW ANSWERS

1. Diesel fuel is different from gasoline; diesel engines do not use spark plugs or carburetors. Both types are four stroke engines; each is an internal combustion engine.

2. Some of the thermal energy is converted to mechanical energy in the power stroke, forcing the piston to move; the rest is wasted thermal energy transferred to the environment.

3. Apply: No; the more heat allowed to enter the refrigerator, the more heat the refrigerator will move back into the kitchen. Much electrical energy will be wasted.

4. Connect to Chemistry: Chemical potential energy is converted to thermal energy in the power stroke as the fuel is burned.

ACTIVITY 6-2

30 minutes

OBJECTIVE: Construct and **analyze** a model of a four-stroke engine.

PROCESS SKILLS applied in this activity:
▶ **Observing** in Procedure Steps 4-7.
▶ **Analyzing** in Analyze Question 1.
▶ **Modeling** in Procedure Steps 4-7.

COOPERATIVE LEARNING
Use the Science Investigation Team strategy. Each member can operate a different part of the engine: carburetor, intake and exhaust valves, and piston.

TEACHING THE ACTIVITY

Troubleshooting: Insert glass tubing prior to the activity. This will both save time and increase safety.
▶ Students should prepare by reading pages 148-149 about internal combustion engines.
▶ Torch paper can be used to generate smoke. Otherwise, you should use paper towels.
▶ Soft rubber tubing and strong pinch clamps are needed to avoid gas leaks.
▶ Use the activity to discuss the use of models to study specific parts of a complex problem.

PROGRAM RESOURCES

From the **Teacher Resource Package** use:

Activity Worksheets, pages 49-50, Activity 6-2: The Four-Stroke Engine.

Activity
ASSESSMENT
Performance: To further assess students' understanding of engines, see USING LAB SKILLS, Question 12, on page 154.

The Four-Stroke Engine

You have learned to analyze many situations for the transfers between potential and kinetic energy in a system. As you examine the piston movements in a four-stroke engine can you identify and detect changes in kinetic and potential energy? In this activity you will use a model of a four-stroke engine to demonstrate such changes.

Materials
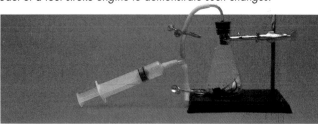
- matches
- flask, 250-mL
- glass or plastic "T"
- pinch clamps (2)
- large syringe, plastic
- rubber tubing (3 pieces)
- small piece of cloth or yarn
- rubber stopper, 2-hole, with glass tubing

Procedure
1. *Set up a model* four stroke engine as shown.
2. *Prepare a data table* like the one shown. As you complete each step, identify the stroke and *record your observations.*
3. With all clamps closed, ignite a small piece of cloth or yarn and drop it in the flask. **CAUTION:** *Exercise caution when using open flames.* Allow the flask, representing the carburetor, to fill with smoke.
4. With the piston inside the syringe, open the intake clamp and pull the piston down.
5. Close the intake clamp and push the piston up into the syringe.
6. Release the piston and *observe* what happens.
7. Open the exhaust clamp and push the piston up into the syringe.
8. Close the exhaust clamp and repeat Steps 4-7.

Analyze
1. During which stroke are the smoke particles most widely separated?
2. What happens to the smoke particles when the intake clamp is closed and the piston moves into the syringe?
3. What happens when the piston is released?
4. What happens to the smoke particles when the exhaust clamp is opened and the piston moves into the syringe?
5. During what strokes are both clamps closed?

Conclude and Apply
6. In this model, what does the smoke represent in Steps 4 and 5? In Step 7?
7. When would be the best instant to explode a fuel-air mixture?
8. In which stroke is kinetic energy changed to potential energy? Potential to kinetic?

Data and Observations
Sample Data

Step	Stroke	Observations
4	intake	intake clamp open; piston moves out of syringe; smoke from carburetor fills syringe
5	compression	both clamps closed; piston moves into syringe; particles of smoke squeezed together
6	power	both clamps closed; pressure of gases squeezed at top of syringe forces piston to move out
7	exhaust	exhaust clamp open; piston moves into syringe; smoke is pushed out through exhaust clamp

152 USING THERMAL ENERGY

ANSWERS TO QUESTIONS
1. intake stroke
2. The smoke particles are compressed—squeezed together.
3. It moves downward in the syringe.
4. Smoke particles are pushed out through the clamp by the piston.
5. during the compression and power strokes
6. In Steps 4 and 5, the smoke represents the fuel-air mixture; in Step 7, it represents exhaust gases.
7. when the piston is at the top of its stroke and the fuel-air mixture is most compressed

8. Kinetic energy is changed to potential energy during the compression stroke. Potential energy is changed to kinetic energy during the power stroke.

SUMMARY

6-1: Moving Thermal Energy

1. Thermal energy can be transferred by conduction, convection, and radiation. Conduction and convection can only occur when matter is present. Radiation does not require matter.
2. Materials that do not allow heat to move through them easily are insulators. Conductors allow heat to move through them easily.
3. Insulation slows down or prevents the movement of thermal energy.

6-2: Heating Systems

1. Heating systems are generally identified by the medium that transfers the thermal energy. The three most common types of heating systems are hot water, steam, and hot air.
2. A solar heating system converts radiant energy from the sun to thermal energy.
3. Passive solar systems have no devices to transfer heat from one part of the system to another.

Active systems use fans or pumps to serve this purpose.

6-3: Science and Society: Thermal Pollution

1. Thermal pollution adversely affects living things.
2. Specific practices have been identified that can greatly reduce thermal pollution at the source.

6-4: Using Heat to Do Work

1. Heat engines are devices that convert thermal energy produced by burning fuel into mechanical energy. In an internal combustion engine, fuel is burned inside the engine. In an external combustion engine, fuel is burned outside the engine.
2. Heat movers move thermal energy from one place and release it in another place. In many cases, this transfer is from cooler to warmer regions.

KEY SCIENCE WORDS

a. combustion
b. conduction
c. convection
d. cooling tower
e. external combustion engine
f. fluid
g. heat engine
h. heat mover
i. heat pump
j. insulator
k. internal combustion engine
l. radiation
m. radiator
n. solar collector
o. solar energy
p. thermal pollution

UNDERSTANDING VOCABULARY

Match each phrase with the correct term from the list of Key Science Words.

1. energy transfer by direct contact of particles
2. energy transfer by movement of particles from place to place
3. energy transfer by invisible waves
4. material that resists the flow of heat
5. device that absorbs the sun's radiant energy
6. device that converts thermal energy into mechanical energy
7. rapid burning
8. a device that transfers thermal energy from one place to another
9. device in which warm water is cooled by fans or by evaporation
10. a device designed to heat the air that comes in contact with it

USING THERMAL ENERGY **153**

CHAPTER
REVIEW

SUMMARY

Have students read the summary statements to review the major concepts of the chapter.

UNDERSTANDING VOCABULARY

1.	b	6.	g
2.	c	7.	a
3.	l	8.	h
4.	j	9.	d
5.	n	10.	m

ASSESSMENT
Portfolio

Encourage students to place in their portfolios one or two items of what they consider to be their best work. For each item, ask students to explain why that item was chosen and what they learned from it. Items might be selected from the following.
- Connect to Chemistry answer, p. 140
- Connect to Earth Science answer, p. 146
- In Your Journal entry, p. 149

Performance

Additional performance assessments may be found in *Performance Assessment* and *Science Integration Activities* that accompany **Merrill Physical Science.** Performance Task Assessment Lists and rubrics for evaluating these activities and other products generated throughout the chapter can be found in Glencoe's *Performance Assessment in Middle School Science.*

OPTIONS

ASSESSMENT

To assess student understanding of material in this chapter, use the resources listed.

👥 COOPERATIVE LEARNING

Consider using cooperative learning in the THINK AND WRITE CRITICALLY, APPLY, and MORE SKILL BUILDERS sections of the Chapter Review.

PROGRAM RESOURCES

From the **Teacher Resource Package** use:
Chapter Review, pages 15-16.
Chapter and Unit Tests, pages 32-35, Chapter Test.

CHAPTER
REVIEW

CHECKING CONCEPTS

1. b	**6.** b
2. a	**7.** c
3. d	**8.** a
4. a	**9.** d
5. a	**10.** d

USING LAB SKILLS

ASSESSMENT

Use these alternate lab exercises to assess students' understanding of the skills used in this chapter.

11. The warmer, less dense water should rise to the top. All the water in the beaker will mix as it reaches the same temperature.

12. An actual engine uses a combustible material to force the piston down, which converts potential to kinetic energy. The exhaust in the Activity is chemically different from the air-gas mixture in a real engine.

THINK AND WRITE CRITICALLY

13. Initially, the bottom of the pot and the soup near the pot bottom are heated by conduction. Some of the energy of the burner top is transferred to the particles of the pot bottom, which transfers energy to the soup. As the bottom portion of the soup becomes warm, the cooler, denser liquid sinks, forcing the warmer liquid to rise. This movement transfers heat throughout the liquid by convection.

14. Convection currents are created when one part of a fluid is heated. The cooler, denser fluid moves down and forces the warmer, less dense fluid to rise, creating a convection current. Winds and ocean currents are examples of convection currents in nature.

15. Darker materials absorb radiation more effectively. When layers of clothing are worn, a thin layer of insulating air will be present between each layer of clothing.

16. In passive solar heating, radiant energy is directed onto a material that will absorb the energy, convert it to thermal energy, and transfer it to the surroundings as heat. In active solar

CHECKING CONCEPTS

Choose the word or phrase that completes the sentence or answers the question.

1. Which is not a method of heat transfer?
- **a.** conduction
- **c.** radiation
- **b.** insulation
- **d.** convection

2. In _____, fuel is burned inside chambers called cylinders.
- **a.** internal combustion engines
- **b.** external combustion engines
- **c.** heat pumps
- **d.** steam engines

3. Waste gases are removed during the _____ of a four stroke engine.
- **a.** power stroke
- **c.** compression stroke
- **b.** intake stroke
- **d.** exhaust stroke

4. Which material is a poor insulator of heat?
- **a.** aluminum
- **c.** air
- **b.** feathers
- **d.** plastic

5. A _____ is an example of a heat mover.
- **a.** refrigerator
- **c.** combustion engine
- **b.** steam engine
- **d.** four stroke engine

6. In which of these forms is water not a fluid?
- **a.** liquid water
- **c.** water vapor
- **b.** ice
- **d.** steam

7. Heat can move easily through a good _____.
- **a.** insulator
- **c.** conductor
- **b.** carburetor
- **d.** collector

8. Which of these does not require the presence of particles of matter?
- **a.** radiation
- **c.** convection
- **b.** conduction
- **d.** combustion

9. In order for radiant energy to change to thermal energy, it must be _____.
- **a.** reflected
- **c.** convected
- **b.** conducted
- **d.** absorbed

10. A(n) _____ is a two-way heat mover.
- **a.** refrigerator
- **c.** air conditioner
- **b.** steam engine
- **d.** heat pump

USING LAB SKILLS

11. Review Activity 6-1 on page 141. What do you think would happen if you were to use a funnel to add warm water (colored red) to the bottom of a beaker of cold water? Explain your answer.

12. Study the four stroke engine model in Activity 6-2 on page 152. Explain how this model differs from an actual engine.

THINK AND WRITE CRITICALLY

Answer the following questions in your Journal using complete sentences.

13. Describe all of the ways in which energy is transferred while a pot of soup is heated on an electric stove. Indicate how each type of energy transfer takes place.

14. Explain how convection currents are created. Describe two examples of convection currents that occur in nature.

15. Why is winter clothing generally darker in color than summer clothing? Explain why wearing two or three layers of clothing helps to keep you warmer in cold weather than does one thick layer.

16. Compare and contrast passive and active solar heating. What basic principle are both systems based on?

17. Describe some causes and effects of thermal pollution. Suggest some solutions to this environmental problem.

heating, the thermal energy is transferred by the use of mechanical devices. Both systems are based on the idea that radiant energy is changed to thermal energy when it is absorbed.

17. Most thermal pollution is produced by industries that use water as a coolant, and then release heated water back into the body of water from which it came. The effect of this action is to raise the temperature of the body of water, which can make it unfit for plant and animal life to exist. The best way to prevent such pollution is to cool the water before returning it to the environment.

APPLY

18. Student responses will vary, but may include such analogies as energy being passed on to a pack of billiard balls when one ball is struck.

19. Radiant energy from the sun strikes materials inside a car and is absorbed, changing to thermal energy. Thermal energy is transferred as heat. The increase in heat causes the temperature inside the car to rise.

20. Student answers will vary, but should include dark-colored materials that will absorb radiant energy and layers of fibers

APPLY

18. The energy transfer shown in Figure 6-1 on page 135 takes place at the particle level of matter. Thus, the transfer of energy cannot be observed directly. Think of an analogy or model using visible objects that you could use to demonstrate the process of conduction.
19. Explain why the inside of an automobile left sitting in direct sunlight for several hours becomes very warm.
20. Design a line of clothing to be used on an Arctic expedition. Describe the articles of clothing and explain why each will keep the wearer warm in extremely cold conditions.
21. The engines of many high-performance cars have four valves per cylinder rather than the usual two-valve arrangement. These engines also have fuel injectors at each cylinder rather than a single carburetor. How do these differences improve the performance of the engine?
22. Describe how an automobile air conditioner using Freon gas works. Explain why the engine must be running in order for the air conditioner to work.

MORE SKILL BUILDERS

If you need help, refer to the Skill Handbook.

1. **Interpreting Data:** Using the R-values given in Table 6-1 on page 139, design an energy-efficient house. Indicate the type and thickness of the different materials to be used in constructing the walls and ceilings.
2. **Sequencing:** Order the events that occur in the removal of heat from an object by a refrigerator. Start with the placing of a warm object in the refrigerator and finish with the change in Freon from a gas to a liquid.

3. **Concept Mapping:** Complete the following events chain to show how an active solar heating system works.

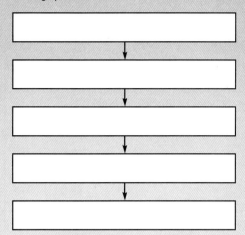

4. **Recognizing Cause and Effect:** Describe the probable effect of each of the following problems that might occur in a fuel-injected gasoline engine. Indicate the engine stroke that will be affected. (a) exhaust valve stuck closed; (b) clogged fuel injector; (c) bad spark plug; (d) intake valve will not close.
5. **Using Variables, Constants, and Controls:** Design an experiment to test the effects of surface area and length of a material on heat conduction. Indicate your hypothesis, controls, and constants. How will you organize and interpret your data?

PROJECTS

1. Design and construct an insulated container using household materials.
2. Research the development of the automobile engine. Construct a time line showing the most significant events.

USING THERMAL ENERGY **155**

---

that will trap air and reduce the loss of body heat. Also, reflective linings could be used to reflect thermal energy.
21. Increasing the number of valves increases the amount of fresh air taken into the cylinder during the intake stroke and decreases the amount of exhaust remaining. More air can burn more fuel. The fuel injectors provide a more even distribution of fuel. Both help to increase efficiency of combustion and thus increase power.
22. As liquid Freon moves through the air conditioner it evaporates, removing thermal energy from the interior of the car. This thermal energy is then released to the warmer air outside the car. This process requires work to be done by the car's engine.

MORE SKILL BUILDERS

1. **Interpreting Data:** Student responses will vary, but the combinations of suggested materials and/or their thicknesses should give total R-values of at least 19 for the walls and 30 for the roof.
2. **Sequencing:** Liquid Freon evaporates, removing thermal energy from the interior of the refrigerator; compressing the gas raises its temperature; heat flows from the gas to the exterior air, causing the Freon gas to condense to a liquid.
3. **Concept Mapping:**

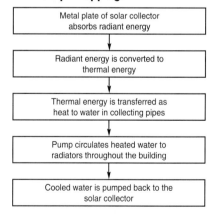

---

4. Recognizing Cause and Effect: (a) Exhaust gases will not be removed during the exhaust stroke, which will limit the amount of fuel-air mixture entering during the intake stroke. (b) The amount of fuel being mixed with air during the intake stroke will be reduced, thus reducing the effectiveness of the power stroke. (c) The fuel-air mixture will not be properly ignited, thus reducing the power stroke. (d) The fuel-air mixture that enters during the intake stroke will be pushed out of the stuck valve during the compression stroke, thus reducing the power stroke.

5. Using Variables, Constants, and Controls: Student responses will vary, but a sample hypothesis is that increasing surface area increases thermal conduction. Controls would include varying the surface area. Constants would include the type of material tested. Data analysis may include a line graph.

CHAPTER
7 Machines

CHAPTER SECTION	OBJECTIVES	ACTIVITIES
7-1 Why We Use Machines (2 days)	1. **Explain** how machines make work easier. 2. **Calculate** mechanical advantage.	**Activity 7-1:** *Invent a Machine!*, p. 162
7-2 The Simple Machines (2 days)	1. **Describe** the six types of simple machines. 2. **Calculate** the mechanical advantage for different types of simple machines.	**Activity 7-2:** *Levers*, p. 171
7-3 Human-Powered Flying Machines Science & Society (1 day)	1. **Analyze** the simple machines in a human-powered air-craft. 2. **Consider** the value of experiments with no obvious practical value.	
7-4 Using Machines (2 days)	1. **Recognize** the simple machines that make up a compound machine. 2. **Calculate** the efficiency of a machine. 3. **Describe** the relationship between work, power, and time.	**MINI-Lab:** *Can you measure the power of a toy car?* p. 177
Chapter Review		

ACTIVITY MATERIALS

FIND OUT	ACTIVITIES		MINI-LABS

Page 157
round pencils (several)
stiff ruler
2 books
	7-1 Invent a Machine!, p. 162
	brick
	book
	string
	pencils (2)
	hard board
	pulley
	ring stand and ring
		7-2 Levers, p. 171
		sheet of paper,
		  20 cm x 28 cm
		  (8-1/2 " × 11")
		coins (3) (quarter,
		  dime, nickel)
		balance
		metric ruler
			Can you measure the power of a toy car? p. 177
			wind-up toy car
			inclined plane board
			stopwatch or timer
			  with second hand
			meterstick
			spring scale

CHAPTER FEATURES	TEACHER RESOURCE PACKAGE	OTHER RESOURCES
Skill Builder: *Recognizing Cause and Effect*, p. 161	**Ability Level Worksheets** ♦ **Study Guide**, p. 30 ● **Reinforcement**, p. 30 ▲ **Enrichment**, p. 30 **Activity Worksheets**, pp. 55, 56	**STVS:** Disc 1, Side 2
Problem Solving: *How Do You Use Your Arm as a Lever?* p. 165 **Skill Builder:** *Making and Using Tables*, p. 170	**Ability Level Worksheets** ♦ **Study Guide**, p. 31 ● **Reinforcement**, p. 31 ▲ **Enrichment**, p. 31 **Activity Worksheets**, pp. 57, 58 **Critical Thinking/Problem Solving**, p. 13 **Transparency Masters**, pp. 25, 26	**Color Transparency 13,** Classes of Levers **Laboratory Manual 14,** Balanced Levers **Laboratory Manual 15,** Pulleys **Science Integration Activity 7**
You Decide! p. 173	**Ability Level Worksheets** ♦ **Study Guide**, p. 32 ● **Reinforcement**, p. 32 ▲ **Enrichment**, p. 32 **Cross-Curricular Connections**, p. 11	
Technology: *Micromachines*, p. 177 **Skill Builder:** *Concept Mapping*, p. 178	**Ability Level Worksheets** ♦ **Study Guide**, p. 33 ● **Reinforcement**, p. 33 ▲ **Enrichment**, p. 33 **Activity Worksheets**, p. 61 **Concept Mapping**, pp. 19, 20 **Science and Society**, p. 11 **Transparency Masters**, pp. 27, 28	**Color Transparency 14,** A Compound Machine **Laboratory Manual 16,** The Bicycle: A Well-Engineered Machine **STVS:** Disc 1, Side 2
Summary Think & Write Critically Key Science Words Apply Understanding Vocabulary More Skill Builders Checking Concepts Projects Using Lab Skills	**ASSESSMENT RESOURCES** **Chapter Review**, pp. 17, 18 **Chapter Test**, pp. 36-41 **Performance Assessment in Middle School Science**	**Chapter Review Software** **Test Bank** **Alternate Assessment** **Performance Assessment** **STVS:** Disc 1, Side 2

♦ **Basic**   ● **Average**   ▲ **Advanced**

ADDITIONAL MATERIALS		
SOFTWARE	**AUDIOVISUAL**	**BOOKS/MAGAZINES**
Learning All About Machines and Mechanics, Queue. *Mechanics*, Queue. *Miner's Cave*, MECC. *Work, Friction, and Machines;* Queue. *Work and Machines*, Queue.	*Inclined Planes*, Video, Coronet. *Levers, Video*, Coronet. *Machine Story*, Video, Pyramid. *Machines*, Video, Journal Films. *Pulleys*, Video, Coronet. *Simple Machines*, Video, AIT. *Simple Machines: Inclined Planes and Levers*, Video, Britannica. *Simple and Compound Machines: How They Work*, Laserdisc, AIMS Media. *Wheels and Axles*, Video, Coronet. *Working Together*, Video, Coronet	Ardley, Neil. *The Science Book of Machines.* San Diego: Harcourt Brace Jovanovich, 1992. Gonick, Larry, and Art Huffman. *The Cartoon Guide to Physics.* NY: Harper Perennial, 1991. Lampton, Christopher. *Seesaws, Nutcrackers, Brooms: Simple Machines That Are Really Levers.* Brookfield, CT: Millbrook, 1991. Lampton, Christopher. *Marbles, Roller Skates, Doorknobs: Simple Machines That Are Really Wheels.* Brookfield, CT: Millbrook, 1991.

7
MACHINES

THEME DEVELOPMENT: A simple machine is a system that has work done on it. It, in turn, does work on an object or another system. Emphasize the input-output nature of simple and compound machines throughout the chapter.

CHAPTER OVERVIEW

▶ **Section 7-1:** Simple machines are introduced and characterized in this section. The concept of mechanical advantage is developed.

▶ **Section 7-2:** This section classifies simple machines into six types and discusses how they can be conceptualized into two broad categories: levers and inclined planes.

▶ **Section 7-3: Science and Society:** A report on human-powered flight asks students to query the advantages and disadvantages of research that doesn't have apparent or immediate application.

▶ **Section 7-4:** Compound machines are discussed using a bicycle as an example. The concepts of efficiency and power of a machine are introduced and developed.

CHAPTER VOCABULARY

machine	pulley
simple machine	wheel and
effort force	axle
resistance force	inclined plane
ideal machine	screw
mechanical	wedge
advantage	compound
lever	machine
fulcrum	efficiency
effort arm	power
resistance arm	watt

C H A P T E R

7 Machines

156

OPTIONS

⚡ For Your Gifted Students

▶ Have students design and build a compound machine that performs a task. They should name the machine and create an advertisement for their invention. The students can present their advertisements to the class as they might appear on radio, television, or in a magazine. Students should be able to identify the simple machines involved. They may wish to research how one receives a patent and contact the U.S. Patent Office.

⚡ For Your Mainstreamed Students

▶ Have students contribute objects and pictures of simple machines to form a display. Students can label the objects and pictures and categorize them by the type of simple machine or compound machine each represents.

People use machines to make jobs easier. What comes to mind when you think of machines? You might list washing machines, computers, and microwave ovens as devices. There are also many machines that do not need electricity to operate and some that have no moving parts.

FIND OUT!

Do this activity to show how you can reduce the effort needed to move an object.

Stack two books on a flat desk or table and use one hand to push them along the surface. Now put several round pencils under the bottom book and push the books again. Are they easier to push?

Remove the pencils and position the books so they just hang over the edge of the desk. *Experiment* with different ways to lift the books. Place your fingertips under the bottom book and lift the books with your fingers. Set the books flat on the surface and slide a stiff ruler under the edge of the bottom book. Push up on the ruler to lift the books. (Make sure not to break the ruler.) Is it easier to lift the books using the ruler?

Gearing Up
Previewing the Chapter

Use this outline to help you focus on important ideas in this chapter.

Section 7-1   Why We Use Machines
- ▶ What Are Simple Machines?
- ▶ Advantages of Simple Machines

Section 7-2   The Simple Machines
- ▶ Levers
- ▶ Pulleys
- ▶ Wheel and Axle
- ▶ Inclined Plane
- ▶ Screw and Wedge

Section 7-3   Science and Society
Human-Powered Flying Machines
- ▶ Pedaling through the Sky

Section 7-4   Using Machines
- ▶ Compound Machines
- ▶ Efficiency
- ▶ Power

Previewing Science Skills
- ▶ In the **Skill Builders,** you will recognize cause and effect, make and use tables, and map concepts.
- ▶ In the **Activities,** you will describe, measure in SI, and experiment.
- ▶ In the **MINI-Lab,** you will observe and measure in SI.

What's next?

You've shown that work can be made easier by reducing friction and using simple devices to reduce the amount of force you have to exert to move something. Now find out about some different devices used to make work easier, how they operate, and how much easier they make your work.

157

INTRODUCING THE CHAPTER
Use the Find Out activity to introduce students to the concept of machines as devices that make doing a job or task easier.

FIND OUT!
Materials: Obtain stiff rulers and several boxes of round pencils for the activity and a large coffee can, its plastic lid, and enough marbles to fill the lid for the Demonstration.

Cooperative Learning: Have Problem Solving Teams determine if the length of the ruler inserted under the books has any effect on making the books easier to lift.

Teaching Tips
- ▶ To increase the sturdiness of the rulers, secure two together with tape or rubber bands.
- ▶ **Demonstration:** Fill the plastic lid of a coffee can with marbles and place the can on top of them. Allow students to turn the can. Point out that the marbles demonstrate how ball bearings are devices that reduce effort.

Gearing Up
Have students study the Gearing Up feature to familiarize themselves with the chapter. Discuss the relationships of the topics in the outline.

What's Next?
Before beginning the first section, make sure students understand the connection between the Find Out activity and the topics to follow.

VideoDisc
STVS: Factory of the Future, Disc 1, Side 2

ASSESSMENT OPTIONS

PORTFOLIO
Refer to page 179 for suggested items that students might select for their portfolios.

PERFORMANCE ASSESSMENT
See page 179 for additional Performance Assessment options.
Process
Skill Builders, pp. 161, 170, 178
MINI-Lab, p. 177
Activities 7-1, p. 162; 7-2, p. 171
Using Lab Skills, p. 180

CONTENT ASSESSMENT
Assessment—Oral, pp. 169, 176
Section Reviews, pp. 161, 170, 173, 178
Chapter Review, pp. 179–181
Mini Quizzes, pp. 160, 165, 169

GROUP ASSESSMENT
Opportunities for group assessment occur with Cooperative Learning Strategies and Flex Your Brain Activities.

PREPARATION

SECTION BACKGROUND

▶ A machine can be thought of as a system that transfers mechanical energy. A simple machine transfers energy in one movement.

▶ A machine can multiply forces, distances, or speeds at which the forces are delivered; because of the conservation of energy, it cannot do more than one at a time.

▶ The mechanical advantage of a machine indicates the factor by which it multiplies an effort force.

PREPLANNING

▶ Prepare for Activity 7-1 by obtaining one brick for each lab group.

1 MOTIVATE

▶ Have students list various simple tasks done at home or at school and discuss how different tools or devices help make doing the tasks easier. For example, to tighten a screw into a piece of wood (the task), the student would probably choose a screwdriver (the tool). The blade of a screwdriver turns the head of the screw and drives it into the wood as the handle of the screwdriver is turned (how it functions).

Cooperative Learning: Using the Numbered Heads Together strategy, have each group decide upon an example of a complex machine and an example of a simple machine. Have the groups share examples. Discuss how each group defined the terms *machine, complex,* and *simple.* Compare the definitions.

7-1 Why We Use Machines

New Science Words

machine
simple machine
effort force
resistance force
ideal machine
mechanical advantage

Objectives

▶ Explain how machines make work easier.
▶ Calculate mechanical advantage.

What Are Simple Machines?

Have you used any machines today? You probably know that a bicycle is a machine. Pencil sharpeners and can openers are also machines. Even if you haven't used any of these things, you have probably used at least one machine today. If you turned a doorknob or twisted off a bottle cap, you have used a machine. A **machine** is a device that makes work easier.

Some machines are powered by engines or electric motors; others are people-powered. Some machines are very complex; others are quite simple. A **simple machine** ❶ is a device that does work with only one movement. There are six types of simple machines, examples of which are pictured below. You'll learn more about each type in a later section of this chapter.

OPTIONS

Meeting Different Ability Levels

For Section 7-1, use the following **Teacher Resource Masters** depending upon individual students' needs.

◆ **Study Guide Master** for all students.

● **Reinforcement Master** for students of average and above average ability levels.

▲ **Enrichment Master** for above average students.

Additional Teacher Resource Package masters are listed in any PROGRAM RESOURCES boxes that are in the section. The additional masters are appropriate for all students.

◆ **STUDY GUIDE** 30

STUDY GUIDE   Chapter 7
Why We Use Machines   Text Pages 158–162

In each of the following statements, a term has been scrambled. Unscramble the term and write it on the line provided.

resistance 1. The force applied by a machine to overcome gravity or friction is the *sitrencea* force.
effort   2. The force that is applied to the machine is the *oftref* force.
work   3. When a force is applied through a distance, *krow* is done.
machine   4. A device that makes work easier is a *himcane.*
input   5. The work done on a machine is work *puint.*
ideal   6. A machine in which work input is equal to work output is an *ideal* machine.
simple   7. A device that does work with only one movement is a *plame* machine.
advantage   8. The number of times a machine multiplies the effort force is the mechanical *gavetadna.*
output   9. The work done by a machine is work *putuot.*
            10. A machine makes work easier by changing the size or direction of the *roef* exerted on it.

In the blank write the term that correctly completes each statement about the equations given.
11. In the equation $MA = F_r / F_e$,
    a. MA stands for ___ mechanical advantage
    b. F_r stands for ___ resistance force
    c. F_e stands for ___ effort force
12. In the equation $W = F \times d$,
    a. W stands for ___ work
    b. F stands for ___ force
    c. d stands for ___ distance
13. In the equation $W_{in} = F_e \times d_e$,
    a. W_{in} stands for ___ work input
    b. d_e stands for ___ the distance the effort force is exerted
14. In the equation $W_{out} = F_r \times d_r$,
    a. W_{out} stands for ___ work output
    b. d_r stands for ___ the distance the resistance force moves

30   Copyright Glencoe Division of Macmillan/McGraw-Hill
                        Users of Merrill Physical Science have the publisher's permission to reproduce this page.

Advantages of Simple Machines

Suppose you wanted to pry the lid off a paint can with a screwdriver. You'd slip the end of the screwdriver blade under the edge of the can lid and push down on the handle. You would do work on the screwdriver and the screwdriver would do work on the lid.

Recall from Chapter 5 that work is done when a force is exerted through a distance. A machine makes work easier by changing the force you exerted on it in size, direction, or both. For example, when you use a screwdriver to lift a can lid, as shown in Figure 7-1, both the size and direction of the force you exert on the screwdriver are changed. The force you exert on the screwdriver is less than the force exerted by the screwdriver on the lid. So as you push down, the screwdriver pushes the lid up.

When you use a simple machine, you are trying to move something that resists being moved. You are trying to overcome some force of resistance, usually gravity (weight) or friction. For example, when you use a crowbar to move a large rock, you are working against gravity—the weight of the rock. When you use a screwdriver to move a paint can lid, you are working against friction—the friction between the lid and the can.

② Two forces are involved when a machine is used to do work. The force applied *to* the machine is called the **effort force (F_e)**. The force applied *by* the machine to overcome resistance due to gravity or friction is called the **resistance force (F_r)**. In the can lid example, you apply the effort force to the screwdriver handle. The resistance force is the force the screwdriver applies to the lid.

③ There are also two kinds of work to be considered when a machine is used—the work done *on* the machine and the work done *by* the machine. The work done on the machine is called work input (W_{in}); the work done by the machine is called work output (W_{out}). Recall that work is the product of force and distance: $W = F \times d$. Work input is the product of the effort force and the distance that force is exerted: $W_{in} = F_e \times d_e$. Work output is the product of the resistance force and the distance that force moves: $W_{out} = F_r \times d_r$.

Remember that energy is always conserved. So, you can never get more work out of a machine than you put in. In other words, W_{out} can never be greater than W_{in}. In fact, whenever a machine is used, some energy is

In Your JOURNAL

Look around your classroom and locate a simple machine. **In your Journal,** write a paragraph describing the effort force and the resistance force of this machine. Does this machine change the size or direction of the force you exerted on it?

What forces are always involved when a machine is used to do work?

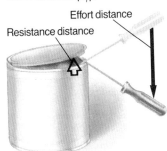

Figure 7-1. To lift the lid with the screwdriver, the effort distance (d_e) must be greater than the resistance distance (d_r).

Effort distance

Resistance distance

TYING TO PREVIOUS KNOWLEDGE: Have students recall from Section 5-1 the scientific meaning of *work*. Point out that in this section they will use this definition to learn how machines make accomplishing work easier.

In Your JOURNAL

Answers will vary, but be sure students distinguish between F_e and F_r.

2 TEACH

Key Concepts are highlighted.

CONCEPT DEVELOPMENT

▶ $W_{in} = W_{out}$ is a consequence of the conservation of energy. To transfer mechanical energy to a machine, work is done on the machine. The machine, in turn, does work on the object. Because the amount of energy transferred to a machine must equal the energy transferred by the machine,

$$W_{in} = W_{out}$$

▶ In an ideal machine, all the work done to the machine becomes useful work done by the machine. However, in the real world, some mechanical energy is converted to heat through work done to overcome friction. Therefore, the amount of *observed* output work is always less than the amount of input work.

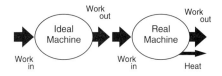

REVEALING MISCONCEPTIONS

▶ Some students may think that machines make work easier by reducing the amount of work that has to be done. Point out that machines actually require more work than does the task itself. Machines allow us to multiply our force, speed, or distance, but not our energy.

● **REINFORCEMENT** 30

▲ **ENRICHMENT** 30

CONCEPT DEVELOPMENT

▶ Point out that because $MA = F_r/F_e$, $F_e \times MA = F_r$. The value of MA indicates how much the effort force has been multiplied by the machine.

▶ Have students consider a tennis racket with an MA of 1/2. If a player swings the racket with a force of 60 N, the racket will deliver a force of only 30 N to the ball. However, point out that if the player moves the handle at a speed of 5 m/s, the racket strings will strike the ball at 10 m/s.

PRACTICE PROBLEM ANSWER

1. $MA = \dfrac{F_r}{F_e}$

$F_e = \dfrac{F_r}{MA} = \dfrac{2000 \text{ N}}{10} = 200 \text{ N}$

TEACHER F.Y.I.

▶ From the equation, $W_{in} = W_{out}$, it follows that $d_e/d_r = F_r/F_e$ The right side of the equation is the definition of MA. The left side is defined as the *ideal mechanical advantage, IMA*. The MA of a machine is always less than its IMA because of friction.

CHECK FOR UNDERSTANDING

Use the Mini Quiz to check for understanding.

MINI QUIZ

Use the Mini Quiz to check students' recall of chapter content.

① A simple machine is a device that does work with only one _____ . *movement*

② The force applied to a machine is called the _____ . *effort force*

③ The force applied by a machine is called the _____ . *resistance force*

④ The number of times a machine multiplies the effort force is the _____ of the machine. *mechanical advantage*

Connect to...
Life Science

The effort force is exerted by the muscles in the breast of the bird, and the resistance force is that of the wing pushing up on the bird's body.

EcoTip

Use a human-powered machine and save energy resources. Use hand-operated tools to trim your lawn or remove snow from your sidewalk. You'll help to save natural resources and you'll get a little exercise, too.

Connect to...
Life Science

Birds fly using their wings to move them through the air. Identify the resistance and effort forces for this simple machine.

---

changed to heat due to friction. So, W_{out} is always smaller than W_{in}.

To understand how machines work, it helps to imagine a frictionless machine in which no energy is converted to heat. Such an **ideal machine** is one in which work input equals work output. For an ideal machine,

$$W_{in} = W_{out}$$
$$F_e \times d_e = F_r \times d_r$$

In most cases, a machine multiplies the force applied to it—F_r is greater than F_e. So, in order for W_{in} to equal W_{out}, the effort force must travel farther than the resistance force—d_e must be greater than d_r.

Think again about the can lid example. The distance you move the screwdriver handle (d_e) is greater than the distance the screwdriver blade moves the lid (d_r). So, the blade must exert more force on the lid (F_r) than you exert on the handle (F_e). The machine multiplies your effort, but you must move the handle a greater distance.

The number of times a machine multiplies the effort force is the **mechanical advantage (MA)** of the machine. **④** To calculate mechanical advantage, you divide the resistance force by the effort force.

$$MA = \frac{\text{resistance force}}{\text{effort force}} = \frac{F_r}{F_e}$$

EXAMPLE PROBLEM: Calculating Mechanical Advantage

Problem Statement:	A worker applies an effort force of 10 N to pry open a window that has a resistance of 500 N. What is the mechanical advantage of the crowbar?
Known Information: Strategy Hint: Mechanical advantage has no units.	resistance force, F_r = 500 N effort force, F_e = 10 N
Unknown Information:	mechanical advantage (MA)
Equation to Use:	$MA = \dfrac{F_r}{F_e}$
Solution:	$MA = \dfrac{500 \text{ N}}{10 \text{ N}} = 50$

PRACTICE PROBLEM

Strategy Hint: Rearrange the equation.

1. Find the effort force needed to lift a 2000-N rock, using a jack with a mechanical advantage of 10.

OPTIONS

INQUIRY QUESTIONS

▶ **How is the MA of a crowbar affected if it bends as it is used?** *The MA decreases because some force applied to the bar does work in bending it. Thus, the amount of work delivered by the machine is less.*

▶ **In the Example Problem on this page, the window moved 1 cm and the end of the crowbar moved 60 cm. How much mechanical energy was converted to heat?**
$W_{in} = 10 \text{ N} \times 0.60 \text{ m} = 6 \text{ J}$
$W_{out} = 500 \times 0.01 \text{ m} = 5 \text{ J}$
$W_{in} - W_{out} = 6 \text{ J} - 5 \text{ J} = 1 \text{ J}$

Some machines don't multiply force. Instead, they change the direction of the effort force. For example, when you pull down on the cord of window blinds, the blinds go up. Only the direction of the force changes; the effort force and resistance force are equal, so the mechanical advantage is 1.

Other machines have mechanical advantages that are less than 1. Such machines are used to increase the distance an object moves or the speed at which it moves.

Think again about all the machines you've seen in use today. Was the mechanical advantage in each case greater than, less than, or equal to 1?

SECTION REVIEW

1. Explain how simple machines can make work easier without violating the law of conservation of energy.
2. A carpenter uses a claw hammer to pull a nail from a board. The nail has a resistance of 2500 N. The carpenter applies an effort force of 125 N. What is the mechanical advantage of the hammer?
3. **Apply:** Give an example of a simple machine you've used recently. How did you apply effort force? How did the machine apply resistance force?
4. **Connect to Life Science:** In the example of a flying bird, why doesn't the wing push the bird down when it moves upward?

☑ Recognizing Cause and Effect

Skill Builder

When you operate a machine, it's often easy to observe cause and effect. For example, when you turn a doorknob, the latch in the door moves. Give five examples of machines and describe one cause-and-effect pair in the action of each machine. If you need help, refer to Recognizing Cause and Effect in the **Skill Handbook** on page 679.

7-1   WHY WE USE MACHINES   **161**

Skill Builder

Answers will vary. Examples are:
1. Screwdriver—turn the handle and screw is driven into wood
2. C-clamp—turn the lever and objects are forced together
3. Hatchet—strike wood and it splits
4. Nutcracker—apply force on the handles and nut cracks
5. Bottle lid—turn lid and bottle opens or closes

Skill Builder
ASSESSMENT
Performance: Bring a simple machine to class, preferably one familiar to most students. Have students write a short paragraph describing its cause-and-effect actions.

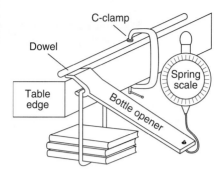
CHAPTER 7   **161**

DESIGNING AN EXPERIMENT
Invent a Machine!

OBJECTIVE: **Invent** ways to use common implements as simple machines to accomplish a given task.

Time: One class period for pre-lab discussion and experiment; one-half class period to conduct Going Further investigations.

Process Skills applied in this activity are **experimenting, observing, describing,** and **communicating.**

PREPARATION
Be sure each group has a complete set of the suggested materials.

 Cooperative Learning: Assign groups of two or three.

SAFETY
Caution students to keep their fingers out from under the brick if it is lifted above the surface by a machine.

THINKING CRITICALLY
A machine can be any device that makes work easier, but a simple machine does work with only one movement. Simple machines may multiply force or distance, but they cannot multiply energy.

TEACHING THE ACTIVITY
*Refer to the **Activity Worksheets** for additional information and teaching strategies.*

• You may wish to add other materials, such as masking tape or rulers.

• Add any additional restrictions you think might make this more interesting, but encourage students to be creative.

• You might wish to announce a role change every 10 minutes to ensure that all students are active participants in both manipulating materials and recording procedures.

PROGRAM RESOURCES
From the **Teacher Resource Package** use:

Activity Worksheets, pages 55-56, Activity 7-1: Invent a Machine!

Have you ever tried to move something that was too heavy or too large to lift yourself? Could you invent a machine to help you?

Getting Started
In this activity, you will design a machine to move a brick from one location to another using materials from a limited list. **CAUTION:** *If the brick is elevated from the table, be sure to keep your fingers away from the area beneath the brick.*

Thinking Critically
How does a simple machine differ from the general definition of a machine?

Materials
Your cooperative group will use:
• brick
• book
• string
• pencils (2)
• hard board
• pulley
• ring stand and ring

— **Try It!** —

NOTE: While conducting this activity:
• Do not move or touch the brick with your hands.

• Only one person at a time may apply force to the brick.
1. Place the brick and the book about 30 cm apart on the tabletop.
2. Use any of the materials to move the brick until it rests on top of the book.
3. Keep a carefully written record of your attempts, especially any failures. *Describe* what you did and what happened.
4. *Experiment* with as many different ways as you can think of to accomplish this task.

Summing Up/Sharing Results
Of the different methods you tried, which one do you think worked the best? Explain why you prefer this method.

Going Further!
Try to use the same method to move the brick back to its original place. Will your preferred method work in reverse? Explain why or why not.

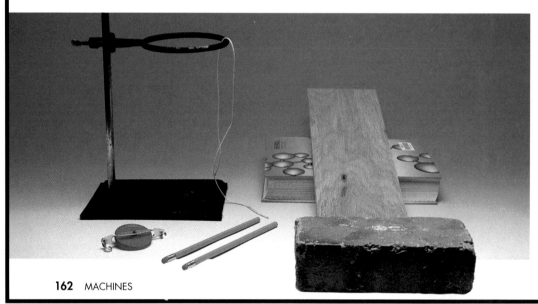

162 MACHINES

SUMMING UP/SHARING RESULTS
Student answers will vary, but be sure they clearly state their methods and reasons. The machines identified may include nonmachine terms such as *rope* or *platform;* they will learn this more specifically in the next section. The levers (pencils or boards) probably had the greatest MA.

GOING FURTHER!
Each team should write an analysis of why their method did or did not work in reverse.

Activity
ASSESSMENT
Oral: Evaluate students' understandings of machine design by encouraging them to connect this activity to large-scale examples. Ask students to identify any actual machines they may have used as models in designing their methods. For example, window blinds and cranes both make use of pulleys to lift objects.

The Simple Machines 7-2

Objectives

▶ Describe the six types of simple machines.
▶ Calculate the mechanical advantage for different types of simple machines.

Levers

If you've ever ridden a seesaw, pried the cap from a bottle of soda pop, or swung a tennis racket, you have used a lever. A **lever** is a bar that is free to pivot, or turn, about a fixed point. The fixed point of a lever is called the **fulcrum** (FUL krum). The part of the lever on which the effort force is applied is called the **effort arm.** The part of the lever that exerts the resistance force is called the **resistance arm.**

Suppose you are using a crowbar to pry the lid from a crate. You can see in Figure 7-2 that the edge of the crate acts as the fulcrum. You push down on the effort arm of the crowbar. The bar pivots about the fulcrum, and the resistance arm exerts a force on the lid, lifting it upward.

Figure 7-2. The crowbar is being used as a lever. The edge of the crate acts as the fulcrum.

New Science Words

lever
fulcrum
effort arm
resistance arm
pulley
wheel and axle
inclined plane
screw
wedge

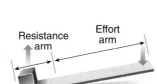

7-2 THE SIMPLE MACHINES **163**

PREPARATION

SECTION BACKGROUND

▶ The six types of simple machines—lever, pulley, wheel and axle, inclined plane, wedge, and screw—fall into two broad categories: levers and inclined planes. Pulleys and wheels and axles are leverlike machines. Wedges and screws are grouped with inclined planes.

▶ The mechanical advantage of every simple machine depends upon its design and is calculated by comparing its F_r to its F_e.

1 MOTIVATE

▶ Have students discuss how various kitchen utensils, such as knives, spoons, spatulas, whisks, and hand mixers, fit the definition of a simple machine. Ask students to find similarities among the functions and shapes of the utensils.

TYING TO PREVIOUS KNOWLEDGE: Have students recall from the last section the definition of *mechanical advantage.* Point out that in this section they will learn how the design of a simple machine affects its mechanical advantage.

Cooperative Learning: Assign one of the six simple machines to each team of 3-4 students. Each group will have two class periods to prepare a presentation about their machine. They should define their machine, identify its important parts, and give a demonstration of its use. Encourage creativity, such as using a knife to cut some brownies to share.

MULTICULTURAL PERSPECTIVE

The Great Pyramids

The great pyramids in Egypt were constructed using inclined planes to move the stones into place. One of them, the pyramid of Cheops, covers 5.2 hectares and contains over 2.25×10^6 blocks that average 2×10^3 kg each. Most modern cranes would not be able to lift stones that heavy, so it is easy to understand why the Egyptians would need to find an alternative to lifting the stones. That alternative was the inclined plane, which allowed them to move the heavy blocks with smaller forces exerted over a longer period of time. For example, let's assume you want to move an object to a height of 10 m, but you cannot lift it. However, you can push it up a plane inclined at 10°. Since the length of the inclined plane is equal to the height divided by the sine of 10°, this means you must push the object 58 m to get it 10 m off the ground.

Key Concepts are highlighted.

CONCEPT DEVELOPMENT

▶ Provide students with many opportunities to manipulate levers. Allow ample time for them to locate the fulcrum and identify the effort arm and resistance arm in each lever.

TEACHER F.Y.I.

▶ The mechanical advantages discussed in this section are ideal mechanical advantages of simple machines. The two terms are synonymous if we assume that no mechanical energy is converted to heat.

CROSS CURRICULUM

▶ **Language Arts:** Have students look up the word *lever* in a dictionary. Students should find that it comes from the Latin root *levare* (to lift). Ask a volunteer to explain how the meaning of the word reflects its root.

PRACTICE PROBLEM ANSWER

$$MA = \frac{L_e}{L_r} = \frac{140 \text{ cm}}{20 \text{ cm}} = 7$$

Connect to... Life Science

Answer: Curls and leg lifts are two examples.

In Your JOURNAL

In your Journal, write a separate paragraph on each class of lever. Describe at least two examples of each class, identifying the effort force, resistance force, and fulcrum. Use Figure 7-3 to help you.

Connect to... Life Science

Weightlifting tones and strengthens muscles. Describe a weightlifting exercise that uses part of your body as a lever. Identify the effort and resistance forces and the fulcrum.

The type of lever shown in Figure 7-2 makes work easier by multiplying your effort force. Like all simple machines, this lever has a mechanical advantage. You've learned that the mechanical advantage of any machine can be calculated by dividing the resistance force by the effort force. You can also use the lengths of the arms of a lever to find the mechanical advantage of the lever. The length of the effort arm is the distance from the fulcrum to the point where effort force is applied. The length of the resistance arm is the distance from the fulcrum to the point where the resistance force is applied. The following equation, which assumes no friction, can be used to find the ideal mechanical advantage of any lever:

$$MA = \frac{\text{length of effort arm}}{\text{length of resistance arm}} = \frac{L_e}{L_r}$$

EXAMPLE PROBLEM: Mechanical Advantage of a Lever

Problem Statement: A worker uses an iron bar to raise a manhole cover weighing 65 N. The effort arm of the lever is 60 cm long. The resistance arm is 25 cm long. What is the mechanical advantage of the bar?

Known Information:
Strategy Hint: Which equation for mechanical advantage will you use?

length of effort arm, L_e = 60 cm
length of resistance arm, L_r = 25 cm

Unknown Information: mechanical advantage (*MA*)

Equation to Use:
$$MA = \frac{L_e}{L_r}$$

Solution:
$$MA = \frac{60 \text{ cm}}{25 \text{ cm}} = 2.4$$

PRACTICE PROBLEM

Strategy Hint: Find the lengths of the effort arm and the resistance arm.

1. You use a crowbar 140 cm long as a lever to lift a large rock. The rock is 20 cm from the fulcrum. You push down on the other end of the crowbar. What is the *MA* of the lever?

There are three different types, or classes, of levers. These classes are based on the positions of the effort force, resistance force, and fulcrum. Figure 7-3 shows the three classes of levers.

OPTIONS

Meeting Different Ability Levels

For Section 7-2, use the following **Teacher Resource Masters** depending upon individual students' needs.

◆ **Study Guide Master** for all students.

● **Reinforcement Master** for students of average and above average ability levels.

▲ **Enrichment Master** for above average students.

Additional Teacher Resource Package masters are listed in any PROGRAM RESOURCES boxes that are in the section. The additional masters are appropriate for all students.

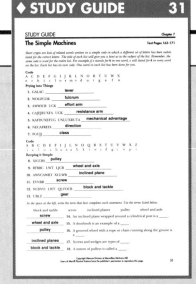

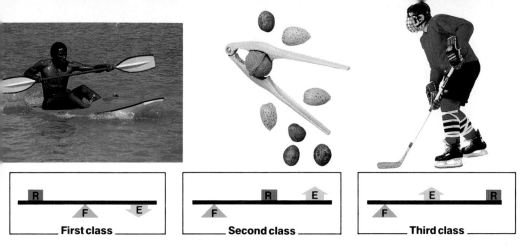

R		
	F	E
First class		

	R	E
F		
	Second class	

	E	R
F		
	Third class	

Figure 7-3. The classes of levers differ in the positions of the effort force, the resistance force, and the fulcrum.

If you look at the examples of third class levers, you will see that the effort arm is always shorter than the resistance arm. So, the *MA* of a third class lever is always less than 1. This means that a third class lever does not multiply force. A third class lever multiplies the distance the effort force travels.

PROBLEM SOLVING

How Do You Use Your Arm as a Lever?

The muscles and bones of your body work together as levers. Try contracting your biceps muscle to see how a simple body lever works.

The two bones in your forearm act as the bar of the lever. Because the elbow is the point where the arm lever pivots, it is the fulcrum. The bones in your forearm are attached to the upper arm bone by ligaments at the elbow. When you contract your biceps, this muscle exerts an effort force on the forearm bones to pull them upward. The entire forearm is the resistance force. What class of lever is being demonstrated when you raise your forearm?

Think Critically: Identify the fulcrum, effort force, and resistance force when you lower your arm, using the triceps muscle on the back of your upper arm.

165

► It isn't necessary to know the exact location of F_e, F_r, and the fulcrum to classify a lever. All one needs to know is what is in-between. In a first class lever, the fulcrum is located somewhere between the effort force and the resistance force. In a second class lever, F_r is in-between, and in a third class lever, F_e is in-between.

MINI QUIZ

Use the Mini Quiz to check students' recall of chapter content.

1. A _____ is a bar that is free to turn about a fixed point. *lever*
2. The fixed point of a lever is called the _____ . *fulcrum*
3. The _____ is the part of a lever on which the effort force is applied. *effort arm*
4. The _____ is the part of a lever that exerts the resistance force. *resistance arm*

Cooperative Learning: Assign Problem Solving Teams to identify bones that act as levers shown in cardboard skeletons displayed at Halloween. From the functioning of each bone, have the team determine if it is a first, second, or third class lever.

PROBLEM SOLVING

When you raise your forearm, the muscles and bones are a third class lever.

Think Critically: The elbow is the fulcrum. The effort force is exerted by the triceps. The bones of the forearm are the resistance force.

CONCEPT DEVELOPMENT

▶ **Demonstration:** Show that each strand of a single, movable pulley system supports half the resistance force. Weigh the pulley and a small attached weight. Attach a spring scale to each end of the cord that passes through the pulley and suspend the pulley and weight from the scales. Have a volunteer read each scale. Remove one spring scale and attach that end of the string to a ring stand. Have a volunteer read the spring scale supporting the pulley. Stand a meterstick behind the pulley system and have a volunteer measure the distance the weight moves as you pull the spring scale upward 20 cm. From the values of d_e and d_r show that the MA of a single, movable pulley is 2.

▶ **Demonstration:** Show how a single, fixed pulley is related to a first class lever by placing a piece of brightly colored tape across the diameter of a large pulley. Use it as a single, fixed pulley to lift a small weight. Have students observe that the tape rotates around the center of the wheel much like a lever. Have the students identify the fulcrum, L_e, and L_r. Point out that a single, fixed pulley can be conceptualized as a first class lever with an MA of 1. (L_e and L_r are equal.) Repeat the demonstration using the pulley as a single, movable pulley. Have students observe that the tape rotates around the end opposite the effort force. From their observations have them realize that a single, movable pulley can be conceptualized as a second class lever with an MA of 2. (L_e is twice as long as L_r.)

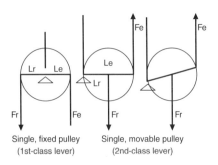

Single, fixed pulley
(1st-class lever)   Single, movable pulley
(2nd-class lever)

PROGRAM RESOURCES

Use **Laboratory Manual 14,** Balanced Levers.

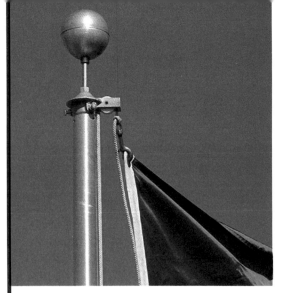

Figure 7-4. This single fixed pulley changes the direction of the effort force.

Pulleys

Have you ever seen someone raise a flag on a flagpole? A pulley is used to help get the flag to the top of the pole. A **pulley** is a grooved wheel with a rope or a chain running along the groove. Figure 7-4 shows a typical pulley.

A pulley works something like a first class lever. Instead of a bar, a pulley has a rope. The axle of the pulley acts like the fulcrum. The two sides of the pulley are the effort arm and the resistance arm.

Pulleys can be fixed or movable. A fixed pulley is attached to something that doesn't move, such as a ceiling, wall, or tree. A fixed pulley can change the direction of an effort force. When you pull down on the effort arm with the rope, the pulley raises the object attached to the resistance arm. Because the resistance arm and effort arm are of equal length, the MA of a fixed pulley is 1. Thus, a fixed pulley does not multiply the effort force.

A movable pulley is attached to the object being moved, as shown in Figure 7-5. The difference between a fixed pulley and a movable pulley is shown in Figure 7-6. Unlike the fixed pulley, a movable pulley does multiply the effort force. Because a movable pulley multiplies force, its MA is greater than 1. In fact, the MA of a single movable pulley is 2. This means that an effort force of 1 N will lift a weight (resistance) of 2 N. In order to conserve energy, the effort distance must be twice as large as the resistance distance.

Fixed and movable pulleys can be combined to make a system of pulleys called a block and tackle. Depending on the number of pulleys used, a block and tackle can have a large mechanical advantage. The mechanical advantage of any ideal pulley or pulley system is equal to the number of ropes that support

Figure 7-5. A movable pulley is attached to the resistance. A block and tackle, like the one shown, multiplies the effort force and changes its direction.

OPTIONS

INQUIRY QUESTIONS

▶ **What class of lever is the screwdriver shown in Figure 7-1 on page 159?** *first* **How could it be used as a second class lever to open the lid?** *Pivot the screwdriver at its tip and push up.* **Would the screwdriver used as a second class lever have a greater or lesser MA than used as shown? Explain.** *The MA would be less. In both levers, the L_e is the same. However, when the screwdriver is used as a second class lever, L_r is greater, which reduces the ratio of L_e to L_r.*

▶ **Why can't a second class lever be designed to have an MA less than 1?** *In a second class lever, L_e is always longer than L_r, because the resistance force must be located between the fulcrum and the location of the effort force. Thus, L_e is always greater than L_r, and their ratio, MA, is always greater than 1.* **Can a third class lever have an MA greater than 1?** *no*

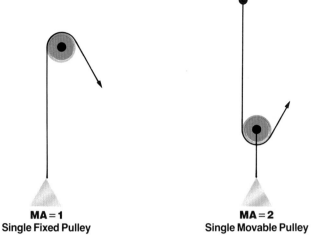
MA = 1
Single Fixed Pulley

MA = 2
Single Movable Pulley

MA = 4
Block and Tackle

Figure 7-6. The mechanical advantage of each type of pulley can be found by counting every support rope except the effort rope.

the resistance weight. As Figure 7-6 shows, the only rope that does not support the resistance weight is the rope leading from the pulley system to the effort force.

Wheel and Axle

Look closely at a doorknob or the handle of a water faucet. Do they look like simple machines to you? Do they seem to make work easier? If you don't think so, remove the knob or handle from its narrow shaft. Now try opening the door or turning on the water by rotating that shaft with your fingers. After a few minutes, you'll appreciate the fact that the knob and handle, together with their shafts, do make work easier. They are machines.

Doorknobs and faucet handles are examples of a wheel and axle. A **wheel and axle** is a simple machine consisting of two wheels of different sizes that rotate together. An effort force is usually applied to the larger wheel. The smaller wheel, called the axle, exerts the resistance force. In many cases the larger wheel doesn't look like a typical circular wheel. It may be a crank handle, like that of an ice cream freezer or a meat grinder. But it always travels in a circle.

Figure 7-7. A water faucet is an example of a wheel and axle. Without the faucet handle (wheel), the shaft of the faucet (axle) is difficult to turn.

CONCEPT DEVELOPMENT

Cooperative Learning: Have Problem Solving Teams demonstrate the MAs of the pulley systems shown in Figure 7-6.

▶ Repeat the previous demonstration to help students conceptualize a wheel and axle as a lever. Use a large wheel and axle, and indicate the radius of the wheel and the radius of the axle each with a different color of tape.

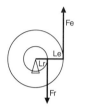
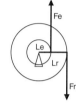

Wheel and Axle (MA > 1)
(2nd-class lever)

Wheel and Axle (MA < 1)
(3rd-class lever)

▶ Have students bring in photographs of steering columns from automobile advertisements. Have students point out the various levels on the column and identify the steering wheel as a wheel and axle. Show how the steering wheel can also be visualized as a lever.

Cooperative Learning: Assign Problem Solving Teams to demonstrate that a single pulley can have two different MAs depending on how it is used.

PROGRAM RESOURCES

Use **Laboratory Manual 15,** Pulleys.

INQUIRY QUESTIONS

▶ A person uses a block and tackle to lift an automobile engine that weighs 1800 N. The person must exert a force of 300 N to lift the engine. How many ropes support the engine? Explain how you know. *For any machine,*

$$MA = \frac{resistance\ force}{effort\ force} = \frac{1800\ N}{300\ N} = 6.$$

In a pulley system, the MA equals the number of supporting ropes.

▶ The MA of a single fixed pulley is 1. What, then, is gained by using a fixed pulley? Give two examples. *Answers will vary but should reflect the idea that it allows a change of direction. A fixed pulley allows a person to use his or her weight to exert a downward force to raise an object. In addition, exerting a downward force is more convenient. Fixed pulleys may be used to raise objects to high places while the person stays at ground level.*

CONCEPT DEVELOPMENT
▶ Have students refer to the two sets of gears shown in Figure 7-9. Ask them to identify the set in which the gears will move in the same direction (drive chain) and the set in which they will move in opposite directions (mesh teeth).

TEACHER F.Y.I.
▶ In mesh teeth gears, the MA is equal to the number of teeth on the effort gear, N_e, divided by the number of teeth on the resistance gear, N_r. In mesh gears, the size, number, and spacing of teeth must be precise for the gears to operate smoothly.

CROSS CURRICULUM
▶ **Mathematics:** Supply the students with silhouettes of several common wheels and axles, such as screwdrivers, house keys, and beaters from an electric mixer; or ask them to trace similar items at home and bring the tracings to class. Have them cut out the silhouettes or tracings, fold each along the center of the wheel and axle, unfold the paper, and measure the approximate radius of the wheel and the radius of the axle for each item. Allow the students to use calculators to determine the MA of each item and relate this value to the task that the item is used for.

PRACTICE PROBLEM ANSWER
$$MA = \frac{r_w}{r_a} = \frac{24 \text{ cm}}{4 \text{ cm}} = 6$$

PROGRAM RESOURCES
From the **Teacher Resource Package** use:

Critical Thinking/Problem Solving, page 13, How Was Stonehenge Built?

Science Integration Activity 7

Figure 7-8. The length of the crank handle represents the radius of the wheel in this ice cream maker.

It might help to think of a wheel and axle as being a lever attached to a shaft. The radius of the wheel is the effort arm, and the radius of the axle is the resistance arm. The center of the axle is the fulcrum. As with the lever, the ideal mechanical advantage of a wheel and axle can be calculated by dividing the radius of the wheel (effort arm) by the radius of the axle (resistance arm).

$$MA = \frac{\text{radius of wheel}}{\text{radius of axle}} = \frac{r_w}{r_a}$$

EXAMPLE PROBLEM: Calculating MA of a Wheel and Axle

Problem Statement:
In the ice cream freezer shown in Figure 7-8, the wheel has a radius of 20 cm. The axle has a radius of 15 cm. What is the mechanical advantage of the wheel and axle?

Known Information:
Strategy Hint: What happens to the units when you divide?
radius of wheel, r_w = 20 cm
radius of axle, r_a = 15 cm

Unknown Information:
mechanical advantage (MA)

Equation to Use:
$$MA = \frac{r_w}{r_a}$$

Solution:
$$MA = \frac{20 \text{ cm}}{15 \text{ cm}} = 1.3$$

PRACTICE PROBLEM
Strategy Hint: Use the diameter to find the radius of circle.

1. An automobile steering wheel having a diameter of 48 cm is used to turn the steering column, which has a radius of 4 cm. What is the MA of this wheel and axle?

OPTIONS

ENRICHMENT
▶ Have students research various types of gears, such as *helical, bevel, planetary,* and *worm;* display them to the class as working models and discuss their uses.
▶ Have interested students research how simple machines were used in early civilizations such as Babylon, Egypt, China, and Inca.
▶ Have interested students research and build an Archimedes' screw.

INQUIRY QUESTIONS
▶ **On a boat, a winch consisting of a long crank attached to the center of a cylinder raises and lowers the anchor. The crank is 80 cm long and the cylinder is 20 cm in diameter. What is the MA of the winch? How much force will be needed to raise a 600-N anchor?** *The radius of the cylinder is 20 cm/2 = 10 cm. MA = radius of wheel/ radius of axle = 80 cm/10 cm = 8. For any machine, MA = resistance force/effort force. Therefore, 8 = 600 N/effort force. Effort force = 600 N/8 = 75 N.*

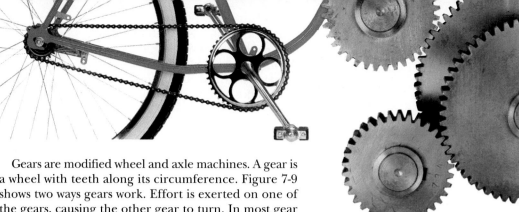

Gears are modified wheel and axle machines. A gear is a wheel with teeth along its circumference. Figure 7-9 shows two ways gears work. Effort is exerted on one of the gears, causing the other gear to turn. In most gear systems, the larger gear is the effort gear. The mechanical advantage of a pair of gears is found by dividing the radius of the effort gear by the radius of the resistance gear. This is known as the gear ratio of the pair.

Figure 7-9. In both cases, turning one gear causes the other gear to turn.

Inclined Plane

Suppose you had to move a heavy box from the ground up onto a porch. Would you rather lift the box straight up or slide it up a ramp? The ramp would make your job easier. A ramp **⑤** is a type of **inclined plane,** a sloping surface used to raise objects.

The amount of work done on the box is the same whether you lift it straight up or slide it up the ramp. But remember that work has two parts, force and distance. When you lift the box straight up, the distance is small, but the force is large. Using the ramp, you must cover more distance, but you exert less force.

You can calculate mechanical advantage of an ideal inclined plane using distances, just as you did for a lever.

$$MA = \frac{\text{effort distance}}{\text{resistance distance}} = \frac{\text{length of slope}}{\text{height of slope}} = \frac{l}{h}$$

Figure 7-10. The ramp is an example of an inclined plane.

Screw and Wedge

⑥ The screw and the wedge are examples of inclined planes that move. A **screw** is an inclined plane wrapped in a spiral around a cylindrical post. If you look closely

▶ **Demonstration:** Show that screws and wedges can be conceptualized as inclined planes. Using a straightedge and a pencil, draw a diagonal on one piece of typing paper and then on another. Highlight the diagonals with a brightly colored marker. Cut each piece of paper along its diagonal to form four right triangles. Starting with the narrow edge of one triangle, wrap it around a pencil to form a screw. Join the bases of two other triangles to form a wedge. Have students compare the inclined plane, represented by the remaining triangle, the screw, and the wedge. Point out that the screw can be conceptualized as a spiral inclined plane and a wedge can be conceptualized as a double inclined plane.

▶ In levers, pulleys, and wheels and axles, the effort and resistance forces are in the same or opposite directions. In inclined planes, screws, and wedges, the forces act mostly perpendicular. For example, the force applied to a wood screw is in the same plane as the head of the screw. However, the resistance force is along the shaft of the screw, which is perpendicular to the head of the screw. Therefore, twisting a screw partially embedded in a piece of wood will either raise or lower it. Have students analyze a jar lid as a screw.

MINI QUIZ

Use the Mini Quiz to check students' recall of chapter content.

⑤ **A ramp is an example of a simple machine called a(n) _____ .** *inclined plane*

⑥ **A(n) _____ is an inclined plane wrapped in a spiral around a cylindrical post.** *screw*

⑦ **Chisels, knives, and axes are examples of _____ .** *wedges*

CHECK FOR UNDERSTANDING

Ask questions 1-2 and the **Apply** and **Connect to Life Science** questions in the Section Review.

ASSESSMENT—ORAL

▶ **How does the direction of the slant of the threads of a screw determine its motion up and down (vertical motion) as it is twisted?** *Threads that spiral up to the right (as in most screws) will cause the screw to move in the direction of its tip when the head is twisted clockwise.* **How does the direction of the slant of the threads on the mouth of a jar compare to that of its lid (or a bolt and its nut)?** *The threads on the mouth usually spiral up to the right and those of its lid spiral down to the right.*

▶ **Explain why the MA of a wedge is equal to a, the distance from the tip of the wedge to the middle of its base, divided by b, the length of its base.** *When the wedge has been completely driven into an object, the effort force has moved the distance a. The resistance force moved the distance b. The MA, which is d_e/d_r, is the same as a/b.*

Figure 7-11. The blade of the axe and the threads of the screw are special types of inclined planes.

at a screw, you'll see that the threads form a tiny ramp that runs from its tip to near its top. As you turn the screw, the threads seem to pull the screw into the wood. The wood seems to slide up the inclined plane. Actually, the plane slides through the wood.

A **wedge** is an inclined plane with one or two sloping sides. Chisels, knives, and axe blades are examples. A typical inclined plane stays in one place while materials move along its surface. With a wedge, the material remains in one place while the wedge moves through it.

Perhaps you've noticed that the six types of simple machines are all variations of two basic machines—the lever and the inclined plane. As you go about your daily activities, look for examples of each type of simple machine. See if you can tell how each makes work easier.

SECTION REVIEW

1. Give one example of each kind of simple machine. Use examples different from the ones in the text.
2. Explain why the six kinds of simple machines are really variations on just two basic machines.
3. **Apply:** When would the friction of an inclined plane be useful?
4. **Connect to Life Science:** If you were in a wheelchair and knew you needed an MA of 20 to move up 0.8 m, what simple machine would you ask for and how big would it have to be?

Skill Builder

☑ **Making and Using Tables**

Organize information about the six kinds of simple machines into a table. Include the type of machine, an example of each type, and a brief description of how it works. You may include other information if you wish. If you need help, refer to Making and Using Tables in the **Skill Handbook** on page 686.

Levers

ACTIVITY 7-2
40 minutes

Did you ever play on a seesaw when you were younger? Wasn't it much easier to balance your friend on the other end if both of you weighed about the same? If your friend was lighter, you probably moved toward the fulcrum to balance the seesaw. How did this help? Moving toward the fulcrum shortened the effort arm. In this activity, you will balance a lever to determine the mass of a coin.

Materials
- sheet of paper, 20 cm × 28 cm (8½" × 11")
- coins, 3 (quarter, dime, nickel)
- balance
- metric ruler

Procedure
1. Make a lever by folding the paper into a strip 3 cm wide by 28 cm long.
2. Mark a line 2 cm from one end of the paper strip. Label this line *Resistance*.
3. Slide the other end of the paper strip over the edge of a table until the strip begins to teeter on the edge. Mark a line across the paper at the table edge and label this line *Effort*.
4. *Measure* the mass of the paper to the nearest 0.1 g. Write this mass on the *Effort* line.
5. Center a dime on the *Resistance* line.
6. Locate the fulcrum by sliding the paper strip until it begins to teeter on the edge. Mark the balance line. Label it *Fulcrum #1*.
7. *Measure* the lengths of the resistance arm and the effort arm to the nearest 0.1 cm.

8. *Calculate* the MA of the lever.
9. Multiply the MA times the mass of the lever to find the mass of the coin.
10. Repeat Steps 5 through 9 with the nickel and then with the quarter. Mark the fulcrum line #2 for the nickel and #3 for the quarter.

Analyze
1. In this activity, is the effective total length of the lever a constant or a variable?
2. Are the lengths of the resistance and effort arms constants or variables?
3. What provides the effort force?
4. What does it mean if the MA is less than 1.0?

Conclude and Apply
5. Is it necessary to have the resistance line 2.0 cm from the end of the paper?
6. The calculations are done as if the entire weight of the paper is located at what point?
7. Why can mass units be used in place of force units in this kind of problem?

OBJECTIVE: Calculate the mechanical advantage of levers to balance unequal forces.

PROCESS SKILLS applied in this activity:
▶ **Measuring** in Procedure Steps 1-7.
▶ **Using Numbers** in Procedure Steps 8 and 9.
▶ **Interpreting** in Analyze Questions 1-3.

TEACHING THE ACTIVITY
Troubleshooting: It is advisable to demonstrate the activity before students work in the lab.

▶ This activity applies the idea that a rigid object can act as though its entire mass is located at its center of gravity. One end of the lever is located at the center of gravity of the paper, and the other end is located near one end of the paper. The coin is placed with its center of gravity right on the lever's end mark.

▶ Have students draw the effective lever and fulcrum on the paper between the effort and resistance lines. Point out that the rest of the paper is not considered part of the lever but provides effort force and support.

▶ Allow students to check mass calculations by using a balance.

▶ The following equations are needed for Procedure Steps 8 and 9.

Step 8: $IMA = \dfrac{L_e \text{ (paper)}}{L_r \text{ (coin)}}$

Step 9: $MA = \dfrac{F_r \text{ (coin)}}{F_e \text{(paper)}}$

Mass and force are proportional, so $M_r \text{ (coin)} = M_e \text{ (paper)} \cdot MA$

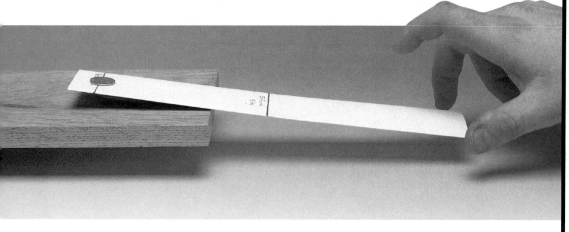

ANSWERS TO QUESTIONS
1. The lever's total length is a constant.
2. The lengths of effort and resistance arms are variables.
3. Gravity provides the effort force.
4. The force to move the lever is more than the weight that is moved.
5. No, the resistance line can be placed at any convenient location.
6. The calculations assume the entire weight of the lever is located at the center of gravity of the paper.

7. The forces on both ends of the lever are caused by gravity acting with the same ratio of force to mass.

Activity Assessment
For further assessment of this activity, see USING LAB SKILLS Question 11 on page 180.

PROGRAM RESOURCES
From the **Teacher Resource Package** use:
  Activity Worksheets, pages 57-58, Activity 7-2: Levers.

PREPARATION

SECTION BACKGROUND

▶ The first demonstrably successful human-powered flight took place on August 23, 1977, when Bryan Allen flew the *Gossamer Condor* along a 1.6 km, figure-8 course to capture the £50 000 Kremer prize.

1 MOTIVATE

▶ **Demonstration:** Blow across a strip of paper held close to your mouth to demonstrate that moving air can provide lift. Make sure students understand that an airplane is lifted by the air moving over and under the wing, not by the propeller. Due to the shape of the wing, air moves faster across the top than across the bottom. So, the air on the bottom exerts a greater force.

2 TEACH

Key Concepts are highlighted.

Connect to...
Life Science

You would need a healthy diet and exercise to achieve a lean, muscular build and to increase your endurance for sustained effort.

PROGRAM RESOURCES

From the **Teacher Resource Package** use:

Cross-Curricular Connections, page 11, The Myth of Daedalus.

Activity Worksheets, page 5, Flex Your Brain.

Objectives

▶ Analyze the simple machines in a human-powered aircraft.
▶ Consider the value of experiments with no obvious practical value.

Connect to...
Life Science

Suppose you were preparing to pilot a human-powered flying machine. How would you train for such a task? Consider diet, exercise, and overall fitness.

Pedaling Through the Sky

Can you imagine how it would feel to pedal a bicycle through the air? That's probably how Greek cycling champion Kanellos Kanellopoulos felt in 1988, when he flew the Daedalus, a human-powered aircraft, 115 kilometers across the Aegean Sea.

Designed at the Massachusetts Institute of Technology, the Daedalus has pedals like a bicycle. The pilot applies an effort force to the pedals, and the force is transferred, through gears, to a propeller. The plane is human-powered because the pilot's legs are the only source of power.

In designing the plane, engineers did experiments to find out exactly how much power would be needed to fly it. One earlier model required about 1.5 watts of power for every pound the pilot weighed. That wasn't good enough. Even a well-conditioned pilot would not be able to provide enough power to fly the plane only 80 kilometers. By redesigning the aircraft, the engineers came up with a version that needed less power.

OPTIONS

Meeting Different Ability Levels

For Section 7-3, use the following **Teacher Resource Masters** depending upon individual students' needs.

◆ **Study Guide Master** for all students.

● **Reinforcement Master** for students of average and above average ability levels.

▲ **Enrichment Master** for above average students.

Additional Teacher Resource Package masters are listed in any **PROGRAM RESOURCES** boxes that are in the section. The additional masters are appropriate for all students.

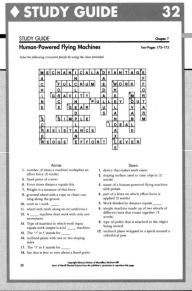

◆ STUDY GUIDE   32

STUDY GUIDE   Chapter 7
Human-Powered Flying Machines   Text Pages 172–173

Solve the following crossword puzzle by using the clues provided.

Across

1. number of times a machine multiplies an effort force (2 words)
5. fixed point of a lever
8. Force times distance equals this.
9. Weight is a measure of this force.
7. grooved wheel with a rope or chain running along the groove
10. work in = work ____
11. wheel with teeth along its circumference
13. A ____ machine does work with only one movement.
14. Type of machine in which work input equals work output is a(n) ____ machine.
15. The "r" in *F₁* stands for ____.
16. inclined plane with one or two sloping sides
17. The "e" in *F₂* stands for ____.
18. bar that is free to turn about a fixed point

Down

1. device that makes work easier
2. sloping surface used to raise objects (2 words)
3. name of a human-powered flying machine with pedals
4. part of a lever on which effort force is applied (2 words)
5. Work divided by distance equals ____.
6. simple machine made up of two wheels of different sizes that rotate together (3 words)
8. type of pulley that is attached to the object being moved
12. inclined plane wrapped in a spiral around a cylindrical post

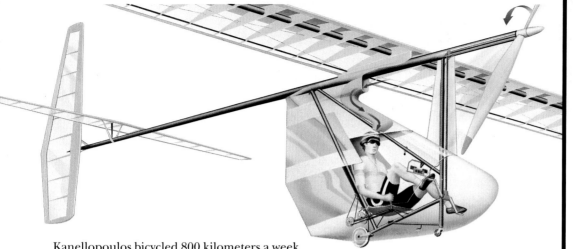

Kanellopoulos bicycled 800 kilometers a week to train for the flying feat. During the flight, he pedalled for nearly four hours, swigging a special high-energy drink until he complained that his stomach was full and "sloshing around."

As Kanellopoulos soared 12 meters above the sea, the director of the Daedalus project mused, "This is insane, but wonderful." Just 9 meters away from shore, a gust of wind snapped the tail off the Daedalus, and the plane fell on a raft. Daedalus was a mess, but Kanellopoulos was safe, and the flight was declared a success.

SECTION REVIEW

1. Look at the simple diagram of the Daedalus. How many simple machines can you identify?
2. Would you feel differently about the value of the Daedalus project if Kanellopoulos had been hurt when the plane fell into the sea?
3. **Connect to Life Science:** Daedalus flew 115 km in the 4-hour flight. Is this faster or slower than most birds?

You Decide!

The researchers who worked on Daedalus often are asked if the project had any practical value. Can you think of any useful applications of their research? Do you think it is worthwhile to spend time and money on research that has no immediate practical applications? What would help you decide whether a research project is worth doing?

SCIENCE & SOCIETY

173

CONCEPT DEVELOPMENT

▶ Students may not realize that an energy production of 1.5 watts/pound is quite large. A student (70 lb) climbing a flight of stairs produces about 2 watts/pound. Ask them if they think they could maintain that rate for four hours—equivalent of climbing 20 000 steps!

CHECK FOR UNDERSTANDING

Ask questions 1 and 2 and the **Connect to Life Science** quesiton in the Section Review.

RETEACH

Demonstration: Fly a rubber-band powered model airplane. Have students compare the time of flight and the complexities of the Daedalus to those of the model airplane.

EXTENSION

For students who have mastered this section, use the **Reinforcement** and **Enrichment** masters or other OPTIONS provided.

3 CLOSE

? **FLEX Your Brain**

Use the Flex Your Brain activity to have students explore IMPROVING THE DAEDALUS.

ASSESSMENT

Portfolio: Use the Flex Your Brain activity to reinforce critical-thinking and problem-solving skills. In Step 2, students might list what they know about paper airplanes.

SECTION REVIEW ANSWERS

1. Responses will vary. Accept all reasonable responses.
2. Student responses will vary.
3. **Connect to Life Science:** Kanellopoulos' speed was 115 km/4 h=29 km/h or 8 m/s. This would be very slow for a bird.

PREPARATION

SECTION BACKGROUND
▶ How effectively a machine transfers energy is measured by its efficiency. The rate at which it transfers energy is measured by its power.

PREPLANNING
▶ You will need a wind-up toy car for each group conducting the MINI-Lab.

1 MOTIVATE

Cooperative Learning: Using the Numbered Heads Together strategy, have groups attempt to classify a fingernail clipper.

TYING TO PREVIOUS KNOWLEDGE:
Have students recall what a simple machine does. In this section they will see how combining simple machines also makes work easier.

VideoDisc
STVS: Micro-Machine Shop, Disc 1, Side 2

PROGRAM RESOURCES

From the **Teacher Resource Package** use:

Transparency Masters, pages 27-28, A Compound Machine.

Concept Mapping, pages 19-20.

Use **Color Transparency** number 14, A Compound Machine.

7-4 Using Machines

New Science Words
compound machine
efficiency
power
watt

Objectives
▶ Recognize the simple machines that make up a compound machine.
▶ Calculate the efficiency of a machine.
▶ Describe the relationship between work, power, and time.

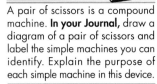

In Your JOURNAL
A pair of scissors is a compound machine. **In your Journal,** draw a diagram of a pair of scissors and label the simple machines you can identify. Explain the purpose of each simple machine in this device.

Figure 7-12. A bicycle is made up of many simple machines that work together.

Compound Machines

Many machines that you use, such as a lawn mower or a pencil sharpener, are made up of several simple machines. A combination of two or more simple machines is a **compound machine.** Even a tool as simple as an axe is a compound machine made up of a wedge and a lever.

Often the simple machines that make up a compound machine are concealed. However, in one familiar compound machine—the bicycle—many of the simple machines are visible and easily recognized.

Look at the bicycle in Figure 7-12. The pedal mechanism is a wheel-and-axle system made up of two wheels

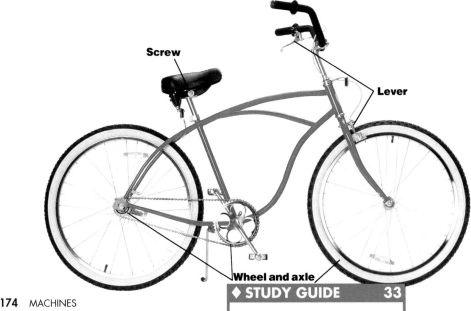

Screw

Lever

Wheel and axle

174 MACHINES

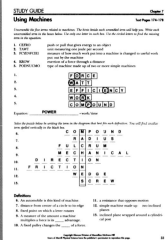

OPTIONS

Meeting Different Ability Levels
For Section 7-4, use the following **Teacher Resource Masters** depending upon individual students' needs.
◆ **Study Guide Master** for all students.
● **Reinforcement Master** for students of average and above average ability levels.
▲ **Enrichment Master** for above average students.
Additional Teacher Resource Package masters are listed in any **PROGRAM RESOURCES** boxes that are in the section. The additional masters are appropriate for all students.

attached to the same axle. Each pedal moves in a circle, like a wheel. The axle is a gear. The effort force exerted on the pedals by the rider turns this pedal gear. The bicycle chain transfers the force to a smaller gear attached to the rear wheel. This wheel gear is actually the effort wheel of the rear wheel-and-axle system. As the wheel gear turns, it causes the rear wheel to turn, and the wheel exerts the resistance force on the road. Because the wheel gear is smaller than the pedal gear that drives it, the rear wheel turns faster than the pedals do.

The overall mechanical advantage of a bicycle is the ratio of the resistance force exerted by the tires on the road to the effort force exerted by the rider on the pedals. The bicycle shown in Figure 7-12 has only two gears. Its gear ratio is fixed, so its mechanical advantage cannot be changed. This makes it a one-speed bike. A ten-speed bike has two pedal gears and five wheel gears. By shifting gears, the rider can change gear ratios, which changes the mechanical advantage and helps the rider maintain a steadier rate of pedaling in different terrain.

A bicycle has many other simple machines. Some of these machines are shown in Figure 7-12. See if you can tell what each does. Can you think of any others?

Efficiency

You learned earlier that some of the energy put into a machine is lost as thermal energy produced as a result of friction. So the work put out by a machine is always less than the work put into the machine.

Efficiency is a measure of how much of the work put into a machine is changed to useful work put out by a machine. The higher the efficiency of a machine, the greater the amount of work input is changed to useful work output. Efficiency is calculated by dividing work output by work input and is usually expressed as a percentage.

$$\text{efficiency} = \frac{W_{out}}{W_{in}} \times 100\% = \frac{F_r \times d_r}{F_e \times d_e} \times 100\%$$

Why must the efficiency of a machine always be less than 100 percent? Can you think of ways to increase the efficiency of a machine?

Figure 7-13. The rear wheel of a ten-speed bicycle has five different gears.

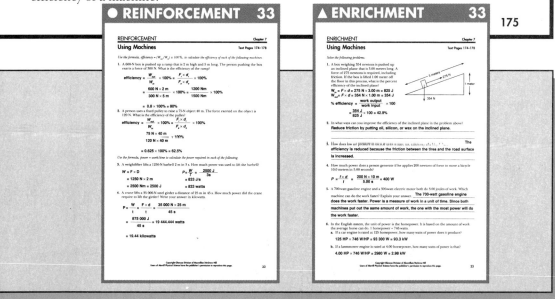

175

2 TEACH

Key Concepts are highlighted.

CONCEPT DEVELOPMENT

▶ **Demonstration:** Set up a meterstick as a lever with a fulcrum located at the 0-cm mark. Hang a heavy weight at the 33-cm mark and connect a single, movable pulley to the meterstick with a wire tie at the 99-cm mark. Raise and lower the lever using the pulley string. Have students determine that the machine is a compound machine by identifying the lever and pulley. The resistance force of the pulley is actually driving the lever. Have students identify the meterstick as a second class lever and have them calculate its MA.
$MA = L_e/L_r$ = 99 cm/33 cm = 3
Have them recall that the MA of a single, movable pulley is 2. Attach a spring scale to the string and record the force needed to raise and lower the lever. Measure the weight. From these values, calculate the MA of the compound machine.

▶ The following diagram illustrates energy transfers in a compound machine.

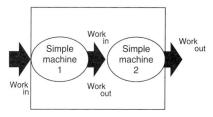

Compound machine

STUDENT TEXT QUESTION

▶ Page 175, paragraph 5: **Why must the efficiency of a machine always be less than 100 percent?** *In any machine, the work put out by a machine* (W_{out}) *is always less than the work put into it* (W_{in}) *because some mechanical energy is converted to thermal energy in the machine.*

In Your JOURNAL

Scissors contain wedges and levers. The levers transfer and change the direction of force, and the wedges, or blades, use the force to cut the material.

CONCEPT DEVELOPMENT

▶ The mechanical advantage of a compound machine is the product of the individual mechanical advantages of the simple machines that make it up. In a simple machine, the output force is equal to the input force multiplied by the MA of the machine: $F_r = F_e \times MA$. In a compound machine, the output force of one of its simple machines becomes the input force of another. For a compound machine made of two simple machines,

$$F_r = MA_2 \times MA_1 \times F_e$$

PRACTICE PROBLEM ANSWER

Given: $F_r = 65$ N; $F_e = 72$ N

$d_r = d_e$

$$\text{efficiency} = \frac{F_r \times d_r}{F_e \times d_e} \times 100\%$$

$$= \frac{65 \text{ N}}{72 \text{ N}} \times 100\%$$

efficiency = 90%

REVEALING MISCONCEPTIONS

▶ Have students discuss their understanding of efficiency. Have them focus their discussion on doing a task, such as mowing a lawn. Some will interpret efficiency as doing a task quickly. Others may interpret efficiency as doing a task with less energy. As you develop the concept of efficiency, contrast its meaning with these misconceptions.

MINI QUIZ

Use the Mini Quiz to check students' recall of chapter content.

1. A(n) _____ is a combination of two or more simple machines. *compound machine*

2. _____ is a measure of how much of the work put into a machine is changed to useful work put out by a machine. *Efficiency*

Connect to... Chemistry

Answer: Graphite is made of carbon and rubs off in thin layers. The layers coat the surfaces where parts rub and reduce friction.

EXAMPLE PROBLEM: Calculating Efficiency

Problem Statement: A sofa weighing 1500 N must be placed in a truck bed 1.0 m off the ground. A worker uses a force of 500 N to push the sofa up an inclined plane that has a slope length of 4.0 m. What is the efficiency of the inclined plane?

Known Information:
Strategy Hint: Can your answer be greater than 100 percent?

resistance force, $F_r = 1500$ N
resistance distance, $d_r = 1.0$ m
effort force, $F_e = 500$ N
effort distance, $d_e = 4.0$ m

Unknown Information: efficiency

Equation to Use: $\text{efficiency} = \dfrac{F_r \times d_r}{F_e \times d_e} \times 100\%$

Solution: $\text{efficiency} = \dfrac{1500 \text{ N} \times 1.0 \text{ m}}{500 \text{ N} \times 4.0 \text{ m}} \times 100\% = 75\%$

PRACTICE PROBLEM

Strategy Hint: How is this problem different from the sample problem?

1. Using a fixed pulley, you exert a 72-N force to raise a 65-N object. What is the efficiency of the pulley?

Connect to... Chemistry

A material called graphite is sometimes used as a lubricant to increase the efficiency of machines. Find out what element graphite is made of and why it eases the movement of machines.

Many machines can be made more efficient by reducing friction. This is usually done by adding a lubricant, such as oil or grease, to surfaces that rub together. After a time, dirt will build up on the grease or oil, and the lubricant will lose its effectiveness. The dirty lubricant should be wiped off and replaced with clean grease or oil. Can you think of any other ways to increase the efficiency of a machine?

Power

Suppose you and a friend are pushing boxes of books up a ramp to load them into a truck. The boxes weigh the same, but your friend is able to push a box a little faster than you can. Your friend moves a box up the ramp in 30 seconds. It takes you 45 seconds. Do you both do the same amount of work on the books? Yes. This is true because the boxes weighed the same and were moved the same distance. The only difference is in the time it takes you and your friend to do the work.

OPTIONS

ASSESSMENT—ORAL

▶ **What part of the axe is a lever?** *the handle* **What class of lever is it?** *third* **What are the benefits of attaching a wedge to a lever to make an axe?** *The axe increases the speed of the effort force through the lever and changes the direction of the effort force through the wedge.*

▶ **Use the information presented in the text to explain if the MA of a one-speed bike is greater or less than 1.** *The resistance distance is greater than the effort distance because the rear wheel goes faster than the pedal wheel, . The MA must be less than 1 because d_e is less than d_r.* **What do you gain by using a one-speed bike?** *speed* **What do you lose?** *force*

TECHNOLOGY

Micromachines

Imagine a robot the size of a flyspeck. Thousands of these robots could be injected into your bloodstream to clean out deposits or to identify and destroy bacteria, viruses, and cancer cells. This is the future predicted by a new group of engineers called micromechanical engineers.

These engineers use a sculpting process similar to that used in microelectronics to create mechanical devices a few microns thick. (A human hair is about 75 microns

across.) The sculpting is done in silicon, which at this size demonstrates a strength similar to that of steel.

Micromechanical sensors are already widely used to detect pressure, acceleration, and temperature. However, these sensors are passive. Tiny robots will produce micromachines that can make things move. Recently, scientists at the University of California at Berkeley constructed a rotary motor that is only about two-thirds the diameter of a human hair. The central motor is 0.002 inches across, and the rotor arm is about the size of a red blood cell. Although working on this very small scale still involves many unknowns, the possibilities are enormous.

Think Critically: What are some of the problems encountered by mechanical engineers that may be quite different in machines constructed at the micron level?

Your friend has more power than you have. **Power** is the rate at which work is done. In other words, power is a measure of the amount of work done in a certain amount of time. To calculate power, divide the work done by the time required to do the work.

$$\text{power} = \frac{\text{work}}{\text{time}}$$

$$P = \frac{W}{t}$$

Power is measured in watts, named for James Watt, the inventor of the steam engine. A **watt (W)** is one joule per second. A watt is pretty small—about equal to the power used to raise a glass of water from your knees to your

MINI-Lab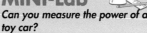

Can you measure the power of a toy car?

Wind up a toy car and place it at the bottom of an inclined plane. Adjust the angle of the inclined plane so the car will reach the top at the *slowest* speed possible. *Measure* the time in seconds for the car to travel to the top. *Measure* the weight of the car in newtons. *Measure* the height of the inclined plane in meters. Use weight and height to calculate the work in joules. Divide work by time to get power in watts.

TECHNOLOGY

▶ For more information on micromachines, see "Micromachine Magic" by Robert Gannon, *Popular Science*, March 1989, pp. 89-92.

▶ Have students observe a silicon chip and a human hair together under a microscope. Use this comparison to develop the concept of scale and to introduce the micron. **Think Critically:** At the micron level, qualities such as smoothness, friction, and lubrication may be very different from the same qualities in objects of normal size.

CONCEPT DEVELOPMENT

▶ To introduce the concept of power, pose the following questions. Suppose two students are asked to unpack identical cartons of books. One student completes the job in 10 minutes, whereas the other takes 20 minutes. Which student worked harder? Which student did more work? Develop the idea of power, the rate of work, by asking students what they mean when they say someone worked harder at a task.

MINI-Lab

Materials: inclined plane board, stopwatch, meterstick, spring scale, and wind-up car

Teaching Tips

▶ Any toy that will travel up an incline can be used. Encourage students to bring their own.

Answers to Questions

▶ Answers will vary. Expect answers in the 0.01 watt range.

ENRICHMENT

▶ Have interested students demonstrate the gears of a ten-speed bike. Ask them to discuss the ten possible combinations of gears between the two pedal gears and the five rear-wheel gears. Have them relate the function of each combination in terms of starting, gaining speed, and climbing. Gear ratios could also be calculated.

▶ Have interested students compile a listing of power ratings and efficiency ratings for various appliances. Encourage them to investigate if the two are related.

PROGRAM RESOURCES

From the **Teacher Resource Package** use:

Activity Worksheet, page 61, MINI-Lab: Can you measure the power of a toy car?

Science and Society, page 11, Will Robots Take Away Jobs?

Use **Laboratory Manual 16,** The Bicycle: A Well-Engineered Machine.

MINI-Lab

ASSESSMENT

Performance: For further assessment, refer to USING LAB SKILLS Question 12 on page 180.

CONCEPT DEVELOPMENT

▶ Power is the rate at which energy is converted. For example, a 100-W light bulb converts 100 joules of electrical energy into 100 joules of radiant energy and heat during one second.

▶ Machines and appliances can be compared by their power ratings.

CROSS CURRICULUM

▶ **Health:** Nutritionists recommend a daily diet of about 5 000 000 J (1200 C) to maintain health. Show students that this diet would generate an average power of 58 W.

$$\frac{5\ 000\ 000\ J}{24\ h \times 60\ min/h \times 60\ s/min}$$

PRACTICE PROBLEM ANSWER

$P = \dfrac{F \times d}{t} = \dfrac{25\ 000\ N \times 30\ m}{60\ s}$

$= 12\ 500\ W$ or $12.5\ kW$

CHECK FOR UNDERSTANDING

Ask questions 1-2 and the **Apply** and **Connect to Life Science** questions from the Section Review.

RETEACH

Cooperative Learning: Have Problem Solving Teams determine a method for calculating the amount of power a student generates while climbing a flight of stairs.

EXTENSION

For students who have mastered this section, use the **Reinforcement** and **Enrichment** masters or other OPTIONS provided.

3 CLOSE

SECTION REVIEW ANSWERS

1. Student responses will vary. Accept all reasonable responses.

2. By definition, *power* is a measure of the amount of work done in a given amount of time.

3. Apply: For a given amount of work put into the mower, the work put out by the mower will increase.

4. Connect to Life Science: Predators should have greater power than their prey for at least short durations to be able to overtake them.

EXAMPLE PROBLEM: Calculating Power

Problem Statement:	A figure skater lifts his partner, who weighs 450 N, 1 m in 3 s. How much power is required?
Known Information:	force, $F = 450\ N$
Strategy Hint: Remember that work = force × distance.	distance, $d = 1\ m$
	time, $t = 3\ s$
Unknown Information:	power (P)
Equation to Use:	$P = \dfrac{W}{t} = \dfrac{F \times d}{t}$
Solution:	$P = \dfrac{450\ N \times 1\ m}{3\ s} = 150\ W$

PRACTICE PROBLEM

Strategy Hint: Should your answer be in watts or kilowatts?

1. A 500-N passenger is inside a 24 500-N elevator that rises 30.0 m in exactly 1 minute. How much power is needed for the elevator's trip?

mouth in one second. Because the watt is such a small unit, large amounts of power often are expressed in kilowatts. One kilowatt (kW) equals 1000 watts.

SECTION REVIEW

1. Give an example of a compound machine. What are the simple machines that make it up?
2. How are power, work, and time related?
3. **Apply:** You buy a secondhand lawn mower with an efficiency of 30 percent. By repairing and lubricating it, you increase its efficiency to 40 percent. How does this affect the work put out by the lawn mower for a given amount of work put in?
4. **Connect to Life Science:** How is power related to the success of a predator in hunting?

Skill Builder

☑ Concept Mapping

Make an events chain concept map to show how some of the simple machines in a bicycle work together to move the bicycle. Start with the feet applying force to the pedals. If you need help, refer to Concept Mapping in the **Skill Handbook** on pages 684 and 685.

Skill Builder

Feet apply force to pedals
↓
Pedals move in a circle around axle
↓
Force is transferred from pedals to wheels through gears and chain
↓
Wheels exert resistance force on road surface

Skill Builder

ASSESSMENT

Performance: Have students number the steps in this map and correlate them with a picture of a bicycle by writing the number of the step next to the portion affected by it.

SUMMARY

7-1: Why We Use Machines

1. A machine makes work easier by changing the size of the force applied to it, the direction of that force, or both.

2. The number of times a machine multiplies the force applied to it is the mechanical advantage of the machine.

7-2: The Simple Machines

1. A lever is a bar that is free to pivot about a fixed point called a fulcrum. A pulley is a grooved wheel with a rope running along the groove. A wheel and axle consists of two differently sized wheels that rotate together. An inclined plane is a sloping surface used to raise objects. The screw and the wedge are special types of inclined planes.

2. Each type of simple machine has a specific equation for calculating its mechanical advantage. Each equation is related to the distance the effort force moves divided by the distance the resistance force moves.

7-3: Science and Society: Human-Powered Flying Machines

1. Simple machines can be combined to increase force and transfer that force from one place to another. Using a combination of simple machines, a human was able to propel a specially built airplane for a distance of more than 100 kilometers. The effort force for this flight was exerted by the pilot's legs.

2. Any experiment may have practical value that is not obvious at first.

7-4: Using Machines

1. A combination of two or more simple machines is called a compound machine.

2. The efficiency of any machine is a ratio of the work put into the machine to the useful work put out by the machine.

3. Power is a measure of the amount of work done in a certain amount of time. The SI unit of power is the watt, which is equivalent to one joule per second.

KEY SCIENCE WORDS

a. **compound machine**
b. **efficiency**
c. **effort arm**
d. **effort force**
e. **fulcrum**
f. **ideal machine**
g. **inclined plane**
h. **lever**
i. **machine**
j. **mechanical advantage**
k. **power**
l. **pulley**
m. **resistance arm**
n. **resistance force**
o. **screw**
p. **simple machine**
q. **watt**
r. **wedge**
s. **wheel and axle**

UNDERSTANDING VOCABULARY

Match each phrase with the correct term from the list of Key Science Words.

1. any device that accomplishes work with only one movement
2. force applied by a machine
3. a device in which work output equals work input
4. a bar that pivots about a fixed point
5. two differently sized wheels that rotate together
6. a combination of simple machines
7. the work output of a machine divided by the work input
8. the rate at which work is done
9. the fixed point of a lever
10. an inclined plane wrapped around a cylinder

MACHINES **179**

CHAPTER
REVIEW

SUMMARY

Have students read the summary statements to review the major concepts of the chapter.

UNDERSTANDING VOCABULARY

1. p		**6.** a	
2. n		**7.** b	
3. f		**8.** k	
4. h		**9.** e	
5. s		**10.** o	

ASSESSMENT
Portfolio

Encourage students to place in their portfolios one or two items of what they consider to be their best work. For each item, ask students to explain why that item was chosen and what they learned from it. Items might be selected from the following.

- Practice Problem calculations and answer, p. 160
- Enrichment research, p. 168
- Activity 7-2 calculations and answers, p. 171

Performance

Additional performance assessments may be found in *Performance Assessment* and *Science Integration Activities* that accompany **Merrill Physical Science.** Performance Task Assessment Lists and rubrics for evaluating these activities and other products generated throughout the chapter can be found in Glencoe's *Performance Assessment in Middle School Science.*

OPTIONS

ASSESSMENT

To assess student understanding of material in this chapter, use the resources listed.

👥 COOPERATIVE LEARNING
Consider using cooperative learning in the THINK AND WRITE CRITICALLY, APPLY, and MORE SKILL BUILDERS sections of the Chapter Review.

PROGRAM RESOURCES

From the **Teacher Resource Package** use:

Chapter Review, pages 17-18.

Chapter and Unit Tests, pages 36-39, Chapter Test.

Chapter and Unit Tests, pages 40-41, Unit Test.

REVIEW

CHECKING CONCEPTS

1. b	6. b
2. b	7. a
3. a	8. b
4. c	9. b
5. d	10. a

USING LAB SKILLS

ASSESSMENT

Use these alternate lab exercises to asess students' understanding of the skills used in this chapter.

11. Changing the position of the resistance line will affect the position of the fulcrum when the lever is balanced. The calculations using L_e and L_r should account for this, and the masses of the coins should measure the same.

12. Have a partner time you as you walk up a ramp at maximum speed. Determine your weight in Newtons and measure the vertical height of the incline in meters. Use $P = F \times d/t$ to determine your power in watts.

THINK AND WRITE CRITICALLY

13. Simple machines can make work easier by: (a) multiplying the effort force, as with a first class lever; (b) changing the direction of the applied force, as with a single, fixed pulley; (c) increasing the distance through which the resistance force moves, as with a third class lever.

14. Most machines increase the amount of work done by increasing the amount of friction involved in doing the work. However, the applied force is smaller.

15. A fixed pulley changes the direction of the effort force; it does not multiply that force. A fixed pulley is similar to a first class lever. A single, movable pulley moves with the resistance. It multiplies the force by 2. Such a pulley is similar to a second class lever.

16. The MA of an inclined plane can be increased by increasing its length (or decreasing its height). Sharpening a knife has the effect of increasing the length of the *inclined plane*.

REVIEW

CHECKING CONCEPTS

Choose the word or phrase that completes the sentence or answers the question.

1. There are _____ types of simple machines.
- **a.** 3
- **b.** 6
- **c.** 8
- **d.** 10

2. Which of these cannot be done by a machine?
- **a.** multiply force
- **b.** multiply energy
- **c.** change direction of a force
- **d.** work

3. In an ideal machine, the work input _____ work output.
- **a.** is equal to
- **b.** is greater than
- **c.** is less than
- **d.** is independent of

4. The _____ of a machine is the number of times it multiplies the effort force.
- **a.** efficiency
- **b.** power
- **c.** mechanical advantage
- **d.** resistance

5. To raise a resistance 4 meters, the effort rope of a fixed pulley must move _____.
- **a.** 2 meters
- **b.** 8 meters
- **c.** 1 meter
- **d.** 4 meters

6. The mechanical advantage of a pulley system in which 5 ropes support an object is _____.
- **a.** 2.5
- **b.** 5
- **c.** 10
- **d.** 25

7. In a wheel and axle, the resistance force is usually exerted by the _____.
- **a.** axle
- **b.** larger wheel
- **c.** gear ratio
- **d.** pedals

8. The MA of an inclined plane 8 meters long and 2 meters high is _____.
- **a.** 2
- **b.** 4
- **c.** 16
- **d.** 8

9. As the efficiency of a machine increases, the _____ of the machine increases.
- **a.** work input
- **b.** work output
- **c.** friction
- **d.** MA

10. The MA of an inclined plane can be increased by _____.
- **a.** increasing the length
- **b.** increasing the height
- **c.** decreasing the length
- **d.** making its surface smoother

USING LAB SKILLS

11. In Activity 7-2 on page 171, you determined the mass of several coins using a lever. Move the resistance line 4 cm from the edge of the paper and repeat the experiment. Are your results affected?

12. You measured the power of a toy car in the MINI-Lab on page 177. Design a procedure to determine your own power as you walk up an incline. Conduct your experiment.

THINK AND WRITE CRITICALLY

Answer the following questions in your Journal, using complete sentences.

13. Describe and give examples of three ways that a simple machine can make work easier.

14. If machines make work easier, explain why most machines actually increase the amount of work you do in accomplishing a task.

15. Distinguish between a fixed pulley and a single movable pulley and describe the advantages of using each. Compare each type of pulley to its corresponding class of lever.

16. Explain how sharpening a knife changes its MA.

17. The efficiency of an automobile is usually expressed in terms of gas mileage. How can changing the engine oil increase the gas mileage of the automobile?

---

17. Oil lubricates engine parts, thereby reducing friction and making the engine more efficient.

APPLY

18. $MA = \dfrac{F_r}{F_e} = \dfrac{200 \text{ N}}{250 \text{ N}} = 0.8$

19. The fulcrum should be moved toward the adult, which increases the length of the effort arm of the child's lever. Thus, the MA of the child's lever is increased, and the effort force exerted by the child is multiplied.

20. The screwdriver is being used as a wheel and axle, with the handle acting as the wheel. Thus, the screwdriver with the fat handle will have a greater MA. The length is irrelevant.

21. efficiency $= \dfrac{W_{out}}{W_{in}}$

$= \dfrac{2000 \text{ N} \times 2 \text{ m}}{1250 \text{ N} \times 4 \text{ m}} \times 100\% = 80\%$

22. $P = \dfrac{W}{t} = \dfrac{F \times d}{t}$

$= \dfrac{500 \text{ N} \times 3 \text{ m}}{5 \text{ s}}$

$= 300 \text{ watts or } 0.3 \text{ kW}$

APPLY

18. A cyclist applies a force of 250 N to the pedals of a bicycle. If the rear wheel applies a force of 200 N to the road surface, what is the *MA* of the bicycle?

19. An adult and a small child get on a seesaw that has a movable fulcrum. When the fulcrum is in the middle, the child can't lift the adult. How should the fulcrum be moved so that the two can seesaw? Explain your answer.

20. You have two screwdrivers. One is long with a thin handle, and the other is short with a fat handle. Which would you use to drive a screw into a board? Explain your choice.

21. Using a ramp 4 meters long, workers apply an effort force of 1250 N to move a 2000-N crate onto a platform 2 meters high. What is the efficiency of the ramp?

22. How much power does a person weighing 500 N need to climb a 3-meter ladder in 5 seconds?

MORE SKILL BUILDERS

If you need help, refer to the Skill Handbook.

1. **Outlining:** Make an outline describing the six types of simple machines. Be sure the outline indicates the two major types of simple machines and includes the following for each type of machine: (1) a description; (2) how it works; (3) a method for finding its *MA*; (4) an example.

2. **Making and Using Graphs:** A lever has a fixed effort arm length of 40 cm. Calculate the effort force needed to raise a 10-N object with these resistance arm lengths: 80 cm, 40 cm, 20 cm, and 10 cm. Construct a line graph relating these resistance arm lengths to effort force. Describe the relationship between these two variables.

3. **Interpreting Scientific Illustrations:** Study the diagram of a garden hoe and answer the questions.
   a. What type of machine does the diagram represent? (Be specific.)
   b. What does the longer arrow represent?
   c. What does point A represent?
   d. What is represented by segment AC? Segment AB?
   e. What is the *MA* of this machine?
   f. How does this machine make work easier?

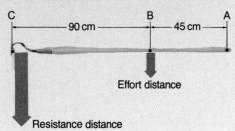

Effort distance

Resistance distance

4. **Measuring in SI:** The SI unit of power, the watt, is a derived unit. Using the definition of power, develop the formula for calculating power and determine the fundamental SI units for expressing power.

PROJECTS

1. Divide the class into teams of 3 or 4 students each. Have the members of each team spend one week daily identifying, describing, and classifying as many simple machines as they can find at school and at home. At the end of the week, each team should report their findings. Members should be prepared to support their own classifications and to challenge classifications they feel are incorrect.

2. Design a human-powered machine of some kind. Describe the simple machines used in your design and tell what each of these machines does.

4. **Measuring in SI:** Power is the rate at which work is done, or $P = W/t$. Power is expressed in watts. Using $F \times d$ to represent work, the formula for power becomes $P = (F \times d)/t$. So, a watt is the name for the derived unit newton • meter per second.

MORE SKILL BUILDERS

1. **Outlining:** Outlines may vary somewhat, but should resemble the following general scheme. Each lettered subhead should have the three subdivisions shown for A.
   I. Levers
      A. lever
         1. description
         2. how it works
         3. method for finding *MA*
         4. examples
      B. pulley
      C. wheel and axle
   II. Inclined Planes
      A. ramp
      B. screw
      C. wedge

2. **Making and Using Graphs:**

$MA = \dfrac{L_e}{L_r}$	$F_e = \dfrac{F_r}{MA}$
$\dfrac{40}{80} = 0.5$	$\dfrac{10}{0.5} = 20$ N
$\dfrac{40}{40} = 1$	$\dfrac{10}{1} = 10$ N
$\dfrac{40}{20} = 2$	$\dfrac{10}{2} = 5$ N
$\dfrac{40}{10} = 4$	$\dfrac{10}{4} = 2.5$ N

The effort force and the length of the resistance arm are directly related.

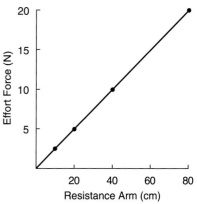

3. **Interpreting Scientific Illustrations:**
   a. third class lever
   b. the distance the resistance moves
   c. fulcrum
   d. AC = resistance arm; AB = effort arm
   e. $MA = \dfrac{L_e}{L_r} = \dfrac{45 \text{ cm}}{135 \text{ cm}} = 0.33$
   f. The machine increases the distance the resistance moves for a given movement of the effort.

Objective

In this unit-ending feature, the unit topic, *Energy and Motion,* is extended into other disciplines. Students will see how energy and motion are re-lated to events occurring around the planet.

Motivate

Cooperative Learning: Assign one Connection to each group of students. Using the Expert Teams strategy have each group research to find out more about the geographic location of the Connection—its climate, culture, flora and fauna, and ecological issues.

Teaching Tips

▶ Ask students to look for the relationship between energy and motion in each of the items in this feature.

▶ Ask students to explain the motion involved in each Connection. Then ask them to describe the kind of energy involved in each one.

Wrap-Up

Conclude this lesson by asking students to describe how energy changes form in each of the Connections.

OCEANOGRAPHY

Background: Earth rotates once on its axis every 24 hours, while the moon orbits Earth. Before the moon returns to the same position overhead, Earth has rotated for 24 hours, 50 minutes. High tides occur when the moon is overhead or exactly on the opposite side of Earth. Because of this, high tides usually occur every 12 hours, 15 minutes.

Discussion: Ask students how tides might differ if Earth had two moons.

Answer to Question: Although the sun has much more mass than the moon, it is much farther away.

Extension: Have students find out how the Amazon River in South America is affected by tides.

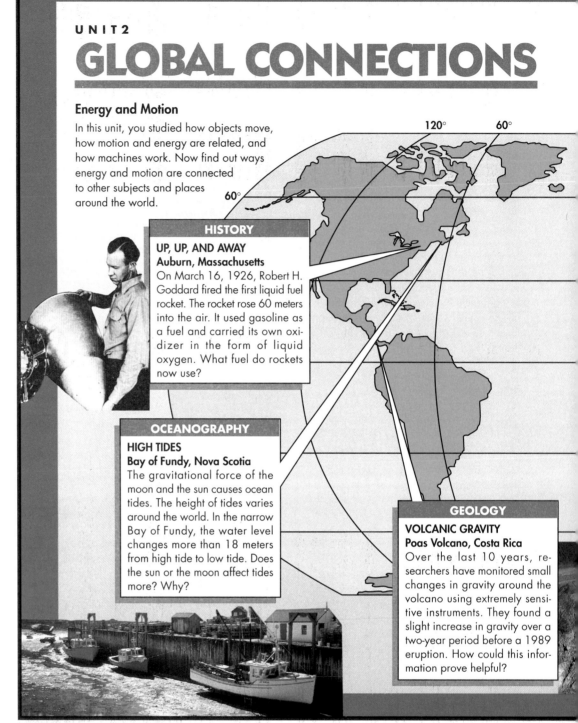

UNIT 2
GLOBAL CONNECTIONS

Energy and Motion

In this unit, you studied how objects move, how motion and energy are related, and how machines work. Now find out ways energy and motion are connected to other subjects and places around the world.

HISTORY
UP, UP, AND AWAY
Auburn, Massachusetts
On March 16, 1926, Robert H. Goddard fired the first liquid fuel rocket. The rocket rose 60 meters into the air. It used gasoline as a fuel and carried its own oxidizer in the form of liquid oxygen. What fuel do rockets now use?

OCEANOGRAPHY
HIGH TIDES
Bay of Fundy, Nova Scotia
The gravitational force of the moon and the sun causes ocean tides. The height of tides varies around the world. In the narrow Bay of Fundy, the water level changes more than 18 meters from high tide to low tide. Does the sun or the moon affect tides more? Why?

GEOLOGY
VOLCANIC GRAVITY
Poas Volcano, Costa Rica
Over the last 10 years, researchers have monitored small changes in gravity around the volcano using extremely sensitive instruments. They found a slight increase in gravity over a two-year period before a 1989 eruption. How could this information prove helpful?

HISTORY

Background: The Chinese had used rockets during the Middle Ages. But until the 20th century rockets used gunpowder which is a fuel mixed with an oxidizer.

Discussion: Discuss with students the importance of an oxidizer to a rocket in traveling in space. Ask why a rocket traveling to the moon needs to carry a supply of liquid oxygen.

Answer to Question: Rockets now use liquid hydrogen as fuel and still carry liquid oxygen as the oxidizer.

Extension: Have students prepare a poster showing the structure of different kinds of rockets.

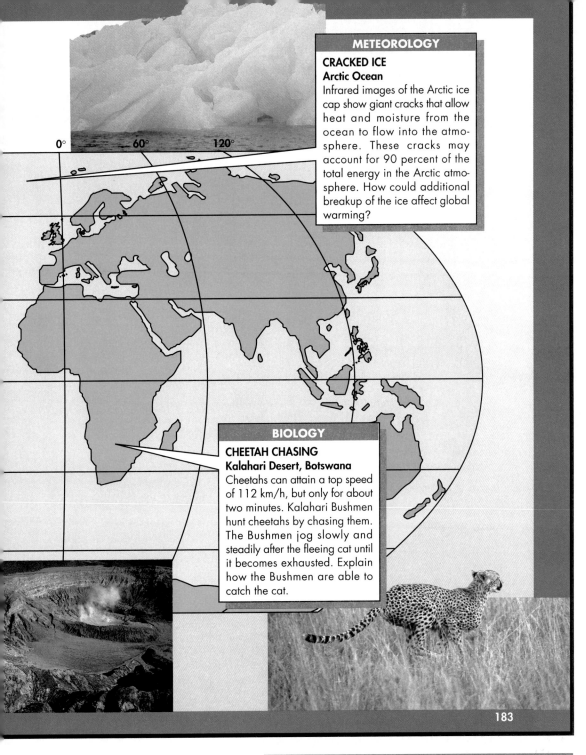

Background: Researchers inferred that the increase in gravity was likely due to the intrusion of dense molten magma into the volcano's cone before the eruption.

Discussion: Tell students that gravity decreased before the eruption of another volcano, probably because gas pockets formed in the magma, lowering its density. Discuss the possibility and practicality of determining a characteristic profile of each volcano in order to predict eruptions.

Answer to Question: The information might be used to help predict volcanic eruptions before they occur.

Extension: Have students research other methods that scientists use to predict volcanic eruptions.

METEOROLOGY

CRACKED ICE
Arctic Ocean

Infrared images of the Arctic ice cap show giant cracks that allow heat and moisture from the ocean to flow into the atmosphere. These cracks may account for 90 percent of the total energy in the Arctic atmosphere. How could additional breakup of the ice affect global warming?

METEOROLOGY

Background: The temperature of the ocean beneath the Arctic ice cap is about 40 degrees warmer than the Arctic air. Human activities which added more energy to the atmosphere could increase the breakup of the ice caps.

Discussion: Discuss the effects of global warming on the polar ice caps. Tell students that melting of the ice caps could raise sea level as much as 60 meters. Ask what effect this would have on the United States.

Answer to Question: If more energy escapes into the atmosphere, it could increase global warming.

Extension: Have students draw on a map the areas of the United States that would be below sea level if the polar ice caps melted.

BIOLOGY

CHEETAH CHASING
Kalahari Desert, Botswana

Cheetahs can attain a top speed of 112 km/h, but only for about two minutes. Kalahari Bushmen hunt cheetahs by chasing them. The Bushmen jog slowly and steadily after the fleeing cat until it becomes exhausted. Explain how the Bushmen are able to catch the cat.

183

BIOLOGY

Background: When comparing the speeds of various animals and humans, the maximum speeds attained are measured over varying distances. For a cheetah (112 km/h) to catch a gazelle (80 km/h), the cheetah must first get close enough so it can quickly catch the gazelle.

Discussion: In track, the cheetah could be compared to a sprinter, while the Bushmen are like marathon runners. Ask students to describe the motion of both in terms of speed and acceleration.

Answer to Question: The Bushmen can outlast the cheetah and catch up to the cat, which must slow down.

Extension: Have students research the maximum speeds of various other animals.

HVAC TECHNICIAN

Background: HVAC technicians may be self-employed or they may work for companies that install and service equipment. The technicians travel from location to location to install and service equipment. Some companies have HVAC technicians on staff to service the equipment in their buildings.

Related Career	Education
Machinist	high school
Boiler operator	high school
Power plant operator	technical school
Mechanical engineer	college degree

Career Issue: Refrigerators and air conditioners use coolants that contain ozone-eroding CFCs. In the process of servicing and repairing these units, technicians sometimes release these gases into the air. Technology exists to capture these gases, rather than release them into the atmosphere.

What do you think? Ask students if they think technicians should be required to capture and recycle CFCs from refrigeration units.

AERONAUTICAL ENGINEER

Background: Aeronautical engineers work for private companies or for the federal government. Some aeronautical engineers specialize in the design of spacecraft.

Related Career	Education
Air traffic controller	college degree
Commercial pilot	college degree
Aircraft mechanic	technical school
Tool and die maker	high school

Career Issue: Many people think more research and testing should be done to assure the safety of airplanes.

What do you think? Do students believe airplanes are safe enough now? Should the government require stricter safety standards?

CAREERS

HVAC TECHNICIAN

Heating, ventilation, and air-conditioning (HVAC) technicians work on equipment that heats and cools homes, schools, offices, and other buildings. Some technicians specialize in one of these areas, while others are skilled in all of them. They install, maintain, and repair units from the size of a room air conditioner to a central heating and cooling system for a large building.

If you're interested in becoming an HVAC technician you should take high school classes in math and physics and have mechanical aptitude. Some technicians learn the trade by working for several years as helpers with experienced technicians. Others take a two- or three-year program at a vocational or technical school.

For Additional Information

Contact the American Association of Heating, Refrigeration, and Air-Conditioning Engineers, 1791 Tullie Circle NE, Atlanta, Georgia 30329.

AERONAUTICAL ENGINEER

Aeronautical engineers design airplanes. They usually begin with a drawing that uses mathematics and engineering principles. Often they use computers to help them in the study and design of airplanes. Aeronautical engineers also use computers to simulate how the airplane they are designing will perform in flight. When the engineer has completed a design, a small model is built based on the design.

If you're interested in becoming an aeronautical engineer you should take classes in mathematics and physics in high school. Aeronautical engineers must have a college degree in engineering and may have advanced degrees.

For Additional Information

Contact the American Institute of Aeronautics and Astronautics, 555 West 57th Street, New York, New York 10019.

UNIT READINGS

▶Laithwaite, Eric. *Force: The Power Behind Movement.* Danbury, CT: Watts, 1986.
▶Santray, Laurence. *Heat.* Mahwah, N J: Troll, 1985.
▶Zubrowski, Bernard. *Raceways: Having Fun With Balls and Tracks.* New York: Morrow, 1985.

184

UNIT READINGS

Background
▶ *Force: The Power Behind Movement* looks at the basic principles that bridge the gap between pure science and the everyday world.
▶ *Heat* is an introduction to thermodynamics.
▶ *Raceways: Having Fun With Balls and Tracks* includes activities that demonstrate velocity and acceleration.

More Readings
1. Watson, Philip. *Super Motion.* New York, NY: Lothrop, 1982. This book contains experiments to explore aspects of force and motion.
2. Kilgore, Jim. "The Art and Science of Punting." *Scholastic Science World.* November 20, 1987, pp. 28–29. Explains how a football punter can take advantage of the laws of projectile motion.

Dolphins

by Jacques-Yves Cousteau and Philippe Diole

This passage that follows is a brief account of Jacques Cousteau's first encounter with dolphins.

The cruiser *Primauguet* cut through the water at full speed, its prow rising and falling among the waves and raising a great wave of its own as it pushed irresistibly through the liquid wall of the sea. It was an impressive sight. The cruiser, a ship of the French Navy, had just been released from dry dock and we were testing her in the waters of the Far East. At that moment, the *Primauguet's* engines were wide open, and we were moving at a speed of 33.5 knots.

I was standing on the bridge, enthralled by the performance of the mighty cruiser as it cut through the sea with incredible violence. Then, I glanced to starboard. A school of dolphins was alongside, their fins regularly appearing then disappearing beneath the surface, their dark backs moving with graceful power through the rough water. I watched. And suddenly I realized that the dolphins were moving faster than the *Primauguet*. Swimming some thirty or forty feet away from the cruiser and parallel to her, they were passing her! I could hardly believe my eyes.

Then, suddenly, the lead dolphin altered his course and cut toward our prow.

When he reached the crest of the wave raised by the thrust of the *Primauguet's* engines, he hovered there until he was displaced by another dolphin, and then another. The dolphins had devised a game which they played in the midst of the waves: one by one, in turn, they rode the crest of the cruiser's wave, directly before our prow, for two or three minutes, then let themselves be carried to starboard or port so that the next dolphin could have his turn. It was an astonishing spectacle, but its importance to me at that time was practical rather than aesthetic. I realized that the school of dolphins, in catching up to and then passing the *Primauguet* as it moved at full power, must have been swimming at a speed of no less than fifty miles per hour!

That was forty years ago. Since then, I have had many encounters with dolphins, but I have never forgotten my first impression of those great mammals as they materialized in front of the *Primauguet's* stern—faster, and infinitely more maneuverable, than the best machines that human ingenuity had yet been able to devise.

In Your Own Words

▶ Write a brief, descriptive essay about energy and motion involved in an encounter you have had with an animal.

185

Source: Jacques-Yves Cousteau and Philippe Diole. *Dolphins.* New York, NY: A & W Visual Library, 1975.
Biography: Jacques-Yves Cousteau has dedicated his life to exploration of the sea. In 1950, he converted a minesweeper into a research vessel. Since then, he and the crew of the *Calypso* have traveled the world on scientific expeditions. He has filmed many of his adventures for television and has authored numerous books. Philippe Diole is a journalist, archaeologist, and diver. He has dived on many of *Calypso's* expeditions and been coauthor of many of Cousteau's books.

TEACHING STRATEGY

Have students read through the passage by Cousteau. Then have them respond to the discussion questions below.

Discussion Questions

1. **From the passage given here, why does Cousteau feel his observations about dolphins are important?** *Although he is impressed by the aesthetics of the dolphins' movements, he is more interested in the practical information he has learned—that is, about the incredible speed of the dolphins and their ability to change directions.*

2. **From the passage given here, how does Cousteau compare dolphins with machines?** *He describes dolphins as being faster and much more maneuverable than the best machines yet devised by humans.*

Other Works

▶ Other books by Cousteau and Diole include: *Diving for Sunken Treasure; The Whale: Mighty Monarch of the Sea;* and *Octopus and Squid: The Soft Intelligence.*

VideoDisc

STVS: Prop-Fan Propellers, Disc 1, Side 2

Classics

Walker, Jeral. *Roundabout: The Physics of Rotation in the Everyday World.* New York, NY: Freeman and Company, 1985. Explains circular motion and how Newton's laws apply.

In Unit 3, students are introduced to the physical and chemical classification of matter. The unit begins by describing the characteristics of the states of matter by the kinetic theory, continues by differentiating between physical and chemical properties, introduces the periodic table as a means of organizing elements, and relates chemical properties to atomic structure.

CONTENTS

ADVANCE PREPARATION

Activities
▶ **Activity 11-1, page 273,** calls for egg cartons. Have students begin saving them now.

Field Trips and Speakers
▶ Arrange to have an industrial safety officer visit the classroom to discuss how chemicals are important in his or her work.

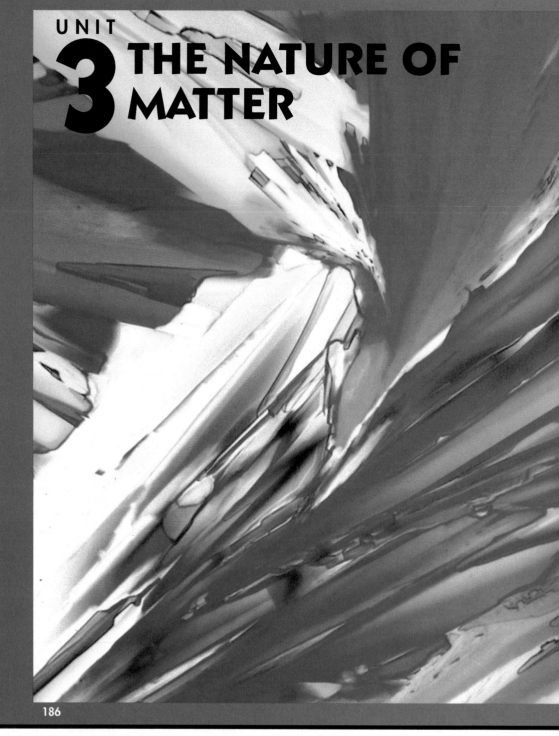

186

OPTIONS

Cross Curriculum
Have students list symbols that are introduced in other classes and their meanings. For example, in history class, *ca* in front of dates, such as ca 1850, means *approximately.* Students should be able to list many math symbols, such as $+$, $\times$, Δ, or $\div$.

Science at Home
Have students monitor television, magazines, and newspapers to find the uses of models. Have them list the circumstances and how the model was used to convey information. For example, an advertisement may show a floor plan of a model home. This shows the basic features but does not require that every home is exactly like the model.

What's Happening Here?

The micrograph at the left shows a crystal of sodium thiosulfate ($Na_2S_2O_3$). Photographed in polarized light sodium thiosulfate, called *hypo*, is one of the chemicals used to develop photos. The atomic structure of sodium thiosulfate caused its crystals to form in this way. Atomic structure is one of the topics you'll study in Unit 3. Is matter made of other structures besides crystals? How is matter classified? What bonds hold it together? In Unit 3 you'll find the answers to these questions.

UNIT CONTENTS

187

What's Happening Here?
▶ Have students look at the photos and read the text. Ask them to tell you what's happening here. Point out to students that in this unit they will be studying the structure of matter and how its structure determines its characteristics and behavior.

▶ **Background:** In an electron microscope, beams of electrons are reflected by matter and then are refracted, that is, focused—not by lenses as light is in an optical microscope, but by electric fields—onto a phosphorescent screen, which is then photographed. The properties of electrons and their role in the structure of matter are discussed in Chapter 13.

Previewing the Chapters
▶ Have students use the figures and charts displayed in the unit to investigate the ways in which matter can be classified, such as state (pages 190-193); mixture or substance, element or compound (page 222); ionic compound or covalent compound (pages 276-277). Have them discuss into what categories they can place sodium thiosulfate now and what new information they would have to obtain to further classify it.

Tying to Previous Knowledge
▶ Have students identify changes that occur when one bakes a cake. Lead them through mixing the dry ingredients, adding eggs, milk, and flavoring to the dry mixture, and baking it. Ask them to discuss what clues (visual, tactile, olfactory) they use to determine if a change has happened. Ask them to list other processes that indicate chemical changes.

▶ Use the **inquiry questions** in the OPTIONS box to discuss classifying materials as solids, liquids, and gases.

Multicultural Awareness
Encourage students to select an element from the periodic table and use reference books to find out the nationality of the person who discovered the element.

Inquiry Questions
▶ **How would you classify ice? Why?** *Solid. Accept all reasonable answers. It is "hard."*
▶ **How would you classify water? Why?** *Liquid. Accept all reasonable answers. It "pours."*
▶ **Discuss the characteristics you would use to classify butter and fog.** *Butter keeps its shape and melts at a certain temperature; therefore, it is a solid. Fog has characteristics of air, so it must be a gas. However, it feels wet, so it must contain liquid, too.*

CHAPTER

8 Solids, Liquids, and Gases

CHAPTER SECTION	OBJECTIVES	ACTIVITIES
8-1 Matter and Temperature (2 days)	1. **Describe** the four states of matter. 2. **Use** the kinetic theory of matter to explain the characteristics of solids, liquids, and gases. 3. **Explain** the thermal expansion of matter.	**Activity 8-1:** *Properties of Liquids,* p. 197
8-2 Water—Earth's Vital Liquid Science & Society (1 day)	1. **Describe** how people use and pollute water. 2. **Discuss** how people can save water and stop pollution.	
8-3 Changes in State (1 day)	1. **Interpret** state changes in terms of the kinetic theory of matter. 2. **Account** for the energy of the heats of fusion and vaporization in state changes.	**MINI-Lab:** *What energy changes take place during evaporation?* p. 201
8-4 Behavior of Gases (2 days)	1. **Explain** how a gas exerts pressure on its container. 2. **State** and **explain** how the pressure of a container of gas is affected when the volume is changed. 3. **Explain** the relationship between the temperature and volume of a gas.	**Activity 8-2:** *More Than Just Hot Air,* p. 208
8-5 Uses of Fluids (2 days)	1. **State** Archimedes' principle and **predict** whether an object will sink or float in water. 2. **State** Pascal's principle and **describe** the operation of a machine that uses Pascal's principle. 3. **State** Bernoulli's principle and **describe** a way that Bernoulli's principle is applied.	**MINI-Lab:** *How does applied pressure affect different areas of a fluid?* p. 210
Chapter Review		

ACTIVITY MATERIALS

FIND OUT	ACTIVITIES		MINI-LABS	
Page 189 soccer ball 1 pump 1 inflation needle 1 gauge	**8-1 Properties of Liquids, p. 197** dropper food coloring wooden stick paper cup graduated cylinder 4% solution of powdered borax in water 4% solution of polyvinyl alcohol (PVA) in water goggles, apron	**8-2 More Than Just Hot Air, p. 208** string, marking pen meterstick bucket of ice water heat-proof glove/tongs beaker of boiling water thermometer goggles 2 medium, round balloons	**What energy changes take place during evaporation? p. 201** dropper rubbing alcohol	**How does applied pressure affect different areas of a fluid? p. 210** dropper 2-liter plastic soda bottle

CHAPTER FEATURES	TEACHER RESOURCE PACKAGE	OTHER RESOURCES
Problem Solving: *Breakfast with Grandmother,* p. 196 **Skill Builder:** *Making and Using Tables,* p. 196	**Ability Level Worksheets** ◆ *Study Guide,* p. 34 ● *Reinforcement,* p. 34 ▲ *Enrichment,* p. 34 **Activity Worksheets,** pp. 5, 63, 64 **Transparency Masters,** pp. 29, 30	**Color Transparency 15,** States of Matter **Laboratory Manual 17,** Density of a Liquid; **18,** Densities of Solutions **STVS:** Disc 1, Side 2
You Decide! p. 199	**Ability Level Worksheets** ◆ *Study Guide,* p. 35 ● *Reinforcement,* p. 35 ▲ *Enrichment,* p. 35 **Cross-Curricular Connections,** p. 12 **Science and Society,** p. 12	**STVS:** Disc 6, Side 2 **Science Integration Activity 8**
Skill Builder: *Concept Mapping,* p. 203	**Ability Level Worksheets** ◆ *Study Guide,* p. 36 ● *Reinforcement,* p. 36 ▲ *Enrichment,* p. 36 **Concept Mapping,** pp. 21, 22 **Actvity Worksheets,** p. 69	
Technology: *Gaseous Research Giants,* p. 206 **Skill Builder:** *Hypothesizing,* p. 207	**Ability Level Worksheets** ◆ *Study Guide,* p. 37 ● *Reinforcement,* p. 37 ▲ *Enrichment,* p. 37 **Activity Worksheets,** pp. 5, 65, 66	**Laboratory Manual 19,** The Behavior of Gases **STVS:** Disc 1, Side 1
Skill Builder: *Measuring in SI,* p. 214	**Ability Level Worksheets** ◆ *Study Guide,* p. 38 ● *Reinforcement,* p. 38 ▲ *Enrichment,* p. 38 **Critical Thinking/Problem Solving,** p. 14 **Activity Worksheets,** pp. 5, 70 **Transparency Masters,** pp. 31, 32	**Color Transparency 16,** Archimedes' Principle **STVS:** Disc 1, Side 2
Summary Think & Write Critically Key Science Words Apply Understanding Vocabulary More Skill Builders Checking Concepts Projects Using Lab Skills	**ASSESSMENT RESOURCES** **Chapter Review,** pp. 19, 20 **Chapter Test,** pp. 53-56 **Performance Assessment in** **Middle School Science**	**Chapter Review Software** **Test Bank** **Alternate Assessment** **Performance Assessment**

◆ **Basic**   ● **Average**   ▲ **Advanced**

ADDITIONAL MATERIALS

SOFTWARE	AUDIOVISUAL	BOOKS/MAGAZINES
All About Matter, AIMS Media. *Forces in Liquids and Gases,* Wm. K. Bradford Publishing Co. *Ideal Gases,* Queue. *Introduction to General Chemistry: Gas Laws,* EduQuest. *It's a Gas,* Diversified Educational Enterprises, Inc.	*Airplanes and How They Fly,* Video, Coronet. *Buoyancy,* Video, Coronet. *Crystals,* Video, Journal Films. *The Energy of Matter in Three States,* Video, Lucerne Media. *Floating and Sinking,* Laserdisc, Journal Films. *Magnetic Confinement,* Video, Insight Media. *The Molecular Theory of Matter,* Video, Britannica.	Fine, Gerald J. "Glass and Glassmaking." *Journal of Chemical Education,* Sept. 1991, pp. 765-760. Friedhoffer, Robert. *Matter and Energy.* NY: Watts, 1993. Mellett, Peter and Jane Rossiter. *Liquids in Action.* NY: Watts, 1993. Mercer, Ian. *Crystals.* Cambridge, MA: Harvard University Press, 1990.

THEME DEVELOPMENT: The energy content, or temperature, of particles plays a major role in determining their state of matter. The kinetic theory of matter presents a way for students to visualize atoms and molecules in motion and to form a mental model of the states of matter.

CHAPTER OVERVIEW

▶ **Section 8-1:** The kinetic theory of matter explains why solids, liquids, gases, and plasmas behave differently.

▶ **Section 8-2: Science and Society:** Students learn how they use, pollute, and can conserve water.

▶ **Section 8-3:** The kinetic theory is applied to explain how thermal energy affects changes of state.

▶ **Section 8-4:** After *pressure* is defined, the relationships among volume, pressure, and temperature in gases are explored.

▶ **Section 8-5:** Characteristics of fluids are discussed by exploring the discoveries of Archimedes, Pascal, and Bernoulli.

CHAPTER VOCABULARY

states of matter	pressure
kinetic theory	pascal
of matter	Boyle's Law
crystals	Charles's Law
plasma	buoyant force
thermal	Archimedes'
expansion	principle
polluted water	Pascal's
evaporation	principle
condensation	Bernoulli's
heat of fusion	principle
heat of	
vaporization	

188

OPTIONS

 For Your Gifted Students

Have students form a hypothesis about the effect of fluid density on the buoyant force exerted on an object. Determine the density of water and a saturated salt solution by measuring the mass of a known volume. For objects that will sink, buoyant force can be measured by hanging the object by a thread from a spring scale and observing the apparent weight loss when it is immersed. For floating objects, also determine how much weight must be added to the object to sink it.

 For Your Mainstreamed Students

This chapter deals with the changes matter undergoes as a result of temperature. There is little substitute for tactile and/or visual experiences with matter. The aim should be to make sure students can correctly identify a state of matter and relate its overall characteristics. Changes in state can easily be related to the events students observe in the kitchen.

Perhaps you have seen bicycle tires or a soccer ball lose pressure and soften with a change of the seasons. Do objects lose pressure only if they leak air? Or does this mean a change in temperature affects pressure?

FIND OUT!

Do this activity to find out if the temperature and pressure of air are related.

Using a hand pump, pressure gauge, and an inflation needle, inflate a soccer ball until the gauge reads 20 lb/sq in. Drop the ball and have a partner measure the height of the first bounce. Next, submerge the ball in a bucket of ice water for 10 minutes and then use the needle and gauge to *measure* the pressure of the ball. Drop the cold ball from the same height as before and have your partner *measure* its first bounce. Then submerge the ball in warm water for 10 minutes (or longer) and repeat both measurements. What do you *infer* about the relationships among pressure, bounce heights, and temperature?

Gearing Up
Previewing the Chapter

Use this outline to help you focus on important ideas in this chapter.

Previewing Science Skills

▶ In the Skill Builders, you will make and use a table, make a concept map, hypothesize, and measure in SI.
▶ In the Activities, you will observe, interpret data, infer, hypothesize, measure, and classify.
▶ In the MINI-Labs, you will observe and hypothesize.

What's next?

You have shown that temperature affects the pressure of air. You will learn more about the behavior of gases as you read the pages that follow.

189

INTRODUCING THE CHAPTER
Use the Find Out activity to introduce students to the relationship that exists between temperature and pressure of gases. Inform students that they will be learning more about temperature and its effects on matter as they read the chapter.

FIND OUT!
Preparation: Obtain soccer balls and inflation equipment from students or from your school's athletic department.
Materials: one soccer ball, one pump, one inflation needle, and one gauge per group
Teaching Tips
▶ If there are gauges available that read in kilopascals, inform students that 20 lb/sq in. is about 140 kPa.
▶ Do not allow students to hold the ball underwater with their hands.
▶ Remind students to drop the ball from the same height each time. Therefore, they will have to measure the starting height of the first drop.
▶ Three or four setups should be enough to get good comparisons.

Gearing Up
Have students study the Gearing Up feature to familiarize themselves with the chapter. Discuss the relationships of the topics in the outline.

What's Next?
Before beginning the first section, make sure the students understand the connection between the Find Out activity and the topics to follow.

PROGRAM RESOURCES
From the **Teacher Resource Package** use:
   Transparency Masters, pages 29-30, States of Matter.
Use the **Color Transparency** number 15, States of Matter.

ASSESSMENT OPTIONS

PORTFOLIO
Refer to page 215 for suggested items that students might select for their portfolios.

PERFORMANCE ASSESSMENT
See page 215 for additional Performance Assessment options.
Process
Skill Builders, pp. 196, 203, 214
MINI-Labs, pp. 201, 210
Activities 8-1, p. 197; 8-2, p. 208
Using Lab Skills, p. 216

CONTENT ASSESSMENT
Assessment—Oral, pp. 194, 209
Skill Builder, p. 207
Section Reviews, pp. 196, 199, 203, 207, 214
Chapter Review, pp. 215-217
Mini Quizzes, pp. 194, 202, 205, 211

GROUP ASSESSMENT
Opportunities for group assessment occur with Cooperative Learning Strategies and Flex Your Brain Activities.

PREPARATION

SECTION BACKGROUND

▶ All true solids are crystalline. Their crystal shape reflects the original arrangement of atoms and molecules.

▶ The kinetic theory of matter assumes that particles of matter are in constant motion and undergo perfectly elastic collisions. That is, they lose no energy in collisions.

▶ Particles of liquids have little, if any, more spacing than those of solids. For water, liquid particles are actually closer together than those of the solid. Thus, ice is less dense and floats in liquid water.

▶ As more molecules of air are added to a tire, the number of collisions per second increases as the distance between molecules decreases. A single gas molecule undergoes several billion collisions per second.

▶ Because it is made of charged particles, plasma is greatly affected by electric and magnetic fields.

PREPLANNING

▶ For Activity 8-1, make enough 4% sodium borate and polyvinyl alcohol solutions for your lab groups.

1 MOTIVATE

▶ Ask your students if they have ever heard of fuel line freeze-up or engine vapor lock. With vapor lock, fuel vaporizes at a hot spot causing a fuel line to partially fill with gas. A car's fuel pump is designed to pump a liquid, not a gas. In summer, the gasoline can vaporize in the fuel line. In winter, water from condensation in the gas tank can freeze and block the fuel line. Discuss with students how temperature affects the state of matter.

8-1 Matter and Temperature

New Science Words

states of matter
kinetic theory of matter
crystals
plasma
thermal expansion

Objectives

▶ Describe the four states of matter.
▶ Use the kinetic theory of matter to explain the characteristics of solids, liquids, and gases.
▶ Explain the thermal expansion of matter.

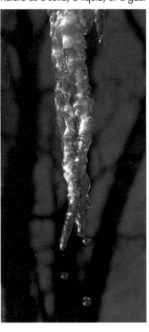

Figure 8-1. Water can exist in nature as a solid, a liquid, or a gas.

States of Matter

After swimming on a very hot day Eli was having a refreshing glass of ice water. As he rested by the pool, the water on his arm evaporated and the ice cubes melted in his glass. In how many different forms does the water in this example exist? Ice, liquid water, and water vapor are examples of the three most familiar states of matter—solid, liquid, and gas.

All matter takes up space and has mass, yet matter can exist in different states. There are four **states of matter**—solid, liquid, gas, and plasma. The state of a sample of matter depends on its molecular motion as measured by temperature. For example, water ordinarily exists as ice at low temperatures and as liquid water at moderate temperatures. At higher temperatures, water changes to the gas state as water vapor. At still higher temperatures, thousands of degrees hotter than those the day Eli was swimming, the matter in water would become plasma. Each state has characteristics that are used to identify it, as you'll see.

Solids

A metal spoon, a cube of sugar, and a piece of cement are classified as solids. Every solid has a definite shape and a definite volume. For example, a metal spoon stays spoon-shaped whether it's in your hand or in a glass of water. And because no ordinary amount of force can squeeze the spoon into a smaller space, it has a definite volume.

OPTIONS

Meeting Different Ability Levels

For Section 8-1, use the following **Teacher Resource Masters** depending upon individual students' needs.

◆ **Study Guide Master** for all students.
● **Reinforcement Master** for students of average and above average ability levels.
▲ **Enrichment Master** for above average students.

Additional Teacher Resource Package masters are listed in any PROGRAM RESOURCES boxes that are in the section. The additional masters are appropriate for all students.

◆ **STUDY GUIDE** 34

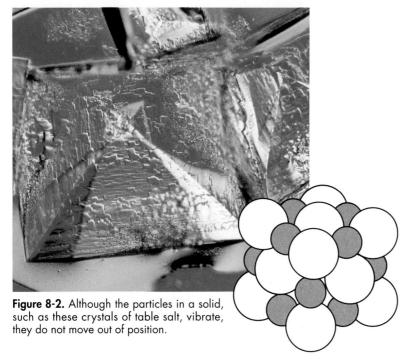

Figure 8-2. Although the particles in a solid, such as these crystals of table salt, vibrate, they do not move out of position.

What accounts for the characteristics of solids? Tiny particles in constant motion make up all matter. This idea is called the **kinetic theory of matter.** The particles in solid matter are held very close together by forces between them. This is why a solid can't be squeezed into a smaller space. The particles can vibrate against their neighbors, but can't move out of position. Thus, they can't move over or around each other. This explains why a solid holds its shape.

In most solids, the particles are arranged in repeating geometric patterns. These arrangements form **crystals.** Different kinds of solids have crystals of different shapes. With a magnifier you can see that salt crystals are little cubes. A snowflake is a crystal of water that has the shape of a hexagon.

Some materials such as glass, many plastics, and some kinds of wax, appear to be solids but are not made of crystals. They are often called amorphous solids. The word *amorphous* means having no form. Many scientists think some of these noncrystalline materials should be classified as very thick liquids.

Why does a solid hold its shape?

191

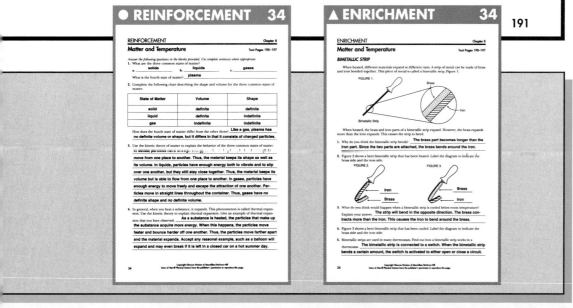

TYING TO PREVIOUS KNOWLEDGE: Remind students that their bodies contain three of the four states of matter. Ask them to give examples such as bones, blood, and exhaled air.
▶ Students should realize that temperature changes cause changes in matter. Ask if they have ever noticed cracking or clanking noises when a furnace or radiator is turned on. The noises come from the expansion of the pipes as they heat up.

OBJECTIVES AND SCIENCE WORDS: Have students review the objectives and science words to become familiar with this section.

2 TEACH

Key Concepts are highlighted.

CONCEPT DEVELOPMENT

▶ If possible, obtain some moth crystals to use in teaching this section. As you discuss solids, have a student place some moth crystals in a test tube. Stopper the tube and pass it around the class so students can observe the crystalline form.

▶ Have students observe the regular shape of salt crystals under a microscope or with a hand lens.

Cooperative Learning: Assign Problem Solving Teams. Have each team prepare a written statement explaining how refineries solve the problems of fuel line freeze-up and vapor lock. They will find that refineries change gasoline blends for different seasons and different geographical locations.

CONCEPT DEVELOPMENT

▶ As you discuss liquids, melt moth crystals in an unstoppered test tube placed in a beaker of boiling water. Relate the role of energy to the melting process. Use the kinetic theory to explain to your students what is happening on a molecular level.

Cooperative Learning: Use the Science Investigation strategy with groups of three. Have one student place 5 drops of vanilla flavoring into a balloon, blow up the balloon, and tie it closed. Have a second student smell near the surface of the balloon. The student should be able to detect the aroma of vanilla as it evaporates inside the balloon. The balloon may feel cool where the liquid is evaporating on the inside. Have the third student monitor, confirm, and record the group's observations. Ask the group to explain its observations using the kinetic theory. The students should conclude that the moving molecules of vanilla passed between the molecules of the stretched balloon.

TEACHER F.Y.I.

▶ Some liquids can be instantaneously changed into solids by high voltage. These liquids are called ER (electro-rheological) fluids. In the future these ER fluids may be used in robots.

VideoDisc

STVS: Droplets, Disc 1, Side 2

Students should describe an increase in motion as particles change from solid to liquid to gas or a decrease in motion as the change is from gas to liquid to solid.

Liquids

If you don't eat it quickly enough, a solid scoop of ice cream will turn into a liquid, taking the same shape as your bowl or cup. A liquid flows and takes the shape of its container. However, like solids, liquids can't normally be squeezed to a smaller volume. If you push down on a liter of water with a moderate amount of force, its volume will remain a liter.

Just as the kinetic theory explains the properties of solids, it also explains the properties of liquids. Because a liquid can't be squeezed, its particles must also be very close together, like those of a solid. However, they have enough kinetic energy to move over and around each other. This movement of particles lets a liquid flow and take the shape of its container. Thus, orange juice poured into a glass will take the shape of the glass.

Because its particles are held very close together, almost as close as those of a solid, liquid matter does have a definite volume. If you pour 1 liter of orange juice into a 2-liter bottle, it will not spread out to fill the bottle. Likewise, you couldn't force the liter of juice into a half-liter container. The two containers in Figure 8-4 contain the same volume of juice.

Figure 8-3. The particles in a liquid are close together, but have enough energy to vibrate over and around one another.

In Your JOURNAL

In your Journal, describe how the motion of the particles changes when matter changes from one state to another.

Figure 8-4. Although its volume does not change, the shape of a liquid depends on the shape of its container.

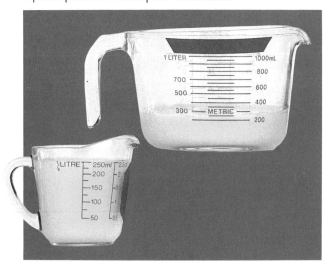

OPTIONS

INQUIRY QUESTIONS

▶ Sometimes expensive glassware is called "crystal." Explain why this term is incorrectly used. *Glass is not crystalline; it is amorphous.*
▶ Is there anything wrong with saying, "This bottle is half filled with carbon dioxide gas?" *Yes, a gas occupies all the space available in its container.*

▶ When water changes from the liquid state to the solid state, it expands and becomes less dense. What happens during freezing, in terms of particle spacing and arrangement? List a physical property of ice that results from this change. *The particles change from a jumbled arrangement to a regular arrangement. The spacing is greater in the solid than in the liquid. Ice floats in liquid water.*

Gases

You may have pumped air into a basketball, tire, or balloon and noticed that the air takes the shape of the object. Gases are "springy"—they expand or contract to fill the space available to them and can be squeezed into a smaller space. A gas has neither a definite shape nor a definite volume.

According to the kinetic theory of matter, the particles of a gas have enough energy to separate completely from one another. Therefore, the particles are free to move in all directions and spread evenly throughout their container. Because the particles are not close together, they can also be squeezed into a smaller space. When you pump up a bicycle tire, you are forcing more and more air particles into the same space.

Compare the models of a solid, a liquid, and a gas shown in Figure 8-6. How are they different?

Plasma

So far you've learned about the three familiar states of matter. But none of these is the most common state of matter in the universe. For example, 99 percent of the

Figure 8-5. The particles in a gas have enough energy to spread widely apart from one another.

Figure 8-6. The diagrams below show the spacing and arrangements of the particles in the three familiar states of matter.

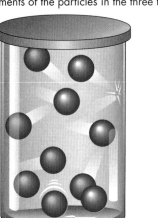

Gas   Liquid   Solid

REVEALING MISCONCEPTIONS

▶ Many students have the impression that the particle spacing of liquids is an average of the spacing in solids and gases. If this were true, liquids would be "springy" like a gas, and hydraulic machines would not work. In addition, the expansion of water upon freezing directly contradicts this assumption.

CONCEPT DEVELOPMENT

▶ **Demonstration:** On the overhead projector, in a clear plastic lid from a box of greeting cards, place five marbles. Agitate the box to simulate gas molecules in motion. Increase the amount of agitation of the box lid to simulate the effect of increasing the temperature of a gas. Point out the more frequent and forceful collisions. Relate student observations to the properties and particle model of a gas.

CROSS CURRICULUM

▶ **Art and Design:** As students visit shopping malls, have them observe how the states of matter are used to decorate and make shopping more pleasant. Have them write about what they saw, such as waterfalls, helium balloons, marble floors, fluorescent and neon lighting.

STUDENT TEXT QUESTION

▶ Page 193, paragraph 3: **How are the models of solids, liquids, and gases different?** *The particles of solids are close together in a regular arrangement. The particles of liquids are close together but jumbled. The particles of gases are far apart and are able to move freely.*

TEACHER F.Y.I.

▶ Oxygen gas molecules have an average speed of 1700 km/h.
▶ Crystals grown on Earth have between 1000 and 10 000 defects per square centimeter. In orbiting space stations, ultrapure crystals can be grown without using a container in "zero-gravity" conditions. Pure crystals will enable computers to operate faster and the laser in a CD player to be more durable.

▶ Heating matter to temperatures above 5000°C produces a plasma.

▶ In the formation of a plasma, the collisions between the particles are so violent that electrons are removed from atoms.

CROSS CURRICULUM

▶ **Space Science:** A plasma engine is being designed as an advanced propulsion unit for space vehicles. The charged particles moving away from the spacecraft at high speeds cause the ship to move in the opposite direction just as the exhaust gases from a jet engine push an airplane forward.

Answer: Blood plasma and muscle plasma have substances dissolved in a dense fluid that can be shaped into various forms. Plasma, as described in physical science, may also take various forms. In life science, plasma is formed at typically encountered temperatures and does not involve only charged particles.

CHECK FOR UNDERSTANDING

Use the Mini Quiz to check for understanding.

MINI QUIZ

Use the Mini Quiz to check students' recall of chapter content.

❶ **Name the four states of matter.** *solid, liquid, gas, plasma*

❷ **Which state of matter has definite shape and definite volume?** *solid*

❸ **According to the kinetic theory, what is all matter composed of?** *tiny particles in constant motion*

❹ **What happens to the average speed of the particles of matter as it is heated?** *It increases.*

❺ **What happens to most matter when it is heated?** *It expands.*

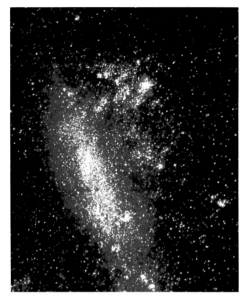

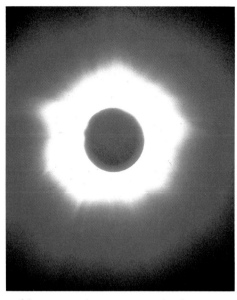

Figure 8-7. Most of the matter in the universe is in the plasma state. The stars at the center of this nebula and the sun contain plasma.

The word *plasma* is from a Greek word that means "something that can be formed or molded." Compare and contrast plasma as it is used in life science to plasma as it is used in physical science.

Did You Know?

The sun is getting smaller, having lost over 400 km of radius in the past 50 years.

mass of our solar system is contained in the sun. The most common form of matter in the universe is the type found in stars like the sun. Such matter is called plasma.

Plasma is a gaslike mixture of positively and negatively charged particles. You know that particles of matter move faster as the matter is heated to higher temperatures. The faster they move, the greater the force with which they bump into other particles, or collide. As matter is heated to *very* high temperatures, the particles begin to collide violently. As a result, the particles break up into the smaller particles they are made of. These particles are electrically charged.

Besides light from the sun, you can observe the effects of plasma in your home or school. When a fluorescent light is switched on, electricity causes particles of mercury gas inside the tube to form plasma.

Thermal Expansion

You have learned how the kinetic theory accounts for characteristics of different states of matter you see and touch every day. The kinetic theory also explains other things you may have observed.

194 SOLIDS, LIQUIDS, AND GASES

OPTIONS

ASSESSMENT—ORAL

▶ Whether or not a sample of matter has a definite volume relates to a property called compressibility. Compare the compressibility of solids, liquids, and gases. *Solids and liquids are not compressible. Gases are compressible.*

▶ Whether or not a sample of matter takes the shape of its container relates to a property called fluidity. Compare the fluidity of solids, liquids, and gases. *Solids are not fluid. Liquids and gases are fluid.*

▶ Give an example of a situation that demonstrates that liquids are fluid but not compressible. *Answers will vary. Students may mention hydraulic devices, the force of fast-running water, or the pain of a "belly flop" dive into the water.*

For example, have you ever noticed the strips of metal that run across the floors and up the walls in long hallways of concrete and steel buildings? Maybe you've seen these strips in your school. These strips usually cover gaps in the building structure called expansion joints. Expansion joints allow the building to expand in hot weather and shrink in cold weather without cracking the concrete. As you drive onto or off a bridge, you will usually pass over a large steel expansion joint as shown in Figure 8-8.

Almost all matter expands as it gets hotter and contracts when it cools. This characteristic of matter is called **thermal expansion.** How does the kinetic theory of matter explain thermal expansion? In a solid, forces between the particles hold them together. As the solid is heated, these particles move faster and faster and vibrate with more force. As a result, the particles spread apart slightly in all directions and the solid expands. The same effect also occurs in liquids and gases.

You can compare thermal expansion to a crowd of people. When the people are quiet and still, they are able to stand close together. As the people become restless, they jostle one another and the crowd spreads out.

What is the purpose of expansion joints in buildings?

⑤

EcoTip

Make your own air freshener. Put vinegar, a few spices, and a little cinnamon in a small glass jar. Heat the jar in the microwave oven for one minute and then place it where you need it most.

Figure 8-8. Expansion joints in a bridge allow the structure to expand in warm weather without cracking.

RETEACH

Provide the students who have not demonstrated mastery with the crossword puzzle and have them write the clues for each word. Then give the entire class a blank crossword and the clues to solve it.

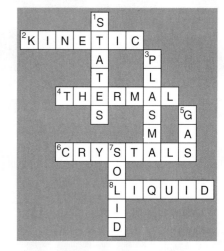

EXTENSION

For students who have mastered this section, use the **Reinforcement** and **Enrichment** masters or other OPTIONS provided.

3 CLOSE

▶ Ask questions 1-3 and the **Apply** and **Connect to Life Science** questions, in the Section Review.

?   **FLEX Your Brain**

Use the Flex Your Brain activity to have students explore the STATES OF MATTER. Guide students to associate the states with their physical characteristics and their particle models. You could direct students to explore state changes in preparation for Section 8-3.

ASSESSMENT

Portfolio: Use the Flex Your Brain activity to reinforce critical-thinking and problem-solving skills. In Step 2, students might list the different states of matter.

▶ Have a group of students prepare a bulletin board on the states of matter and their particle models.

PROBLEM SOLVING

This method of opening jars can easily be demonstrated to the class. Remind students that most metals have a much lower specific heat than glass or plastic. Therefore, the lid increases in temperature much faster than the jar does.

Think Critically: As the lid's temperature rises, it undergoes thermal expansion making it a little looser on the jar.

SECTION REVIEW ANSWERS

1. Both solids and liquids have a definite volume because their particles are closely packed. Solids have a definite shape, but liquids take the shape of the container. The particles of solids are held in place by attractive forces. The particles of liquids have enough energy to tumble over and around one another.

2. The material is a gas because it expanded to occupy all the space available in the container.

3. The particles of copper move more slowly as it cools. Attractive forces then pull them closer together.

4. Apply: Glass lacks the rigid crystal structure shown in a crystalline solid. Over time it flows downward.

5. Connect to Life Science: Water is heated to dissolve the gelatin. As the dissolved ingredients in the liquid cool, the particles slow to the extent that attractive forces hold the particles close enough together to form a solid.

Skill Builder
ASSESSMENT
Oral: After students have made their tables, select objects from the classroom and ask students to describe the particles and their movements within the selected objects.

 P R O B L E M   S O L V I N G

Breakfast with Grandmother

Jose was visiting his grandmother. On Saturday morning, he woke to the smell of muffins baking. He dressed quickly and ran down the stairs and into the kitchen.

Grandmother was taking the muffins out of the oven. She asked Jose to get a jar of jam and open it. Jose tried to remove the metal lid, but no matter how hard he tried, the lid would not budge. At his grandmother's suggestion, Jose ran hot water over the lid before trying again to remove the lid, and then it came off easily.

Think Critically: How did hot water affect the metal lid? Why was the lid easier to remove after running hot water over it?

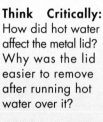

SECTION REVIEW

1. Compare the characteristics of solids and liquids.
2. You pour 500 mL of a green material into a 1-liter flask and stopper it. The material completely fills the flask. What state of matter is the material? Explain how you know.
3. In terms of particle motion, explain why copper shrinks when it cools.
4. **Apply:** In very old houses, the window glass is thicker at the bottom of the panes than at the top. How can you account for this thickening?
5. **Connect to Life Science:** Food preparation often involves energy changes. Identify the important energy changes that occur in the preparation of a gelatin dessert.

 **Skill Builder**

☑ **Making and Using Tables**

Make a table to classify several materials as a solid, liquid, gas, or plasma. Include columns for properties and a description of particles for each state. If you need help, refer to Making and Using Tables in the **Skill Handbook** on page 686.

Skill Builder

Possible Solution

State	Properties	Particle description	Examples
Solid	Definite shape and volume	Closely packed; do not easily change position	ice, sugar
Liquid	Definite volume; takes shape of container	Closely packed; able to move past one another	milk, mercury in thermometer
Gas	Occupies shape and volume of container	Spread apart; free to move in all directions	oxygen, steam
Plasma	Occupies shape and volume of container	Gaslike mix of negatively and positively charged particles	mercury vapor in fluorescent tube, sun and stars

Properties of Liquids

Why is a soft drink considered a liquid? Why is a hamburger considered a solid? Each state of matter has its own characteristics that allow us to classify it as that state. How can the properties of a material be used to classify it?

Materials

- dropper
- food coloring
- wooden stick
- paper cup
- graduated cylinder
- 4% solution of powdered borax in water
- 4% solution of polyvinyl alcohol (PVA) in water
- goggles
- apron

Procedure

1. Copy the data table and use it to record your observations of the new material.
2. Using a graduated cylinder, *measure* 30 mL (cm^3) of PVA solution into a paper cup. Add two drops of food coloring.
3. Using a dropper, add about 3 mL (cm^3) of borax solution to the PVA in the cup and begin to stir vigorously with a wooden stick.
4. After it has been stirred for 2 minutes, what is the consistency of the material?
5. Transfer the material to your hand. **CAUTION:** *Do not taste or eat the material and be sure to wash your hands after the activity.* Rate the ease with which the material flows.
6. Form the material into a ball and then place it in the cup to test its ability to take the shape of its container.
7. *Compare* the volume of the new material with the volume of the original material before stirring.

Analyze

1. Is the new material most like a gas, a liquid, or a solid?
2. What other materials have you seen that have properties similar to this one?
3. Considering the slow flow of the new material, how would you rate the strength of the attraction among its particles?

Conclude and Apply

4. Using the kinetic theory of matter, how would you describe the closeness of the particles of matter in the new material?
5. How can properties of this material be used to *classify* it?

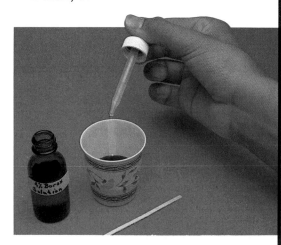

Data and Observations

Sample Data

Property	Observation	Interpretation
Ability to flow	Yes, but slowly (high viscosity)	Molecules hold to each other, but not as much as solids
Shape change	Does change shape	Molecules do allow movement
Volume change	No change	Molecules are not totally free to fill up any volume

OBJECTIVE: Observe the properties of a material and classify it according to state.

PROCESS SKILLS applied in this activity:
▶ **Measuring** in Procedure Steps 2 and 3.
▶ **Classifying** in Analyze Questions 1 and 2.
▶ **Formulating models** in Conclude and Apply Question 4.

COOPERATIVE LEARNING
Organize Science Investigation groups. If possible, have no more than three students per group. Have three or four groups compare results and form generalized conclusions.

TEACHING THE ACTIVITY
▶ **Troubleshooting:** In order to properly mix the borax and PVA, students must stir the solutions quickly and continuously. Do not allow students to taste the resulting gel or take it out of the classroom. Spills may be cleaned up with water.
▶ The new material is a polymer that is very much like products sold in toy stores under names like Slime. Encourage students to make comparisons to commercial products.
▶ To prepare 4% borax solution, dissolve 12 g sodium borate in 288 mL of hot water with constant stirring. Cool before using.
▶ To prepare 4% PVA solution, add 40 g of 98% hydrolyzed PVA to 960 mL H$_2$O. Heat to 80°C with constant stirring. Cool before using.

Activity
ASSESSMENT
Performance: To further assess students' understanding of properties of liquids, see USING LAB SKILLS, Question 11, on page 216.

ANSWERS TO QUESTIONS

1. a liquid
2. Slime, gelatin dessert, jellies, mucus
3. The particles are fairly strongly attracted. They hold into a certain volume and do not fill the container as a gas would. However, unlike a solid they are not attracted strongly enough to hold the material into a definite shape.
4. The particles are close together because the material cannot be pressed into a smaller space.
5. It exhibits the properties of flow, indefinite shape, and constant volume. Therefore, it is classified as a liquid.

PROGRAM RESOURCES
From the **Teacher Resource Package** use:
Activity Worksheets, pages 63-64, Activity 8-1: Properties of Liquids.

SCIENCE & SOCIETY **8-2 Water—Earth's Vital Liquid**

PREPARATION

SECTION BACKGROUND
► Find out what the water sources for your community are and how water for human consumption is treated. Is water in short supply in your area? Why? Is polluted water a problem where you live? Why? You may want to assign these areas of concern for student investigation.

1 MOTIVATE

► **Demonstration:** Measure 100 mL of water into a graduated cylinder. Ask a student to remove one milliliter using a medicine dropper and place it on a watch glass. The amount of water in the watch glass, when compared to the original 100 mL, represents the approximate percentage of fresh water available on Earth.

TYING TO PREVIOUS KNOWLEDGE:
Ask students to list the ways they have used water since they awoke this morning. Ask them how much of the water was reusable when they finished with it.

Connect to...
Life Science

Answer: 65 percent by mass

2 TEACH

Key Concepts are highlighted.

VideoDisc
STVS: Purifying with Plants, Disc 6, Side 2

New Science Words
polluted water

Connect to...
Life Science

The human body needs water to carry out many chemical reactions. Approximately what percentage of the mass of a human body is water?

What percentage of the water on Earth is available fresh water?

Objectives
► Describe how people use and pollute water.
► Discuss how people can save water and stop pollution.

Will There Be Enough Water?

For living things, like yourself, the most important liquid on Earth is fresh water. It is not as abundant as you might think. Fresh water, which is water that is not salty, makes up only 0.75 percent of the water available on Earth in the liquid state.

How much water do you think you use in a day? Take a guess. Did you say 1700 gallons? For the average person in the United States, that's the correct answer! Each person uses about 200 gallons a day for cooking, bathing, toilet use, and heating and cooling homes. Add to this the 750 gallons per person a day used to produce materials and energy, and another 750 gallons per person a day used to water crops. Table 8-1 lists only a few ways you use water indirectly as well as directly.

Table 8-1

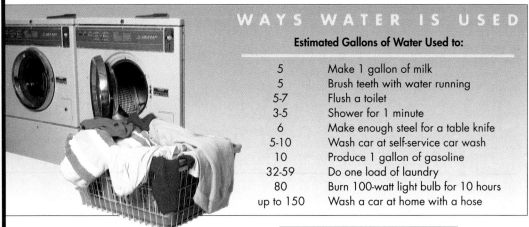

WAYS WATER IS USED	
Estimated Gallons of Water Used to:	
5	Make 1 gallon of milk
5	Brush teeth with water running
5-7	Flush a toilet
3-5	Shower for 1 minute
6	Make enough steel for a table knife
5-10	Wash car at self-service car wash
10	Produce 1 gallon of gasoline
32-59	Do one load of laundry
80	Burn 100-watt light bulb for 10 hours
up to 150	Wash a car at home with a hose

198 SOLIDS, LIQUIDS, AND GASES

OPTIONS

Meeting Different Ability Levels
For Section 8-2, use the following **Teacher Resource Masters** depending upon individual students' needs.
◆ **Study Guide Master** for all students.
● **Reinforcement Master** for students of average and above average ability levels.
▲ **Enrichment Master** for above average students.
Additional Teacher Resource Package masters are listed in any **PROGRAM RESOURCES** boxes that are in the section. The additional masters are appropriate for all students.

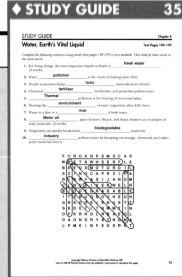
◆ **STUDY GUIDE** **35**

STUDY GUIDE — Chapter 8
Water, Earth's Vital Liquid — Text Pages 198–199

Complete the following sentences using words from pages 198-199 in your textbook. Then look for these words in the word search.

1. For living things, the most important liquid on Earth is _____ **fresh water** _____. (2 words)
2. Water _____ **pollution** _____ is the result of making water dirty.
3. People sometimes dump _____ **toxic** _____ materials down drains.
4. Chemical _____ **fertilizer** _____, herbicides, and pesticides pollute water.
5. _____ **Thermal** _____ pollution is the heating of rivers and lakes.
6. Heating the _____ **environment** _____ of water organisms often kills them.
7. Water in a lake or a _____ **river** _____ is fresh water.
8. _____ **Motor oil** _____, paint thinner, bleach, and drain cleaners are examples of toxic materials. (2 words)
9. Organisms can quickly break down _____ **biodegradable** _____ materials.
10. _____ **Industry** _____ pollutes water by dumping raw sewage, chemicals, and radioactive materials into it.

Not only do humans use huge amounts of fresh water, humans also pollute natural supplies of this liquid. **Polluted water** refers to water that contains such high levels of unwanted materials that it is unacceptable for drinking or other specific purposes.

Water that runs off land after rain falls and snow melts may wash animal and plant wastes into our water supplies. Human activities in cities may contaminate rivers with raw sewage. Fertilizers, pesticides, and herbicides used on farms may enter the groundwater. Toxic chemicals from home use may end up in our water supply if they are not disposed of properly.

Another form of water pollution can occur when electrical generating plants or industries release large amounts of heated water into rivers. The excess heat in the water is called thermal pollution. If water temperature is changed too much, some organisms that live in the water will die.

One way to reduce water pollution is to use products that are safer for the environment. Scientists are also trying to develop better ways to contain and dispose of industrial and farming by-products.

SECTION REVIEW

1. What are two main reasons that there could be a shortage of clean water?
2. List five sources of water pollution.
3. **Connect to Physics:** Explain why water is a good choice to use to absorb the heat produced in electric power plants.

You Decide!

The amount of water used by each person can be reduced 15 to 25 percent without any noticeable change in lifestyle. What are five things you could do to use less water or reduce water pollution?

SCIENCE & SOCIETY

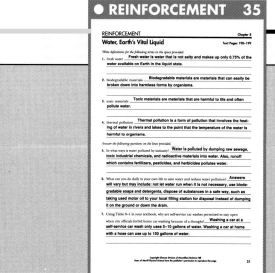

PROGRAM RESOURCES

From the **Teacher Resource Package** use:

Cross-Curricular Connections, page 12, Watersheds and Water Quality.

Science and Society, page 12, Is Your Water Safe?

Activity Worksheets, page 5, Flex Your Brain.

Science Integration Activity 8

CHECK FOR UNDERSTANDING

▶ Ask questions 1-2 and the **Connect to Physics** question in the Section Review.

RETEACH

▶ **Demonstration:** Filter vinegar through filter paper. Test the filtrate with litmus paper to show that dissolved chemicals cannot be filtered out.

EXTENSION

For students who have mastered this section, use the **Reinforcement** and **Enrichment** masters or other OPTIONS provided.

3 CLOSE

? FLEX Your Brain

Use the Flex Your Brain activity to have students explore WATER POLLUTION.

SECTION REVIEW ANSWERS

1. wasteful use and pollution of water
2. Answers will vary, but may include toxic industrial chemicals, toxic household chemicals, chemical fertilizers, pesticides, herbicides, radioactive materials, raw sewage, heat from electric power plants.
3. **Connect to Physics:** Water has a high specific heat and can absorb much heat per gram before its temperature increases significantly.

YOU DECIDE!
SCIENCE & SOCIETY

Answers will vary, but should include (a) ways to use less water, (b) using nontoxic or biodegradable materials at home, and (c) participating in the political process.

PREPARATION

SECTION BACKGROUND
▶ Substances that have weak inter-molecular forces evaporate easily and melt or boil at relatively low temperatures.
▶ Before a substance reaches its melting or boiling point, added energy increases the motion (kinetic energy) of the particles and the temperature increases.

PREPLANNING
▶ The MINI-Lab requires rubbing alcohol and droppers.

1 MOTIVATE

▶ **Demonstration:** Solid iodine sublimes easily. Place a few crystals of solid iodine in a stoppered test tube or glass flask. A pale violet color will be visible to students. **CAUTION:** *Iodine vapors are toxic.* Ask students to suggest a mechanism for this phenomenon based on the particle models of the states of matter.

TYING TO PREVIOUS KNOWLEDGE:
Ask students to recall how cold they felt when they got out of the water after swimming when a strong breeze was blowing.
▶ Ask your class if anyone has seen dry ice subliming. Ask them to describe what they saw. If possible, obtain a piece for your students to observe. **CAUTION:** *Use gloves when handling dry ice. Never place dry ice in a closed container.*

8-3 Changes in State

New Science Words
evaporation
condensation
heat of fusion
heat of vaporization

Objectives
▶ Interpret state changes in terms of the kinetic theory of matter.
▶ Account for the energy of the heats of fusion and vaporization in state changes.

Kinds of State Changes

If you've ever seen ice cream melt before you could eat it, you have seen matter change state. Solid ice crystals in the ice cream melt when they change from the solid state to the liquid state. In melting, a solid changes into a liquid. You put water in the freezer to make ice cubes. In freezing, matter changes from the liquid state to the solid state.

When you boil water, you observe another change of state, called vaporization. In boiling, you add heat to a liquid until it reaches a temperature at which it changes to bubbles of gas below its surface. But liquids don't need to boil to change to a gas. In **evaporation,** a liquid changes to a gas gradually at temperatures below the boiling point. When you come out of a pool into warm air, water on

Figure 8-9. When water boils, bubbles of gas particles form below the surface, rise to the top, and escape (a). When a liquid evaporates, individual gas particles escape from the surface (b).

200 SOLIDS, LIQUIDS, AND GASES

OPTIONS

Meeting Different Ability Levels
For Section 8-3, use the following **Teacher Resource Masters** depending upon individual students' needs.
◆ **Study Guide Master** for all students.
● **Reinforcement Master** for students of average and above average ability levels.
▲ **Enrichment Master** for above average students.
Additional Teacher Resource Package masters are listed in any PROGRAM RESOURCES boxes that are in the section. The additional masters are appropriate for all students.

◆ STUDY GUIDE   36

STUDY GUIDE   Chapter 8
Changes in State   Text Pages 200–203

Solve the following crossword puzzle by using the clues provided.

Across
3. The state of a material depends on this.
5. change of a solid directly to a gas
9. When ice melts, the particles of solid water _____ energy.
10. gaseous water
12. energy needed to change a material from solid to liquid (5 words)
15. change of a liquid to gas below the boiling point
16. has definite volume but no definite shape
17. The kinetic energy of a substance is the _____ kinetic energy of its particles.
18. to change from a liquid to a gas at temperatures above those normal to the liquid state
19. process that occurs during boiling

Down
1. to change from solid to liquid
2. energy needed to change a material from liquid to gas (3 words)
4. occurs when a gas cools and changes to a liquid
6. Liquids have a definite volume and _____.
7. a unit of heat
8. no definite shape, no definite volume
11. theory used to explain changes of state
13. has a definite volume and shape
14. determined by motion and spacing of particles

your skin soon evaporates. You'll see later how this drying helps cool you.

Have you noticed that ice cubes shrink when they've been in the freezer a long time? This shrinkage happens because of another change of state called sublimation. In **sublimation**, a solid changes directly to a gas without going through the liquid state.

You see another change of state when your glass of ice-cold soft drink "sweats." The drops of water on your glass appear when gaseous water condenses from the air onto the cold surface. **Condensation** takes place when a gas changes to a liquid. Generally, a gas will condense when cooled to its boiling point.

Figure 8-10. Gaseous water in the air often condenses on cool surfaces.

Heat and State Changes

The kinetic theory of matter explains changes of state. Suppose you take some ice cubes from your freezer and put them in a beaker. Then, as you heat them, you measure the temperature of the cubes every 30 seconds. You will find that the temperature rises steadily as the cubes absorb thermal energy. Figure 8-11 on the next page plots these temperature changes.

After 5 minutes, the cubes warm up to 0°C and begin to melt. But the temperature stops rising and stays at 0°C while the cubes melt. What is happening to the energy? The particles of the solid water are absorbing energy. This energy enables them to overcome forces that hold them in place. Then the particles are free to tumble over one another. In other words, they have become particles of water in the liquid state.

The amount of energy needed to change a material from the solid state to the liquid state is the **heat of fusion** of that material. For water, the heat of fusion is 334 kJ/kg. This means that it takes 334 kJ of energy to melt 1 kg of ice without changing its temperature from 0°C.

What is the heat of fusion of a material?

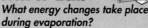

MINI-Lab

What energy changes take place during evaporation?

④ Use a dropper to place five drops of rubbing alcohol on the back of your hand. Wait for two minutes. What sensations did you feel? What change of state did you *observe*? Is energy entering or leaving your hand? Where does the energy for this process come from?

Connect to... Life Science

Answer: As liquid nitrogen changes to a gas, it must absorb energy from its surroundings. There is a very quick loss of energy from the wart.

ANSWERS TO QUESTIONS

1. a liquid
2. Slime, gelatin dessert, jellies, mucus
3. The particles are fairly strongly attracted. They hold into a certain volume and do not fill the container as a gas would. However, unlike a solid they are not attracted strongly enough to hold the material into a definite shape.
4. The particles are close together because the material cannot be pressed into a smaller space.

MINI-Lab

Materials: dropper, rubbing alcohol

Teaching Tips

▶ Emphasize that an input of energy is required for continued evaporation.

▶ Discuss the function of perspiration during hot weather and physical exertion.

Results: In a short time, the alcohol will evaporate completely. Students will feel a cooling sensation.

▶ Have students compare what they feel in still air and when blowing gently across the hand.

Answers to Questions

Hands felt cooler. Evaporation was observed. Energy for evaporation came mostly from the skin.

MINI-Lab

ASSESSMENT

Oral: Have students explain how the panting of a dog regulates its body temperature.

PROGRAM RESOURCES

From the **Teacher Resource Package** use:

Activity Worksheets, page 69, MINI-Lab: What energy changes take place during evaporation?

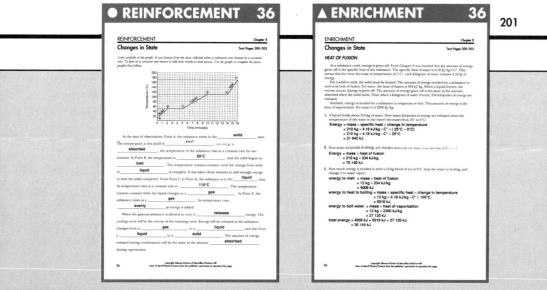

1 **Define melting.** *A solid changes to a liquid.*

2 **Define evaporation.** *A liquid gradually changes to a gas at temperatures below the boiling point.*

3 **Define sublimation.** *A solid changes directly to a gas.*

4 **Define condensation.** *A gas changes to a liquid.*

5 **How much energy is needed to melt 1000 grams of ice at 0°C?** *334 kJ*

CROSS CURRICULUM

▶ **Geology:** Have students read about the mechanism and energy source for geysers. Yellowstone Park's Old Faithful geyser is a well known example of a change in state involving the boiling of water. Geothermal energy provides the heat of vaporization.

REVEALING MISCONCEPTIONS

▶ Students tend to believe that ice is always at its freezing temperature. In reality, it can become colder like any other solid after freezing.

CONCEPT DEVELOPMENT

▶ The amount of energy required to change liquid particles to gas particles at the boiling point of the liquid depends on the pressure applied to them. Thus, water inside a pressure cooker boils at a temperature higher than water's normal boiling point. Conversely, water at high altitudes boils at a lower temperature.

In Your JOURNAL

Answer: The spill has a greater surface area so its rate of evaporation is faster.

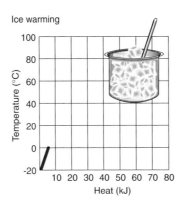

Ice warming

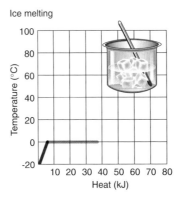

Ice melting

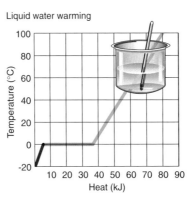

Liquid water warming

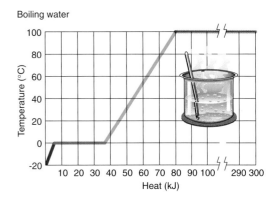

Boiling water

Suppose after the cubes melt, you continue to heat the liquid water. The temperature rises once again. When the water begins to boil, the temperature reads 100°C and rises no further. Again, the water particles are absorbing energy, and they overcome attractive forces holding them together in the liquid state. The particles can separate to great distances from one another. They are becoming particles of gaseous water, steam. The amount of energy needed to change a material from a liquid to a gas is the **heat of vaporization** of that material. For water, the heat of vaporization is 2260 kJ/kg.

After the water has boiled away, the temperature of the steam rises rapidly. Suppose you condense the steam back into liquid water and then freeze the liquid into ice. You must remove all the energy you added before. And the temperature would stay at 100°C while the steam condensed and at 0°C while the ice froze.

You can also use the kinetic theory to explain how water evaporates from your skin and how it cools you. When a liquid evaporates, the particles do not all have the same kinetic energy. Many fast-moving particles break away from the liquid and become a gas. As these fast-moving water particles leave, the average kinetic energy of the remaining particles becomes less. As a result, the temperature of the remaining water goes down. Because the water is now cooler than your skin, it takes heat from your skin and cools you.

Figure 8-11. The warming and melting of ice and the warming and boiling of water.

OPTIONS

INQUIRY QUESTIONS

▶ Some liquids have much stronger attractive forces between particles than others. Suggest how the amount of attractive force affects the boiling point of a liquid. *The higher the attractive force, the higher the boiling point—provided other factors are equal.*

▶ Under the oceans, hot lava erupts from cracks in Earth's crust. The water boils when heated by the molten rock. Explain why steam bubbles are never observed at the ocean's surface. *The steam loses heat and condenses as it rises.*

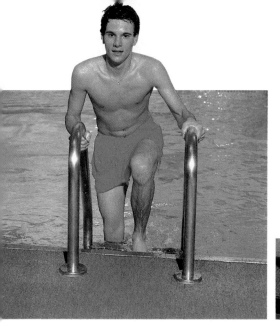
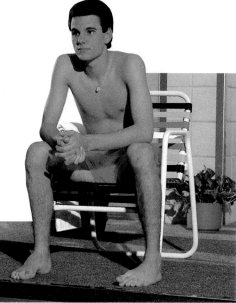

Figure 8-12. In warm air, water soon evaporates from wet skin and hair.

SECTION REVIEW

1. Name and describe the state changes in which a solid or a liquid changes to a gas.
2. Use the kinetic theory to explain melting.
3. What happens to the energy put into a liquid during boiling?
4. **Apply:** Steam must lose its heat of vaporization in order to condense. How does this fact help explain why steam causes more severe skin burns than water at its boiling point?
5. **Connect to Earth Science:** Carbon dioxide makes up about 0.03 percent of our atmosphere. Solid carbon dioxide, or *dry ice*, changes directly to a gas without becoming a liquid. What is this process called?

JOURNAL

A glass of water and a puddle of water, both containing the same volume of water, are left to evaporate. Which do you think will evaporate sooner? Write and explain your answer **in your Journal**.

☑ Concept Mapping

Use a cycle map to show the changes in particles as cool water boils, changes to steam, and then changes back to cool water. If you need help, refer to Concept Mapping in the **Skill Handbook** on pages 684 and 685.

Skill Builder

8-3   CHANGES IN STATE   **203**

Skill Builder

Cool water

heat lost →

heat added →

Hot water

Particles close, tumbling over one another

Hot water

Particles move slower; attractive forces pull them together, forming liquid. (Condensation)

Steam

Particles still close but moving faster

Particles absorb energy, overcoming attractive forces, forming a gas. (Boiling)

heat lost

heat added

CHECK FOR UNDERSTANDING
Ask questions 1-3 and the **Apply** and **Connect to Earth Science** questions in the Section Review.

RETEACH

Cooperative Learning: Use the Paired Partner strategy. Have each partner draw and label a particle model of one of the three common states of matter and write a state change that could occur starting from the state drawn. Students should then exchange papers and make a particle sketch representing the indicated state change. Repeat until all states and possible changes are exhausted.

EXTENSION

For students who have mastered this section, use the **Reinforcement** and **Enrichment** masters or other OPTIONS provided.

3 CLOSE

▶ **Demonstration:** In novelty stores, one can purchase a "drinking bird." If a student has one, have him or her bring it to class and explain how it works. The water evaporates from the head to cool and condense the vapors of the volatile liquid inside.

SECTION REVIEW ANSWERS

1. Boiling: Gas bubbles form within the liquid at the boiling point. Sublimation: A solid changes directly to a gas. Evaporation: Particles of a liquid gain enough energy to escape from the surface of the liquid.

2. Particles absorb enough energy to overcome some attractive forces and become free enough to tumble over one another.

3. The energy is used in overcoming the attractive forces that hold the liquid particles close to one another.

4. Apply: If steam touches the skin, steam will condense and give up its heat of vaporization there. Liquid water at its boiling temperature does not have heat of vaporization to lose.

5. Connect to Earth Science: sublimation

PREPARATION

SECTION BACKGROUND

▶ Gas molecules are much smaller than the distance between the molecules.

▶ The gas laws treat gases as though they are ideal gases. In ideal gases, each molecule has no volume, and there is no attraction between molecules. Most gases behave almost like ideal gases at normal pressures and temperatures.

PREPLANNING

▶ A supply of ice will be needed for Activity 8-2. Two balloons will be needed per lab team.

1 MOTIVATE

▶ **Demonstration:** Fill a small glass to overflowing with water. Hold a 3 x 5-inch card on top of the glass and invert it. Ask your students what they think will happen if you take your hand away. Remove your hand from beneath the card. Air pressure will hold the card on the inverted glass. Point out that air pressure acts in all directions.

▶ A newton is about the weight of a stick of butter. If students imagine the butter spread over a square meter surface, they have an idea of a pascal of pressure.

TEACHER F.Y.I.

▶ Safety, handling, and gas mileage suffer when drivers fail to inflate automobile tires properly. Some cars have in-wheel pressure sensors that cause a light on the instrument panel to go on if any tires are underinflated.

New Science Words

pressure
pascal
Boyle's law
Charles's law

Objectives

▶ Explain how a gas exerts pressure on its container.
▶ State and explain how the pressure of a container of gas is affected when the volume is changed.
▶ Explain the relationship between the temperature and volume of a gas.

Figure 8-13. The force of particles of air in constant motion colliding with the inside walls of a tire keeps the tire inflated.

Pressure

Every time you feel the wind on your face, you observe the behavior of a gas—rather, the mixture of gases that is Earth's air, or atmosphere. Even when the wind is calm, the air exerts a force called pressure.

What causes the pressure of a gas? Particles of matter are very small—many billions of particles of air fill an inflated toy balloon. When riding on a bike, you're riding on pockets of colliding air particles inside your tires. You have learned that the particles of air, like those in all gases, are constantly moving. They're free to fly about and collide with anything in their way. The collisions with the inside walls keep the balloons or tires inflated and cause the force that you feel when you squeeze them.

The total amount of force exerted by a gas depends on the size of its container. **Pressure** is the amount of force exerted per unit of area. ❶

$$P = F/A$$

The **pascal** (Pa) is the SI unit of pressure. One pascal of pressure is a force of one newton per square meter. This is a very small pressure unit, so most pressures are given in kilopascals (kPa).

Earth's atmosphere exerts a pressure on everything within it. At sea level, atmospheric pressure is 101.3 kPa. ❷ This means that at Earth's surface, the atmosphere exerts a force of about 100 000 newtons on every square meter. This amount of force is equal to a weight of 100 000 newtons—about the weight of a large truck.

204 SOLIDS, LIQUIDS, AND GASES

OPTIONS

Meeting Different Ability Levels

For Section 8-4, use the following **Teacher Resource Masters** depending upon individual students' needs.

◆ **Study Guide Master** for all students.
● **Reinforcement Master** for students of average and above average ability levels.
▲ **Enrichment Master** for above average students.

Additional Teacher Resource Package masters are listed in any **PROGRAM RESOURCES** boxes that are in the section. The additional masters are appropriate for all students.

◆ **STUDY GUIDE** 37

STUDY GUIDE   Chapter 8
Behavior of Gases   Text Pages 204–206

Use the words in the box to fill in the blanks.

force	constantly	size	absolute	liquids
increase	volume	boiling	decrease	pressure
kinetic	particles	kilopascals	larger	decrease
pressure	Charles's	Boyle's	temperature	increased

Gases in Earth's atmosphere exert _____**pressure**_____ on everything. According to the _____**kinetic**_____ theory, the particles of a gas are _____**constantly**_____ moving. Every time gas particles hit something and bounce off, they exert a tiny force. Pressure is this amount of _____**force**_____ exerted per unit of area. Air pressure at sea level is 101.3 _____**kilopascals**_____.

The amount of force exerted by a gas depends on the _____**size**_____ of its container. _____**Boyle's**_____ law states that if a sample of gas is kept at constant _____**temperature**_____, decreasing the volume will _____**increase**_____ the pressure the gas exerts. If you increase the volume, the pressure will _____**decrease**_____.

According to the kinetic theory, if you do not change the amount of gas or its temperature but _____**decrease**_____ the size of the container, the particles will strike the walls more often and the pressure will rise. When the size of the container is _____**larger**_____, the pressure is smaller because the _____**particles**_____ hit the walls less often.

According to _____**Charles's**_____ law, if a sample of gas is kept at constant _____**pressure**_____, the volume increases if the temperature is _____**increased**_____. Charles's measurements suggested that the _____**volume**_____ of a gas would become zero at a temperature of –275°C. The temperature –275°C is called _____**absolute**_____ zero. All gases become _____**liquids**_____ when cooled to their _____**boiling**_____ points.

Copyright Glencoe Division of Macmillan/McGraw-Hill
Users of Merrill Physical Science have the publisher's permission to reproduce this page.   37

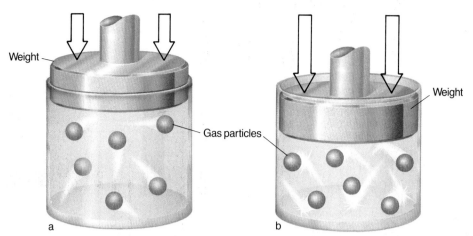

Weight

Gas particles

a   b

Weight

Boyle's Law

Suppose you have some gas in a sealed flexible container, such as a balloon. You can squeeze or stretch the container without changing the amount of gas trapped inside.

The pressure of a gas depends on how often its particles strike the walls of the container. If you squeeze some gas into a smaller space, its particles will strike the walls more often, giving an increased pressure. This behavior explains why when you squeeze a balloon into a smaller space, it causes the balloon to push back with more force. The reverse happens too. If you give the gas particles more space, they will hit the walls less often and the gas pressure will be reduced. Robert Boyle (1627-1691), a British scientist, described this property of gases. According to **Boyle's law,** if you decrease the volume of a container of gas, the pressure of the gas will increase, provided the temperature does not change. Increasing the volume causes pressure to drop. As you'll see, it is important that the temperature remains constant.

Charles's Law

If you've seen a hot-air balloon in the sky, you know gases become less dense when heated. Jacques Charles (1742-1823) was a French scientist who studied gases. According to **Charles's law,** the volume of a gas increases with increasing temperature, provided the pressure does not change. As with Boyle's law, the reverse is true,

Figure 8-14. If you increase the pressure on air in an enclosed space (a), the volume of the air in the enclosed space decreases, (b).

In Your JOURNAL

In your Journal, write a plan to help you remember that Charles's law relates temperature and volume and Boyle's law relates pressure and volume.

⑶

⑷

● **REINFORCEMENT**   37

▲ **ENRICHMENT**   37

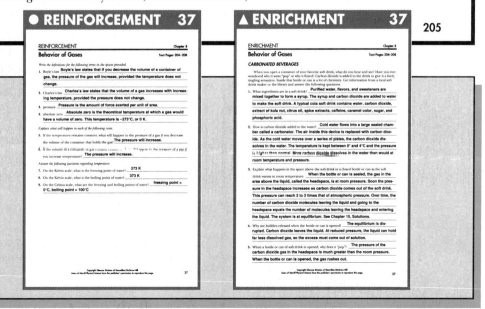

205

TYING TO PREVIOUS KNOWLEDGE: Ask a student who swims frequently to describe the feeling he or she has when diving below the surface. The skin is sensitive to pressure only when it is not normal atmospheric pressure.

VideoDisc

STVS: Schlieren Photography, Disc 1, Side 1

2 TEACH

Key Concepts are highlighted.

CONCEPT DEVELOPMENT

▶ **Demonstration:** Put approximately 20 mL of water into an empty aluminum soft drink can, and place it on a hot plate to boil. After the can has filled with steam, grasp it with tongs or a hot pad and quickly plunge the can *inverted* into a large beaker of ice water. The sudden drop of pressure inside the can and atmospheric pressure will quickly crush the can.

MINI QUIZ

Use the Mini Quiz to check students' recall of chapter content.

① **Force per unit area is a measure of _____.** *pressure*

② **Average sea level air pressure is _____ kPa.** *101.3*

③ **With temperature held constant, when the volume of a gas increases, the pressure will _____.** *decrease*

④ **With pressure held constant, as a gas is heated, the volume will _____.** *increase*

In Your JOURNAL

Plans may include relating the letter *C* to both Charles and Celsius, reflecting temperature. Or, when someone is under pressure, their emotions may be near the *boil*ing point, relating pressure and *Boyle's* law.

TECHNOLOGY

For more information on research balloons, see "NASA's Giant Research Balloons Are Out of Sight," by James R. Chiles, *Smithsonian*, Jan. 1987, pp. 82-91.

Think Critically: Balloons are less expensive than rockets and satellites. Balloons can float within the atmosphere at a controlled altitude carrying instruments that can make measurements in the immediate surroundings, rather than observing the surroundings from above.

Connect to...
Physics

Answer: Inversely related means that, as one variable increases, the other variable decreases.

CROSS CURRICULUM

▶ **Meteorology:** Bring an aneroid barometer to class. Have the students record the pressure each day and the outside weather conditions for several days. Ask them to search the data for correlations. They may observe that on days of low pressure it tends to be cloudy with precipitation, while on days of high pressure it may be clear.

CHECK FOR UNDERSTANDING

Ask questions 1-2 and the **Apply** and **Connect to Physics** questions in the Section Review.

RETEACH

Have students place a small air sample in a re-sealable plastic bag in the freezer overnight. Remove the bag from the freezer, and with the bag sealed, warm it with a hair dryer. Have them explain their observations. Remind them of Charles's law if necessary.

EXTENSION

For students who have mastered this section, use the **Reinforcement** and **Enrichment** masters or other OPTIONS provided.

TECHNOLOGY

Gaseous Research Giants

Imagine a balloon so immense that, when fully inflated, it will hold a volume of gas equivalent to 168 Goodyear blimps! Scientists are sending such balloons into the stratosphere, the layer of the atmosphere that is above 99 percent of Earth's air. These giant balloons are filled with helium gas, which gives them their lift. One of these balloons may hoist a load higher than a cruising jumbo jet, but lower than an orbiting satellite in space. The initial volume of helium required to lift the load might be the size of a small house. In the stratosphere, the volume may reach the size of 283 of the houses!

Scientists use the balloons for research. For example, a load of equipment may gather data on how ozone gas is formed in the upper atmosphere. Ozone helps protect life by absorbing a potentially dangerous form of energy given off by the sun. Because the sky is clear in the stratosphere, another load may be a telescope for studying the energy given off by the sun and other stars. Such studies help scientists understand the makeup and behavior of matter.

Think Critically: For some kinds of research, why do scientists launch giant balloons into the stratosphere instead of launching satellites into outer space where there is no air?

Connect to...
Physics

Boyle's law shows that, at constant temperature, gas volume and pressure are inversely related. What is meant by the term *inversely related*?

also. A gas shrinks with decreasing temperature. Figure 8-15 shows a demonstration of Charles's law.

Using his law, Charles was able to calculate the temperature at which a gas would have a volume of zero. The kinetic theory would say that this is the temperature at which all particle motion of matter should stop. Charles found this temperature to be $-273°C$, or 0 K, also called absolute zero. In reality, gases cannot be cooled to zero volume. Instead, they condense to liquids when cooled to their boiling points.

206 SOLIDS, LIQUIDS, AND GASES

OPTIONS

INQUIRY QUESTIONS

▶ **Scuba divers breathe compressed air. Will a full tank of air last longer if the diver is ten meters below the surface or is at twenty meters?** *At greater depths the pressure on the compressed air is even greater. Each breath contains more air particles. Therefore, the tank would last longer at ten meters.*

▶ **When a helium-filled rubber balloon is released outdoors, will it break or come down to Earth intact? Explain your answer.** *The pressure on the balloon decreases with altitude. It will expand and burst.*

▶ **Yeast put into bread dough reacts with sugar to produce carbon dioxide gas, which becomes trapped in the dough. During baking, the yeast organisms are killed, but the bread continues to rise. Explain why.** *The trapped gas expands with increasing temperature.*

▶ **In theory, a gas at a temperature of absolute zero would have zero volume. Why would it never actually achieve this volume?** *It condenses into a liquid and freezes into a solid.*

You can explain Charles's law by using the kinetic theory of matter. As a gas is heated, its particles move faster and faster, and its temperature increases. Because the gas particles move faster, they begin to strike the walls of their container more often and with more force. If the walls are free to move, the gas pushes the walls out and expands.

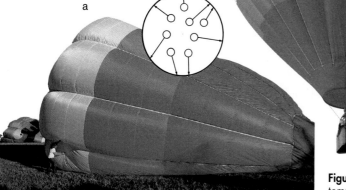

a

b

Figure 8-15. If you increase the temperature of the air in a balloon (a), the volume of the air in the balloon also increases (b).

SECTION REVIEW

1. When you bounce a basketball on the floor, the air pressure inside the ball increases for a moment. Explain why this increase occurs.
2. Why does a closed, empty 2-liter plastic soft-drink bottle "cave in" when placed in a freezer?
3. **Apply:** Labels on cylinders of compressed gases state the highest temperature to which the cylinder may be exposed. Give a reason for this warning.
4. **Connect to Physics:** Using the kinetic theory, explain why automobile drivers are more likely to experience tire blowouts on hot summer days.

✉ **Hypothesizing**

Skill Builder

A bottle containing ammonia begins to leak. An hour later you can smell ammonia almost everywhere, especially near the bottle. State a hypothesis to explain your observations. If you need help, refer to the **Skill Handbook,** page 682.

Skill Builder
ASSESSMENT
Portfolio: After students have stated their hypotheses, have each of them explain an experiment that would show a way to test the hypothesis.

PROGRAM RESOURCES

From the **Teacher Resource Package** use:
Activity Worksheets, page 5, Flex Your Brain.
Use **Laboratory Manual 19,** The Behavior of Gases.

---

3 CLOSE

? **FLEX Your Brain**

Use the Flex Your Brain activity to have students explore BEHAVIOR OF GASES. This could be made more concrete by asking students to visualize the behavior of gases trapped in balloons or inflated balls during changes of temperature, pressure, or volume.

ASSESSMENT
Portfolio: Use the Flex Your Brain activity to reinforce critical-thinking and problem-solving skills. In Step 2, students might list effects of temperature and pressure on volume.

SECTION REVIEW ANSWERS

1. The ball is momentarily compressed to a smaller volume resulting in a momentary increase in pressure.
2. The air particles in the "empty" bottle decrease in average velocity as the temperature drops. Thus they collide less frequently with the walls of the bottle. The pressure inside the bottle decreases, but the atmospheric pressure on the outside remains the same. Because the walls are relatively flexible, the bottle decreases in volume.
3. **Apply:** With increasing temperatures, gas particles move faster, striking the walls of their container more often. If the walls are not free to move, the gas cannot expand. Thus, the pressure builds up instead, and the cylinder may explode. Every gas container has a maximum safe pressure, thus a maximum safe temperature.
4. **Connect to Physics:** On warmer days, more heat energy transfers from the pavement to the air particles in the tires, making them move faster. Thus, there are more collisions with the inside of the tire, and pressure increases.

Skill Builder

The bottle of ammonia gives off ammonia gas. Gases are made of particles that spread farther and farther apart as they move from a bottle into a room. Thus, the ammonia is more concentrated near the bottle and less concentrated farther away.

ACTIVITY 8-2

OBJECTIVE: **Design and carry out an experiment** to show the relationship between temperature and volume of a gas.
Time: 40 minutes

PROCESS SKILLS applied in this activity are **observing and inferring, recognizing cause and effect, measuring, interpreting data,** and **hypothesizing.**

PREPARATION

COOPERATIVE LEARNING: Divide the class into Science Investigation Teams.

SAFETY

Caution students to wear goggles. Do not heat balloons directly with a hot plate or flame or immerse balloon in hot water. When working with heat or steam, use tongs and heat-proof gloves.

HYPOTHESIZING

A possible hypothesis would be that if the temperature of a gas sample is increased or decreased, then its volume will also increase or decrease.

TEACHING THE ACTIVITY

*Refer to the **Activity Worksheets** for additional information and teaching strategies.*
►You may want to assist students with finding the volume of the balloon; $V = C^3/59$. This formula is derived from the formulas $V = \frac{4}{3}\pi r^3$ and $r = C/(2\pi)$.

SUMMING UP/ SHARING RESULTS

► The volume of the gas increased as the temperature was raised. The volume decreased and the temperature was decreased.
► Correct hypotheses are supported by

DESIGNING AN EXPERIMENT
More Than Just Hot Air

One of the major points of the kinetic theory of matter is that all matter is composed of tiny, rapidly moving particles. The evidence for this has been indirect evidence. In this activity you will investigate how changing the temperature of a sample of a gas affects the volume of gas. Find out what hot air can do!

Getting Started

You need to find the volume of a gas, air, inside an approximately spherical volume, a balloon. The two variables you will use for the gas are temperature and volume. How is the circumference of a sphere used to find its volume? Be sure to use a thermal mitt when working near steam.

Hypothesizing

Within your group, write a **hypothesis** about how changing the temperature of gas will alter the volume of the gas.

Materials

Your cooperative group will use:
• string
• marking pen
• meterstick
• bucket of ice water
• tongs
• heat-proof glove
• beaker of boiling water
• thermometer
• goggles
• two medium, round balloons

◼ Try It! ◼

1. Inflate the two balloons to the same size and tie them closed.
2. Use string to determine the circumference of each balloon. Find the volume of each and record the room temperature. Mark dots on the balloon so that you can always put the string around the same place on the balloon when other measurements are needed.

3. Use one balloon to place the trapped air in a colder temperature. Determine both the colder temperature and the resulting volume.
4. Use the other balloon to determine the change in the volume of the air at a hotter temperature.
CAUTION: *Use heat-proof gloves and tongs to handle the balloon near heated air or steam.*

Summing Up/Sharing Results

• What pattern did you *observe* when you compared the air volumes at different temperatures? Compare your findings with those of other groups.
• How do the results of this experiment help you evaluate your **hypothesis**?
• Use the kinetic theory to explain how air molecule movements are related to the volumes of the balloons.

Going Further!

Use the class data to *make a graph* of temperatures and volumes found in this investigation. What relationship between temperature and gas volume can you draw from this graph? If you extended the graph to show zero volume, at what temperature would this occur?

---

the direct temperature-volume relationship, as stated in Charles's law.
► As a gas is heated, the average speed of its particles increases, increasing the number of collisions with the inside of the balloon. Thus, the volume must increase if pressure is kept constant. The converse explanation applies for lower temperatures.

GOING FURTHER!

The graph suggests a direct relationship between the temperature and volume of a gas. Extending to zero volume results in a predicted temperature of approximately –273°C.

Activity
ASSESSMENT
Oral: Ask students to explain the "Do not incinerate; contents under pressure." caution that is found on many aerosol cans.

Uses of Fluids

Objectives

▶ State Archimedes' principle and predict whether an object will sink or float in water.
▶ State Pascal's principle and describe the operation of a machine that uses Pascal's principle.
▶ State Bernoulli's principle and describe a way that Bernoulli's principle is applied.

New Science Words

buoyant force
Archimedes' principle
Pascal's principle
Bernoulli's principle

Archimedes' Principle

Have you ever relaxed by floating quietly on your back in a swimming pool? You seem weightless as the water supports you. If you climb slowly out of the pool you feel as if you gain weight. The farther out you climb, the more you have to use your muscles to support yourself. When you were in the pool, you experienced buoyancy. Buoyancy is the ability of a fluid—a liquid or a gas—to exert an upward force on an object immersed in it. This force is called **buoyant force.**

The amount of buoyant force determines whether an object will sink or float in a fluid. If the buoyant force is

Figure 8-16. Forces acting on person lying on the floor beside a pool (a) and in water (b).

OPTIONS

ASSESSMENT—ORAL

▶ **Air-filled soap bubbles sink at a slower rate in air than does a small balloon of equal size. Explain why.** *Buoyant force acts on both. However, the rubber compresses the air and increases its density. Therefore, the net downward force is greater on the balloon.*

▶ **When a weather balloon is released, it is partially filled with helium gas. Describe what happens to the balloon's volume as it goes up.** *Atmospheric pressure decreases; volume increases.*

PROGRAM RESOURCES

From the **Teacher Resource Package** use:
Critical Thinking/Problem Solving, page 14, Hydraulics.
Transparency Masters, pages 31-32, Archimedes' Principle.
Use **Color Transparency** number 16, Archimedes' Principle.

PREPARATION

SECTION BACKGROUND

▶ An object's density, not its weight, determines whether it will sink or float.
▶ As with any other machines, those that employ Pascal's principle are limited in that the work done by the machine cannot be greater than the work done on the machine.
▶ Bernoulli's principle applies to both liquids and gases.

PREPLANNING

▶ Check the margin for materials needed in the demonstrations to determine in advance which ones you will choose to do.

1 MOTIVATE

▶ **Demonstration:** Place an egg in a beaker of tap water. It sinks. Place another egg in a beaker of saturated salt solution. It floats. Discuss swimming in a freshwater pool and in the ocean as it relates to buoyancy.

TYING TO PREVIOUS
KNOWLEDGE: Ask students to recall when they have seen hydraulic or pneumatic devices being used. Common examples are bulldozers, jackhammers, door closers, and pneumatic impact tools. All of these devices make use of Pascal's principle.

VideoDisc

STVS: Laminar Flow over Airplane Wings, Disc 1, Side 2
STVS: Cutting with Water, Disc 1, Side 2

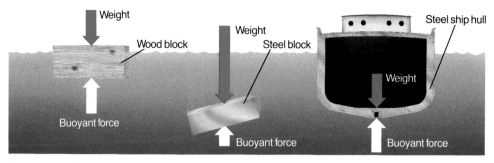

Figure 8-17. Forces act on a wood block, a steel block, and a steel ship hull in water.

2 TEACH

Key Concepts are highlighted.

CONCEPT DEVELOPMENT

▶ Discuss with your class how each of the following demonstrations makes Archimedes' principle visible. Use the principle to explain why the various objects sink or float.

▶ **Demonstration:** Place an unopened aluminum can of diet cola and one of non-diet cola in a water-filled aquarium. The can of sugar-free Cola is less dense and will float.

▶ **Demonstration:** Place an ice cube in a beaker of water. It floats. Place an ice cube in a beaker of rubbing alcohol. It sinks.

MINI-Lab
How does applied pressure affect different areas of a fluid? Draw water into a dropper and place it into a 2-L soft drink bottle that is filled with water to within 1 cm of the top. Suck in or squeeze out water from the dropper until it just barely floats. *Observe* and record how increasing the amount of water inside the dropper affects its density. Put the cap tightly back on the bottle. Squeeze the bottle. What effect does the applied pressure have on the dropper?

210 SOLIDS, LIQUIDS, AND GASES

less than the object's weight, the object will sink. If the buoyant force equals the object's weight, the object floats. Sometimes the buoyant force on an object is greater than its weight. This force is what seems to pull a helium-filled balloon upward in the air. When the balloon is released, the unbalanced buoyant force causes the balloon to accelerate upward.

Archimedes, a Greek mathematician who lived in the third century B.C. made a discovery about buoyancy. According to **Archimedes' principle**, the buoyant force on an object in a fluid is equal to the weight of the fluid displaced by the object. If you place a block of pine wood in water, it will push water out of the way as it begins to sink—but only until the weight of the water it displaces equals the block's weight. The block floats at this level, as shown in Figure 8-17.

Suppose you drop a solid steel block the same size as the wood block into water. When the steel block is placed in the water, the steel block begins to push aside water as it sinks. Buoyant force begins to push up on the block. However, the density of steel is much greater than that of wood. So the buoyant force never becomes great enough to equal the weight of the steel block, and it sinks to the bottom.

How, then, does a steel ship float? Suppose you formed the steel block into a large hollowed-out bowl shape. As this shape sinks into water, it displaces much more water than the solid block. Soon, it displaces enough water to equal the weight of the steel, and it floats.

Pascal's Principle

If you dive underwater, you can feel the pressure of the water all around you. You live at the bottom of Earth's atmosphere, which also is a fluid that exerts a pressure.

This pressure is also all around you, even though you don't feel it. Blaise Pascal (1623-1662), a French scientist, discovered a useful property of fluids. **Pascal's principle** states that pressure applied to a fluid is transmitted unchanged throughout the fluid. For example, when you squeeze one end of a balloon, the balloon pops out on the other end. When you squeeze one end of a toothpaste tube, toothpaste emerges from the other end.

Figure 8-18. When you apply pressure on one end of an inflated balloon, the pressure is transmitted throughout the fluid—that is, the air—in the balloon.

Hydraulic machines that move very heavy loads use Pascal's principle. Maybe you've seen a car raised using a hydraulic lift. Look at Figure 8-19 to see how a machine of this type works. A small cylinder and a large cylinder are connected by a pipe. The cross section of the small cylinder has an area of 5 cm². The cross section of the large cylinder is 50 cm². Each cylinder is filled with a hydraulic fluid, usually oil, and has a piston that rests on the oil's surface.

Suppose you apply 500 N of force to the small piston. Therefore the pressure on the small piston is:

$$P = F/A = 500 \text{ N}/5 \text{ cm}^2 = 100 \text{ N/cm}^2.$$

Pascal's principle says that this pressure is transferred unchanged throughout the liquid. Therefore, the large piston will also have a pressure of 100 N/cm² applied to it. But the area of the large piston is 50 cm². So, the total force on the large piston is 100 N/cm² × 50 cm² = 5000 N. With this hydraulic machine, you could use your weight to lift something ten times as heavy as yourself. What action must be increased when using this machine?

State Pascal's principle.

②

Connect to...
Physics

Designers of dams and levees must consider the same properties of fluids that Pascal noticed. Which levee would experience more water pressure, one that is next to a large lake that has a depth of three meters or a levee next to a small pond that has a depth of six meters? Explain your choice.

③

Figure 8-19. A hydraulic lift is a machine that makes use of Pascal's principle.

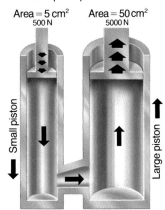

Area = 5 cm²   Area = 50 cm²
500 N   5000 N

Small piston   Large piston

211

CHECK FOR UNDERSTANDING
Use the Mini Quiz to check for understanding.

MINI QUIZ

Use the Mini Quiz to check students' recall of chapter content.

① **The cause of buoyant force was first explained by _____ .**
Archimedes

② **The discovery that pressure is exerted in all directions throughout a fluid was made by _____ .**
Pascal

③ **Hydraulic jacks that move heavy loads make use of _____ principle.**
Pascal's

RETEACH
Have students test several objects that sink or float in water. Encourage students to explain why each object sinks or floats. Have students use density, volume, and mass in their explanations.

EXTENSION
For students who have mastered this section, use the Reinforcement and Enrichment masters or other OPTIONS provided.

STUDENT TEXT QUESTION
▶ Page 211, paragraph 4: **What action must be increased when using a hydraulic lift?** *the distance the effort force moves*

Connect to...
Physics

Answer: The pressure at the bottom of the pond is greater because it depends on the depth. The more water above the bottom of the levee, the more force per area is exerted on the levee.

PROGRAM RESOURCES
From the **Teacher Resource Package** use:
Activity Worksheets, page 70, MINI-Lab: How does applied pressure affect different areas of a fluid?

▶ Use the following demonstrations to illustrate Bernoulli's principle.

▶ **Demonstration:** Connect the hose to the exhaust side of a wet vac. Use a vertical stream of air to support a table tennis ball.

▶ **Demonstration:** Connect a water aspirator to a lab sink's faucet. Connect about a meter of tubing to the aspirator arm. Turn on the water and allow students to experience the low pressure created by the rapid flow of water through the wasp-waisted shape of the aspirator's venturi.

MULTICULTURAL PERSPECTIVE

Kayaks and Boomerangs

Many cultures have understood the principles discussed in this chapter, even if they did not scientifically name them. Boomerangs make use of Bernoulli's principle. The boomerang is like a curved wing, and its differences in thickness allow it to "fly." Several cultures, including some native Americans, used nonreturning boomerangs to hunt birds and small animals. The most famous boomerangs are those developed by societies in eastern and western Australia. These form either a deep, even curve, or a straight-sided angle with the ends of the arms twisted in opposite directions. These shapes affect the spin of the flight so that the boomerang completes a circle approximately 45 meters wide, then several small circles as it returns to the thrower.

Kayaks make use of buoyancy principles. These canoes, still used by the Inuit, also known as the Eskimo, skim the water and are ideal for hunting because they are virtually noiseless. The Inuit traditionally used kayaks for hunting seals in the sea and caribou swimming in lakes and rivers. Seal or other animal skins are shrunk over a wooden frame, and the canoe is propelled by a double-bladed paddle. The canoe is completely enclosed except for a center cockpit. Air pressure keeps the skin boat buoyant.

Bernoulli's Principle

It took humans thousands of years to learn to do what birds do naturally—fly, glide, and soar. Obviously it was no simple task to build a machine that could lift itself off the ground and fly with people aboard. The ability of an airplane to rise into the air is an example of another property of fluids called Bernoulli's principle. Daniel Bernoulli (1700-1782) was a Swiss scientist who studied the properties of moving fluids such as water and air. He published his discovery in 1738. According to **Bernoulli's principle,** as the velocity of a fluid increases, the pressure exerted by the fluid decreases.

Figure 8-20. If you hang a piece of paper and then blow across its surface, the paper rises.

To demonstrate Bernoulli's principle, blow across the surface of a sheet of paper, as in Figure 8-20. The paper will rise. The velocity of the air you blew over the top surface of the paper is greater than that of the quiet air below it. As a result, the downward air pressure above the paper decreases. The higher air pressure below the paper exerts a net force that pushes the paper upward.

212 SOLIDS, LIQUIDS, AND GASES

OPTIONS

ENRICHMENT

▶ Use tape and rubber bands to seal a plastic garbage bag around a wet-vac hose attached to the exhaust side. Place a cafeteria tray on top of the flattened plastic bag. Place a large mass on the tray and raise it by inflating the bag. Fire rescue trucks use air bags to upright flipped cars and trucks at an accident scene.

▶ If the auto shop at your local vocational school has a hydraulic lift, arrange for your students to see it in operation. Point out that, unlike the idealized diagram shown in the text, the lift has no single narrow column. Rather, there may be a reciprocating piston and a valve system that allow more oil to enter on each stroke. Also, there may be other types of oil pressure pumps.

Figure 8-21. The design of airplane wings is an application of Bernoulli's principle.

Now look at the curvature of the airplane wing in Figure 8-21. As the wing moves forward, the air passing over it must travel farther than air passing below it. To take the same time to get to the rear of the wing, air must travel faster over the top of the wing than below it. Thus, the pressure above the wing is less than the pressure below it. The result is a net upward force on the wing, lifting the airplane in flight.

Baseball pitchers also use Bernoulli's principle. If the pitcher puts a spin on the ball, air moves faster along the side of the ball that is spinning away from the direction of the throw. Look at Figure 8-22. The ball's spin results in a net force that pushes the ball toward the low-pressure direction. The force gives the ball a curve.

Fluids flow faster when forced to flow through narrow spaces. As a result of this speed increase, the pressure of the fluid drops. This reduction in pressure in these spaces is an example of Bernoulli's principle called the Venturi effect. A dramatic demonstration of the Venturi effect has occurred in cities where the wind is forced between rows of skyscrapers. The reduced air pressure outside of buildings during strong winds has caused

How does a difference in air pressure help an airplane to fly?

❓ FLEX Your Brain

Use the Flex Your Brain activity to have students explore the PROPERTIES OF FLUIDS.

ASSESSMENT

Portfolio: Use the Flex Your Brain activity to reinforce critical-thinking and problem-solving skills. In Step 2, students might list the properties that they know.

SECTION REVIEW ANSWERS

1. Shape the concrete into a hollowed-out boat shape so that it displaces enough water to equal its weight.

2. The machine in the example multiplies forces by ten. Therefore, a force of 2000 N would have to be applied to the small piston.

3. As the velocity of a fluid increases, the pressure exerted by the fluid decreases. Air is a fluid. An airplane's wing is shaped such that air flows at a greater velocity over its upper surface. The difference in pressure above and below the wing creates a net upward force that helps lift the plane.

4. Apply: The air in the balloon is compressed compared to normal air and thus has a greater density. The weight of the denser air along with the weight of the rubber itself is greater than the buoyant force of the surrounding air. Therefore, the balloon sinks.

5. Connect to Life Science: A small amount of pressure on the fluid in the leg can be used to make enough pressure to cause the entire leg to extend.

Skill Builder
ASSESSMENT

Performance: Have students repeat the Skill Builder using, instead of water, salt water with a density of 1.3 g/cm³. By what percentage would the buoyant force be increased? *27 percent increase to 1.5 N*

PROGRAM RESOURCES

From the **Teacher Resource Package** use:

Activity Worksheets, page 5, Flex Your Brain.

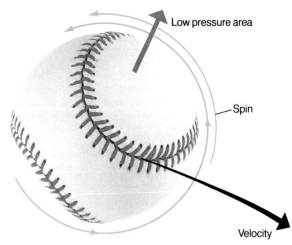

Low pressure area

Spin

Velocity

Figure 8-22. Air moves faster along the side of a spinning ball that is moving away from the direction of the throw.

windows to be forced out by the higher air pressure inside the buildings.

SECTION REVIEW

1. How is it possible that a boat made of concrete can float?
2. If you wanted to lift an object weighing 20 000 N, how much force would you have to apply to the small piston in Figure 8-19?
3. State Bernoulli's principle and tell how it helps produce lift on an airplane.
4. **Apply:** If you fill a balloon with air, tie it off, and release it, it will fall to the floor. Why does it fall instead of float?
5. **Connect to Life Science:** Spiders extend their legs by using a pressurized fluid that can be forced into their legs. How is this an example of a hydraulic system that uses Pascal's principle?

☑ Measuring in SI

The density of water is 1.0 g/cm³. How many kilograms of water does a submerged 120-cm³ block of concrete displace? One kilogram weighs 9.8 N. What is the buoyant force on the block? If you need help, refer to Chapter 2 and to Measuring in SI in the **Skill Handbook** on page 680.

Skill Builder

A submerged block of 120 cm³ displaces 120 cm³ of water. The mass of water displaced is therefore 120 cm³ × 1.0 g/cm³ = 120 g. Converting to kilograms, 120 g ÷ 1000 g/kg = 0.12 kg. The buoyant force on the block is then 0.12 kg × 9.8 N/kg = 1.2 N.

You can extend the Skill Builder by posing the following question. **Suppose the mass of the block is 90 grams. If a diver carries it underwater, will it float or sink?** *It will float because the downward force of gravity is about 0.9 N, which is less than the upward buoyant force.*

CHAPTER REVIEW

SUMMARY

8-1: Matter and Temperature
1. There are four states of matter: solid, liquid, gas, and plasma.
2. According to the kinetic theory, all matter is made of constantly moving particles.
3. Most matter expands when heated and contracts when cooled.

8-2: Science and Society: Water—Earth's Vital Liquid
1. Fresh water on Earth is scarce, and this water is often wasted or polluted.
2. There are many ways in which people can save water and stop its pollution.

8-3: Changes in State
1. Changes of state can be interpreted in terms of the kinetic theory of matter.
2. The energy of the heat of fusion and the heat of vaporization overcomes attractive forces between particles of matter.

8-4: Behavior of Gases
1. Gas pressure is caused by its moving particles colliding with the inside walls of its container.
2. Boyle's law states that the volume of a gas decreases when the pressure increases, at constant temperature.
3. Charles's law states that the volume of a gas increases when the temperature increases, at constant pressure.

8-5: Uses of Fluids
1. Archimedes' principle states that the buoyant force on an object in a fluid is equal to the weight of the fluid displaced.
2. Pascal's principle states that pressure applied to a fluid is transmitted unchanged throughout the fluid.
3. Bernoulli's principle states that the pressure exerted by a fluid decreases as its velocity increases.

KEY SCIENCE WORDS

a. Archimedes' principle
b. Bernoulli's principle
c. Boyle's law
d. buoyant force
e. Charles's law
f. condensation
g. crystal
h. evaporation
i. heat of fusion
j. heat of vaporization
k. kinetic theory of matter
l. pascal
m. Pascal's principle
n. plasma
o. polluted water
p. pressure
q. states of matter
r. thermal expansion

UNDERSTANDING VOCABULARY

Match each phrase with the correct term from the list of Key Science Words.

1. The volume of a gas is reduced when the temperature is decreased.
2. water that exceeds government limits for impurities
3. liquid changes to gas below the boiling point
4. amount of force exerted per unit of area
5. The buoyant force on an object in a fluid equals the weight of the displaced fluid.
6. the SI unit of pressure
7. particles are arranged in regular patterns
8. a gaslike mixture of charged particles
9. Matter is made of tiny, moving particles.
10. energy needed for a liquid to boil

SOLIDS, LIQUIDS, AND GASES **215**

CHAPTER REVIEW

SUMMARY

Have students read the summary statements to review the major concepts of the chapter.

UNDERSTANDING VOCABULARY

1. e	6. l
2. o	7. g
3. h	8. n
4. p	9. k
5. a	10. j

ASSESSMENT
Portfolio
Encourage students to place in their portflios one or two items of what they consider to be their best work. For each item, ask students to explain why that item was chosen and what they learned from it. Items might be selected from the following.
- Enrichment research, p. 193
- Activity 8-1 observations and answers, p. 197
- Cross Curriculum observations and inferences, p. 206

Performance
Additional performance assessments may be found in *Performance Assessment* and *Science Integration Activities* that accompany **Merrill Physical Science.** Performance Task Assessment Lists and rubrics for evaluating these activities and other products generated throughout the chapter can be found in Glencoe's *Performance Assessment in Middle School Science.*

OPTIONS

ASSESSMENT
To assess student understanding of material in this chapter, use the resources listed.

COOPERATIVE LEARNING
Consider using cooperative learning in the THINK AND WRITE CRITICALLY, APPLY, and MORE SKILL BUILDERS sections of the Chapter Review.

PROGRAM RESOURCES
From the **Teacher Resource Package** use:
Chapter Review, pages 19-20.
Chapter and Unit Tests, pages 53-56, Chapter Test.

CHECKING CONCEPTS

1. a		**6.** a	
2. d		**7.** a	
3. c		**8.** b	
4. b		**9.** d	
5. c		**10.** c	

USING LAB SKILLS

ASSESSMENT

Use these alternate lab exercises to assess students' understanding of skills used in this chapter.

11. Student answers may include following all the same steps in the procedure, but seal some of the new product in plastic bags. Then place the sealed bags in ice water that is at various temperatures. Try to manipulate the product to see how it responds at each temperature. The kinetic theory would predict slower-moving particles at lower temperatures.

12. Student data should show Kelvin temperatures obtained by adding 273 to each Celsius reading. The plot should still indicate a straight line that, when extended to zero volume, shows zero Kelvin degrees.

THINK AND WRITE CRITICALLY

13. Some water is suitable for watering plants, gardens, and lawns. Some used wash water is suitable for presoaking clothes yet to be washed. Other answers are possible.

14. Because gases can be squeezed into smaller spaces, more gas can be added to a room, no matter how much is already present.

15. The hot tea transfers energy to particles in the glass and the ice. The tea cools, because its particles now have a lower average kinetic energy. The glass warms as its particles absorb energy from the tea. The ice absorbs energy from the tea. Ice will melt after its temperature is raised to 0°C and energy equal to its heat of fusion is absorbed.

16. Water vapor in the air is cooled by the glass. The particles lose energy and condense.

CHECKING CONCEPTS

Choose the word or phrase that completes the sentence.

1. The temperature at which all particle motion of matter would stop is _____.
   a. absolute zero   **c.** 0°C
   b. its melting point   **d.** 273°C

2. The state of matter that has a definite volume and a definite shape is _____.
   a. gas   **c.** plasma
   b. liquid   **d.** solid

3. The most common state of matter is _____.
   a. gas   **c.** plasma
   b. liquid   **d.** solid

4. Pressure is measured in _____.
   a. grams   **c.** newtons
   b. kilopascals   **d.** kilograms

5. Pascal's principle is the basis for _____.
   a. aerodynamics   **c.** hydraulics
   b. buoyancy   **d.** changes of state

6. Bernoulli's principle explains why _____.
   a. airplanes fly   **c.** pistons work
   b. boats float   **d.** ice melts

7. Particles are completely separated from each other in a(n) _____.
   a. gas   **c.** solid
   b. liquid   **d.** amorphous material

8. The state of the matter in the sun and other stars is primarily _____.
   a. amorphous   **c.** liquid
   b. plasma   **d.** gas

9. In general, as a solid is heated, it _____.
   a. becomes a gas   **c.** contracts
   b. condenses   **d.** expands

10. A material's heat of fusion gives the amount of energy needed to _____.
   a. condense a gas   **c.** melt a solid
   b. boil a liquid   **d.** evaporate a liquid

USING LAB SKILLS

11. In Activity 8-1 on page 197, you made a substance that had some unusual properties. A variable that you did not change was temperature. Suggest a way to investigate the properties of the substance at cold temperatures. Apply what you have learned about the kinetic theory of matter to make some predictions.

12. Look back at your data table from Activity 8-2 on page 208. Using the volume and temperature data you collected, you were able to show a direct relationship between the variables. Convert the temperature readings in your data from Celsius to Kelvin and replot the data. Is the volume-temperature relationship the same? At what temperature would the volume be zero?

THINK AND WRITE CRITICALLY

Answer the following questions in your Journal using complete sentences.

13. How might waste water in the home be recycled instead of being poured into the sewer system?

14. Why would it be incorrect to say, "This room is full of air"?

15. What energy changes occur when hot tea is poured over ice?

16. Use the kinetic theory to explain why liquid water forms on the outside of a glass of cold lemonade.

17. Why might rocks in a creek hurt your feet more than the same rocks would in deeper water?

---

17. The deeper water exerts a much greater buoyant force on your body, reducing the downward force of your feet on the rocks.

18. Use Charles's and Boyle's laws to explain why you should check your tire pressure when the temperature changes.

19. Explain how food might get "freezer burn." How might you prevent it?

20. Alcohol evaporates more quickly than does water. What can you tell about the forces between the alcohol particles?

21. Why do aerosol cans have a "do not incinerate" warning?

22. Applying pressure lowers the melting point of ice. Why might an icy road at −1°C be more dangerous than an icy road at −10°C?

MORE SKILL BUILDERS

If you need help, refer to the Skill Handbook.

1. **Observing and Inferring:** Infer the effect related to air pressure that a large truck passing a small car would have on the car.

2. **Making and Using Graphs:** A group of students heated ice until it melted and then turned to steam. They measured the temperature each minute and graphed the results. Their graph is provided below. In terms of the energy involved, explain what is happening at each letter (a, b, c, d) in the graph.

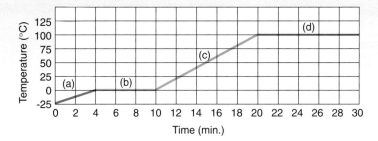

3. **Sequencing:** Sequence the changes in state that occur when ice is heated until it becomes steam and then the steam is cooled until it is ice again.

4. **Interpreting Data:** As elevation increases, boiling point decreases. List each of the following locations as at sea level, above sea level, or below sea level. (Boiling point of water in °C is given.) Death Valley (100.3), Denver (94), Madison (99), Mt. Everest (76.5), Mt. McKinley (79), New York City (100), Salt Lake City (95.6)

5. **Recognizing Cause and Effect:** List possible effects for each of the following causes.
   a. Perspiration evaporates.
   b. Pressure on a balloon decreases.
   c. Your buoyant force equals your weight.

PROJECTS

1. What would happen to an unprotected person at the bottom of the ocean or in outer space? Research the effects of pressure changes on the human body and write a report.

2. Research crystal growing and what conditions are needed to grow a perfect crystal. Grow crystals of several different materials and display them.

SOLIDS, LIQUIDS, AND GASES **217**

18. According to Charles's law, as the temperature of a gas changes, so does the volume. As the volume changes, so does the pressure, according to Boyle's law. Point out that "bleeding" hot tires to lower the pressure is not advisable.

19. Ice in the food sublimes, drying out the food. This can be prevented by wrapping the food in airtight packaging such as foil or by using heavy plastic containers.

20. The forces between the alcohol particles are probably weaker than those between the water particles.

21. According to Charles's law, as temperature increases, gases tend to expand. However, because the can is not free to expand, pressure builds up and the can may explode.

22. If the ice is just below its normal melting point, pressure, such as that applied by tires, will melt it and form a slippery layer of liquid water on the ice. At lower temperatures, the pressure of the tires may not be enough to melt the ice.

MORE SKILL BUILDERS

1. **Observing and Inferring:** When the car and truck are side by side, the space between them is narrow. The air passing through this space must travel faster. This lowers the air pressure and the higher pressure, on the other side of the car pushes the car toward the truck.

2. **Making and Using Graphs:**
   a. Ice is warming to its melting point.
   b. Ice is absorbing energy equal to its heat of fusion. Ice melts.
   c. Liquid water warms.
   d. Liquid absorbs energy equal to its heat of vaporization. Liquid boils.

3. **Sequencing:** melting, boiling, condensation, freezing

4. **Interpreting Data:** Above: Denver, Madison, Mt. Everest, Mt. McKinley, Salt Lake City
At: New York City
Below: Death Valley

5. **Cause and Effect:** Student answers may vary. Sample answers are given.
   a. Skin feels cooler.
   b. Volume increases.
   c. You float.

Classification of Matter

CHAPTER SECTION	OBJECTIVES	ACTIVITIES
9-1 Composition of Matter (2 days)	1. **Distinguish** between substances and mixtures. 2. **Compare** and **contrast** solutions, colloids, and suspensions.	**Activity 9-1:** *Elements, Compounds, and Mixtures,* p. 225
9-2 Smog, A Mixture in the Environment Science & Society (1 day)	1. **Identify** smog as a harmful colloid by its properties. 2. **Describe** how smog is formed and suggest several ways to eliminate it.	
9-3 Describing Matter (2 days)	1. **Give examples** of physical properties. 2. **Distinguish** between physical and chemical changes. 3. **Distinguish** between chemical and physical properties. 4. **State** and **explain** the law of conservation of mass.	**Activity 9-2:** *Checking Out Chemical Changes,* p. 236
Chapter Review		

ACTIVITY MATERIALS

FIND OUT	ACTIVITIES		MINI-LABS
Page 219 crushed calcium carbonate tablets (10 g) 20 g sand 30 g small gravel 5 g water paper cup	**9-1 Elements, Compounds, and Mixtures, p. 225** plastic freezer bag containing tagged items: copper foil small package of salt piece of solder aluminum foil chalk piece of granite sugar water in a vial	**9-2 Checking Out Chemical Changes, p. 236** goggles 0.5 g baking soda small evaporating dish hand lens 3 cm^3 of 4M hydrochloric acid 10-cm^3 graduated cylinder electric hot plate	

CHAPTER FEATURES	TEACHER RESOURCE PACKAGE	OTHER RESOURCES
Problem Solving: *Jason Makes a Colloid*, p. 223 **Skill Builder:** *Concept Mapping*, p. 224	**Ability Level Worksheets** ◆ **Study Guide**, p. 39 ● **Reinforcement**, p. 39 ▲ **Enrichment**, p. 39 **Activity Worksheets**, pp. 72, 73 **Concept Mapping**, pp. 23, 24 **Transparency Masters**, pp. 33, 34	**Color Transparency 17**, Classification of Matter **Laboratory Manual 20**, Chromatography **STVS:** Disc 2, Side 1 Disc 6, Side 2 **Science Integration Activity 9**
You Decide! p. 227	**Ability Level Worksheets** ◆ **Study Guide**, p. 40 ● **Reinforcement**, p. 40 ▲ **Enrichment**, p. 40	**STVS:** Disc 6, Side 2 Disc 7, Side 2
Technology: *Aerogels—Next to Nothing at All*, p. 231 **Skill Builder:** *Observing and Inferring*, p. 235	**Ability Level Worksheets** ◆ **Study Guide**, p. 41 ● **Reinforcement**, p. 41 ▲ **Enrichment**, p. 41 **Activity Worksheets**, pp. 5, 74, 75 **Critical Thinking/Problem Solving**, p. 15 **Cross-Curricular Connections**, p. 13 **Science and Society**, p. 13 **Transparency Masters**, pp. 35, 36	**Color Transparency 18**, Conservation of Matter **Laboratory Manual 21**, Properties of Matter **STVS:** Disc 2, Side 1
Summary · Think & Write Critically Key Science Words · Apply Understanding Vocabulary · More Skill Builders Checking Concepts · Projects Using Lab Skills	**ASSESSMENT RESOURCES** **Chapter Review**, pp. 21, 22 **Chapter Test**, pp. 57-60 **Performance Assessment in Middle School Science**	**Chapter Review Software** **Test Bank** **Alternate Assessment** **Performance Assessment**

◆ Basic ● Average ▲ Advanced

ADDITIONAL MATERIALS		
SOFTWARE	**AUDIOVISUAL**	**BOOKS/MAGAZINES**
Air Pollution, EME. *Colloid*, Queue. *Structure of Matter*, Classroom Consortia Media. *Solutions*, J&S Software. *Physical or Chemical*, EME.	*Chemical Changes All About Us*, Video, Coronet. *Elements, Compounds, and Mixtures*; Video, Coronet. *Evidence for the Atomic-Molecular Theory*, Video, Britannica. *Matter and the Molecular Theory*, Video, Coronet. *Physical Changes All About Us*, Video, Coronet.	Cornell, John. *Experiments with Mixtures*. 2nd ed. New York: Wiley, John & Sons, Inc., 1990. Gordon, J. E. *The Science and Structures of Materials*. New York: Scientific American Library, 1988. *Scientific American* 255, no. 4 (October 1986). The whole issue is devoted to materials.

9
CLASSIFICATION OF MATTER

THEME DEVELOPMENT: Patterns of change is one of the major themes emphasized in this text. In Chapter 9 the student learns to classify matter by observing the patterns that occur when it undergoes physical and chemical change.

CHAPTER OVERVIEW

▶ **Section 9-1:** This section introduces the student to the vocabulary used by scientists when classifying matter. Also, it distinguishes between true substances and various kinds of mixtures.

▶ **Section 9-2: Science and Society:** Students learn how smog is made. The class will be asked to think about long-term solutions to air pollution.

▶ **Section 9-3:** Physical and chemical properties and physical and chemical changes are described and related to the students' daily living in this section.

CHAPTER VOCABULARY

element
compounds
substance
heterogeneous mixture
homogeneous mixture
solution
colloid
suspension
Tyndall effect
smog
physical property
physical change
chemical change
chemical property
law of conservation of mass

CHAPTER
9 Classification of Matter

218

OPTIONS

For Your Gifted Students

Have students add equal amounts of soil, clay, sand, gravel, and pebbles to a gallon jar. Enough cold water should be added so the jar is almost full. Students should stir or shake the mixture thoroughly and predict the order in which the materials will settle and explain why. They should prepare a list of variables that would control the rate of settling. Have them test salt water and hot water to see if the order and rate of deposition of the material changes.

For Your Mainstreamed Students

Have students place filter paper over the end of a vacuum cleaner hose opening. They should clean a part of the room and then examine the filter paper through a microscope or hand lens. Can any of the particles be identified? They can sample other locations and compare. Squares of nylon stocking mounted on cardboard frames can be hung outside to test the effect of air pollution. Damage will appear under a hand lens as broken fibers.

Did you ever watch a construction crew pour concrete for a building? What is this material? Actually, you can't classify fresh concrete as one of the states of matter. Rather, it is a mixture of solids—portland cement, sand, rocks—and a liquid, water.

FIND OUT!

Do this activity to make some classroom concrete and observe its properties.

Mix thoroughly in a paper cup 10 g of crushed calcium carbonate tablets; 20 g of sand; 30 g of small, clean rocks; and 5 g of water. Describe the appearance and state of the mixture. Allow to dry overnight and *observe* again.

Gearing Up
Previewing the Chapter

Use this outline to help you focus on important ideas in this chapter.

Section 9-1   Composition of Matter
▶ Substances
▶ Mixtures
▶ Solutions
▶ Colloids and Suspensions
Section 9-2   Science and Society
Smog, a Mixture in the Environment
▶ Visible Air Pollution
Section 9-3   Describing Matter
▶ Physical Properties
▶ Physical Changes
▶ Chemical Changes
▶ Chemical Properties
▶ The Conservation of Mass

Previewing Science Skills
▶ In the Skill Builders, you will make a concept map and observe and infer.
▶ In the Activities, you will classify, make and use tables, observe, and hypothesize.

What's next?

You have made a sample of concrete, a useful mixture. Study Chapter 9 for a better understanding of mixtures and the physical and chemical properties of matter.

219

INTRODUCING THE CHAPTER
Use the Find Out activity to introduce students to the classification of matter. Inform students that they will be learning more about kinds of matter and how matter changes as they read the chapter.

FIND OUT!
Preparation: Gather the materials to be used in this Find Out activity.
Materials: calcium carbonate, sand, small gravel, water, paper cup
Teaching Tips
▶ A calcium carbonate-based antacid tablet may be used as a source of calcium carbonate.
Cooperative Learning: Use the Science Investigation Team strategy and have each team prepare a slightly different mixture. By varying the proportions of the mixture, the properties will change. Teams could use 12 g, 10 g, 8 g, 6 g, and 4 g of calcium carbonate. The amounts of the other materials would be kept the same.
▶ The concrete that has dried can be tested for strength. Remove it from the paper cup, drop each piece from the same height, and observe the amount of shattering to determine its strength.
▶ Emphasize the heterogeneous nature of the concrete.

Gearing Up
Have students study the Gearing Up feature to familiarize themselves with the chapter. Discuss the relationships of the topics in the outline.

What's Next?
Before beginning the first section, make sure students understand the connection between the Find Out activity and the topics to follow.

ASSESSMENT OPTIONS

PORTFOLIO
Refer to page 237 for suggested items that students might select for their portfolios.

PERFORMANCE ASSESSMENT
See page 237 for additional Performance Assessment options.
Process
Skill Builder, p. 224
Activities 9-1, p. 225; 9-2, p. 236
Using Lab Skills, p. 238

CONTENT ASSESSMENT
Assessment—Oral, p. 230
Skill Builder, p. 235
Section Reviews, pp. 224, 227, 235
Chapter Review, pp. 237-239
Mini Quizzes, pp. 223, 232, 234

GROUP ASSESSMENT
Opportunities for group assessment occur with Cooperative Learning Strategies and Flex Your Brain Activities.

PREPARATION

SECTION BACKGROUND

▶ In science, the word *substance* is limited to elements and compounds. More than nine million substances are known to chemists. A system of classification is necessary.

▶ A heterogeneous mixture is one that is composed of more than one phase. A phase is any region with a uniform set of properties.

▶ Solutions are not necessarily liquid. Air is a gaseous solution. Most alloys of metals are solid solutions.

▶ Colloids are composed of two phases, the dispersed phase and the continuous phase.

PREPLANNING

▶ To prepare for Activity 9-1, label seven items and place them in a plastic bag for each activity group.

▶ Several demonstrations are offered. Scan them to see which ones you want to do and gather the materials needed.

▶ Begin using the wall periodic table to point out element names and symbols. Becoming familiar with the table now will serve students well in upcoming chapters.

1 MOTIVATE

▶ **Demonstration:** Obtain five small clear glass bottles. In the first, place some copper metal and label it. In the second, place some sulfur and label it. Leave the third empty and label it oxygen. In the fourth bottle, place a little copper and sulfur. Leave plenty of space. The fifth bottle should contain copper(II) sulfate, $CuSO_4$. Use these bottles to demonstrate elements, compounds, and mixtures. Aid students in forming mental models of chemically combined compounds versus mixtures.

VideoDisc

STVS: Shock Impact Gun, Disc 2, Side 1

STVS: Pollution Record in Lake Sediments, Disc 6, Side 2

9-1 Composition of Matter

New Science Words

element
compounds
substance
heterogeneous mixture
homogeneous mixture
solution
colloid
suspension

Objectives

▶ Distinguish between substances and mixtures.
▶ Compare and contrast solutions, colloids, and suspensions.

Substances

You can easily tell whether a line is drawn in ink or pencil. The lines look different because they are made of different materials. Look at the parts of a pencil. Notice that it's made of several kinds of materials. You could classify the materials of the pencil according to the four states of matter. Another way to classify materials is by the particles they are made of.

The particles that make up all matter are called atoms. If all the atoms in a sample of matter are alike, that kind of matter is an **element.** The carbon in a pencil point, the oxygen in the air, and the copper in a penny are all examples of elements. Altogether, there are 109 recognized elements. The names of all the elements are in the periodic table on pages 258-259. You will learn more about the other information in the table in later chapters.

Materials called **compounds** are made from atoms of two or more elements that are combined. The ratio of the different atoms in a compound is always the same. For example, the elements hydrogen and oxygen can combine to form the compound water. The atoms of elements in water are present in the ratio of two hydrogen atoms to one oxygen atom.

Figure 9-1. A pencil is made up of several different materials.

OPTIONS

Meeting Different Ability Levels

For Section 9-1, use the following **Teacher Resource Masters** depending upon individual students' needs.

◆ **Study Guide Master** for all students.

● **Reinforcement Master** for students of average and above average ability levels.

▲ **Enrichment Master** for above average students.

Additional Teacher Resource Package masters are listed in any PROGRAM RESOURCES boxes that are in the section. The additional masters are appropriate for all students.

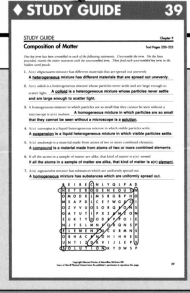

◆ STUDY GUIDE 39

STUDY GUIDE Chapter 9

Composition of Matter Text Pages 220-225

One key term has been scrambled in each of the following statements. Unscramble the term. On the line provided, rewrite the entire statement with the unscrambled term. Then find each unscrambled key term in the hidden word puzzle.

1. A(n) *rtlegenoeeuos* mixture has different materials that are spread out unevenly.
   A heterogeneous mixture has different materials that are spread out unevenly.

2. A(n) *oidllc* is a heterogeneous mixture whose particles never settle and are large enough to scatter light. **A colloid is a heterogeneous mixture whose particles never settle and are large enough to scatter light.**

3. A homogeneous mixture in which particles are so small that they cannot be seen without a microscope is a(n) *toulsion*. __ **A homogeneous mixture in which particles are so small that they cannot be seen without a microscope is a solution.**

4. A(n) *sunsnopsei* is a liquid heterogeneous mixture in which visible particles settle.
   A suspension is a liquid heterogeneous mixture in which visible particles settle.

5. A(n) *onudmcpo* is a material made from atoms of two or more combined elements.
   A compound is a material made from atoms of two or more combined elements.

6. If all the atoms in a sample of matter are alike, that kind of matter is a(n) *normel*.
   If all the atoms in a sample of matter are alike, that kind of matter is a(n) element.

7. A(n) *oogeeunshom* mixture has substances which are uniformly spread out.
   A homogeneous mixture has substances which are uniformly spread out.

Figure 9-2. Sugar is a compound of carbon, oxygen, and hydrogen.

When was the last time you ate a compound whose elements are a black solid and two invisible gases? One compound that fits this description is sugar. You can recognize sugar by its white crystals and sweet taste. But the elements that form sugar—carbon, hydrogen, and oxygen—are neither white nor sweet, Figure 9-2. Like sugar, compounds usually have a very different appearance from the elements that make them up.

Oxygen, carbon, water, sugar, baking soda, and salt are examples of materials classified as substances. A **substance** is either an element or a compound. Elements and compounds cannot be broken down or separated by physical processes.

Mixtures

When you have a sore throat, do you gargle with salt water? Salt water is classified as a mixture. A mixture is a material made up of two or more substances, and salt and water are different substances.

Unlike compounds, mixtures do not always contain the same amounts of different substances. You may be wearing clothing made of permanent-press fabric. This fabric is woven from fibers of two compounds—polyester and cotton. The fabric may contain varying amounts of polyester and cotton, as shown in Figure 9-3. Fabric with more polyester is more resistant to wrinkling than is fabric with less polyester.

Figure 9-3. Permanent-press fabrics are mixtures that have variable composition.

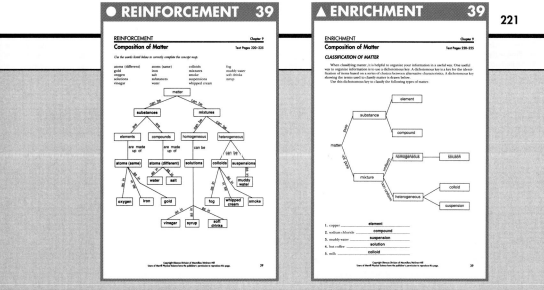

● **REINFORCEMENT 39**

▲ **ENRICHMENT 39**

221

TYING TO PREVIOUS KNOWLEDGE: Ask a student to describe the phases present in an ice cream soda. The ice cream, flavored syrup, soda water, whipped cream, and cherry will probably be mentioned. Compounds, heterogeneous mixtures, homogeneous mixtures, and colloids are present in the ice cream soda.

2 TEACH

Key Concepts are highlighted.

CONCEPT DEVELOPMENT

▶ Exhibit some of the elements from a chemical stockroom, such as Fe, C, Cu, Zn, and S.

▶ It is very important that students recognize the difference between combining and mixing substances, even if they do not know the mechanisms involved. Exhibit obvious substances and mixtures such as those used in the Motivate feature. Ask students to classify them as substances or mixtures and to characterize their composition. You can model the difference between mixing and combining by comparing wooden balls or marbles in a shallow container with modeling clay balls in a similar container. As you shake the container, the clay balls will adhere (combine) while the other balls only mix together. To emphasize the point, the clay spheres should be further stuck together so that their individual natures are lost.

PROGRAM RESOURCES

From the **Teacher Resource Package** use:

Transparency Masters, pages 33-34, Classification of Matter.

Science Integration Activity 9

Use **Color Transparency** number 17, Classification of Matter.

► The word *substance* is popularly used to refer to any kind of matter. Make sure students realize that its scientific usage is limited to either an element or a compound.

CONCEPT DEVELOPMENT

► **Demonstration:** Partially fill a petri dish with water and place it on the overhead projector. Place a crystal of potassium permanganate, $KMnO_4$, in the water, and have the students observe the purple streamers as you stir the water *very* gently. Emphasize that a solution is completely homogeneous on a molecular level because the constant motion of the particles of matter enables a thorough mixing.

► **Demonstration:** Place sugar in a glass of cold tea so that some remains undissolved on the bottom of the glass (heterogeneous). Transfer the mixture to a beaker and warm gently, stirring until the sugar dissolves in the hot tea (homogeneous). Introduce the idea that temperature (energy) often determines the form of a mixture.

CROSS CURRICULUM

► **Language Arts:** Have a group of volunteers prepare a crossword puzzle using the vocabulary words of this lesson. Shown here is one possibility.

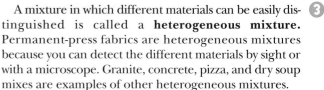

A mixture in which different materials can be easily distinguished is called a **heterogeneous mixture.** Permanent-press fabrics are heterogeneous mixtures because you can detect the different materials by sight or with a microscope. Granite, concrete, pizza, and dry soup mixes are examples of other heterogeneous mixtures.

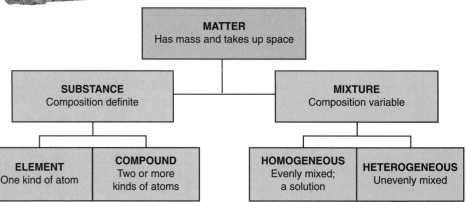

Figure 9-4. Every sample of matter is an element, a compound, or a mixture.

Solutions

The salt water you gargle with looks like water and tastes salty. Like a polyester-cotton fabric, salt water is in some ways similar to the substances it contains. But you can't see the particles in salt water even with a microscope. A material in which two or more substances are uniformly spread out is a **homogeneous mixture.**

Have you ever looked closely at a bottle of white vinegar? Vinegar is a liquid solution made mostly of acetic acid and water. It appears clear, even though it is made up of particles of acetic acid in water. A **solution** is another name for a homogeneous mixture. Particles in solutions are so small that they cannot be seen even with a microscope. The particles have diameters of about 0.000 000 001 m (1 nm). The particles will also never settle to the bottom of their container. Solutions remain constantly and uniformly mixed.

Figure 9-5. Vinegar is a liquid solution containing acetic acid and water.

222 CLASSIFICATION OF MATTER

OPTIONS

INQUIRY QUESTIONS

► **When a soft drink is opened, the solution becomes a heterogeneous mixture. Describe what happens and explain why the result is heterogeneous.** *The pressure of carbon dioxide in the bottle is reduced by opening the bottle, and the excess dissolved gas bubbles out of solution.*

► **Explain why a solution is always a mixture, but not every mixture is a solution.** *All solutions are homogeneous mixtures because they are mixed at the molecular level. Some mixtures, such as a pizza, are heterogeneous* and therefore cannot be solutions.

► **How would you explain to a person that paint is not a substance?** *True substances, elements and compounds, cannot be separated physically. Paint, left standing, will separate and must be stirred before using. In addition, the person can see that the paint contains materials that evaporate, leaving dry paint behind.*

Jason Makes a Colloid

Jason makes a colloid to use on sand-wiches. His friends think that his colloid tastes better than store-bought mayonnaise, although it is similar.

To make the colloid, Jason pours 60 cm³ of vinegar into a blender. He then adds 30 cm³ of sugar and blends until dissolved. Next, he adds 5 cm³ of dry mustard, one clove of fresh garlic, a pinch of salt, and one egg. He blends these ingredients until they are well mixed. While the blender is still on, he slowly adds 180 cm³ of vegetable oil in a steady stream. He continues blending until the colloid is thick.

At what stages in the preparation of his recipe does Jason have homogeneous and heterogeneous mixtures?

Think Critically: How can mayonnaise be distinguished from a solution?

Colloids and Suspensions

When you drink a glass of whole or low-fat milk, you are drinking a mixture of water, fats, proteins, and other substances. Milk is a colloid. A **colloid** is a heterogeneous mixture that, like a solution, never settles. Unlike the particles in a solution, the particles in a colloid are large enough to scatter light. Milk appears white because its particles scatter light. Gelatin is a colloid that may seem to be clear until you shine a light on it. Then you see that its particles also scatter light.

In what way is a colloid like a solution?

⑤  **Connect to...**
Life Science

Most milk containers carry the label *Homogenized*. Find out what part of the milk is homogenized and describe the process.

Figure 9-6. A beam of light goes straight through a solution (left) but is scattered by a colloid (right).

Answers to Questions: The vinegar is homogeneous. Adding sugar gives a heterogeneous mixture until the sugar dissolves. At this point, the mixture is again homogeneous. After the mustard is added, the mix-ture remains heterogeneous.
Think Critically: Mayonnaise, like milk, appears white and opaque because it scatters light. This light-scattering property makes it possi-ble to classify mayonnaise as a colloid.

CONCEPT DEVELOPMENT

▶ The motion of colloidal particles is called Brownian motion. This observed, constant motion is direct evidence for the kinetic theory of matter.
▶ Ask students why it is important to follow directions to shake well before taking a medication.

 **Connect to...**
Life Science

Answer: Homogenized milk is made by passing the fat globules through a uniform sieve that forms the fat into more easily dispersed particles.

CHECK FOR UNDERSTANDING

Use the Mini Quiz to check for under-standing.

MINI QUIZ

Use the Mini Quiz to check students' recall of chapter content.

① If all the atoms of a sample of mat-ter are alike, the matter is a(n) _____ . *element*
② Substances made from a combina-tion of two or more elements are called _____ . *compounds*
③ A mixture that is not the same throughout is called a(n) _____ mixture. *heterogeneous*
④ A mixture that is the same through-out is called a(n) _____ mixture or _____ . *homogeneous, solution*
⑤ A heterogeneous mixture that never settles is called a(n) _____ . *colloid*

ENRICHMENT

▶ Have a student prepare and present a brief report on Brownian motion and its cause. Brownian motion can be seen in a suspension of very fine dust, pollen, or bacte-ria in water. The student could set up a micro-scope and slide to demonstrate the effect. High magnification is needed.
▶ Some gas masks use the principle of adsorption to filter poisonous gases from the air. Because they are so finely divided, col-loidal particles have a very large surface area compared to a solid chunk of the same

material. Have interested students research how gas masks work. Be sure they discover the concept of surface adsorption by col-loidal particles.

PROGRAM RESOURCES

From the **Teacher Resource Package** use:
Concept Mapping, pages 23-24.
Use **Laboratory Manual 20,** Chroma-tography.

Table 9-1

COMPARING SOLUTIONS, COLLOIDS, AND SUSPENSIONS

Description	Solutions	Colloids	Suspensions
Settle upon standing	No	No	Yes
Can be separated using filter paper	No	No	Yes
Sizes of particles	0.1-1 nm	1-100 nm	Greater than 100 nm
Scatter light	No	Yes	Yes

In Your JOURNAL

In your Journal, make a list of the liquids you consumed yesterday. Classify each as a solution, a colloid, or a suspension.

Some mixtures are neither solutions nor colloids. If you fill a glass with pond water, you may notice that the water is slightly muddy. If you let it stand long enough, the silt will fall to the bottom of the glass and the water will clear. Muddy water is a suspension. A **suspension** is a heterogeneous mixture containing a liquid in which visible particles settle.

You can use the information in Table 9-1 to classify different kinds of mixtures.

SECTION REVIEW

1. How is a container of hydrogen gas and oxygen gas different from a container of water vapor?
2. Distinguish between a substance and a mixture.
3. **Apply:** Why do the words "Shake well before using" on a bottle of fruit juice indicate that the juice is a suspension?
4. **Connect to Life Science:** Carbon dioxide, a product of respiration, is composed of one carbon atom and two oxygen atoms. Is carbon dioxide a compound or a mixture?

Skill Builder

☑ Concept Mapping

Make a network tree to show types of liquid mixtures. Include these terms: *homogeneous mixtures, heterogeneous mixtures, solutions, colloids,* and *suspensions.* If you need help, refer to Concept Mapping in the **Skill Handbook** on pages 684 and 685.

RETEACH

Fill a large jar with water. Using a large stainless steel spoon, dissolve some sugar in the water. Follow this with some food coloring. Pour in some sand and stir. Finally, add a dropperful of milk. Stop stirring and allow everything to stand. Have a student describe the contents of the jar at each step using terms from this section. Note: Don't forget the metal spoon. Stainless steel is a solid solution (alloy) containing iron, chromium, and other metals.

EXTENSION

For students who have mastered this section, use the **Reinforcement** and **Enrichment** masters or other OPTIONS provided.

3 CLOSE

▶ Ask questions 1-2 and the **Apply** and **Connect to Life Science** questions in the Section Review.

▶ Have a scientist from a nearby water treatment plant come and describe how mud, algae, bacteria, and harmful chemicals are detected and removed from your drinking water. As an alternative, have a team videotape an interview at the water treatment plant.

SECTION REVIEW ANSWERS

1. The hydrogen and oxygen are separate, uncombined elements. The water vapor is a compound made from these elements.

2. A substance is either an element or a compound. It has a specific composition. A mixture contains two or more substances. The composition of a mixture can vary.

3. Apply: The label indicates that the juice must contain materials that have settled out and must be resuspended.

4. Connect to Life Science: compound

Skill Builder

```
                Mixtures
          ┌────────┴────────┐
        include          include
          │                 │
   Homogeneous        Heterogeneous
    mixtures             mixtures
          │                 │
      which are       which can be
          │            ┌────┴────┐
      Solutions     Colloids  Suspensions
```

Skill Builder
ASSESSMENT
Portfolio: Display some liquid mixtures and have students use their network tree to classify the liquids.

Elements, Compounds, and Mixtures

Elements, compounds, and mixtures all contain atoms. In elements, the atoms all have the same identity. In compounds, two or more elements have been combined in a fixed ratio. In a mixture, the ratio of substances present can vary. Can you observe these differences among elements, compounds, and mixtures?

Materials
- plastic freezer bag containing tagged items
- copper foil
- small package of salt
- piece of solder
- aluminum foil
- chalk (calcium carbonate) or baking soda (sodium hydrogen carbonate)
- piece of granite
- sugar water in a vial

Procedure
1. Copy the data table and use it to record your observations.
2. Obtain a prepared bag of numbered objects.
3. Use the table below to identify each object and *classify* it as either an element, a compound, a heterogeneous mixture, or a homogeneous mixture. The names of all the elements appear in the periodic table on pages 258-259. Any of the objects that are compounds have been named as examples in Section 9-1.

Data and Observations Sample Data

Object	Identity	Classification
1	copper	element
2	salt	compound
3	solder	homogeneous mixture
4	aluminum	element
5	chalk	compound
6	granite	heterogeneous mixture
7	sugar/water	homogeneous mixture

Analyze
1. If you know the name of a substance, how can you find out if it is an element?
2. How is a compound different from a mixture?
3. Were the mixtures you identified homogeneous or heterogeneous?

Conclude and Apply
4. Examine the contents of your refrigerator at home. *Classify* what you find as elements, compounds, or mixtures.
5. If they are described, all materials can be classified. What are the differences among elements, compounds, and mixtures?

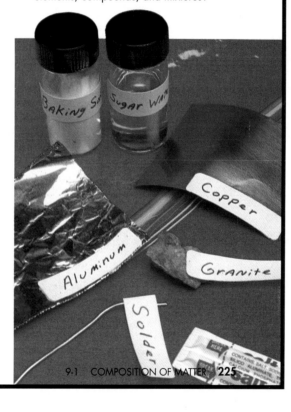

9-1 COMPOSITION OF MATTER **225**

OBJECTIVE: Classify materials based on their appearance and chemical makeup.

PROCESS SKILLS applied in this activity:
▶ **Observing** in Procedure Step 3.
▶ **Classify** in Procedure Step 3.

👥 COOPERATIVE LEARNING
Use the Science Investigation strategy in groups of three. One student can examine the periodic table to search for elements. Have another student identify compounds and mixtures. The third can collect and evaluate decisions and fill out the data table.

TEACHING THE ACTIVITY
Alternate Materials: Any equivalent assortment that students can identify may be substituted. Pictures of materials may be substituted for actual objects.
Troubleshooting: Make sure vials are tightly sealed.
▶ Introduce formulas for the compounds or have students look them up.
▶ If you have not done so already, this would be a good time to hang a large periodic table on the wall.

PROGRAM RESOURCES
From the **Teacher Resource Package** use: **Activity Worksheets,** pages 72-73, Activity 9-1: Elements, Compounds, and Mixtures.

ANSWERS TO QUESTIONS
1. See if it appears on the periodic table.
2. A compound is a substance that consists of chemically combined elements. A mixture consists of various substances not chemically combined.
3. Solder and sugar water were homogeneous. Granite was heterogeneous.
4. Answers will vary but may include: milk, heterogeneous mixture; water, compound; and tea, homogeneous mixture. Students will find few, if any, elements.

5. Elements are homogeneous substances having a specific composition consisting of only one kind of atom. Compounds are also homogeneous and have a specific composition, but they consist of two or more kinds of atoms chemically combined. Mixtures do not have a specific composition and may consist of varying amounts of two or more substances.

Activity
ASSESSMENT
Content: To further assess students' understanding of elements, compounds, and mixtures, see USING LAB SKILLS, Question 11, on page 238.

PREPARATION

SECTION BACKGROUND

▶ The word *smog* was first used in 1905 as a combination of *smoke* and *fog*. Today smog contains pernitric acid, carbon monoxide, ozone, organic peroxy compounds, and aldehydes.

Connect to...
Earth Science

Answer: obsidian

1 MOTIVATE

▶ **Demonstration:** Fill a small aquarium tank with water. Add a few drops of milk to give the water a "foggy" blue appearance. This colloid can be used as a model for atmospheric smog. Show that a beam of light from a projector passes through the clear water invisibly but it is visible and scattered when colloidal particles are present.

TYING TO PREVIOUS KNOWLEDGE:
Have students recall and discuss where they have observed litter or pollution caused by improperly discarded items. Point out that air pollution is equivalent to littering the air with waste gases and particles.

VideoDisc
STVS: Arctic Haze, Disc 6, Side 2
STVS: Children and Smog, Disc 7, Side 2

 **SCIENCE & SOCIETY**

9-2 Smog, a Mixture in the Environment

New Science Words
Tyndall effect
smog

Objectives
▶ Identify smog as a harmful colloid by its properties.
▶ Describe how smog is formed and suggest several ways to eliminate it.

Connect to...
Earth Science

The ash from volcanoes is not the type of ash that comes from combustion. It consists of small solid or porous particles of a type of hard, glassy rock. What is the name of this rock?

Did You Know?

One out of three Americans lives in an area where the air standards of the Clean Air Act are violated.

Visible Air Pollution

Have you ever watched the beam of a searchlight zoom across the night sky? The beam forms when light from the searchlight is scattered by invisible bits of dust and droplets of water in the air. The scattering of light by particles in a mixture is called the **Tyndall effect.** You can see the Tyndall effect in all colloids. As you recall, a colloid is a mixture in which the particles are invisible and never settle. However, the particles in the mixture are large enough to scatter light. Fog is a mixture of water droplets in air. The water droplets scatter light, causing the fog to appear cloudy or hazy. The air above large cities sometimes appears hazy. The haze is often smog.

Smog is a form of air pollution. It is a colloid of small, invisible pieces of solid materials mixed with the gases that make up air. Some of the solid material in smog is dust. The dust can occur naturally. It may come from

OPTIONS

Meeting Different Ability Levels
For Section 9-2, use the following **Teacher Resource Masters** depending upon individual students' needs.
◆ **Study Guide Master** for all students.
● **Reinforcement Master** for students of average and above average ability levels.
▲ **Enrichment Master** for above average students.

◆ **STUDY GUIDE** 40

STUDY GUIDE   Chapter 9
Smog, A Mixture in the Environment   Text Pages 226-227

Use the following words and phrases to write a paragraph about smog.

mixture	colloid	air	dust storms
forest fires	ash and soot	automobile exhaust	volcanic eruptions
industrial wastes	trapped air layers	pollution	smog alert

Paragraphs will vary but should be judged on content related to Lesson 9-2.

_____
_____
_____
_____
_____
_____
_____
_____

40

loose soil blown upward by the wind or from ash from volcanic eruptions and forest fires. However, smog also contains solid materials that are not produced naturally. In the early 1900s, ash and soot from burning coal produced most of the dust in smog. Today, unburned compounds in automobile exhaust account for most of the particles of solids in smog. Other sources of solid materials in the air are gasoline stations, industrial plants, hair sprays, spray paints, forest fires, woodburning stoves, and fireplaces.

Normally, warm air will rise in the atmosphere. However, sometimes a layer of warm air will be trapped beneath a layer of colder air. The constant motion of the warm air mixes the dust and other solid particles in the air, producing the colloid smog. Within the smog, harmful compounds begin to form. These compounds cause eye irritation and can cause lung damage. Sometimes city governments must declare smog alerts. These alerts advise elderly people and people with respiratory problems to remain indoors. Industries are asked to cut back their use of fuels, and nonessential traffic is restricted. Winds eventually blow smog away from the cities over which it forms.

SECTION REVIEW

1. Why does smog appear hazy?
2. How does smog form?
3. **Connect to Earth Science:** If warm air usually rises in the atmosphere, is warm air less dense or more dense than cold air? Explain your answer.

You Decide!

One way to reduce air pollution is to reduce the consumption of gasoline. Suppose there were a bill in Congress to raise gasoline taxes and use the proceeds to help clean up the environment. Would you want your representatives to vote for the higher taxes? Why or why not?

SCIENCE & SOCIETY

● **REINFORCEMENT** 40   ▲ **ENRICHMENT** 40

REINFORCEMENT   Chapter 9
Smog, A Mixture in the Environment   Text Pages 226–227

WHEN DO 50 + 50 = 95?

Read the following paragraphs. Answer the questions and make drawings in the spaces provided.

Karen did an activity in science class. She measured 50 mL of alcohol into one graduated cylinder and 50 mL of water into another graduated cylinder. She then emptied the 50 mL of alcohol into a 100-mL graduated cylinder. Then she emptied the 50 mL of water into the same 100-mL graduated cylinder that contained the alcohol. She then observed and recorded the total volume as 95 mL. Karen thought that she made a mistake in measuring, so she repeated the entire procedure and again observed that the total volume was 95 mL.

How could this be? She asked her teacher what she had done wrong. Her teacher said that Karen would be able to explain the results if she thought about it for a while.

Karen went home from school and made some popcorn. To 500 mL of popped popcorn she added 25 mL of salt and noted that the total volume did not go above 500 mL. Karen then watched her four-year-old neighbor playing in his sandbox. He emptied a container of sand into a pail filled with pebbles, but his pail did not overflow. Karen could not wait until she went to school the next day. She could now explain how 50 + 50 = 95.

1. What explanation was Karen going to give in science class? **There could be small spaces between the particles of alcohol and water. The water particles go in between the alcohol particles and take up some of this empty space.**

2. Make drawings to help you explain.

a. water particles   b. alcohol particles   c. alcohol and water particles

3. How can Karen's science class explanation help you understand how smog conditions worsen in a city in a period of one day? **There is a lot of empty space between air particles. This empty space can hold more pollution particles if the air is trapped over the city.**

40   Copyright Glencoe Division of Macmillan/McGraw-Hill
Users of Merrill Physical Science have the publisher's permission to reproduce this page.

ENRICHMENT   Chapter 9
Smog, A Mixture in the Environment   Text Pages 226–227

PHOTOCHEMICAL SMOG

Photochemical smog is a type of smog caused by the action of sunlight on exhaust gases from factories and automobiles. The chemicals involved in photochemical smog include the following.

A. Nitrogen monoxide (NO). It is formed in the atmosphere from oxygen and nitrogen and from combustion in automobiles.

B. Nitrogen dioxide (NO_2). It is made from the reaction of nitrogen monoxide and oxygen in the atmosphere. It has a pungent, irritating odor and has an orange-brown color.

C. Ozone (O_3). It is produced from the photochemical reaction of nitrogen monoxide, nitrogen dioxide, and sunlight. It is a powerful oxidant and can crack rubber, corrode metals, and damage plant and animal tissues.

D. Hydrocarbons. These are organic materials that escape from gasoline tanks or are emitted during incomplete combustion of gasoline. These can cause burning eyes, are

harmful to people with respiratory or heart disease, can injure plants, and can damage rubber and paint.

Data Table. Chemicals in Photochemical Smog

Time	Pollutant Level, parts per million (ppm) by volume			
	Hydrocarbons	NO	NO_2	O_3
Midnight	0.18	0.07	0.06	0.01
2 AM	0.18	0.09	0.06	0.02
4 AM	0.19	0.10	0.06	0.02
6 AM	0.26	0.12	0.09	0.03
8 AM	0.40	0.11	0.15	0.04
10 AM	0.35	0.03	0.14	0.07
Noon	0.28	0.01	0.08	0.12
2 PM	0.21	0.02	0.07	0.15
4 PM	0.18	0.02	0.07	0.12
6 PM	0.17	0.04	0.06	0.07
8 PM	0.17	0.05	0.06	0.02
10 PM	0.18	0.07	0.06	0.01

Analyze and Conclude

1. At what time do the concentrations of both nitrogen oxides and hydrocarbons peak? **about 8 AM**

What could cause these high concentrations? **morning rush hour traffic—more automobile exhaust gases**

2. As the concentration of NO_2 is increasing, the concentration of NO is decreasing. How can you explain this? **NO + oxygen make NO_2**

3. Ozone in the upper atmosphere is important in protecting us from ultraviolet light. Near the ground ozone is a pollutant. Using the data table, determine which chemicals are near minimum levels when ozone is at its maximum level. **NO, NO_2 students may include hydrocarbons**

What does this tell you about the production of ozone in polluted air? **These chemicals, along with sunlight, make ozone.**

4. What steps can be taken to reduce photochemical smog? **Sample answers include: Reduce the level of polluting chemicals. Put less reliance on polluting fuels—convert to cleaner fuels.**

40   Copyright Glencoe Division of Macmillan/McGraw-Hill
Users of Merrill Physical Science have the publisher's permission to reproduce this page.

227

2 TEACH

Key Concepts are highlighted.

CONCEPT DEVELOPMENT
▶ Many of the components of smog are a result of sunlight-activated chemical reactions. This photochemical smog is a significant problem in areas that experience temperature inversions.

CHECK FOR UNDERSTANDING
Ask questions 1-2 and the **Connect to Earth Science** question in the Section Review.

RETEACH
Clap two used chalkboard erasers together so that the fine chalk dust drifts down. Shine a flashlight beam through the dust to show the Tyndall effect.

EXTENSION
For students who have mastered this section, use the **Reinforcement** and **Enrichment** masters or other OPTIONS provided.

3 CLOSE

▶ Use the You Decide feature as the basis for a panel discussion or a debate.

SECTION REVIEW ANSWERS
1. The colloidal particles in smog scatter light.
2. Dust and other pollutant particles mix with and build up in the air.
3. Connect to Earth Science: Less dense, because the particles in warm air have more kinetic energy. The particles spread out more than do the particles in cooler air.

YOU DECIDE!

SCIENCE & SOCIETY

Many conclusions are possible and may be debated by students. You could make this an exercise in risk-benefit analysis, leading to a discussion of how much pollution should be tolerated.

PREPARATION

SECTION BACKGROUND

▶ Physical changes don't alter the identity of a substance. Pounding, pulling, cutting, dissolving, melting, or boiling don't produce a new substance with new properties, the mark of a chemical change.

▶ Evidence that a chemical change may have occurred includes formation of a precipitate, evolution or absorption of heat or light, evolution of a gas, or a color change.

▶ Chemical properties cannot be tested without altering the identity of the substance being tested.

▶ Since Einstein wrote $E = mc^2$, mass and energy have been thought of as being equivalent. Mass can be changed into energy and energy can be changed into mass. However, the law of conservation of mass, as stated here, holds true for everyday physical and chemical changes.

▶ The French scientist Lavoisier first stated the law of conservation of mass. He was executed in 1794 during the French Revolution.

PREPLANNING

▶ For Activity 9-2, you will need to prepare dilute 4M hydrochloric acid.

▶ Several demonstrations are offered. Scan them to see which ones you want to do and gather the materials needed.

STUDENT TEXT QUESTIONS

▶ Page 228, paragraph 1: **Does all matter have properties?** *Yes. All matter can be described by its properties.*

▶ Page 228, paragraph 2: **What physical property of a nail is measured with a balance?** *its mass*

9-3 Describing Matter

New Science Words

physical property
physical change
chemical change
chemical property
law of conservation of mass

Objectives

▶ Give examples of physical properties.
▶ Distinguish between physical and chemical changes.
▶ Distinguish between chemical and physical properties.
▶ State and explain the law of conservation of mass.

Physical Properties

You can bend an empty aluminum can. But you can't bend a piece of chalk. Chalk doesn't bend—it breaks. Brittleness is a characteristic that describes a piece of chalk. Its color and shape also describe the chalk. A **physical property** is any characteristic of a material that you can observe without changing the substances that make up the material. You can describe matter using physical properties. Does all matter have properties?

Figure 9-7. What are the physical properties of the balloons and the gas inside them?

Some physical properties describe the appearance of an object. For example, you might describe an iron nail as a pointy-ended cylinder made of dull, gray-colored solid. By describing the shape, color, and state of the nail, you have listed several of its physical properties. Some physical properties can be measured. For instance, you could use a metric ruler to measure another property of the nail—its length. What physical property of the nail is measured with a balance?

228 CLASSIFICATION OF MATTER

OPTIONS

Meeting Different Ability Levels

For Section 9-3, use the following **Teacher Resource Masters** depending upon individual students' needs.

◆ **Study Guide Master** for all students.

● **Reinforcement Master** for students of average and above average ability levels.

▲ **Enrichment Master** for above average students.

Additional Teacher Resource Package masters are listed in any PROGRAM RESOURCES boxes that are in the section. The additional masters are appropriate for all students.

◆ **STUDY GUIDE** 41

STUDY GUIDE   Chapter 9
Describing Matter   Text Pages 228–236

Complete the following by filling in each blank with the correct term.

Scientists try to explain how changes in substances take place. By applying energy, you can tear a sheet of paper into pieces and cause a(n) _____physical_____ _____change_____ in the paper. If you place a balloon filled with air into the refrigerator, the balloon will get smaller. The balloon undergoes a(n) _____physical_____ _____change_____. On a hot summer day, water vapor will condense into water droplets on the outside of a glass of iced tea. The glass of iced tea is a(n) _____mixture_____ of sugar, tea, lemon, and water. Ice is water in the solid state. The density of ice is less than that of liquid water. Therefore, ice floats on the tea. The melting point of ice is 0°C. This temperature is also the freezing point of liquid water. Water is a clear, colorless _____liquid_____ at room temperature. The words *clear* and *colorless* describe two _____physical_____ _____properties_____ of water. The melting of the ice in iced tea is a(n) _____physical_____ _____change_____.

In comparison, a(n) _____chemical_____ _____change_____ produces new substances. When a candle burns, physical and _____chemical_____ changes take place. The _____melting_____ of the wax is a physical change. The melted wax is now in the liquid state. However, when burning occurs, a(n) _____chemical_____ _____change_____ takes place. The melted wax, as it burns, combines with gaseous oxygen in air. After the chemical change, water vapor and carbon dioxide gas are formed. The mass of all substances before a chemical change _____is_____ _____equal_____ _____to_____ the mass of all substances after a chemical change.

Copyright Glencoe Division of Macmillan/McGraw-Hill
Users of Merrill Physical Science have the publisher's permission to reproduce this page.   41

If you had some water in a test tube, you might measure its volume and temperature and describe its odor. Each characteristic is a physical property. Some physical properties describe the behavior of a material or a substance. As you may know, all objects made of iron are attracted by a magnet. Attraction by a magnet is a property of the substance iron. Every substance has physical properties that distinguish it from other substances. Examples of physical properties you have learned about are color, shape, size, density, melting point, and boiling point.

Do you pick out the grapes in a fruit salad and eat them first, last, or maybe not at all? If you do, you are using physical properties to identify the grapes and separate them from the other fruits in the mixture. Figure 9-8 shows a mixture of pebbles and sand. You can identify the pebbles and grains of sand by differences in color, shape, and size. By sifting the mixture, you can quickly separate the pebbles from the grains of sand because they have different sizes.

Look at the mixture of iron filings and sand shown in Figure 9-9. It would be impossible to separate this mixture with a sieve because the filings and grains of sand are the same size. A more efficient way is to pass a magnet through the mixture. When you pass a magnet through the mixture, the magnet attracts the iron filings and pulls them from the sand. In this way, the difference in a physical property, such as attraction to a magnet, can be used to separate substances in a mixture.

Figure 9-8. This mixture of pebbles and sand could be separated with a sifter.

Connect to... Earth Science

Recycling conserves natural resources. In some large recycling projects it is difficult to separate aluminum metal from scrap iron. What physical properties of the two metals would help you separate them?

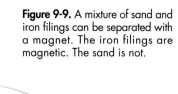

Figure 9-9. A mixture of sand and iron filings can be separated with a magnet. The iron filings are magnetic. The sand is not.

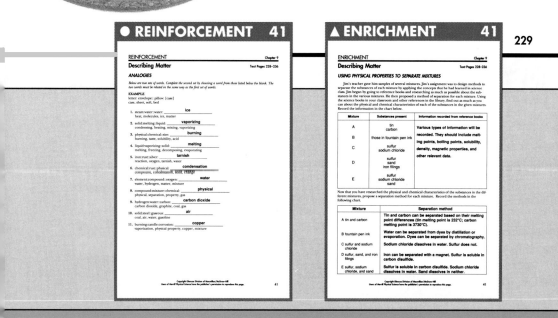

229

List five examples of physical changes in water.

Physical Changes

If you break a piece of chalk, it loses its original size and shape. You have caused a change in some of its physical properties. But you have not changed the identities of the substances that make up the chalk.

The changes that you studied in Chapter 8 are all examples of physical changes. When a substance freezes, boils, evaporates, sublimes, or condenses, it undergoes physical changes. There are energy changes during these changes in state, but the kind of substance—the identity of the element or compound—does not change.

As shown in the picture above, iron will change states if it absorbs enough energy. In each state it will have physical properties that identify it as the substance iron. A change in size, shape, or state of matter is called a **physical change.** Sometimes a color change indicates a physical change. Physical changes do not change the identities of the substances in a material.

Just as physical properties can be used to separate mixtures, so can physical changes. For example, if you let salt water stand, you'll find at a later time that

OPTIONS

TECHNOLOGY

Aerogels—Next to Nothing at All

Imagine a block of gelatin dessert in which all of the liquid has been replaced with air. It might look like a frozen cloud and would be called an aerogel.

Light passing through the tiny pores and microscopic framework of an aerogel is bent, giving the aerogel a bluish color against a dark background and a yellowish color in the light. Unlike a solid, the framework is so weakly connected that the aerogel is a poor conductor of heat. Therefore, an aerogel is an excellent insulator. The insulating property of aerogels has caught the interest of industry. Thus, you may soon see aerogels used as insulation in everything from refrigerators to double pane windows.

Think Critically: What property of aerogels might limit their use as an insulator in double pane windows?

the water has evaporated, leaving salt crystals inside the glass. The process of evaporating water from salty seawater is used to produce drinking water.

Chemical Changes

In any physical change of a material, the substances in the material do not change their identities. But you know that substances do change their identities. Fireworks explode, matches burn, eggs rot, and bikes and car bodies rust. What do changes in these materials have in common?

Burned toast, burned soup, and burned steak all smell burned. The smell is different from the smell of bread, soup, or steak. The odor is a clue that a new substance

In Your JOURNAL

Over the past couple of days you have observed or been part of many chemical and physical changes. **In your Journal,** list five chemical changes and five physical changes that you have noticed in the past two days.

TECHNOLOGY

For more information on aerogels, see "Super Fluff" by Robert Pool, *Discover*, Aug. 1990, p. 26, and "The Art of Making Insubstantial Things" by Ivan Amato, *Science News*, Nov. 17, 1990, p. 316.

Think Critically: The bluish or yellowish color may limit its use in standard windows.

CONCEPT DEVELOPMENT

▶ Students enjoy learning about chemical changes by seeing them occur. You can demonstrate the types of evidence that indicate chemical change.

▶ **Demonstration:** A precipitate can be formed by mixing tap water, which will probably contain some chloride, and a few drops of 0.1M silver nitrate solution. A white precipitate of silver chloride will form, indicating a chemical change.

▶ **Demonstration:** The evolution of heat and light can be demonstrated by striking a match and letting it burn.

▶ **Demonstration:** The evolution of a gas can be demonstrated by mixing baking soda with vinegar in the bottom of a large flask or jar. Carbon dioxide gas, water, and sodium acetate are the products. Pour the denser-than-air carbon dioxide gas onto a burning candle to show students how it can be used in fire extinguishers.

TEACHER F.Y.I.

▶ Physical and chemical changes are always accompanied by energy changes. The energy changes occur between a system and its surroundings. A system is that piece of the universe under consideration, for example, a flask and its contents. Everything else is the surroundings.

In Your JOURNAL

Check student entries for misconceptions about physical and chemical changes.

ENRICHMENT

▶ Some of the chemical changes that occur in the body take in energy, and others release energy. Have students gather information about the Calorie content of some common foods. Then have them research activities to find out how many Calories are used. Students should compute the energy value of a typical meal and then determine how long they would have to perform various activities in order to use up that energy. Be sure students include basal metabolic rates.

PROGRAM RESOURCES

From the **Teacher Resource Package** use:
Cross-Curricular Connections, page 13, Physical and Chemical Properties and Changes.

Use the Mini Quiz to check students' recall of chapter content.

1 **Which kind of property can be determined without changing the identity of a material?** *physical property*

2 **A change in size, shape, or state of matter is called a(n) _____ change.** *physical*

3 **A change of one substance into a different substance is a(n) _____ change.** *chemical*

4 **Rusting is a chemical change because iron and oxygen combine to form a new _____ .** *substance*

CROSS CURRICULUM

▶ **History:** Nitrates are a primary ingredient in explosives and gun powder. Before World War I, Germany had to import nitrates from South America. Because the British navy could have cut off this supply, Germans looked for alternate sources of nitrates. Fritz Haber discovered a way to make ammonia from nitrogen and hydrogen. Friedrich Ostwald later discovered a method to oxidize the ammonia to form nitrate. The motivation for these scientists' research was not to enable Germany to make explosives, but to make inexpensive fertilizer available to Europe's worn out farmland. Interested students could read about Haber's and Ostwald's lives and work.

PROGRAM RESOURCES

From the **Teacher Resource Package** use:

Critical Thinking/Problem Solving, page 15, Ethanol versus Gasoline.

Science and Society, page 13, Motor Vehicle Pollution.

has been produced. A change of one substance in a material to a different substance is a **chemical change.** There 3 are many signs that can tell you when a chemical change has taken place. For example, the foaming of an antacid tablet in a glass of water and the smell in the air after a thunderstorm indicate that new substances have been produced. In some chemical changes a rapid production of energy, such as the light and sound of an exploding firecracker, is a clue.

When iron is exposed to the oxygen and water in the air, the iron and oxygen slowly form a new substance, 4 rust. When hydrogen gas is burned in a rocket engine, the elements hydrogen and oxygen combine to form water. Burning and rusting are chemical changes because different substances are produced.

232 CLASSIFICATION OF MATTER

OPTIONS

INQUIRY QUESTIONS
▶ Classify each of the following as a chemical or a physical change: (a) fading of dye in cloth; (b) growth of a plant; (c) formation of clouds in the air. *(a) chemical; (b) chemical; (c) physical*

▶ Classify each of the following as a heterogeneous mixture, an element, a compound, or a solution: (a) air; (b) table salt; (c) apple; (d) silver; (e) hot tea; (f) box of cake mix; (g) copper. *(a) solution; (b) compound; (c) heterogeneous mixture; (d) element; (e) solution;*

(f) heterogeneous mixture; (g) element

ENRICHMENT
▶ Ask a student to research how crude oil can be obtained from shale or oil sands through chemical and physical means. In one method, the shale is crushed and then placed into a retort, where it is heated with superheated steam, which vaporizes the oil. The vapors are condensed, and the oil is refined.

Chemical Properties

Look at Figure 9-10. You have probably seen this warning on cans of paint thinners and lighter fluids for charcoal grills. The warning indicates that these liquids burn quickly. The tendency of a substance to burn is an example of a chemical property. A **chemical property** is a characteristic of a substance that indicates if it can undergo a certain chemical change. Many substances are flammable or combustible. Knowing which materials contain substances that have this chemical property allows you to use them safely.

Science and READING

When iron has turned to rust, why would the mass of the rust be more than the mass of the iron?

Figure 9-10. Flammability or combustibility is a chemical property of some materials used in the home.

If you look around a drugstore, you might notice that many medicines are stored in dark bottles. These medicines contain compounds with a similar chemical property. Chemical changes will take place in the compounds if they are exposed to light. What physical property do these bottles have in common?

Even though there are thousands of substances and billions of mixtures, they do share a few common physical and chemical properties. You can use these properties to study matter further.

EcoTip

Cleaners with the words *warning*, *caution*, or *poison* on them can be dangerous to you and to the environment. Call the local EPA to find out how to dispose of them when they are no longer needed.

Science and READING

Nearly all chemistry books discuss rusting in some detail as a basic example of chemical change. When iron rusts, it combines with oxygen from the air. After rusting, all the iron that was originally there is still there. The added oxygen results in an increased mass. Rust is a hydrated form of Fe_2O_3.

CONCEPT DEVELOPMENT

▶ The chemical properties of a substance depend on the action of the substance in the presence of other substances or added energy.

▶ Some examples of chemical properties are (1) changes in the presence of light, (2) flammability, (3) reacts with oxygen in air, (4) reacts with water, (5) reacts with acid, (6) is decomposed by electricity, (7) produces a gas when heated, and (8) forms a precipitate in the presence of a base.

▶ Examples of reactions that occur from the above list of chemical properties are (1) photographs and dyes fade, (2) paper and wood burn, (3) white phosphorus ignites in air, (4) Li, Na, and K react with water, (5) zinc metal reacts in acid, (6) electrolysis of water, (7) metal carbonates produce CO_2 when heated, and (8) some metals form insoluble hydroxides.

▶ You can use the two lists above to prepare a matching quiz for students who like to be challenged.

REVEALING MISCONCEPTIONS

▶ Use the Ecotip on page 233 to clear up the common misconception that proper disposal of all household chemicals is to put them down the drain.

▶ Have students make posters for display in their homes that give specific disposal instructions for common household chemical wastes such as paint, used oil, outdated medications, and so on.

STUDENT TEXT QUESTION

▶ Page 233, paragraph 2: **What physical property do these bottles have in common?** *They do not allow light to pass through.*

MULTICULTURAL PERSPECTIVE

A-maize-ing!

Corn, scientifically known as *Zea mays*, has been part of human life for thousands of years. It originated in North, Central, and South America, but quickly spread to widely diverse areas. Today a corn crop matures somewhere in the world every month of the year. The U.S. produces almost half of the world's total corn production, but other major growers include Brazil, Mexico, Romania, South Africa, and India.

Corn, when subjected to various physical and chemical changes, has been used in many ways by humans. Different colors of corn have different properties and are used for different purposes. Blue corn, for example, is used to prepare ritual meals among the Hopi. Ground into meal, maize forms a dough (masa) used to make flat corn pancakes called tortillas that form the basis of many dishes. Maize is also used to feed livestock; cobs are used as fuel; fermented corn produces an alcoholic beverage; and oil made from corn is used to fry foods as well.

▶ You may want to contrast an ordinary chemical reaction with a nuclear reaction when you discuss the law of conservation of mass. The formula $E = mc^2$ shows that mass is converted to energy in a nuclear reaction. When nuclear reactions are considered, the law becomes the law of conservation of mass-energy. This law simply states that the sum of mass and energy remains constant.

CHECK FOR UNDERSTANDING

Use the Mini Quiz to check for understanding.

MINI QUIZ

Use the Mini Quiz to check students' recall of chapter content.

⑤ Which kind of property indicates whether a substance can undergo a certain chemical change? *chemical*

⑥ Which law states that matter can be neither created nor destroyed during a chemical change? *law of conservation of mass*

⑦ The mass of substances remaining after a chemical change _____ the mass of substances present before the change. *equals*

RETEACH

Cooperative Learning: Use the Paired Partner strategy to have students prepare two sets of flash cards. Have students write the new science words in this section on one side of each set. On the reverse side of one set, write the definition of the term. On the other set, write examples for each term. Use the cards to provide drill and practice for students who need remediation.

EXTENSION

For students who have mastered this section, use the **Reinforcement** and **Enrichment** masters or other OPTIONS provided.

What are some signs of a chemical change when a log burns?

The Conservation of Mass

Suppose you burn a large log on a campfire until nothing is left but a small pile of ashes. During the burning, smoke, heat, and light are given off. It's easy to see that a chemical change occurs. At first, you might also think that matter was lost during this change, because the pile of ashes looks much smaller than the log. In fact, if you could measure both the mass of the log and the mass of the ashes, the mass of the ashes would be less than that of the log. But suppose that during the burning, you could collect all the oxygen in the air that was combined with the log during the burning. And suppose you could also collect all the smoke and gases that escape from the burning log and measure their masses, too. Then you would find that there is no loss of mass during the burning.

Not only is there no loss of mass during burning; there is no loss or gain of mass during any chemical change. In other words, matter is neither created nor destroyed during a chemical change. This statement is known as the **law of conservation of mass.** According to this law, the mass of all substances present before a chemical change equals the mass of all the substances remaining

Figure 9-11. Although you can't see the gases used or formed when a log burns, there is no loss or gain of mass.

234 CLASSIFICATION OF MATTER

OPTIONS

ENRICHMENT

▶ Chemical changes occur when some photosensitive chemicals are exposed to light. If your school has a darkroom, have interested students develop film and print pictures and enlargements. For more depth, students could find books and articles on photographic chemistry. There may be a student photographer who is willing to demonstrate the use of the darkroom and chemicals used in photography to interested students after school.

PROGRAM RESOURCES

From the **Teacher Resource Package** use:
Transparency Masters, pages 35-36, Conservation of Matter.
Use **Color Transparency** number 18, Conservation of Matter.
Use **Laboratory Manual 21,** Properties of Matter.

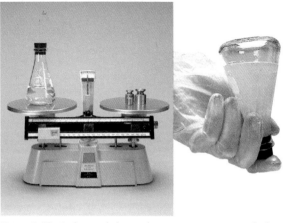

Figure 9-12. A chemical change between two compounds demonstrates the law of conservation of mass.

(7) after the change. What evidence is there in Figure 9-12 that a chemical change has occurred? How do the pictures illustrate the law of conservation of mass?

SECTION REVIEW

1. In terms of substances, explain why evaporation of water is a physical change and not a chemical change.
2. Give an example of a chemical change that occurs when you prepare a meal.
3. Why is being flammable a chemical property rather than a physical property?
4. **Apply:** The law of conservation of mass applies to physical changes as well as to chemical changes. How might you demonstrate this law for melting ice?
5. **Connect to Earth Science:** When acids are added to rocks containing a carbonate, bubbles form. Is this evidence of a physical change or a chemical change? Explain your answer.

☑ Observing and Inferring

Observe a burning candle. What evidence do you have that there are chemical and physical changes in the candle as it burns? If you need help, refer to Observing and Inferring in the **Skill Handbook** on page 678.

Skill Builder

Skill Builder

Evidence of chemical changes includes the production of heat and light, the smell of something burning, the darkening of the wick, and the production of smoke (soot) and water vapor. Evidence of physical changes includes the melting and hardening (solidification) of the wax; the change in the shape, mass, and length of the candle; and the shortening of its wick.

Skill Builder
ASSESSMENT
Oral: Display several similar, but slightly different, candles. Have a student describe a secretly selected candle using only its physical properties. The other students then try to identify the candle.

STUDENT TEXT QUESTIONS

▶ Page 235, paragraph 1: **What evidence is there that a chemical change has occurred?** *A precipitate has formed and a color change has taken place.* **How do these pictures demonstrate the law of conservation of mass?** *Even though a change takes place, no mass is lost or gained.*

3 CLOSE

? FLEX Your Brain

Use the Flex Your Brain activity to have students explore CHEMICAL CHANGES.

ASSESSMENT

Portfolio: Use the Flex Your Brain activity to reinforce critical-thinking and problem-solving skills.

▶ Ask questions 1-4 and the **Apply** and **Connect to Earth Science** questions in the Section Review.

SECTION REVIEW ANSWERS

1. During evaporation, the units of water change from being close together as a liquid to being much farther apart as a gas. The makeup of the water units is unchanged.
2. Answers may vary but could include toasting bread, rising and browning of pancakes on a grill, searing of meat in a pan. Processes involving only melting or mixing should not be included.
3. Flammability is a material's tendency to catch fire in air. Burning is a chemical change because substances change to new substances.
4. Apply: Measure the mass of a closed container of ice. Allow the ice to melt and measure the mass again. There should be no change in mass.
5. Connect to Earth Science: Chemical change; a new substance is formed.

PROGRAM RESOURCES

From the **Teacher Resource Package** use:

Activity Worksheets, page 5, Flex Your Brain.

ACTIVITY 9-2

OBJECTIVE: Design and carry out an experiment to show evidence of a chemical change.
Time: one class period

PROCESS SKILLS applied in this activity are **Observing and Inferring, Recognizing Cause and Effect, Interpreting Data,** and **Making and Using Tables.**

PREPARATION

Prepare dilute (4M) HCl by slowly adding 330 cm³ of stock concentrated (12M) HCl to 660 cm³ of distilled water in a well-ventilated area. Allow solution to cool before use.

Cooperative Learning: Use the Science Investigation Team strategy. One student should have the specific task of monitoring the drying process.

SAFETY

Caution students to avoid direct contact with HCl, immediately flushing any affected area with water, and to avoid inhaling HCl fumes. Do not substitute any containers that may not be heat resistant for the evaporating dishes.

THINKING CRITICALLY

Different substances have different sets of chemical properties.

TEACHING THE ACTIVITY

Refer to the Activity Worksheets for additional information and teaching strategies.
▶ If time or supplies are limited, you may measure out the baking soda into watch glasses before starting class.
▶ The solution should be dried at a slow enough rate to avoid splattering. Turn off the hot plate as the solution approaches dryness and let residual heat finish the drying process.
▶ The chemical reaction involved is $NaHCO_3 + HCl \rightarrow NaCl + CO_2 + H_2O$.

SUMMING UP/SHARING RESULTS

▶ Bubbles formed after HCl was added to baking soda. The dried product seemed not to react with HCl.

DESIGNING AN EXPERIMENT
Checking Out Chemical Changes

As you have learned, simply mixing materials together does not always cause a chemical change. There must be some evidence that a new product has been formed before you can state that a chemical change has taken place. What evidence indicates a chemical change?

Getting Started
In this activity you will be gathering evidence of a chemical change. Some clues that a new product has been formed include those mentioned on page 232. **CAUTION:** *Hydrochloric acid is corrosive and can burn the skin; report and clean up any spills immediately. Avoid touching any glassware that could become hot during a chemical change.*

Thinking Critically
What factors make one substance different from another substance?

Materials
Your cooperative group will use:
- safety goggles
- baking soda
- small evaporating dish
- hand lens
- dilute hydrochloric acid
- 10-cm³ graduated cylinder
- electric hot plate

Try It!

1. Read the procedure steps and *make a data table* to record your data. Place approximately 0.5 g of baking soda in an evaporating dish. Examine the substance with a hand lens and record your observations.
2. Slowly add 1 cm³ of dilute hydrochloric acid to the 0.5 g of baking soda in the dish. Record any changes you *observed.*
3. Slowly add 1 cm³ more acid to the dish. Heat the dish until the contents become dry, and let it cool. Examine the contents of the dish with the hand lens and record your observations.
4. Add another 1 cm³ of acid to the material in the dish. Record your observations.

Summing Up/Sharing Results
- Compare and contrast your observations when acid was added to the baking soda and when acid was added to the product.
- Do you now have enough evidence to describe this reaction as a chemical change?

Going Further!
If you had used vinegar, which contains acetic acid, instead of hydrochloric acid, what results might be the same and what results might be different?

▶ New products were produced. The dried material had new physical and chemical properties. These were evidence of a chemical change.

GOING FURTHER!
Results using vinegar would be similar to those using HCl except that more vinegar must be used to produce the same results.

Activity
ASSESSMENT
Performance: To further assess students' understanding of chemical changes, see USING LAB SKILLS, Question 12, on page 238.

PROGRAM RESOURCES
From the **Teacher Resource Package** use: **Activity Worksheets,** pages 74-75, Activity 9-2: Checking Out Chemical Changes.

SUMMARY

9-1: Composition of Matter
1. Elements and compounds are substances; a mixture is composed of two or more substances.
2. A solution is a homogeneous mixture. Colloids and suspensions are two kinds of heterogeneous mixtures.

9-2: Science and Society: Smog, a Mixture in the Environment
1. Smog is a form of air pollution that can be identified as a colloid by the Tyndall effect.
2. Ways to eliminate smog include reducing the use of materials responsible for air pollution.

9-3: Describing Matter
1. Physical properties are characteristics of materials that you can observe without changing the identities of the substances themselves.
2. In physical changes, substances in materials do not change. In chemical changes, substances in materials change to different substances.

3. Physical properties can be observed without changing substances; chemical properties indicate chemical changes substances can undergo.
4. The law of conservation of mass states that during any chemical change, matter is neither created nor destroyed.

KEY SCIENCE WORDS

a. **chemical change**
b. **chemical property**
c. **colloid**
d. **compound**
e. **element**
f. **heterogeneous mixture**
g. **homogeneous mixture**
h. **law of conservation of mass**
i. **physical change**
j. **physical property**
k. **smog**
l. **solution**
m. **substance**
n. **suspension**
o. **Tyndall effect**

UNDERSTANDING VOCABULARY

Match each phrase with the correct term from the list of Key Science Words.

1. a colloidal form of air pollution
2. mixture of parts that can be easily distinguished
3. all atoms in a sample are alike
4. change in size, shape, or state
5. change of substance to a different substance
6. combined atoms of two or more elements
7. either an element or a compound
8. mixture that scatters light and never settles
9. an indication of whether a chemical change can occur in a substance
10. In a chemical change, matter is neither created nor destroyed.

CLASSIFICATION OF MATTER **237**

SUMMARY

Have students read the summary statements to review the major concepts of the chapter.

UNDERSTANDING VOCABULARY

1. k	**6.** d
2. f	**7.** m
3. e	**8.** c
4. i	**9.** b
5. a	**10.** h

ASSESSMENT
Portfolio
Encourage students to place in their portfolios one or two items of what they consider to be their best work. For each item, ask students to explain why that item was chosen and what they learned from it. Items might be selected from the following.
- Enrichment research, p. 223
- Activity 9-1 observations and answers, p. 225
- Skill Builder observations, p. 235

Performance
Additional performance assessments may be found in *Performance Assessment* and *Science Integration Activities* that accompany **Merrill Physical Science.** Performance Task Assessment Lists and rubrics for evaluating these activities and other products generated throughout the chapter can be found in Glencoe's *Performance Assessment in Middle School Science.*

OPTIONS

ASSESSMENT
To assess student understanding of material in this chapter, use the resources listed.

👥 COOPERATIVE LEARNING
Consider using cooperative learning in the THINK AND WRITE CRITICALLY, APPLY, and MORE SKILL BUILDERS sections of the Chapter Review.

PROGRAM RESOURCES
From the **Teacher Resource Package** use:
Chapter Review, pages 21-22.
Chapter and Unit Tests, pages 57-60, Chapter Test.

CHECKING CONCEPTS

1. b	**6.** a
2. a	**7.** d
3. b	**8.** c
4. a	**9.** b
5. d	**10.** b

USING LAB SKILLS

ASSESSMENT

Use these alternate lab exercises to assess students' understanding of skills used in this chapter.

11. Fresh milk and spoiled milk are both examples of heterogeneous mixtures.

12. You could not conclude that the substances were the same unless you could determine that all the products of the reactions were the same. Both substances could react with acid in a similar way, producing similar, but not identical, substances.

THINK AND WRITE CRITICALLY

13. Answers might include color, mass, smell, taste, temperature, state of milk, state of carton, volume, texture, density, and shape.

14. Table salt has properties different from those of sodium or chlorine alone.

15. Gels and many thick liquids such as paints and glues are actually colloids.

16. The iron in the nail is not lost. It merely combines with oxygen. The mass of the rusty nail equals the mass of the original nail plus the mass of the oxygen that reacted with it.

17. Many substances are dissolved in ocean water, forming a solution. There are also many small particles suspended in the water. These particles will settle out upon standing.

CHECKING CONCEPTS

Choose the word or phrase that completes the sentence or answers the question.

1. A copper wire will bend. This is an example of _____.
   a. a chemical property   **c.** conservation
   b. a physical property   **d.** an element

2. Which of the following is *not* an element?
   a. water   **c.** oxygen
   b. carbon   **d.** hydrogen

3. An example of a chemical change is _____.
   a. boiling   **c.** evaporation
   b. burning   **d.** melting

4. Gelatin is an example of a _____.
   a. colloid   **c.** substance
   b. solution   **d.** suspension

5. A sunbeam is an example of _____.
   a. an element   **c.** a suspension
   b. a solution   **d.** the Tyndall effect

6. Most smog is now caused by _____.
   a. automobile exhaust   **c.** dust
   b. burning coal   **d.** factories

7. The red color of a rose is a _____.
   a. chemical change   **c.** physical change
   b. chemical property **d.** physical property

8. The process of evaporating water from seawater for drinking is a _____.
   a. chemical change   **c.** physical change
   b. chemical property **d.** physical property

9. Which warning label indicates a chemical property of the material being labeled?
   a. "Fragile"   **c.** "Handle with Care"
   b. "Flammable"   **d.** "Shake Well"

10. Which of the following is a substance?
   a. colloid   **c.** mixture
   b. element   **d.** solution

USING LAB SKILLS

11. In Activity 9-1 on page 225 you classified different materials as to whether each was an element, a compound, a homogeneous mixture, or a heterogeneous mixture. Fresh milk from the grocery store would be classified as what type of material? If milk were allowed to spoil, what type would it be?

12. In Activity 9-2 on page 236 you investigated how chemical changes could be identified. If two white substances both react with acid to produce bubbles, can you conclude that they are the same substance? Explain your answer.

THINK AND WRITE CRITICALLY

Answer the following questions in your Journal using complete sentences.

13. Describe a carton of milk using its physical properties.

14. The soft metal sodium and the greenish gas chlorine combine to form table salt, sodium chloride. How do you know table salt is a compound?

15. The word *colloid* means "gluelike." Why was *colloid* chosen to name these mixtures?

16. Use a nail rusting in air to explain the law of conservation of mass.

17. Mai says that ocean water is a solution. Ed says that ocean water is a suspension. Are they both correct?

18. Rust is formed from oxygen and iron. How might you keep an iron pipe from rusting?
19. By mistake, sugar was put into some dry rice. How might you separate the mixture?
20. Not all solutions are liquid. Why is a metal alloy, such as brass, considered a solution?
21. Use what you know about suspensions to explain why deltas form at the mouths of large rivers.
22. Why do many medications have instructions to "shake well before using"?

MORE SKILL BUILDERS

If you need help, refer to the Skill Handbook.

1. **Recognizing Cause and Effect:** List at least two causes of smog and two effects of smog.
2. **Making and Using Tables:** Different colloids may involve different states. For example, gelatin is formed from solid particles in a liquid. Complete the following table, using these common colloids: smoke, marshmallow, fog, paint.

Colloid	Example
Gas in solid	
Solid in liquid	
Solid in gas	
Liquid in gas	

3. **Comparing and Contrasting:** In terms of suspensions and colloids, compare and contrast a glass of milk and a glass of grapefruit juice.
4. **Interpreting Data:** Starting with a 25-cm³ sample of pond water, Hannah poured 5 cm³ through a piece of filter paper. She repeated this with four more pieces of filter paper. She dried each piece of filter paper and measured the mass of the sediment. Why did the last sample have a higher mass than did the first sample?
5. **Using Variables, Constants, and Controls:** Marcos took a 100-cm³ sample of a suspension, shook it well, and divided it equally into four different test tubes. He placed one test tube in a rack, one in very hot water, one in warm water, and the fourth in ice water. He then observed the time it took for each suspension to settle. What was the variable in the experiment? What was one constant?

PROJECTS

1. Research the smog problem in Los Angeles. Report on what causes the problem, what health and other problems are caused by the smog, and possible solutions to the problem.
2. Make a display of an example of a solution, a heterogeneous mixture, a colloid, and a suspension. Label each and explain their differences.

CLASSIFICATION OF MATTER **239**

18. Coat the iron with paint, grease, or other material that will prevent oxygen from coming into contact with the iron. Water is also necessary for common rusting, but students may not know that.
19. A possible solution would be to dissolve the sugar in water and filter the mixture.
20. Brass is a homogeneous mixture of atoms of different metals, primarily copper and zinc.
21. As the river water flows rapidly, particles are kept suspended by the water's motion. As the river widens at the delta, the water slows down, allowing particles to settle out.
22. Because some liquid medications are suspensions, some of their substances will settle out. These substances need to be resuspended evenly before the medication is used.

MORE SKILL BUILDERS

1. **Recognizing Cause and Effect:** Causes include dust, ash, unburned materials, and spray products. Effects include health problems, restrictions on industry and traffic, and a drop in tourism.
2. **Making and Using Tables:** The table should be completed as follows: gas in solid, marshmallow; solid in liquid, paint; solid in gas, smoke; liquid in gas, fog.
3. **Comparing and Contrasting:** They are alike in that both have small particles suspended in a liquid. The particles of the juice will settle out. Thus, the juice is a suspension. The milk does not settle and is therefore a colloid.
4. **Interpreting Data:** The pond water could have been a suspension. As the experiment progressed, settling out was taking place. Thus, each succeeding filter paper received more sediment.
5. **Using Variables, Constants, and Controls:** The variable was temperature. Constants include the volume.

10 Atomic Structure and the Periodic Table

CHAPTER SECTION	OBJECTIVES	ACTIVITIES
10-1 Structure of the Atom (2 days)	1. **List** the names and symbols of common elements. 2. **Describe** the present model of the atom. 3. **Describe** how electrons are arranged in an atom.	**Activity 10-1:** *Models of Atomic Structure,* p. 247
10-2 Smaller Particles of Matter Science & Society (1 day)	1. **Identify** quarks as particles of matter that make up protons and neutrons. 2. **Explain** how protons can be broken apart.	
10-3 Masses of Atoms (2 days)	1. **Compute** the atomic mass and mass number of an atom. 2. **Identify** and **describe** isotopes of common elements. 3. **Interpret** the average atomic mass of an element.	**Activity 10-2:** *Candy-Covered Isotopes,* p. 254
10-4 The Periodic Table (2 days)	1. **Describe** the periodic table of elements and use it to find information about an element. 2. **Distinguish** between a group and a period. 3. **Use** the periodic table to classify an element as a metal, nonmetal, or metalloid.	**MINI-Lab:** *What are the advantages of a periodic table?* p. 257
Chapter Review		

ACTIVITY MATERIALS

FIND OUT	ACTIVITIES		MINI-LABS
Page 241 assorted small nuts, bolts, and washers toothpicks modeling clay	**10-1 Models of Atomic Structure, p. 247** magnetic board about 20 cm × 27 cm 1 0.5-cm piece and 20 1-cm pieces of magnetic tape circles of paper: white, 4-cm wide red, 1-cm wide marker	**10-2 Candy-Covered Isotopes, p. 254** 4 red and 3 green candy-coated peanuts 2 red and 3 green candy-coated chocolates 2 sealable plastic bags	**What are the advantages of a periodic table?** p. 257 assorted pencils and pens large table surface

CHAPTER FEATURES	TEACHER RESOURCE PACKAGE	OTHER RESOURCES
Skill Builder: *Concept Mapping,* p. 246	**Ability Level Worksheets** ◆ **Study Guide,** p. 42 ● **Reinforcement,** p. 42 ▲ **Enrichment,** p. 42 **Cross-Curricular Connections,** pp. 15, 16 **Activity Worksheets,** pp. 5, 78, 79	**STVS:** Disc 2, Side 2
You Decide! p. 249	**Ability Level Worksheets** ◆ **Study Guide,** p. 43 ● **Reinforcement,** p. 43 ▲ **Enrichment,** p. 43	
Problem Solving: *Ivan's Isotopes,* p. 252 **Skill Builder:** *Making and Using Tables,* p. 253	**Ability Level Worksheets** ◆ **Study Guide,** p. 44 ● **Reinforcement,** p. 44 ▲ **Enrichment,** p. 44 **Critical Thinking/Problem Solving,** p. 16 **Activity Worksheets,** pp. 80, 81	**Science Integration Activity 10**
Technology: *Seeing Atoms,* p. 261 **Skill Builder:** *Making and Using Graphs,* p. 262	**Ability Level Worksheets** ◆ **Study Guide,** p. 45 ● **Reinforcement,** p. 45 ▲ **Enrichment,** p. 45 **Concept Mapping,** pp. 25, 26 **Cross-Curricular Connections,** p. 14 **Science and Society,** p. 14 **Activity Worksheets,** pp. 5, 84 **Transparency Masters,** pp. 37-40	**Color Transparency 19,** The Periodic Table **Color Transparency 20,** The Periodic Table—Blank **Laboratory Manual 22,** Chemical Activity **STVS:** Disc 2, Side 1
Summary Think & Write Critically Key Science Words Apply Understanding Vocabulary More Skill Builders Checking Concepts Projects Using Lab Skills	**ASSESSMENT RESOURCES** **Chapter Review,** pp. 23, 24 **Chapter Test,** pp. 61-64 **Performance Assessment in** **Middle School Science**	**Chapter Review Software** **Test Bank** **Alternate Assessment** **Performance Assessment**

◆ **Basic**   ● **Average**   ▲ **Advanced**

ADDITIONAL MATERIALS

SOFTWARE	AUDIOVISUAL	BOOKS/MAGAZINES
The Atom and Its Nucleus, Queue. *Atomic Structure and Chemistry,* Queue. *Atoms,* J and S. Software. *Atoms and Elements,* Queue. *Chemistry: The Periodic Table,* MECC. *Classifying Elements,* Queue. *Learning All About Atoms and Atomic Energy,* Queue. *Molecules and Atoms: Exploring the Essence of Matter,* Queue. *Periodic Law,* EME Corp. *Periodic Table,* EME Corp. *The Structure of Matter,* Queue.	*The Atom,* Video, Insight Media. *The Atom: A Closer Look,* Video, Coronet. *Atoms and Compounds: An Illustrated History,* Video, Lucerne Media. *How We Found Out About Atoms,* Video, Hawkhill *Models of the Atom,* Video, Guidance Associates. *The Periodic Table and Periodicity,* Video, Coronet. *The Periodic Table,* Video, Lucerne Media. *The Story of the Atom,* Video, Hawkhill.	Asimov, Issac. *Atom: Journey Across the Subatomic Cosmos.* NY: Dutton, 1991. Crawford, Mark. "Racing after the Z Particle." *Science,* August 26, 1988, pp. 1031-1032. Fisher, A. "Hunting Neutrinos." *Popular Science,* May 1988, pp. 72-74, 115. Mebane, Robert C., and Thomas R. Rybolt. *Adventures with Atoms and Molecules, Book IV: Chemistry Experiments for Young People.* Hillside, NJ: Enslow, 1992.

THEME DEVELOPMENT: Scale and structure as a theme are developed through a presentation of atomic structure and the periodic table. The structure of an atom is related to its position on the periodic table.

CHAPTER OVERVIEW

▶ **Section 10-1:** This section introduces the general structure of the atom. The makeup of the nucleus and electron cloud are described.

▶ **Section 10-2: Science and Society:** The student learns how a supercollider can reveal subatomic particles.

▶ **Section 10-3:** In this section, the student learns that atoms of different elements have different masses. The term *isotope* is introduced, and the concept of average atomic mass is developed.

▶ **Section 10-4:** The student learns how the periodic table organizes elements into groups and periods related to atomic structure. Students are introduced to dot diagrams of atoms.

CHAPTER VOCABULARY

chemical	isotopes
symbol	average
nucleus	atomic mass
electrons	periodic table
protons	groups
neutrons	dot diagram
atomic number	periods
electron cloud	metals
quarks	nonmetals
mass number	metalloids

CHAPTER

10 Atomic Structure and the Periodic Table

240

OPTIONS

 For Your Gifted Students

Have students design and name their own element. Have them diagram the electron arrangement in the appropriate energy levels, the protons, and the neutrons. Students should find the correct position of their element in the periodic table according to group and period and predict its physical characteristics. If there is an existing element in the same position, they should check the properties against their predictions.

 For Your Mainstreamed Students

Obtain samples of several elements, such as tin, sulfur, copper, carbon, iron, aluminum, lead, zinc, gold, silver. Let students examine and record the characteristics of each element. They should look for such properties as color, hardness, texture, brittleness, and the like. Students can compare their lists. They can play a game in which one student lists characteristics and others try to identify the element.

Did you ever go stargazing at a planetarium? If so, you may have seen a globular cluster like the one in the picture. The appearance of this collection of stars resembles one model of the structure of the atom. What are some other models of the atom?

FIND OUT!

In this activity, you will make another kind of model of an atom.

Your teacher will give you a certain number of bolts, nuts, and/or washers. Each group in the class will get different numbers of the pieces of hardware. Bury your hardware in a piece of modeling clay. Form the clay into a ball so that you can't see the hardware. Trade clay balls with another group that started with different kinds and/or numbers of hardware pieces. You have made a kind of model of an atom. Using toothpicks to stick into the ball, try to *analyze* how many of each hardware piece are hidden in the clay without pulling it apart. Now you have used indirect evidence, as scientists do, to *infer* the identify and count the hidden parts of your model atom.

Previewing Science Skills
► In the Skill Builders, you will make a concept map, make and use a table, and make and use a graph.
► In the Activities, you will build models, infer, compare and contrast, and interpret data.
► In the MINI-Lab, you will observe and infer.

What's next?

You have investigated one simple model of an atom. In the pages that follow, you will learn about scientists' models of atoms.

241

ASSESSMENT OPTIONS

PORTFOLIO
Refer to page 263 for suggested items that students might select for their portfolios.

PERFORMANCE ASSESSMENT
See page 263 for additional Performance Assessment options.
Process
Skill Builders, pp. 246, 253, 262
MINI-Lab, p. 257
Activities 10-1, p. 247; 10-2, p. 254
Using Lab Skills, p. 264

CONTENT ASSESSMENT
Assessment—Oral, p. 258
Section Reviews, pp. 246, 249, 253, 262
Chapter Review, pp. 263-265
Mini Quizzes, pp. 245, 252, 259, 260

GROUP ASSESSMENT
Opportunities for group assessment occur with Cooperative Learning Strategies and Flex Your Brain Activities.

INTRODUCING THE CHAPTER
Use the Find Out activity to introduce students to atomic structure and the problems that faced scientists who tried to determine atomic structure. Inform students that they will be learning more about the structure of atoms as they read the chapter.

FIND OUT!
Preparation: Collect small nuts, bolts, and washers. Determine how much clay will be needed to bury a cluster of hardware.
Materials: assorted small nuts, bolts, and washers; toothpicks; modeling clay
Cooperative Learning: Use Science Investigation Groups of three. Have one student form the model out of sight of the other two.
Teaching Tips
► Have students prepare the clay balls the day before the activity. Have lumps of clay contain one, two, or three pieces of hardware.
► Have students prepare a detailed, full-scale map of the interior of the clay ball. Have students stick a broken-off toothpick in a permanent location on the ball as a point of reference. Record the position of each toothpick probe and the result. An *0* on the map means the probe hit nothing; an *X* on the map indicates that the probe touched a piece of hardware.

Gearing Up
Have students study the Gearing Up feature to familiarize themselves with the chapter. Discuss the relationships of the topics in the outline.

What's Next?
Before beginning the first section, make sure students understand the connection between the Find Out activity and the topics to follow.

PREPARATION

SECTION BACKGROUND

▶ The International Union of Pure and Applied Chemistry (IUPAC) has adopted a three-letter symbol for elements beyond 103. The symbols represent the names, which themselves are made up of Latin and Greek prefixes for the corresponding atomic numbers.

▶ Ca. 400 B.C., Democritus proposed that all matter was composed of small particles he called *atomos*. It wasn't until 1808 that Dalton restated this as a part of the atomic theory of matter.

▶ Atomic numbers were first assigned to elements as a result of the work of Henry Moseley. In 1913, Moseley used X rays to differentiate among the atomic nuclei of different elements.

▶ In 1913, Niels Bohr described the planetary model of the atom. Schrödinger later used quantum mechanics to describe the electron clouds around the nucleus.

PREPLANNING

▶ Try to have a wall-size copy of the periodic table available to refer to during this and following chapters. This display will help reinforce the use of the table as a source of information about elements.

▶ To prepare for Activity 10-1, cut and glue the magnetic tape to the backs of the paper circles. Allow the glue to dry overnight. As an alternative, obtain magnetic tape that has one peel-and-stick side.

STUDENT TEXT QUESTION

▶ Page 242, paragraph 2: **Which symbols in Table 10-1 might come from Latin?** *Cu, Au, Fe, Hg, K, Ag, Na*

10-1 Structure of the Atom

New Science Words

chemical symbol
nucleus
electrons
protons
neutrons
atomic number
electron cloud

Objectives

▶ List the names and symbols of common elements.
▶ Describe the present model of the atom.
▶ Describe how electrons are arranged in an atom.

Table 10-1

Chemical Symbols

Do the letters C, Al, He, and Ag mean anything to you? Each letter or pair of letters is a **chemical symbol,** which is an abbreviated way to write the name of an element. The black material on a burned match is carbon—C. You may wrap food in foil made of aluminum—Al. Did you ever lose a balloon filled with helium—He? You often use coins that contain copper—Cu.

Chemical symbols consist of one capital letter or a capital letter plus one or two small letters. For some elements, the symbol is the first letter of the element's name. For other elements, the symbol is the first letter of the name plus another letter from its name. Some symbols, such as Ag, are derived from Latin. *Argentum* is Latin for silver. Which symbols in Table 10-1 might come from Latin?

SYMBOLS OF SOME ELEMENTS

Element	Symbol	Element	Symbol	Element	Symbol
Aluminum	Al	Gold	Au	Mercury	Hg
Calcium	Ca	Hydrogen	H	Nitrogen	N
Carbon	C	Helium	He	Oxygen	O
Chlorine	Cl	Iodine	I	Potassium	K
Copper	Cu	Iron	Fe	Silver	Ag
Fluorine	F	Magnesium	Mg	Sodium	Na

Matter and Atoms

The idea of atoms began more than 2400 years ago with Greek thinkers, who defined atoms as the smallest parts of matter. Today scientists consider atoms to be the basic building blocks of matter. The atom consists of a positively

OPTIONS

Meeting Different Ability Levels

For Section 10-1, use the following **Teacher Resource Masters** depending upon individual students' needs.

◆ **Study Guide Master** for all students.
● **Reinforcement Master** for students of average and above average ability levels.
▲ **Enrichment Master** for above average students.

Additional Teacher Resource Package masters are listed in any PROGRAM RESOURCES boxes that are in the section. The additional masters are appropriate for all students.

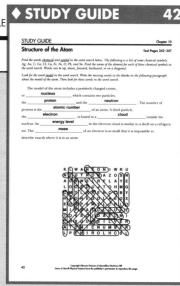

charged center, or **nucleus,** surrounded by negatively charged particles called **electrons.** The two major kinds of particles in the nucleus are **protons** and **neutrons.** The mass of a proton is about the same as that of a neutron. The mass of an electron is about 1/2000 the mass of a proton. The electron's mass is so small that it is considered negligible when finding the mass of an atom. The nucleus contains most of the mass of the atom.

A neutron is neutral, which means it has no charge. A proton has a positive charge. As a result, the net charge on the nucleus is positive. The amount of positive charge on a proton is equal to the amount of negative charge on an electron. Table 10-2 summarizes this information about the three particles in an atom.

Science and READING

The element platinum has an interesting history. Find out why it was called fool's silver.

Table 10-2

COMPARISON OF PARTICLES IN AN ATOM			
	Relative Mass	Charge	Location in the Atom
Proton	1	1+	Part of nucleus
Neutron	1	none	Part of nucleus
Electron	0	1–	Moves around nucleus

The **atomic number** of an atom is the number of protons in its nucleus. Every atom of the same element has the same number of protons. For example, every carbon atom has 6 protons. Therefore, it has the atomic number 6. Atoms of different elements have different numbers of protons. For example, every carbon atom has 6 protons, but every oxygen atom has 8 protons.

The number of electrons in a neutral atom is equal to the number of protons. A neutral carbon atom, then, has 6 electrons because it has 6 protons. Because the numbers of positively charged protons and negatively charged electrons in an atom are equal, the atom as a whole is electrically neutral.

How is the number of electrons in an atom related to the number of protons?

Table 10-3

ATOMIC NUMBER OF SOME ELEMENTS			
Atom	Number of Protons	Number of Electrons	Atomic Number
Carbon	6	6	6
Aluminum	13	13	13
Helium	2	2	2
Silver	47	47	47

● **REINFORCEMENT 42**

REINFORCEMENT   Chapter 10
Structure of the Atom   Text Pages 243–247

Use the clues to complete the puzzle.
Across
3. Scientist who developed the planetary model of the atom
7. Element 105
11. Region surrounding the nucleus which is occupied by electrons
13. Atomic number of fluorine (spelled out)
14. Center of atom
15. Symbol for sodium
16. Symbol for silver
18. Fe is the symbol.
21. Name of element used in fluorescent signs
22. Atom of an element with a different number of neutrons
23. Sum of protons and neutrons
25. Only element with atoms which do not have neutrons

Down
1. Element often made into electrical wire
2. Number of protons in an atom
4. Name of element whose symbol is Ru
5. Negatively charged particle
6. Mixture of mostly nitrogen and oxygen
8. 1/12 the mass of a carbon-12 atom
9. Helps us understand something that we cannot see directly
10. These are like shelves where electrons can be found.
12. Equal in number to the number of protons
14. A particle with approximately the same mass as a proton
17. Element used in balloons
19. Element name of radioactive gas that can accumulate in houses
20. Positively charged particle in nucleus
24. The building block of matter

▲ **ENRICHMENT 42**

ENRICHMENT   Chapter 10
Structure of the Atom   Text Pages 242–247

MENTAL MODEL OF THE SIZE OF ATOMS

Before performing this activity, review the following operations using scientific (exponential) notation.

A. When adding or subtracting exponential numbers, exponents must be the same.
$5 \times 10^4 + 4 \times 10^6 = 9 \times 10^6$ $2 \times 10^6 + 0.3 \times 10^6 = 2 \times 10^6 + 3 \times 10^6 = 5 \times 10^6$
$5 \times 10^6 - 0.1 \times 10^8 = 5 \times 10^6 - 1 \times 10^6 = 2 \times 10^6$
B. When multiplying numbers in exponential notation, multiply the numbers and add the exponents.
$(6 \times 10^4)(3 \times 10^6) = 18 \times 10^{10} = 1.8 \times 10^{11}$ $(2 \times 10^4) \times 4 = 8 \times 10^4$
C. When dividing numbers in exponential notation, divide the numbers and subtract the exponents.
$(6 \times 10^4) \div (3 \times 10^6) = 2 \times 10^{-2}$ $(8 \times 10^4) \div 2 = 4 \times 10^4$
D. To find the power of an exponential number, raise the number to the power and multiply the exponent by the power.
$(3 \times 10^4)^3 = 9 \times 10^{12}$ $(3 \times 10^6)^3 = 27 \times 10^{18} = 2.7 \times 10^{19}$
E. To find the root of a number in exponential notation, take the root of the number and divide the exponent by the root.
$\sqrt{16 \times 10^6} = 4 \times 10^3$ $\sqrt[3]{8 \times 10^9} = 2 \times 10^3$

Suppose you had a cube of copper metal. Using a balance, you found the copper cube had a mass of 106 grams. Using the *Handbook of Chemistry and Physics,* you found that the density of copper is 9.0 g/cm³. There are 6.02×10^{23} atoms. Use this information to answer the following questions.

1. What is the volume of the copper cube?
$Density = \frac{mass}{volume}$ $V = \frac{M}{D} = \frac{106 \text{ g}}{9.0 \text{ g/cm}^3} = 11.8 \text{ cm}^3$

2. Using the volume from question 1, what is the length, width, and height of the copper cube?
$L \times W \times H = V$ $L = W = H = \sqrt[3]{11.8 \text{ cm}^3} = 2.28 \text{ cm}$

3. How many copper atoms are in the cube?
64 g Cu/6.02 × 10²³ atoms = 106 g/x atoms $x = 1.00 \times 10^{24}$ atoms Cu in cube

4. Suppose you had as many sheets of paper as you had atoms in question 3. If each sheet of paper had a thickness of 0.1 mm (1 × 10⁻⁴ m), how high, in meters would your stack of papers be?
$1.00 \times 10^{24} \text{ sheets} \times \frac{1.00 \times 10^{-4}}{1 \text{ sheet}} = 1.00 \times 10^{20} \text{ m}$

5. Light travels about 9.5×10^{15} meters in a year. How many light years high would your stack of paper be?
$1.00 \times 10^{20} \text{ m} \times \frac{1 \text{ light year}}{9.5 \times 10^{15} \text{ m}} = 10\ 526 \text{ light years}$

243

Copyright Glencoe Division of Macmillan/McGraw-Hill
Users of *Merrill Physical Science* have the publisher's permission to reproduce this page.

Copyright Glencoe Division of Macmillan/McGraw-Hill
Users of *Merrill Physical Science* have the publisher's permission to reproduce this page.

1 MOTIVATE

▶ Obtain a periodic table that is in Spanish or French from your school's foreign language teacher. Explain that the chemical symbols are the same for all languages.

TYING TO PREVIOUS KNOWLEDGE: An example of symbols and names that students are already familiar with are traffic signs that convey safety information. Students will probably also know a few names, chemical symbols, and formulas for some common substances, such as table salt, $NaCl$; cane sugar, $C_{12}H_{22}O_{11}$; and water, H_2O. Encourage your students by informing them that they will learn many more symbols and formulas during this and the next chapter.

2 TEACH

Key Concepts are highlighted.

CONCEPT DEVELOPMENT

▶ For students who enjoy history, you can share the following information. By 1700, thirteen elements had been identified in their pure form. When Mendeleev proposed his periodic table in 1869, chemists knew of 26 elements. In 1908, Moseley used X rays to determine the atomic numbers of 81 elements. Today, 109 elements have been discovered or synthesized.

REVEALING MISCONCEPTIONS

▶ Students often do not realize the importance of capital and lowercase letters in chemical symbols. For example, *CO* and *Co* do not have the same meaning. Point out that carbon monoxide is not the same as an atom of cobalt.

VideoDisc

STVS: Neutron Activation Analysis of Paintings, Disc 2, Side 2

▶ You may want to review Rutherford's gold foil experiment with the class. Alpha particles hit gold foil. Most passed through, indicating that the atom is mostly empty space. However, some particles were deflected by a small, dense, positively charged nucleus. Details may be found in most high school chemistry texts.

▶ Emphasize that Bohr's planetary model of the atom is not the best model for science students to visualize. Encourage them to think about electrons occupying probability clouds.

▶ **Demonstration:** Place a small scoop of sesame seeds inside a balloon. Inflate it and tie it closed. Shake the seeds around the balloon to simulate electrons moving about the nucleus. Their pattern of motion mimics that of electrons in an electron cloud.

▶ A dart board and repeated throws of one dart can be used as a model of the hydrogen atom with its one electron. The pattern of holes in the dart board represents the electron cloud around the nucleus.

▶ A multi-electron atom can have concentric spheres of electron clouds, called energy levels, around the nucleus. Students have seen layers of clouds in the sky when lower clouds are covered by a higher overcast.

CROSS CURRICULUM

▶ **Design and Engineering:** Both engineers and scientists often use models to predict the behavior of actual objects. An airplane model is constructed and tested in a wind tunnel before the prototype is built. Design flaws can be corrected because a model behaves just like the real thing. Sometimes computer models are used instead of physical models. Our model of the atom should also allow us to explain how the real atom behaves.

Connect to...
Earth Science

Answer: In the Bohr model, electrons orbit the nucleus in much the same way planets orbit the sun.

Figure 10-1. A globe is a physical model, unlike a scientific model, which is a mental picture.

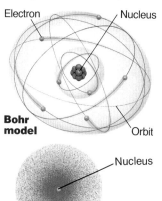

Electron   Nucleus

Bohr model   Orbit

Nucleus

Electron cloud model

Figure 10-2. The top illustration is an early model of an atom with defined paths for electrons. The lower illustration is a later model showing a region where electrons are likely to be.

Connect to...
Physics

The Bohr model of the atom is also called the planetary model of the atom. Explain why the term *planetary model* is used.

Figure 10-3. In an atom as wide as a football field, the nucleus would be as wide as a paper clip wire.

Models of the Atom

As scientists continued to study matter and atoms, they tried to form a mental picture or model of what an atom might look like. A model helps us understand something we cannot see directly, usually because it is too large or too small. A good model of the atom must explain all the information about matter and atoms. As more information was collected, scientists changed their models. Therefore, the model of the atom we use today is the result of the work of many scientists.

One of the early models of an atom looked like the top one in Figure 10-2. It was developed by Niels Bohr in 1913. Bohr pictured the atom as having a central nucleus with electrons moving around it in well-defined paths, or orbits.

In 1926, scientists developed a better model of the atom. In this model, the electrons moved about in a region called an **electron cloud** (Figure 10-2). This cloud surrounds the nucleus of the atom. It describes the region where an electron is likely to be at any time. The diameter of the nucleus is about 1/100 000 the diameter of the electron cloud. Suppose you built a model of an atom with an electron cloud as wide as a football field. The atom's nucleus would be about the thickness of the wire in a paper clip!

Because the electron's mass is so small, it is impossible for you—or anyone—to describe exactly where it is as it moves in the atom. All anyone can give

OPTIONS

INQUIRY QUESTIONS

▶ **Democritus stated his belief that matter was composed of atoms around 400 B.C. John Dalton proposed his atomic theory in 1808 A.D. Science has advanced rapidly since the acceptance of the atomic theory. Why didn't the ancient Greeks make similar advances? Hint: Research the influence of Aristotle's ideas about matter.** *Aristotle's idea that matter was continuous prevailed. Many of Aristotle's ideas were accepted without question until the 17th and 18th centuries.*

ENRICHMENT

▶ By assigning each student a scientist to research, you can have the class prepare a time line mural on the bulletin board to show how each contributed to our knowledge of the atom. You can assign the following names: Empedocles, Democritus, Lucretius, Aristotle, Newton, Boyle, Lavosier, Proust, Dalton, Avogadro, Gay-Lussac, Millikan, J. J. Thomson, Geiger, Rutherford, Bohr, De Broglie, Planck, Chadwick, Pauli, Schrödinger, Einstein, Heisenberg, Becquerel, and Curie.

is its probable location. Describing the electron's location around a nucleus is like trying to describe your location in your science class at any given moment. Your most probable location during the class is at your desk. Other possible, though less probable, locations are at the pencil sharpener and at the teacher's desk.

The electron cloud represents the probable locations of electrons within an atom. As a model of the electron cloud you could use the spray of water drops from a rotary lawn sprinkler. Each drop represents a probable location of an electron in the cloud. As you can see in Figure 10-4, most of the drops are near the center of the spray. In an atom, the most probable location of electrons is in the electron cloud about the nucleus.

Energy Levels of Electrons

The electrons in an atom make up the electron cloud. Within the electron cloud, electrons are at various distances from the nucleus. Electrons near the nucleus have low energy. Electrons farther away have higher energy. You can represent the energy differences of the electrons by picturing the atom as having energy levels.

Energy levels are somewhat like shelves of a refrigerator door. A carton on the lowest shelf represents an electron in the lowest energy level. The difference in spacing of the shelves could indicate the differences in the amount of energy the electrons in that level can have. Shelves of a refrigerator door can usually hold the same number of cartons. Unlike these shelves, each energy level of an atom has a different maximum number of electrons it can hold. The lowest energy level can hold just two electrons. The second energy level can hold eight electrons, and the third energy level, 18 electrons.

Figure 10-4. You can compare the spray of water from a rotary lawn sprinkler to an electron cloud.

What does the electron cloud represent?

Did You Know?

One ounce of gold can be made into a wire 50 miles long.

PROGRAM RESOURCES

From the **Teacher Resource Package** use:
Cross-Curricular Connections, page 15, Alchemy.
Cross-Curricular Connections, page 16, The Name Game.

REVEALING MISCONCEPTIONS

▶ Be certain that your students understand that the electron does not go around the nucleus like a train on a track.

CROSS CURRICULUM

▶ **Meteorology:** Fog can vary in density as is measured by visibility. Some aircraft need 1200 feet of visibility to take off. The electron cloud for the hydrogen atom varies in its density also. It is less dense far from the nucleus than it is near the nucleus.

CHECK FOR UNDERSTANDING

Use the Mini Quiz to check for understanding.

MINI QUIZ

Use the Mini Quiz to check students' recall of chapter content.

1. **An abbreviated way to write an element's name is to use a(n) _____ .** *chemical symbol*
2. **An atom's nucleus contains _____ .** *protons and neutrons*
3. **An atom's atomic number is the number of ____ in its nucleus.** *protons*
4. **Electrons move around the nucleus in a region called an electron _____ .** *cloud*
5. **Electrons near the nucleus have low _____ .** *energy*
6. **The electron capacities of the first three energy levels are 2, 8, and ____ .** *18*

RETEACH

Have each student complete a duplicate of Table 10-2 that has one item missing from each of the three lines of information.

EXTENSION

For students who have mastered this section, use the **Reinforcement** and **Enrichment** masters or other OPTIONS provided.

3 CLOSE

▶ Ask questions 1-3 and the **Apply** and **Connect to Physics** questions in the Section Review.

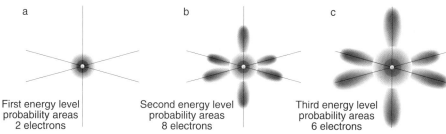

a

b

c

First energy level
probability areas
2 electrons

Second energy level
probability areas
8 electrons

Third energy level
probability areas
6 electrons

Figure 10-5. A sulfur atom has 16 electrons distributed in three energy levels. Each of the colored regions at each level can hold a maximum of two electrons. To get a complete picture, (b) and (c) should be placed on top of (a).

Sulfur's atomic number is 16. It has 16 protons and 16 electrons. Two of these electrons are in the first energy level, eight are in the second energy level, and six are in the third energy level. The electron arrangement of sulfur is shown in Figure 10-5.

Table 10-4

ELECTRONS IN ENERGY LEVELS	
Energy Level in Atom	Maximum Number of Electrons
1	2
2	8
3	18
4	32

SECTION REVIEW

1. Write the chemical symbols for the elements carbon, aluminum, hydrogen, oxygen, and sodium.
2. List the names, charges, and locations of three kinds of particles that make up an atom.
3. What does an electron cloud represent?
4. **Apply:** How might an electric fan that is turned on be a model of an atom? How is the fan unlike an atom?
5. **Connect to Physics:** When a glass rod is rubbed with silk, the rod becomes positively charged. What type of particle in the atoms in the rod has been removed?

Skill Builder

☑ **Concept Mapping**

Make a concept map for the parts of an atom. Include the following terms: *electron cloud, nucleus, electrons, protons,* and *neutrons.* Also provide the charge of each part. If you need help, refer to Concept Mapping in the **Skill Handbook** on pages 684 and 685.

Use the Flex Your Brain activity to have students explore ATOMIC STRUCTURE.

ASSESSMENT
Portfolio: Use the Flex Your Brain activity to reinforce critical-thinking and problem-solving skills. In Step 2, students might list what particles make up an atom.

SECTION REVIEW ANSWERS
1. C, Al, H, O, Na
2. proton: positive, nucleus; neutron: no charge, nucleus; electron: negative, surrounding nucleus
3. the region where electrons are likely to be in an atom
4. Apply: The visual blur formed by the moving blades can be a model for an electron cloud surrounding the nucleus of an atom. The blades form a blurry cloud and appear to be everywhere at once. Unlike electrons, the blades move in a flat plane in definite paths, whereas electrons have a spherical distribution.
5. Connect to Physics: electron

Skill Builder
ASSESSMENT
Select several elements. Tell students how many protons, neutrons, and electrons are in an atom of each. Have students model a nucleus of an atom of each element.

PROGRAM RESOURCES
From the **Teacher Resource Package** use: **Activity Worksheets,** page 5, Flex Your Brain.

Skill Builder

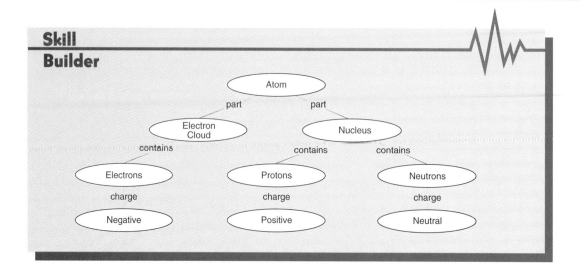

Models of Atomic Structure

Building a model can help you understand how a complex system operates. Something as simple as observing the release of an inflated balloon can give you information about the forces involved in launching rockets. Building and using a model for an atom can help you understand how the main parts of an atom relate to each other.

Materials

- magnetic board about 20 cm × 27 cm
- one 0.5-cm piece and 20 1-cm pieces rubber magnetic tape
- circles of white paper 4 cm wide
- circles of red paper 1 cm wide
- marker

Procedure

1. Choose an element with an atomic number of 1 through 20. Determine the number of each kind of particle needed to make up an atom of that element.
2. Use a marker to write the number of protons and neutrons on a paper circle. This represents the nucleus of the atom.
3. Use a 0.5-cm magnetic strip to attach the model nucleus to one side of a magnetic board.
4. Attach the red paper circles to the 1-cm magnetic strips. Arrange these model electrons in energy levels around the nucleus. Use as many of these electrons as you need for your element.

5. Remove either the model nucleus or the model electrons from the magnetic board and ask classmates to identify the element.
6. Repeat Steps 1 through 5 for another element.

Analyze

1. In a neutral atom, which particles will always be present in equal numbers?
2. **Hypothesize** what you think would happen to the charge of an atom if one of the electrons were removed from the atom.
3. Except for hydrogen, how many first level electrons did each selected atom contain?

Conclude and Apply

4. How is this model of an atom similar to an actual atom?
5. Name two differences, other than size, between your model and an actual atom.
6. What happens to the atom if one proton is removed from the nucleus and one electron is also removed?

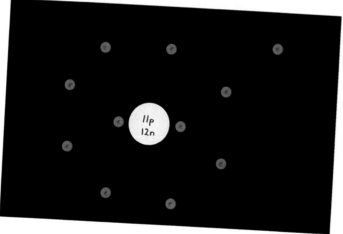

OBJECTIVE: Formulate models of atomic structure and **identify** atoms by their structures.

PROCESS SKILLS applied in this activity:
▶ **Formulating models** in Procedure Steps 2, 3, and 4.
▶ **Inferring** in Conclude and Apply Questions 5 and 6.

COOPERATIVE LEARNING
Organize the class into Science Investigation Groups of three or four. Have one student or pair construct the atom's nucleus and present it to the other two students, who must then decide on the electron arrangement.

TEACHING THE ACTIVITY
Alternate Materials: Painted steel rectangular snack trays may work well as magnetic boards. Use the bottom if there is a distracting design. Another possibility is to use carpet squares and the stiff half of Velcro strips.
Troubleshooting: Make sure the atom models are correctly constructed before having the class identify them. Going beyond element 20 requires a more detailed understanding of the distribution of electrons in energy levels.
▶ Peel-and-stick magnetic plastic tape is sold in most craft and hobby shops.

Activity
ASSESSMENT
Content: To further assess students' understanding of atomic structure, see USING LAB SKILLS, Question 11, on page 264.

ANSWERS TO QUESTIONS

1. protons and electrons
2. The number of protons would be one greater than the number of electrons. Therefore the atom would have a positive charge.
3. two
4. Answers will vary but should reflect the ideas that the numbers of protons and electrons are equal, the protons and neutrons are localized in the nucleus, and that electrons are distributed in energy levels outside the nucleus.

5. Answers will vary. Possible answers include the facts that the model's electrons are not moving, the model is two-dimensional, and the electrons would be distributed much farther from the nucleus if the model were to scale.
6. The atom becomes a different element with an atomic number one less than that of the original atom.

PREPARATION

SECTION BACKGROUND
▶ Quarks are described as having properties called flavors, such as charm, truth, and beauty. Quarks also have properties called colors: red, green, and blue. These terms are simply arbitrary labels for properties.

1 MOTIVATE

▶ **Demonstration:** Place a glass bottle in a heavy cloth bag. Drop it to break the bottle. Place the pieces on a newspaper. Ask students if they think they could reconstruct the bottle by studying the pieces. Relate this to the work of scientists who smash atoms in a supercollider. They study the pieces to learn more about the whole particle.

TYING TO PREVIOUS KNOWLEDGE:
Have students recall that National Transportation Safety Board investigators collect the pieces after an airplane crash to determine the cause of the accident.

2 TEACH

Key Concepts are highlighted.

CONCEPT DEVELOPMENT
▶ **Demonstration:** The magnets in particle accelerators are electromagnets, which can change polarity quickly to alternately pull and push the protons. Use a 6-volt battery connected to many turns of insulated wire wrapped around a large nail to demonstrate an electromagnet.

CHECK FOR UNDERSTANDING
Ask questions 1-2 and the **Connect to Physics** question in the Section Review.

New Science Words

quarks

Objectives

▶ Identify quarks as particles of matter that make up protons and neutrons.
▶ Explain how protons can be broken apart.

Looking for Quarks

You know that protons, electrons, and neutrons make up atoms. Are these particles made up of even smaller particles? Theories propose that electrons are not made of any smaller particles. Protons and neutrons, however, are made up of smaller particles called **quarks.** So far, experiments have shown evidence for five types of quarks, and a sixth type is predicted. A particular arrangement of three quarks held together with strong nuclear force produces a proton. Another arrangement of three quarks produces a neutron.

Fermilab, in Batavia, Illinois, houses a machine that can generate the tremendous forces that are required to study quarks. This machine, the Tevatron, is approximately 6.4 km in circumference. Electric and magnetic fields are used to accelerate, focus, then collide fast-moving protons. Studying the collisions can reveal information about the inner structure of the atom.

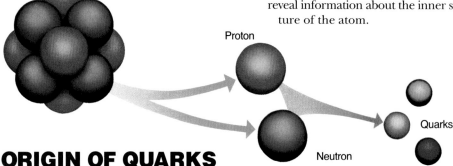

ORIGIN OF QUARKS

Proton

Neutron

Quarks

248 ATOMIC STRUCTURE AND THE PERIODIC TABLE

OPTIONS

Meeting Different Ability Levels
For Section 10-2, use the following **Teacher Resource Masters** depending upon individual students' needs.
◆ **Study Guide Master** for all students.
● **Reinforcement Master** for students of average and above average ability levels.
▲ **Enrichment Master** for above average students.

◆ **STUDY GUIDE** 43

STUDY GUIDE   Chapter 10
Smaller Particles of Matter   Text Pages 248–249

Circle the correctly spelled vocabulary word in each row.

1. quark   qarck   quork   (quark)
2.(proton)   protahn   protan   prohton
3. neutron   neutran   (neutron)   nuetron
4.(research)   research   reserch   research
5.(nucleus)   nucatron   nuclius   nucleas
6. element   (element)   elliment   ellament
7. elektron   electran   (electron)   eleckron
8. What is a supercollider? Briefly, describe how a supercollider can be used to study the nature of matter.   **A supercollider is a gigantic accelerator that is used to accelerate two beams of protons going in opposite directions. When they are going at almost 300 000 m/s the two beams are aimed in such a way that there is a head-on collision. The impact of the collision will break the protons into quarks.**

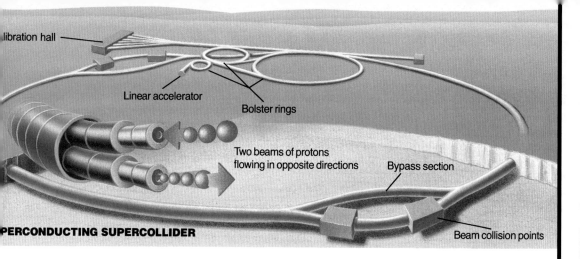

libration hall

Linear accelerator

Bolster rings

Two beams of protons
flowing in opposite directions

Bypass section

PERCONDUCTING SUPERCOLLIDER

Beam collision points

Scientists had proposed an even larger and more powerful machine. The newest device, called the Superconducting Supercollider, or SSC, was to be built in Waxahachie, Texas. In October, 1993, the United States Congress cancelled the project because of its expense. If built, it would have had a circumference of 80 km. With speeds approaching 300 000 000 m/s, the protons' collisions may have revealed more about the nature of quarks.

Connect to...
Earth Science

Current theory proposes that all quarks were present in the first seconds of the universe. What is the name scientists have given to this theory about the formation of the universe?

SECTION REVIEW

1. What are quarks?
2. Describe the supercollider.
3. **Connect to Physics:** How long would it take for a proton to travel 80 km if a proton travels at a speed of 300 000 000 m/s?

You Decide!

Supporters of the supercollider say that it would have helped scientists to better understand what matter is made of and how matter behaves. They point out that the money spent would have created new technology and thousands of new jobs. Critics argue that important, smaller research projects may have been cancelled because of lack of funds due to the supercollider's high costs. What factors do you think are important in evaluating scientific research like the supercollider? Why?

SCIENCE & SOCIETY

● **REINFORCEMENT** 43

▲ **ENRICHMENT** 43

3 CLOSE

▶ Have students do library research to determine the current status of the supercollider project.

SECTION REVIEW ANSWERS

1. Quarks are small particles of matter that make up protons and neutrons.
2. The supercollider consists of an 80-km track surrounded by powerful electric and magnetic fields.
3. Connect to Physics:

$$\frac{80 \text{ km}}{1} \times \frac{1000 \text{ m}}{1 \text{ km}} \times \frac{1 \text{ s}}{300\,000\,000 \text{ m}}$$
= 0.000 27 s

Connect to...
Earth Science

Answer: the Big Bang Theory

YOU DECIDE!

SCIENCE & SOCIETY

Answers will vary. Students should give sound support for their positions. If your class has students accustomed to debate, you could organize two teams to research and debate the topic.

SECTION BACKGROUND

▶ The choice of the first atomic mass standard was arbitrary. For a long time chemists used an atomic mass scale based on oxygen-16. In 1961, it was agreed to use carbon-12 as the standard for atomic mass.

▶ The term *atomic weight* is incorrect even though it has been used for many years. Your students will quickly learn from your correct examples and frequent use of *atomic mass.*

▶ Be certain students understand that isotopes of the same element are alike chemically, but different in mass.

▶ The atomic number is designated by the letter *Z* and the mass number by the letter *A*. The number of neutrons in an atom can be calculated using the formula $A - Z$.

▶ The mass of 1 u is approximately 1.67×10^{-24} g.

PREPLANNING

▶ To prepare for Activity 10-2, you will need to obtain the candy-coated peanuts and candy-coated chocolates. Sort out the needed number of different colors and place them in plastic bags.

1 MOTIVATE

▶ Use the Problem Solving feature on page 252 to show your students the relevance of the topic.

TYING TO PREVIOUS

KNOWLEDGE: Students have previously studied mass in different contexts. Refresh their memories by asking them to relate their concepts of mass. Make sure they are not confusing mass with volume.

In Your JOURNAL

Boron is used in some lightweight alloys, in laundry aids, in boric acid, and rocket fuels.

10-3 Masses of Atoms

New Science Words

mass number
isotopes
average atomic mass

Objectives

▶ Compute the atomic mass and mass number of an atom.
▶ Identify and describe isotopes of common elements.
▶ Interpret the average atomic mass of an element.

Atomic Mass

What is the atomic mass unit?

You may have guessed that the mass of an atom is *very* small. Yet, scientists are able to measure that mass with great accuracy. They can even measure the masses of protons and neutrons. The unit of measurement of those particles is the atomic mass unit (u). In fact, the mass of a proton or a neutron is almost equal to 1 u. This is not a coincidence—the unit was defined that way. The atomic mass unit is defined as one-twelfth the mass of a carbon atom containing six protons and six neutrons. Remember that the mass of a carbon atom is in its nucleus because the atom's six electrons have a negligible mass. Therefore, each of the 12 particles in the nucleus must have a mass nearly equal to one-twelfth the mass of the carbon atom. Thus, a proton or a neutron has a mass of about 1 u.

To help you understand this, suppose you have an egg carton containing six brown eggs and six white eggs, as shown in Figure 10-6. You could define a mass unit as one-twelfth the mass of the entire dozen. Because the carton itself has very little mass, the mass of each egg, brown or white, would be equal to your defined unit.

Figure 10-6. You can compare a carton of eggs to a carbon atom.

OPTIONS

Meeting Different Ability Levels

For Section 10-3, use the following **Teacher Resource Masters** depending upon individual students' needs.

◆ **Study Guide Master** for all students.
● **Reinforcement Master** for students of average and above average ability levels.
▲ **Enrichment Master** for above average students.

Additional Teacher Resource Package masters are listed in any PROGRAM RESOURCES boxes that are in the section. The additional masters are appropriate for all students.

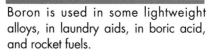

◆ STUDY GUIDE   44

Mass Number

The **mass number** of an atom is the sum of the number of protons and the number of neutrons in the nucleus of an atom. As you can see in Table 10-5, the mass number of an atom is almost equal to the mass of its most common form, expressed in atomic mass units.

If you know the mass number and the atomic number of an atom, you can then calculate the number of neutrons. The number of neutrons is equal to the atomic number subtracted from the mass number:

number of neutrons = mass number − atomic number

Table 10-5

MASS NUMBERS OF SOME ATOMS					
Element	Symbol	Protons	Neutrons	Mass Number	Average Atomic Mass*
Boron	B	5	6	11	10.81
Carbon	C	6	6	12	12.01
Oxygen	O	8	8	16	16.00
Sodium	Na	11	12	23	22.99
Copper	Cu	29	34	63	63.55

* to two decimal places

Isotopes

Not all the atoms of an element have the same number of neutrons. Atoms of the same element that have different numbers of neutrons are called **isotopes.**

Suppose you have a sample of the element boron. Naturally occurring atoms of boron have mass numbers of 10 or 11. How many neutrons are there in a boron atom? It depends upon which boron atom you are referring to. Obtain the number of protons from Table 10-5 and use the formula above to calculate that a boron atom may contain five or six neutrons. Use the example on the left to help you.

B
Boron

11 mass number
−5 number of protons
6 number of neutrons

10 mass number
−5 number of protons
5 number of neutrons

Figure 10-7. Boron has two naturally occurring isotopes.

● REINFORCEMENT 44

▲ ENRICHMENT 44

251

2 TEACH

Key Concepts are highlighted.

CONCEPT DEVELOPMENT

▶ The proton, 1.0073 u, and the neutron, 1.0087 u, are essentially equal in mass. The mass of the electron is extremely small, 0.000 549 u, or about 1/2000 the mass of a proton.

▶ Emphasize the fact that nearly all the mass of the atom is located in the nucleus.

▶ For most calculations in science, the average atomic mass is used rather than the mass of just one isotope.

▶ Emphasize that not all isotopes of an element are present in equal amounts. Just as in a class, not all students earn the same quiz grade. However, there is a class average for the quiz. Use this analogy to reinforce the idea of average atomic mass for an element.

REVEALING MISCONCEPTIONS

▶ The word *isotope* sometimes conjures up thoughts of dangerous radioactive materials. Before discussing isotopes, have members of the class tell what the word brings to mind. They should understand that nearly all elements exist as mixtures of isotopes and that many are not radioactive.

CROSS CURRICULUM

▶ **Medicine:** Nuclear radiation therapy is very successful for some cancers. Have interested students research the production and medical uses of radioactive isotopes.

TEACHER F.Y.I.

▶ Eighty percent of all nuclear waste comes from hospitals where nuclear medicine is practiced.

Use the Mini Quiz to check students' recall of chapter content.

1 One-twelfth of the mass of carbon-12 is defined as one atomic _____ .
mass unit

2 The sum of the protons and neutrons in an atom is the atom's _____ . *mass number*

3 Atoms of the same element that have different masses are called _____ . *isotopes*

4 Most elements have more than one isotope, so the atomic mass on the periodic table is a(n) _____ . *average*

RETEACH

To model the concept of average atomic mass, determine the average weight of the students in your class after each records his or her weight, to the nearest ten pounds, on a folded piece of paper.

EXTENSION

For students who have mastered this section, use the **Reinforcement** and **Enrichment** masters or other OPTIONS provided.

PROBLEM SOLVING

Think Critically: Refer students to the first two sections of Chapter 24 for additional information on this topic. The iodine-131 atom has too many neutrons for the number of protons to be stable. With too few or too many neutrons, the isotope is likely to be radioactive.

Connect to... Life Science

Answer: Carbon-14 is radioactive and thus decays over time. The amount of carbon-14, compared to the amount of carbon-12, present in the remains of an organism may be used to determine the age of the remains.

 Proton

 Neutron

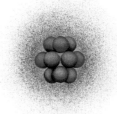 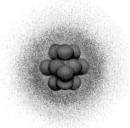

Figure 10-8. The two isotopes of boron have different numbers of neutrons and different mass numbers.

Figure 10-8 shows models of the two isotopes of boron. Because the numbers of neutrons in the isotopes are different, the mass numbers are also different. You use the name of the element followed by the mass number of the isotope to identify each isotope: boron-10 and boron-11. Because most elements have more than one isotope, each element is given an average atomic mass. The **average atomic mass** of an element is the average mass of the mixture of its isotopes.

PROBLEM SOLVING

Ivan's Isotopes

After carrying out many medical tests, the doctor found a tumor in Ivan's thyroid gland. The doctor decided to treat the tumor with iodine -131, an isotope of iodine. Ivan asked her how the treatment would work. She explained that atoms of some isotopes, like iodine -131, are unstable. Iodine -131 atoms have too many neutrons for the number of protons. The nucleus in an unstable isotope rearranges itself spontaneously, resulting in the release of energy called radiation.

The thyroid gland absorbs iodine because the gland needs iodine to function properly. The doctor told Ivan the tumor cells in his thyroid are more sensitive to radiation than the healthy thyroid cells. A controlled dose of radiation from the iodine-131 would kill more tumor cells than healthy cells.

Think Critically: Why is iodine -131 unstable? Why is the number of neutrons in an atom important in the field of medicine?

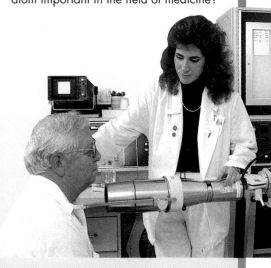

OPTIONS

INQUIRY QUESTIONS

▶ Both X-ray radiation and nuclear radiation can be used in the treatment of cancer. How do they differ? How do they work against a tumor? *The X ray is a form of radiant energy. Nuclear radiation can be of two types—particle radiation such as alpha and beta, or an energy wave called gamma radiation. All can disrupt the DNA molecules of actively dividing tumor cells.*

PROGRAM RESOURCES

From the **Teacher Resource Package** use:
Critical Thinking/Problem Solving, page 16, Carbon-14 Dating.
Science Integration Activity 10

For example, four out of five atoms of boron are boron-11, and one out of five is boron-10. Thus, in an average sample of five atoms of boron, four atoms are likely to have a mass of 11 u. One atom will have a mass of 10 u. If you measured the mass of the five atoms, you would find it to be 54 u. The average atomic mass of the boron mixture is 54 u divided by five, or 10.8 u. That is, the average atomic mass of the element boron is 10.8 u. Note that the average atomic mass of boron, given in Table 10-5, is close to the mass of its most abundant isotope, boron-11.

For another example, hydrogen has three isotopes—hydrogen-1, hydrogen-2, and hydrogen-3. Each has one proton. How many neutrons does each have? The most abundant isotope is hydrogen-1, and the element's average atomic mass is 1.008. The average atomic mass of each element can be found in the periodic table of elements. ④

SECTION REVIEW

1. A chlorine atom has 17 protons and 18 neutrons. What is its mass number? What is its atomic number?
2. How are the isotopes of an element alike and how are they different?
3. **Apply:** Chlorine is used to treat most city water systems. The atomic number of chlorine is 17. The two naturally occurring isotopes of chlorine are chlorine-35 and chlorine-37. The average atomic mass of chlorine is 35.45 u. Why does this indicate that most chlorine atoms contain 18 neutrons?
4. **Connect to Life Science:** An isotope of phosphorus used to treat bone cancer is phosphorus-30. Another isotope is phosphorus-31. What are two reasons why most of the phosphorus in your food must be phosphorus-31 and not phosphorus-30?

Connect to... Life Science

Living organisms on Earth contain carbon. Carbon-12 makes up 99 percent of this carbon. Carbon-13 and carbon-14 make up the other 1 percent. Which isotopes are archaeologists most interested in when they determine the age of carbon-containing remains? Explain your answer.

☑ Making and Using Tables

Construct a table organizing information about the atomic numbers, atomic mass numbers, and the number of protons, neutrons, and electrons in atoms of oxygen-16 and oxygen-17. If you need help, refer to Making and Using Tables in the **Skill Handbook** on page 686.

Skill Builder

---

3 CLOSE

▶Ask questions 1-3 and the **Apply** and **Connect to Life Science** questions in the Section Review.

SECTION REVIEW ANSWERS

1. 35, 17
2. They have the same number of protons (atomic number) but different numbers of neutrons resulting in a different mass number.
3. **Apply:** An atom of chlorine has 17 protons. Because the average atomic mass is close to 35, most atoms of chlorine would have 18 neutrons, giving a mass number of 35.
4. **Connect to Life Science:** Living things that make up our food source could not themselves survive with large quantities of a radioactive isotope. The average atomic mass of phosphorus is very near 31, indicating that most naturally occurring atoms of phosphorus are P-31, which is not radioactive.

Skill Builder

Comparing Isotopes of Oxygen

Isotope	oxygen-16	oxygen-17
Atomic number	8	8
Protons	8	8
Electrons	8	8
Neutrons	8	9
Mass number	16	17

Skill Builder
ASSESSMENT

Content: Have students add their neutron and proton values to make sure it equals the mass number.

ENRICHMENT

Have students work these problems.

▶ **What is the weighted average for a class of 24 students on a quiz if 5 students earn a grade of 100, and 19 students earn a grade of 80?** $\frac{5}{24}(100\%) + \frac{19}{24}(80\%) = 84.2\%$

▶ **What is the average atomic mass of silicon if 92.21% of its atoms have mass 27.977 u, 4.70% have mass 28.976 u, and 3.09% have mass 29.974 u?** $0.9221 (27.977 \, u) + 0.0470 (28.976 \, u) + 0.0309 (29.974 \, u) = 28.1 \, u$

▶ **What is the average atomic mass of hafnium if, out of every 100 atoms, 5 have mass 176 u, 19 have mass 177 u, 27 have mass 178 u, 14 have mass 179 u, and 35 have mass 180 u?** *179 u*

▶ **Compute the average atomic mass of silver if 51.83% of the atoms in nature have a mass of 106.905 u and 48.17% have a mass of 108.905 u.** *107.9 u*

ACTIVITY 10-2

OBJECTIVE: Design and carry out an **experiment** to show how average atomic mass is found.
Time: 30 minutes if candies are pre-sorted.

PROCESS SKILLS applied in this activity are **comparing and contrasting, calculating,** and **interpreting data.**

PREPARATION
Have candy samples sorted and placed in sealed plastic bags. If students are not permitted to open the bags, samples may be used by more than one class.

Cooperative Learning: Divide the class into Science Investigation Teams.

SAFETY
Caution students to keep the bags closed and not eat the candy.

THINKING CRITICALLY
The atomic mass unit compares all atomic masses to a standard mass. In the activity, students can compare the mass of all of a color of candy to a standard that has been set for that color.

TEACHING THE ACTIVITY
*Refer to the **Activity Worksheets** for additional information and teaching strategies.*
• Review with your students the process used to find weighted averages. Use examples that are familiar to students, such as finding average grades if numbers of each letter grade are known.
• Several different types of candy may be used. Other colors may be substituted so long as each set is all the same color.

SUMMING UP/SHARING RESULTS
• $\dfrac{4 \times 2\ \text{rcu} + 2 \times 1\ \text{rcu} = 1.7\ \text{rcu}}{6\ \text{red candies}}$
• Sample student answer might be green candy unit (gcu).
• Average masses were not the same because different units and different numbers of each type of candy were used.

DESIGNING AN EXPERIMENT
Candy-Covered Isotopes

The extremely small size of atoms makes it impossible to count or determine atomic mass in a direct manner. Scientists do, however, have an instrument called a mass spectrometer that can supply both mass and relative numbers of atoms for isotopes. With that data average atomic masses can be calculated. How does a mass spectrometer operate?

Getting Started
Review how the average mass of boron was calculated on page 253. In this activity, a certain color of candy will represent a sample of an element. Using both chocolate-centered candy and peanut-centered candy can be a *model* for two isotopes of the element. Can you determine the average mass of this "element"?

Thinking Critically
Average atomic masses are based on atomic mass units. Without having a balance to *measure* the actual mass of a piece of candy, how can you use the atomic mass unit as a model to determine the average mass of your sample of candy?

Materials
Your cooperative group will use the following:
• one bag containing four red peanut-centered candies and two red chocolate-centered candies
• one bag containing three green peanut-centered candies and three green chocolate-centered candies

Data and Observations

┤ Try It! ├

1. Within your group assume that the red peanut-centered candies have two times the mass of the red chocolate centered candies. The chocolate-centered pieces have a mass of one red candy unit (rcu).
2. Find the average mass of the red candy. Report your value using the correct unit.
3. Repeat this procedure for the green candy, using a different unit that your group defines.

Summing Up/Sharing Results
• In this activity, the green candies represent atoms of a different element. What unit did you use for the average mass of the green candies?
• Why were the average masses of the samples not the same?

Going Further!
If another bag of red candies contains eight peanut-centered pieces, how many chocolate-centered pieces are needed to produce the same average mass as was found in the activity?

Sample Data

	Peanut	Chocolate	Average
	candy × mass	candy × mass	$\dfrac{\text{total mass}}{\text{total candies}}$
Red	4 x 2 = ⑧	2 x 1 = ②	$\dfrac{8 + 2}{4 + 2} = 1.7$
Green	3 x 4 = ⑫	3 x 3 = ⑨	$\dfrac{12 + 9}{3 + 3} = 3.5$

GOING FURTHER!
The new bag of red candy should contain four pieces of chocolate-centered candy. The 2 : 1 ratio of peanut to chocolate should be maintained for all samples to produce the same average mass.

PROGRAM RESOURCES
From the **Teacher Resource Package** use:
Activity Worksheets, pages 80-81, Activity 10-2: Candy-Covered Isotopes.

ACTIVITY ASSESSMENT
To further assess students' understanding of finding average atomic mass, see USING LAB SKILLS, Question 12, on page 264.

The Periodic Table 10-4

Objectives

▶ Describe the periodic table of elements and use it to find information about an element.

▶ Distinguish between a group and a period.

▶ Use the periodic table to classify an element as a metal, nonmetal, or metalloid.

New Science Words

periodic table
groups
dot diagram
periods
metals
nonmetals
metalloids

Structure of the Periodic Table

Remember the last time you sat on a swing and moved back and forth, over and over? Your movement was periodic. *Periodic* means "repeated in a pattern." Look at a calendar. The days of the week are periodic because they repeat themselves every seven days. The calendar is a periodic table of days. You use calendars to organize your time.

In the late 1800s, Dimitri Mendeleev, a Russian chemist, searched for a way to organize the elements. He arranged all the elements known at that time in order of increasing atomic masses. He discovered that there was a pattern to the properties of the elements. This pattern was periodic. The arrangement of elements according to repeated changes in properties is called a **periodic table** of elements. Look at the early periodic table at the right.

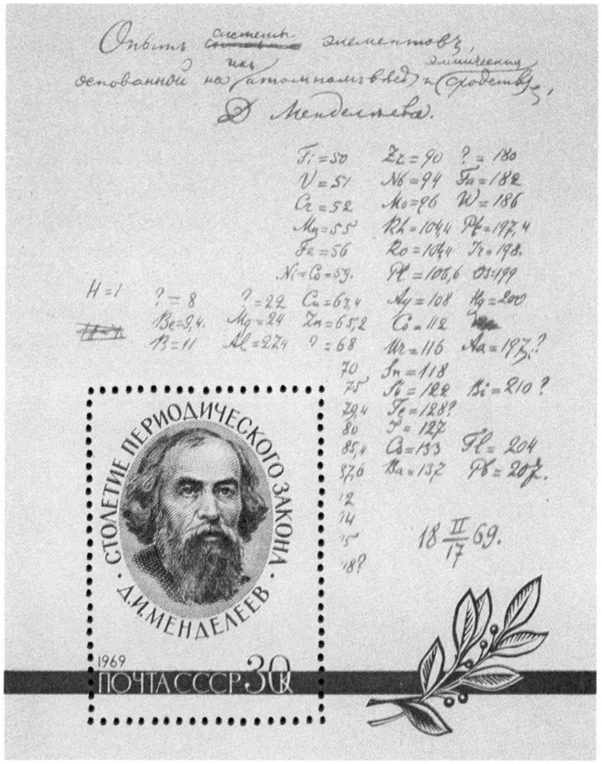

Figure 10-9. In his first periodic table, Mendeleev wrote question marks in spaces for elements not yet discovered.

10-4 THE PERIODIC TABLE **255**

SECTION 10-4

PREPARATION

SECTION BACKGROUND

▶ Dimitri Ivanovich Mendeleev was born in Siberia, the last of 14 or 17 children, depending on which record you accept. His father died when Mendeleev was very young. His mother took him to St. Petersburg (Leningrad) for education. She died shortly after their arrival. He graduated from college at the top of his class and then studied in France and Germany. In 1866, he became professor of chemistry at the University of St. Petersburg.

▶ Mendeleev predicted the existence of six undiscovered elements—scandium, gallium, germanium, technetium, rhenium, and polonium.

▶ Mendeleev's first three predictions, made in 1871, were confirmed by 1885.

PREPLANNING

▶ Collect assorted pens and pencils for the MINI-Lab on page 257.

▶ If you have not already obtained one, you should have a display-size periodic table available.

1 MOTIVATE

▶ **Demonstration:** Using a battery-powered conductivity tester, touch the instrument's probes to samples of elements. Your high school physics teacher may have a conductivity tester that you can borrow. Students can begin to classify elements as conductors and nonconductors. Use this activity to lead into a discussion about the need to classify elements.

TYING TO PREVIOUS KNOWLEDGE: The books in the library are classified so that a student can quickly find a book on a particular subject. The elements are classified and arranged on the periodic table. The periodic table contains a library of useful information for the scientist.

OPTIONS

INQUIRY QUESTIONS

Ask these questions as students study pages 255-257.

▶ **The nitrogen family of elements begins with a nonmetal and ends with a metal, bismuth. Can you explain such a wide variety of properties within group 15? Hint: The less attracted the outer-level electrons are, the more metallic the element.** *The size of the atom increases as you go down the family. Thus, the attraction for the outer electrons is less. Nitrogen is much smaller and has five closely held outer electrons.*

▶ **The noble gases (group 18) are chemically inert under most reaction conditions. What does chemically "inert" mean? What feature of outer electron structure do all noble gases share?** *The elements usually do not react with other elements. With the exception of helium, all have eight outer-level electrons.*

CONCEPT DEVELOPMENT

▶ Emphasize the meaning of the word *periodic*. The properties of the elements are a periodic function of their atomic numbers because of repeating similarities in their outer electron structures.

▶ In the time of Mendeleev, energy levels and sublevels had not been discovered. He didn't even have a modern concept of what an atom was. His predictions, based solely on physical and chemical properties, were a remarkable achievement.

MULTICULTURAL PERSPECTIVE
Left-handed or Right?

One of the foundations of physics was the law of atomic parity. This law states that like atomical particles always act alike and that an atomic system is identical in nature to its own mirror image. Dr. Chien-Shiung Wu was able to experimentally disprove this basic law.

Dr. Wu's experiment showed that atomic particles are either "right-handed" or "left-handed" and have different patterns of behavior. Dr. Wu's colleagues in the study were awarded the Nobel prize in 1957 for their theoretical contributions to the project, but Dr. Wu was overlooked.

Dr. Wu, born near Shanghai, China, immigrated to the U.S. in 1936 to do graduate work at the University of California at Berkeley. Today Dr. Wu is a highly honored scientist. She participated in the development of the nuclear bomb for the U.S. government. At the age of 27, she served briefly as a physics instructor at Princeton — at a time when Princeton would not accept women as students. Dr. Wu was the first woman to receive the Comstock Prize for the National Academy of Sciences and the Research Corporation Award. In 1976, she received the U.S. Medal of Science.

Currently, Dr. Wu is working in the field of biophysics to find a cure for sickle-cell anemia, a genetic disease found in high frequency in people of African ancestry.

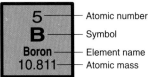

Figure 10-10. The periodic table shows the symbol, name, atomic number, and atomic mass of each element.

Mendeleev's periodic table had blank spaces. He looked at the properties and atomic masses of the elements surrounding these blank spaces. From this information, he predicted the properties and the mass numbers of new elements that had not yet been discovered. Sometimes you make predictions like this. Suppose someone crossed out a date on a calendar, as shown. You could predict the missing date by looking at the surrounding dates. Mendeleev's predictions proved to be quite accurate. Scientists later discovered elements, such as germanium, having the properties that he had predicted (Table 10-6).

Although Mendeleev's arrangement of elements was successful, it did need some changes. On Mendeleev's table, the atomic mass gradually increased from left to right in each row. If you look at the modern periodic table as shown on pages 258 and 259, you will see several examples, such as cobalt and nickel, where the mass decreases from left to right. However, you may notice that the atomic number always increases from left to right. The work of Henry G.J. Moseley, a young English scientist, in 1913 led to the arrangement of elements based on their properties and atomic numbers instead of an arrangement based on atomic masses.

Each box in the periodic table contains information about the elements that you studied earlier in this chapter. Look at Figure 10-10. This box represents the element boron. The atomic number, chemical symbol, name, and average atomic mass are included in this box. The boxes for all of the elements are arranged in order of their atomic numbers.

Table 10-6

"EKASILICON" (GERMANIUM)

Properties	Predicted	Actual
Atomic mass	72	72.6
Density	5.5 g/cm³	5.35 g/cm³
Color	dark gray	gray-white
Effect of water	none	none
Effect of acid	slight	HCl: no effect
Effect of base	slight	KOH: no effect

OPTIONS

Meeting Different Ability Levels

For Section 10-4, use the following **Teacher Resource Masters** depending upon individual students' needs.

◆ **Study Guide Master** for all students.

● **Reinforcement Master** for students of average and above average ability levels.

▲ **Enrichment Master** for above average students.

Additional Teacher Resource Package masters are listed in any **PROGRAM RESOURCES** boxes that are in the section. The additional masters are appropriate for all students.

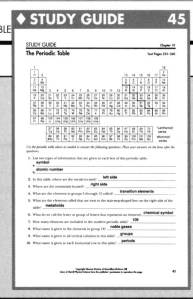

◆ STUDY GUIDE 45

Groups of Elements

The vertical columns in the periodic table are called **groups,** or families. The groups are numbered 1 through 18. Elements in each group have similar properties. For example, Figure 10-11 shows rings made of three elements in Group 11, copper—Cu, silver—Ag, and gold—Au. These elements have similar properties. Each is a shiny metal and a good conductor of electricity and heat.

④

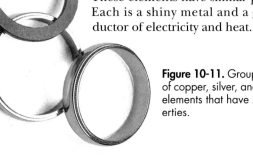

Figure 10-11. Group 11 consists of copper, silver, and gold, three elements that have similar properties.

Why do elements in a group have similar properties? It is because they have similar electron arrangements. Think about how the properties of different kinds of balls are related to their shape. You expect a soccer ball and a basketball to bounce in similar ways because they have similar shapes. But a football will bounce differently, because it has a different shape.

Atoms of different elements have different numbers of electrons. However, atoms of different elements may have the same number of electrons in their outer energy levels. It is the number of electrons in the outer energy level that determines the chemical properties of the element. Different elements with the same number of electrons in their outer energy level have similar chemical properties. These outer electrons are so important that a special way to represent them has been developed. A **dot diagram** uses the symbol of the element and dots to represent the electrons in the outer energy level.

⑤

257

MINI-Lab

What are the advantages of a periodic table?

Observe the mass and other properties of your pen or pencil, such as color and composition. With your class, develop a "periodic table" of pens and pencils. Arrange similar pens and pencils in columns and in order of mass. What can you say about (a) the properties of the elements and (b) the masses of the elements in a column, or group, of the periodic table?

MINI-Lab

Materials: assorted pencils and pens, large table surface

Teaching Tips:
► Discuss with students the reasons for their arrangements. Make sure they have examined the properties of objects as they are arranged within columns.

Expected Results
Students should be able to place all wooden pencils in one column, mechanical pencils in another column, stick pens in another column, retractable pens in another column, and so on.

Answers to Questions
Within a column on the periodic table, the elements have similar properties and the same number of electrons in their outer energy level. Masses increase from top to bottom in a column.

MINI-Lab
ASSESSMENT
Performance: Have students properly place another pen or pencil in their arrangement. Note the placement based on properties.

CONCEPT DEVELOPMENT
► Take every opportunity to point out elements on the periodic table and stress the relationship between electron structure and an element's position on the table.

PROGRAM RESOURCES
From the **Teacher Resource Package** use:

Activity Worksheets, page 84, MINI-Lab: What are the advantages of a periodic table?

Use **Laboratory Manual 22,** Chemical Activity.

CONCEPT DEVELOPMENT

▶ The spectrum of color across the periodic table shown here is designed to illustrate and reinforce the increasing nonmetallic character of elements as you read from left to right across the table. The redder the coloration of the element box, the greater the metallic character of the element. The bluer the box, the more nonmetallic the element. Notice that the elements along the stairstep line have both metallic and nonmetallic characteristics. These elements are the metalloids.

▶ Note also that the elements with the greatest metallic character are in the lower left corner of the table. Atoms of these elements are large, having several levels of electrons. As a result, their outer electrons are relatively distant from the nucleus and thus are loosely held. This fact causes the elements to be highly reactive because they lose outer electrons easily.

▶ Elements that are most nonmetallic in behavior are in the upper right of the table (disregarding the noble gases, Group 18). Atoms of these elements are small and have nearly full outer electron levels. Consequently, these elements attract electrons strongly and are highly reactive.

▶ The noble gases are technically nonmetals in physical character, but are extremely unreactive and, therefore, form a separate group with their own distinct properties.

▶ Hydrogen, by its electron arrangement, is part of Group 1. However, because it has only one electron energy level that can hold only two electrons, it has its own unique set of properties. Therefore, it is colored differently from the other elements.

▶ List the elements in the first six periods that would be out of order if the table were arranged by atomic mass. The elements Ar, K, Co, Ni, Te, and I would be out of order.

▶ Johann Dobereiner, a German scientist, and John Newlands from England made early attempts at classifying the elements. Dobereiner arranged elements in groups of three called triads. Newlands' law of octaves had the eighth element repeating the properties of the first. The noble gases had not yet been discovered.

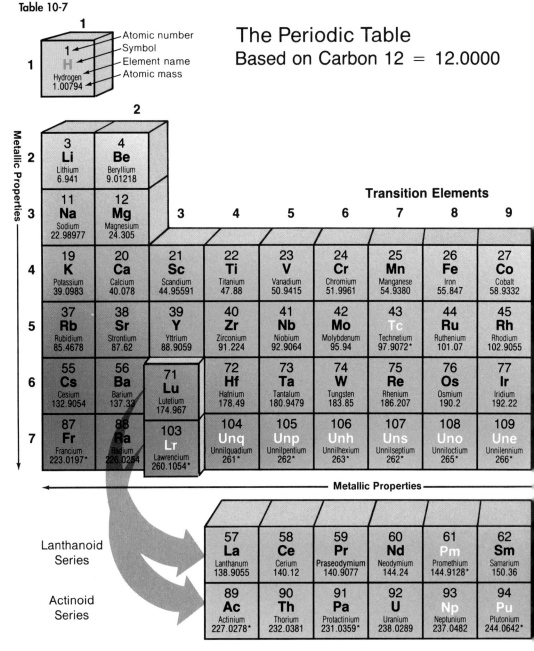

Table 10-7

The Periodic Table
Based on Carbon 12 = 12.0000

*Mass of isotope with longest half-life, that is, the most stable isotope of the element

OPTIONS

ASSESSMENT—ORAL

▶ **Iodine is used in many commercial chemicals and dyes. What is the name of the group to which iodine belongs? What is the meaning of the group name?** *halogens, Greek for "salt formers"*

▶ **Calcium compounds in the soil are absorbed by grass which is eaten by cows and made into milk. In your body, calcium is found in teeth and bones. Assume that some radioactive strontium-90 has accidentally been released into the atmosphere. Is there cause for concern? Explain.** *Yes. Sr-90 will* take the place of Ca because it is in the same group. After the Chernobyl accident in 1986, milk in the affected area had to be discarded because it was radioactive.

▶ **There are seven numbered rows on the periodic table. What does this tell you about atoms of elements in the seventh row?** *These atoms have electrons in seven energy levels.*

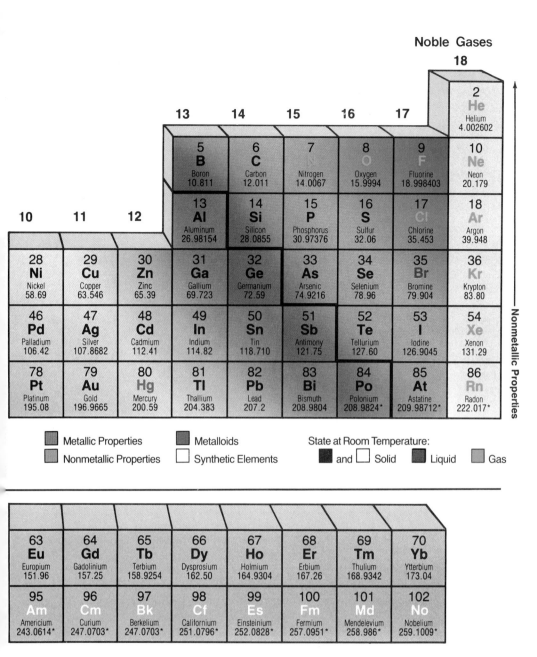

			13	14	15	16	17	Noble Gases 18
								2 **He** Helium 4.002602
			5 **B** Boron 10.811	6 **C** Carbon 12.011	7 N Nitrogen 14.0067	8 O Oxygen 15.9994	9 F Fluorine 18.998403	10 **Ne** Neon 20.179
10	11	12	13 **Al** Aluminum 26.98154	14 **Si** Silicon 28.0855	15 **P** Phosphorus 30.97376	16 **S** Sulfur 32.06	17 Cl Chlorine 35.453	18 **Ar** Argon 39.948
28 **Ni** Nickel 58.69	29 **Cu** Copper 63.546	30 **Zn** Zinc 65.39	31 **Ga** Gallium 69.723	32 **Ge** Germanium 72.59	33 **As** Arsenic 74.9216	34 **Se** Selenium 78.96	35 **Br** Bromine 79.904	36 **Kr** Krypton 83.80
46 **Pd** Palladium 106.42	47 **Ag** Silver 107.8682	48 **Cd** Cadmium 112.41	49 **In** Indium 114.82	50 **Sn** Tin 118.710	51 **Sb** Antimony 121.75	52 **Te** Tellurium 127.60	53 **I** Iodine 126.9045	54 **Xe** Xenon 131.29
78 **Pt** Platinum 195.08	79 **Au** Gold 196.9665	80 **Hg** Mercury 200.59	81 **Tl** Thallium 204.383	82 **Pb** Lead 207.2	83 **Bi** Bismuth 208.9804	84 **Po** Polonium 208.9824*	85 **At** Astatine 209.98712*	86 **Rn** Radon 222.017*

Nonmetallic Properties →

■ Metallic Properties ■ Metalloids State at Room Temperature:
■ Nonmetallic Properties □ Synthetic Elements ■ and □ Solid ■ Liquid ■ Gas

63 **Eu** Europium 151.96	64 **Gd** Gadolinium 157.25	65 **Tb** Terbium 158.9254	66 **Dy** Dysprosium 162.50	67 **Ho** Holmium 164.9304	68 **Er** Erbium 167.26	69 **Tm** Thulium 168.9342	70 **Yb** Ytterbium 173.04
95 **Am** Americium 243.0614*	96 **Cm** Curium 247.0703*	97 **Bk** Berkelium 247.0703*	98 **Cf** Californium 251.0796*	99 **Es** Einsteinium 252.0828*	100 **Fm** Fermium 257.0951*	101 **Md** Mendelevium 258.986*	102 **No** Nobelium 259.1009*

CONCEPT DEVELOPMENT

▶ You may have older tables in which groups are numbered with Roman numerals and letters. The American Chemical Society in recent years has recommended the use of periodic tables numbered 1 through 18.

▶ Remind students that all atoms of the same element contain the same number of protons.

▶ Inform students that scientists use the periodic table to make predictions every day. Atomic and ionic radii, ionization energy, electron affinity, electronegativity, melting point, and oxidation number can all be predicted from the periodic table.

▶ Learning to draw dot diagrams will help students in the future as they relate reactivity to the outer arrangement of electrons. The octet of outer electrons is particularly stable, as are filled and half-filled sublevels.

MINI QUIZ

Use the Mini Quiz to check students' recall of chapter content.

① **The arrangement of elements according to repeated changes in properties is called the _____ .** *periodic table*

② **_____ used his table to make predictions about undiscovered elements.** *Mendeleev*

③ **The elements on the periodic table are arranged in order of increasing atomic _____ .** *number*

④ **Vertical columns on the periodic table are called _____ .** *groups or families*

⑤ **The number of outermost electrons determines the _____ of an element.** *chemical properties*

VideoDisc

STVS: Images of Atoms, Disc 2, Side 1

ENRICHMENT

▶ The chemical symbols for the following elements are not abbreviations of their English names. Have students use reference books to determine the symbols for the following elements and the names upon which the symbols are based: Copper: *Cu, cuprum;* Gold: *Au, aurum;* Iron: *Fe, ferrum;* Lead: *Pb, plumbum;* Tin: *Sn, stannum;* Mercury: *Hg, hydroargyrum;* Silver: *Ag, argentum;* Sodium: *Na, natrium;* Potassium: *K, kalium;* Antimony: *Sb, stibnum;* Tungsten: *W, wolfram*

PROGRAM RESOURCES

From the **Teacher Resource Package** use:
Cross-Curricular Connections, page 14, La Tabla Periodica
Transparency Masters, pages 37-38, The Periodic Table.
Transparency Masters, pages 39-40, The Periodic Table—Blank.
Use **Color Transparency** number 19, The Periodic Table.
Use **Color Transparency** number 20, The Periodic Table—Blank.

► If you have less common forms of the periodic table, you may want to bring them to class. There are circular ones and one in the shape of a figure eight.

► Point out and encourage students to learn the trends contained in the periodic table so they can be good predictors. It is easier to learn a trend than to learn about each individual element in a period or group.

CROSS CURRICULUM

► **Language Arts:** The names of the elements have an interesting history. Have each student pick three elements and write a short essay on how they were named.

Connect to...
Physics

Answers: Mercury solidifies at approximately –39°C. Bromine solidifies at approximately –7°C.

CHECK FOR UNDERSTANDING

Use the Mini Quiz to check for understanding.

MINI QUIZ

Use the Mini Quiz to check students' recall of chapter content.

6 **The halogens are found in which group?** *17*

7 **The noble gases are found in which group?** *18*

8 **Horizontal rows on the periodic table are called _____ .** *periods*

9 **Elements next to the stair-step line are called _____ .** *metalloids*

10 **Groups 3 through 12 are called the _____ metals.** *transition*

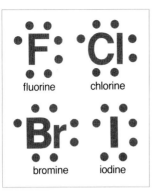

fluorine   chlorine

bromine   iodine

Connect to...
Physics

Use the periodic table on pages 258-259 to find the names of the two elements that are liquids at room temperature. Find out the temperatures at which these liquids become solids.

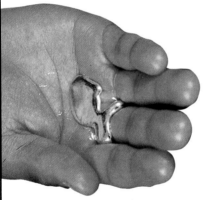

260 ATOMIC STRUCTURE AND THE PERIODIC TABLE

Figure 10-12. In each of these dot diagrams, the seven dots represent seven outer electrons.

For example, the dot diagrams of the atoms of the elements in Group 17, called the halogens, are shown in 6 Figure 10-12. They all have seven electrons in their outer energy levels. One similar property of the halogens is the ability to form compounds with elements in Group 1. 7 The elements in Group 18 are known as noble gases. Noble gases do not usually form compounds. We say they are stable, or unreactive. The atoms of all the noble gases except helium have outer energy levels that contain eight electrons, as shown in Figure 10-13. You will learn more about the significance of electron arrangement of elements in later chapters.

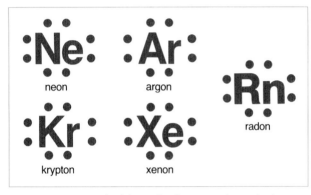

neon   argon

krypton   xenon   radon

Figure 10-13. In each of these dot diagrams, the eight dots represent eight outer electrons.

Periods of Elements

The horizontal rows of elements in the periodic table 8 are called **periods.** Notice the stair-step line on the right side of the periodic table. All the elements to the left of this line, except hydrogen, are metals. Iron, zinc, and copper are examples of metals. Most **metals** have the common properties of existing as solids at room temperature and being shiny and good conductors of heat and electricity.

Figure 10-14. Gallium is a metal that has a low melting point.

OPTIONS

ENRICHMENT

► Mendeleev arranged his periodic table in order of increasing atomic mass. The modern table is arranged by atomic number. Have students find out why the table was first arranged in mass order. Mendeleev had no knowledge of atomic numbers.

► Lothar Meyer, a German, published a table similar to Mendeleev's about the same time. Have students find out why he is not credited with the invention. Mendeleev used his own table to predict six undiscovered elements.

► Cut 3" × 5" cards in half. Have each student select a group and record the name, symbol, and atomic number on one card for each element in that group. Tape the cards together to form a large periodic table. Use this table to reinforce the objective of this section.

TECHNOLOGY

Seeing Atoms

For more than 50 years, scientists have been able to see extremely tiny things with electron microscopes. But it was less than twenty years ago that scientists first saw atoms with scanning probe microscopes. These microscopes are the result of a new approach to how we see objects. Instead of shining light or a beam of electrons on an object, these new microscopes drag a probe across the surface of an object. The position of the probe is then changed and it is dragged across the surface again. This process, called scanning, is repeated many times to build an image of the peaks and valleys on the surface of the object. Scanning is like going into a dark room and using your hand as a probe to feel a chair to determine its shape, instead of shining a light on it.

The key development in the invention of the scanning probe microscope was a system that moves the probe in precise steps smaller than the width of an atom. In addition to seeing atoms, these probes enable scientists to move single atoms. Scientists at IBM used xenon atoms to spell out "IBM" in letters only five atoms tall! This ability to handle materials on an atom-by-atom basis could lead to ways of developing new materials that, up until now, were just not possible.

Think Critically: Scientists are using scanning probe microscopes to view atoms. Atoms range in radius from 0.053 nm for hydrogen to 0.27 nm for francium. What everyday objects, like two kinds of balls, would represent this range in size?

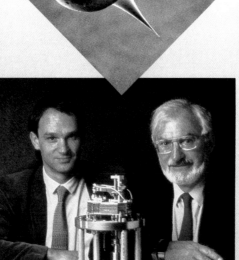

Those elements to the right of the stair-step line on the periodic table are classified as **nonmetals.** Oxygen, nitrogen, and carbon are examples of nonmetals. At

10-4   THE PERIODIC TABLE   **261**

TECHNOLOGY

For more information on imaging atoms, read "Seeing Atoms" by James Trefil, *Discover*, June 1990, pp. 55-60.

Think Critically: The radii given are in a ratio of approximately 1:5. Size comparisons could include a golf ball and a volleyball.

RETEACH

Cooperative Learning: Using an appropriate strategy such as Expert Teams, organize eight class groups. Have them devise dot diagrams for the first 18 elements in the periodic table. Each group should be assigned one of the major groups—1, 2, and 13 through 18. Once the correct diagrams are established, have the groups enter their diagrams in a large table on the chalkboard or on roll paper. Point out the electron similarity in each group and the repeating pattern in the periods.

EXTENSION

For students who have mastered this section, use the **Reinforcement** and **Enrichment** masters or other OPTIONS provided.

3 CLOSE

▶ Ask questions 1-3 and the **Apply** and **Connect to Life Science** questions in the Section Review.

? FLEX Your Brain

Use the Flex Your Brain activity to have students explore the PERIODIC TABLE.

ASSESSMENT

Portfolio: Use the Flex Your Brain activity to reinforce critical-thinking and problem-solving skills. In Step 2, students might list the people who developed systems for classifying elements.

ENRICHMENT

▶ Have a student use a calendar to illustrate the concept of periodicity.

▶ The radius of an atom increases down through a group. Ask students to explain why this occurs. *There are additional energy levels around the nucleus.*

▶ Research the activity series of the metals. Point out that an element's activity is related to its position on the periodic table.

PROGRAM RESOURCES

From the **Teacher Resource Package** use:

Concept Mapping, pages 25-26.

Science and Society, page 14, Steel and Aluminum Beverage Cans.

Activity Worksheets, page 5, Flex Your Brain.

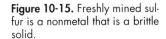
SECTION REVIEW ANSWERS

1. N, nitrogen, 7, 14.01
   Ca, calcium, 20, 40.08
   Kr, krypton, 36, 83.80
   W, tungsten, 74, 183.85
   Note: These atomic masses are rounded to two decimal places.

2. nitrogen, period 2, group 15
   sodium, period 3, group 1
   iodine, period 5, group 17
   mercury, period 6, group 12

3. K, potassium, metal
   Si, silicon, metalloid
   Ba, barium, metal
   S, sulfur, nonmetal

4. **Apply:** It is a liquid at room temperature, and like other metals, it conducts electricity.

5. **Connect to Life Science:** Both microscopes are used to see small objects. The scanning microscope uses a change in probe position instead of light. Compound microscopes cannot be used to see items as small as those seen using a scanning microscope.

Skill Builder

The graph should indicate 77% of the elements are metals, 8% are metalloids, and 15% are nonmetals.

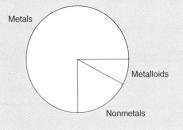

Metals

Metalloids

Nonmetals

Skill Builder
ASSESSMENT

Performance: If a sensitive balance is available, have students determine the mass of their pie graphs. After then cutting the graph into parts, have students mass each piece and determine what percentage of the whole each slice represents.

Figure 10-15. Freshly mined sulfur is a nonmetal that is a brittle solid.

Where are the metalloids located in the periodic table?  ⑨

room temperature, most nonmetals are gases and some are brittle solids. Most nonmetals do not conduct heat and electricity well.

The elements next to the stair-step line are **metalloids,** because they have properties of both metals and nonmetals. Boron and silicon are examples of metalloids.

⑩ Elements in Groups 3 through 12 are called the transition elements. They are metals but have properties not found in elements of other groups. Copper and iron are examples of common transition elements.

From the periodic table on pages 258-259, choose a synthetic element and write a brief biography of the element **in your Journal.** Include information about the element's name, location of the synthesis research, and the people responsible.

SECTION REVIEW

1. Use the periodic table to find the name, atomic number, and average atomic mass of the following elements: N, Ca, Kr, and W.
2. Give the period and group in which each of these elements is found: nitrogen, sodium, iodine, and mercury.
3. Write the name of each of these elements and classify it as a metal, a nonmetal, or a metalloid: K, Si, Ba, and S.
4. **Apply:** What property of mercury makes it different from other metals and also makes it useful in thermometers and silent light switches?
5. **Connect to Life Science:** Compare and contrast the main features of a scanning probe microscope and a compound microscope.

Skill Builder

☑ **Making and Using Graphs**

Construct a pie graph showing the elements classified as metals, metalloids, and nonmetals. If you need help, refer to Making and Using Graphs in the **Skill Handbook** on page 687.

OPTIONS

ENRICHMENT

▶ Have a student research alchemists' symbols and use them to prepare a bulletin board.

▶ Barium compounds are very toxic. Small doses are fatal. Determine why barium compounds are used when making gastrointestinal X rays. *Barium sulfate is opaque to X rays. It is also very insoluble in water. Therefore, there is little danger in having barium sulfate in the intestines. Very little barium would pass into the bloodstream.*

SUMMARY

10-1: Structure of the Atom

1. A chemical symbol is a shorthand way of writing the name of an element.

2. An atom consists of a nucleus made of protons and neutrons surrounded by an electron cloud.

3. The electrons in an atom are arranged in several energy levels, each of which is able to hold a certain number of electrons.

10-2: Science and Society: Smaller Particles of Matter

1. Quarks are particles of matter that make up protons and neutrons.

2. Protons can be broken into quarks by having them collide while traveling near the speed of light.

10-3: Masses of Atoms

1. The number of neutrons in an atom can be computed by subtracting the atomic number from the mass number.

2. The isotopes of an element are atoms of that same element that have different numbers of neutrons.

3. The average atomic mass of an element is the average mass of the mixture of its isotopes.

10-4: The Periodic Table

1. The periodic table of elements is an arrangement of elements according to repeated changes in properties.

2. In the periodic table, the 109 elements are arranged in 18 vertical columns, or groups, and seven horizontal rows, or periods.

3. Metals are found at the left of the periodic table, nonmetals at the right, and metalloids along the line that separates the metals from the nonmetals.

KEY SCIENCE WORDS

a. **atomic number**
b. **average atomic mass**
c. **chemical symbol**
d. **dot diagram**
e. **electron cloud**
f. **electron**
g. **group**
h. **isotopes**
i. **mass number**
j. **metalloid**
k. **metal**
l. **neutron**
m. **nonmetal**
n. **nucleus**
o. **periodic table**
p. **period**
q. **proton**
r. **quarks**

UNDERSTANDING VOCABULARY

Match each phrase with the correct term from the list of Key Science Words.

1. an abbreviated way to write the name of an element
2. an atomic particle with no charge
3. atoms of the same element with different numbers of neutrons
4. average mass of the mixture of isotopes
5. positively charged center of an atom
6. particles that make up protons and neutrons
7. the region formed by electrons
8. the number of protons in the nucleus
9. total number of protons and neutrons in the nucleus
10. a horizontal row in the periodic table

SUMMARY

Have students read the summary statements to review the major concepts of the chapter.

UNDERSTANDING VOCABULARY

1. c	**6.** r
2. l	**7.** e
3. h	**8.** a
4. b	**9.** i
5. n	**10.** p

ASSESSMENT
Portfolio

Encourage students to place in their portfolios one or two items of what they consider to be their best work. For each item, ask students to explain why that item was chosen and what they learned from it. Items might be selected from the following.

- Enrichment research, p. 245
- Activity 10-1 observations and answers, p. 247
- Skill Builder concept map, p. 246

Performance

Additional performance assessments may be found in *Performance Assessment* and *Science Integration Activities* that accompany **Merrill Physical Science**. Performance Task Assessment Lists and rubrics for evaluating these activities and other products generated throughout the chapter can be found in Glencoe's *Performance Assessment in Middle School Science*.

OPTIONS

ASSESSMENT

To assess students' understanding of material in this chapter, use the resources listed.

👥 COOPERATIVE LEARNING

Consider cooperative learning in the THINK AND WRITE CRITICALLY, APPLY, and MORE SKILL BUILDERS sections of the Chapter Review.

PROGRAM RESOURCES

From the **Teacher Resource Package** use:

Chapter Review, pages 23-24.

Chapter and Unit Tests, pages 61-64, Chapter Test.

CHECKING CONCEPTS

1. d	**6.** c
2. c	**7.** d
3. b	**8.** a
4. b	**9.** d
5. a	**10.** b

USING LAB SKILLS

ASSESSMENT

Use these alternate lab exercises to assess students' understanding of skills used in this chapter.

11. osmium; 16

12. $\dfrac{3 \times 4 + 2 \times 3 + 1 \times 2}{6} = 3.3$

THINK AND WRITE CRITICALLY

13. The tendency of the moving electron to escape is balanced by the electrical attraction of the positive nucleus for the negative electron.

14. Because the names of several elements may start with the same letter, a second letter may be needed to distinguish them.

15. Silver atoms have an atomic number of 47 and therefore contain 47 protons.

Mass of atoms in sample

= 52 (60 + 47) + 48 (62 + 47)

= 52 × 107 + 48 × 109

= 5564 + 5232

= 10 796

Average atomic mass

= $\dfrac{10\,796}{52 + 48}$ = 107.96

16. Protons are thought to be composed of smaller particles called quarks. Electrons, however, cannot be broken down into smaller particles.

17. They are called nucleons because they are the particles that make up the nucleus.

CHECKING CONCEPTS

Choose the word or phrase that completes the sentence or answers the question.

1. The state of matter of most of the elements to the left of the stair-step line in the periodic table is _____.
- **a.** gas
- **b.** liquid
- **c.** plasma
- **d.** solid

2. If a pattern repeats itself, it is _____.
- **a.** isotopic
- **b.** metallic
- **c.** periodic
- **d.** transition

3. _____ is an element that would have similar properties to those of neon.
- **a.** Aluminum
- **b.** Argon
- **c.** Arsenic
- **d.** Silver

4. Boron is a _____.
- **a.** metal
- **b.** metalloid
- **c.** noble gas
- **d.** nonmetal

5. The element potassium is a _____.
- **a.** metal
- **b.** metalloid
- **c.** nonmetal
- **d.** transition element

6. The element bromine is a _____.
- **a.** metal
- **b.** metalloid
- **c.** nonmetal
- **d.** transition element

7. The halogens are those elements in Group _____.
- **a.** 1
- **b.** 11
- **c.** 15
- **d.** 17

8. In its group, nitrogen is the only element that is a _____.
- **a.** gas
- **b.** metalloid
- **c.** metal
- **d.** liquid

9. _____ is a shiny element that conducts electricity and heat well.
- **a.** Chlorine
- **b.** Sulfur
- **c.** Hydrogen
- **d.** Magnesium

10. The atomic number of Re is 75. The atomic mass of one of its isotopes is 186. How many neutrons are in an atom of this isotope?
- **a.** 75
- **b.** 111
- **c.** 186
- **d.** 261

USING LAB SKILLS

11. In Activity 10-1 on page 247, you made a model to help find the relationship among protons, neutrons, and electrons. Which element has 114 neutrons, 76 protons, and 76 electrons?

12. In Activity 10-2 on page 254, you found what is known as a weighted average. In many schools a weighted average provides a student's grade point average, or GPA. If a letter grade of A equals four points; a B, three; a C, two; and a D, one, find the GPA if the student made three A's, two B's, and one C.

THINK AND WRITE CRITICALLY

Answer the following questions in your Journal using complete sentences.

13. Why do electrons keep moving around the nucleus and not away from the atom?

14. Why do some chemical symbols have one letter and some have two letters?

15. A silver sample contains 52 atoms, each having 60 neutrons, and 48 atoms, each having 62 neutrons. What is the sample's average atomic mass?

16. According to currently accepted ideas, how do protons and electrons differ in structure?

17. Why are protons and neutrons also known as nucleons?

18. We know that properties of elements are periodic. List at least two other things in nature that are periodic.

19. Lead and mercury are two pollutants in the environment. From information about them in the periodic table, why are they called "heavy metals"?

20. Ge and Si are used in making semiconductors. Are these two elements in the same group or the same period?

21. U and Pu are named for objects in nature. What are these objects, and what other element is named after a similar object?

22. Ca is used by the body to make bones and teeth. Radioactive Sr is in nuclear waste. Why is this Sr hazardous to people?

MORE SKILL BUILDERS

If you need help, refer to the Skill Handbook.

1. Making and Using Tables: Use the periodic table to list a metal, a metalloid, and a nonmetal with five outer-level electrons.

2. Comparing and Contrasting: From the information found in the periodic table and reference books, compare and contrast the properties of chlorine and bromine.

3. Interpreting Data: If scientists have determined that a neutral atom of rubidium has an atomic number of 37 and a mass number of 85, how many protons, neutrons, and electrons does the atom have?

4. Sequencing: What changes in the periodic table would occur in Periods 1 through 4 if the elements are arranged according to increasing average atomic mass instead of atomic number? How do we know that arrangement by atomic number is correct?

5. Concept Mapping: As a star dies, it becomes more dense. Its temperature rises to a point where He nuclei are combined with other nuclei. When this happens, the atomic numbers of the other nuclei are increased by 2, because each gains the two protons contained in the He nucleus. For example, Cr fused with He becomes Fe. Complete the concept map below showing the first four steps in He fusion.

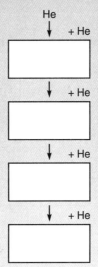

PROJECTS

1. Do research on the attempts made by Johann Dobereiner and John Newlands to classify the elements. Write a report on your findings.

2. Make a display of samples or pictures of several elements. List the name, symbol, atomic number, average atomic mass, and several uses for each element.

3. Research and report on models of the atom from the time of the ancient Greeks until the present.

ATOMIC STRUCTURE AND THE PERIODIC TABLE **265**

18. Possible answers are tides, time of day, seasons, and moon phases.
19. They have relatively high atomic masses.
20. the same group
21. They are planets. Neptunium is also named for a planet.
22. Calcium and strontium are in the same group and therefore have similar properties. Strontium, like calcium, is easily absorbed into the body.

MORE SKILL BUILDERS

1. Making and Using Tables: metal, bismuth; metalloid, antimony or arsenic; nonmetal, nitrogen or phosphorus

2. Comparing and Contrasting: The chemical properties of chlorine and bromine would be similar because they are in the same group. At room temperature, bromine is a liquid, whereas chlorine is a gas. Bromine atoms have a greater mass than do chlorine atoms. It is also reasonable to assume that a bromine atom is larger than a chlorine atom because the bromine atom has one more level of electrons.

3. Interpreting Data: 37 protons, 37 electrons, 48 neutrons

4. Sequencing: Argon and potassium would be reversed as would nickel and cobalt. The resulting arrangement would cause the elements to appear in groups with other elements that do not share their properties.

5. Concept Mapping: See below.

He $\xrightarrow{\text{+ He}}$ Be $\xrightarrow{\text{+ He}}$ C $\xrightarrow{\text{+ He}}$ O $\xrightarrow{\text{+ He}}$ Ne

11 Chemical Bonds

CHAPTER SECTION	OBJECTIVES	ACTIVITIES
11-1 Why Atoms Combine (2 days)	**1. Describe** how a compound differs from the elements it is composed of. **2. Explain** what a chemical formula represents. **3. State** a reason why chemical bonding occurs.	**Activity 11-1:** *Eggshell Electrons,* p. 273
11-2 Hazardous Compounds at Home **Science & Society** (1 day)	**1. Describe** the dangers posed by hazardous compounds in the home. **2. Demonstrate** an understanding of ways to avoid hazardous compounds or ways to use them safely.	
11-3 Kinds of Chemical Bonds (2 days)	**1. Describe** ionic bonds and covalent bonds. **2. Identify** the particles produced by ionic bonding and by covalent bonding. **3. Distinguish** between a nonpolar covalent bond and a polar covalent bond.	**Activity 11-2:** *Become a Bond Breaker,* p. 281
11-4 Formulas and Names of Compounds (2 days)	**1. Explain** how to determine oxidation numbers. **2. Write formulas** for compounds from their names. **3. Name** compounds from their formulas. **4. Describe** hydrates and their formulas.	**MINI-Lab:** *How does heat affect a hydrate?* p. 287
Chapter Review		

ACTIVITY MATERIALS

FIND OUT	ACTIVITIES		MINI-LABS

Page 267
steel wool
2 test tubes of the
  same size
1 beaker or jar
	11-1 Eggshell Electrons,
	p. 273
	modified egg carton
	marbles
		11-2 Become a Bond Breaker, p. 281
		1 tablespoon each of
		  crushed ice, sugar,
		  and salt
		3 test tubes
		wire test tube holder
		laboratory burner
		goggles
		timer
			How does heat affect a hydrate? p. 287
			white paper
			glass stirring rod
			solution containing
			  1 g $CoCl_2 \cdot 6H_2O$
			  in 35 mL of water
			laboratory burner

CHAPTER FEATURES	TEACHER RESOURCE PACKAGE	OTHER RESOURCES
Skill Builder: *Making and Using Tables*, p. 272	**Ability Level Worksheets** ◆ **Study Guide,** p. 46 ● **Reinforcement,** p. 46 ▲ **Enrichment,** p. 46 **Science and Society,** p. 15 **Activity Worksheets,** pp. 5, 86, 87 **Transparency Masters,** pp. 41, 42	**Color Transparency 21,** Chemical Bonding **Laboratory Manual 23,** The Six Solutions Problem **STVS:** Disc 1, Side 1
You Decide! p. 275	**Ability Level Worksheets** ◆ **Study Guide,** p. 47 ● **Reinforcement,** p. 47 ▲ **Enrichment,** p. 47 **Concept Mapping,** pp. 27, 28 **Critical Thinking/Problem Solving,** p. 17	**STVS:** Disc 2, Side 1
Technology: *Bond Busters*, p. 279 **Skill Builder:** *Concept Mapping*, p. 280	**Ability Level Worksheets** ◆ **Study Guide,** p. 48 ● **Reinforcement,** p. 48 ▲ **Enrichment,** p. 48 **Activity Worksheets,** pp. 88, 89	**Laboratory Manual 24,** Chemical Bonds **STVS:** Disc 2, Side 1 **Science Integration Activity 11**
Problem Solving: *The Packet of Mystery Crystals*, p. 288 **Skill Builder:** *Using Variables, Constants, and Controls*, p. 288	**Ability Level Worksheets** ◆ **Study Guide,** p. 49 ● **Reinforcement,** p. 49 ▲ **Enrichment,** p. 49 **Cross-Curricular Connections,** p. 17 **Activity Worksheets,** pp. 5, 92 **Transparency Masters,** pp. 43, 44	**Color Transparency 22,** Oxidation Numbers of Elements
Summary Key Science Words Understanding Vocabulary Checking Concepts Using Lab Skills Think & Write Critically Apply More Skill Builders Projects	**ASSESSMENT RESOURCES** **Chapter Review,** pp. 25, 26 **Chapter Test,** pp. 65-68 **Unit Test,** pp. 69, 70 **Performance Assessment in** Middle School Science	**Chapter Review Software** **Test Bank** **Alternate Assessment** **Performance Assessment**

◆ **Basic**   ● **Average**   ▲ **Advanced**

ADDITIONAL MATERIALS

SOFTWARE	AUDIOVISUAL	BOOKS/MAGAZINES
Atoms and Molecules, AIMS Media. *Bonding,* J and S Software. *Chemicals of Life I,* EduQuest. *Covalent Bonds—Covalent Structures,* Queue. *Covalent Bonds—Electron Orbitals,* Queue. *Introduction to General Chemistry: Inorganic Nomenclature,* EdQuest. *Ionic Bonds,* Queue. *Molecules and Atoms: Exploring the Essence of Matter,* Queue. *Writing Chemcial Formulas,* Queue.	*Atoms and Molecules,* Video, Insight Media. *Chemical Bonding and Atomic Structure,* Video, Insight Media. *Chemical Bonding and Atomic Structure,* Video, Coronet. *Exploring Matter: Chemical Change,* Video, Britannica. *How Atoms Combine,* Video, Coronet. *Molecular Bonding: A Union of Atoms,* Video, Lucerne Media.	Block, B. Peter, et al. *Inorganic Chemical Nomenclature.* Washington, D.C.: American Chemical Society, 1990. Borman, Stu. "New Tin-Based Propellane May Shed Light on Bonding Questions." *Chemical and Engineering News* 67, August 7, 1989, pp. 29-31. Gray, Harry B. *Chemical Bonds: An Introduction to Atomic and Molecular Structure.* Redwood City, CA: Benjamin-Cummings Publishing Co., 1973.

THEME DEVELOPMENT: Stability, a theme of the textbook, is described in terms of chemical stability. The relationship between an atom's electron structure and its stability is discussed. A study of chemical bonding further develops the theme. Chemical properties such as corrosiveness, flammability, and toxicity are related to stability.

CHAPTER OVERVIEW

▶ **Section 11-1:** Atoms react to form chemically stable substances that are held together by chemical bonds and are represented by chemical formulas.

▶ **Section 11-2: Science and Society:** Students learn that care must be exercised when using many chemicals found in the home.

▶ **Section 11-3:** Ionic, polar covalent, and covalent bonds are conceptualized in this section as are the resulting polar and nonpolar molecules.

▶ **Section 11-4:** Oxidation numbers are used to introduce formula writing and naming for both binary and polyatomic compounds. This section also introduces students to hydrates.

CHAPTER VOCABULARY

chemical	covalent bond
formula	polar
chemically	molecule
stable	nonpolar
chemical bond	molecule
toxic	oxidation number
corrosive	binary compound
ion	polyatomic ion
ionic bond	hydrate

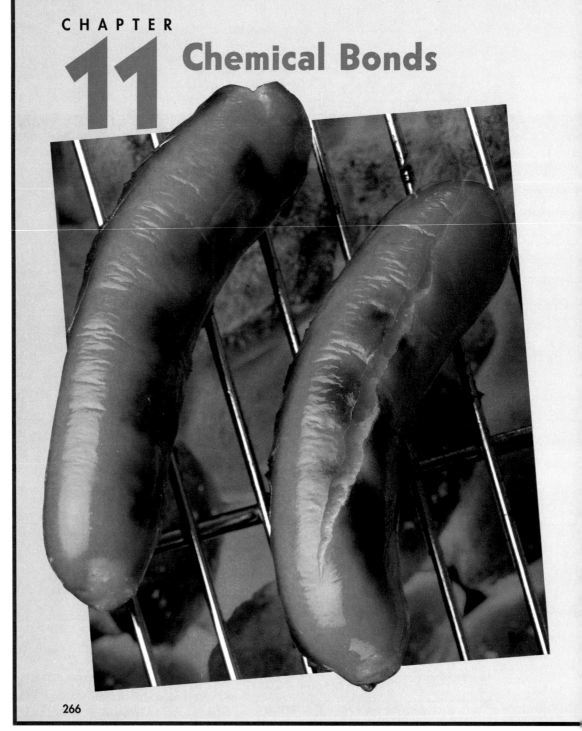

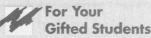

266

OPTIONS

For Your Gifted Students

A concept that may be particularly interesting for gifted students is the relationship between an element's electron structure and bonding that involves more than outer level electrons. Using a high school text, point out the text that explains bonding involving transition metals scandium through zinc. Students may be challenged to understand how other bonding theories explain attractions between atoms.

For Your Mainstreamed Students

Students can make a survey of all the hazardous materials found in their homes and school. They could prepare a poster display using magazine pictures of these materials and write a paragraph for each that lists the hazards and the proper disposal of the material.

The use of physical models to show atomic structure and bonding is particularly important for students who have impaired vision.

Whenever you watch charcoal burning, you observe a change in which chemical bonds form. These bonds form between the carbon in the charcoal and oxygen in the air. What is another chemical change in which oxygen bonds with another element?

FIND OUT!

Do this simple activity to find out how oxygen can bond with another element.

Stuff some wet steel wool into the bottom of a test tube. Invert the test tube in a beaker of water. Invert a tube containing only air beside the first one. Adjust the water levels in both tubes so that they are equal, with the water rising about 1 cm above the openings of the test tubes. Let the tubes stand a few days. What evidence of chemical change do you *observe?*

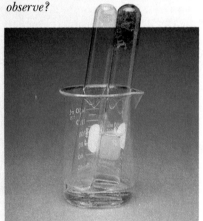

Gearing Up
Previewing the Chapter
Use this outline to help you focus on important ideas in this chapter.

Previewing Science Skills
▶ In the Skill Builders, you will make and use a table, make a concept map, and use variables, constants, and controls.
▶ In the Activities, you will observe, compare, classify, and infer.
▶ In the MINI-Lab, you will observe and infer.

What's next?

You have shown that moist iron rusts as it combines with the oxygen in a test tube of air. You will learn more about how elements combine as you read the pages that follow.

267

INTRODUCING THE CHAPTER
Use the Find Out activity to introduce students to chemical bonding. Inform students that they will be learning more about chemical formulas and bonds as they read the chapter.

FIND OUT!
Preparation: Some steel wool has an oily coating to prevent rust. If you suspect this, wash the steel wool in soapy water and rinse thoroughly before using.

Materials: steel wool, two test tubes of the same size, and one beaker or jar for each group

Cooperative Learning: Use the Paired Partners strategy if you have enough materials. Have students speculate on the reason for the empty test tube. Ask them to form a common hypothesis about the results.

Teaching Tips
▶ Students can adjust water levels in the tubes by tilting them slightly near the surface of the water.
▶ Tubes should rest securely on the bottom of beaker. If they tend to float, pour some water out of the beaker.
▶ If you have some very large test tubes, set up a large-scale version of the activity as a demonstration.
▶ Water should rise one-fifth of the way up the tube that contains the steel wool. Remind students that the air is 20 percent oxygen, as the activity demonstrates. The remainder is mainly nitrogen and argon.

Gearing Up
Have students study the Gearing Up feature to familiarize themselves with the chapter. Discuss the relationships of the topics in the outline.

What's Next?
Before beginning the first section, make sure students understand the connection between the Find Out activity and the topics to follow.

ASSESSMENT OPTIONS

PORTFOLIO
Refer to page 289 for suggested items that students might select for their portfolios.

PERFORMANCE ASSESSMENT
See page 289 for additional Performance Assessment options.
Process
Skill Builders, pp. 272, 280
MINI-Lab, p. 287
Activities 11-1, p. 273; 11-2, p. 281
Using Lab Skills, p. 290

CONTENT ASSESSMENT
Assessment—Oral, pp. 278, 285
Skill Builder, p. 288
Section Reviews, pp. 272, 275, 280, 288
Chapter Review, pp. 289-291
Mini Quizzes, pp. 271, 279, 285

GROUP ASSESSMENT
Opportunities for group assessment occur with Cooperative Learning Strategies and Flex Your Brain Activities.

11-1 Why Atoms Combine

PREPARATION

SECTION BACKGROUND

▶ An atom with a full outer energy level is chemically stable, or unreactive. For most atoms, this condition means having eight outer electrons. For this reason, this principle is called the octet rule. Note, however, if the first energy level is the outer level, only two electrons are needed for the level to be full.
▶ Electrons can be simultaneously attracted by two nuclei. The attractive force is called a chemical bond.
▶ Most metals have three or fewer outer electrons and tend to lose electrons to form positive ions.
▶ Most nonmetals have five or more outer electrons and tend to gain electrons to form negative ions.

PREPLANNING

▶ To prepare for Activity 11-1, prepare modified egg carton and package marbles for each laboratory team.

1 MOTIVATE

▶ **Demonstration:** Two elements combining in a dramatic way can be shown by reacting 3 g of zinc dust with 2 g of iodine crystals. Place them in a test tube. Shake to mix, then clamp the tube securely upright. Add 1 mL water to start the reaction. **CAUTION:** *The reaction gives off heat and a toxic vapor. Perform only outdoors or in a fume hood.* Point out that the elements become more stable by combining. Tell students that they will learn to name and write the formula for the product of this reaction, zinc iodide.

STUDENT TEXT QUESTION

▶ Page 268, paragraph 3: **How are the properties of table salt different from those of sodium and chlorine?** *Table salt is a white, crystalline, nonpoisonous solid. Sodium is a silvery-colored soft metal. Chlorine is a greenish, poisonous gas.*

New Science Words

chemical formula
chemically stable
chemical bond

Objectives

▶ Describe how a compound differs from the elements it is composed of.
▶ Explain what a chemical formula represents.
▶ State a reason why chemical bonding occurs.

Did You Know?

In the last two centuries, industrialization has greatly increased the amounts of the compound carbon dioxide in Earth's atmosphere. This increase is, in part, responsible for recent trends in global warming.

Figure 11-1. When iron rusts, iron and oxygen combine to form a new substance.

Compounds

Most of the matter around you is in the form of compounds or mixtures of compounds. The water you drink, the carbon dioxide you exhale, and the salt you put on food are examples of compounds.

Some of the matter around you is in the form of elements, such as iron and oxygen. But, like many other pairs of elements, iron and oxygen tend to unite chemically to form a compound when the conditions are right. You know how iron in moist steel wool exposed to oxygen forms rust, a compound. Rusting is a chemical change because a new substance, rust, is produced.

Compounds have properties unlike those of their elements. Table salt, for example, is composed of the elements sodium and chlorine. Sodium is a shiny, soft, gray metal that reacts violently with water. Chlorine is a greenish-yellow gas that can kill an animal that inhales a few deep breaths of the gas. These elements combine to form table salt, or sodium chloride. Look at Figure 11-2. How are the properties of table salt different from those of sodium and chlorine?

OPTIONS

Meeting Different Ability Levels

For Section 11-1, use the following **Teacher Resource Masters** depending upon individual students' needs.
◆ **Study Guide Master** for all students.
● **Reinforcement Master** for students of average and above average ability levels.
▲ **Enrichment Master** for above average students.
Additional Teacher Resource Package masters are listed in any PROGRAM RESOURCES boxes that are in the section. The additional masters are appropriate for all students.

◆ **STUDY GUIDE** 46

STUDY GUIDE   Chapter 11
Why Atoms Combine   Text Pages 268-273

The definitions of several key terms about how atoms combine are given below. In the blanks, write the term from the word list that makes each definition complete.

atoms   chemical symbol   compound   electrons   force
number   ratios   elements   energy level

1. **Chemical formula** tells what **elements** make up a **compound** and the **ratios** of the atoms of those elements.
2. **Subscript:** a **number** in a chemical formula written after a **chemical symbol** that tells how many atoms of an element are in a unit of the compound
3. **Chemically stable:** condition of an atom when its outer **energy level** is completely filled with **electrons**
4. **Chemical bond:** in a compound, the **force** that holds the **atoms** together

Use the diagram below to select eight letters to form a word found in this chapter. Use the statements as hints to help you select the correct letters. Circle each letter as you find it in the diagram. Write the word in the space provided. Then define the term.

1. The first letter must be in the triangle and in the circle, but not in the rectangle.
2. The second letter must be in the triangle only.
3. The third letter must be in the circle, triangle, and rectangle.
4. The fourth letter must be in the rectangle only.
5. The fifth letter must be in the circle only.
6. The sixth letter must be in both the rectangle and the triangle, but not in the circle.
7. The seventh letter must be in both the rectangle and circle, but not in the triangle.
8. The eighth letter must be in the part of the rectangle that is below the triangle.

The word is c o m p o u n d Definition: A **compound** is a substance composed of two or more elements chemically combined.

46   Copyright Glencoe Division of Macmillan/McGraw-Hill

Figure 11-2. Sodium, a soft, gray metal, combines with chlorine, a greenish-yellow gas, to form sodium chloride, a white crystalline solid.

Formulas

Do you recall that the chemical symbols Na and Cl represent sodium and chlorine? When written as NaCl, the symbols make up a formula, or chemical shorthand, for the compound sodium chloride. Another formula you may recognize is H_2O, for water. The formula is a combination of the symbols H and O and the subscript number 2. *Subscript* means "written below." A subscript number written after a symbol tells how many atoms there are of that element in a unit of the compound. If a symbol has no subscript, there's one atom of that element. The formula H_2O, then, shows there are two atoms of hydrogen for one atom of oxygen in one unit of the compound water. Put another way, the ratio of hydrogen atoms to oxygen atoms in water is 2 to 1.

Look at the formula for iron (III) oxide: Fe_2O_3. The symbol for iron, Fe, is followed by the subscript 2, and the symbol for oxygen, O, is followed by the subscript 3. For two atoms of iron there are three atoms of oxygen in the compound. That is, the ratio of iron atoms to oxygen atoms in iron (III) oxide is 2 to 3.

Baking soda is found in many foods. What is its chemical formula? How many oxygen atoms are found in one unit of baking soda?

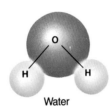

Water

Carbon dioxide

Figure 11-3. These models show the ratios and the arrangements of atoms in water and carbon dioxide.

● **REINFORCEMENT** 46

▲ **ENRICHMENT** 46

269

TYING TO PREVIOUS KNOWLEDGE: Ask students to think of how the pieces of a jigsaw puzzle interlock to form a complete picture. In a similar way, atoms can bond together to form a compound. The atoms combine in a definite ratio and in a definite order in a way similar to the way the puzzle pieces combine.

2 TEACH

Key Concepts are highlighted.

CONCEPT DEVELOPMENT

▶ Until recently, no rules were followed in naming elements. Some element names are based on German, Greek, or Latin roots. Some are based on names of geographic locations. Some are named to honor scientists.

▶ You may want to review that the atom has a positive nucleus that is surrounded by negative electrons.

▶ Using the periodic table on pages 258-259, students should be able to look up the names or symbols of elements and thus become familiar with their locations on the table.

▶ The driving force that causes a chemical reaction to go to completion is the atom's tendency to become stable. Typically, this involves a completed outer energy level of eight electrons.

Answers: $NaHCO_3$; 3

VideoDisc

STVS: Photo-Acoustic Cell, Disc 1, Side 1

▶ Geology: The names that geologists use for gemstones and other crystals are not the same names used by chemists. A quartz crystal is silicon dioxide. Fool's gold, iron pyrite, is named iron sulfide, and fluorite is calcium fluoride. Have students research common names, chemical names, and chemical formulas for other gems and minerals.

CONCEPT DEVELOPMENT

**▶ To help your students better understand chemical stability, you can use the concept of potential energy. A book held above a desk has potential energy depending on its height above the desk. The book can become more stable by falling to the desk, losing energy in the process. When atoms bond together and become more stable, energy is usually given off.

STUDENT TEXT QUESTIONS

▶ Page 270, paragraph 1: What elements are in each compound listed in Table 11-1? What is the ratio of atoms in each compound? *Refer to Table 11-1. Aid students in picking individual element symbols out of formulas and in interpreting the formulas. For example, silicon dioxide is made up of silicon and oxygen in a 1:2 ratio.*

Science and READING

The names of chemical compounds listed on product labels are often different from those in chemistry textbooks. Manufacturers often give trade names to chemicals that will be sold by their companies. The International Union of Pure and Applied Chemists (I.U.P.A.C.) uses a system that involves Roman numerals for charges on some atoms. For example, some anticavity toothpastes contain stannous fluoride. The IUPAC name is tin(II) fluoride.

Table 11-1

SOME FAMILIAR COMPOUNDS		
Familiar Name	Chemical Name	Formula
Lye	Sodium hydroxide	$NaOH$
Vinegar	Acetic acid	$HC_2H_3O_2$
Ammonia	Ammonia	NH_3
Grain alcohol	Ethanol	C_2H_5OH
Sand	Silicon dioxide	SiO_2
Battery acid	Sulfuric acid	H_2SO_4
Stomach acid	Hydrochloric acid	HCl
Milk of magnesia	Magnesium hydroxide	$Mg(OH)_2$
Cane sugar	Sucrose	$C_{12}H_{22}O_{11}$

Science and READING

Check the labels on the products you find in your home. Look in such places as the medicine cabinet, the refrigerator, and the cupboard under the sink. Match the name of the active ingredient with a formula, and vice versa, for as many products as you can.

The **chemical formula** for any compound tells what elements it contains and the ratio of the atoms of those elements. What elements are in each compound listed in Table 11-1? What is the ratio of atoms in each compound?

Chemically Stable Atoms

What causes elements to form compounds? Look again at the periodic table on pages 258 and 259. It lists 109 elements, most of which can, and often do, combine with other elements. But the six noble gases in Group 18 seldom combine with other elements. Why do the noble gases almost never form compounds? The reason is that the arrangement of electrons in their atoms makes them chemically stable, or resistant to change.

What electron arrangements make atoms stable? An atom is **chemically stable** if its outer energy level is completely filled with electrons. For the atoms of most elements, the outer energy level is filled when it contains eight electrons. Atoms of the noble gases neon, argon, krypton, xenon, and radon all contain eight electrons in the outermost energy level. For atoms of helium, the outermost energy level is filled when it has two electrons.

Figure 11-4 shows dot diagrams of some of the noble gases. Remember that a dot diagram of an atom shows

2

OPTIONS

INQUIRY QUESTIONS

▶ Hot packs are used by athletic trainers. When the chemicals inside the plastic bag are mixed, a chemical reaction occurs. Describe what you think is happening in terms of bonding and energy. *As mixing takes place, some bonds are broken and new bonds formed. More energy is released by the new bonds than is required to break original bonds.*

▶ Atoms of some elements will bond with another atom of the same element. The molecules they form are called diatomic molecules. The oxygen gas you breathe is diatomic, O_2. Why would like atoms bond together? *They share electrons, giving each atom eight electrons in the outer energy level.*

▶ Potassium permanganate is used to control odors around paper mills and animal feedlots. How many oxygen atoms are in its formula, $KMnO_4$? *4*

▶ When would a chemist want to produce a chemical that was unstable? *rocket fuel, explosive*

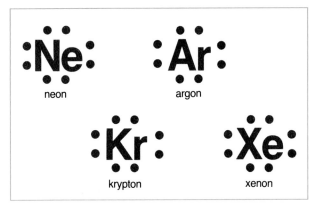

neon   argon

krypton   xenon

Figure 11-4. Dot diagrams of neon—Ne, krypton—Kr, argon—Ar, and xenon—Xe

the number of electrons in its outer energy level. Notice that each of these elements has eight outer electrons. Because each noble gas has an outer level that is filled with electrons, each of these elements is chemically stable. Thus, the noble gases don't form compounds naturally. A few compounds of xenon and radon have been prepared in the laboratory under special conditions. Each atom of all the elements *except* the noble gases has from one to seven electrons in its outer energy level. These atoms tend to lose, gain, or share electrons with other atoms. It is the gaining, losing, or sharing of electrons that causes chemical changes. In one of these ways, an atom may have its outer energy level filled, like a noble gas.

Losing, gaining, and sharing electrons are the means by which atoms become stable and form chemical bonds. A **chemical bond** is a force that holds together the atoms in a substance. When a chemical bond forms between sodium and chlorine, each sodium atom loses one electron and each chlorine atom gains one. As a result, each atom in sodium chloride, NaCl, now has eight electrons in its newly formed outer energy level. Figure 11-5 illustrates this process. Why is the compound sodium chloride stable?

What is a chemical bond?

Figure 11-5. When sodium combines with chlorine, each sodium atom loses an electron and each chlorine atom gains an electron.

sodium atom   chlorine atom   sodium chloride

CONCEPT DEVELOPMENT

▶ The material in this section can be abstract for some students. It may be helpful to have students draw the electron structures of the simpler elements, emphasizing the outer-level electron arrangement and relating this to the element's position on the periodic table.

▶ Relate the bonding between sodium and chloride ions to electrostatic attraction ("static cling"). The same force is involved. Do a quick demonstration of electrostatic attraction by rubbing a plastic ruler with a wool cloth and showing that they attract. Reinforce the idea that a chemical bond is a real physical force and not just an idea on paper.

STUDENT TEXT QUESTION

▶ Page 271, paragraph 2: **Why is the compound sodium chloride stable?** *because both sodium and chlorine now have eight electrons in the outer level*

MINI QUIZ

Use the Mini Quiz to check students' recall of chapter content.

1 **What is used in a formula to tell the number of atoms of an element in a compound?** *subscript*
2 **When the outer energy level of an atom is filled with electrons, the atom is chemically _____ .** *stable*
3 **What happens when electrons are gained, shared, or lost?** *chemical changes*
4 **What do we call a force that holds atoms together in a substance?** *chemical bond*

CHECK FOR UNDERSTANDING

Ask questions 1-3 and the **Apply** and **Connect to Earth Science** questions in the Section Review.

RETEACH

▶ Ask students why they think each compound listed in Table 11-1 on page 270 is a stable compound. The answer, except for hydrogen, is that all atoms present are stable because they have an outer level with eight electrons.

ENRICHMENT

▶ The chemical symbols that are used today are relatively modern. Students may want to research the ancient history of the first symbols used for elements and compounds.
▶ The noble gases used to be called the inert gases. In 1962, some were caused to react. Have a student research noble gas compounds and how they are made.
▶ Have a student determine the chemical formulas of some common compounds found in soft drinks.

PROGRAM RESOURCES

From the **Teacher Resource Package** use:
  Science & Society, page 15, Biodegradability.
  Activity Worksheets, page 5, Flex Your Brain.
  Transparency Masters, pages 41-42, Chemical Bonding.
Use **Color Transparency** number 21, Chemical Bonding.
Use **Laboratory Manual 23,** The Six Solutions Problem.

EXTENSION

For students who have mastered this section, use the **Reinforcement** and **Enrichment** masters or other OPTIONS provided.

STUDENT TEXT QUESTION

▶ Page 272, paragraph 1: **How is the bond in Cl₂ different from the bond in NaCl?** *It is formed by sharing electrons rather than by attraction between oppositely charged particles brought about by electron transfer.*

Answer: A chemical bond is a condition in which a force holds atoms together in a substance. The force may result from the sharing or loss or gain of electrons. Atoms generally fill their outer energy levels when they bond, becoming more stable.

3 CLOSE

? FLEX Your Brain

Use the Flex Your Brain activity to have students explore COMPOUNDS.

ASSESSMENT

Portfolio: Use the Flex Your Brain activity to reinforce critical-thinking and problem-solving skills. In Step 2, students might list differences between compounds and other materials.

SECTION REVIEW ANSWERS

1. The properties of the elements are replaced by the properties of the compound they form.
2. (a) CaF_2 , (b) Al_2S_3
3. The compounds that are formed are chemically more stable than the elements.
4. Apply: sodium, carbon, and oxygen, in the ratio of 2 to 1 to 3
5. Connect to Earth Science:

Figure 11-6. Dot diagram for the formation of chlorine gas, Cl₂, from two atoms of chlorine

In Your JOURNAL

A chemical bond is not a thing that can be touched. Using electron arrangements, energy, and stability, write **in your Journal** a paragraph describing a chemical bond.

What makes most atoms chemically unstable?

In chlorine gas, two chlorine atoms share electrons. In its formula, Cl_2, the subscript 2 shows that there are two atoms bonded together. Look at Figure 11-6. How is the bond in Cl_2 different from the bond in NaCl?

As you have read, compounds make up most of the matter around you. Why is this so? The answer is that the arrangements of electrons in most atoms make them chemically unstable. By sharing or transferring electrons, the atoms achieve more stable arrangements of electrons.

SECTION REVIEW

1. What happens to the properties of elements when atoms form compounds?
2. Write formulas for (a) a compound with one calcium atom and two fluorine atoms and (b) a compound with two aluminum atoms and three sulfur atoms.
3. Why do most elements tend to form compounds?
4. **Apply:** The label on a box of washing soda states that it contains Na_2CO_3. Name the elements in this compound. In what ratio are they present?
5. **Connect to Earth Science:** Calcium chloride is sometimes used on dirt roads to keep dust levels lower and reduce wind erosion. Calcium and chlorine are in a 1:2 ratio in this compound. Draw the electron dot diagram for the formation of calcium chloride.

Skill Builder ☑ Making and Using Tables

The compounds in Table 11-1 on page 270 that contain carbon are classified as organic, and the others are classified as inorganic. Reorganize the contents of the table using these groups. If you need help, refer to Making and Using Tables in the **Skill Handbook** on page 686.

Skill Builder

Type of Compound	Familiar Name	Chemical Name	Formula
Organic	vinegar	acetic acid	$HC_2H_3O_2$
	grain alcohol	ethanol	C_2H_5OH
	cane sugar	sucrose	$C_{12}H_{22}O_{11}$
Inorganic	lye	sodium hydroxide	$NaOH$
	ammonia	ammonia	NH_3
	sand	silicon dioxide	SiO_2
	battery acid	sulfuric acid	H_2SO_4
	stomach acid	hydrochloric acid	HCl
	milk of magnesia	magnesium hydroxide	$Mg(OH)_2$

Eggshell Electrons

Electrons are so small that you cannot see them. But you can make a model that shows how electrons are arranged in bonded atoms.

Materials
- modified egg carton
- marbles

Procedure
1. Obtain a modified egg carton and marbles from your teacher. The carton will represent the first and second energy levels of an atom, and the marbles will represent electrons.
2. Place one marble in each receptacle of the carton. Start with the pair of receptacles representing the first energy level of the atom.
3. Place the remaining marbles in receptacles representing the second energy level. In which column would your element appear on the periodic chart?
4. *Compare* your model with those of your classmates. Find one or more other cartons that, when combined with yours, will make it possible for each of the two cartons to have eight marbles in its second energy level.
5. Make a list of the combinations you were able to make with your classmates' models.

Analyze
1. Generally, do groups of metals on the periodic table have more or fewer electrons in their outer energy levels than do nonmetals?
2. The combinations you found could represent chemical formulas. Why did some formulas require more than one atom of an element?

Conclude and Apply
3. Would your *model* be more likely to represent a metal or a nonmetal atom? Explain.
4. What group of elements would your *model* be in if you received eight marbles? Explain.

11-1 WHY ATOMS COMBINE **273**

OBJECTIVE: Infer chemical formulas by **making models** of outer electron levels.

PROCESS SKILLS applied in this activity:
▶ **Classifying** in Procedure Step 3.

👥 COOPERATIVE LEARNING
Use the Science Investigation Team strategy in pairs. Further group five teams together to find all compound possibilities.

TEACHING THE ACTIVITY
Alternate Materials: Substitutes for marbles could include buttons, candy, or beans.

Troubleshooting: Remind students that these examples do not include the transition metals. These egg carton "atoms" can represent the elements in the first two rows of the periodic table.

▶ Using the egg carton, block off two of the egg receptacles and review with students the capacity of first and second energy levels.

▶ Give different numbers of marbles to different students so that all elements from lithium through fluorine are represented. Depending on the size of your class, have students add or remove marbles to change their element models and increase the number of matchup possibilities.

▶ To answer the question in Procedure Step 3, direct students to count the marbles in the second energy level. Have them count over the same number of columns in Period 2.

▶ Monitor students so that they discover simple matchups such as LiF and progress to compounds such as BeF_2, Li_2O, BeO, and Be_3N_2. Remind them that atoms can achieve stability by losing, gaining or sharing electrons.

ANSWERS TO QUESTIONS
1. Metals have fewer outer level electrons than do nonmetals.

2. Some formulas require more than one atom of each element because two atoms combined do not provide enough electrons for both to have eight.

3. Answers will vary. Usually fewer than four outer electrons indicates a metal. Four or more usually indicates a nonmetal.

4. Eight marbles indicates a Group 16 element. These atoms have six outer electrons.

PROGRAM RESOURCES
From the **Teacher Resource Package** use:
Activity Worksheets, pages 86-87, Activity 11-1· Eggshell Electrons.

Activity
ASSESSMENT
Content: Have students check their combinations of atoms to make sure full energy levels are evident.

PREPARATION

SECTION BACKGROUND
▶ One quart of oil can contaminate one million liters of drinking water because it forms a very thin film on the surface of the water.

Connect to...
Life Science

Answer: Fluorine is toxic. Fluorine compounds are found in many tooth-pastes, mouthwashes, and drinking water supplies.

1 MOTIVATE

▶ Have students brainstorm a list of household chemicals they think are corrosive, toxic, or flammable.

2 TEACH

Key Concepts are highlighted.

CONCEPT DEVELOPMENT
▶ Nearly every chemical has potential benefits and associated risks. Whether a chemical poses a benefit or a risk often is determined by the amount of chemical present.

VideoDisc
STVS: Dealing with Hazardous Materials, Disc 2, Side 1

PROGRAM RESOURCES
From the **Teacher Resource Package** use:

Concept Mapping, page 27.

Critical Thinking/Problem Solving, page 17, Groundwater Pollution.

Activity Worksheets, page 5, Flex Your Brain.

New Science Words
toxic
corrosive

Connect to...
Life Science

Consult a reference book to find out if fluorine is toxic, corrosive, or flammable. Fluorine compounds, however are commonly used to help you become healthier. What are two materials that contain fluorine compounds?

Objectives
▶ Describe the dangers posed by hazardous compounds in the home.
▶ Demonstrate an understanding of ways to avoid hazardous compounds or ways to use them safely.

Corrosive, Flammable, and Toxic Compounds

In 1989, the oil tanker *Exxon Valdez* spilled 11 million gallons of oil. This was one of the worst oil spills in history. People were shocked and outraged. But think about this. Every year do-it-yourself oil changers improperly dispose of 176 million gallons of oil. This is equal to 16 *Exxon Valdez* spills! One quart of oil, if improperly handled, can contaminate 250 000 gallons of drinking water. Oil and many other common household products are hazardous. This means that they contain compounds that can affect the health and safety of people.

Hazardous household chemicals can be toxic, corrosive, or flammable. Compounds that are **toxic** are poisonous. Toxic compounds are in products such as disinfectants, insect sprays, medicine, and antifreeze. Compounds that are **corrosive** attack and destroy metals, human tissues, and other materials. Corrosive compounds are found in battery acid, drain and oven cleaners, bleach, and toilet cleaners. Compounds that are flammable burn readily. Flammable compounds include ingredients of gasoline, paint thinner, and some aerosols.

Toxic, corrosive, and flammable compounds threaten the health and safety of people in their homes. These materials can poison children and pets and pose fire hazards. They may cause cancer and other diseases. When people handle or dispose of hazardous chemicals improperly, they can pollute air, soil, and water. Many times people dump these materials into sewer systems. Hazardous compounds can pass unchanged through septic systems and water treatment plants and into clean

OPTIONS

Meeting Different Ability Levels
For Section 11-2, use the following **Teacher Resource Masters** depending upon individual students' needs.
◆ **Study Guide Master** for all students.
● **Reinforcement Master** for students of average and above average ability levels.
▲ **Enrichment Master** for above average students.
Additional Teacher Resource Package masters are listed in any PROGRAM RESOURCES boxes that are in the section. The additional masters are appropriate for all students.

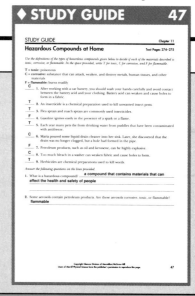

Table 11-2

ALTERNATIVES TO HAZARDOUS HOME CHEMICALS

Product	Safer Alternatives
Aerosols	Use gels, lotions, and nonaerosol sprays.
Chlorine bleach	Use dry bleach or borax.
Moth balls	Use cedar chips.
Toilet bowl cleaners	Use nonphosphate detergents and baking soda.
Drain cleaners	Use a plumbing snake or a plunger to unplug drains.
Window cleaner	Use 2 teaspoons of vinegar in a quart of water and wipe dry with newspaper.
Insecticides	Provide houses and the proper environment in your yard to attract birds, bats, toads, and snakes to eat insects. Use window screens.

water supplies. Hazardous chemicals dumped on soil and in landfills can pollute groundwater supplies. Freon from refrigerators and air conditioners is thought to contribute to the destruction of the ozone layer. Evaporated gasoline also pollutes the air.

How can you and your family remain healthy and safe and prevent pollution? Some suggestions are: (1) Use safer alternatives to hazardous materials, as suggested in Table 11-2. (2) Recycle oil, antifreeze, and used batteries. (3) If you must purchase a hazardous product, buy only the amount you need, or give the excess to someone who will use it. (4) Store hazardous materials in their original containers, away from children. (5) Keep hazardous materials that easily evaporate in tightly closed containers. (6) Share your knowledge of the problem of hazardous household compounds with others.

EcoTip

Instead of using poisonous chemical sprays, chase away insect pests by planting chrysanthemums near your doorways or in your garden.

SECTION REVIEW

1. What are three types of hazardous compounds that may be found in many household products?
2. What are five ways you can protect yourself and the environment from hazardous materials?
3. **Connect to Earth Science:** If one quart of oil pollutes 250 000 gallons of water, what is the ratio of oil to water?

You Decide!

Your neighbor changes his own automobile oil. Several times you have seen him dump the used liquids at the edge of his property and yours. What should you do?

SCIENCE & SOCIETY

CHECK FOR UNDERSTANDING
Ask questions 1 and 2 and the **Connect to Earth Science** question in the Section Review.

RETEACH
Cooperative Learning: Have Expert Teams survey their apartments or houses for hazardous chemicals.

EXTENSION
For students who have mastered this section, use the **Reinforcement** and **Enrichment** masters or other OPTIONS provided.

3 CLOSE

? FLEX Your Brain

Use the Flex Your Brain activity to have students explore HAZARDOUS COMPOUNDS.

SECTION REVIEW ANSWERS
1. corrosive, toxic, or flammable
2. Sample answers are given. (1) Substitute safe materials. (2) Do not pour hazardous materials on the ground. (3) Store hazardous materials in a safe place. (4) Recycle materials. (5) Educate others.
3. **Connect to Earth Science:**
$250\ 000\ \text{gal} \times \dfrac{4\ \text{qt}}{1\ \text{gal}} = 1\ 000\ 000\ \text{qt}$
Ratio is 1:1 000 000.

YOU DECIDE! **SCIENCE & SOCIETY**

Find out from your local environmental agency how to dispose properly of such materials. Explain to your neighbor why it is dangerous to dump the materials and offer advice you learned about disposal or recycling.

PREPARATION

SECTION BACKGROUND

▶ An atom's electronegativity is the tendency of the atom to attract a pair of electrons in a bond.

▶ Excluding noble gases, elements in the upper right of the periodic table have high electronegativities. Those in the lower left have low electronegativities.

▶ An ionic bond results from electron transfer between two atoms that differ greatly in electronegativity.

▶ A covalent bond results from the sharing of a pair of electrons between two atoms that are close in electronegativity.

▶ In a polar covalent bond between two atoms, there is unequal sharing of the electron pair due to a moderate difference in electronegativity.

PREPLANNING

▶ For Activity 11-2 you will need sugar, salt, and finely crushed ice.

▶ If you have not done so, consider making magnetic "electrons" to manipulate on a magnetic chalkboard or file cabinet in order to model bonding between atoms.

1 MOTIVATE

▶ **Demonstration:** The formation of an ionic bond occurs when a piece of magnesium ribbon is burned. **CAUTION:** *Hold the burning ribbon inside a can so that the bright light cannot be directly observed.* The reaction is

$$2Mg + O_2 \rightarrow 2MgO.$$

TYING TO PREVIOUS

KNOWLEDGE: Recall that elements with three or fewer electrons are metals. Metals tend to lose electrons to form positive ions. Nonmetals generally have five or more outer electrons. Nonmetals tend to gain electrons to form negative ions. In both cases, the ions have achieved full outer energy levels.

New Science Words

ion
ionic bond
covalent bond
polar molecule
nonpolar molecule

Objectives

▶ Describe ionic bonds and covalent bonds.
▶ Identify the particles produced by ionic bonding and by covalent bonding.
▶ Distinguish between a nonpolar covalent bond and a polar covalent bond.

Figure 11-7. When placed in contact with each other, sodium and chlorine combine explosively.

Ions and Ionic Bonds

The brilliant flash in the photograph in Figure 11-7 shows what happens when sodium is put in a flask of chlorine gas. (**CAUTION:** *It is very dangerous to handle or mix sodium and chlorine—do not try it.*) Recall how the atoms of these elements—sodium and chlorine—bond chemically when mixed. An atom of sodium has one electron in its outer energy level, as shown below. When the atom loses that electron, its second energy level is then outermost and complete, because it contains eight electrons. But the atom now has 11 protons, with a total charge of 11+, and 10 electrons, with a total charge of 10–. Because $(11+) + (10-) = 1+$, the atom has a net positive charge of 1+. Atoms that have charges are called ions. Thus, the sodium atom, Na, that has lost an electron is now a sodium ion, Na^+. You write the symbol for the ion with a superscript plus sign to indicate its charge. *Superscript* means "written above."

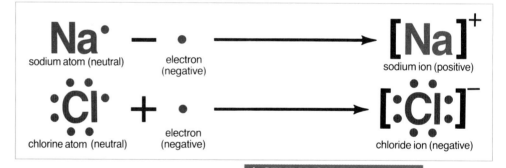

OPTIONS

Meeting Different Ability Levels

For Section 11-3, use the following **Teacher Resource Masters** depending upon individual students' needs.

◆ **Study Guide Master** for all students.
● **Reinforcement Master** for students of average and above average ability levels.
▲ **Enrichment Master** for above average students.

Additional Teacher Resource Package masters are listed in any **PROGRAM RESOURCES** boxes that are in the section. The additional masters are appropriate for all students.

◆ **STUDY GUIDE** 48

STUDY GUIDE · Chapter 11
Kinds of Chemical Bonds · Text Pages 276–281

In the blank, write the letter of the term that is defined by each phrase.

b 1. force that holds together the atoms in a compound
a. chemical formula · b. chemical bond

b 2. an atom that has an electrical charge
a. element · b. ion

a 3. molecule that does not have oppositely charged ends
a. nonpolar molecule · b. ion

b 4. molecule that has oppositely charged ends
a. covalent molecule · b. polar molecule

b 5. number and sign written by the symbol of an ion to indicate its charge
a. subscript · b. superscript

a 6. force of attraction between the opposite charges of the ions in an ionic compound
a. ionic bond · b. polar bond

a 7. bond that forms between atoms when they share electrons
a. covalent bond · b. polar bond

In the blank, write the letter of the term or phrase that correctly completes each statement.

b 8. In the symbol Na⁺, the + sign is a ____.
a. subscript · b. superscript

a 9. A chloride ion, Cl⁻, has ____.
a. a negative charge · b. no charge

a 10. The compound NaCl is an example of ____.
a. an ionic compound · b. a polar compound

b 11. When Na⁺ and Cl⁻ unite to form the compound NaCl, the compound that forms is ____.
a. positively charged · b. neutral

____ 12. Neutral particles formed as a result of the sharing of electrons are called ____.
a. molecules · b. ions

b 13. At room temperature, most covalent compounds are ____.
a. solids · b. liquids or gases

a 14. At room temperature, most ionic compounds are ____.
a. solids · b. liquids or gases

48

A chlorine atom has seven electrons in its outer energy level. When the atom gains an electron, its outermost energy level contains eight electrons. But the atom now has 17 protons, with a total charge of 17+, and 18 electrons, with a total charge of 18–. Because (17+) + (18–) = 1–, the atom has a net negative charge of 1–. In other words, it is now a chloride ion, which you write with a superscript minus sign, Cl^-, to indicate its charge. The compound NaCl as a whole, however, is neutral, because the total net positive charge equals the total net negative charge.

An **ion** is an atom that is either positively or negatively charged. Compounds made up of ions are ionic compounds, and the bonds that hold them together are ionic bonds. An **ionic bond** is the force of attraction between the opposite charges of the ions in an ionic compound.

Figure 11-9 shows another example of ionic bonding—the formation of magnesium fluoride, MgF_2. When magnesium reacts with fluorine, a magnesium atom loses two electrons and becomes a positively charged ion, Mg^{2+}. Notice that you write 2+ on the symbol for magnesium to indicate the ion's net charge. At the same time, each of the two fluorine atoms gains one electron and becomes a negatively charged fluoride ion, F^-. The compound as a whole is neutral. Why? Because the sum of the net charges on all three ions is zero.

Molecules and Covalent Bonds

Most atoms become more chemically stable by sharing electrons, rather than by losing or gaining electrons. In Figure 11-6 on page 272, you saw how two chlorine atoms share electrons. Notice that the chlorine parti-

Figure 11-8. Dot diagram for sodium chloride, NaCl

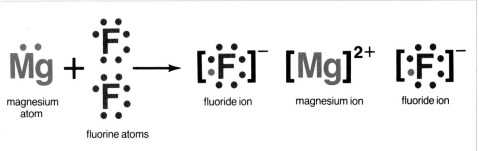

sodium chloride

Why is the charge on a magnesium ion positive?

In Your JOURNAL

Its use in food accounts for less than 15 percent of the use of table salt, sodium chloride. **In your Journal,** write a paragraph describing other uses of NaCl.

Figure 11-9. Dot diagram for magnesium fluoride, MgF_2

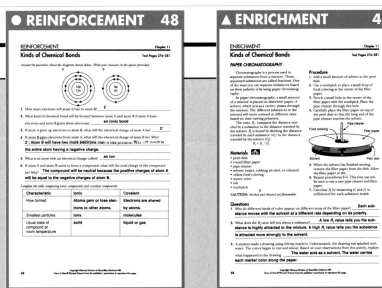

magnesium atom

fluorine atoms

fluoride ion

magnesium ion

fluoride ion

In Your JOURNAL

Answer: Approximately 50 percent of NaCl is used to make other substances, such as chlorine and sodium hydroxide.

2 TEACH

Key Concepts are highlighted.

CONCEPT DEVELOPMENT

▶ Ask students to hypothesize about the differences in melting points between ionic and covalent compounds. Ask them to give reasons for their hypotheses.

▶ A covalent bond can be thought of as a spring that allows the bonded atoms to stretch and bend.

REVEALING MISCONCEPTIONS

▶ Students often think that a chemical bond physically links atoms just as a nail holds two pieces of wood together. Emphasize that bonding is the result of attractive forces.

CROSS CURRICULUM

▶ **Medicine:** Cyanoacrylate, known as Super Glue, can be used in place of sutures in some types of surgery. Super Glue forms chemical bonds with the surface molecules that are being joined together.

VideoDisc

STVS: Snowflakes, Disc 2, Side 1

● REINFORCEMENT 48

REINFORCEMENT   Chapter 11
Kinds of Chemical Bonds   Text Pages 276–281

Answer the questions about the diagram shown below. Write your answers in the space provided.

1. How many electrons will atom A lose to atom B? _____ 2
2. What kind of chemical bond will be formed between atom A and atom B if atom A loses electrons and atom B gains these electrons? _____ an ionic bond
3. If atom A gives up electrons to atom B, what will the electrical charge of atom A be? _____ 2+
4. If atom B gains electrons from atom A, what will the electrical charge of atom B be? Why? 2–; Atom B will have two more electrons than it has protons. This will result in the entire atom having a negative charge.
5. What is an atom with an electrical charge called? _____ an ion
6. If atom A and atom B unite to form a compound, what will the total charge of the compound be? Why? The compound will be neutral because the positive charges of atom A will be equal to the negative charges of atom B.

Complete the table comparing ionic compounds and covalent compounds.

Characteristic	Ionic	Covalent
How formed	Atoms gain or lose electrons to other atoms.	Electrons are shared by atoms.
Smallest particles	ions	molecules
Usual state of compound at room temperature	solid	liquid or gas

▲ ENRICHMENT 48

ENRICHMENT   Chapter 11
Kinds of Chemical Bonds   Text Pages 276–281

PAPER CHROMATOGRAPHY

Chromatography is a process used to separate substances from a mixture. These separated substances are called fractions. One of the ways you can separate substances based on their polarity is by using paper chromatography.

In paper chromatography, a small amount of a mixture is placed on absorbent paper. A solvent, which acts as a carrier, passes through the mixture. The different substances in the mixture will move outward at different rates based on their varying polarities.

The ratio, R_f, compares the distance traveled by a substance to the distance traveled by the solvent. R_f is found by dividing the distance traveled by each substance (D_s) by the distance traveled by the solvent (D_f).
$$R_f = D_s / D_f$$

Materials
• petri dish
• round filter paper
• pipe cleaner
• solvent (water, rubbing alcohol, or ethanol)
• yellow food coloring
• metric ruler
• ink
• toothpick
CAUTION: *Alcohol and ethanol are flammable.*

Procedure
1. Add a small amount of solvent to the petri dish.
2. Use a toothpick to place a small drop of food coloring at the center of the filter paper.
3. Punch a small hole in the center of the filter paper with the toothpick. Place the pipe cleaner through this hole.
4. Carefully place the filter paper on top of the petri dish so that the long end of the pipe cleaner touches the solvent.
5. When the solvent has finished moving, remove the filter paper from the dish. Allow the filter paper to dry.
6. Repeat procedures 2–5. This time use ink. Be sure to use a new pipe cleaner and filter paper.
7. Calculate R_f by measuring D_s and D_f in millimeters for each substance tested.

Questions
1. Why do different bands of color appear on different areas of the filter paper? Each substance moves with the solvent at a different rate depending on its polarity.
2. What does the R_f value tell you about a substance? A low R_f value tells you the substance is highly attracted to the mixture. A high R_f value tells you the substance is attracted more strongly to the solvent.
3. A student made a drawing using felt-tip markers. Unfortunately, the drawing was splashed with water. The colors began to run and smear. Based on your observations from this activity, explain what happened to the drawing. The water acts as a solvent. The water carries each marker color along the paper.

277

Why is a chlorine molecule neutral?

Figure 11-10. Dot diagrams for the formation of nitrogen gas, N_2, from two atoms of nitrogen

Figure 11-11. Dot diagram and model for a molecule of hydrogen chloride

cle, Cl_2, is not charged—it is neutral. The chlorine is not in the form of ions, but molecules. Neutral particles formed as a result of electron sharing are called molecules.

A bond that forms between atoms when they share electrons is known as a **covalent bond**. In the case of chlorine, a covalent bond is formed between two atoms of the same element. Covalent bonds also form between atoms of nitrogen, the gas that makes up most of the air. As you can see in Figure 11-10, two atoms of nitrogen in N_2 share six electrons, forming three covalent bonds between the atoms.

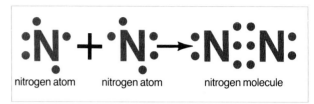

nitrogen atom   nitrogen atom   nitrogen molecule

Polar and Nonpolar Molecules

Atoms in molecules do not always share electrons equally. An example is a molecule of hydrogen chloride, HCl. A water solution of HCl is hydrochloric acid, which is used in laboratories, to clean metal, and in your stomach to digest food. The chlorine atom has a stronger attraction for electrons than does the hydrogen atom. As a result, the electrons they share in hydrogen chloride will spend more time near the chlorine atom than near the hydrogen atom. This type of molecule is called polar. *Polar* means "having two opposite ends." A **polar molecule** is one that has a positive end and a negative end.

Water is another example of a compound with polar molecules, as shown in Figure 11-12. A water molecule contains two polar covalent bonds, one between each hydrogen atom and the oxygen atom. The oxygen atom

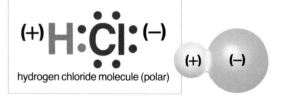

hydrogen chloride molecule (polar)

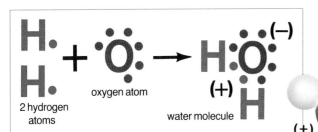

Figure 11-12. Dot diagram and model for a molecule of water

has a stronger attraction for electrons than the hydrogen atoms do. As a result, the oxygen end of the water molecule is negative and the hydrogen end of the molecule is positive.

Bond Busters

Toxic compounds with names such as vinyl chloride, benzene, and pentachlorophenol are among the pollutants that human activities generate in huge amounts and that damage the environment. One way to get rid of toxic compounds is to change them chemically into other, harmless compounds. That is, the chemical bonds holding together the atoms in molecules of toxic compounds must be broken. Then the atoms could bond into different molecules of less harmful substances.

Scientists are now enlisting new strains of microbes as bond busters to change toxic compounds into nontoxic ones. The microbes eat the compounds, which change chemically as they are digested. To create a strain of pollutant-eating microbes, scientists first add a pollutant to a population of microbes. Most of the microbes die, leaving only the hardiest ones to reproduce. Scientists then seed polluted soil with these microbes and add

fertilizer and oxygen to promote their growth. The microbes break down the toxic compounds and then, with the food source gone, the microbes die.

At least 1000 different strains of bacteria and fungi are now helping to get rid of pollutants. The biggest advantage of the microbial approach is that instead of relocating the pollutants—by moving toxic substances to other places—the microbes destroy them.

Think Critically: What would be the disadvantages of using microbes compared to removing or burning contaminated soil?

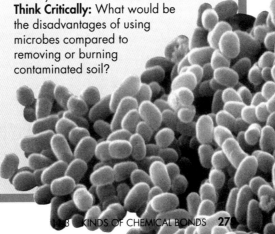

11-3 KINDS OF CHEMICAL BONDS **277**

MULTICULTURAL PERSPECTIVE
Ocher

Ocher is an iron oxide (Fe_2O_3) that occurs naturally. It is formed by the weathering of silicate rocks and has been used since prehistoric times. Archaeological evidence along with observation of contemporary, nonindustrial societies, indicates that ocher is used in a variety of ways. Ocher can be used for treatment of wounds, to tan hides, and as a pigment for art and body decoration. It was used prehistorically to produce the rock paintings at Lascaux and other sites, and continues to be used for artwork today. It comes in a variety of colors depending on the percentage of iron oxide present. Where the pigment is almost completely iron oxide, the color is yellowish. With less iron oxide, the color varies from yellow-brown to red-orange. Hematite ore, one source of ocher that can be ground to produce a bright red ore, appears to have been mined in Swaziland, Africa as early as 44 thousand years ago. Other iron oxide ores produce different colors: black (magnetite), yellow (limonite), and brown (siderite and pyrite).

CHECK FOR UNDERSTANDING

Have students match the type of bonding in a compound with the state(s) of matter that compound is likely to be in at room temperature. Ask them to explain their reasoning.

RETEACH

Have students draw pencil models of substances using dot structures and label them as having ionic or covalent bonds. **HINT:** Elements that are close together on the periodic table often are covalently bonded.

EXTENSION

For students who have mastered this section, use the **Reinforcement** and **Enrichment** masters or other OPTIONS provided.

3 CLOSE

▶ Ask questions 1 and 2 and the **Apply** and **Connect to Earth Science** questions in the Section Review.

SECTION REVIEW ANSWERS

1. In ionic bonds, ions are held together by opposite charges. In covalent bonds, atoms share electrons. Both are attractive forces.

2. a. ionic bonds—positive and negative ions; b. polar covalent bonds—polar molecules (Note: If the molecule is symmetrical, it may not be polar even though it has polar bonds.); c. nonpolar covalent bonds—nonpolar molecules

3. Apply:

$$[Mg]^{2+} \ [:\overset{..}{\underset{..}{O}}:]^{2-}$$

4. Connect to Earth Science: Each aluminum atom can lose three electrons. Each oxygen atom can gain two electrons.

2(3+) + 3(2–) = 6 – 6 = 0

Skill Builder
ASSESSMENT
Performance: Assign a compound to each student and ask him or her to follow it through the concept map, identifying each component.

Figure11-13. Sugar is an example of a covalent compound that has polar molecules.

As a group, do ionic compounds have higher or lower melting points than covalent compounds?

Some molecules, such as those of nitrogen, are nonpolar because the two nitrogen atoms share their electrons equally. A **nonpolar molecule** is one that does not have oppositely charged ends. Look again at the diagram of a nitrogen molecule in Figure 11-10 on page 278.

You have read about two main ways chemical bonding takes place, producing two kinds of compounds—ionic and covalent. Ionic compounds are usually formed by bonding between a metal and a nonmetal. Bonds between nonmetal atoms are covalent. Most ionic compounds are crystalline solids with high melting points. Many covalent compounds are liquids or gases at room temperature. In later chapters, you will learn more about compounds of each type.

SECTION REVIEW

1. Compare ionic and covalent bonds.
2. What type of particle is formed by the following bonds: (a) ionic (b) polar covalent (c) nonpolar covalent?
3. **Apply:** Magnesium burns to form magnesium oxide. The reaction produces a bright light. This is the reaction in flash bulbs. Draw the dot diagram of magnesium oxide.
4. **Connect to Earth Science:** Aluminum oxide, Al_2O_3, can be produced during space shuttle launches. Prove that the sum of the positive and negative charges in a unit of Al_2O_3 equals zero.

Skill Builder

☒ **Concept Mapping**

Using the following terms, make a network tree concept map of chemical bonding: *ionic, covalent, ions, positive ions, negative ions, molecules, polar, nonpolar.* If you need help, refer to Concept Mapping in the **Skill Handbook** on pages 684 and 685

Skill Builder

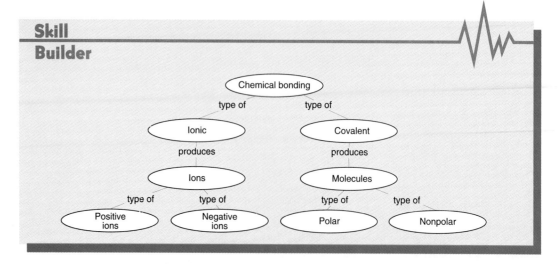

ACTIVITY 11-2 — DESIGNING AN EXPERIMENT
Becoming a Bond Breaker

Ionic bonding involves attractions between ions. Covalent bonding is found within molecules. Think about how the attractions between the basic units, ions or molecules, of a substance can affect certain properties of the substance. You are about to test your ideas by using heat to overcome the attractions between the units within several substances.

Getting Started

Melting a substance overcomes the attractions between the basic units of the substance. You need to determine a way to use heat to overcome the attractions between ions in an ionic substance and between molecules in a covalent substance. Be sure to wear safety goggles and be cautious when using the laboratory burner.

Hypothesizing

Write a **hypothesis** that relates the ease of melting of a substance to the type of bonding between its particles.

Materials

Your cooperative group will use:
- 1 tablespoon each of crushed ice, table salt and sugar
- 1 wire test-tube holder
- 3 test tubes
- goggles
- laboratory burner
- timer

 Try It!

1. After designing your experiment, make a data table to use to record your data.
2. In conducting your experiment, you may heat each substance individually in a test tube. Decide within your group what variables you need to control during the heating process. Use a timer to help you measure heating times. Do not heat any substance longer than five minutes.

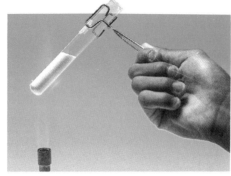

Summing Up/Sharing Results

- How does melting time relate to the attractions between the particles in a substance?
- Which substance has the strongest attractions between its particles? Which substance has the weakest attractions?
- *Classify* each of the substances as having either ionic or covalent bonds.
- How might your results change if you used different amounts of each of the three substances?

Going Further!

- Candle wax is an easy substance to melt. Do you think the basic units in wax are likely to be ions, or are they molecules?
- Table salt, NaCl, is difficult to melt. Use a reference book to find the melting point of table salt. Assume your laboratory burner reaches the temperature of 600°C. If you had heated the table salt longer would it have melted?

OBJECTIVE: Design and carry out an experiment to show how melting properties of substances relate to the type of bonding found in the substance.
Time: one class period

PROCESS SKILLS applied in this activity are **observing, inferring,** and **comparing.**

PREPARATION

Cooperative Learning: Divide the class into Science Investigation Teams.

SAFETY

Caution students to be careful around the hot burner and the heated materials.

HYPOTHESIZING

Students may hypothesize that the more easily melted a substance is, the less attraction the particles have for each other.

TEACHING THE ACTIVITY

*Refer to the **Activity Worksheets** for additional information and teaching strategies.*
- Discuss with students the importance of constants. Measuring differing amounts of the three substances and holding the test tubes in different parts of the flame may affect results.
- Review the chemical formulas of the the substances NaCl, H_2O, and $C_{12}H_{22}O_{11}$.
- Assist students in adjusting the air-gas mix in their burners so that the flames are blue, not yellow.

PROGRAM RESOURCES

From the **Teacher Resource Package** use:

Activity Worksheets, pages 88-89, Activity 11-2: Become a Bond Breaker.

SUMMING UP/SHARING RESULTS

- The more quickly a substance melts, the less attraction between the particles.
- Salt has the strongest attractions; water has the weakest.
- Salt is ionic. Water and sugar are covalent.
- The more material present in a sample, the longer it will take to melt. For example, a large chunk of ice may show little sign of melting in a minute, but a small piece will melt quickly.

GOING FURTHER!

- Wax contains covalent molecules.
- The melting point of NaCl is 801°C. Longer heating would not melt the salt.

Activity ASSESSMENT

Portfolio: Have students construct a table that reports their observations of the three substances during the heating process. Note that their observations should contain references to time intervals.

PREPARATION

SECTION BACKGROUND

▶ As a general rule, the oxidation numbers of metals can be predicted from their outer electron configuration. Metals with one outer-level electron (Group 1) have an oxidation number of 1+. Those with two electrons have an oxidation number of 2+ and so on. Most transition metals have variable oxidation numbers.

▶ The oxidation number of nonmetals can be predicted from their outer electron configuration. Those with seven outer-level electrons (one less than eight) have an oxidation number of 1− and so on.

▶ The noble gases have an oxidation number of zero because they have eight outer electrons.

▶ Many compounds have water molecules as a part of the crystal. The compounds are referred to as hydrates.

PREPLANNING

▶ Cobalt(II) chloride hexahydrate is needed for the MINI-Lab in this section. You may want to have some plaster of paris, calcium sulfate dihydrate, available too.

1 MOTIVATE

▶ **Demonstration:** Exhibit 4 g of powdered sulfur and 7 g of iron filings. Point out the yellow color of sulfur and use a magnet to demonstrate the magnetic properties of iron. Mix them on a piece of paper and pour into a test tube. Behind a shield, heat the tube using a burner until the contents glow red. Then, plunge it into a beaker of water to break the test tube. The students will notice that the product is not yellow or magnetic.

Fe + S ⟶ FeS.

Use the demonstration to introduce oxidation numbers, formula writing, and naming.

11-4 Formulas and Names of Compounds

New Science Words

oxidation number
binary compound
polyatomic ion
hydrate

Objectives

▶ Explain how to determine oxidation numbers.
▶ Write formulas for compounds from their names.
▶ Name compounds from their formulas.
▶ Describe hydrates and their formulas.

Oxidation Numbers

The people in these two pictures seem to have little in common. Yet, in a sense, the medieval alchemist is the ancestor of the modern chemist. Both are shown at work investigating matter. Notice how each would write symbols for the elements silver and sulfur. Silver tarnish is silver sulfide, a compound of silver and sulfur. If the alchemist knew the composition of silver tarnish, how might he write its formula? The modern chemist does know its composition; she would write it Ag_2S. When you get to the end of this section, you, too, will know how to write such formulas.

What two elements are present in tarnish?

OPTIONS

Meeting Different Ability Levels

For Section 11-4, use the following **Teacher Resource Masters** depending upon individual students' needs.

◆ **Study Guide Master** for all students.
● **Reinforcement Master** for students of average and above average ability levels.
▲ **Enrichment Master** for above average students.

Additional Teacher Resource Package masters are listed in any **PROGRAM RESOURCES** boxes that are in the section. The additional masters are appropriate for all students.

◆ STUDY GUIDE 49

STUDY GUIDE   Chapter 11
Formulas and Names of Compounds   Text Pages 282–288

Match each term in Column II with its description in Column I. Write the letter of the correct term in the space provided.

	Column I		Column II
i	1. prefix meaning six	a.	bi-
g	2. prefix meaning many	b.	ion
a	3. prefix meaning two	c.	binary
c	4. compound composed of two elements	d.	anhydrous
b	5. positively or negatively charged atom	e.	polyatomic ion
e	6. positively or negatively charged group of atoms	f.	subscript
j	7. compound that has water chemically attached to its ions	g.	poly-
h	8. number assigned to an element to show its combining ability in a compound	h.	oxidation number
d	9. without water	i.	hydrate
f	10. number that tells how many atoms of an element are in a unit of the compound	j.	hexa-

The words in each group below are related. Write a sentence, using all the words in the group, that shows how the words are related.

Example: Student responses may vary. Check to be sure students have written complete sentences using all terms.
compound, properties, elements
The properties of a compound differ from the properties of the elements making up the compound.

1. hydrate, water, ions   A hydrate is a compound that has water chemically attached to its ions.

2. oxidation number, element, compound   The oxidation number of an element can be used to determine its combining ability in a compound.

3. zero, oxidation numbers, noble gases   The oxidation numbers of the noble gases are zero.

4. oxidation number, Roman numeral, element   The name of a compound containing an element with more than one oxidation number must include a Roman numeral after the name of the element.

Copyright Glencoe Division of Macmillan/McGraw-Hill
Users of Merrill Physical Science have the publisher's permission to reproduce this page.   49

You can figure out formulas with the help of oxidation numbers. What are these numbers? An **oxidation number** is a positive or negative number assigned to an element to show its combining ability in a compound. In other words, an oxidation number indicates how many electrons an atom has gained, lost, or shared when bonding with other atoms. For example, when sodium forms an ion, it loses an electron and has a charge of 1+. So the oxidation number of sodium is 1+. And when chlorine forms an ion, it gains an electron and has a charge of 1–. So the oxidation number of chlorine is 1–.

Oxidation numbers are often a periodic property of elements. The red numbers printed on the periodic table shown in Figure 11-14 are the oxidation numbers for these elements in many of their binary compounds. *Bi-* means "two," and a **binary compound** is one that is composed of two elements. Sodium chloride is an example of a binary compound.

Like sodium, each metal in Group 1 loses its one outer electron in bonding, so each of these elements has an oxidation number of 1+. Remember, losing electrons produces a positive oxidation number in an element. Each metal in Group 2 loses both its outer electrons in bonding, so each has an oxidation number of 2+.

Like chlorine, each of the nonmetals in Group 17 gains one electron in bonding, so each of these elements has an oxidation number of 1–. Remember, gaining electrons

What does an oxidation number indicate?

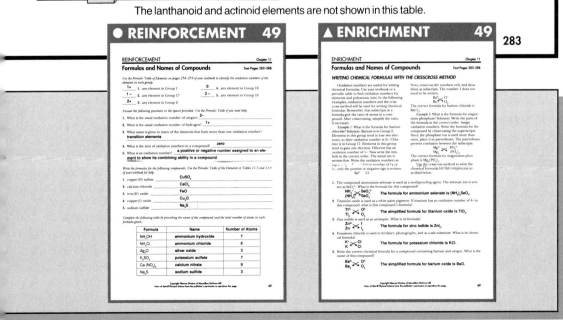

Figure 11-14. Part of the periodic table, with oxidation numbers for elements in Groups 1, 2, 13, 14, 15, 16, 17, and 18

* In Group 14, Sn and Pb also exhibit 2 + oxidation states.

The lanthanoid and actinoid elements are not shown in this table.

TYING TO PREVIOUS KNOWLEDGE: Ask students to write on the chalkboard the chemical formulas for as many compounds as they remember. Use the formulas to introduce oxidation numbers, formula writing, and naming.

2 TEACH

Key Concepts are highlighted.

CONCEPT DEVELOPMENT

▶ Give each student a blank copy of the periodic table. Have students write the oxidation numbers of Groups 1, 2, 13, 14, 15, 16, 17, and 18 at the top of each column.

▶ To help students write compound formulas correctly, remind them:

• The oxidation number of hydrogen in most compounds is 1+.

• The oxidation number of oxygen in most compounds is 2–.

• The sum of the oxidation numbers of all the atoms in a compound formula must equal zero.

• In compounds, the elements of Groups 1 and 2 and aluminum have positive oxidation numbers of 1+, 2+, and 3+, respectively.

▶ It is best that students not be required to memorize oxidation numbers but rather relate them to atomic structure and to an atom's position on the periodic table, when possible.

REVEALING MISCONCEPTIONS

▶ Explain that oxidation numbers are used as an aid in understanding atomic structure and in writing formulas correctly. Formula writing is not just a reasoning exercise but represents a way of predicting the composition of actual chemical substances formed in real chemical processes.

copper(I)	Cu^+
copper(II)	Cu^{2+}
iron(II)	Fe^{2+}
iron(III)	Fe^{3+}
chromium(II)	Cr^{2+}
chromium(III)	Cr^{3+}
lead(II)	Pb^{2+}
lead(IV)	Pb^{4+}

Figure 11-15. Here are some elements that have variable oxidation numbers. Not all possible oxidation numbers are shown.

Connect to...
Physics

Magnetism and CrO_2 are present in audio tapes. Another oxide of chromium is Cr_2O_3, which is used in stainless steel. What is the oxidation number of chromium in each of these compounds?

produces a negative oxidation number in an element. Each nonmetal in Group 16 gains two electrons in bonding, so each has an oxidation number of 2–.

Some elements have more than one oxidation number. Copper, as you can see in Figure 11-15, can be either Cu^+ or Cu^{2+}. In the name of a compound of copper, the Roman numeral equals the oxidation number of copper in that compound. Thus, the oxidation number of copper in copper(II) oxide is 2+. Iron may be Fe^{2+} or Fe^{3+}. Thus, the oxidation number of iron in iron(III) oxide is 3+.

Formulas for Binary Compounds

Once you know how to find the oxidation numbers of elements in binary compounds, you can write formulas by using these rules: (1) Write first the symbol of the element with the positive oxidation number. Hydrogen and all metals have positive oxidation numbers. (2) Then write the symbol of the element with the negative oxidation number. (3) Add subscripts so that the sum of the oxidation numbers of all the atoms in the formula is zero.

EXAMPLE PROBLEM: Writing Formulas for Binary Compounds

Problem Statement:

What is the formula of a compound composed of only sulfur and aluminum?

Problem-Solving Steps:

1. Write the symbol of the positive element followed by the symbol of the negative element.

   Al   S

2. Look up oxidation numbers for each element. Write oxidation numbers above the symbols.

   3+   2–
   Al   S

3. Write in subscripts so that the sum of the oxidation numbers is zero.

   3+   2–
   Al_2 S_3

4. Check to see if the sum of the oxidation numbers is zero.

   $2(3+) + 3(2–) = (6+) + (6–) = 0$

Solution:

Final Formula: Al_2S_3

PRACTICE PROBLEMS

<u>Strategy Hint:</u> Be sure to use the smallest possible subscript numbers to make the sum zero.
<u>Strategy Hint:</u> The Roman numeral II tells you the oxidation number of copper.

1. Write the formula for the binary compound of calcium and oxygen.
2. Write the formula of the binary compound of copper(II) and sulfur.

284 CHEMICAL BONDS

OPTIONS

Naming Binary Compounds

You can name a binary compound from its formula by using these rules: (1) Write the name of the first element. (2) Write the root of the name of the second element. (3) Add the ending *-ide* to the root. Table 11-3 lists several elements and their *-ide* counterparts. For example, $CaCl_2$ is named calcium chloride.

To name compounds of elements having two or more oxidation numbers you must first figure out the oxidation numbers of the elements. Study the next example problem and do the practice problems.

Figure 11-16. Many binary compounds of transition elements, such as copper(II) chloride and cobalt chloride, are brightly colored.

EXAMPLE PROBLEM: Naming Some Binary Compounds

Problem Statement:

What is the name of CrO?

Problem-Solving Steps:

1. Write the name of the positive element.

chromium

2. If this element has more than one oxidation number, use the oxidation number of the negative element to figure out the oxidation number of the positive element. Write this number as a Roman numeral after the name of the element.

$? + (2-) = 0; ? = 2+$
Cr   O
chromium (II)

3. Add the root of the name of the second element, followed by *-ide*.

Solution: chromium(II) oxide

PRACTICE PROBLEM

Strategy Hint: For names of elements with more than one oxidation number, remember to include the Roman numeral. For names of non-metals in binary compounds use Table 11-3.

1. Name the following compounds:
   Li_2S, MgF_2, FeO, CuCl

Table 11-3

ELEMENTS IN BINARY COMPOUNDS	
Element	***-ide* Naming**
Chlorine	Chloride
Fluorine	Fluoride
Nitrogen	Nitride
Oxygen	Oxide
Phosphorus	Phosphide
Sulfur	Sulfide

CONCEPT DEVELOPMENT

▶ Emphasize that a Roman numeral indicates the oxidation number of an ion whose oxidation number varies. It is as important as the name of the element.

▶ **Demonstration:** To show that like charges repel and opposites attract to form chemical compounds, place two 25-cm-long pieces of cellophane tape on a plastic surface side by side. Pull both up at the same time. They will then have like charges. Bring the two pieces toward each other and watch them repel. Then put one piece down on the plastic surface. Place a second piece on top of it. Pull them off the plastic surface, and then separate them. They will have opposite charges, and, as you bring them close together, they will attract.

MINI QUIZ

Use the Mini Quiz to check students' recall of chapter content.

1 **An element's combining ability in a compound is designated by its _____ .** *oxidation number*

2 **A compound formed from two elements is called a(n) _____ .** *binary compound*

3 **Elements that lose one electron take on an ion charge of _____ .** *1+*

4 **How do you show the oxidation number of a metal having more than one possible oxidation number when naming a compound?** *Use a Roman numeral.*

5 **In a correct formula for a compound, the oxidation numbers of all atoms add up to _____ .** *zero*

PRACTICE PROBLEM ANSWERS

Note: Have students check Figure 11-15 on page 284 for elements with variable oxidation numbers. Many more elements than the ones in the list are variable. However, those listed are the only variable elements used in this text unless specifically stated in a problem.

1. lithium sulfide
2. magnesium fluoride
3. iron(II) oxide
4. copper(I) chloride

ASSESSMENT—ORAL

▶ State the formula for each of the following:
a. magnesium nitride Mg_3N_2
b. aluminum oxide Al_2O_3
c. lithium fluoride LiF
d. lead(IV) oxide PbO_2
e. chromium(II) bromide $CrBr_2$
▶ Element A has oxidation numbers of 2+ and 3+. Element Z has oxidation numbers of 2− and 3−. What are possible formulas if A and Z bond together? AZ, A_3Z_2, A_2Z_3

PROGRAM RESOURCES

From the **Teacher Resource Package** use:
Cross-Curricular Connections, page 17, Restoration of the Sistine Chapel
Transparency Masters, pages 43-44, Oxidation Numbers of Elements.
Use **Color Transparency** number 22, Oxidation Numbers of Elements.

CONCEPT DEVELOPMENT

▶ Remind students that polyatomic ions act as a single group. Thus, they should be treated very much like a single element when writing formulas.

▶ Students will probably want to use parentheses in formulas when they are not needed. Remind them that parentheses are to be used only around polyatomic ions when more than one is needed to make the formula electrically neutral.

STUDENT TEXT QUESTIONS

▶ Page 286, paragraph 1: **What four elements does NaHCO₃ contain?** *sodium, hydrogen, carbon, and oxygen*

▶ Page 286, paragraph 2: **What is the name of Sr(OH)₂?** *strontium hydroxide*

PRACTICE PROBLEM ANSWERS

1. 1+ 2–
Na SO₄
Therefore, Na₂SO₄ gives a sum of zero for charges.

2. 2+ 1–
Mg ClO₃
Therefore, the formula is Mg(ClO₃)₂.

CROSS CURRICULUM

▶ **Geology:** Calcium sulfate dihydrate is plaster of paris. It is also called gypsum. When seawater evaporated from shallow pools, beds of gypsum were formed. One of these gypsum beds is the Paris Basin in France.

STUDENT TEXT QUESTIONS

▶ Page 287, paragraph 2: **How does cobalt chloride detect water vapor?** *by changing color as it forms a hydrate*

▶ Page 287, paragraph 4: **How would you write the formula for this powder (anhydrous plaster of paris)?** *CaSO₄*

Table 11-4

POLYATOMIC IONS		
Charge	Name	Formula
1+	Ammonium	NH_4^+
1–	Acetate	$C_2H_3O_2^-$
	Chlorate	ClO_3^-
	Hydroxide	OH^-
	Nitrate	NO_3^-
2–	Carbonate	CO_3^{2-}
	Sulfate	SO_4^{2-}
3–	Phosphate	PO_4^{3-}

Compounds with Polyatomic Ions

Not all compounds are binary. Have you ever used baking soda in cooking, as a medicine, or to brush your teeth? Baking soda, which has the formula $NaHCO_3$, is an example of a compound that is not binary. What four elements does it contain? Some compounds, including baking soda, are composed of more than two elements because they contain polyatomic ions. The prefix *poly-* means "many," so *polyatomic* means "having many atoms." A **polyatomic ion** is a positively or negatively charged group of atoms. So the compound as a whole contains three or more elements.

Table 11-4 lists several polyatomic ions. To name a compound that contains one of these ions, write first the name of the positive element. For a compound of the ammonium ion, NH_4^+, write ammonium first. Then use Table 11-4 to find the name of the polyatomic ion. For example, K_2SO_4 is potassium sulfate. What is the name of $Sr(OH)_2$?

To write formulas for compounds containing polyatomic ions, follow the rules for writing formulas for binary compounds, with one addition. Write parentheses around the group representing the polyatomic ion when more than one of that ion is needed.

EXAMPLE PROBLEM: Writing Formulas with Polyatomic Ions

Problem Statement:
Problem-Solving Steps:

1. Write symbols and oxidation numbers for calcium and the nitrate ion.

2. Write in subscripts so that the sum of the oxidation numbers is zero. Enclose the NO_3 in parentheses.

Solution:

What is the formula for calcium nitrate?

2+ 1–
Ca NO_3

2+ 1–
Ca $(NO_3)_2$

Final formula: $Ca(NO_3)_2$

PRACTICE PROBLEMS

Strategy Hint: When only one polyatomic ion is needed in a formula, do not enclose the ion in parentheses.

Strategy Hint: Because the subscript *3* in ClO_3 is part of the ion, it should not be changed when written as part of a formula.

1. What is the formula for sodium sulfate?

2. What is the formula for magnesium chlorate?

OPTIONS

INQUIRY QUESTIONS

▶ **Use Table 11-4 to write the formulas for the following:**
a. iron(III) nitrate *Fe(NO₃)₃*
b. calcium carbonate *CaCO₃*
c. aluminum acetate *Al(C₂H₃O₂)₃*
d. ammonium phosphate *(NH₄)₃PO₄*

▶ **Use Table 11-4 to write the names of the following compounds:**
a. NaOH *sodium hydroxide*
b. KClO₃ *potassium chlorate*
c. CuSO₄ *copper(II) sulfate*
d. NH₄Cl *ammonium chloride*

Hydrates

Some ionic compounds may have water molecules as part of their structure and written into their formulas. These compounds are called hydrates. A **hydrate** is a compound that has water chemically attached to its ions. *Hydrate* comes from a word that means water. For example, when a water solution of cobalt chloride evaporates, pink crystals that contain six water molecules for each unit of cobalt chloride are formed. The formula for this compound is $CoCl_2 \cdot 6H_2O$ and its name is cobalt chloride hexahydrate. *Hexa-* means "six." You can remove water from these crystals by heating them. The resulting blue compound is called anhydrous, which means without water. The blue paper in Figure 11-17 has been soaked in cobalt chloride solution and heated.

Like many anhydrous compounds, cobalt chloride gains water molecules easily. You may have seen "weather predictors" made from blue paper that turns pink in humid air. The paper contains cobalt chloride. How does it detect water vapor?

Have you ever made a mold or cast with plaster of paris? If so, you have made a hydrate. Plaster of paris is the anhydrous form of calcium sulfate dihydrate, $CaSO_4 \cdot 2H_2O$. When you mix plaster of paris with water, it absorbs water and changes chemically into the hydrate.

Water in a hydrate has lost its properties because it is chemically attached. Not all crystals are hydrates. The only way to detect the presence of water in crystals is to heat the solid material and see if it gives off steam and changes to powder. For example, if you heat hardened plaster of paris, it will give off steam, crumble, and become powdery. How would you write the formula for this powder?

You have learned how to write formulas of binary ionic compounds and of compounds containing polyatomic ions. Using oxidation numbers to write formulas, you can predict the ratio in which atoms of elements may combine to form compounds. You have also seen how hydrates have water molecules as part of their structure and formulas. As you study the chapters that follow, you will see many uses of formulas.

Figure 11-17. The paper strips have been soaked in a solution of $CoCl_2$. The blue strips have been heated to drive water molecules out of the crystals.

MINI-Lab

How does heat affect a hydrate?
Using a light pink solution of $CoCl_2 \cdot 6H_2O$ as ink and a glass rod as a pen, write your name on white paper. After you have allowed the writing to air dry, it should be nearly invisible. Next, *carefully* wave the paper above a flame until you *observe* the writing starting to appear blue. What part of the $CoCl_2 \cdot 6H_2O$ was changed? How does heat affect a hydrate? What term is applied to the compound after it has been heated?

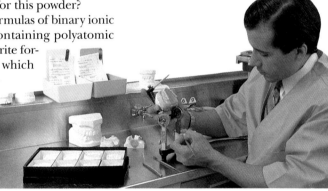

EXTENSION

For students who have mastered this section, use the **Reinforcement** and **Enrichment** masters or other OPTIONS provided.

 PROBLEM SOLVING

Think Critically: The silica gel would absorb the water and form a hydrate. It was packed with the VCR to absorb water molecules, thus helping to prevent corrosion of the metal parts of the VCR.

3 CLOSE

? **FLEX Your Brain**

Use the Flex Your Brain activity to have students explore CHEMICAL FORMULAS.

ASSESSMENT

Portfolio: Use the Flex Your Brain activity to reinforce critical-thinking and problem-solving skills. In Step 2, students might list examples of chemical formulas.

▶ Have students write their own definitions of the word *chemical*. Their definitions should approximate the definition of *substance* in Chapter 9. The definition should be rational and without the negative connotations so often given it in popular media.

SECTION REVIEW ANSWERS

1. sodium iodide, iron(III) iodide, potassium sulfate, ammonium bromide
2. (a) Li_2S, (b) $Ca(C_2H_3O_2)_2$, (c) BaO
3. (a) $CoCl_2$, (b) $CaSO_4 \cdot 2H_2O$
4. Apply: KNO_3
5. Connect to Earth Science: $2(Fe) + 3(2^-) = 0$; $Fe = 3+$

 P R O B L E M   S O L V I N G

The Packet of Mystery Crystals

When a new video cassette recorder (VCR) was delivered to Peter's home, he was eager to start using it to tape programs. So he asked for and got the job of unpacking the VCR. When he lifted the instrument from the carton, a small flat packet fell out. A label on the packet read "Contains silica gel. Do not eat."

Peter was curious about the contents of the packet, so he looked up "silica gel" in a reference book. There he read that silica gel is the anhydrous form of silica, a mineral that consists mainly of silicon(IV) oxide, SiO_2.

Think Critically: What would silica gel do if water molecules were in the air? Why was the packet of silica gel placed in the carton with the VCR?

SECTION REVIEW

1. Name the following: NaI, FeI_3, K_2SO_4, NH_4Br.
2. Write formulas for (a) lithium sulfide, (b) calcium acetate, and (c) barium oxide.
3. Write formulas for the following: (a) the anhydrous form of $CoCl_2 \cdot 6H_2O$ and (b) calcium sulfate dihydrate.
4. **Apply:** Plant food may list potassium nitrate as one ingredient. What is the formula for this compound?
5. **Connect to Earth Science:** A common iron ore is hematite, Fe_2O_3. What is the oxidation number of iron in this ore?

 **Skill Builder**

☑ Using Variables, Constants, and Controls

Design an experiment to distinguish between crystals that are hydrates and those that are not. Include crystals of iron(II) chloride, copper(I) nitrate, and crystals of sucrose. If you need help, refer to Using Variables, Constants, and Controls in the **Skill Handbook** on page 682.

Skill Builder

Heat crystals of each substance and observe whether or not they give off steam and turn powdery. Add water to the powder. If the original types of crystals form, then the substance was a hydrate. Crystals of iron(III) chloride and copper(II) nitrate are both hydrates, whereas sucrose is not. When sucrose is heated, it decomposes and gives off water vapor, leaving the black carbon as a residue that will not dissolve in water nor form sugar crystals.

Skill Builder
ASSESSMENT
Content: Have students explain why hydrates are heated in their experiments.

SUMMARY

11-1: Why Atoms Combine
1. The properties of compounds are generally different from those of the elements they contain.
2. A chemical formula for a compound indicates the composition of a unit of the compound.
3. Chemical bonding occurs when atoms of most elements become more stable by gaining, losing, or sharing electrons.

11-2: Science and Society: Hazardous Compounds at Home
1. Compounds that are toxic, corrosive, or flammable are hazardous.
2. There are many ways in which people can protect their health and the environment from hazardous compounds in the home.

11-3: Kinds of Chemical Bonds
1. Ionic bonds between atoms are formed by the attraction between ions, and covalent bonds are formed by the sharing of electrons.

2. Ionic bonding produces charged particles called ions. Covalent bonding produces units called molecules.
3. The unequal sharing of electrons produces compounds that contain polar bonds, and the equal sharing of electrons produces nonpolar compounds.

11-4: Formulas and Names of Compounds
1. An oxidation number indicates how many electrons an atom has gained, lost, or shared when bonding with other atoms.
2. In the formula of an ionic compound, the element or ion with the positive oxidation number is written first, followed by the one with the negative oxidation number.
3. The name of a binary compound is derived from the names of the two elements it contains.
4. A hydrate is a compound that has water chemically attached to its ions and written into its formula.

KEY SCIENCE WORDS

a. **binary compound**
b. **chemical bond**
c. **chemical formula**
d. **chemically stable**
e. **corrosive**
f. **covalent bond**
g. **hydrate**
h. **ion**
i. **ionic bond**
j. **nonpolar molecule**
k. **oxidation number**
l. **polyatomic ion**
m. **polar molecule**
n. **toxic**

UNDERSTANDING VOCABULARY

Match each phrase with the correct term from the list of Key Science Words.

1. a charged group of atoms
2. a compound composed of two elements
3. a molecule with opposite charges on each end
4. a positively or negatively charged atom
5. a chemical bond between oppositely charged ions
6. chemical bond formed from shared electrons
7. crystalline substance that contains water
8. outer energy level is filled with electrons
9. shows an element's combining ability
10. tells which elements are in a compound and their ratios

CHEMICAL BONDS **289**

CHAPTER
REVIEW

SUMMARY

Have students read the summary statements to review the major concepts of the chapter.

UNDERSTANDING VOCABULARY

1. l	**6.** f
2. a	**7.** g
3. m	**8.** d
4. h	**9.** k
5. i	**10.** c

ASSESSMENT
Portfolio
Encourage students to place in their portfolios one or two items of what they consider to be their best work. For each item, ask students to explain why that item was chosen and what they learned from it. Items might be selected from the following:
• Flex Your Brain, p. 275
• Activity 11-2 results and Assessment table, p. 281
• Skill Builder experiment design, p. 288

Performance
Additional performance assessments may be found in *Performance Assessment* and *Science Integration Activities* that accompany **Merrill Physical Science.** Performance Task Assessment Lists and rubrics for evaluating these activities and other products generated throughout the chapter can be found in Glencoe's *Performance Assessment in Middle School Science.*

ASSESSMENT
To assess student understanding of material in this chapter, use the resources listed.

👥 COOPERATIVE LEARNING
Consider using cooperative learning in the THINK AND WRITE CRITICALLY, APPLY, and MORE SKILL BUILDERS sections of the Chapter Review.

PROGRAM RESOURCES
From the **Teacher Resource Package** use:
Chapter Review, pages 25-26.
Chapter and Unit Tests, pages 65-68, Chapter Test.
Chapter and Unit Tests, pages 69-70, Unit Test.

CHECKING CONCEPTS

1. b	6. d
2. c	7. b
3. c	8. b
4. c	9. a
5. a	10. d

USING LAB SKILLS

ASSESSMENT

Use these alternate lab exercises to assess students' understanding of skills used in this chapter.

11. Calcium chloride is an ionic compound with a high melting point. Lard has covalent bonds between carbon atoms and between carbon and hydrogen atoms. It has a low melting point.

12. A dilute $CoCl_2 \cdot 6H_2O$ solution could be absorbed onto some white paper. On dry days the water would tend to go into the air, resulting in a blue color. On more humid days the water would be reabsorbed, turning the color pink.

THINK AND WRITE CRITICALLY

13. The molecule is composed of one atom of carbon and two atoms of oxygen.

14. Atoms can lose, gain, or share electrons to become more stable.

15. Chromium is a transition element and has two different oxidation numbers.

16. The hydroxide ion, OH^-, in $Mg(OH)_2$ is a polyatomic ion that acts as a unit when it combines with the magnesium ion.

17. XZ, X_2Z_3, X_2Z_5, X_3Z_5

CHECKING CONCEPTS

Choose the word or phrase that completes the sentence or answers the question.

1. The elements that are least likely to react with other elements are the _____.
   - a. metals
   - b. noble gases
   - c. nonmetals
   - d. transition elements

2. The oxidation number of Fe in Fe_2S_3 is _____.
   - a. 1+
   - b. 2+
   - c. 3+
   - d. 4+

3. The name of CuO is _____.
   - a. copper oxide
   - b. copper(I) oxide
   - c. copper(II) oxide
   - d. copper(III) oxide

4. The formula for iron(III) chlorate is _____.
   - a. $FeClO_3$
   - b. $FeCl$
   - c. $Fe(ClO_3)_3$
   - d. $FeCl_3$

5. Which of the following is a nonpolar molecule? _____
   - a. N_2
   - b. H_2O
   - c. NaCl
   - d. HCl

6. The number of electrons in the outer energy level of Group 17 elements is _____.
   - a. 1
   - b. 2
   - c. 17
   - d. 7

7. An example of a binary compound is _____.
   - a. O_2
   - b. NaF
   - c. H_2SO_4
   - d. $Cu(NO_3)_2$

8. An example of an anhydrous compound is _____.
   - a. H_2O
   - b. $CaSO_4$
   - c. $CuSO_4 \cdot 5H_2O$
   - d. $CaSO_4 \cdot 2H_2O$

9. An atom that has gained an electron is a _____.
   - a. negative ion
   - b. positive ion
   - c. polar molecule
   - d. nonpolar molecule

10. An example of a covalent compound is _____.
    - a. sodium chloride
    - b. calcium fluoride
    - c. calcium chloride
    - d. water

USING LAB SKILLS

11. Calcium chloride is sometimes used in winter to help melt ice. Lard is mostly made from carbon and hydrogen and may be used in cooking. Using the same techniques that you used in Activity 11-2 on page 281, what would you predict about the bonding types and melting points of these two materials?

12. In the MINI-Lab on page 287, you found that the cobalt chloride hydrate changed color as the water part of the molecule was attached or removed. Devise a way that this could be used to determine the humidity in your classroom.

THINK AND WRITE CRITICALLY

Answer the following questions in your Journal using complete sentences.

13. What does the formula CO_2 tell you about a molecule of carbon dioxide?

14. By what three ways can atoms become chemically stable?

15. How can chromium form two different compounds with oxygen?

16. Why is the formula for milk of magnesia written $Mg(OH)_2$ instead of MgO_2H_2?
17. What compounds can be formed from element X, with oxidation numbers 3+ and 5+, and element Z, with oxidation numbers 2− and 3−? Write their formulas.

APPLY

18. Anhydrous magnesium chloride is used to fireproof wood. Draw a dot diagram of magnesium chloride.
19. Baking soda, sodium hydrogen carbonate, and vinegar, which contains hydrogen acetate, can be used as household cleaners. Write the chemical formulas for these two compounds.
20. Artificial diamonds are made using thallium carbonate. If thallium has an oxidation number of 1+, what is the formula for the compound?
21. Ammonium sulfate is used as a fertilizer. What is its chemical formula?
22. The formula for a compound that composes kidney stones is $Ca_3(PO_4)_2$. What is the chemical name of this compound?

MORE SKILL BUILDERS

If you need help, refer to the Skill Handbook.

1. **Comparing and Contrasting:** Compare and contrast polar and nonpolar molecules.
2. **Interpreting Scientific Illustrations:** Write the name and formula for the compound illustrated below.

3. **Hypothesizing:** Several uses of HCl were given to you in Section 11-3. HF is another acid and is used to etch glass. If HCl is hydrochloric acid, what would be the name of HF?
4. **Observing and Inferring:** Ammonia gas and water react to form household ammonia, NH_4OH. If the formula for water is H_2O, what is the formula for ammonia gas?
5. **Concept Mapping:** In photosynthesis, green plants, in sunlight, convert carbon dioxide and water to glucose, $C_6H_{12}O_6$, and oxygen, O_2. In respiration, glucose and oxygen react to produce carbon dioxide and water and release energy. In the following map, write in the formulas of the molecules and the names of the processes.

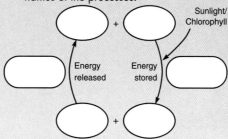

PROJECTS

1. One common form of phosphorus, white phosphorus, has the formula P_4 and is formed by four covalently bonded phosphorus atoms. Make a model of this molecule, showing that all four atoms are now chemically stable.
2. More sulfuric acid, H_2SO_4, is made in the United States than is any other chemical. Research the production and uses of sulfuric acid and write a report on your findings.

APPLY

18.

$$[:\ddot{C}l:]^- \ [Mg]^{2+} \ [:\ddot{C}l:]^-$$

19. $NaHCO_3$ (baking soda); $HC_2H_3O_2$ (vinegar)
20. Tl_2CO_3
21. $(NH_4)_2SO_4$
22. calcium phosphate

MORE SKILL BUILDERS

1. **Comparing and Contrasting:** Both molecules have covalent bonds. Polar molecules always have polar bonds and a slight charge on each end. Nonpolar molecules have no charged ends.
2. **Interpreting Scientific Illustrations:** hydrogen sulfide, H_2S
3. **Hypothesizing:** hydrofluoric acid
4. **Observing and Inferring:** NH_3

---

5. **Concept Mapping:**

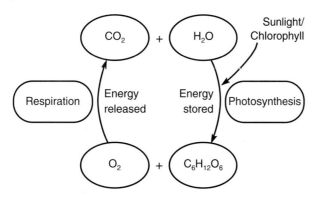

Objective

In this unit-ending feature, the unit topic, "The Nature of Matter," is extended into other disciplines. Students will see how knowledge of matter influences events around the planet.

Motivate

Cooperative Learning: Assign one Connection to each group of students. Using the Expert Teams strategy, have each group research to find out more about the geographic location of the Connection—its climate, culture, flora and fauna, and ecological issues.

Teaching Tips

▶ Tell students to keep in mind while they are reading this feature the connection between knowledge about the nature of matter and how that knowledge is applied.

▶ Ask students to hypothesize about how new knowledge about the nature of matter might affect their lives in the future.

Wrap-Up

Conclude this lesson by having students discuss how the events discussed in these Connections affected other parts of the world.

METEOROLOGY

Background: Hail is a form of precipitation that occurs mostly during the warm, summer months. It consists of lumps of ice that form within cumulonimbus clouds—the clouds that produce thunderstorms.

Discussion: Discuss the effects of a hailstorm on crops, buildings, cars, and other materials.

Answer to Question: Hailstones start as ice crystals (solids) within a storm cloud. Strong updrafts within the cloud toss the crystals up and down, and droplets of water (liquid) freeze in layers (solid) around the ice crystals. When the hailstones become too heavy, they fall to the ground.

Extension: Have students describe experiences they have had with hailstorms.

GLOBAL CONNECTIONS

The Nature of Matter

In this unit, you studied what matter is, how it is classified, and how it is put together. Now find out how matter is connected to other subjects and places around the world.

METEOROLOGY

THE SKY IS FALLING
Central Kansas
The largest hailstone ever measured fell in Kansas during a September, 1970, thunderstorm. It was almost 14 cm in diameter—the size of a grapefruit. The noise of the hailstones hitting buildings during the storm sounded like exploding bombs. How do hailstones form and what changes in state are involved?

SOCIAL STUDIES

STEAM POWER
New Orleans, Louisiana
By the early 1900s, boats with steam-driven paddle wheels traveled the length of the Mississippi River, carrying passengers and farm goods and opening up the frontier to settlers. Find out how the development of steam engines also affected farming in the Midwest.

BIOLOGY

DEEP-SEA LIFE
Galápagos Islands
Ocean vents that release mineral-rich hot water form the basis of food chains that do not depend on light or photosynthesis. Bacteria around the vents obtain energy from the oxidation of sulfur compounds from the vent. In what lake have scientists found similar vents?

BIOLOGY

Background: In 1977, in the Pacific Ocean near the Galápagos Islands, the first vents were found. Vents have been discovered in at least 20 areas on the ocean floor.

Discussion: Discuss how, up to the time of this discovery, scientists believed that all food chains depended on organisms that used sunlight to produce food in the process of photosynthesis. Ask students to predict what might happen to the life around the vents if the chemicals given off at the vents changed.

Answer to Question: Scientists have recently discovered the first freshwater vents in Lake Baikal in Siberia.

Extension: Have students research the variety of life found around the ocean vents.

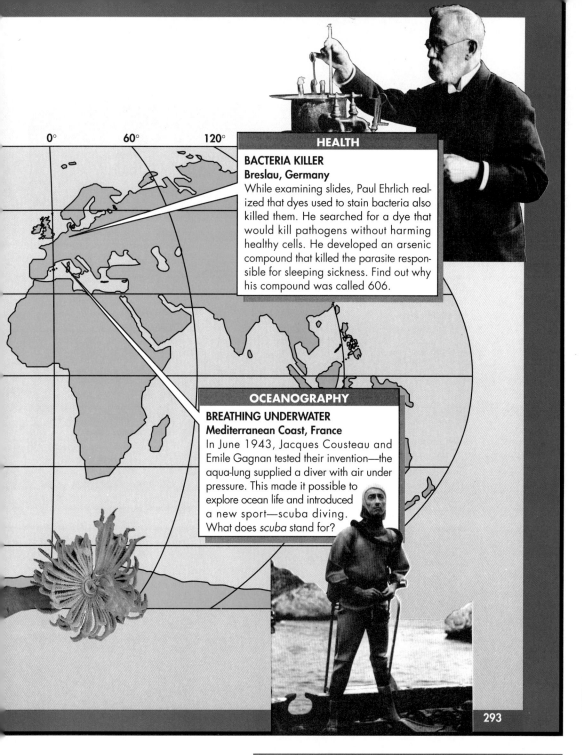

Background: Before the invention of the aqualung, divers had to use a heavy diving suit that required a lifeline with air pumped down from the surface.

Discussion: Discuss how the behavior of gases explains the operation of the aqualung. Ask students what happens to air remaining in the tank, as the diver uses up some of the air.

Answer to Question: *Scuba* stands for self-contained underwater breathing apparatus.

Extension: Have students find out why scuba divers sometimes suffer from "the bends" and how this condition is related to the gas laws.

SOCIAL STUDIES

Background: The steamboat was important in the United States because so much of the country was linked by large rivers. Competition among builders of steamboats led to rapid improvement in their designs and speed.

Discussion: Ask students to describe the change of state that occurs in steam engines and how Boyle's and Charles's laws are involved in a steam engine.

Answer to Question: With steam-powered threshers, farmers could thresh 30 times more wheat per day than they could have by hand.

Extension: Ask students to prepare biographical sketches of some of the early pioneers in the development of steam engines.

HEALTH

BACTERIA KILLER
Breslau, Germany

While examining slides, Paul Ehrlich realized that dyes used to stain bacteria also killed them. He searched for a dye that would kill pathogens without harming healthy cells. He developed an arsenic compound that killed the parasite responsible for sleeping sickness. Find out why his compound was called 606.

OCEANOGRAPHY

BREATHING UNDERWATER
Mediterranean Coast, France

In June 1943, Jacques Cousteau and Emile Gagnan tested their invention—the aqua-lung supplied a diver with air under pressure. This made it possible to explore ocean life and introduced a new sport—scuba diving. What does *scuba* stand for?

HEALTH

Background: The painstaking methods Ehrlich used for finding chemicals to kill bacteria and other pathogens opened the way for the discovery of many other medicines.

Discussion: Tell students that 606 was later discovered to be a cure for syphilis. Discuss the significance of finding chemical compounds that could cure diseases.

Answer to Question: Ehrlich tested every arsenic-based compound he could find on laboratory mice, but most would not kill bacteria. Finally the 606th one he tested worked.

Extension: Ask students to find out how research on new drugs is carried out.

HYDRAULIC ENGINEER

Background: Some hydraulic engineers work for county, state, or federal government agencies. Others work for large construction companies that build bridges and dams.

Related Career	Education
Construction worker	high school
Hydrologist	college degree
Equipment operator	technical school
Architect	college degree

Career Issue: Many groups are against the construction of new dams for flood control, to create recreational areas, or power generation because of the damage it does to the environment. **What do you think?** Ask students to discuss how they would decide whether or not a new dam should be built on a river in your area.

CHEMISTRY TEACHER

Background: Chemistry teachers must not only have a good understanding of chemistry, but also must be able to explain the subject to students. Chemistry teachers teach in public and private schools, as well as in colleges.

Related Career	Education
Research chemist	graduate degree
Teacher's aide	high school
Science supervisor	college degree
School nurse	college degree

Career Issue: Some people think that students should be required to take more science classes, particularly chemistry and physics, to better prepare them for the technological world in which they live. **What do you think?** Lead students in a discussion of their own attitudes toward more stringent science requirements in high school.

HYDRAULIC ENGINEER

Hydraulic engineers use a knowledge of fluids to design bridges, levees, and dams. They must study bodies of water to find out about drainage and water supplies. They also need to know how a bridge, levee, or dam will be affected by the normal water pressure, as well as extra pressure exerted by water from heavy storms. Hydraulic engineers must be sure that the structures they design will not collapse after a storm.

If you're interested in becoming a hydraulic engineer, you should like working with measurements, formulas, statistics, and graphs. In high school, you should take math, physics, and chemistry classes. Hydraulic engineers have at least a bachelor's degree, and many have advanced degrees.

For Additional Information
Contact the American Society of Civil Engineers, 345 E. 47th Street, New York, New York 10017.

CHEMISTRY TEACHER

A *chemistry teacher* works with students to help them learn about chemistry and how it is a part of their everyday lives. Chemistry teachers must make daily lesson plans, set up laboratory activities, demonstrate experiments, and work with students having different backgrounds and interests.

If you're interested in becoming a chemistry teacher, you should enjoy math and science classes, and should like working with young people. Many colleges and universities offer programs for bachelor's and master's degrees in chemistry and chemical education.

For Additional Information
Contact the National Science Teachers Association, 1742 Connecticut Avenue, NW, Washington, DC 20009-1171.

UNIT READINGS

▶ Hamilton, J.H. and Maruhn, J.A. "Exotic Atomic Nuclei." *Scientific American*, July, 1986, pp. 80-89.
▶ Maxwell, James C. *Maxwell on Molecules and Gases.* Cambridge, MA: MIT Press, 1986.
▶ Sprackling, Michael. *Liquids and Solids.* New York: Methuen, 1985.

294

UNIT READINGS

Background
▶ *Maxwell on Molecules and Gases* is a collection of classic writings.
▶ *Liquids and Solids* describes properties of these familiar states of matter.

More Readings
Mebane, Robert C. and Rybolt, Thomas R. *Adventures with Atoms and Molecules: Chemistry Experiments for Young People.* Hillside, NJ: Enslow, 1985. Thirty experiments that answer fundamental questions about the nature of matter.

Classics
▶ Chester, Michael. *Particles.* New York, NY: Macmillan, 1978. An introduction to the world of atomic and subatomic particles.

Connections

by James Burke

The passage that follows describes the invention of the barometer.

In June 1644, Torricelli wrote to a colleague and friend in Rome, Michelangelo Ricci, to explain an experiment carried out by his own assistant Vincenzo Viviani, to which he added drawings in the margin. Viviani had filled a 6-foot long tube with mercury and upended it in a dish full of the same metal, with the open end of the tube beneath the surface of the mercury in the dish. When he took his finger away from the open end of the tube, the mercury in it ran out into the dish, but stopped when the mercury column left in the tube was still about 30 inches above the dish. Torricelli reasoned that the weight of the air pressing on the mercury in the dish had to be exactly equal to the weight of the mercury left in the tube. If there were no weight of air, all the mercury in the tube would have run out into the dish. If this were so, he wrote, "we live submerged at the bottom of an ocean of air." What was more, in the space at the top of the tube left by the mercury was the thing thought to be impossible: a vacuum. Torricelli wrote that if he was right, the pressure of the air in our atmospheric ocean must vary according to how far up or down in the ocean we are.

Ricci, realizing that current church opinion in Rome would not take kindly to these arguments (since if they were true several things followed, such as the existence of interplanetary vacuum, with sun-orbiting planets), made a copy of Torricelli's letter and sent it to a priest in Paris, Father Marin Mersenne.... the first thing he did was send another copy of it to a friend who was interested in the same problem, the son of a Paris tax inspector, Blaise Pascal. Two years after receiving the letter (he had been busy meanwhile in the Paris gambling halls working on laws-of-chance mathematics) Pascal found himself in Rouen. It was here that he repeated Torricelli's experiment, to check it; only he did it full-scale, with water. Unfortunately he was in no position to check the second part of the argument—there were no mountains around Rouen. However, Pascal had a brother-in-law called Francois Perier who lived in central France, in Clermont Ferrand, which is surrounded by mountains. So Pascal wrote to Perier, asking him to take things to the next stage.

In Your Own Words

1. Pascal asked his brother-in-law, Perier, to take things to the next stage. If you had been Perier, what would you have done next?
2. How might Pascal's knowledge of Torricelli's barometer have influenced him in his discovery of Pascal's principle?

295

Source: Burke, James. *Connections.* Little, Brown and Company, Boston MA: 1978.

Biography: James Burke was born in 1936 in England and is a graduate of Oxford University. He was the BBC's chief reporter on the *Apollo* moon missions. The book is the companion volume to the television series produced by the BBC and broadcast over PBS stations in 1979. Burke served as the host of the television series. Research and filming for the television series and the book took Burke to 23 countries and took over two years to complete.

TEACHING STRATEGY

Have students read through the passage by James Burke. Then have them respond to the discussion questions below.

Discussion Questions

1. **How does Burke say the church in Rome would react to Torricelli's discoveries? Why do you think this is the case?** *The text says the church would not take kindly to the discoveries. The Roman Catholic church was very powerful during the 1600s and if any scientist disagreed with the position of the church, he could be tried for heresy.*

2. **What significance does Burke give to Father Mersenne?** *Father Mersenne served as the link between the scientists of the day. If he had not had so many contacts, and had not copied and sent letters, many scientists would have been unaware of what others were working on and what discoveries had been made.*

Other Works

▶ Other books on this subject include: Middleton, W.E. Knowles. *The History of the Barometer.* Baltimore, MD: John Hopkins University Press, 1964. Mesnard, Jean. *Pascal, His Life and Works.* London: Harvill Press, 1952.

In Unit 4, students build on the broad classification of substances, elements and compounds, that they studied in Chapter 9. The common properties and uses of elements categorized as metals, nonmetals, mixed groups, and synthetic elements are discussed and related to their positions in the periodic table. The common structures and characteristics of organic and biological compounds are then explored. Students are then introduced to materials science with a discussion of alloys, ceramics, plastics, and composites.

CONTENTS

ADVANCE PREPARATION

Audiovisuals:
Show one or more of the listed audiovisuals.
▶ *Metals*, slides/cassette, Science Software.
▶ *The Halogens*, slides/cassette, Science Software.
▶ *The Noble Gases*, film, Science Software.

Field Trips and Speakers
▶ Arrange for a certified gemologist or polymer chemist to visit your class.
▶ Arrange for a representative from your school's food service department to visit your class.

U N I T

4 KINDS OF SUBSTANCES

296

OPTIONS

Cross Curriculum
▶ Have students begin research on the composition of coins used in the United States and other countries.

Cooperative Learning: Have students track the price of gold or crude oil by monitoring television and newspapers. Ask them to present the data as graphs and discuss the results. Have them relate any fluctuations in the prices to world events discussed in social studies.

Science at Home
Cooperative Learning: Assign groups of students to determine community disposal and/or recycling methods for metals, paper, and plastic. Have students describe major differences between the substances and explain why proper handling of each is important.

▶ Have students list various products found around the home that include imitation or artificial flavorings or scents. Have students research what these artificial scents and flavorings are and how they are made.

What's Happening Here?

Even after you think *you're* done with a piece of chewing gum, look again—it still has plenty of stretch and give for the shoe of the next passerby. Chewing gum gets its stretch from its structure—a special arrangement of atoms called a polymer. A gum drop model of the chewing gum polymer is shown below. In this unit you'll learn about polymers and many other kinds of substances—metal, non-metal, organic, biological—and the special properties of each. But hey, next time put your gum in the trash.

UNIT CONTENTS

297

Multicultural Awareness

Have interested students research the contributions of Oriental, African, and Native American cultures to the development of ceramics and metallurgy.

Inquiry Questions

Use the following discussion questions to focus a discussion on the properties of organic and synthetic compounds.

▶ **What characteristic does this chewing gum display?** *Accept all reasonable answers.*

"stretchiness," elasticity, "rubbery"

▶ **What other materials displayed in the photograph have similar characteristics?** *Sole of shoe (tennis shoe, sneaker)*

▶ **How is this characteristic useful in materials and products that you are familiar with?** *Elastic material in cuffs, waistbands, and neck openings keeps clothing in place; clothing made from latex material is form fitting for more comfort, less hazardous for exercising and biking; rubber soles give bounce and cushion the feet; "rubber" surgical gloves afford protection.*

INTRODUCING THE UNIT

What's Happening Here?

▶ Point out to students that in this unit they will be studying how the structure of a substance accounts for its properties and its uses. They will also study how substances can be altered to produce new materials.

▶ **Background:** Chewing gum contains a gum base that gives it its elastic properties. At one time, most gum bases consisted of *chicle*, a coagulation of the latex obtained from the sapodilla tree. Today most gum base consists of synthetic polymers of polyvinyl acetate,

$$-CH_2-\underset{\underset{\underset{CH_3}{C=O}}{O}}{\overset{H}{\underset{|}{C}}}-CH_2-\underset{\underset{\underset{CH_3}{C=O}}{O}}{\overset{H}{\underset{|}{C}}}-CH_2-\underset{\underset{\underset{CH_3}{C=O}}{O}}{\overset{H}{\underset{|}{C}}}-$$

or [unvulcanized] styrene-butadiene rubber (most common synthetic rubber),

both of which are manufactured from petroleum products.

Previewing the Chapters

Cooperative Learning: Have groups of students classify the materials in classroom objects using charts and photographs in this unit.

Tying to Previous Knowledge

▶ Have students collect high-tech mail order catalogues and read advertisements for new and improved products and the materials from which they are made. Have students list the materials and their properties.

▶ Use the **inquiry questions** in the OPTIONS box to discuss organic and synthetic compounds.

12 Elements and Their Properties

CHAPTER SECTION	OBJECTIVES	ACTIVITIES
12-1 Metals (2 days)	1. **Describe** the properties of a typical metal. 2. **Identify** the alkali and alkaline earth metals. 3. **Differentiate** among three groups of transition elements.	**MINI-Lab:** *How is metallic bonding related to the flexibility of a metal?* p. 301
12-2 Synthetic Elements **Science & Society** (1 day)	1. **Distinguish** among elements classified as lanthanoids, actinoids, and transuranium elements. 2. **Compare** the pros and cons of synthesizing elements.	
12-3 Nonmetals (2 days)	1. **Recognize** hydrogen as a nonmetal. 2. **Compare** and **contrast** properties of the halogens. 3. **Describe** properties and uses of the noble gases.	**Activity 12-1:** *Nonmetal Reaction,* p. 315
12-4 Mixed Groups (2 days)	1. **Distinguish** among metals, nonmetals, and metalloids in Groups 13 through 16 of the periodic table. 2. **Describe** the nature of allotropes. 3. **Recognize** the significance of differences in crystal structure in carbon.	**Activity 12-2:** *Slippery Carbon,* p. 322
Chapter Review		

ACTIVITY MATERIALS

FIND OUT	ACTIVITIES		MINI-LABS
Page 299 paper clips tongs sodium chloride strontium chloride copper(II) sulfate burner (gas) distilled water small beakers	**12-1 Nonmetal Reaction, p. 315** large test tube large wooden match 20 mL liquid laundry bleach (5% sodium hypochlorite) 0.5 g cobalt chloride goggles	**12-2 Slippery Carbon, p. 322** thin spaghetti polystyrene sheet toothpicks small gum drops flat cardboard scissors	**How is metallic bonding related to the flexibility of a metal? p. 301** pieces of thin iron wire (such as hairpins) tongs burner beaker of cold water

CHAPTER FEATURES	TEACHER RESOURCE PACKAGE	OTHER RESOURCES
Technology: *Metallic Moments,* p. 305 **Skill Builder:** *Interpreting Scientific Illustrations,* p. 307	**Ability Level Worksheets** ◆ **Study Guide,** p. 50 ● **Reinforcement,** p. 50 ▲ **Enrichment,** p. 50 **Activity Worksheets,** pp. 5, 100 **Critical Thinking/Problem Solving,** p. 18 **Cross-Curricular Connections,** p. 18 **Transparency Masters,** pp. 45, 46	**Color Transparency 23,** Metallic Bonding **STVS:** Disc 2, Side 1 **Science Integration Activity 12**
You Decide! p. 309	**Ability Level Worksheets** ◆ **Study Guide,** p. 51 ● **Reinforcement,** p. 51 ▲ **Enrichment,** p. 51	
Skill Builder: *Making and Using Graphs,* p. 314	**Ability Level Worksheets** ◆ **Study Guide,** p. 52 ● **Reinforcement,** p. 52 ▲ **Enrichment,** p. 52 **Activity Worksheets,** pp. 94, 95 **Science and Society,** p. 16	**Laboratory Manual 25,** Preparation of Carbon Dioxide; **26,** Preparation of Hydrogen; **27,** Preparation of Oxygen **STVS:** Disc 2, Side 2
Problem Solving: *The "Lead" in a Pencil,* p. 318 **Skill Builder:** *Concept Mapping,* p. 321	**Ability Level Worksheets** ◆ **Study Guide,** p. 53 ● **Reinforcement,** p. 53 ▲ **Enrichment,** p. 53 **Activity Worksheets,** pp. 96, 97 **Concept Mapping,** pp. 29, 30 **Transparency Masters,** pp. 47, 48	**Color Transparency 24,** Allotropes of Carbon **STVS:** Disc 2, Side 1
Summary Think & Write Critically Key Science Words Apply Understanding Vocabulary More Skill Builders Checking Concepts Projects Using Lab Skills	**ASSESSMENT RESOURCES** **Chapter Review,** pp. 27, 28 **Chapter Test,** pp. 80-83 **Performance Assessment in Middle School Science**	**Chapter Review Software** **Test Bank** **Alternate Assessment** **Performance Assessment**

◆ **Basic**   ● **Average**   ▲ **Advanced**

ADDITIONAL MATERIALS

SOFTWARE	AUDIOVISUAL	BOOKS/MAGAZINES
Chemaid: Introduction to the Periodic Table, Ventura Educational Systems. *Element Hunt,* Queue. *Elements,* Queue. *Hydrogen Spectrum,* Scott Foresman & Co. *Introduction to General Chemistry: The Elements,* EduQuest. *Mystery Matter,* MECC.	*Buckyballs—A New Molecule for a New Chemistry,* Video, Hawkhill. *Carbon,* Video, Lucerne Media. *Metals,* Video, Journal Films. *Of Metals and Men,* Video, Insight Media. *Oxygen,* Video, Lucerne Media.	Colin, Norman. "Uranium Enrichment," *Science,* May 22, 1987, pp. 906-908. Heiserman, David L. *Exploring Chemical Elements and Their Compounds.* PA: TAB, 1992.. Matthews, G. J. *Origin and Distribution of the Elements.* Teaneck, NJ: World Scientific Pub., 1988. Ruben, Samuel. *Handbook of the Elements.* Peru, IL: Open Court Publishing Co., 1985.

THEME DEVELOPMENT: Scale and structure as a theme is developed through a presentation of metallic and nonmetallic properties of elements and their positions on the periodic table based on their atomic structures.

CHAPTER OVERVIEW

▶ **Section 12-1:** The properties of metals are presented and explained by a study of metallic bonding. The alkali metal and alkaline earth metal families, as well as transition elements, are studied in detail.

▶ **Section 12-2: Science and Society:** The student is introduced to the synthetic elements, which are important in some useful devices.

▶ **Section 12-3:** The properties of hydrogen, the halogens, and noble gases are developed in detail. The properties of nonmetals are contrasted with those of metals.

▶ **Section 12-4:** Within some groups on the periodic table there are nonmetals, metalloids, and metals. These groups are studied in Section 12-4.

CHAPTER VOCABULARY

malleable	transuranium
ductile	elements
metallic	diatomic
bonding	molecule
radioactive	sublimation
element	semiconductors
transition	allotropes
elements	

CHAPTER

12 Elements and Their Properties

298

OPTIONS

For Your Gifted Students

Students could observe flame tests for various metallic elements. Single-displacement reactions in which the more active halogen, chlorine, replaces less active halogens, bromine and iodine, from their halide salts are also interesting. In addition, these reactions illustrate and reinforce the pattern of varying chemical activity within a family. Observe proper precautions when allowing students to perform any laboratory experiments.

For Your Mainstreamed Students

Try to have mainstreamed students distinguish metals and nonmetals on the basis of their properties. Because metals are used much more often in their elemental form than are nonmetals, students should survey how metals are used in the home and relate those uses to metallic properties. Examples include heat conductivity (cooking utensils and radiators), electrical conductivity (wiring and plugs), and malleability and strength (the structure of washers and refrigerators).

Did you know that the Chinese invented fireworks hundreds of years ago? They used certain substances mixed with gunpowder —which they also invented—to produce colorful explosions.

FIND OUT! 🐦

In this activity, observe the colors some compounds give to a flame.

Using tongs, hold a clean paper clip in a flame until no additional color is seen in the flame. Dip the paper clip in a solution of copper(II) sulfate and hold it in the flame again. *Observe* and *record* the color produced. Repeat the procedure using strontium chloride, and again using sodium chloride. *Using variables, constants, and controls*, how might you find out which element in each compound causes the color? Test your **hypothesis.** Besides fireworks, what do you think is another use for brightly colored flames?

Gearing Up
Previewing the Chapter
Use this outline to help you focus on important ideas in this chapter.

Previewing Science Skills
  ▶ In the **Skill Builders,** you will interpret scientific illustrations, make and use a graph, and make a concept map.
  ▶ In the **Activities,** you will observe, compare, predict, infer, and build a model.
  ▶ In the **MINI-Lab,** you will observe and draw a conclusion.

What's next?

Read Chapter 12 to learn more about elements that give colors to flames and fireworks. You will also study other properties of elements.

299

ASSESSMENT OPTIONS

PORTFOLIO
Refer to page 323 for suggested items that students might select for their portfolios.

PERFORMANCE ASSESSMENT
See page 323 for additional Performance Assessment options.
Process
Skill Builders, pp. 314, 321
MINI-Lab, p. 301
Activities 12-1, p. 315; 12-2, p. 322
Using Lab Skills, p. 324

CONTENT ASSESSMENT
Assessment—Oral, pp. 312, 318
Skill Builder, p. 307
Section Reviews, pp. 307, 309, 314, 321
Chapter Review, pp. 323-325
Mini Quizzes, pp. 303, 306, 309, 313, 319, 320

GROUP ASSESSMENT
Opportunities for group assessment occur with Cooperative Learning Strategies and Flex Your Brain Activities.

INTRODUCING THE CHAPTER
Use the Find Out activity to introduce students to metals and nonmetals. Inform students that they will be learning about the properties of elements as they read the chapter.

FIND OUT!
Preparation: Make three concentrated salt solutions before class using distilled water.
Materials: paper clips, tongs, sodium chloride, strontium chloride, copper(II) sulfate, gas burner, distilled water, small beakers

👥 **Cooperative Learning:** Use the Science Investigation Team strategy to answer the questions. Each member of the group should test one element in the flame.
Teaching Tips
▶ **CAUTION:** *Have students wear goggles and aprons and be cautious working with open flames. The paper clip will become very hot.*
▶ It is important that the burners be adjusted to a blue flame. In a darkened room, sodium compounds give a fluffy yellow flame, strontium compounds give a red flame, and copper compounds give a pale green flame.
▶ For a dramatic demonstration, darken the room and place one of the three salts in a paper or plastic bag. Shake the bag and then open it near the air intake of the burner. The flame will turn color and will be visible all over the room as the dust enters the burner flame.
▶ **Answers to Questions:** Test other combinations of the same ions. For instance, test a different sodium compound and a different chlorine compound. Uses include signal and warning flares.

Gearing Up
Have students study the Gearing Up feature to familiarize themselves with the chapter. Discuss the relationships of the topics in the outline.

What's Next?
Before beginning the first section, make sure students understand the connection between the Find Out activity and the topics to follow.

PREPARATION

SECTION BACKGROUND

▶ As the atomic numbers of the alkali metals increase: the atoms become larger, the outer electrons are farther from the nucleus, lower level electrons shield the effect of the more positive nucleus, and outer electrons are held less tightly. This results in more chemically active atoms.

▶ Electron energy levels are made up of sublevels that are given labels of *s, p, d,* or *f.* The highest-energy electrons for elements in Groups 1-2 are in the *s* sublevel, in the *p* sublevel for Groups 13-18, and in the *f* sublevel for the lanthanoids and actinoids. The transition elements are those elements whose highest-energy electrons are in the *d* sublevels. These partially filled *d* sublevels cause the chemical properties to be different from those of other metals.

1 MOTIVATE

▶ **Demonstration:** Have a student wearing leather gloves attempt to tear an aluminum can into two pieces by gripping the ends and twisting in one direction. It will twist but not tear. Use a stiff, L-shaped piece of metal to scratch the protective plastic film off the inside of the can in a line around the middle. Put 125 mL of water into the can. Then add 100 mL concentrated hydrochloric acid. **CAUTION:** *Hydrochloric acid is corrosive and gives off harmful fumes. Place can inside a large beaker.* After a few minutes the acid will partially dissolve the can where the plastic film has been scratched away. Rinse completely. You can now easily tear the treated can as you introduce the properties of metals.

New Science Words

malleable
ductile
metallic bonding
radioactive element
transition elements

Objectives

▶ Describe the properties of a typical metal.
▶ Identify the alkali and alkaline earth metals.
▶ Differentiate among three groups of transition elements.

Properties of Metals

Have you ever seen very old jewelry or statues made of gold and copper? These were the two first metals that people discovered, thousands of years ago. The use of silver and tin soon followed. Then came iron. But aluminum—the metal used in your soft drink cans—wasn't discovered until a little more than 100 years ago.

Gold, copper, silver, tin, iron, and aluminum are typical metals. What do these and other metals have in common? Most metals are hard, shiny solids. Metals are also good conductors of both heat and electricity. These properties make metals suitable for uses ranging from kitchen pots and pans to wires for electric appliances. Because metals reflect light well, they are used in mirrors. Metals are **malleable,** which means they can be hammered or rolled into sheets. Metals are also **ductile,** which means they can be drawn into wires.

Figure 12-1. Gold is so malleable it can be rolled into thin sheets. Very thin gold sheets, called gold leaf, were used to plate this dome.

300 ELEMENTS AND THEIR PROPERTIES

OPTIONS

Meeting Different Ability Levels

For Section 12-1, use the following **Teacher Resource Masters** depending upon individual students' needs.

◆ **Study Guide Master** for all students.
● **Reinforcement Master** for students of average and above average ability levels.
▲ **Enrichment Master** for above average students.

Additional Teacher Resource Package masters are listed in any PROGRAM RESOURCES boxes that are in the section. The additional masters are appropriate for all students.

Figure 12-2. Metals are ductile, which means they can be drawn into wires.

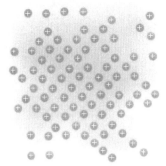

Figure 12-3. In metallic bonding, the outer level electrons from the atoms surround the remaining positively charged ions.

The atoms of metals generally have from one to three electrons in their outer energy levels. Metals tend to give up electrons easily. Remember from Chapter 11 what happens when metals combine with nonmetals. The atoms of the metals tend to lose electrons to the atoms of nonmetals, forming ionic bonds. The other type of bond you have studied is the covalent bond, which generally forms between atoms of nonmetals.

A third type of bonding, neither ionic nor covalent, occurs among the atoms in a metal. In **metallic bonding,** positively charged metallic ions are surrounded by a "sea of electrons." Outer level electrons are not held tightly to their particular nucleus. Rather, the electrons move freely among many positively charged ions. The electrons form a cloud around the ions of the metal as shown in Figure 12-3.

Metallic bonding explains many of the properties of metals. For example, when a metal is hammered or drawn into a wire, it does not break because the ions are in layers that slide past one another. And because the outer level electrons are weakly held, metals are good conductors of electricity.

Look at the periodic table on pages 258-259. How many of the elements in the table are classified as metals? Except for hydrogen, all the elements in Groups 1 through 12 are metals. You will read about metals in some of these groups in this section. Some other metals are discussed in later sections.

Connect to... Earth Science

Stalactites and stalagmites are hanging and rising formations found in caves. These formations are mostly calcium carbonate, $CaCO_3$. How many electrons has calcium given up in forming this compound?

MINI-Lab

How is metallic bonding related to the flexibility of a metal?
Carefully, using tongs, hold two pieces of thin wire in a flame until they are red hot. Drop one wire into a beaker of cold water. Let the other wire slowly cool. Be sure both wires cool to room temperature. Try to bend quickly both pieces of wire. What do you *observe* about the flexibility of the wires? How can metallic bonding be used to explain what you observe?

---

2 TEACH

Key Concepts are highlighted.

CONCEPT DEVELOPMENT

▶ Have your students memorize the properties of metals. They will not have to memorize the properties of nonmetals because they are opposite to those of metals.

Connect to... Earth Science

Answer: two

MINI-Lab

Materials: pieces of thin iron wire, such as hairpins; tongs; burner; beaker of cold water
Teaching Tips
▶**CAUTION:** *Students should wear goggles. Warn students to be careful not to drop red-hot wires.*
▶Place the cold water near the flame so that the wire is thoroughly hot when it is immersed.
▶**Expected Results:** The slowly cooled wire retains its normal flexibility while the quickly cooled wire becomes brittle.
▶**Answers to Questions:** Layers of atoms can move past one another. When heated, the structure becomes jumbled and unstable. Quick cooling "freezes" the atoms in these positions. Slow cooling allows the atoms to resume normal positions.

MINI-Lab
ASSESSMENT

Content: Check student responses to determine if they have clearly shown the concept of the "sea of electrons" as a way to explain their results.

● REINFORCEMENT 50   ▲ ENRICHMENT 50   301

► Some people think that any amount of salt, NaCl, in the diet is harmful. Too much can cause health problems, but so can too little. The Na^+ ion from the salt is needed to help maintain the body's electrolyte balance. The Cl^- ion is used to produce HCl in the stomach.

CROSS CURRICULUM

► **Medicine:** Sodium and potassium ions are essential to the proper functioning of the human nervous system. The nerve cell axons do not conduct electricity. The sodium or potassium ions move through the cell membrane changing the potential. This change moves down the axon like a wave at a rate of 30-50 m/s.

CONCEPT DEVELOPMENT

► **Demonstration:** Use an electrical conductivity checker to show the contrast between metals and nonmetals. To show differences in heat conductivity, place a metal and a wooden spoon in a beaker of boiling water. After a few minutes, have the students carefully check the temperature of each spoon's handle.

► **Demonstration:** To show how layers of metal atoms slide past each other making a metal malleable, place a clear plastic box lid on the overhead projector. Add metal shot (BBs) to the box. The metal shot will form into rows that you can move with a short piece of wood.

► You may want to inform students that alkali metals are stored under mineral oil because they react violently with water, releasing hydrogen gas. The oil keeps the metal from the water vapor and oxygen in the air.

► Ask students what they think about when the word *radiation* is mentioned. Radioactive sources release radiation that is different from the radiation of a light or heat source. You may want to introduce radioactivity here but reserve most of the content for later in the textbook.

VideoDisc

STVS: Sea Urchins and Power Plants, Disc 2, Side 1

1
3 **Li** Lithium 6.941
11 **Na** Sodium 22.98977
19 **K** Potassium 39.0983
37 **Rb** Rubidium 85.4678
55 **Cs** Cesium 132.9054
87 **Fr** Francium 223.0197*

The Alkali Metals

The elements in Group 1 of the periodic table are the alkali metals. Like other metals generally, these metals are shiny, malleable, and ductile. They are good conductors of both heat and electricity. The alkali metals are highly reactive metals. For this reason, they are found in nature only in compounds.

Each atom of an alkali metal has one electron in its outer energy level. This electron is given up when an alkali metal combines. The result is a positively charged ion in a compound such as sodium chloride, NaCl, or potassium bromide, KBr. As shown in Figure 12-4, you can use flame tests to identify compounds of alkali metals.

Alkali metals and their compounds have many and varied uses. You and other living things need potassium and sodium compounds—such as table salt, NaCl—to stay healthy. Doctors use lithium compounds to treat bipolar disorder. The operation of some photocells depends upon rubidium or cesium compounds.

Francium, the last element in Group 1, is extremely rare and also radioactive. The nucleus of a **radioactive element** breaks down and gives off particles and energy. You will study radioactive elements later.

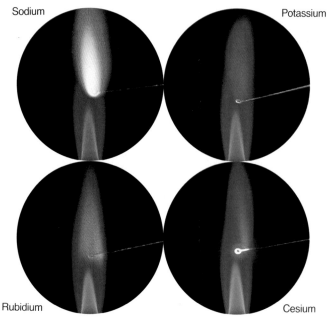

Figure 12-4. Alkali metals and their compounds give distinctive colors to flames.

OPTIONS

INQUIRY QUESTIONS

► **When doctors prescribe a low salt (sodium) diet, they often suggest KCl as a salt substitute. How can the two elements' biochemistries be similar?** *Both Na and K have one outer electron and react in a similar manner with other elements.*

► **The potassium ion helps regulate heartbeat and other nerve transmission. What are some sources of potassium in your diet?** *Bananas, peaches, and orange juice may be mentioned.*

PROGRAM RESOURCES

From the **Teacher Resource Package** use:

Transparency Masters, pages 45-46, Metallic Bonding.

Science Integration Activity 12 Use **Color Transparency** number 23, Metallic Bonding.

The Alkaline Earth Metals

The alkaline earth metals make up Group 2 of the periodic table. Like the alkali metals, these metals are shiny, malleable, ductile, and so reactive that they are not found free in nature. Each atom of an alkaline earth metal has two electrons in its outer energy level. These electrons are given up when an alkaline earth metal combines. The result is a positively charged ion in a compound such as calcium fluoride, CaF_2, or barium chloride, $BaCl_2$.

Emeralds and aquamarines are gemstone forms of beryl, a mineral that contains beryllium. Do you watch fireworks on the Fourth of July? The brilliant red in fireworks is produced by compounds of strontium.

Magnesium can be made into a fine wire that burns so brightly it is used in some photographic flashbulbs. Magnesium metal is also used in fireworks to produce brilliant white. Magnesium's lightness and strength account for its use in cars, planes, and spacecraft. Magnesium is also used to make such things as household ladders and baseball and softball bats.

Calcium is seldom used as a free metal, but its compounds are needed for life. Calcium carbonate in your bones helps make them strong. Marble and limestone

Figure 12-5. Bones contain calcium carbonate. Magnesium burns easily and is used in bats.

4
Be
Beryllium
9.01218

12
Mg
Magnesium
24.305

20
Ca
Calcium
40.078

38
Sr
Strontium
87.62

56
Ba
Barium
137.33

88
Ra
Radium
226.0254

What metal is part of the compound chlorophyll?

Figure 12-6. The colors of these gems are due to compounds of transition elements.

Which elements are able to create a magnetic field?

are calcium carbonate. Most life on Earth depends upon chlorophyll, a magnesium compound that enables plants to make food.

Some barium compounds are used to diagnose digestive disorders. The patient swallows a barium compound, which can absorb X rays. As the barium compound goes through the digestive tract, a doctor can study the X rays. Radium, the last element in Group 2, is radioactive. It was once used to treat cancers. Today, other radioactive substances are replacing radium in cancer therapy.

Transition Elements

An iron nail, a copper wire, and a silver dime are examples of objects made from transition elements. The **transition elements** are those elements in Groups 3 through 12 of the periodic table. Typical transition elements are metals and have one or two electrons in the outer energy level. These metals are less active than those in Groups 1 and 2.

Many gems contain brightly colored compounds of transition elements. Brilliant cadmium yellow and cobalt blue paint pigments are made from compounds of transition elements. But cadmium and cobalt paints are so toxic that their use is now limited.

Iron, Cobalt, and Nickel

Iron, cobalt, and nickel form a unique cluster of transition elements. The first elements in Groups 8, 9, and 10, respectively, are known as the iron triad. The elements that make up the triad are the only elements known to create a magnetic field.

25 **Mn** Manganese 54.9380	26 **Fe** Iron 55.847	27 **Co** Cobalt 58.9332	28 **Ni** Nickel 58.69	29 **Cu** Copper 63.546
43 **Tc** Technetium 97.9072*	44 **Ru** Ruthenium 101.07	45 **Rh** Rhodium 102.9055	46 **Pd** Palladium 106.42	47 **Ag** Silver 107.8682

304 ELEMENTS AND THEIR PROPERTIES

Iron is second only to aluminum among the metals in abundance in Earth's crust. As the main component of steel, iron is the most widely used of all metals. Some steels also contain cobalt. Nickel is added to other metals to give them strength. Nickel is also often used to give a shiny, protective coating to other metals, as shown in the picture above.

 T E C H N O L O G Y

Metallic Moments

A large radio antenna was folded into a compact shape and launched into space. Once in orbit it absorbed heat from the sun and unfolded as a working antenna! This antenna was made of Nitinol, a mixture of nickel and titanium.

Nitinol is one of a class of metal mixtures, or alloys, that is able to remember an earlier shape. About 20 of the transition elements can form shape memory alloys (SMAs). If you bend and then heat an object made from an SMA, it returns to its original shape. Products made from SMAs include eyeglass frames, orthodontic wires, and electrical connectors.

Because SMAs absorb heat and convert it to mechanical energy, they are used in heat engines. A device that delivers small doses of medication into veins uses SMA power.

Think Critically: Elements that can form SMAs are found in Groups 3 through 12 of the periodic table. What are some other common properties of these elements?

12-1   METALS   **305**

CONCEPT DEVELOPMENT
▶ **Demonstration:** With 4 hairpins and a burner, you can show the heat treatment of iron by the following methods.

Spring Steel: Spring steel is the way the hairpins come. Have a student bend one open and report what is observed and felt. Use tongs and heat the curved end of the other 3 pins in the flame and easily open them straight. Heating expands the metal allowing the layers of atoms to more easily slide over one another.

Annealed Steel: Use tongs to hold the 3 straightened pins vertically in the flame until all 3 are glowing red. *Very* slowly raise the pins up and out of the flame so the cooling process will be slow. This grows large body-centered cubic crystals that easily slip over each other. These 3 pins have been annealed or softened.

Case Hardened Steel: When cool, bend all 3 pins into the shape of a fish hook. One is a control. Heat the other two in the flame until red hot. Quickly quench them in a beaker of cold water. The crystals are very small, resulting in a hard, brittle metal. Attempt to unbend one hook. It breaks easily.

Tempered Steel: Tempered steel is both springy and hard. Take the remaining hardened hook, hold it with tongs and very slowly lower it into the upper part of a burner flame until the gray color changes to a gun-metal blue color (oxide). Slowly remove the hook from the flame before it glows red. After the hook has slowly cooled, attempt to unbend it. The hook has regained its springiness, and is harder than the annealed form.

 T E C H N O L O G Y

For more information on shape memory alloys, see "Memory Metals Inc.," by Daniel Wiener, *Fortune*, April 28, 1986, p. 88; and "Shape Memory Phenomena," by Ahmad Golestaneh, *Physics Today*, April 1984, pp. 62-70.

Think Critically: The transition elements are chemically less active than the metals in Groups 1 and 2. The transition elements form many colored compounds and have a variety of oxidation states.

Use the Mini Quiz to check for understanding.

MINI QUIZ

Use the Mini Quiz to check students' recall of chapter content.

6 What metal is found in chlorophyll? *magnesium*

7 Groups 3 through 12 are known as the _____ elements. *transition*

8 What unique property does the iron triad of iron, cobalt, and nickel have? *magnetism*

9 Copper, silver, and gold are known as the _____ metals. *coinage*

10 The only metal that is a silvery liquid at room temperature is _____ . *mercury*

RETEACH

Have each student make one flash card listing an element, its group (or *transition element* if it is one) and its properties. Use the cards to provide review and reinforcement of the entire section.

EXTENSION

For students who have mastered this section, use the **Reinforcement** and **Enrichment** masters or other OPTIONS provided.

PROGRAM RESOURCES

From the **Teacher Resource Package** use:

Activity Worksheets, page 5, Flex Your Brain.

Copper, Silver, and Gold

11		
29 **Cu** Copper 63.546		
47 **Ag** Silver 107.8682		
79 **Au** Gold 196.9665		

Can you name the main metals in the coins in the photograph below? They are copper, silver, and gold, the three elements in Group 11. They are so unreactive that they are found as elements in nature. For centuries, these metals have been widely used as coins. For this reason, they are known as the coinage metals. **9**

Copper is often used in electric wiring, because of its superior ability to conduct electricity and its relatively low cost. Can you imagine a world without photographs and movies? Because silver iodide and silver bromide break down when exposed to light, these compounds are used to make photographic film and paper. Much silver is also used in jewelry. The yellow color, relative softness, and rarity of gold account for its use in jewelry.

Zinc, Cadmium, and Mercury

12		
30 **Zn** Zinc 65.39		
48 **Cd** Cadmium 112.41		
80 **Hg** Mercury 200.59		

Zinc, cadmium, and mercury make up Group 12 of the periodic table. Zinc combines with oxygen in the air to form a thin protective coating of zinc oxide on the surface of the metal. Zinc is often used to coat, or plate, other metals, such as iron. Cadmium is also used in plating and in rechargeable batteries.

Mercury is a silvery, liquid metal used in thermometers, thermostats, switches, and batteries. Mercury is poisonous, **10** and mercury compounds can accumulate in the body. People have died of mercury poisoning that resulted from eating fish from mercury-contaminated water.

306 ELEMENTS AND THEIR PROPERTIES

OPTIONS

MULTICULTURAL PERSPECTIVE

That'll be two cowries and a whale's tooth...
Coinage metals got their name from their use as money, but anything that people agree to accept as a medium of exchange can and has been used as money. The wampum that native Americans used consisted of beads made from shells. Cowries shells in India, whales' teeth in Fiji, and stone disks in Yap (a Pacific Island), have all served in monetary systems. The use of metals for exchange appears around 7000 BC in the Middle East. Cast-bronze animal shapes were used first, followed by more easily cast wedges. Gold and silver began to be used as well, because they were more valuable than bronze. True coins, of standard weight and value, were probably first produced by the Lydians of Anatolia (modern-day Turkey) in 640 BC. They used a naturally occurring alloy of gold and silver called electrum. The gold content of electrum varied, however, so value wasn't truly standardized. Eventually, the purity and weight of gold and silver in coins was certified by the government.

Figure 12-7. Mercury is liquid at room temperature (left). Metallic copper is found in nature (right).

Look at the periodic table on pages 258-259. Which elements do you think of as being typical metals? Probably transition elements, because they occur in nature as elements, and thus are familiar. Group 1 and Group 2 metals are not found in nature except in compounds.

SECTION REVIEW

1. You are given a piece of the element palladium. How would you test it to see if it is a metal?
2. On the periodic table, how does the arrangement of the iron triad differ from the arrangements of the coinage metals and of the zinc group?
3. **Apply:** If X stands for a metal, how can you tell from the formulas XCl and XCl$_2$ which compound contains an alkali metal and which contains an alkaline earth metal?
4. **Connect to Physics:** Platinum spark plugs are now used in some internal combustion engines. Find out the advantages of platinum spark plugs.

Why are transition metals more familiar to us than are Group 1 and Group 2 metals?

In your Journal, write a paragraph about how a metallic element has affected your life.

☑ Interpreting Scientific Illustrations

Draw dot diagrams to show the similarity among chlorides of three alkali metals: lithium chloride, sodium chloride, and potassium chloride. If you need help, refer to Interpreting Scientific Illustrations in the **Skill Handbook** on page 689.

INQUIRY QUESTIONS

▶ Silver conducts electricity better than gold does and is less expensive. However, gold is used to plate electrical contacts in high quality switches and in computers. Why is gold preferable to silver for this use? *Silver is more reactive than gold and tarnishes by combining with pollutants in air.*

▶ Catalytic converters on cars contain platinum, palladium, and rhodium. Research the purpose of the converter and how these elements work in the converter. *The converter cleans the exhaust gases of unburned hydro-*carbons and converts CO to CO_2 and NO to N_2. *The elements are surface catalysts. The combustion products are held on the hot surface of the metal and further reacted with oxygen.*

▶ One gram of some metals can be drawn into a thin wire that is over 100 meters in length. Explain how the bonding in metals makes this possible. *The electrons in metals are not attracted to a particular positive ion. When the metal is stretched, the positive ions can move past each other and still be bonded.*

---

3 CLOSE

❓ FLEX Your Brain

Use the Flex Your Brain activity to have students explore PROPERTIES OF ELEMENTS.

ASSESSMENT
Portfolio: Use the Flex Your Brain activity to reinforce critical-thinking and problem-solving skills. In Step 2, students might list properties of metals.

▶ Ask questions 1-2 and the **Apply** and **Connect to Physics** questions in the Section Review.

SECTION REVIEW ANSWERS
1. Find out if it is hard and shiny, is a good conductor of heat and electricity, and is malleable and ductile.
2. Iron, cobalt, and nickel are successive metals in the same period. Copper, silver, and gold are all in Group 11. Zinc, cadmium, and mercury are all in Group 12.
3. Apply: Chlorine bonds by gaining or sharing one electron. Alkali metals can lose one electron, so they would form the compound XCl. Alkaline earth metals have two outer electrons, so they would form compounds XCl$_2$.
4. Connect to Physics: Platinum spark plugs last about six times as long, burn more cleanly, give better fuel economy, and are more reliable.

Skill Builder

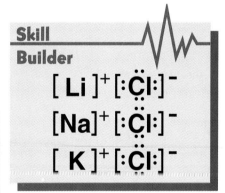

Skill Builder
ASSESSMENT
Oral: Ask students to list at least two ways that the three drawn structures are alike. All the Group 1 ions are 1+; all formulas show a 1:1 ratio between ions.

PREPARATION

SECTION BACKGROUND
▶ Elements with atomic numbers greater than 92 have been produced using other elements to bombard target elements.

1 MOTIVATE

▶ Ask the class if they have ever heard of Merlin in King Arthur's court. He was an alchemist. He tried to change common metals into gold. Today this can be accomplished in a nuclear reactor. Ask your class why they think today's scientists do not convert iron into gold. Mined gold is cheaper.

2 TEACH

Key Concepts are highlighted.

CONCEPT DEVELOPMENT
▶ Bring a portable smoke detector to class, open it and show the class the case where the americium is.

Connect to...
Physics

Answer: Typically, the production of these elements is difficult to confirm. There has been some controversy as to who discovered them first. Therefore, IUPAC now uses more generic names.

New Science Words

transuranium elements

Objectives

▶ Distinguish among elements classified as lanthanoids, actinoids, and transuranium elements.
▶ Compare the pros and cons of synthesizing elements.

Why Make Elements?

Did you know that the smoke alarm in your home may contain americium? This element does not form naturally. Because it can be made only in a laboratory, americium is called a synthetic element. Currently, there ❶ are 19 synthetic elements. One of these, technetium, is a period-5 transition metal. The other synthetic elements are found in periods 6 and 7.

What synthetic element is used in smoke alarms?

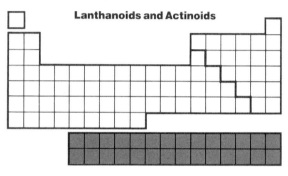
Lanthanoids and Actinoids

If you look at the periodic table on pages 258-259, you will see breaks in periods 6 and 7. The first break includes a series of 14 elements with atomic numbers of 57 through ❷ 70. The second break includes those elements with atomic numbers ranging from 89 to 102. The two series include elements that have similar electron structures and similar properties. They also include 11 of the 19 synthetic elements.

The picture tube in your color TV contains pigments that glow bright red when struck by electrons. These pigments are oxides of europium and ytterbium, two lanthanoids. A lanthanoid is an element with an atomic

308 ELEMENTS AND THEIR PROPERTIES

OPTIONS

Meeting Different Ability Levels
For Section 12-2, use the following **Teacher Resource Masters** depending upon individual students' needs.
◆ **Study Guide Master** for all students.
● **Reinforcement Master** for students of average and above average ability levels.
▲ **Enrichment Master** for above average students.

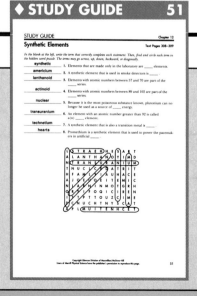
◆ **STUDY GUIDE** 51

number of 57-70. The lanthanoid series contains one synthetic element, promethium, used to power pacemakers and artificial hearts.

③ Americium is one of the ten synthetic elements in the actinoid series. An actinoid is an element with an atomic number of 89-102. One important actinoid you may have heard of is uranium.

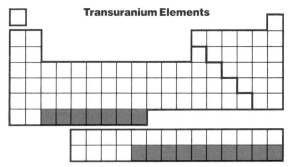

Transuranium Elements

④ All elements with atomic numbers higher than that of uranium are synthetic elements called **transuranium elements**. One of these is plutonium.

Plutonium has been used in nuclear reactors, such as the reactor shown in the photo, and in nuclear warheads. Because it is the most poisonous substance known, its production has been banned in the United States. Other transuranium elements in the actinoid series are used as nuclear energy sources for generating electric power and in nuclear weapons. All synthetic elements are radioactive and some can be very harmful.

SECTION REVIEW

1. Compare the lanthanoid and actinoid series.
2. What are the transuranium elements?
3. **Connect to Earth Science:** One use of technetium is to prevent corrosion of iron. Why do you think technetium is not found in nature?

You Decide!

Plutonium was banned in the United States after much debate. Suppose you had to vote on a petition to ban the production of another synthetic element. What information would you want to help you decide how to vote?

Connect to...
Physics

The elements with atomic numbers greater than 103 have been given names that reflect their atomic numbers. Find out why these elements are not named after people or places.

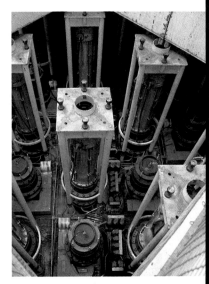

SCIENCE & SOCIETY

CHECK FOR UNDERSTANDING

Use the Mini Quiz to check for understanding.

MINI QUIZ

Use the Mini Quiz to check students' recall of chapter content.

① **Of the 109 known elements, how many are synthetic?** *19*
② **Elements having atomic numbers between 57 and 70 are classified as ____ .** *lanthanoids*
③ **Elements having atomic numbers between 89 and 102 are classified as ____ .** *actinoids*
④ **A transuranium element has an atomic number greater than that of ____ .** *uranium*

RETEACH

Have your students use a blank copy of the periodic table to record the symbol, name, and atomic number of the 19 synthetic elements.

EXTENSION

For students who have mastered this section, use the **Reinforcement** and **Enrichment** masters or other OPTIONS provided.

3 CLOSE

SECTION REVIEW ANSWERS

1. Both series contain 14 elements. The lanthanoids are in Period 6 and one is a synthetic element. Actinoids are in Period 7; 10 are synthetic elements.

2. Period 7 elements with atomic numbers greater than 92

3. Connect to Earth Science: Technetium is radioactive and unstable. Any that might have been formed in nature has decayed.

YOU DECIDE!
SCIENCE & SOCIETY

Answers will vary. Students should discuss its technological and economic benefits (medicine, national security) and its liabilities (toxicity, disposal problems).

● REINFORCEMENT 51

REINFORCEMENT   Chapter 12
Synthetic Elements   Text Pages 308-309

Use the periodic table on pages 258-259 of your textbook to answer questions 1-8.

1. What is the name of the group of elements with atomic numbers of 57-70? __lanthanoid series__

2. What is the name of the group of elements with atomic numbers 89-102? __actinoid series__

3. In what period do the elements in the actinoid series belong? __period 7__

4. In what period do the elements in the lanthanoid series belong? __period 6__

5. How many elements make up the lanthanoid series __14__

6. a. Which element in the lanthanoid series has the highest atomic number? __ytterbium__
   b. What is the atomic mass of this element? __173.04__

7. a. Which element in the actinoid series has the greatest atomic number? __nobelium__
   b. How many protons are in the nucleus of one atom of this element? __102__

8. List the names of the elements that make up the lanthanoid series in order from greatest atomic mass to least atomic mass. __ytterbium, thulium, erbium, holmium, dysprosium, terbium, gadolinium, europium, samarium, promethium, neodymium, praseodymium, cerium, lanthanum__

9. How does the lanthanoid series compare to the actinoid series? __They both include elements that have similar electron structures and similar properties.__

10. What is one practical use of the elements europium and ytterbium? __Oxides of these elements are used in the picture tubes of television sets.__

11. Which elements in the actinoid series are transuranium elements? __neptunium, plutonium, americium, curium, berkelium, californium, einsteinium, fermium, mendelevium, and nobelium__

Copyright Glencoe Division of Macmillan/McGraw-Hill
Users of Merrill Physical Science have the publisher's permission to reproduce this page.   51

▲ ENRICHMENT 51

ENRICHMENT   Chapter 12
Synthetic Elements   Text Pages 308-309

NAMING OF NEW ELEMENTS

You have just discovered a new element that has an atomic number of 110. In the past, you could have named the element as you wished. But what happens if another person discovered and named the element about the same time? What would be the official name of the element?

Scientists in both the United States and the Soviet Union claim discovery of elements 104 and 105. Because of the confusion about what to name these new elements, the International Union for Pure and Applied Chemistry (IUPAC) decided that a system was needed to officially name new elements. The systematic names are alternatives to the already trivial names approved by the IUPAC for elements 101, 102, and 105 (mendelevium, nobelium, and hahnium). Each element must be named using the approved names.

The IUPAC guidelines for new chemical names are as follows.
1. The name is derived directly from the atomic number of the element using the

following numerical roots:
0 = nil
1 = un
2 = bi
3 = tri
4 = quad
5 = pent
6 = hex
7 = sept
8 = oct
9 = enn

2. The roots are put together in order of the digits which make up the atomic number. The name is ended by ium to spell out the name. The final n of enn is removed when it occurs before nil. The final i of bi and oct is removed when it occurs before ium.
3. The symbol of the element is composed of the initial letters of the numerical roots which make up the name.
4. The numerical root is pronounced with a long o, to rhyme with moon.

Conclude and Apply

1. Write the IUPAC approved names and the symbols for the elements that would have the following atomic numbers. The first one is given as an example.

104	Unnilquadium Unq		108	Unniloctium Uno
105	Unnilpentium Unp		109	Unnilennium Une
106	Unnilhexium Unh		110	Unununnilium Uun
107	Unnilseptium Uns		120	Unbinilium Ubn

2. What are the advantages and disadvantages of using the IUPAC system to name new compounds? __advantage, no confusion over naming elements; disadvantage, takes some of the uniqueness out of finding and naming elements__

Copyright Glencoe Division of Macmillan/McGraw-Hill
Users of Merrill Physical Science have the publisher's permission to reproduce this page.   51

PREPARATION

SECTION BACKGROUND

▶ Atoms of most nonmetals have five or more outer electrons, and tend to gain electrons to complete their outer energy levels.

▶ Hydrogen has unique properties and is usually considered as a group by itself. Hydrogen can react by gaining, losing, or sharing its electron.

▶ As the atomic numbers of the halogens increase, the atoms become larger, the outer electrons are farther from the nucleus, the nucleus has less attraction for electrons of other atoms, and the atoms become less active.

▶ The noble gases were considered to be inert until 1962 when xenon and oxygen difluoride were combined in a nickel tube at 300°C under pressure to produce xenon difluoride.

PREPLANNING

▶ To prepare for Activity 12-1 you will need laundry bleach and wooden matches.

▶ You may want to prepare a collection of nonmetals to have on display for the class to see. A piece of roll sulfur, some coal, and a few crystals of iodine in a sealed bottle can be used.

1 MOTIVATE

▶ **Demonstration:** Use a piece of roll sulfur to visually reinforce the properties of nonmetals. Show the class the dull surface before you cover it with a cloth and using a hammer, break off a piece. Students will see that it is brittle and powdery, not malleable. Use an electrical conductivity checker to demonstrate that sulfur is a nonconductor.

▶ Remind students that, in general, the properties of metals are the opposite of those of nonmetals.

VideoDisc
STVS: Radon Danger, Disc 2, Side 2

12-3 Nonmetals

New Science Words

diatomic molecule
sublimation

Objectives

▶ Recognize hydrogen as a nonmetal.
▶ Compare and contrast properties of the halogens.
▶ Describe properties and uses of the noble gases.

Properties of Nonmetals

Figure 12-8 shows that you're mostly made of oxygen, carbon, hydrogen, and nitrogen. Calcium, a metal, and other elements make up the remaining four percent of your body's weight. Phosphorus, sulfur, and chlorine are among other elements found in your body. These elements are among those classified as nonmetals.

Look at the periodic table on pages 258 and 259. How many elements are nonmetals? Notice that most nonmetals are gases at room temperature. Several nonmetals are solids, and one nonmetal is a liquid.

In contrast to metals, solid nonmetals are dull. Because they are brittle and powdery, they are neither malleable nor ductile. The electrons in most nonmetals are tightly attracted and are more restricted to one atom. So, as a group, nonmetals are poor conductors of heat and electricity.

Most nonmetals form both ionic and covalent compounds. When nonmetals gain electrons from metals, the nonmetals become negative ions in ionic compounds. An example of such an

carbon 18%

calcium 2.0%

nitrogen 3.0%

hydrogen 10%

other elements 2.0%

oxygen 65%

TOTAL: 100%

Figure 12-8. Most of your body weight consists of compounds of nonmetals.

310   ELEMENTS AND THEIR PROPERTIES

OPTIONS

Meeting Different Ability Levels

For Section 12-3, use the following **Teacher Resource Masters** depending upon individual students' needs.

◆ **Study Guide Master** for all students.
● **Reinforcement Master** for students of average and above average ability levels.
▲ **Enrichment Master** for above average students.

Additional Teacher Resource Package masters are listed in any PROGRAM RESOURCES boxes that are in the section. The additional masters are appropriate for all students.

◆ **STUDY GUIDE** 52

STUDY GUIDE   Chapter 12
Nonmetals   Text Pages 310–315

Use the clues given below and the letters you have been given to identify each of the missing terms in the puzzle. Write one letter in each space.

Clues
1. only nonmetal on left side of the periodic table
2. only liquid nonmetal
3. kind of bond that forms a salt
4. Two atoms of the same element, when bonded, form a(n) _____ molecule.
5. most chemically active element
6. type of bond formed when nonmetals combine with other nonmetals
7. process by which a solid, such as iodine, changes directly to a gas
8. Its name means "salt-former."
9. common name for the elements that make up group 18 of the periodic table

1. H Y D R O G E N
2. B R O M I N E
3. I O N I C
4. D I A T O M I C
5. F L U O R I N E
6. C O V A L E N T
7. S U B L I M A T I O N
8. H A L O G E N
9. N O B L E G A S E S

52   Copyright Glencoe Division of Macmillan/McGraw-Hill
Users of Merrill Physical Science have the publisher's permission to reproduce this page.

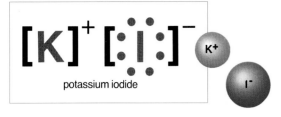

potassium iodide

Figure 12-9. Nonmetals form both ionic and covalent compounds.

ammonia

ionic compound is potassium iodide, KI, which is found in iodized table salt. KI is formed from the nonmetal iodine and the metal potassium. On the other hand, when bonded with other nonmetals, atoms of nonmetals usually share electrons and form covalent compounds. An example is ammonia, NH_3, the gas you can smell when you open a bottle of household ammonia.

The noble gases, Group 18, make up the only group of elements that are all nonmetals. Group 17 elements, except for astatine, are also nonmetals. Several other nonmetals, found in Groups 13 through 16, will be discussed later. Except for hydrogen, all of the nonmetals are located on the right side of the periodic table.

Hydrogen

Do you know that 90 percent of all the atoms in the universe are hydrogen? Most hydrogen on Earth is found in the compound water. When water is broken down into its elements, hydrogen forms as a gas made up of diatomic molecules. A **diatomic molecule** consists of two atoms of the same element. Thus, the formula for hydrogen gas is H_2.

Hydrogen is highly reactive. A hydrogen atom has a single electron, which the atom shares when it combines with other nonmetals. Hydrogen burns in oxygen to form water, H_2O. In forming water, hydrogen shares electrons with oxygen. Hydrogen also shares electrons with chlorine to produce hydrogen chloride, HCl.

Hydrogen may gain an electron when it combines with alkali and alkaline earth metals. The compounds formed are hydrides, such as sodium hydride, NaH.

Figure 12-10. Hydrogen gas, which consists of diatomic molecules, combines with oxygen in an oxyhydrogen torch.

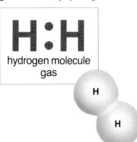

hydrogen molecule gas

● **REINFORCEMENT** 52

REINFORCEMENT   Chapter 12
Nonmetals   Text Pages 310–315

Complete the following table that compares the properties of metals and nonmetals by supplying the information required.

Characteristic	Metal	Nonmetal
Appearance of solid	shiny	dull
Is it malleable?	yes	no
Is it ductile?	yes	no
Does it conduct heat?	yes	no
Does it conduct electricity?	yes	no
Most common state at room temperature	solid	gas
Type(s) of bonding	metallic and ionic	ionic and covalent

In the spaces provided, list two properties for each nonmetal listed. Answers may vary. Accept all correct responses.

1. Hydrogen _gas, forms diatomic molecules, highly reactive_
2. Fluorine _active gas, forms diatomic molecules, 7 electrons in outer energy level_
3. Chlorine _gas, forms diatomic molecules, 7 electrons in outer energy level_
4. Bromine _liquid at room temperature, 7 electrons in outer energy level_
5. Iodine _shiny, gray solid, sublimates, 7 electrons in outer energy level_
6. Helium _2 electrons in outer energy level, not reactive, gas_
7. Neon _8 electrons in outer energy level, not reactive, gas_

Answer the following questions on the lines provided.

8. How does helium differ from the other noble gases? _Helium has two electrons in its outer energy level. The remaining noble gases each have eight electrons in their outer energy._

9. How does bromine differ from the other nonmetals? _Bromine is the only nonmetal that is a liquid at room temperature._

10. How does the location of hydrogen on the periodic table differ from the locations of the other nonmetals? _Hydrogen is the only nonmetal on the left side of the periodic table._

52

▲ **ENRICHMENT** 52

ENRICHMENT   Chapter 12
Nonmetals   Text Pages 310–315

THE HALOGENS

The halogens are the most reactive metallic family. Fluorine is the most reactive nonmetal. All the halogens are in the gas state are highly toxic and thus are very hazardous to handle.

Halogen atoms form stable diatomic molecules. High temperatures are required to disrupt these molecules and form single atoms. Chlorine atoms have been detected near the sun's surface, where the temperature is about 6000°C. At more moderate temperatures, chlorine atoms react with each other to form chlorine molecules:

$2Cl(g) \rightarrow Cl_2(g)$

Each halogen has seven electrons in its outer energy level. Each chlorine atom achieves a stable electron arrangement by sharing its one

unshared electron. The result is the diatomic chlorine molecule.

It is possible to relate the melting and boiling points of the halogens to the forces acting between molecules. On the graph below, plot the melting point versus atomic number and boiling point versus atomic number from the information in the table. Use your graph to answer the questions that follow.

Element	Atomic number	MP (K)	BP (K)
Fluorine	9	55	85
Chlorine	17	172	239
Bromine	35	266	332
Iodine	53	387	457

Room temperature = 22°C = 295 K

Questions

1. The temperatures given above are in kelvin (K) units. Why is that easier to graph than using the Celsius temperature scale? _The kelvin scale doesn't have any temperatures with negative values, 0 K = −273°C._

2. Which of the halogens are gases at room temperature (295 K)? _fluorine, chlorine_ Which is a liquid? _bromine_ Which is a solid? _iodine_

3. What does the graph tell you about the atomic number of a halogen and the forces between molecules? _As the atomic number of the halogen increases, the forces holding the halogen molecules together get stronger._

52

311

TYING TO PREVIOUS
KNOWLEDGE: Many students have seen a picture of the airship *Hindenburg* when it crashed in New Jersey in 1937. The hydrogen gas explosion and fire brought an end to commercial lighter-than-air craft service. Ask students what they can infer about the properties of hydrogen.

2 TEACH

Key Concepts are highlighted.

CONCEPT DEVELOPMENT

▶ **Demonstration:** A small amount of hydrogen gas can be generated by placing a piece of mossy zinc in a large test tube. Add 4 mL of 6M sulfuric acid and stopper the test tube with a 1-hole stopper fitted with a 90° glass bend. **CAUTION:** *The acid is corrosive.* Use an empty, inverted test tube to collect the hydrogen gas by the downward displacement of air. A burning wood splint can be used to show that the gas is flammable. **CAUTION:** *Use an explosion shield. Never produce more than a small test tube of explosive hydrogen gas.*

▶ Tell students that hydrogen gas is being investigated as a nonpolluting fuel for autos, buses, and planes. The flammable gas can be used to heat homes in winter with no danger of carbon monoxide poisoning.

REVEALING MISCONCEPTIONS

▶ Ask students what gas is used to fill balloons that are lighter than air. Some think that hydrogen rather than helium is used. Help students eliminate this confusion between the two gases by asking why helium is used instead of hydrogen gas. Show a picture of the burning *Hindenburg* to help students remember the flammability of hydrogen.

17
9 **F** Fluorine 18.998403
17 **Cl** Chlorine 35.453
35 **Br** Bromine 79.904
53 **I** Iodine 126.9045
85 **At** Astatine 209.98712*

The Halogens

Look how bright these high-tech lamps are in Figure 12-11. Their light and that of the headlights of some cars is supplied by halogen light bulbs. These bulbs contain small amounts of bromine or iodine. These elements, as well as fluorine, chlorine, and astatine, are called halogens and are found in Group 17.

Figure 12-11. The halogens bromine and iodine are used in the bulbs of halogen lamps such as these.

Because an atom of a halogen has seven electrons in its outer energy level, only one electron is needed to complete this energy level. If a halogen gains an electron from a metal, an ionic compound, called a salt, is formed. The word *halogen* means "salt former." In the gaseous state, the halogens form diatomic covalent molecules and can be identified by their distinctive colors.

Fluorine is the most chemically active of all the elements. Hydrofluoric acid, a mixture of hydrogen fluoride and water, is used to etch glass and to "frost" the inner surfaces of light bulbs. Other fluorides are added to toothpastes and to city water systems to prevent tooth decay. Does your community add fluorides to its water?

Connect to...
Earth Science

Compounds called chlorofluorocarbons have been used in refrigeration systems. If released, these compounds destroy ozone in the atmosphere. Draw the electron dot diagram for CF_2Cl_2.

Figure 12-12. In the gaseous state, the halogens chlorine, bromine, and iodine have distinctive colors.

312 ELEMENTS AND THEIR PROPERTIES

The odor near swimming pools is the odor of chlorine. Chlorine compounds are used to disinfect water. Chlorine, the most abundant halogen, is obtained from seawater. Household and industrial bleaches used to whiten flour and paper contain chlorine compounds.

⑤ Bromine, the only nonmetal that is liquid at room temperature, is extracted from compounds in seawater. Other bromine compounds are used as dyes in cosmetics.

Iodine, a shiny gray solid at room temperature, is obtained from brine. When heated, iodine changes directly to a purple vapor. The process of a solid changing directly to a vapor without forming a liquid is called **sublimation.** Recall that sublimation accounts for ice cubes shrinking in freezers. Iodine is essential in your diet for the production of the hormone thyroxin and to prevent goiter, an enlarging of the thyroid gland in the neck.

As you have read, both silver iodide and silver bromide are also used to produce photographic paper and film.

Astatine, the last member of Group 17, is radioactive and very rare. But it has many properties similar to those of the other halogens.

The Noble Gases

Why are the noble gases called "noble"? It was known that these gases did not naturally form compounds. Thus, they were thought of as the nobility of elements, because nobles did not mix with common folk. In the early 1960s scientists were able to prepare some compounds of noble gases.

Figure 12-14. "Neon" signs contain several noble gases.

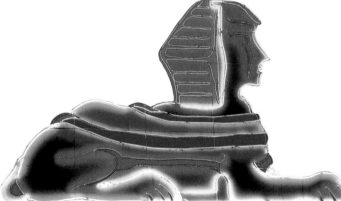

Figure 12-13. Dyes in some cosmetics contain bromine compounds.

18
2 **He** Helium 4.002602
10 **Ne** Neon 20.179
18 **Ar** Argon 39.948
36 **Kr** Krypton 83.80
54 **Xe** Xenon 131.29
86 **Rn** Radon 222.017*

TEACHER F.Y.I.

▶ In 1962, xenon gas reacted with other elements for the first time. Neils Bartless conducted the experiment. See *Science,* Vol. 138, October 12, 1962, for an example of the initial reports.

CONCEPT DEVELOPMENT

▶ Ask students to bring in pictures of "neon" signs. Red-orange lights are from neon, yellow from helium, blue from xenon, purple from argon, and white from krypton.

▶ **Demonstration:** A safe way to show that hydrofluoric acid will etch glass is to dip a glass plate into hot paraffin, thoroughly coating both sides. Use a piece of metal wire to scratch through the cooled wax, making an exposed design. Wearing rubber gloves and goggles, in a fume hood, place 12 g of calcium fluoride in a plastic dish. Add enough concentrated sulfuric acid to the dish to cover the glass plate. **CAUTION:** *Acid is corrosive.* Place the glass plate in the dish and cover it with a plastic lid for 20 minutes. Use tongs to remove the glass plate and rinse the acid off in water. Use a large beaker of boiling water to remove the wax from the glass plate. The HF fumes will have etched the design onto the glass plate.

CHECK FOR UNDERSTANDING

Use the Mini Quiz to check for understanding.

MINI QUIZ

Use the Mini Quiz to check students' recall of chapter content.

1 In what state are most nonmetals at room temperature? *gases*

2 When hydrogen burns in air, what product forms? *water*

3 Group 17 elements are also called _____ . *halogens*

4 Which element is the most chemically active nonmetal? *fluorine*

5 Which nonmetal is a liquid at room temperature? *bromine*

ENRICHMENT

▶ Polychlorinated biphenyls, PCBs, have had effects on human health. Have a student research PCBs. Why they were invented; what their use was; and how scientists are removing them from the environment are some of the questions the student's research should answer. PCBs are a group of chlorinated hydrocarbons that are nonflammable, inexpensive, and stable, but carcinogenic. They were used to cool transformers on power lines. They are difficult to remove from the environment.

PROGRAM RESOURCES

From the **Teacher Resource Package** use:
Science and Society, page 16, Americium and Smoke Detectors.
Use **Laboratory Manual 26,** Preparation of Hydrogen; **27,** Preparation of Oxygen; **25,** Preparation of Carbon Dioxide.

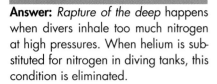
In Your JOURNAL

Answer: *Rapture of the deep* happens when divers inhale too much nitrogen at high pressures. When helium is substituted for nitrogen in diving tanks, this condition is eliminated.

3 CLOSE

▶ Ask questions 1-3 and the **Apply** and **Connect to Life Science** questions in the Section Review.

SECTION REVIEW ANSWERS
1. by sharing its electron or by gaining an electron to form a hydride
2. Like other halogens, bromine has 7 outer-level electrons and gains one electron to form a negative ion. It also bonds covalently with other atoms and exists as diatomic molecules. Bromine is the only halogen in the liquid state at room temperature.
3. They are chemically stable. Therefore they can be used to maintain a chemically inert environment around reactive materials.
4. Apply: Hydrofluoric acid is very reactive and will react with glass. It must be stored in bottles made of more inert material.
5. Connect to Life Science: covalent

Skill Builder
ASSESSMENT
Performance: Using their graph, have students predict the ratio of solid elements to the total of gas and liquid elements. Have them check this ratio by using the periodic table on pages 258-259.

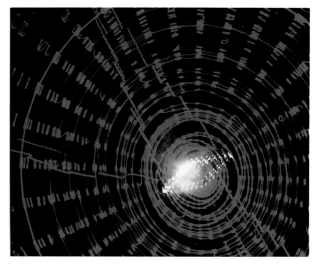

Figure 12-15. Noble gases are used to produce laser light shows.

What are some uses of the noble gases?

As you recall, each element in Group 18 is stable because its outer energy level is full. The stability of the noble gases plays an important role in their uses, such as those shown in Figures 12-14 and 12-15.

Both the halogens and the noble gases illustrate that each element in a group has some similar properties but also has unique properties and uses.

SECTION REVIEW

1. What are two ways in which hydrogen combines with other elements?
2. Compare bromine to the other halogens.
3. What property of noble gases makes them useful?
4. **Apply:** Why must hydrofluoric acid always be stored in plastic bottles?
5. **Connect to Life Science:** Chlorine and oxygen can combine to form a compound that can kill harmful microscopic organisms in water. What type of bond would you predict for this compound?

Skill Builder ☑ Making and Using Graphs

Prepare a bar graph comparing nonmetals and metals as solids, liquids, and gases at room temperature. If you need help, refer to Making and Using Graphs in the **Skill Handbook** on page 687.

314 ELEMENTS AND THEIR PROPERTIES

Skill Builder

Note: No metalloids (B-At) are included in the count. All synthetic elements are counted as solid metals

Bar graph: Number of Elements (y-axis, 0-100) vs State at Room Temperature (x-axis: Solid, Liquid, Gas)

■ Metals □ Nonmetals

Nonmetal Reaction

If you examine the label on some common household bleach you will likely find that the active ingredient is NaClO, sodium hypochlorite. In this activity, you will remove the oxygen from this compound. What common chemical property does oxygen have that will help you identify it?

Materials

- large test tube
- large wooden match
- 20 mL liquid laundry bleach (5% sodium hypochlorite)
- 0.5 g cobalt chloride
- goggles

Procedure

1. Put on safety goggles.
2. Carefully pour about 20 mL of liquid laundry bleach into a large test tube.
3. Add about 0.5 g of cobalt chloride to the bleach.
4. A gas will start to form in the liquid. Place your thumb loosely over the opening of the tube until you feel some slight pressure, but do not attempt to prevent the escape of the gas from the tube.
5. Have a classmate carefully bring a lighted match near the opening of the tube.
6. Blow out the flame of the match and insert the glowing end of the match into the upper half of the tube.

Analyze

1. An increase in the amount of oxygen in a container can cause a glowing match to burst into flame. Were the bubbles given off in your tube oxygen? Explain your answer.
2. Look at the formula for sodium hypochlorite present in bleach, NaClO. What two nonmetals does this compound contain?

Conclude and Apply

3. Liquid bleach is sometimes used as a disinfectant in kitchens. As the sodium hypochlorite in bleach decomposes, or breaks down, what product do you *predict* might appear?
4. Sunlight can also decompose hypochlorite. *Examine* the materials used to make containers of different sizes and brands of bleach. In what way are the containers all alike? Suggest a reason for this similarity.

PROCESS SKILLS applied in this activity:
▶ **Observing** in Procedure Step 6.
▶ **Predicting** in Conclude and Apply Question 3.
▶ **Comparing** in Conclude and Apply Question 4.

COOPERATIVE LEARNING
Use the Paired Partners strategy, dividing the tasks of the activity and having students work together to answer questions.

TEACHING THE ACTIVITY
Alternate Materials: Crystals of $CuSO_4$ or $FeSO_4$ should also work well with chlorine bleach. Try before using.
Troubleshooting: Try out the reaction using materials students will use. The reaction mixture may foam upward. Make sure the tubes are large enough to contain the reaction. Adjust quantities if needed.
▶ The 0.5 g of $CoCl_2$ does not need to be exact. You could measure out the quantity and exhibit to students so they can approximate the amount. This will save time in measuring.
▶ The reaction mixture will turn black when the $CoCl_2$ is added.
▶ Demonstrate the proper technique for gently placing the thumb over the tube.

Activity
ASSESSMENT
Performance: To further assess students' understanding of measurement systems, see USING LAB SKILLS, Question 11, on page 324.

ANSWERS TO QUESTIONS
1. Yes. The glowing match burst into flame.
2. chlorine and oxygen
3. Oxygen could be a product of bleach decomposition. So might chlorine.
4. Containers are made of opaque materials. This keeps out light that could decompose the bleach.

PROGRAM RESOURCES
From the **Teacher Resource Package** use: **Activity Worksheets,** pages 94-95, Activity 12-1: Nonmetal Reaction.

PREPARATION

SECTION BACKGROUND

▶ Of the elements in Group 13, aluminum has the greatest number of practical uses. With three outer electrons, it is less metallic than the Group 1 and 2 metals.

▶ The elements of Group 14 generally react by sharing electrons. However, the tendency of these elements to lose electrons—their metallic nature—increases as the atomic number increases.

▶ Pure oxygen is extracted from liquefied air, compressed, and sold in cylinders. It is most often used in the production of steel and in medicine, rocket fuel, and welding torches.

PREPLANNING

▶ Assemble the materials needed for Activity 12-2. The polystyrene foam sheets can be obtained from a hardware store or a vinyl siding company. Students can bring spaghetti and gum drops from home.

1 MOTIVATE

▶ Have the class recall that life on this planet is based primarily on the chemistry of carbon, oxygen, and nitrogen. Ask them if they think it is possible for other life-forms to exist in the universe. Ask students which elements could be a basis of those life-forms. Very different life-forms have been found deep in oceans near volcanic vents. They thrive on normally poisonous gases such as hydrogen sulfide.

12-4 Mixed Groups

New Science Words

semiconductors
allotropes

Objectives

▶ Distinguish among metals, nonmetals, and metalloids in Groups 13 through 16 of the periodic table.
▶ Describe the nature of allotropes.
▶ Recognize the significance of differences in crystal structure in carbon.

Locating the Mixed Groups

Can an element be both a metal and a nonmetal? In a sense, some elements are. They are the metalloids, which have both metallic and nonmetallic properties. A metalloid may conduct electricity better than many nonmetals but not as well as some metals. In the periodic table, the metalloids are the elements located along the stair-step line. The mixed groups—13, 14, 15, and 16—contain metals, nonmetals, and metalloids.

What kinds of properties do metalloids have?

The Boron Group

Boron, a metalloid, is the first element in Group 13. If you look around your home, you may find two compounds of boron. One of these is boric acid, a mild antiseptic. The other is borax, used in laundry products to soften water. Less familiar are the boranes, compounds of boron used in fuels for rockets and jet planes.

Aluminum, a metal, is also in Group 13. Aluminum is the most abundant metal in Earth's crust. You use aluminum in soft drink cans, foil wrap, and cooking pans. You may also see aluminum on the sides of buildings. And because aluminum is both strong and light, it is used to build airplanes.

When you operate electronic equipment, such as calculators, you may be using another metal in Group 13. These metals are gallium, indium, and thallium, used to produce semiconductors. **Semiconductors** conduct an electric current under certain conditions. You will learn more about semiconductors in Chapter 23.

13

5
B
Boron
10.811

13
Al
Aluminum
26.98154

31
Ga
Gallium
69.723

49
In
Indium
114.82

81
Tl
Thallium
204.383

316 ELEMENTS AND THEIR PROPERTIES

OPTIONS

Meeting Different Ability Levels

For Section 12-4, use the following **Teacher Resource Masters** depending upon individual students' needs.

◆ **Study Guide Master** for all students.

● **Reinforcement Master** for students of average and above average ability levels.

▲ **Enrichment Master** for above average students.

Additional Teacher Resource Package masters are listed in any PROGRAM RESOURCES boxes that are in the section. The additional masters are appropriate for all students.

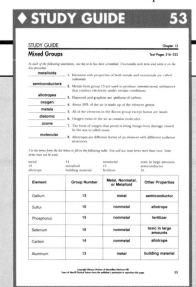

◆ **STUDY GUIDE** **53**

STUDY GUIDE Chapter 12

Mixed Groups
Text Pages 316–322

In each of the following statements, one key term has been scrambled. Unscramble each term and write it on the line provided.

metalloids 1. Elements with properties of both metals and nonmetals are called *tallemoids*.

semiconductors 2. Metals from group 13 are used to produce *smonitdcuers*, substances that conduct electricity under certain conditions.

allotropes 3. Diamond and graphite are *sllotrape* of carbon.

oxygen 4. About 20% of the air is made up of the element *genyox*.

metals 5. All of the elements in the Boron group except boron are *mstea*.

diatomic 6. Oxygen exists in the air as *comdiait* molecules.

ozone 7. The form of oxygen that protects living things from damage caused by the sun is called *ozeon*.

molecular 8. Allotropes are different forms of an element with different *mlaecuolr* structures.

Use the terms from the list below to fill in the following table. You will use some terms more than once. Some terms may not be used.

metal	14	nonmetal	toxic in large amounts
13	metalloid	15	semiconductor
allotrope	building material	fertilizer	16

Element	Group Number	Metal, Nonmetal, or Metalloid	Other Properties
Gallium	13	metal	semiconductor
Sulfur	16	nonmetal	allotrope
Phosphorus	15	nonmetal	fertilizer
Selenium	16	nonmetal	toxic in large amounts
Carbon	14	nonmetal	allotrope
Aluminum	13	metal	building material

Copyright Glencoe Division of Macmillan/McGraw-Hill

Users of Merrill Physical Science have the publisher's permission to reproduce this page. 53

The Carbon Group

Each element in Group 14, the carbon family, has four electrons in its outer energy level. But here much of the similarity ends. Carbon is a nonmetal; silicon and germanium are metalloids; tin and lead are metals.

What do the diamond in a diamond ring and the graphite in your pencil have in common? It may surprise you to learn that they are both carbon. How can this be? Diamond and graphite are examples of allotropes. **Allotropes** are different forms of the same element having different molecular structures. Look at the diagrams. Graphite is a black powder that consists of hexagonal layers of carbon atoms. In the hexagons, each carbon atom is bonded to three other carbon atoms. The fourth electron of each atom is bonded weakly to the layer next to it. This structure allows the layers to slide easily past one another, making graphite an excellent lubricant.

14

6
C
Carbon
12.011

14
Si
Silicon
28.0855

32
Ge
Germanium
72.59

50
Sn
Tin
118.710

82
Pb
Lead
207.2

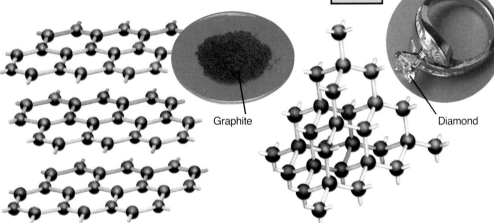

Graphite

Diamond

● **REINFORCEMENT 53**

▲ **ENRICHMENT 53**

TYING TO PREVIOUS KNOWLEDGE:
Help students to recall information about Groups 13-16 presented in Chapter 10 when they learned about the periodic table. Remind students about the number of outer electrons in each group and how these electrons relate to the element's chemical behavior.

OBJECTIVES AND SCIENCE WORDS:
Have students review the objectives and science words to become familiar with this section.

2 TEACH

Key Concepts are highlighted.

CONCEPT DEVELOPMENT

▶ Build a model of a boron or aluminum compound to show students. There are three bonds directed at a 120° bond angle. The structure is trigonal planar.

▶ **Demonstration:** Have a student remove the label from an empty tin (actually iron) can and leave the can outside for two days and nights. Beside it, place a similar aluminum can. Bring both cans to class on the third day. The oxidation resistance of aluminum will be obvious. Ask students why they think the iron reacted while the aluminum did not. Iron atoms are larger and electrons are farther away from the nucleus and less tightly held.

▶ If you have an old calculator that doesn't work, remove the circuit board with the computer chip on it. Show this to the class as you discuss semiconductors. Save the board for Chapter 23.

▶ As you discuss carbon, display a large lump of coal, graphite flakes, and a fake diamond. This visual emphasis will help students remember allotropes.

If possible, have assorted grades of pencils available for students to try. A book that uses the pencil as a central theme in a discussion of design and engineering technology is *The Pencil: A History of Design and Circumstance* by Henry Petroski, New York: Knopf, 1990.
Think Critically: Because graphite acts as a lubricant, it is safe to assume that the softest pencil (No. 1) contains more graphite than the hardest pencil (No. 3).

CONCEPT DEVELOPMENT

▶ **Demonstration:** Each student can build one unit cell of a diamond. The cells can then be connected to make a model that accurately demonstrates why a diamond is so hard. Duplicate four equilateral triangles for each student. Have the student cut out each triangle, leaving a tab on each edge. Tape or glue the triangles together to form a tetrahedron. Stack the tetrahedrons together in a clear plastic sweater storage box. The interlocking network of tetrahedrons represents the rigid crystal structure of a diamond.

Cooperative Learning: Send an Expert Team to a jewelry store to interview a jeweler about diamonds. Have students make an appointment in advance so they can talk to a certified gemologist about a stone's carat weight, cut, and clarity. Perhaps the jeweler could visit the school and talk to the class.

▶ Bring a soccer ball to class to show students the basic shape of the C_{60} molecules of buckminsterfullerene.

VideoDisc

STVS: Glass Making for Science, Disc 2, Side 1

The "Lead" in a Pencil

In a pencil factory, ground graphite crystals are mixed with clay to make the pencil "lead." The graphite-clay mixture is then shaped into long thin rods.

The rods are cut, dried, and heated. Grooves shaped to fit the rods are cut into half blocks of wood. The grooves are coated with glue, and then the rods are placed into the grooves. The other half of the block of wood is placed on the first half. After the glue has dried, the block is cut into individual pencils. After the pencils are painted, metal bands and erasers are added to make finished pencils.

Think Critically: What makes up the lead of a pencil? How do the amounts of graphite in hard (No. 3), medium (No. 2), and soft (No. 1) pencils compare? Explain your answer.

Buckminsterfullerene

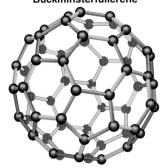

Did You Know?

Synthetic diamonds, used extensively in industry, are made by subjecting graphite to extremely high pressure and temperature.

A diamond is clear and extremely hard. In a diamond, each carbon atom is bonded to four other carbon atoms at the vertices, or corner points, of a tetrahedron. In turn, many tetrahedrons join together to form a giant molecule, sometimes called a macromolecule, in which the atoms are held tightly in a strong crystal structure. This structure accounts for the hardness of diamond. Look at the drawings of the structures of graphite and diamond on page 317. How are the structure and properties of diamond unlike those of graphite?

Recently a third allotrope of carbon, called buckminsterfullerene, has been discovered. Its basic unit is made up of 60 carbon atoms arranged in a shape similar to that of a soccer ball.

Carbon occurs as an element in coal and in compounds in oil, natural gas, and foods. Carbon in these materials may combine with oxygen to produce carbon dioxide, CO_2. Plants combine CO_2 with water to make food. In Chapter 13, you will study other carbon compounds—many essential to life.

Silicon is second only to oxygen in abundance in Earth's crust. Most silicon is found in sand, silicon dioxide, SiO_2,

318 ELEMENTS AND THEIR PROPERTIES

OPTIONS

ASSESSMENT—ORAL

▶ **The carbon family of Group 14 has both metallic and nonmetallic members. How can you distinguish between them?** *The metals have typical metallic properties (luster, conductivity, malleability, and so on) and have positive oxidation numbers. The nonmetals have some typical nonmetallic properties (brittleness, nonconductivity, and so on) and have negative oxidation numbers.*

PROGRAM RESOURCES

From the **Teacher Resource Package** use:
Transparency Masters, pages 47-48, Allotropes of Carbon.
Use **Color Transparency** number 24, Allotropes of Carbon.

and in almost all rocks and soil. The crystal structure of silicon dioxide is similar to the tetrahedrons in diamond. Silicon occurs as two allotropes. One of these is a hard, gray substance, and the other is a brown powder.

What compound has a structure similar to that of diamond?

Figure 12-16. Most gasolines are no longer leaded (left). Pewter contains tin and other metals (right).

Both silicon and germanium, the other metalloid in the carbon group, are used in making semiconductors, which you'll learn about in Chapter 23. Tin and lead are typical metals. Tin is used to coat other metals to prevent corrosion. Tin is also combined with other metals to produce bronze and pewter. Lead was once used widely in paints and antiknock gasoline. But lead is poisonous, so it has been replaced in these materials.

The Nitrogen Group

The nitrogen family makes up Group 15. Each element has five electrons in its outer energy level. These elements tend to share electrons and to form covalent compounds with other elements.

Each breath you take is about 80 percent gaseous nitrogen, as diatomic molecules, N_2. If you look again at Figure 12-8 on page 310, you'll see that nitrogen is the element fourth in abundance in your body. Yet you and other animals and plants can't use nitrogen as N_2. The nitrogen must be combined into compounds, such as nitrates—compounds that contain the nitrate ion, NO_3^-. Much nitrogen is used to make nitrates and ammonia, NH_3, both of which are used in fertilizers.

Connect to...
Life Science

Some plants contain bacteria in their roots that break the bonding in N_2 gas and form useful nitrogen compounds. This process is called nitrogen fixing. Look at the dot diagram for nitrogen gas on page 278. Why is the bonding so difficult to break?

15
7 **N** Nitrogen 14.0067
15 **P** Phosphorus 30.97376
33 **As** Arsenic 74.9216
51 **Sb** Antimony 121.75
83 **Bi** Bismuth 208.9804

REVEALING MISCONCEPTIONS

REVEALING MISCONCEPTIONS
▶ The words *silicon* and *silicone* are often interchanged in everyday usage. Silicon is an element. Silicones are long chains of Si and O bonded to carbon atoms.
▶ Students often hear the term *tin can*. In reality, the metal cans in which food is preserved are iron cans. At one time, all were coated with tin. Today, many have a plastic film lining.

TEACHER F.Y.I.
▶ Some computer bulletin boards have had recipes for making explosives. Advise your students *never* to try making these high-powered nitrogen explosives.

CROSS CURRICULUM
▶ **Political Science:** Nitrogen compounds include ammonia and nitrate fertilizers that help feed the world's population as well as drugs to help treat disease. They also include trinitrotoluene, TNT, that is used in bombs and rockets and other compounds used in poisonous gases. Chemicals are neither good nor bad. People decide how chemicals are to be used. Have a panel discussion on whether scientists should work on development of explosives and poisons.

MINI QUIZ

Use the Mini Quiz to check students' recall of chapter content.

1 **How do we classify an element that has both metallic and nonmetallic properties?** *as a metalloid*
2 **What is the most abundant metal in Earth's crust?** *aluminum*
3 **What do we call substances that conduct an electric current under certain conditions?** *semiconductors*
4 **Different forms of the same element are called _____ .** *allotropes*
5 **Most semiconductors are made from silicon or _____ .** *germanium*

Connect to...
Life Science

Answer: Nitrogen atoms share three pairs of electrons.

ENRICHMENT
▶ Have a student research the meaning of the Greek word *graphein* from which we get our word, *graphite*. It means "to write."
▶ Black lung disease occurs among coal miners. Have a student research the disease and its causes. Have a second student report on how mining practices and equipment have changed to help prevent the disease.
▶ Have students find out why both germanium and silicon are used to make computer chips.

PROGRAM RESOURCES
From the **Teacher Resource Package** use:
Concept Mapping, pages 29-30.

CONCEPT DEVELOPMENT

▶ White phosphorus is very reactive. It is a component in the chemical weapon napalm. Its structure is a tetrahedron with the formula P_4. Red phosphorus is less reactive and is thought to have a chain structure. Black phosphorus is not common but does exist.

▶ **Demonstration:** Students can observe that oxygen supports combustion but does not burn. Place 1 g of MnO_2 in a 600 mL beaker. Slowly add 3% hydrogen peroxide to the beaker. Oxygen gas will be produced. Lower a glowing splint into the beaker. The splint will burst into flame.

CHECK FOR UNDERSTANDING

Use the Mini Quiz to check for understanding.

MINI QUIZ

Use the Mini Quiz to check students' recall of chapter content.

6 How many outer electrons are present in each member of the nitrogen family? *five*

7 The air contains _____ percent nitrogen gas. *about eighty*

8 The air contains _____ percent oxygen gas. *about twenty*

9 What is the chemical formula for ozone? O_3

10 Which Group 16 element is very toxic but is needed in your diet in trace amounts? *selenium*

RETEACH

Have each student in the class prepare a flash card listing one element from Groups 13-16. On one side show the name and symbol, and on the other side write the properties and uses. Use these cards for drill and practice.

EXTENSION

For students who have mastered this section, use the **Reinforcement** and **Enrichment** masters or other OPTIONS provided.

In Your JOURNAL

Answer: Accept student entries that are reasonable and supported. Current suggested selenium intake is less than 0.2 mg per day.

Phosphorus is a nonmetal that has three allotropes. Uses of phosphorus compounds range from water softeners to fertilizers to match heads. Antimony is a metalloid, and bismuth is a metal. Both elements are used with other metals to lower their melting points. It is because of this property that the metal in automatic fire sprinkler heads contains bismuth.

The Oxygen Group

The oxygen group makes up Group 16 on the periodic table. You can live only a short time without the nonmetal oxygen, which makes up about 20 percent of the air. Oxygen exists in the air as diatomic molecules, **⑧** O_2. During electrical storms, some oxygen molecules, O_2, change into ozone molecules, O_3. Do you notice that O_2 and O_3 are allotropes?

Nearly all living things on Earth need free oxygen, as O_2, for respiration. Living things also depend on a layer of ozone, O_3, around Earth for protection from some of **⑨** the sun's radiation, as you will learn in later chapters.

Sulfur is a nonmetal that can exist in allotropes as different-shaped crystals and as a noncrystalline solid. Sulfur combines with metals to form sulfides of such distinctive colors that they are used as pigments in paints.

16
8 **O** Oxygen 15.9994
16 **S** Sulfur 32.06
34 **Se** Selenium 78.96
52 **Te** Tellurium 127.60
84 **Po** Polonium 208.9824*

In Your JOURNAL

Selenium is part of an enzyme in your body and may play an important anticancer role. Too much selenium, however, can be toxic. **In your Journal,** write your opinion about the use of animal testing to determine the effects of selenium on humans.

Figure 12-17 One allotrope of sulfur has eight-sided crystals. The other allotrope, shown in the photo, has needlelike crystals.

OPTIONS

ENRICHMENT

▶ Silicon dioxide (quartz) crystals can be clear and colorless. When they have impurities they become colored gem stones. Research which impurities are in amethyst, emerald, aquamarine, jade, garnet, opal, onyx, and moonstone. For example, Mn and Fe cause quartz to become purple amethyst. An oxide of chromium causes the emerald to be green.

▶ Have students research glass, china and its glazes, and ceramics. Ceramics are clay products such as brick, tile, and terra cotta.

▶ Asbestos contains the element silicon. Ask a student to report on asbestos, its uses, and why it is being removed from buildings.

▶ Photovoltaic solar cells convert sunlight into electricity. Ask a student to read and report on solar cell research.

▶ Fiber optics are used for communication. Have a student report on how these fibers are made and how they work. Fibers are pulled from a melt of pure quartz crystals. The light reflects off the interior walls of the fiber.

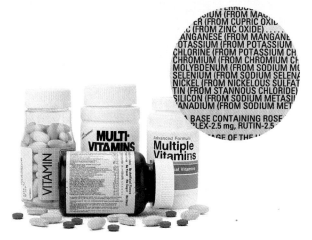

Figure 12-18. Selenium is one of several elements needed by the body in trace amounts.

The nonmetal selenium and two metalloids, tellurium and polonium, are the other Group 16 elements. Selenium is the most common of these. This element is one of several that you need in trace amounts in your diet. Larger amounts of selenium are toxic, however.

SECTION REVIEW

1. Why are Groups 14 and 15 better representatives of mixed groups than are Group 13 or Group 16?
2. How do the allotropes of sulfur differ?
3. Why is graphite a lubricant while a diamond is the hardest gem known?
4. **Apply:** Today aluminum is one of the most plentiful and least expensive of metals. Yet Napoleon III set the table for his most important guests with utensils made of aluminum instead of silver or gold. Why?
5. **Connect to Earth Science:** After being refined from ore, bismuth metal is often used in metal mixtures that need a low melting point, such as those used in fire sprinkler systems. Is bismuth more metallic or less metallic than nitrogen? In compounds, would bismuth be more likely to have a positive oxidation number or a negative oxidation number?

✉ Concept Mapping

Make a concept map for allotropes of carbon, using the terms *graphite*, *diamond*, *buckminsterfullerene*, *sphere*, *hexagon*, and *tetrahedron*. If you need help, see Concept Mapping in the **Skill Handbook** on pages 684 and 685.

Science and WRITING

Fluorescent lamps have been described as a major advantage in the energy conservation movement. Explain how they work and why they are so much better than the incandescent bulb.

Science and WRITING

The filament emits electrons that collide with mercury vapor in the tube. Mercury atoms emit ultraviolet light that causes the phosphor coating on the inside of the tube to glow (fluoresce). Fluorescent lights use about 1/4 the energy of incandescent lights of equivalent brightness but cost more to purchase.

3 CLOSE

▶ Ask questions 1-3 and the **Apply** and **Connect to Earth Science** questions in the Section Review.

SECTION REVIEW ANSWERS

1. Group 13 contains no elements that are clearly nonmetals. Group 16 contains no elements that are clearly metals.

2. Sulfur can exist as differently shaped crystals or a noncrystalline (amorphous) solid.

3. In graphite, carbon is arranged in flat sheets of atoms bonded in a hexagonal pattern. Because the sheets can slide over one another, graphite is a good lubricant. A diamond consists of a network of tetrahedrally bonded carbon atoms. Thus the crystal is essentially a giant molecule that results in an extremely hard gem.

4. Apply: At the time of Napoleon III, who ruled from 1850 to 1870, no reliable method of extracting aluminum from its compounds had been found. As a result, aluminum metal was costly and rare. Aluminum tableware was a sign of great wealth and prestige.

5. Connect to Earth Science: Bismuth is more metallic; positive.

Skill Builder
ASSESSMENT
Performance: Have students extend their concept maps to include any uses they know of for the allotropes.

Skill Builder

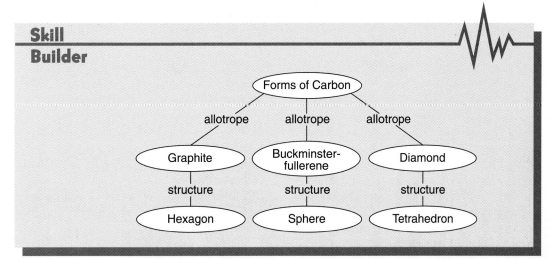

ACTIVITY 12-2

OBJECTIVE: Design and carry out an **experiment** to show a working **model** of the layered graphite structure. Students will determine the cause and effect relationship between bonding and properties.
Time: 30 minutes

PROCESS SKILLS applied in this activity are **making and using models** and **inferring.**

PREPARATION

Cooperative Learning: Use the Science Investigation Group strategy to take advantage of different skills that group members have.

SAFETY

Caution students to use care in working with scissors, especially if they use them to make holes in the polystyrene or cardboard.

THINKING CRITICALLY

You can gather information about the properties of things you cannot see. Models reflect these properties.

TEACHING THE ACTIVITY

*Refer to the **Activity Worksheets** for additional information and teaching strategies.*
• If students are unfamiliar with the behavior of lubricants, have them put together and then take apart a nut and bolt. Then have them repeat the procedure after coating the threads with graphite. Powdered graphite can be messy; use over newspaper and wipe off any excess.
• Polystyrene sheets may be available from hardware stores. They are often used as shims in appliance packaging.
• Have students compare lines made by pencils of various hardnesses and relate the results to the activity.

PROGRAM RESOURCES

From the **Teacher Resource Package** use:

Activity Worksheets, pages 96-97, Activity 12-2: Slippery Carbon.

DESIGNING AN EXPERIMENT
Slippery Carbon

Have you ever tried to turn a key in a sticky lock? Someone may have suggested that you try the lock after adding some graphite to it. Why does this allotrope of carbon have such good lubricating qualities?

Getting Started
You will *make a model* that can be used to determine the *cause and effect* relationship between the graphite's structure and its properties.

Thinking Critically
To represent bonding in graphite you need to *model* a rather strong bond and a weak bond. How can you model something that you cannot see?

Materials
Your cooperative group has the following materials available for use:
• thin spaghetti
• toothpicks
• small gum drops
• polystyrene sheets
• flat cardboard
• scissors

Try It!

1. *Construct a model* that can represent the strong attachments between carbon atoms in a flat, six-sided ring.
2. Connect two of these flat structures with something that will easily break under slight pressure. This structure models weak bonding between layers of carbon atoms.

Summing Up/Sharing Results
• *Compare* your completed graphite model with the structure shown on page 317. How does your model illustrate two types of bonding found in graphite?
• How does the bonding of graphite explain graphite's lubricating properties?

Going Further!
Do you think that buckminsterfullerene could make a good lubricant? Explain your answer.

SUMMING UP/SHARING RESULTS
• Student structures should show a model that represents six carbon atoms bonded together in flat layers that do not break under pressure. These layers may be represented by a hexagonal piece of polystyrene or cardboard. Two flat layers should be connected by easily broken objects, such as spaghetti, that represent the weak bonds in graphite.
• When pressure is applied to graphite, the weak bonds between layers break. This breaking allows one layer of hexagonal structures to move over another layer, causing a lubricating effect.

GOING FURTHER!
The buckminsterfullerene structures are round and could possibly roll over and around each other. Excluding cost considerations, it could be a good lubricant.

Activity
ASSESSMENT
Performance: To further assess students' understanding of bonding in graphite, see USING LAB SKILLS, Question 12, on page 324.

SUMMARY

12-1: Metals

1. A typical metal is a hard, shiny, solid that—due to metallic bonding—is malleable, ductile, and a good conductor of heat and electricity.

2. Groups 1 and 2 on the periodic table are the alkali and alkaline earth metals, which have some similar and some contrasting properties.

3. The iron triad, the coinage metals, and the zinc, cadmium, and mercury group are among the transition elements, which make up Groups 3 through 12 on the periodic table.

12-2: Science and Society: Synthetic Elements

1. The lanthanoids and actinoids have atomic numbers 57-70 and 89-102, respectively, whereas transuranium elements have atomic numbers greater than 92.

2. The making of synthetic elements is a controversial issue.

12-3: Nonmetals

1. As a typical nonmetal, hydrogen is a gas that forms compounds by sharing electrons with other nonmetals and also with metals.

2. All the halogens, Group 17, have seven outer electrons and form both covalent and ionic compounds, but each halogen has some properties unlike the others.

3. The noble gases, Group 18, are elements whose properties and uses are related to their chemical stability.

12-4: Mixed Groups

1. Groups 13 through 16 of the periodic table include metals, nonmetals, and metalloids.

2. Allotropes are different forms of the same element having different molecular structures.

3. The properties of three forms of carbon, graphite, diamond, and buckminsterfullerene, depend upon the differences in their crystal structures.

KEY SCIENCE WORDS

a. allotrope
b. diatomic molecule
c. ductile
d. malleable
e. metallic bonding
f. radioactive element
g. semiconductor
h. sublimation
i. transuranium element
j. transition element

UNDERSTANDING VOCABULARY

Match each phrase with the correct term from the list of Key Science Words.

1. can be drawn out into a wire
2. appears after uranium on the periodic table
3. can be hammered into a thin sheet
4. process of changing directly from a solid to a gas
5. will conduct an electric current under certain conditions
6. different structural forms of the same element
7. composed of two atoms
8. breaks down and gives off particles, radiation, and energy
9. in Groups 3 through 12 on the periodic table
10. Positively charged ions are surrounded by freely moving electrons.

ELEMENTS AND THEIR PROPERTIES **323**

SUMMARY

Have students read the summary statements to review the major concepts of the chapter.

UNDERSTANDING VOCABULARY

1. c   **6.** a
2. i   **7.** b
3. d   **8.** f
4. h   **9.** j
5. g   **10.** e

ASSESSMENT
Portfolio

Encourage students to place in their portfolios one or two items of what they consider to be their best work. For each item, ask students to explain why that item was chosen and what they learned from it. Items might be selected from the following.

• Enrichment interview, p. 305
• Activity 12-1 observations and answers, p. 315
• Skill Builder concept map, p. 321

Performance

Additional performance assessments may be found in *Performance Assessment* and *Science Integration Activities* that accompany **Merrill Physical Science.** Performance Task Assessment Lists and rubrics for evaluating these activities and other products generated throughout the chapter can be found in Glencoe's *Performance Assessment in Middle School Science.*

OPTIONS

ASSESSMENT

To assess student understanding of material in this chapter, use the resources listed.

👥 COOPERATIVE LEARNING

Consider using cooperative learning in the THINK AND WRITE CRITICALLY, APPLY, and MORE SKILL BUILDERS sections of the Chapter Review.

PROGRAM RESOURCES

From the **Teacher Resource Package** use:
Chapter Review, pages 27-28.
Chapter and Unit Tests, pages 80-83, Chapter Test.

CHAPTER

REVIEW

CHECKING CONCEPTS

1. b	**6.** c
2. a	**7.** d
3. d	**8.** d
4. c	**9.** a
5. a	**10.** d

USING LAB SKILLS

ASSESSMENT

Use these alternate lab exercises to assess students' understanding of skills used in this chapter.

11. Carefully place a glowing splint in the gas sample. If the splint bursts into flame, the gas is oxygen. If the glow is extinguished, the gas is probably carbon dioxide.

12. A pencil mark is made on paper when the bonds between the hexagonal layers are broken apart and left on the paper.

THINK AND WRITE CRITICALLY

13. francium, because it is at the bottom of Group 1 and at the left of the table

14. oxygen, silicon, aluminum, and iron, respectively

15. Atoms of gaseous elements other than the noble gases have unstable electron structures. These atoms acquire stable structures by sharing electrons in diatomic molecules. The atoms of a noble gas, on the other hand, are stable and thus do not share electrons to form diatomic molecules. Instead, they occur as single atoms.

16. Elements are grouped on the periodic table according to their atomic numbers and electron arrangements. Hydrogen is placed first because its atomic number is 1. It is placed above the alkali metals because, like those elements, it has one electron in its outer energy level. Note, however, that hydrogen's properties differ from those of Group 1 metals in several significant ways.

17. Zinc, cadmium, and nickel are three metals used to coat other metals to form a protective layer that resists corrosion.

CHAPTER

REVIEW

CHECKING CONCEPTS

Choose the word or phrase that completes the sentence or answers the question.

1. When magnesium and fluorine react, what type of bond is formed?
  a. metallic **c.** covalent
  b. ionic **d.** diatomic

2. What type of bond is found in a piece of pure gold?
  a. metallic **c.** covalent
  b. ionic **d.** diatomic

3. Because electrons move freely in metals, metals are _____.
  a. brittle **c.** dull
  b. hard **d.** conductors

4. The _____ make up the most reactive group of all metals.
  a. iron triad **c.** alkali metals
  b. coinage metals **d.** alkaline earth metals

5. The most reactive of all nonmetals is _____.
  a. fluorine **c.** hydrogen
  b. uranium **d.** oxygen

6. The element _____ is always found in nature combined with other elements.
  a. copper **c.** magnesium
  b. gold **d.** silver

7. The least magnetic of these metals is _____.
  a. cobalt **c.** nickel
  b. iron **d.** titanium

8. Production of the element _____ was banned in the U.S. after much controversy.
  a. ytterbium **c.** americium
  b. promethium **d.** plutonium

9. An example of a radioactive element is _____.
  a. astatine **c.** chlorine
  b. bromine **d.** fluorine

10. The only group that is completely nonmetallic is Group _____.
  a. 1 **c.** 17
  b. 2 **d.** 18

USING LAB SKILLS

11. In a laboratory, some students are investigating a chemical reaction that is producing a gas. They suspect that the gas is either oxygen or carbon dioxide. Suggest a way, based on Activity 12-1 on page 315, that they could decide which gas it is.

12. The model you made in Activity 12-2 on page 322 helps explain the lubricating ability of graphite. Use that same model to explain how the graphite in a pencil is able to leave a mark on a piece of paper.

THINK AND WRITE CRITICALLY

Answer the following questions in your Journal using complete sentences.

13. Reading from top to bottom on the periodic table, metallic properties of elements *increase,* reading from left to right, metallic properties *decrease.* Which element is the most metallic of all? Explain your answer.

14. The most abundant elements in Earth's crust are a nonmetal, a metalloid, and two metals. List the four elements.

15. Why do oxygen and nitrogen occur in the air as diatomic molecules, but argon, neon, krypton, and xenon occur as monatomic molecules?

16. Explain why hydrogen, a nonmetal, is on the metal side of the periodic table.

17. Name three metals used to coat other metals. Why is one metal used to coat another?

APPLY

18. Why was mercury used in clinical thermometers, and why is it no longer used for that purpose?

19. The density of hydrogen is so low that it can be used to fill balloons to make them lighter than air. Why is helium used more frequently?

20. Why is aluminum used instead of steel in building airplanes?

21. Why are silver compounds used in photography? Name two nonmetals extracted from brine that are also part of these compounds.

22. Like selenium, chromium is poisonous but is needed in trace amounts in your diet. How does this information apply to the safe use of vitamin-mineral pills?

MORE SKILL BUILDERS

If you need help, refer to the Skill Handbook.

1. Making and Using Tables: Use the periodic table to classify each of the following as a lanthanoid or actinoid: californium, europium, cerium, nobelium.

2. Comparing and Contrasting: Aluminum is close to carbon on the periodic table. Explain why aluminum is a metal and carbon is not.

3. Observing and Inferring: You are shown two samples of phosphorus. One is white and burns if exposed to air. The other is red and burns if lit. Infer why the properties of two samples of the same element differ.

4. Recognizing Cause and Effect: Plants need nitrogen compounds. Nitrogen-fixing changes free nitrogen into nitrates. Lightning and legumes are both nitrogen-fixing. What are the cause and effect of nitrogen fixing?

5. Concept Mapping: Complete the concept map located to the right for some common metals. You may use symbols for the elements.

PROJECTS

1. Research the pros and cons of using nuclear energy to produce electricity. Prepare a report that includes data as well as your informed opinion on the subject. If several class members do research, conduct a debate on the issue.

2. Research the source, composition, and properties of asbestos. What properties made it suitable for use in construction in the past? How did these same properties cause asbestos to become a health hazard, and what is being done now to eliminate the hazard?

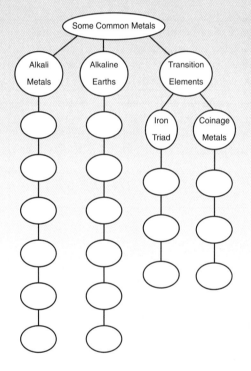

APPLY

18. Mercury remains a liquid throughout the ordinary temperature range and expands as temperature increases. Mercury is poisonous.

19. Hydrogen burns readily in air. Helium is a noble gas and therefore is stable.

20. Aluminum is strong but lightweight. Therefore, it is more fuel efficient than is steel.

21. Some silver compounds change chemically when exposed to light. Bromine and iodine, used to make silver bromide and silver iodide, are obtained from brine.

22. Do not take more than the recommended dosage. Exceeding the trace amounts needed may produce toxic reactions.

MORE SKILL BUILDERS

1. Making and Using Tables: lanthanoids: europium, cerium; actinoids: californium, nobelium

2. Comparing and Contrasting: Aluminum has metallic properties such as being malleable and ductile, and it transfers electrons when it combines with nonmetals. Carbon has none of these properties.

3. Observing and Inferring: They are allotropes of phosphorus, that is, forms of the element with different properties because they have different structures.

4. Recognizing Cause and Effect: Cause: lightning and legumes; Effect: changing atmospheric nitrogen into nitrogen compounds

5. Concept Mapping:

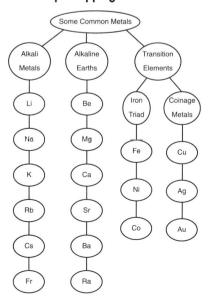

13 Organic and Biological Compounds

CHAPTER SECTION	OBJECTIVES	ACTIVITIES
13-1 Simple Organic Compounds (2 days)	1. **Describe** structures of organic compounds and explain why carbon forms so many compounds. 2. **Distinguish** between saturated and unsaturated hydrocarbons. 3. **Identify** isomers of organic compounds.	**MINI-Lab:** *What structures can octane have?* p. 330
13-2 Other Organic Compounds (2 days)	1. **Describe** characteristics of aromatic compounds. 2. **Classify** groups of organic compounds as substituted hydrocarbons.	**Activity 13-1:** *Alcohols and Organic Acids,* p. 337
13-3 Alternative Sources of Energy Science & Society (1 day)	1. **Describe** the role of biomass as a source of two fuels for increasing our energy supply. 2. **Analyze** the positive and negative effects of the widespread use of ethanol and gasohol.	
13-4 Biological Compounds (2 days)	1. **Describe** the formation of polymers and **discuss** their importance as biological compounds. 2. **Compare** and **contrast** proteins, nucleic acids, carbohydrates, and lipids.	**Activity 13-2:** *Mixing Many Monomers,* p. 346
Chapter Review		

ACTIVITY MATERIALS

FIND OUT	ACTIVITIES		MINI-LABS
Page 327 white bread white paper laboratory burner test tubes	**13-1 Alcohols and Organic Acids, p. 337** test tube and stopper dropper pipet graduated cylinder ethyl alcohol 6 M sodium hydroxide 0.01 M potassium permanganate	**13-2 Mixing Many Monomers, p. 346** paper clips colored index cards	**What structures can octane have? p. 330** gum drops of one color raisins toothpicks

CHAPTER FEATURES	TEACHER RESOURCE PACKAGE	OTHER RESOURCES
Problem Solving: *The Case of the Overripe Tomatoes,* p. 332 **Skill Builder:** *Making and Using Graphs,* p. 333	**Ability Level Worksheets** ◆ **Study Guide,** p. 54 ● **Reinforcement,** p. 54 ▲ **Enrichment,** p. 54 **Activity Worksheets,** pp. 5, 108 **Cross-Curricular Connections,** p. 19 **Transparency Masters,** pp. 49, 50	**Color Transparency 25,** Hydrocarbon Structure **STVS:** Disc 2, Side 1
Skill Builder: *Interpreting Scientific Illustrations,* p. 336	**Ability Level Worksheets** ◆ **Study Guide,** p. 55 ● **Reinforcement,** p. 55 ▲ **Enrichment,** p. 55 **Activity Worksheets,** pp. 102, 103 **Critical Thinking/Problem Solving,** p. 19 **Technology,** pp. 13, 14	**STVS:** Disc 4, Side 1
You Decide! p. 339	**Ability Level Worksheets** ◆ **Study Guide,** p. 56 ● **Reinforcement,** p. 56 ▲ **Enrichment,** p. 56	**STVS:** Disc 4, Side 2 **Science Integration Activity 13**
Technology: *Fake Fats,* p. 344 **Skill Builder:** *Concept Mapping,* p. 345	**Ability Level Worksheets** ◆ **Study Guide,** p. 57 ● **Reinforcement,** p. 57 ▲ **Enrichment,** p. 57 **Activity Worksheets,** pp. 5, 104, 105 **Concept Mapping,** pp. 31, 32 **Science and Society,** p. 17 **Transparency Masters,** pp. 51, 52	**Color Transparency 26,** Biological Polymers **Laboratory Manual 28,** The Breakdown of Starch **Laboratory Manual 29,** Testing for a Vitamin **STVS:** Disc 7, Side 1
Summary Think & Write Critically Key Science Words Apply Understanding Vocabulary More Skill Builders Checking Concepts Projects Using Lab Skills	**ASSESSMENT RESOURCES** **Chapter Review,** pp. 29, 30 **Chapter Test,** pp. 84-87 **Performance Assessment in** **Middle School Science**	**Chapter Review Software** **Test Bank** **Alternate Assessment** **Performance Assessment**

◆ **Basic**   ● **Average**   ▲ **Advanced**

ADDITIONAL MATERIALS

SOFTWARE	AUDIOVISUAL	BOOKS/MAGAZINES
Organic Chemistry, J&S Software. *Polymer Chemistry,* American Chemical Society. *Chemistry of Life,* Queue. *Carbon Chemistry,* J & S Software. *Chemicals of Life II and III,* EduQuest. *Organic Chemistry,* Queue.	*Carbon and Its Compounds,* 2nd ed., Film, Coronet/MTI. *The Carbon Compounds,* Film, SVE. *The Chemistry of Carbohydrates and Lipids,* Video, Insight Media. *Functional Chemistry in Living Cells,* Video, Insight Media. *Methane: The Simplest Hydrocarbon,* Video, Britannica. *Translating the Code: Protein Synthesis,* Video, HRM Video.	Atkins, P.W. *Molecules.* NY: Scientific American Library, 1987. Buscall, R. *Science and Technology of Polymer Colloids.* NY: Elsevier Science Publishing Co., Inc., 1985. Gallant, K.W. and J.M. Railey. *Physical Properties of Hydrocarbons,* Vol. 2, 2nd ed. Houston, TX: Gulf Publishing Co., 1984.

THEME DEVELOPMENT: Scale and structure as a theme of the textbook is developed through a presentation of organic compounds and related biopolymers. The relationships that exist between the structure of organic molecules and the properties of those molecules are described and developed.

CHAPTER OVERVIEW

▶ **Section 13-1:** The unique chemistry of carbon as it forms many different molecular shapes is presented in this section. The student is introduced to saturated and unsaturated hydrocarbons as well as isomers.

▶ **Section 13-2:** Aromatic compounds and substituted hydrocarbons are described in this section.

▶ **Section 13-3: Science and Society:** Biomass conversion as an alternate energy source is described in detail.

▶ **Section 13-4:** This section introduces biochemistry and describes the structure of the main classes of biochemicals: proteins, fats, and carbohydrates. The concept of polymerization is presented to unify the section.

CHAPTER VOCABULARY

organic compounds	biomass
hydrocarbon	biogas
saturated	energy
hydrocarbons	farming
unsaturated	gasohol
hydrocarbons	polymers
isomers	proteins
aromatic compound	nucleic acids
substituted	carbohydrates
hydrocarbon	lipids
alcohol	

326

OPTIONS

 **For Your Gifted Students**

Have students research the structure of DNA and its functions. They can research the bases adenine, guanine, cytosine, and thymine. Have students show the chemical structure of the bases. They can make a three-dimensional model of the double helix and show how the four bases pair. Some students could research the way base sequences code for amino acids in proteins. The students will need to find out how protein is synthesized as a consequence of the DNA code.

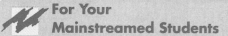 **For Your Mainstreamed Students**

Ask students to make models of organic compounds. They can paint polystyrene foam balls various colors for the specific elements (carbon—black, hydrogen—yellow, and so forth). Have them combine the atoms to make models of the molecules shown in this chapter. This will afford opportunities for visual, tactile, and kinesthetic learning.

Have you heard the saying "You are what you eat"? Actually, many of the same compounds in foods are found in your body. And one special element is basic to these compounds and to other substances made by living things.

FIND OUT!

Do this activity to observe the element that forms from the breakdown of some kinds of materials when they are heated.

Place a small piece of bread in a test tube. Hold the test tube over the flame of a laboratory burner. What do you *observe*? Using a clean test tube and a small amount of paper instead of bread, repeat the procedure. What do you observe this time?

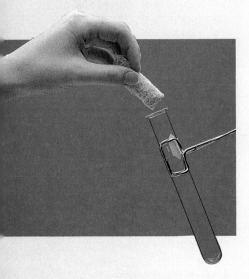

Gearing Up
Previewing the Chapter

Use this outline to help you focus on important ideas in this chapter.

Section 13-1   Simple Organic Compounds
▶ Organic Compounds
▶ Hydrocarbons
▶ Isomers

Section 13-2   Other Organic Compounds
▶ Aromatic Compounds
▶ Substituted Hydrocarbons

Section 13-3   Science and Society
Alternative Sources of Energy
▶ Why Not New Fuels?

Section 13-4   Biological Compounds
▶ Proteins
▶ Nucleic Acids
▶ Carbohydrates
▶ Lipids

Previewing Science Skills

▶ In the Skill Builders, you will make and use a graph, interpret scientific illustrations, and make a concept map.
▶ In the Activities, you will observe, predict, and build models.
▶ In the MINI-Lab, you will build a model, compare, and contrast.

What's next?

You have observed evidence of the presence of carbon in bread and paper, which contain organic compounds. As you study this chapter, you will find out more about organic compounds.

327

INTRODUCING THE CHAPTER
Use the Find Out activity to introduce students to organic and biological compounds. Inform students that they will be learning more about their special chemistry, formulas, and reactions as they read the chapter.

FIND OUT!
Preparation: Cut fresh bread and paper into thin strips, 2 cm long, that will fit into a test tube.
Materials: white bread, white paper, laboratory burner, test tubes
Teaching Tips
▶ Suggest to students that they record the time they begin heating both samples and the time that the first observable change is noticed.
▶ Use this activity to reinforce the evidence of a chemical reaction—color change, odor, and evolution of a gas (water vapor).
▶ Students will notice that both paper and bread turn black. Both will give off water vapor, which will condense inside the test tube.
▶ Because cellulose and starch are chemically similar, students observe similar reactions when paper and bread are heated. Ask the class if this means they can digest paper. The negative answer implies a difference in structure between the two. Digestive enzymes are structurally specific.

Gearing Up
Have students study the Gearing Up feature to familiarize themselves with the chapter. Discuss the relationships of the topics in the outline.

What's Next?
Before beginning the first section, make sure students understand the connection between the Find Out activity and the topics to follow.

ASSESSMENT OPTIONS

PORTFOLIO
Refer to page 347 for suggested items that students might select for their portfolios.

PERFORMANCE ASSESSMENT
See page 347 for additional Performance Assessment options.
Process
Skill Builders, pp. 333, 345
MINI-Lab, p. 330
Activities 13-1, p. 337; 13-2, p. 346
Using Lab Skills, p. 348

CONTENT ASSESSMENT
Assessment—Oral, pp. 336, 342
Skill Builder, p. 336
Section Reviews, pp. 333, 336, 339, 345
Chapter Review, pp. 347-349
Mini Quizzes, pp. 332, 335, 343, 344

GROUP ASSESSMENT
Opportunities for group assessment occur with Cooperative Learning Strategies and Flex Your Brain Activities.

PREPARATION

SECTION BACKGROUND

▶ Organic compounds can be classified as aromatic and aliphatic. Aromatic compounds contain one or more benzene rings. All other hydrocarbons are classified as aliphatic.

▶ A hydrocarbon in which all carbon-carbon bonds are single bonds is called an alkane. This is also called a saturated compound. The general formula for alkanes is C_nH_{2n+2}.

▶ An atom or group of atoms that is attached to a main chain is called a branch or substituent.

▶ An alkene is an unsaturated hydrocarbon that contains a double bond. The general formula for an alkene is C_nH_{2n}.

▶ An alkyne is an unsaturated hydrocarbon that contains a triple bond. The general formula for an alkyne is C_nH_{2n-2}.

PREPLANNING

▶ To prepare for the MINI-Lab on page 330, obtain soft gum drops, raisins, and toothpicks.

1 MOTIVATE

▶ **Demonstration:** Organic compounds, called esters, that smell like pineapple, banana, and wintergreen can easily be prepared by reacting an organic acid with an alcohol. Place 6 mL each of the acid and the alcohol listed below in a test tube. Add 5 drops of concentrated sulfuric acid, mix and heat in a warm water bath. **CAUTION:** *Acid is corrosive. Alcohols are flammable. Butyric acid has a foul odor. Aromas should be checked by using a slight waving motion to direct fumes toward your nose.*

butyric acid + ethanol = pineapple
acetic acid + ethanol = apple
acetic acid + isopentanol = banana
acetic acid + 1-octanol = orange
salicylic acid + methanol = wintergreen
(Salicylic acid is a solid.)

New Science Words

organic compounds
hydrocarbon
saturated hydrocarbons
unsaturated hydrocarbons
isomers

Objectives

▶ Describe structures of organic compounds and explain why carbon forms so many compounds.
▶ Distinguish between saturated and unsaturated hydrocarbons.
▶ Identify isomers of organic compounds.

Organic Compounds

What do cassette tapes and CDs, you, and your athletic shoes have in common? Each is made up mostly of substances called organic compounds. Most compounds that contain the element carbon are **organic compounds**. 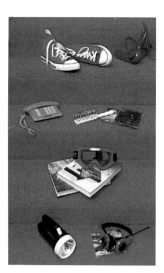 There are several exceptions, such as carbon monoxide, carbon dioxide, and carbonates. More than 90 percent of all compounds are organic compounds.

You probably recognize that the word *organic* is related to *organism*. At one time, scientists assumed that only living organisms could produce organic compounds. However, by 1830 scientists were making organic compounds artificially in laboratories. But scientists didn't change the name of these carbon-containing compounds. Today, most of the millions of different organic compounds that exist are synthetic. The manufacturing of organic compounds is one of world's largest industries. A chemical plant is shown in Figure 13-1 on the next page.

You may be wondering why there are so many organic compounds. There are several reasons related to the element carbon. First, a carbon atom has four electrons in its outer energy level. Recall that this electron arrangement means that each atom can form four covalent bonds with atoms of carbon or with other elements. Four is a large number of bonds compared to the number of bonds that atoms of other elements can form. When carbon atoms bond to form the molecules of some organic compounds, they form long chains. These chains may be

How many covalent bonds can a carbon atom form?

OPTIONS

Meeting Different Ability Levels

For Section 13-1, use the following **Teacher Resource Masters** depending upon individual students' needs.

◆ **Study Guide Master** for all students.
● **Reinforcement Master** for students of average and above average ability levels.
▲ **Enrichment Master** for above average students.
Additional Teacher Resource Package masters are listed in any **PROGRAM RESOURCES** boxes that are in the section. The additional masters are appropriate for all students.

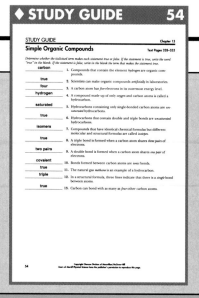

◆ **STUDY GUIDE** 54

STUDY GUIDE   Chapter 13
Simple Organic Compounds   Text Pages 328–333

Determine whether the italicized term makes each statement true or false. If the statement is true, write the word "true" in the blank. If the statement is false, write in the blank the term that makes the statement true.

carbon	1. Compounds that contain the element *hydrogen* are organic compounds.
true	2. Scientists can make organic compounds *artificially* in laboratories.
four	3. A carbon atom has *five* electrons in its outermost energy level.
hydrogen	4. A compound made up of only *oxygen* and carbon atoms is called a hydrocarbon.
saturated	5. Hydrocarbons containing only single-bonded carbon atoms are *unsaturated* hydrocarbons.
true	6. Hydrocarbons that contain double and triple bonds are *unsaturated* hydrocarbons.
isomers	7. Compounds that have identical chemical formulas but different molecular and structural formulas are called *isotopes.*
true	8. A triple bond is formed when a carbon atom shares *three pairs* of electrons.
two pairs	9. A double bond is formed when a carbon atom shares *one pair* of electrons.
covalent	10. Bonds formed between carbon atoms are *ionic* bonds.
true	11. The natural gas *methane* is an example of a hydrocarbon.
triple	12. In a structural formula, three lines indicate that there is a *single* bond between atoms.
true	13. Carbon can bond with as many as *four* other carbon atoms.

continuous or branched. In other compounds the carbon atoms form closed rings. Molecules of organic compounds may contain from one to several thousand carbon atoms.

Second, a carbon atom can form a single, double, or triple bond with another carbon atom. There also can be many different arrangements of single, double, and triple bonds between carbon atoms. Each arrangement forms a molecule of a different organic compound. Finally, a carbon atom can bond with atoms of many other elements, such as hydrogen, oxygen, nitrogen, and chlorine. Carbon forms an enormous number of compounds with hydrogen alone. A compound made up of only carbon and hydrogen atoms is called a **hydrocarbon.** You can learn a lot about other organic compounds by studying hydrocarbons.

Hydrocarbons

Does the furnace, stove, or water heater in your home burn natural gas? Almost all the natural gas people use for these purposes is the hydrocarbon methane. The chemical formula of methane is CH_4. There are two other ways to represent methane. The structural formula in Figure 13-3 shows that four hydrogen atoms are bonded to one

Figure 13-2. Natural pigments like the color of this flamingo are organic compounds.

Figure 13-3. Natural gas is mostly methane, CH_4.

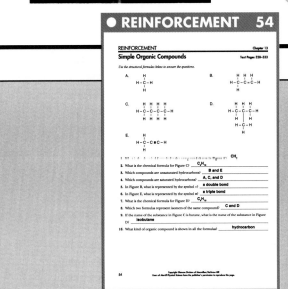

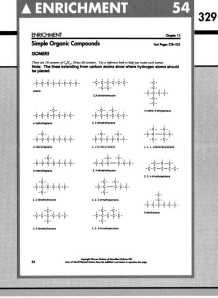

methane
CH_4

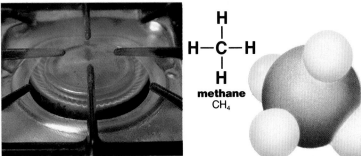

● **REINFORCEMENT** 54

▲ **ENRICHMENT** 54

329

2 TEACH

Key Concepts are highlighted.

CONCEPT DEVELOPMENT

▶ Ask students what is used as a source of raw materials to make organic chemicals. Petroleum is a complex mixture of organic compounds that are used as building blocks for other organic chemicals.

▶ Show ball-and-stick models of methane, ethane, propane, and butane. Point out the structural similarities in a homologous series such as the alkanes.

▶ Bring to class a small propane torch commonly used by plumbers, a butane lighter, and a methane-fired Bunsen burner. Point out that the small molecular masses and nonpolar nature of these fuels result in their being gases at room temperature. Butane is a liquid in the lighter only because it is under pressure. Intermolecular forces are much weaker in small hydrocarbons than in water, which has a similar molecular mass but also has polar attractions. Hydrocarbons are usually nonpolar.

VideoDisc

STVS: Oil Spill Identification, Disc 2, Side 1

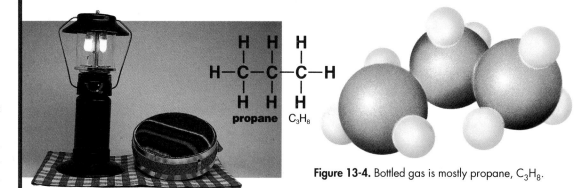

Figure 13-4. Bottled gas is mostly propane, C_3H_8.

MINI-Lab

What structures can octane have?
Octane, C_8H_{18}, is a hydrocarbon in gasoline. Using gum drops for carbon atoms, raisins for hydrogen atoms, and toothpicks for bonds that join the "atoms," *make a model* of one possible structure of octane. Each carbon atom can have four bonds and each hydrogen atom, one bond. *Compare* the structure of your model to those of your classmates.

In Your JOURNAL

Many fuels are mixtures of hydrocarbons. Some hydrocarbons release more energy than do other hydrocarbons when they are burned. **In your Journal,** write a chemical explanation of why fuel prices may vary.

carbon atom in a molecule. Each line between atoms represents a single covalent bond. As you recall, a covalent bond is formed when two atoms share a pair of electrons. The space-filling model in Figure 13-3 shows the relative volumes of the electron clouds in the molecule.

Methane and other hydrocarbons account for more than 90 percent of the energy sources used in homes, schools, industry, and transportation. Hydrocarbons are also important in manufacturing almost all the organic compounds used in products ranging from fertilizers to skateboards.

Some stoves, most outdoor grills, and hot-air balloons burn the bottled gas propane, another hydrocarbon. Its chemical formula is C_3H_8. Look at Figure 13-4. How many

Table 13-1

SOME HYDROCARBONS		
Name	**Chemical Formula**	**Structural Formula**
Methane	CH_4	H‑C‑H (H above and below)
Ethane	C_2H_6	H‑C‑C‑H (H above and below)
Propane	C_3H_8	H‑C‑C‑C‑H (H above and below)
Butane	C_4H_{10}	H‑C‑C‑C‑C‑H (H above and below)
Pentane	C_5H_{12}	H‑C‑C‑C‑C‑C‑H (H above and below)

330   ORGANIC AND BIOLOGICAL COMPOUNDS

Octane has 18 isomers. Shown here are the carbon chains for the isomers. Each student model should match one of these structures.

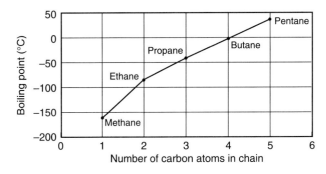

Figure 13-5. Boiling Points of Hydrocarbons in Natural Gas

Connect to...
Earth Science

When engineers separate the hydrocarbons found in crude oil, they use the different boiling points of the hydrocarbons. Using Figure 13-5, what would you predict for the number of carbon atoms in the hydrocarbons that make up kerosene, which has a boiling point around 175°C?

atoms of each element are in a molecule of propane? How many covalent bonds are in each molecule?

In some hydrocarbons, the carbon atoms are joined by single covalent bonds. Hydrocarbons containing only single-bonded carbon atoms are called **saturated hydrocarbons.** The carbon atoms in a molecule of propane are bonded by single covalent bonds. Propane is a saturated hydrocarbon. As you can see, the carbon atoms in propane seem to form a short chain. Propane is a member of a group of saturated hydrocarbons in which the carbon atoms form chains. Table 13-1 lists methane, propane, and three other similar hydrocarbons. Notice how each carbon atom appears to be a link in the chain within the molecule. Figure 13-5 shows a graph of the boiling points of these hydrocarbons. What happens to the boiling point as the number of carbon atoms in the chain increases?

Do you like bananas? They are among the many fruits and vegetables that are often ripened with the help of ethylene. Ethylene is the common name of the hydrocarbon ethene, C_2H_4. Did you ever watch a welder using an acetylene torch? Acetylene is the common name of the hydrocarbon ethyne, C_2H_2. Look at the structural formulas for ethene and ethyne. The double lines between the carbon atoms in ethene represent a double covalent bond. A double covalent bond is the sharing of two pairs of electrons—in other words, four electrons. The three lines in ethyne represent a triple covalent bond. How many pairs of electrons are shared in a triple covalent bond?

Hydrocarbons, such as ethene and ethyne, that contain at least one double or triple bond between carbon atoms are called **unsaturated hydrocarbons.** Remember

Connect to...
Earth Science

Answer: Kerosene is a mixture of hydrocarbons, each having between 10 and 16 carbon atoms per molecule.

CONCEPT DEVELOPMENT

▶ Bring to class examples of saturated and unsaturated fats. Have students read the labels on butter, margarine, solid vegetable shortening, and liquid cooking oils. Discuss the dietary recommendations of health organizations such as the cancer, diabetes, and heart societies. If there is little knowledge among students about this important topic, make research assignments.

▶ **Demonstration:** Bromine bonds to hydrocarbons having double bonds. You can show the presence and reactivity of double bonds by adding a few milliliters of bromine water to cyclohexene in a test tube. Stopper and shake. Use cyclohexane as a comparison. **CAUTION:** *Hydrocarbons are both flammable and toxic. Bromine is a severe skin irritant.* Repeat this test for unsaturation by using various fats and oils.

STUDENT TEXT QUESTIONS

▶ Page 331, paragraph 1: **How many atoms of each element are there in a molecule of propane?** *8 hydrogen, 3 carbon.* **How many covalent bonds are in each molecule?** *10*

▶ Page 331, paragraph 2: **What happens to the boiling points of hydrocarbons as the number of carbon atoms in the chain increases?** *The boiling points become higher.*

▶ Page 331, paragraph 3: **How many pairs of electrons are shared in a triple covalent bond?** *three (six electrons total)*

OPTIONS

INQUIRY QUESTIONS

▶ The general formula for saturated hydrocarbons is C_nH_{2n+2}. Determine the formulas for pentane, which has five carbon atoms, and hexane, which has six. C_5H_{12}, C_6H_{14}.

▶ Write a formula for a nine-carbon saturated hydrocarbon. C_9H_{20}

▶ Which compound—pentane, hexane, or octane—would have the highest boiling point? Give a reason. *octane, because it has the greatest number of carbon atoms giving it the greatest molecular mass*

PROGRAM RESOURCES

From the **Teacher Resource Package** use:

Activity Worksheets, page 108, MINI-Lab: What structures can octane have?

Transparency Masters, pages 49-50, Hydrocarbon Structure.

Use **Color Transparency** number 25, Hydrocarbon Structure.

▶ Write the formulas for ethane, ethene, and ethyne. C_2H_6, C_2H_4, C_2H_2

Think Critically: The avocado was already overripe, so the ripening process continued until it rotted. Ethylene gas given off by the overripe avocado was trapped in the bag, causing the tomatoes to ripen more rapidly than expected.

CHECK FOR UNDERSTANDING

Use the Mini Quiz to check for understanding.

MINI QUIZ

Use the Mini Quiz to check students' recall of chapter content.

1 **Organic compounds contain the element _____ .** *carbon*

2 **How many bonds do carbon atoms form?** *four*

3 **What do you call a compound that is made of only carbon and hydrogen atoms?** *hydrocarbon*

4 **Hydrocarbons that contain only single-bonded carbon atoms are _____ .** *saturated*

5 **Unsaturated hydrocarbons contain at least one of what kinds of bonds between carbon atoms?** *double or triple*

6 **Compounds that have identical chemical formulas but different molecular structures are called _____ .** *isomers*

RETEACH

On a handout, draw structural formulas for several hydrocarbons. Have students write the molecular formula for each and decide if it is a saturated or unsaturated hydrocarbon.

EXTENSION

For students who have mastered this section, use the **Reinforcement** and **Enrichment** masters or other OPTIONS provided.

PROBLEM SOLVING

The Case of the Overripe Tomatoes

Maria helped out at home by preparing dinner on Mondays and Thursdays. She was also responsible for buying any groceries needed to prepare the meals. One Monday Maria bought an overripe avocado to use for guacamole that evening and some green tomatoes to use for a salad on Thursday. She thought the tomatoes would be juicy but still firm by Thursday evening. The grocery clerk put the avocado and tomatoes in a brown paper bag.

When Maria arrived at home, her father decided to take the family out to dinner. So she didn't have to prepare dinner that evening.

On Thursday, Maria opened the paper bag. The avocado was rotten, and the tomatoes were overripe—not firm as she had expected. Maria knew that fruits give off ethylene gas as they ripen. But the tomatoes ripened more quickly than they should have.

Think Critically: Why did the avocado rot? What caused the tomatoes to ripen more rapidly than expected?

that *saturated* hydrocarbons contain only single bonds between carbon atoms. Fats and oils can also be classified as unsaturated or saturated because parts of their molecules are similar to hydrocarbon molecules.

Isomers

Perhaps you have seen or know about butane, a gas sometimes burned in camping stoves and lighters. The chemical formula of butane is C_4H_{10}. Another hydrocarbon also has the same chemical formula as butane. How can this be? The answer lies in the arrangement of the four carbon atoms. Look at Figure 13-6. In a molecule of butane, the carbon atoms form a continuous chain. The carbon chain of isobutane is branched. The arrangement of carbon atoms in each compound changes the shape of the molecule. Isobutane and butane are isomers.

332 ORGANIC AND BIOLOGICAL COMPOUNDS

OPTIONS

INQUIRY QUESTIONS

▶ **Extend your knowledge of hydrocarbons by predicting the shape of a cyclobutane molecule.** *It is square.*

▶ **Explain why a double bond is expected to be stronger than a single bond.** *The electron cloud created by four electrons has a greater attraction for the two nuclei.*

▶ **What can you infer about the length of a double bond when compared to a single bond?** *The double bond is shorter because the extra electrons attract the nuclei closer together.*

PROGRAM RESOURCES

From the **Teacher Resource Package** use:

Cross-Curricular Connections, page 19, How Fattening Is Your Food?

Activity Worksheets, page 5, Flex Your Brain.

6 **Isomers** are compounds that have identical chemical formulas but different molecular structures and shapes. There are thousands of isomers among the hydrocarbons. Table 13-2 summarizes several properties of the two isomers of butane. As you can see, the structure of an isomer does affect some of the compound's properties.

Figure 13-6. Isomers of Butane

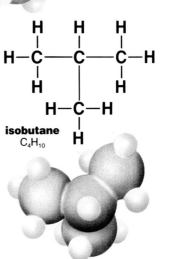

butane C_4H_{10}

Table 13-2

PROPERTIES OF BUTANE ISOMERS		
	Butane	**Isobutane**
Description	Colorless gas	Colorless gas
Density	0.6 kg/L	0.6 kg/L
Melting point	–138°C	–160°C
Boiling point	–0.5°C	–12°C

isobutane
C_4H_{10}

SECTION REVIEW

1. Why can carbon form so many organic compounds?
2. Compare and contrast ethane, ethene, and ethyne.
3. How is an unsaturated hydrocarbon different from a saturated hydrocarbon?
4. **Apply:** Cyclopropane is a saturated hydrocarbon containing three carbon atoms. In this compound, each carbon atom is bonded to two other carbon atoms. Draw its structural formula. Are cyclopropane and propane isomers? Explain.
5. **Connect to Physics:** Propene is used to make the fiber polypropylene, which is used in some insulating fabrics. Propene contains three carbon atoms and one double bond. Draw the structural formula for propene.

☑ **Making and Using Graphs**

Skill Builder

Make a graph of Table 13-1. For each compound, plot the number of carbon atoms on one axis and the number of hydrogen atoms on the other axis. Use the graph to predict the formula of hexane, which has six carbon atoms. If you need help, refer to Making and Using Graphs in the **Skill Handbook** on page 687.

13-1   SIMPLE ORGANIC COMPOUNDS   **333**

▶ Ask questions 1-3 and the **Apply** and **Connect to Physics** questions in the Section Review.

? **FLEX Your Brain**

Use the Flex Your Brain activity to have students explore ORGANIC COMPOUNDS.

ASSESSMENT
Portfolio: Use the Flex Your Brain activity to reinforce critical-thinking and problem-solving skills. In Step 2, students might list examples of isomers.

SECTION REVIEW ANSWERS

1. Carbon can form four covalent bonds with other atoms, including other carbon atoms. Thus carbon atoms can form long, branched chains. Also, the bonds can be single, double, or triple.

2. The three compounds are hydrocarbons, each containing two carbon atoms. Ethane is a saturated hydrocarbon; ethene contains a double covalent bond and ethyne contains a triple covalent bond.

3. A saturated hydrocarbon contains only single bonds between carbon atoms. An unsaturated hydrocarbon contains one or more double or triple bonds between carbon atoms.

4. Apply:

Cyclopropane, C_3H_6, is not an isomer of propane, C_3H_8, because it has a different chemical formula.

5. Connect to Physics:

Skill Builder

Hexane
C_6H_{14}

(Graph: x-axis "Number of carbon atoms" from 1 to 6; y-axis "Number of hydrogen atoms" from 0 to 14)

PREPARATION

SECTION BACKGROUND

▶ Aromatic compounds are economically important to many chemical industries including rubber, plastics, fibers, explosives, paint, and petroleum.

▶ Substituted hydrocarbons are generally more reactive than unsubstituted compounds. A halogen derivative has a halogen substituted for a hydrogen atom.

▶ Many organic compounds contain oxygen. Alcohols, ethers, aldehydes, ketones, carboxylic acids, and esters are classes of oxygen-containing organic chemicals.

▶ The symbol R– represents any hydrocarbon radical. Thus R–OH is the general formula for alcohols, and R–COOH is the general formula for organic acids.

PREPLANNING

▶ For Activity 13-1, prepare a 0.01M solution of potassium permanganate, and a 6.0M solution of sodium hydroxide. Allow the base solution to cool before using.

1 MOTIVATE

▶ Have students turn ahead to the Unit 5 opener on pages 376-377. Stinging insects, such as wasps and ants, are well known. Ask students if they know what causes the pain when they get stung. In some cases, it is formic acid, HCOOH, the simplest organic acid.

VideoDisc

STVS: Bacterial Digestion of Lignin, Disc 4, Side 1

New Science Words

aromatic compound
substituted hydrocarbon
alcohol

Objectives

▶ Describe characteristics of aromatic compounds.
▶ Classify groups of organic compounds as substituted hydrocarbons.

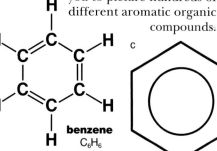

Figure 13-7. Vanilla extract comes from the dried pod of the vanilla orchid, shown above.

Aromatic Compounds

Do you like vanilla ice cream? Perhaps you know that vanilla flavor, like many flavors, is due largely to smell. What you taste is actually vanillin, the compound in vanilla extract that produces the vanilla flavor and smell. Another word for smell is aroma. So you might guess that aromatic compounds are smelly—and most of them are. An **aromatic compound** is a compound that contains the benzene ring structure. Look at a model of benzene, C_6H_6, and its structural formula, Figure 13-8. As you can see, the benzene molecule has six carbon atoms bonded into a ring. The electrons shown as three double bonds and three single bonds that form the ring are actually shared by all six carbon atoms in the ring. This equal sharing of electrons is represented by the special symbol shown in (c). The sharing of these electrons causes the benzene molecule to be very stable. Many compounds contain this stable ring structure.

Knowing the structure of benzene can help you to picture hundreds of different aromatic organic compounds.

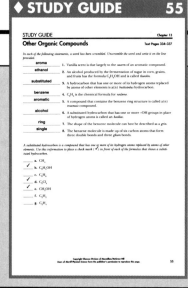

Figure 13-8. Benzene, C_6H_6, can be represented by (a) a space-filling model, (b) a structural formula, or (c) the benzene ring symbol.

334 ORGANIC AND BIOLOGICAL COMPOUNDS

OPTIONS

Meeting Different Ability Levels

For Section 13-2, use the following **Teacher Resource Masters** depending upon individual students' needs.

◆ **Study Guide Master** for all students.
● **Reinforcement Master** for students of average and above average ability levels.
▲ **Enrichment Master** for above average students.

Additional Teacher Resource Package masters are listed in any PROGRAM RESOURCES boxes that are in the section. The additional masters are appropriate for all students.

◆ STUDY GUIDE   55

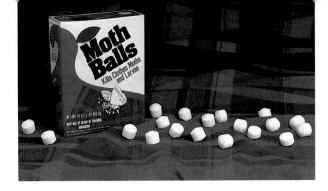

naphthalene
$C_{10}H_8$

Figure 13-9. Moth crystals are naphthalene.

One example is naphthalene. Can you recognize the odor of moth crystals? One type of moth crystals is made of naphthalene, as shown in Figure 13-9. Notice that naphthalene is made up of two fused ring structures.

Substituted Hydrocarbons

Usually, a cheeseburger is a hamburger covered with melted American cheese and served on a bun. However, you can make a cheeseburger with Swiss cheese and serve it on slices of bread. If you ate this cheeseburger, you would notice how the substitutions affect the taste.

Chemists make similar changes to hydrocarbons. These changes produce compounds called substituted hydrocarbons. A **substituted hydrocarbon** has one or more of its hydrogen atoms replaced by atoms of other elements.

For example, a compound used in dry cleaning, tetrachloroethene, C_2Cl_4, is a substituted hydrocarbon. The prefix *tetra-* means "four," and *chloro-* refers to chlorine. Figure 13-10 shows that C_2Cl_4 is formed when four chlorine atoms replace the hydrogen atoms in ethene, C_2H_4.

Have you ever used rubbing alcohol to soothe aching muscles after too much exercise? Did you know you were using a substituted hydrocarbon? Alcohols are an important group of organic compounds. An **alcohol** is formed when –OH groups replace one or more hydrogen atoms in a hydrocarbon, as shown in Figure 13-11. Ethanol, C_2H_5OH, is an alcohol produced by the fermentation of sugar in corn and other grains and in many fruits. Alcoholic beverages contain ethanol. As you will learn in the next section, this alcohol is sometimes added

Connect to... Life Science

In the manufacture of soap, glycerol, an alcohol with three carbon atoms and three –OH groups, is formed. Diagram the structure of glycerol.

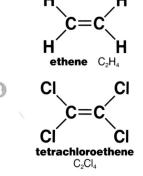

ethene C_2H_4

tetrachloroethene
C_2Cl_4

Figure 13-10. Tetrachloroethene is a substituted hydrocarbon.

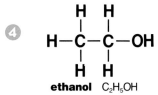

ethanol C_2H_5OH

Figure 13-11. Ethanol is one of many alcohols.

335

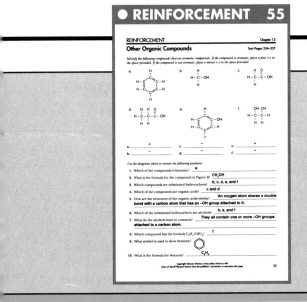

Have students recall and discuss when they have seen explosives such as TNT detonated on TV or in movies. Make a model of benzene. Then, in front of the class, remove a hydrogen atom and replace it with a methyl, –CH₃, group. Now you have toluene. Replace the two hydrogens on either side of the methyl group with two nitro, –NO₂, groups. Remove the hydrogen opposite the methyl and replace it with a third nitro group. You now have a model of trinitrotoluene, TNT.

Connect to... Life Science

2 TEACH

Key Concepts are highlighted.

CONCEPT DEVELOPMENT

▶ Students may want to know that alcohols are defined as poisons because they adversely affect enzyme systems that regulate the speed of chemical reactions. Alcohol slows down the brain's chemistry.

CHECK FOR UNDERSTANDING

Use the Mini Quiz to check for understanding.

MINI QUIZ

Use the Mini Quiz to check students' recall of chapter content.

1. A compound that contains a benzene ring is classified as a(n) _____ compound. *aromatic*
2. Why is the benzene molecule very stable? *Electrons are shared by all six carbon atoms.*
3. Which element has been replaced in a substituted hydrocarbon? *hydrogen*
4. When a hydrogen atom is replaced with an –OH group, the compound formed is a(n) _____. *alcohol*

Have students construct models of substituted hydrocarbons using gumdrops of colors different from those used for the MINI-Lab on page 330.

EXTENSION
For students who have mastered this section, use the **Reinforcement** and **Enrichment** masters or other OPTIONS provided.

3 CLOSE

▶ Ask questions 1-2 and the **Apply** and **Connect to Life Science** questions in the Section Review.

SECTION REVIEW ANSWERS
1. All aromatic compounds contain the benzene ring.
2. (a) Chlorine atoms have replaced the hydrogen atoms in a hydrocarbon; (b) an –OH group has replaced a hydrogen atom in a hydrocarbon; (c) a –COOH group has replaced a hydrogen atom in a hydrocarbon.
3. Apply: A poisonous substance is added to ethanol to deter someone from drinking it; the person will become ill.
4. Connect to Life Science: Ethane is C_2H_6. In C_2H_5Cl, a Cl atom has been substituted for an H atom.

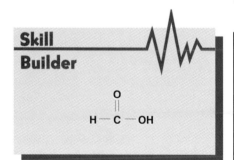

Skill Builder

O
‖
H — C — OH

Table 13-3

COMMON ALCOHOLS				
	Methanol	**Ethanol**	**Isopropyl alcohol (rubbing alcohol)**	**Phenol**
	H H-C-OH H	H H H-C-C-OH H H	H OH H H-C-C-C-H H H H	◯—OH
Uses Fuel	✓	✓		
Cleaner	✓	✓	✓	
Disinfectant		✓	✓	✓
Manufacturing chemicals	✓		✓	✓

H H
H—C—C—H
H H
ethane
C_2H_6

H H
H—C—C—OH
ethanol H H
C_2H_5OH

H O
H—C—C—OH
acetic acid
H CH_3COOH

Figure 13-12. The structures of these compounds are similar.

to gasoline. Ethanol is also a good cleaning fluid because it can dissolve substances that don't dissolve in water. Several alcohols are listed in Table 13-3.

Recall that vinegar contains acetic acid. Acetic acid is an example of an organic acid. Many fruit juices contain similar organic acids. Look at Figure 13-12. The structures of ethane, ethanol, and acetic acid are similar. Do you see that acetic acid is a substituted hydrocarbon?

SECTION REVIEW
1. What do the structures of all aromatic compounds have in common?
2. How is each of the following a substituted hydrocarbon: (a) tetrachloroethene, (b) ethanol, (c) acetic acid?
3. **Apply:** Why is ethanol intended for use as a solvent denatured by the addition of a poisonous substance?
4. **Connect to Life Science:** Chloroethane, C_2H_5Cl, can be used as a spray-on anesthetic for localized injuries. How does chloroethane fit the definition of a substituted hydrocarbon? Diagram its structure.

Skill Builder ☑ **Interpreting Scientific Illustrations**
Formic acid, HCOOH, is the simplest organic acid. Draw its structural formula by referring to Figure 13-12. If you need help, refer to Interpreting Scientific Illustrations in the **Skill Handbook** on page 689.

OPTIONS

ASSESSMENT—ORAL
▶ Write the chemical formula for trichloromethane, commonly called chloroform. $CHCl_3$
▶ Write a formula for methanol. Methyl alcohol or wood alcohol are common names. CH_3OH
▶ When –COOH is substituted for a hydrogen atom, an organic acid forms. Write the formula for ethanoic acid, also known as acetic acid and vinegar. CH_3COOH

PROGRAM RESOURCES
From the **Teacher Resource Package** use:
Technology, pages 13-14, Making Paper Less Perishable.
Critical Thinking/Problem Solving, page 19, Reformulated Gasoline.

Skill Builder
ASSESSMENT
Oral: Ask students to count and report the number of bonds they made to the carbon atom in the structure.

Alcohols and Organic Acids

Have you ever wondered how chemists change one substance into another? You have learned that changing the bonding among atoms holds the key to that process. In this activity you will provide an environment in a test tube that will cause the bonding in an alcohol to change in a way that changes the alcohol into a useful acid.

Materials

- test tube and stopper
- 1 mL 0.01M potassium permanganate solution
- 1 mL 6M sodium hydroxide solution
- 3 drops of ethanol
- goggles
- apron
- graduated cylinder

Procedure

1. Pour 1 mL of 0.01M potassium permanganate solution and 1 mL of 6M sodium hydroxide solution into a test tube. **CAUTION:** *Handle both of these chemicals with care; immediately flush any spill with water.*
2. Add three drops of ethanol to the test tube.
3. Stopper the test tube and gently shake it for one minute. *Observe* and record any changes you notice in the tube for the next five minutes.

Data and Observations Sample Data

Changes in Mixture

Within a few seconds the mixture should change from purple to green. Over the next few minutes the solution should turn brown.

Analyze

1. What is the structural formula for ethanol?
2. What part of a molecule identifies a compound as an alcohol?
3. What part of a molecule identifies a compound as an organic acid?

Conclude and Apply

4. What evidence did you *observe* of a chemical change taking place in the test tube?
5. In the presence of potassium permanganate, an alcohol may undergo a chemical change into an acid. If the alcohol used is ethanol, what would you *predict* to be the formula of the acid produced?
6. The acid from ethanol is found in a common household product. What is the acid's name? In what common household product is the acid found?

OBJECTIVE: **Recognize** the evidence of the chemical reaction of an organic compound.

PROCESS SKILLS applied in this activity:
▶ **Observing** in Procedure Step 3.
▶ **Predicting** in Conclude and Apply Question 5.

COOPERATIVE LEARNING
Use the Science Investigation Team strategy in carrying out the procedure, in observing, and in drawing conclusions.

TEACHING THE ACTIVITY

Alternate Materials: Use 95% ethanol if you have it. If you use ethanol from a drugstore, increase the amount according to the percentage of ethanol in the solution. Five or six drops could be used.

Troubleshooting: Students should observe the reaction mixture carefully to note the two color changes that take place.

▶ Show students how to shake a tube by holding it at the lip with fingers of one hand while swinging it against the palm of the other hand. This method is preferable to shaking it up and down.

▶ Prepare 6.0M NaOH by dissolving 24 g of solid NaOH in 100 mL of distilled water. **CAUTION:** *Sodium hydroxide is very caustic and the solution will become hot. Prepare only in a heat resistant glass container.*

▶ Prepare 0.01M $KMnO_4$ by dissolving 0.16 g $KMnO_4$ in 100 mL of distilled water.

▶ The characteristic odor of acetic acid is unlikely to be noticed. In alkaline solution, the acetic acid formed will rapidly react with the NaOH to form sodium acetate and water.

ANSWERS TO QUESTIONS

1.

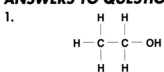

2. the hydroxyl group, –OH
3. the carboxylic acid group, –COOH
4. The color changes from purple to green to brown.

5.

6. acetic acid; in vinegar

Activity
ASSESSMENT
Performance: To further assess students' understanding of alcohols and organic acids, see USING LAB SKILLS, Question 11, on page 348.

PROGRAM RESOURCES
From the **Teacher Resource Package** use:

Activity Worksheets, pages 102-103, Activity 13-1: Alcohols and Organic Acids.

SECTION 13-3

PREPARATION

SECTION BACKGROUND
▶ Synfuels or synthetic fuels are derived from organic sources that are more difficult to convert or are environmentally less acceptable than traditional fuels. Grains, sugars, and wood can produce ethanol and methanol. Tar sands, oil shale, and coal can be used to produce synthetic fuels.

1 MOTIVATE

▶ **Demonstration:** Place a small amount of ethanol in an evaporating dish. Slowly add enough saturated calcium acetate solution to cause the alcohol to solidify. Show the class the jellied alcohol, then darken the room and ignite it. **CAUTION:** *Keep flammable materials clear.* Point out that the flame is burning clean and blue in color. This demonstration shows the class one way that fuels can be modified; burning solids is safer than burning liquids.

VideoDisc
STVS: Water Hyacinth, Disc 4, Side 2

Answer: Accept all supported opinions. Some examples would include biomass, biogas, nuclear, and geothermal.

PROGRAM RESOURCES
From the **Teacher Resource Package** use:

Science Integration Activity 13

13-3 Alternative Sources of Energy

New Science Words

biomass
biogas
energy farming
gasohol

Objectives

▶ Describe the role of biomass as a source of two fuels for increasing our energy supply.
▶ Analyze the positive and negative effects of the widespread use of ethanol and gasohol.

Why Not New Fuels?

What heating fuels have you used today? Probably the main sources of energy you use are natural gas, coal, or petroleum. But did you know that most people in the world rely on biomass for their energy supply? **Biomass** refers to all animal and plant material, both dead and alive. Wood, leaves, animal and human wastes, and food waste are all biomass.

If plant and animal wastes are allowed to rot in the absence of air, bacteria break down the wastes to produce biogas. **Biogas** is mainly methane, just like natural gas. People in rural areas in Third World countries cook, heat their homes, and generate electricity with biogas. China has some four million factories that produce biogas. This fuel is such a promising source of additional energy supplies that proposals have been made for energy farming. **Energy farming** involves growing plants for use as fuel. One proposal is to use the troublesome water hyacinth that clogs waterways.

What is the composition of biomass?

Suppose it was announced that the United States would have no petroleum-based fuels available at the end of next year. **In your Journal**, write what you think would be our most likely alternative energy source. Explain your answer.

OPTIONS

Meeting Different Ability Levels
For Section 13-3, use the following **Teacher Resource Masters** depending upon individual students' needs.

◆ **Study Guide Master** for all students.
● **Reinforcement Master** for students of average and above average ability levels.
▲ **Enrichment Master** for above average students.

Additional Teacher Resource Package masters are listed in any PROGRAM RESOURCES boxes that are in the section. The additional masters are appropriate for all students.

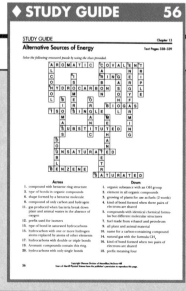

Did you ever see a sign like the one to the right? **Gasohol** is a combination of ethanol and gasoline. If you have ridden in a car fueled with gasohol, you have used a product of biomass. Recall that fermentation produces the ethanol found in alcoholic beverages. The same process of fermentation is used with a variety of grains and fruits to produce ethanol for use as a fuel. Pure ethanol can be used in cars if the engines are modified slightly. Car engines do not have to be modified to burn gasohol. When gasoline is in short supply, gasohol finds wider use.

At first, biogas and gasohol seem like ideal energy sources. Yet producing them commercially results in numerous environmental problems. Among these are disturbing the ecosystem, fertilizer runoff, erosion, and air pollution. The decision for or against large-scale production of biogas and gasohol may not be an easy one.

Clearly the conversion of biomass to easily handled fuels such as methane and ethanol is an interesting possibility for supplying part of our energy needs. But, large-scale tests of energy production from biomass have not yet been carried out in the United States.

SECTION REVIEW

1. In what two major ways is biomass used as a source of fuels?
2. What are the main pros, cons, and concerns related to the use of ethanol in gasohol?
3. **Connect to Earth Science:** Using gasohol helps conserve Earth's resources. When gasohol is made from ethanol and gasoline, is a compound produced, or is a mixture produced? Explain your answer.

You Decide!

Increasing the production and use of both biogas and gasohol may help the United States to cope with petroleum shortages. Should government agencies encourage the production of these fuels? Why or why not?

EcoTip

If you have a garden, grow beans or peas between other plants. The bacteria in the roots of peas and beans supply the soil with nitrogen, which is needed by other plants.

SCIENCE & SOCIETY

● **REINFORCEMENT** 56

▲ **ENRICHMENT** 56

339

---

2 TEACH

Key Concepts are highlighted.

CONCEPT DEVELOPMENT
▶ Ask students how water hyacinths could be used as an energy source.

CHECK FOR UNDERSTANDING
Ask questions 1 and 2 and the **Connect to Earth Science** question in the Section Review.

RETEACH
Have students bring in and report on news articles and photographs of alternative energy sources.

EXTENSION
For students who have mastered this section, use the **Reinforcement** and **Enrichment** masters or other OPTIONS provided.

3 CLOSE

▶ Have students prepare for and stage a debate or a panel discussion of the You Decide feature.

SECTION REVIEW ANSWERS
1. Waste biomass is used as a source of biogas, which is mainly methane. Plant biomass is a source of ethanol used in gasohol.
2. Pro: The use of ethanol in gasohol would reduce dependence on petroleum and would take advantage of agricultural capacity. Con: Growing larger supplies of plants could increase erosion, fertilizer runoff, disturbance of the ecosystem, and air pollution. Also, no one is sure whether gasohol will be cost effective.
3. Connect to Earth Science: Gasohol is a mixture because the ratio of components may vary.

YOU DECIDE!

Answers will vary, but should include reference to pros and cons as summarized in answer to question 2, above.

PREPARATION

SECTION BACKGROUND

▶ Approximately one-half of our non-water mass consists of proteins. These form muscle, cartilage, and tendons. One-half of the protein in the human body is used as biological catalysts called enzymes.

▶ Nucleic acids are polymers of nucleotides. The nucleotide is composed of three parts—a nitrogen base, a sugar, and a phosphate group.

▶ The carbohydrates glycogen, starch, and cellulose differ simply in the way glucose monomers are linked together. The process of breaking down carbohydrates into CO_2 and H_2O is the chief energy source of most organisms.

▶ Lipids can be divided into different groups. One group is fats which are esters formed from glycerol and fatty acids. Fatty acids are carboxylic acids with 12 to 20 carbon atoms in the chain. Steroids are another group of lipids that contain a tetracyclic ring system. Some vitamins are lipids and form another group. Vitamins aid enzyme reactions.

PREPLANNING

▶ To prepare for Activity 13-2, you will need index cards and paper clips. Crayons or colored markers can be used if available.

1 MOTIVATE

▶ **Demonstration:** Before class, prepare a 70-cm-long chain of paper clips and place it in a small box with one end of the chain clipped at the edge of the box. In class, add loose paper clips, monomers, to the same box. Cover the box with your hand and gently shake to simulate a polymerization reaction. Uncover the box and pull out the previously connected paper clips to the amazement of your students.

New Science Words

polymers
proteins
nucleic acids
carbohydrates
lipids

Objectives

▶ Describe the formation of polymers and discuss their importance as biological compounds.
▶ Compare and contrast proteins, nucleic acids, carbohydrates, and lipids.

Proteins

Did you ever loop together strips of paper to make paper chains for decorations? Have you ever strung paper clips together as a prank? Both a paper chain and a string of paper clips are very much like polymers. **Polymers** are ❶ huge molecules made of many smaller organic molecules that have formed new bonds and linked together. The smaller molecules are called monomers. Monomers are usually very similar in size and structure. You can picture a monomer as an individual loop of paper or an individual paper clip. The photograph on the left shows this model of a polymer. As you will see in Chapter 14, plastics are polymers. Many of the important biological compounds in your body also are polymers. Among them are the proteins.

Proteins are polymers formed from organic ❷ compounds called amino acids. Even though there are millions of different proteins, there are only 20 common amino acids.

Different types of ❸ proteins make up many of the tissues in your body, such as muscles and tendons, as well as your hair and fingernails. A protein in your blood called hemoglobin carries oxygen, Figure 13-13.

Figure 13-13. Blood contains a complex protein called hemoglobin.

OPTIONS

Meeting Different Ability Levels

For Section 13-4, use the following **Teacher Resource Masters** depending upon individual students' needs.

◆ **Study Guide Master** for all students.

● **Reinforcement Master** for students of average and above average ability levels.

▲ **Enrichment Master** for above average students.

Additional Teacher Resource Package masters are listed in any **PROGRAM RESOURCES** boxes that are in the section. The additional masters are appropriate for all students.

◆ **STUDY GUIDE** 57

STUDY GUIDE — Chapter 13
Biological Compounds — Text Pages 340–346

Use the clues below to fill in the missing terms in the puzzle. When you have completed the puzzle, another term will be spelled vertically in the section marked A by the black box.

1. C A R B O H Y D R A T E S
2. P R O T E I N S
3. A M I N O
4. P O L Y M E R S
5. M O N O M E R S
6. S U G A R S
7. L I P I D S
8. N U C L E I C A C I D S
9. D N A
10. O I L S

Clues
1. organic compounds in which there are twice as many hydrogen atoms as oxygen atoms
2. organic compounds that make up many of the tissues in the human body
3. acids that make up proteins
4. huge molecules made up of many smaller organic molecules
5. small molecules that make up polymers
6. type of carbohydrate that includes glucose and sucrose
7. group of organic compounds that includes fats and oils
8. polymers that control the activities and reproduction of cells
9. nucleic acid that codes genetic information
10. unsaturated lipids that come mostly from plants

57

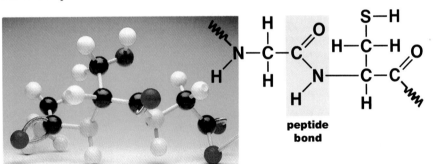

glycine   cysteine

Figure 13-14. Two Amino Acids

The enzymes that regulate chemical reactions in your body are proteins. In fact, proteins account for 15 percent of your weight. That's about half the weight of all materials other than water in your body.

Two amino acids are shown in Figure 13-14. Notice that each molecule of an amino acid contains a –COOH group and an –NH₂ group. The –COOH group is the carboxylic acid group. If you look again at Figure 13-12 on page 336, you'll see that the structure of this group appears also in acetic acid. The –NH₂ group is called the amine group. Both groups appear in every amino acid.

In a protein polymer, peptide bonds link together molecules of amino acids. Peptide bonds form when the amine group of one amino acid combines with the organic acid group of another amino acid. Look at Figure 13-16. You might think of the 20 amino acids as letters of an alphabet. Each protein is a word spelled with these letters. However, unlike English words, words in this alphabet may contain hundreds of letters. Actually, some proteins may contain thousands of amino acids.

Your body makes proteins from amino acids. The amino acids come from eating and digesting foods that contain proteins. Digestion breaks the protein polymers into monomers of amino acids, which your body uses to make new proteins.

In Your **JOURNAL**

Write the word *protein* in your **Journal.** Make as many words as you can from the seven letters found in the word. Explain how this activity is similar to what could be done with seven amino acids being used to make proteins.

Figure 13-15. Some High-Protein Foods

Figure 13-16. The protein molecule contains many peptide bonds.

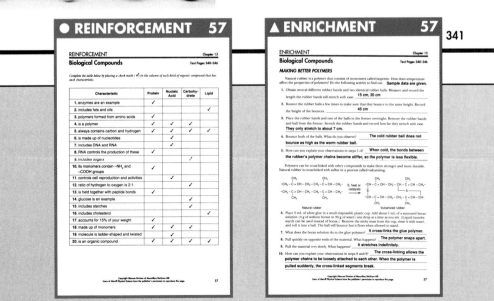

peptide bond

TYING TO PREVIOUS KNOWLEDGE: In the party supplies section of toy stores you can find a spray can of string confetti. This polymer can be shown to students by spraying a string from the can. A 100-g can will produce about 100 meters of polymer for about $2.00.

2 TEACH

Key Concepts are highlighted.

CONCEPT DEVELOPMENT

▶ **Demonstration:** Show students a polymer being formed by making nylon. Commercially available solutions of sebacoyl chloride and 1,6-diaminohexane are available from your science supplier. Layer the two solutions in a small beaker. Using forceps, pick up the center of the film that forms at the interface of the two liquids. Slowly pull the nylon string from the beaker and roll it up on a graduated cylinder that has been wrapped with a paper towel.

▶ **Demonstration:** Plastics are polymers and some are foamed by having gas blown into them. Place a small amount of acetone or alcohol in the bottom of a 600-mL beaker. Add to the solvent a large volume of the polystyrene foam "peanuts" used in shipping containers. Allow the acetone to evaporate overnight. A disc of solid polystyrene will remain.

In Your **JOURNAL**

Answer: The letter sequence can make new words when varied. In a similar way, varying the sequence of a group of amino acids can make new proteins.

REVEALING MISCONCEPTIONS

▶ To many people, *polymer* is another name for plastic. Be certain students understand that plastic is only one of many kinds of polymers.

CROSS CURRICULUM

▶ **Language Arts:** Percy Lavon Julian (1899-1975) synthesized progesterone, testosterone, and cortisone. These are steroids. Have some students research medical uses of steroids, such as treatment of inflammation and estrogen replacement therapy during menopause. Other students could research effects of using steroids in sports and body building. All students should write reports documenting their findings. The school librarian should be advised in advance of this assignment.

CONCEPT DEVELOPMENT

▶ **Demonstration:** Nucleic acids are polymer chains that are cross linked. These cross links are somewhat like the rungs on a ladder. You can demonstrate cross linking by placing 5 mL of Elmer's white glue in a small disposable plastic cup. Add saturated borax solution, 4 g sodium borate in 96 mL water, dropwise as you stir the white glue. About 1 mL of borax solution will be required. A sticky ball will form. Remove it from the cup and rinse it with tap water. Roll it into a ball and bounce it. The borax cross links the polymer chains in the white glue to form a synthetic rubber.

▶ Point out to students the cross linking in DNA using the models pictured in Figure 13-17. In humans, cytosine pairs with thymine while adenine pairs with guanine to form the cross links. The genetic code is the order in which these bases occur.

Did You Know?

Rubber, a natural polymer, is an organic substance that was named because it could be used to rub out pencil marks.

What are nucleotides?

Nucleic Acids

The nucleic acids are another important group of organic compounds that are necessary for life. **Nucleic acids** are polymers that control the activities and reproduction of cells. One kind of nucleic acid, deoxyribonucleic acid (DNA), is found in the nuclei of cells. DNA codes and stores genetic information. Figure 13-17 shows a model of the structure for a portion of the DNA polymer. It resembles a twisted ladder. Like other polymers, DNA is made up of monomers. With the genetic code, DNA controls the production of ribonucleic acid (RNA), another kind of nucleic acid. RNA, in turn, controls the production of proteins that will make new cells.

The monomers that make up DNA are called nucleotides. Each nucleotide looks like one-half of a ladder rung with an attached side piece. As you can see, each pair of nucleotides forms a rung on the ladder, while the side pieces give the ladder a little twist. Because the nucleotides may be made up of different organic compounds, all the ladder rungs are not the same. Unless you're an identical twin, your DNA differs from that of every other person because the nucleotides and their locations are not the same in any two polymers.

Figure 13-17. DNA Models

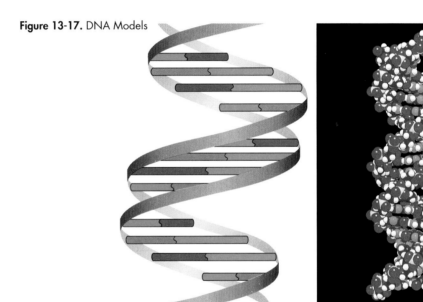

342 ORGANIC AND BIOLOGICAL COMPOUNDS

OPTIONS

ASSESSMENT—ORAL

▶ **What similarities exist between a colored paper chain and a protein?** *Both have small units (monomers) linked together.*

▶ **The DNA molecule is described as a double helix in biology courses. In your textbook, what words are used to describe this structure?** *twisted ladder*

▶ **When two amino acids link together, the bond is called a peptide bond, and the resulting molecule is called a dipeptide. What science word in this section refers to polypeptides?** *proteins*

▶ **Use the percentage value given in the text to calculate the amount of protein in a person whose mass is 50 kg (110 lb of weight).** *7.5 kg (16.5 lb)*

PROGRAM RESOURCES

From the **Teacher Resource Package** use:

Transparency Masters, pages 51-52, Biological Polymers.

Use **Color Transparency** number 26, Biological Polymers.

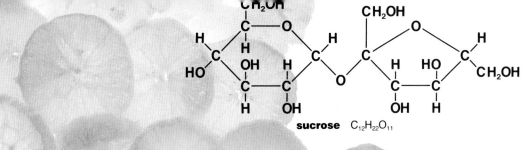

sucrose $C_{12}H_{22}O_{11}$

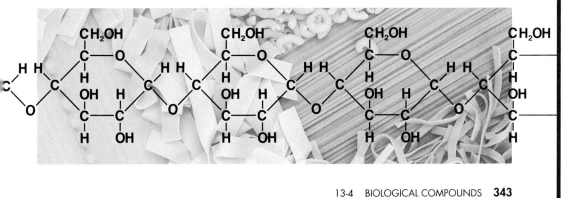

glucose $C_6H_{12}O_6$

Figure 13-18. Sucrose and glucose are sugars found in foods. Fruits contain glucose and another simple sugar called fructose.

What is the formula for the sugar found in your blood?

Figure 13-19. Starch is the major component of pasta.

Carbohydrates

If you hear the word *carbohydrate*, you may think of a sweet fruit or sugary treat. Do you also think of carbohydrate loading by athletes? Runners, for example, often prepare in advance for a long-distance race by eating, or "loading," carbohydrates in starchy foods such as vegetables and pasta. Starches provide high-energy, long-lasting fuel for the body.

⑤ **Carbohydrates** are organic compounds in which there are twice as many hydrogen atoms as oxygen atoms. One group of carbohydrates is the sugars, as shown in Figure 13-18. The sugar glucose is found in your blood and also in many sweet foods such as grapes and honey. The sugar sucrose is common table sugar. By counting the hydrogen and oxygen atoms in each formula, you will see that these sugars are carbohydrates.

⑥ Figure 13-19 shows a part of a starch molecule. Starch is a carbohydrate that is also a polymer. During digestion, sucrose and starch are broken down into monomers of glucose and similar sugars.

13-4 BIOLOGICAL COMPOUNDS **343**

CONCEPT DEVELOPMENT

▶ **Demonstration:** During digestion, enzymes break down starch into monomers of glucose, a simple sugar. Give each student a small piece of cracker or bread and have them chew it many times without swallowing until they notice the taste change. The enzyme ptyalin in the mouth's saliva has already begun the process of breaking the polymeric starch into monomers of the sugar glucose.

▶ Emphasize that carbohydrates are made of carbon, hydrogen, and oxygen. Ask students what some of the end products of cellular respiration are. They exhale carbon dioxide and water vapor. Point out to students that these compounds are made of the elements that make up carbohydrates. Discuss how the energy of the broken chemical bonds is used for life's processes.

▶ **Demonstration:** Place a 100-mL beaker on a tray in a fume hood or outdoors. Half-fill the beaker with sucrose, cane sugar. Add 40 mL of concentrated sulfuric acid to the sugar. **CAUTION:** *Acid is corrosive. The reaction gives off hot gases. Wear goggles and an apron.* Water vapor will be released indicating that hydrogen and oxygen are present. The solid product remaining is easily observed to be carbon. Point out to students that sugars link together to form carbohydrates.

MINI QUIZ

Use the Mini Quiz to check students' recall of chapter content.

① A(n) _____ is formed from many small organic molecules bonded together to form a huge molecule. *polymer*

② Proteins result from the linking of many monomers called _____ . *amino acids*

③ A polymer that makes up muscle, tendons, and hair is _____ . *protein*

④ What type of polymer controls the activities and reproduction of cells? *nucleic acid*

VideoDisc

STVS: Blood Clot Treatment, Disc 7, Side 1

TECHNOLOGY

For more information on fake fats, see "Ersatz Fat: Do New Synthetic Foodstuffs Mean Worry-Free Indulgence?" by Virginia DeMoss, *Bicycling*, June 1990, pp. 112-113.

Think Critically: Although these compounds occur in nature, they are not chemically combined. Once combined, they form a new substance with an entirely new set of properties.

CONCEPT DEVELOPMENT

▶ Materials rich in unsaturated fatty acids from plants are generally oils at room temperature. Saturated fats, such as those from animals and plant oils that have been hydrogenated, tend to be solids at room temperature.

▶ Interested students might want to research the relationship of the lipid cholesterol to heart and artery disease.

CHECK FOR UNDERSTANDING

Use the Mini Quiz to check for understanding.

MINI QUIZ

Use the Mini Quiz to check students' recall of chapter content.

5 Organic compounds that contain twice as many hydrogen atoms as oxygen atoms are classified as _____ . *carbohydrates*

6 Starch is a carbohydrate that is also a(n) _____ . *polymer*

7 Fats, oils, and related compounds make up a group of organic compounds known as _____ . *lipids*

8 Does cholesterol have any good use in the body? *Yes, it is used to build cell membranes.*

Fake Fats

Scientists at a company that produces processed foods have synthesized a molecule that promises the look and "mouth feel" of fats, but with no cholesterol and fewer calories. In a process involving heat and pressure, soybean or some other oil is combined with sugar. The result is a very large, complex molecule called a sucrose polyester. The enzyme responsible for breaking down fats during digestion has no effect on the sucrose polyester. So this "fake fat" passes through the body mostly unchanged.

A second fat substitute has been announced by another company. Because this product is made by combining water with egg or milk protein, its makers maintain that it is all natural. Special techniques shape the proteins into spheres to give the substance the smooth feel of fats. This compound substitutes protein and water for fat, so it is much lower in calories than fat. But because the product forms a gel when it is heated, it is limited to use in uncooked foods.

Think Critically: Both the sugar and oils used in one "fake fat" occur naturally. Why is this fat substitute considered synthetic?

Lipids

Fats, oils, and related compounds make up a group of **7** organic compounds known as **lipids.** Lipids include animal fats, such as butter, and vegetable oils, such as corn oil. Lipids contain the same elements as carbohydrates contain, but in different proportions.

Have you heard that eating too much fat can be unhealthy? You may also have heard that you should substitute unsaturated fats for saturated ones. Fats and oils are similar in structure to hydrocarbons, so they can be classified as saturated and unsaturated, according to the types

Figure 13-20. At room temperature, fats are normally solids, and oils are usually liquids.

OPTIONS

INQUIRY QUESTIONS

▶ **Which of the biological compound classifications would you apply to the components of milk?** *Milk contains minerals, water, lactose (a carbohydrate), casein (protein), vitamins, and fat. All three classifications apply.*

▶**Why do you think unsaturated vegetable oil is less likely to contribute to artery and heart disease than is saturated animal fat?** *The double bonds in the unsaturated oil are more chemically reactive than are single bonds. Thus, the unsaturated oil can be broken down more easily by enzymes in the cell.*

PROGRAM RESOURCES

From the **Teacher Resource Package** use:

Science and Society, page 17, The Cholesterol Controversy.

Concept Mapping, pages 31-32.

Activity Worksheets, page 5, Flex Your Brain.

Use **Laboratory Manual 28,** The Breakdown of Starch; **29,** Testing for a Vitamin.

Figure 13-21. Fats can be classified by the types of bonds in their carbon chains.

of bonds in their carbon chains. Saturated fats contain only single bonds between carbon atoms and unsaturated fats contain at least one double bond. Most animal fats contain a great deal of saturated fats. Oils from plants are mainly unsaturated.

Another lipid found in animal foods is cholesterol. Even if you never eat foods containing cholesterol, your body would make its own supply. Cholesterol is used by the body to build cell membranes and is also found in bile, a digestive fluid. ⑧

There is evidence that too much saturated fat and cholesterol in the diet contributes to heart disease and that unsaturated fats may help to prevent heart disease. A balanced diet includes some fats, just as it includes proteins and carbohydrates.

Connect to... Life Science

Check the label on any available carton of milk. What percentage of fat is in the milk? What are the advantages of drinking lowfat milk?

Which fats, animal or plant, are mainly unsaturated?

SECTION REVIEW

1. What is a polymer? Why are polymers important organic compounds?
2. Compare and contrast proteins and nucleic acids.
3. **Apply:** Is ethanol a carbohydrate? Explain.
4. **Connect to Life Science:** Explain how alteration of DNA structure could affect the function of enzymes in an organism.

☑ Concept Mapping

Use a network tree to describe types of fats including the terms *saturated fats, unsaturated fats, single bonds,* and *double bonds.* If you need help, refer to Concept Mapping in the **Skill Handbook** on pages 684 and 685.

Skill Builder

Skill Builder

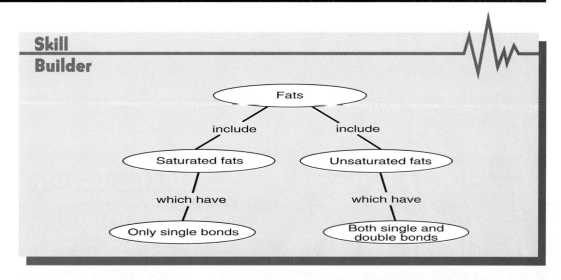

ACTIVITY 13-2

OBJECTIVE: Model the bonding between monomers found in starches and proteins.
Time: 40 minutes

PROCESS SKILLS applied in this activity are **building models, predicting,** and **inferring.**

PREPARATION

Different colored markers may be used on white index cards if colored cards are not available.

Cooperative Learning: Use the Paired Partner strategy to draw structures on cards.

THINKING CRITICALLY

The –OH from one monomer can join with an –H from another monomer, leaving an area on both monomers that can then bond.

TEACHING THE ACTIVITY

Refer to the ***Activity Worksheets*** *for additional information and teaching strategies.*

- Be sure students understand the importance of placing the bonding sites on the edges of the cards.
- The structures for the amino acids glycine and cysteine are shown on page 341 of the student text. Other amino acids may be used in addition to those shown on page 341.

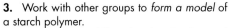

ACTIVITY 13-2 DESIGNING AN EXPERIMENT
Mixing Many Monomers

You may have heard the expression, "You are what you eat." This is true because your digestive system changes food into useful compounds in your body. To better understand this personal chemistry involving biological polymers, this activity directs you to design a model of the bonding involved in glucose and in amino acids.

Getting Started

Review the structures shown in Figures 13-14, 13-16, and 13-18. You will need to know these basic structures in order to make two important biological polymers—protein and starch.

Thinking Critically

How can some monomers, such as amino acids and glucose, bond together to make polymers, such as proteins and starch?

Materials

Your cooperative group will need:
- 2 different colors of index cards
- paper clips

Try It!

1. Draw the structure of glucose on one side of a certain color notecard. Be sure to position your diagram as is shown in the photograph.
2. To represent the attractions involved in bonding, attach a paper clip where the –OH group touches the left edge of the card. Attach another paper clip on the H atom at the opposite side of the card.
3. Work with other groups to *form a model* of a starch polymer.
4. Select another, differently colored index card and draw the structure of a simple amino acid on one side.
5. Use paper clips to locate the most likely area of the molecule for attachment to other amino acids. With the help of amino acid models from other groups, put together a model of a protein.

Summing Up/Sharing Results

What important difference do you notice about the monomer makeup of the two polymer models?

Going Further!

How can you use the same amino acid model cards to form two different protein polymers?

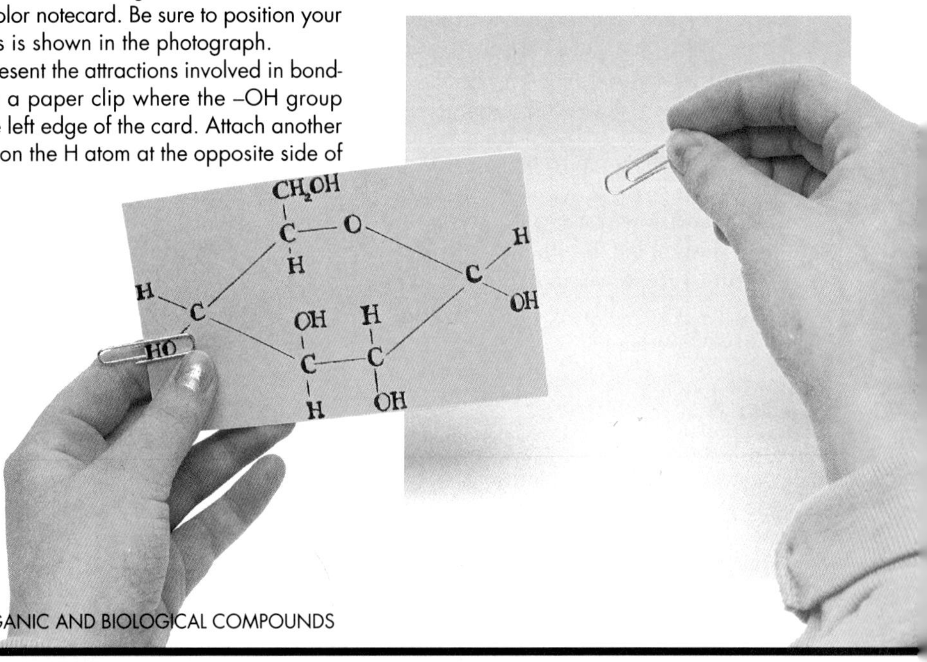

SUMMING UP/SHARING RESULTS

In the starch polymer, the monomer units are identical. In the protein model, the monomers can be from different amino acids.

GOING FURTHER!

When the sequence of amino acid cards is varied, a new protein can be represented. For example, *val-gly-val* is different from *val-val-gly.*

Activity ASSESSMENT

Content: To further assess students' understanding of monomers and polymers, see USING LAB SKILLS, Question 12, on page 348.

PROGRAM RESOURCES

From the **Teacher Resource Package** use:
Activity Worksheets, pages 104-105, Activity 13-2: Mixing Many Monomers

SUMMARY

13-1: Simple Organic Compounds
1. Carbon is an element with a structure that enables it to form a very large number of compounds, known as organic compounds.
2. Saturated hydrocarbons contain only single bonds between carbon atoms, and unsaturated hydrocarbons contain double or triple bonds.
3. Isomers of organic compounds have identical formulas but different molecular shapes.

13-2: Other Organic Compounds
1. Aromatic compounds, many of which have odors, contain the benzene ring structure.
2. A substituted hydrocarbon contains one or more atoms of other elements that have replaced hydrogen atoms.

13-3: Science and Society: Alternative Sources of Energy
1. Biomass is the source of biogas and gasohol, two fuels that can be used to increase our energy supply.
2. Ethanol and gasohol are useful as substitutes for gasoline, but their production may damage the environment.

13-4: Biological Compounds
1. Many important biological compounds are polymers—huge organic molecules made of many smaller units, or monomers.
2. Proteins, nucleic acids, carbohydrates, and lipids are major groups of biological compounds.

KEY SCIENCE WORDS

a. alcohol
b. aromatic compound
c. biogas
d. biomass
e. carbohydrate
f. energy farming
g. gasohol
h. hydrocarbon
i. isomers
j. lipid
k. nucleic acid
l. organic compound
m. polymer
n. protein
o. saturated hydrocarbon
p. substituted hydrocarbon
q. unsaturated hydrocarbon

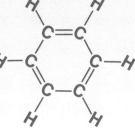

UNDERSTANDING VOCABULARY

Match each phrase with the correct term from the list of Key Science Terms.

1. a combination of ethanol and gasoline
2. a hydrocarbon containing only single bonds
3. all animal and plant material
4. specific type of compound formed when an –OH group replaces one or more hydrogen atoms in a hydrocarbon
5. compounds with identical chemical formulas but different molecular structures
6. a hydrocarbon containing at least one double or triple bond between carbons
7. contains the benzene ring structure
8. a fat, oil, or related compound
9. formed from plant and animal waste
10. growing plants for use as fuel

ORGANIC AND BIOLOGICAL COMPOUNDS **347**

SUMMARY

Have students read the summary statements to review the major concepts of the chapter.

UNDERSTANDING VOCABULARY

1. g	6. q
2. o	7. b
3. d	8. j
4. a	9. c
5. i	10. f

ASSESSMENT
Portfolio
Encourage students to place in their portfolios one or two items of what they consider to be their best work. For each item, ask students to explain why that item was chosen and what they learned from it. Items might be selected from the following.
• Activity 13-1 observations and answers, p. 337
• You Decide answers, p. 339
• Flex Your Brain, p. 345

Performance
Additional performance assessments may be found in *Performance Assessment* and *Science Integration Activities* that accompany **Merrill Physical Science.** Performance Task Assessment Lists and rubrics for evaluating these activities and other products generated throughout the chapter can be found in Glencoe's *Performance Assessment in Middle School Science.*

OPTIONS

ASSESSMENT
To assess student understanding of material in this chapter, use the resources listed.

COOPERATIVE LEARNING
Consider using cooperative learning in the THINK AND WRITE CRITICALLY, APPLY, and MORE SKILL BUILDERS sections of the Chapter Review.

PROGRAM RESOURCES
From the **Teacher Resource Package** use:
Chapter Review, pages 29-30.
Chapter and Unit Tests, pages 84-87, Chapter Test.

CHECKING CONCEPTS

1. b   6. a
2. c   7. b
3. b   8. c
4. a   9. d
5. d   10. d

USING LAB SKILLS

ASSESSMENT

Use these alternate lab exercises to assess students' understanding of skills used in this chapter.

11. Organic acids all must have at least two oxygen atoms to form the —COOH structure.

12. The peptide bonds between amino acids can be broken to release amino acids. The amino acids that you have eaten as proteins can be re-assembled to make needed proteins for your body.

THINK AND WRITE CRITICALLY

13. Organic compounds make up all living things, or things that have lived. In addition to these, many are made artificially. Also, organic compounds have a large amount of structural variation.

14. In a single bond, two atoms share a pair of electrons. In a double bond, the atoms share two pairs of electrons. In a triple bond, three pairs of electrons are shared. (Student diagrams should show four bonds for each carbon atom.)

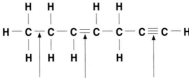

Single bond Double bond Triple bond

15. Marshes have abundant plant and animal life and the water provides a medium for the air-free decomposition of dead organisms.

16. All amino acids contain an —NH$_2$ (amine) group and a —COOH (carboxylic acid) group.

17. One possible answer is shown.

C＝C—C＝C—C＝C

CHECKING CONCEPTS

Choose the word or phrase that completes the sentence or answers the question.

1. A benzene ring is very _____.
   a. rare   **c.** unstable
   b. stable   **d.** saturated

2. Alcohols and organic acids are both _____ hydrocarbons.
   a. aromatic   **c.** substituted
   b. saturated   **d.** unsaturated

3. Two examples of _____ are a dog and a tree.
   a. biogas   **c.** energy farming
   b. biomass   **d.** hydrocarbons

4. Basic units of polymers are _____.
   a. monomers   **c.** plastics
   b. isomers   **d.** carbohydrates

5. Some examples of _____ are enzymes and hemoglobin.
   a. carbohydrates **c.** nucleic acids
   b. lipids   **d.** proteins

6. DNA codes and stores _____.
   a. genetic information **c.** proteins
   b. nucleic acids   **d.** lipids

7. DNA is made up of _____.
   a. amino acids   **c.** polymers
   b. nucleotides   **d.** carbohydrates

8. Glucose and fructose, both C$_6$H$_{12}$O$_6$, are _____.
   a. amino acids   **c.** isomers
   b. alcohols   **d.** polymers

9. If a carbohydrate has 16 oxygen atoms, how many hydrogen atoms does it have?
   a. 4   **c.** 16
   b. 8   **d.** 32

10. Cholesterol is a type of _____.
    a. sugar   **c.** protein
    b. starch   **d.** lipid

USING LAB SKILLS

11. In Activity 13-1 on page 337 you combined organic acids and alcohols. If the formulas of an acid and an alcohol were written as C$_3$H$_8$O and C$_3$H$_6$O$_2$, explain how you could determine which formula is for an acid and which is for an alcohol.

12. In Activity 13-2 on page 346 you showed how monomers can make larger molecules. If reversing this process, where would the structure of a protein most likely break apart? What does your body do with amino acid components from digested proteins?

THINK AND WRITE CRITICALLY

Answer the following questions in your Journal using complete sentences.

13. Why are more than 90 percent of all compounds organic compounds?

14. Use a diagram to explain single, double, and triple bonds in hydrocarbons. Draw a chain of carbon atoms that shows each type of bond.

15. Explain why a marsh provides an environment that produces biogas.

16. Show how the structure of an amino acid explains the term *amino acid*.

17. Some fats are polyunsaturated. Draw a polyunsaturated chain of carbon atoms.

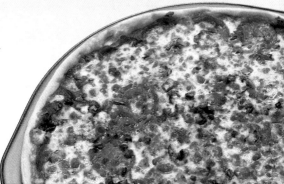

18. Too much saturated fat in the diet is unhealthful. What is the difference in the composition of saturated fat and unsaturated fat?
19. Rubbing alcohol is isopropyl alcohol. How does this differ from propyl alcohol?
20. Carbon tetrachloride, a former dry cleaning fluid, is formed when all the hydrogen in methane is replaced by chlorine. Write the formula for carbon tetrachloride.
21. Explain how biomass has been used as an energy source throughout history.
22. Some vitamins are lipids and won't dissolve in water but will dissolve in other lipids. What is one reason we need fat in our diet?

MORE SKILL BUILDERS

If you need help, refer to the Skill Handbook.

1. **Making and Using Graphs:** Using the following table, plot the number of carbon atoms on one axis and the boiling point on the other axis on a graph. Use the graph to predict the boiling points of butane, octane, and dodecane ($C_{12}H_{26}$).

GRAPH DATA		
Name	**Formula**	**Boiling Point (°C)**
Methane	CH_4	−162
Ethane	C_2H_6	−89
Propane	C_3H_8	−42

2. **Interpreting Scientific Illustrations:** Which of the following terms apply to the illustration below? Terms: alcohol, aromatic, carbohydrate, hydrocarbon, lipid, organic compound, polymer, saturated, substituted hydrocarbon, unsaturated

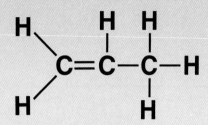

3. **Comparing and Contrasting:** In terms of DNA, compare and contrast identical twins and two people who are not identical twins.
4. **Recognizing Cause and Effect:** Our society has a definite need for more energy farming. List several causes and several effects of this need.
5. **Hypothesizing:** Sarah decided to go on a weight reduction diet. She is eating only lettuce and fruit. What do you predict will happen to Sarah as a result?

PROJECTS

1. Research hydrocarbons containing five carbon atoms. Draw diagrams of their structures, name them, and tell their uses.
2. Survey local gasoline stations and find out if they sell gasohol or sell gasoline. Find out how much of each fuel is sold per month. Display results in a table or graph.
3. Research ways crops are used as energy resources. Report your findings. Suggest how these ways could be implemented locally.

18. Saturated fats contain only single bonds between carbon atoms. Unsaturated fats contain one or more double bonds between carbon atoms.
19. Both compounds contain the same number of each kind of atom, but the arrangements of atoms are different.
20. CCl_4
21. Answers will vary. Answers may include use of wood and peat for fuel.
22. One reason is that fats must be present to dissolve certain vitamins. This group of vitamins is called fat-soluble vitamins.

MORE SKILL BUILDERS

1. **Making and Using Graphs:** Answers should be close to -1°C, 126°C, and 216°C respectively.
2. **Interpreting Scientific Illustrations:** hydrocarbon, organic compound, unsaturated
3. **Comparing and Contrasting:** Characteristics of identical twins are the same because the order of nucleotides in the DNA ladder is the same. Other people are different because the order of nucleotides in the DNA ladder is different.
4. **Recognizing Cause and Effect:** Answers will vary. Causes may include need for a renewable resource and conservation of a dwindling supply of fuel. Possible effects include usage of food-producing land, environmental damage, and increased fuel supply.
5. **Hypothesizing:** Answers will vary. Answers may include negative effects of protein and lipid deficiencies.

14 Useful Materials

CHAPTER SECTION	OBJECTIVES	ACTIVITIES
14-1 Materials with a Past (2 days)	1. **Identify** common alloys and ceramics. 2. **Compare** and **contrast** alloys and ceramics.	**Activity 14-1:** *Preparing an Alloy,* p. 359
14-2 Recycling Science & Society (1 day)	1. **Explain** the importance of recycling solid wastes. 2. **Discuss** ways in which state and local governments encourage recycling of solid waste materials.	
14-3 New Materials (2 days)	1. **Compare** and **contrast** plastics and synthetic fibers. 2. **Describe** a composite.	**Activity 14-2:** *Compose a Composite,* p. 368
Chapter Review		

ACTIVITY MATERIALS

FIND OUT	ACTIVITIES		MINI-LABS	
Page 351 none	**14-1 Preparing an Alloy, p. 359** copper penny zinc, 30 mesh hot plate nitric acid, HNO_3, dilute sodium hydroxide solution, NaOH dilute 2 evaporating dishes tongs	**14-2 Compose a Composite, p. 368** plaster of paris items to embed water aluminum foil, heavy duty measuring cup beaker hammer paper towels		

CHAPTER FEATURES	TEACHER RESOURCE PACKAGE	OTHER RESOURCES
Problem Solving: *Plastics Around You,* p. 355 **Skill Builder:** *Concept Mapping,* p. 358	**Ability Level Worksheets** ◆ *Study Guide,* p. 58 ● *Reinforcement,* p. 58 ▲ *Enrichment,* p. 58 **Activity Worksheets,** pp. 5, 110, 111 **Critical Thinking/Problem Solving,** p. 20 **Cross-Curricular Connections,** p. 20 **Transparency Masters,** pp. 53, 54	**Color Transparency 27,** Steel Alloys **STVS:** Disc 2, Side 1
You Decide! p. 361	**Ability Level Worksheets** ◆ *Study Guide,* p. 59 ● *Reinforcement,* p. 59 ▲ *Enrichment,* p. 59	**STVS:** Disc 2, Side 2 **Science Integration Activity 14**
Technology: *Plastic Parts Instantly,* p. 365 **Skill Builder:** *Observing and Inferring,* p. 367	**Ability Level Worksheets** ◆ *Study Guide,* p. 60 ● *Reinforcement,* p. 60 ▲ *Enrichment,* p. 60 **Activity Worksheets,** pp. 112, 113 **Concept Mapping,** pp. 33, 34 **Science and Society,** p. 18 **Transparency Masters,** pp. 55, 56	**Color Transparency 28,** Production of Nylon **STVS:** Disc 2, Side 1
Summary Think & Write Critically Key Science Words Apply Understanding Vocabulary More Skill Builders Checking Concepts Projects Using Lab Skills	**ASSESSMENT RESOURCES** **Chapter Review,** pp. 31, 32 **Chapter Test,** pp. 88-91 **Unit Test,** pp. 92, 93 **Performance Assessment in** **Middle School Science**	**Chapter Review Software** **Test Bank** **Alternate Assessment** **Performance Assessment**

◆ **Basic**   ● **Average**   ▲ **Advanced**

ADDITIONAL MATERIALS

SOFTWARE	AUDIOVISUAL	BOOKS/MAGAZINES
	Chemistry in Everyday Life, Video, Britannica. *Man-Made Macro Molecules: Polymers,* Video, Insight Media. *Metals and Alloys,* Video, Lucerne Media. *Miracles by Design,* Video, Insight Media. *Plastics,* Video, Britannica. *Recycle,* Laserdisc, AIMS Media. *The Throw Away Society,* Video, Lucerne Media.	Groves, Seli, and Joanna Randolph Rott. *How on Earth Do We Recycle Glass?* Brookfield, CT: Millbrook Press, 1992. Kircher, Harry, Donald Wallace, and Dorothy Gore. *Our Natural Resources and Their Conservation,* 7th ed. Danville, IL: Interstate, 1991. Ross, Bonnie L. *Waste Away: Information and Activities for Investigating Trash Problems and Solutions.* Woodstock, VT: Vermont Institute of Natural Science, 1992.

THEME DEVELOPMENT: Scale and structure as a theme of the textbook is developed by introducing the student to the structure of alloys, ceramics, plastics, synthetic fibers, and composite materials. A discussion of recycling causes the student to think about the scale on which these materials are used and discarded.

CHAPTER OVERVIEW

▶ **Section 14-1:** The section differentiates between an amalgam and other alloys. The uses and properties of ceramic and glass materials are also presented.

▶ **Section 14-2: Science and Society:** Recycling is the focus of this section. Reasons are given for recycling and why recycling is sometimes economically impractical.

▶ **Section 14-3:** This section describes the properties and uses of plastics, synthetic fibers, and composite materials.

CHAPTER VOCABULARY

alloy	cermets
amalgam	recycling
ores	plastic
ceramic	synthetic fiber
glass	composite

CHAPTER

14 Useful Materials

350

OPTIONS

 For Your Gifted Students

Ask students to research the history of the development of plastics. They should find out how plastics have influenced the way we live and how our use of them has affected the environment. Students can make a mural showing the development of plastics, highlighting the historic changes that have taken place in their development. Students may choose instead to make a poster showing the new classifications for recycling plastics.

For Your Mainstreamed Students

▶ Arrange for students to visit a glass recycling or aluminum recycling plant. They should take pictures or make a video of the trip to share with the class as a report.

▶ Students can prepare for Section 14-3 by making a collection of different types of plastics and fabrics made of synthetic fibers. Students should include only those items whose composition can be verified by reading labels, using references, or by talking to knowledgeable people.

The Oscar is an award given for motion-picture excellence. It is a statue that is made of a mixture of copper and tin and covered with a very thin coating of pure gold. The total value of these materials is less than a few hundred dollars. If the Oscar were made of solid gold, it would be worth more than $40 000. Like Oscar, there are many materials, new and old, that are worth more to us than the value of the individual elements that make them up.

FIND OUT!

Do this activity to examine the elements that make up an interesting new material.

A material called dental porcelain may be used to restore damaged teeth to their original appearance. *Predict* what properties this material should have if it is to take the place of tooth enamel.

The basic ingredients of this material are usually silica or alumina. What elements do you think are in these two substances? Clay materials containing some sodium, calcium, and potassium may also be used.

Survey the members of your class as to whether they or members of their families have had dental porcelain used to repair their teeth. In this chapter, you will learn more about how other new materials are used all around you.

Gearing Up
Previewing the Chapter

Use this outline to help you focus on important ideas in the chapter.

Section 14-1   Materials with a Past
► Alloys
► Ceramics
Section 14-2   Science and Society
Recycling
► Why Recycle?
Section 14-3   New Materials
► Plastics
► Composites

Previewing Science Skills
► In the **Skill Builders,** you will map concepts and observe and infer.
► In the **Activities,** you will observe and infer and predict.

What's next?

You have learned that the value or importance of an object often cannot be judged by the value of the materials of which it is composed. Now find out about the composition and properties of some very useful materials.

351

ASSESSMENT OPTIONS

PORTFOLIO
Refer to page 369 for suggested items that students might select for their portfolios.

PERFORMANCE ASSESSMENT
See page 369 for additional Performance Assessment options.
Process
Skill Builder, p. 358
Activities 14-1, p. 359; 14-2, p. 368
Using Lab Skills, p. 370

CONTENT ASSESSMENT
Assessment—Oral, p. 364
Skill Builder, p. 367
Section Reviews, pp. 358, 361, 367
Chapter Review, pp. 369-371
Mini Quizzes, pp. 355, 357, 366

GROUP ASSESSMENT
Opportunities for group assessment occur with Cooperative Learning Strategies and Flex Your Brain Activities.

INTRODUCING THE CHAPTER
Use the Find Out activity to introduce students to useful materials. Inform students that they will be learning more about new and old products of science as they read the chapter.

FIND OUT!
Cooperative Learning: Use the Problem Solving Team strategy to find out information about the composition of silica and alumina and conduct the survey.

Teaching Tips
► Students can contact a local dentist for help in determining the composition and properties of the material.
► Ask if a student has a porcelain repair or crown that they would show to the class.
► Ask students to list the properties that dental porcelain should have. It should be water resistant, the same color as the tooth enamel, durable, and able to withstand staining and both hot and cold temperatures.
► Silica is composed of silicon dioxide, and alumina is aluminum oxide. Both materials are hard, light colored, and relatively inexpensive as raw materials compared to their value as dental porcelain.

Gearing Up
Have students study the Gearing Up feature to familiarize themselves with the chapter. Discuss the relationships of the topics in the outline.

What's Next?
Before beginning the first section, make sure students understand the connection between the Find Out activity and the topics to follow.

PREPARATION

SECTION BACKGROUND

▶ Many common metals are not pure elements, but alloys. Some pairs of metals are soluble in each other in all proportions. Homogeneous examples are Cu/Ni, Cu/Au, W/Mo, Pt/Au. Some pairs that do not dissolve completely and therefore form heterogeneous alloys are Al/Si, Pd/Sn, Cu/Sn, and Ag/Cu.

▶ The solubility of one metal in another is determined mainly by the size of the atoms. Metals with atoms of similar size tend to be soluble in each other. Also, elements whose atoms are very much smaller than the other element are usually soluble. For example, hydrogen dissolves in palladium.

▶ Some dental alloys are also made from silver and tin. Polymers that are cured with ultraviolet light are used where the filling must match the color of the tooth. The metal amalgam filling is more resistant to wear than the polymer fillings.

PREPLANNING

▶ To prepare for Activity 14-1, ask students to bring to class bright, shiny pennies. Pennies dated before 1982 are preferred because they are copper and not copper-clad zinc. If bright pennies are not available, dilute the nitric acid. Prepare the sodium hydroxide solution in advance.

14-1 Materials with a Past

New Science Words

alloy
amalgam
ores
ceramic
glass
cermets

EcoTip

In the United States, 70 percent of all metals used are discarded after a single use.

What is an alloy?

Objectives

▶ Identify common alloys and ceramics.
▶ Compare and contrast alloys and ceramics.

Alloys

Imagine interstate highways without steel bridges, cities without brick buildings, and rooms without glass windows. It's almost impossible because such materials as steel, brick, and glass are part of your everyday life. As you will see, these and many more familiar materials are rooted in discoveries made thousands of years ago.

When a marching band goes by, you can easily recognize the brass section. The instruments are brilliant in both sound and color. Trumpets, trombones, and tubas are made of an alloy called brass. An **alloy** is a mixture of a metal and one or more other elements. An alloy retains the properties common to metals, but it is not a pure metal. Brass is a mixture of copper and zinc. The brass used in musical instruments and in some hardware is composed of about 80 percent copper and 20 percent zinc. Brass of this quality is a solid solution of the two metals. As you recall from Chapter 9, a solution is a homogeneous mixture. Any brass that contains more than 40 percent zinc is a heterogeneous mixture. This means that the mixture of atoms of the two metals is not completely uniform.

Have you ever been awarded a plaque or trophy? Chances are it is made of bronze, an alloy similar to brass. About 5000 years ago, people discovered that a new material could be made by mixing melted copper and tin. The new material—bronze—was stronger and

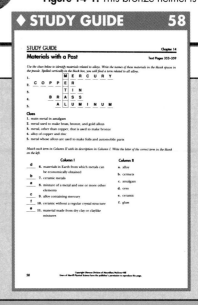

Figure 14-1. This bronze helmet is centuries old.

OPTIONS

Meeting Different Ability Levels

For Section 14-1, use the following **Teacher Resource Masters** depending upon individual students' needs.

◆ **Study Guide Master** for all students.
● **Reinforcement Master** for students of average and above average ability levels.
▲ **Enrichment Master** for above average students.

Additional Teacher Resource Package masters are listed in any **PROGRAM RESOURCES** boxes that are in the section. The additional masters are appropriate for all students.

◆ **STUDY GUIDE** 58

STUDY GUIDE — Chapter 14
Materials with a Past — Text Pages 352–359

Use the clues below to identify materials related to alloys. Write the names of these materials in the blank spaces in the puzzle. Spelled vertically in the black box, you will find a term related to all alloys.

1. M E R C U R Y
2. C O P P E R
3. T I N
4. B R A S S
5. A L U M I N U M

Clues
1. main metal in amalgam
2. metal used to make brass, bronze, and gold alloys
3. metal, other than copper, that is used to make bronze
4. alloy of copper and zinc
5. metal whose alloys are used to make foils and automobile parts

Match each term in Column II with its description in Column I. Write the letter of the correct term in the blank on the left.

Column I	Column II
d 6. materials in Earth from which metals can be economically obtained	a. alloy
b 7. ceramic metals	b. cermets
a 8. mixture of a metal and one or more other elements	c. amalgam
c 9. alloy containing mercury	d. ores
f 10. ceramic without a regular crystal structure	e. ceramic
e 11. material made from dry clay or claylike mixtures	f. glass

more durable than either copper or tin. This first known alloy became so popular and so widely used that a 2000-year span of history is known as the Bronze Age. The Bronze Age ended with the discovery of iron.

Bronze is more expensive than brass, because tin is more expensive than zinc. However, bronze is especially useful in plumbing fixtures and hardware that will be exposed to salt water. Brass is not suitable for such items as boat propellers, because the zinc reacts with minerals in salt water, leaving porous copper behind. The tin in bronze does not react with saltwater minerals.

Metals can be combined with other elements in different amounts to produce many different mixtures. Table 14-1 lists some common alloys. Thousands of alloys have been created since the time bronze was first made.

Table 14-1

COMMON ALLOYS		
Name	Composition	Use
Bronze	copper, tin	jewelry, marine hardware
Brass	copper, zinc	hardware
Sterling silver	silver, copper	tableware
Pewter	tin, copper	tableware
Solder	lead, tin	plumbing
Wrought iron	iron, lead, copper, magnesium	porch railings, fences

An alloy has properties that are different from and more useful than the properties of the elements in it. Look at the bracelet shown in Figure 14-2. It appears to be made of gold. It is actually made of an alloy. As you know, gold is a very bright, very expensive metal that is

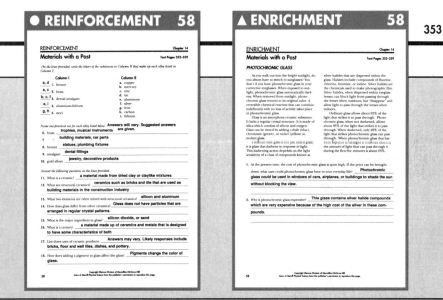

Figure 14-2. Like this bracelet, most gold jewelry is made of a gold-copper alloy.

353

Two ways to describe alloys are substitutional and interstitial. Use a dictionary to determine the meaning of these two words. Then, **in your Journal,** write an explanation of how the definitions could be applied to alloys.

---

1 MOTIVATE

▶**Demonstration:** Obtain clay from the school's art teacher. Have a student divide the clay into two parts. Shape each part into a useful object. Ask the art teacher to fire one piece in a kiln. Allow the second piece to air dry. Have the students examine both ceramic pieces and describe the properties of each. Ask them why they think the properties of the fired and unfired pieces are so different.

TYING TO PREVIOUS KNOWLEDGE: Ask students if they have ever had "gold" chains turn their necks or wrists green. The alloy was mostly copper with very little gold. Emphasize that alloys can vary in composition.

In Your JOURNAL

Answer: *Substitutional* means "replacing something with something else." *Interstitial* means "fitting in between." Some alloys have atoms from one metal substituted by atoms from another metal. Other alloys have smaller atoms between larger metal atoms.

MULTICULTURAL PERSPECTIVE

Aslihan Yener, born in Turkey, moved to the United States when she was six months old. In college, she planned to be a chemist. She returned to Turkey and majored in art history, where she became interested in archaeology. She decided to combine her talents and "to apply atomic bomb techniques to archaeology...by analyzing the lead isotopes in mines and metals throughout the Near East."

The distinct ratios of lead isotopes to other metals in Bronze Age objects are like a fingerprint, matching the object to the mine the metal came from. Yener used this approach to analyze trace elements of lead in silver money, standard weights, and trade items.

Yener has found large Bronze Age industrial parks in the Taurus mountains. She has also located a semisubterranean city built into the mountainside.

2 TEACH

Key Concepts are highlighted.

CONCEPT DEVELOPMENT

▶ Remind students that the strong metallic bond of structural metals, such as iron, chromium, and nickel, makes them hard and strong. It is possible to strengthen softer metals by combining them with harder metals to form alloys.

▶ Bring samples of alloys to class. Hardware stores have brass nuts and bolts. Bronze, stainless steel, and gold jewelry are alloys you can show.

▶ Perform, repeat, or review the demonstration on page 305 in Chapter 12. Softened or annealed steel can be easily shaped into car body parts due to its large crystal size. Hardened steel is used when wear resistance is necessary. Hardened steel is brittle because of its small crystal size. Tempered steel is both hard and strong. It has a springiness because of its intermediate crystal size.

REVEALING MISCONCEPTIONS

▶ Some people believe that galvanized steel is an alloy. Be certain students realize galvanized steel has been coated with zinc. If possible, bring a piece of galvanized metal to class. Students can see the zinc metal crystals on the surface using a hand lens.

Connect to...
Earth Science

Answer: In panning, swirling water rinses less dense particles away from the very dense (19 g/cm³) gold particles. Then the shiny yellow color of gold can be seen.

Connect to...
Earth Science

During the California gold rush, prospectors obtained gold by *panning*. What properties of gold were important in making this technique successful?

soft and bends very easily. Copper, on the other hand, is a somewhat dull, inexpensive metal that is harder than gold. When melted gold and copper are mixed and then allowed to cool, an alloy is formed. It has most of the brilliance of gold and most of the sturdiness of copper. By varying the amounts of gold and copper, alloys with properties designed for different purposes can be produced. Figure 14-3 shows several gold alloys.

The alloys shown in Figure 14-3 contain only two metals. All alloys are not that simple. Do you or someone you know wear dental braces? The wire used in the braces is an alloy of gold, silver, platinum, palladium, zinc, and copper.

Figure 14-3. The pie graphs show the percentages of gold and copper found in the different "gold" objects.

24-karat gold — 100% gold

22-karat gold — 8% copper / 92% gold

14-karat gold — 42% copper / 58% gold

12-karat gold — 50% copper / 50% gold

354 USEFUL MATERIALS

OPTIONS

INQUIRY QUESTIONS

▶ Look at the periodic table and find the locations of copper and zinc. What can be said about the relative sizes of copper and zinc atoms? What alloy is formed by mixing Cu and Zn? What role do you think the relative size of the atoms plays in the formation of this alloy? *The alloy is brass. The atoms are nearly the same size. Elements that have atoms of about the same size tend to form alloys easily.*

▶ What properties would you expect an alloy of iron and chromium to have? *Iron has*

great physical strength and chromium is corrosion resistant. You would expect the alloy to have both these properties.

▶ Brass and gold are the same color. How do they differ in cost, hardness, and tendency to oxidize? *Brass is cheaper and harder than gold. Brass will tarnish or oxidize but gold will not.*

PROBLEM SOLVING

Plastics Around You

Your writing pen, the cover of your notebook, a sandwich bag, and the covering on school desks are all plastics.

Plastics are stronger and more flexible than many natural products. They resist chemical change and wear. They are easy to clean and can be made in a variety of colors.

Many plastics are thermoplastics, which are plastics that soften or fuse when heated and harden again when cooled. The molecules in thermoplastics are linked together to form unbranched chains. Polyethylene, polystyrene, polyvinyl chloride, and nylon are some common thermoplastics.

Thermosets make up another group of plastics. Thermosets become permanently rigid when heated and will not melt again and reharden. The molecules in thermosets consist of chains that are cross-linked. Common thermosets are Formica and Bakelite. What is one advantage of thermoplastics over thermosets?

Think Critically: Classify the materials in the first paragraph as thermoplastics or thermosets.

Some other alloys used by dentists are called amalgams. An **amalgam** is an alloy that contains mercury. Dental amalgams consist of mercury, silver, and zinc. You may have one in your mouth right now. Amalgams are used as fillings for cavities.

As you may have guessed by now, most metallic objects are manufactured from alloys. Various types of steel make up an important group of alloys. Steel production is greater than that of any other alloy. All types of steel are alloys of iron and carbon. You may have seen advertisements for carving knives with blades made of high-carbon steel. The carbon content of this alloy ranges from 1.0 percent to 1.7 percent. Because this steel

Figure 14-4. Surgical steel can be used to join bones together.

 PROBLEM SOLVING

Answers to Questions: Unlike thermosets, thermoplastics can be remelted and used again.

Think Critically: The pen, notebook cover, and plastic bag are thermoplastics. The desk coverings are thermosets.

CONCEPT DEVELOPMENT

▶ Ask students what happens if they accidentally bite down on a piece of aluminum foil. Those who have metal fillings are likely to experience pain. Unlike metals in an electrolyte (saliva) produce an electric current.

MINI QUIZ

Use the Mini Quiz to check students' recall of chapter content.

1. **What kinds of substances make up an alloy?** *a metal and one or more other elements*
2. **Bronze is a mixture of what two elements?** *copper and tin*
3. **How does an alloy compare with the elements it is composed of?** *The properties of the alloy are different and more useful than those of the elements.*
4. **An alloy that contains mercury is called a(n) _____ .** *amalgam*
5. **All types of steel are alloys of iron and _____ .** *carbon*

CROSS CURRICULUM

▶ **Language Arts:** Have students write a science fiction story that makes use of a new alloy with unique properties. In the story, have them tell how the alloy is made and what the properties are. An example is the legend surrounding Jim Bowie's knife. It was said to be made from the metal of a meteorite he found. The metal blade was said to be indestructible, and never needed sharpening.

ENRICHMENT

▶ Have a student who wears dental braces talk to his or her orthodontist and ask which properties are important in the alloy the doctor uses.

▶ Ask a student to ask a dentist about dental amalgams. Why are they preferred over plastic fillings? How are amalgams made? Have the student ask about and research the issue of possible health effects of mercury amalgams.

▶ Ask a student to contact a jeweler and ask about the compositions of gold alloys. Have the student report to the class the meaning of 10-, 14-, and 24-carat gold found in jewelry.

Table 14-2

SOME STEEL ALLOYS			
Name	Composition	Properties	Uses
Manganese	10–18% Mn	very hard	railroads, armor plate, conveyors
Duriron	12–15% Si	acid resistant	pipes, condensers, containers
Nickel	2–5% Ni	elastic, corrosion resistant	gears, drive shafts, cables
Invar	36% Ni	does not expand or contract	measuring tapes, pendulums
Permalloy	78% Ni	magnetic	cables
Stainless	14–19% Cr 7–9% Ni	strong, corrosion resistant	surgical instruments, knives, flatware
High speed	14–20% W, 4% Cr or 6–12% Mo, 4% Cr	keeps hardness at high temperatures	cutting tools, drill bits, saw blades

CROSS CURRICULUM

▶ **Economic Geography:** Have students locate the following countries on a world map. Make signs that show the major elements that are extracted from ores mined in these countries. Canada: Ni, Cu, Nb, Ga, Ta, Zn, Cd, Cs; Mexico: Zn, Sb, Cd, Sr; Brazil: Nb, Mn, Ta; Bolivia: Ag, Sn; Jamaica: Al; Congo: Co, Cu, Sn, Nb, Ta, Au, W, diamonds; South Africa: Cr, Mn, V, Pt; Botswana: Cr, diamonds; Zambia: Co, Au, Mn; Gabon: Mn; U.K.: Pt; Germany: Ga, Cs; Belgium: Co, Sb; Norway: Ni; France: Mn; Commonwealth of Independent States: Cr, Pt; Turkey: Cr; China: Sb; Philippines: Cr; Indonesia: Sn; Malaysia: Ta, Sn; Australia: Al, Mn, Cd; New Caledonia: Ni

Use this map-making exercise to demonstrate how technology depends on Earth's resources.

CONCEPT DEVELOPMENT

▶ **Demonstration:** An empty aluminum soft-drink can may be used to demonstrate the strength of this lightweight metal. The aluminum skin of an airplane must flex many times without tearing. Have a student wearing leather gloves attempt to tear a soft-drink can into two pieces by gripping the ends and twisting in one direction. The can will usually twist but will not tear.

TEACHER F.Y.I.

▶ Living organisms produce ceramic materials, but the processing methods are not well understood. Understanding the growth of biocrystals is the first step to biomimetic processing of ceramics. Bacteria can produce magnetite particles, and yeast can produce small crystals of cadmium sulfide.

VideoDisc

STVS: High-Tech Ceramics, Disc 2, Side 1

EcoTip

During a three-month period, Americans throw away enough aluminum to totally rebuild our entire commercial airline fleet.

is very hard, the knife blades will be very sharp. As you can see from Table 14-2, steels of different compositions are made for different uses.

Aluminum alloys are the second largest group of alloys produced. Aluminum alloys are used to manufacture products ranging from foils used in food wraps to automobile bodies.

In the last decade, aluminum-lithium alloys have become very important. Because lithium is the lightest metal, these alloys are lightweight, yet exceedingly strong. Unlike other alloys, aluminum-lithium alloys maintain their strength at very high temperatures. In the future these alloys may be used to make the bodies of aircraft that will travel near the outer limits of Earth's atmosphere.

Most of the elements needed to make alloys are obtained from ores. **Ores** are materials in Earth from which metals can be economically obtained. The photo to the left shows a sample of silver ore. The silver appears black because it is chemically combined as silver sulfide. Earth also contains clay, which is used in the manufacturing of another important group of useful materials.

6

356 USEFUL MATERIALS

OPTIONS

INQUIRY QUESTIONS

▶ What is the percentage of aluminum metal in a sample of the ore bauxite if 25 g of pure aluminum is processed from 1000 grams of ore? *2.5 percent*
▶ If an iron ore contains two percent iron, how much must be processed to produce one kilogram of iron? *50 kg*
▶ A sample of uranium ore, called pitchblende, is found to contain five percent uranium. How many metric tons of pure uranium can be extracted from 1000 metric tons of ore? *50 metric tons*

PROGRAM RESOURCES

From the **Teacher Resource Package** use:
Critical Thinking/Problem Solving, page 20, Mercury in Dental Amalgam.
Cross-Curricular Connections, page 20, Recycling.
Transparency Masters, pages 53-54, Steel Alloys.
Use **Color Transparency** number 27, Steel Alloys.

Ceramics

Have you ever watched a potter making a bowl? If you have, you know that the potter spins wet clay on a wheel while shaping it into a bowl by hand. The bowl is then heated in a very hot oven, or kiln, to dry it and bring about important chemical changes that harden the material. The bowl is made of a material called ceramic. A **ceramic** is a material made from dried clay or claylike mixtures. People began making ceramic containers thousands of years ago to store food and carry water.

As with alloys, there are thousands of different ceramics. Is your school building made of bricks? Does it have tiled hallways? Bricks and tiles are examples of structural ceramics. Structural ceramics are used by the construction industry because of their rigidity and strength. These ceramics contain silicon or aluminum. These elements can form small, rigid structures that bond together when water is removed. These bonds make the ceramics strong and chemically stable. The porcelain ceramics used on sinks and bathtubs are called whitewares. Figure 14-6 shows examples of several types of ceramics.

Look at some bricks or bathroom tiles, or at the porcelain enamel around the burner plates of a stove. You'll probably see small breaks in their surfaces. These breaks are evidence of one disadvantage of some ceramics: they are so rigid that they crack. If you've ever picked up the

Figure 14-5. This ancient ceramic pottery is made of a mixture of clay and water.

Figure 14-6. The photographs show structural ceramics (left), whitewares (center), and porcelain enamel (right).

CONCEPT DEVELOPMENT

▶ **Demonstration:** Glass is amorphous, which means it has no crystal structure. As in a liquid, the molecules can move past one another. To demonstrate this very slow movement, you can use water glass to make a solid, white "rubber ball." Mix 25 mL of water glass, sodium silicate, with 25 mL of water. In another beaker, mix 18 mL of 95% ethanol with 7 mL of water. Pour the alcohol solution into the beaker containing the water glass solution. Swirl the beaker to mix the two solutions. A white solid forms. Drain off the excess solution. Stack 7–10 paper towels. Dump the solid onto the towels. Gently squeeze the white mass and shape it into a ball. The ball will bounce if you drop it. Place the ball on the lab table. After about 15 minutes have students observe the bottom of the ball. Even though the material seems solid, it has flattened.

CHECK FOR UNDERSTANDING

Use the Mini Quiz to check for understanding.

MINI QUIZ

Use the Mini Quiz to check students' recall of chapter content.

6 **Metals are obtained from materials in Earth called _____ .** *ores*

7 **From what are ceramic materials made?** *clay or claylike mixtures*

8 **A ceramic that does not have a regular crystal structure is called a(n) _____ .** *glass*

9 **Glass is made from sand. What elements make up sand?** *silicon and oxygen*

10 **Materials that have properties of both ceramics and alloys are called _____ .** *cermets*

RETEACH

Have students prepare flash cards with examples of each type of material described in the text. For example, on one side of the card is the word *brick*, and on the other side is the word *ceramic*.

EXTENSION

For students who have mastered this section, use the **Reinforcement** and **Enrichment** masters or other OPTIONS provided.

ENRICHMENT

▶ Kidney stones and gallstones are ceramic-like materials that form in the human body. Ask two students to research one of these and report their findings to the class. How do they form and how can they be prevented? Students may be able to conduct a telephone interview with a doctor.

▶ Have students conduct a survey of ceramic and glass objects they find at home and at school. Students can share their written findings in class the next day. Figure 14-6 will give them some ideas.

▶ Interested students could research high-temperature ceramics, ceramic-metal composites, polymer-ceramic composites, biomimetic ceramics, and oxide-ceramic superconductors.

▶ Pyroceramic materials like Corning Ware, were originally developed as missile nose cones. Pyroceramics can withstand large temperature changes without shattering. Have students research the properties that make them good for the home as well as for nose cones.

? FLEX Your Brain

Use the Flex Your Brain activity to have students explore ALLOYS AND CERAMICS.

ASSESSMENT

Portfolio: Use the Flex Your Brain activity to reinforce critical-thinking and problem-solving skills. In Step 2, students might list examples of alloys and ceramics.

▶ Ask questions 1-4 and the **Apply** and **Connect to Earth Science** questions in the Section Review.

SECTION REVIEW ANSWERS

1. An alloy has metallic properties; it is a mixture of a metal and another element. Responses will vary, but should include alloys discussed in the section.

2. Alloys combine the useful properties of different metals into one material.

3. A ceramic is a material made of dried clay or claylike mixtures. Responses will vary but should include ceramics discussed in the section.

4. A ceramic contains silicon or aluminum, which can form into a strong structure when water is removed.

5. Apply: Ceramic magnets have the magnetic properties of iron.

6. Connect to Earth Science: The lowest percent of iron in a steel listed in Table 14-2 is 22 percent, in permalloy.

Skill Builder
ASSESSMENT

Oral: Have students name an alloy that contains copper and one that contains zinc.

PROGRAM RESOURCES

From the **Teacher Resource Package** use:

Activity Worksheets, page 5, Flex Your Brain.

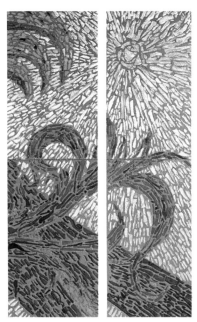

Figure 14-7. The different colors of the glass in this window are produced by pigments added to the glass. Such pigments include cadmium sulfide (red), cerium oxide (yellow), and cobalt oxide (blue).

pieces of a dinner plate you accidentally dropped, you are well aware of this.

Almost half of the ceramics produced today are classified as glasses. A **glass** is a ceramic without a regular crystal structure. Glasses come in thousands of varieties. You are probably most familiar with the type of glass that you see in windows. This glass contains mostly oxygen and silicon, with smaller amounts of sodium and calcium, and a trace of aluminum. The major ingredient that is used to make glass is silicon dioxide, SiO_2—sand.

Glasses can be made to have desired properties by changing the kinds and proportions of elements that make them up. Crystal pendants and vases are made from glass that contains lead as well as silicon and oxygen. Food storage dishes that you can pull from a freezer and place in an oven to heat are glasses that contain boron and magnesium or lithium. As you can see in Figure 14-7, the addition of pigments to a glass alters its appearance.

Do you have magnets stuck to your refrigerator door? If so, chances are they are ceramic magnets. These magnets are examples of cermets. **Cermets,** or ceramic-metals, are materials that have properties of both ceramics and alloys. They are new materials with ancient pasts.

SECTION REVIEW

1. What is an alloy? List names and uses of several alloys.
2. Why are alloys produced?
3. What is a ceramic? List names and uses of several ceramics.
4. Why are ceramics very strong materials?
5. **Apply:** Ceramic magnets demonstrate properties of alloys of what element?
6. **Connect to Earth Science:** The most common iron ore is hematite. Iron can be obtained from hematite and used to make steel. Which steel listed in Table 14-2 has the lowest percentage of iron?

∿ Skill Builder

☑ Concept Mapping

Make a network tree to describe the composition of common alloys using the alloys and elements mentioned in this section. If you need help, refer to Concept Mapping in the **Skill Handbook** on pages 684 and 685.

Skill Builder

You may want to supply students with a list of the alloys to work with.

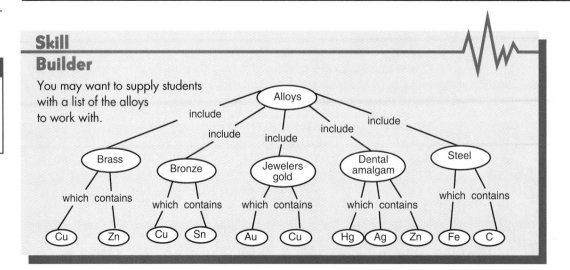

Preparing an Alloy

You have learned that brass is a mixture of copper and zinc. Brass looks very much like gold. In ancient times people called alchemists attempted to change other elements into gold. They never succeeded, but they did produce some alloys.

Materials

- copper penny
- zinc, 30-mesh
- hot plate
- nitric acid, HNO₃, dilute
- sodium hydroxide solution, NaOH, dilute
- evaporating dishes (2)
- tongs

CAUTION: *Acids and bases can cause burns. Rinse spills immediately. Use nitric acid where there is adequate ventilation.*

Procedure

1. CAREFULLY pour enough dilute HNO₃ into one evaporating dish to half fill the dish. Using tongs, grasp the penny and hold it in the acid for about 20 seconds.
2. Still using tongs, remove the penny from the acid and rinse it with cold tap water.
3. Place one teaspoon of 30-mesh zinc in the second evaporating dish. CAREFULLY add dilute NaOH to the dish to a depth of about 2 cm above the zinc.

4. Using tongs, carefully place the penny on top of the zinc. GENTLY heat the contents of the dish and *observe* the color of the penny.
5. Set the control of the hot plate on medium high. Using tongs, carefully remove the penny from the dish and rinse it in cold tap water. Dry the penny and place it on the preheated hot plate until the penny has a golden color.

Analyze

1. Describe the appearance of the penny after it was immersed in the nitric acid. Why did its appearance change?
2. In Step 3, the penny turned a silver color. Was it actually becoming silver? Was it, at this point, an alloy?

Conclude and Apply

3. Do alloys require specific amounts of ingredients to form?
4. What alloy has this procedure produced?
5. Why is heat usually necessary for two metals to combine to form an alloy?

14-1   MATERIALS WITH A PAST   **359**

ANSWERS TO QUESTIONS

1. The dark penny became bright. The nitric acid reacted with surface corrosion and removed it.
2. No, the penny was being coated with fresh zinc. It was not an alloy at this point because the metal atoms had not mixed with each other.
3. No. Most alloys are formed from elements that can dissolve in each other in all proportions.
4. brass

5. Heating increases the motion of the metal atoms, causing the components of the alloy to mix.

OBJECTIVE: **Observe** that the properties of an alloy differ from those of the component metals.

PROCESS SKILLS applied in this activity:
▶ **Observing** in Procedure Steps 4 and 5 and Analyze Question 1.
▶ **Inferring** in Conclude and Apply Questions 3 and 4.

COOPERATIVE LEARNING
If possible, have students work as Paired Partners. This activity does not lend itself to large groups.

TEACHING THE ACTIVITY

Alternate Materials: If you start with clean, shiny pennies, you can have students bypass Procedure Steps 1 and 2. If you do not have 30-mesh zinc, try out any granulated zinc and adjust the time according to your results.

Troubleshooting: The penny should stay in contact with the zinc long enough to become uniformly coated. Turn the penny or push it into the zinc if needed. Warming speeds the reaction.

▶ **CAUTION:** *Do not permit students to carry the coin to the sink to rinse it because acid or alkali will drip.*

▶ Newer pennies that are made of copper-plated zinc can be used if they are shiny and do not require an acid cleaning. Do not heat excessively.

▶ Pennies can also be held with tongs and heated gently at the tip of a burner flame. *Use open flame precautions with this method.* The hot-plate method gives more reliable results.

▶ To prepare dilute nitric acid, carefully add 15 mL of concentrated acid to 85 mL of distilled water with constant stirring.

▶ To prepare 2M sodium hydroxide, dissolve 80 g NaOH in 1000 mL of distilled water. Because the solution will become hot, it should be made well in advance of the activity.

Activity
ASSESSMENT
Performance: To further assess students' understanding of alloys, see USING LAB SKILLS, Question 11, on page 370.

PREPARATION

SECTION BACKGROUND

▶ Families report that they used to generate five garbage bags of trash each week. After recycling, only one bag is sent to the landfill.

1 MOTIVATE

▶Inform students that in 1992, approximately 63 billion aluminum cans were recycled. These cans plus other recycled aluminum provided approximately 30 percent of the aluminum industry's supply of aluminum.

TYING TO PREVIOUS KNOWLEDGE:
Have students discuss where they have observed pollution caused by discarded items.

2 TEACH

Key Concepts are highlighted.

In Your JOURNAL

Answer: Accept all reasonable answers. Students should consider potential recycling possibilities, energy to make both kinds of bags, and utility of the bags.

VideoDisc

STVS: Energy-Integrated Farm, Disc 2, Side 2

New Science Words

recycling

Science and MATH

Choose an item that you could recycle, such as aluminum cans. Save that item for one week, weigh the collected items, and find out how much money they are worth. Calculate how much you could make by recycling for a year.

In Your JOURNAL

When checking out of grocery stores, customers are frequently given a choice of plastic or paper bags for their purchases. **In your Journal,** write a paragraph explaining which you would choose and why.

Figure 14-8. Most solid wastes are buried in sanitary landfills like the one shown here.

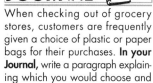

Objectives

▶ Explain the importance of recycling solid wastes.
▶ Discuss ways in which state and local governments encourage recycling of solid waste materials.

Why Recycle?

Think about all the different things that get discarded every day. Paper products, bottles and cans, bicycles and automobiles—the list is endless. In the past few years, major efforts have been made in this country toward recycling some of our solid wastes. **Recycling** is the recovering and processing of waste materials to regain them for human use.

The reasons for recycling materials can be summed up in two words—*preservation* and *conservation*. We need to preserve and conserve natural resources.

Preserving the environment doesn't just mean picking up litter in our parks and along highways. Solid waste must be reduced. Most solid waste is deposited in landfills. Although today's landfills are a great improvement over the old municipal dumps, many are still smelly, unpleasant environmental eyesores. But perhaps more important, many of America's more populous areas are running out of space. For example, some states, such as New Jersey, are forced to transport much of their solid waste to landfills in other states, at considerable cost in money and energy. There's just no room for any more landfills. So, we have to find new ways to deal with solid waste. Recycling is one important way to reduce the amount of solid waste material.

When you think of conservation, you should think of these two things: conserving the raw materials and conserving

360 USE OF MATERIALS

OPTIONS

Meeting Different Ability Levels

For Section 14-2, use the following **Teacher Resource Masters** depending upon individual students' needs.

◆ **Study Guide Master** for all students.

● **Reinforcement Master** for students of average and above average ability levels.

▲ **Enrichment Master** for above average students.

◆ STUDY GUIDE 59

STUDY GUIDE Chapter 14
Recycling Text Pages 360-361

Choose the term from the word list that best completes each statement. Write the term in the blank at the left.

| paper | deposit laws | recycling | solid wastes |
| conservation | pollution | energy | fossil fuels |

recycling 1. The recovering and processing of waste materials to regain them for human use is ____.

paper 2. The recycling of ____ helps to save trees.

solid wastes 3. Most materials that can be recycled are classified as ____.

conservation 4. Using raw materials and energy wisely are examples of ____.

energy 5. Recycling paper and aluminum requires the use of less ____ than is required to make these products from raw materials.

deposit laws 6. Many states now have ____ to encourage recycling of aluminum cans and glass bottles.

fossil fuels 7. Because recycling aluminum uses less electricity than producing new aluminum from raw materials, recycling helps to conserve ____.

pollution 8. As fewer fossil fuels are used to make products that can be made by recycling, air and water ____ is also reduced.

In the space below, list three materials that are currently recycled. Answers may vary. Suggested responses are given. All logical responses should be accepted.

9. **glass**
10. **aluminum**
11. **paper**

59

energy. Consider the three most commonly recycled materials—aluminum, glass, and paper. When an aluminum can or a newspaper is recycled, some aluminum ore is conserved or a tree is saved. But of equal importance, much less energy is needed to process the recycled can or paper. For example, to produce one aluminum can from ore takes 19 times as much electricity as is needed to produce the same can from recycled aluminum.

Thus, recycling helps to conserve our fossil fuels and reduces pollution. In the case of glass, the raw materials—mostly sand—are not in short supply. However, the amount of energy saved by recycling glass is significant.

If recycling is so beneficial, why don't we recycle more materials? For one thing, most factory machines are designed to use raw materials. And in many cases, it is actually less expensive to make something from raw materials than it is to use recycled materials. The entire process of recovering and reusing materials is a very complex one.

In some states, the recycling of certain materials is required by law. People must separate recyclable materials and place them by the curb for pickup. Several states have deposit laws that require people to pay a deposit on all canned and bottled beverages. The deposit is refunded when the bottle or can is returned to the store. As space and raw materials become scarcer, more and more states will turn to recycling. Recycling is definitely the wave of the future.

SECTION REVIEW

1. What are the main reasons for recycling solid wastes?
2. In what two major ways is recycling encouraged in some states?
3. **Connect to Life Science:** How would conserving raw materials be beneficial to plant and animal life?

You Decide!

Assume you are a member of the city council of a town of 200 000 people. Your town is running out of space for storing solid wastes, but the city department responsible for collecting the 400 metric tons of solid waste produced daily is currently spending its total budget. Would you vote for or against a tax increase to develop a program of collecting recyclable materials? Why?

Connect to... Earth Science

Many manufactured products now contain recycled materials. Check at home or at a grocery store to see what products contain or are packaged in recycled materials. What types of paper products frequently contain recycled paper?

SCIENCE & SOCIETY

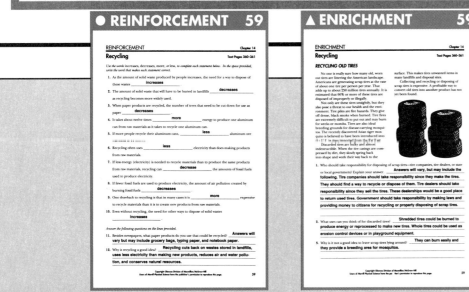

● **REINFORCEMENT** 59

▲ **ENRICHMENT** 59

361

CHECK FOR UNDERSTANDING
▶ Many states have begun plans for state-wide recycling efforts. For example, California's goal is to reduce waste, through recycling, by 50 percent by the year 2000. Have students investigate any such plans their state may have.

RETEACH
Remind students of the law of conservation of mass. It is impossible to throw matter away. There is no "away" because matter is not destroyed in ordinary reactions.

EXTENSION
For students who have mastered this section, use the **Reinforcement** and **Enrichment** masters or other OPTIONS provided.

Connect to... Earth Science

Answer: Notebook paper, newspaper, and bathroom tissue frequently contain recycled paper.

3 CLOSE

▶ Ask questions 1 and 2 and the **Connect to Life Science** question in the Section Review.

SECTION REVIEW ANSWERS
1. We are running out of space for landfills. We can save money by recycling rather than manufacturing from raw materials.
2. Recycling is encouraged in some states by laws requiring recycling and deposits on beverage containers.
3. **Connect to Life Science:** Habitat and natural balance are preserved.

YOU DECIDE!   SCIENCE & SOCIETY

Student responses may vary but should reflect the importance of preservation of the environment and the conservation of raw materials and energy.

PREPARATION

SECTION BACKGROUND

▶ Plastics made by addition polymerization are polyethylene, polypropylene, polyvinyl chloride, polyvinyl acetate, polystyrene, Teflon, and acrylics. In the process of addition polymerization, compounds with double bonds add on to each other end-to-end to form the polymer.

▶ Plastics can also be made by condensation polymerization. Polyesters and polyurethane are made this way. To form one of these polymers, one molecule loses a hydrogen and the next loses a hydroxyl group. The lost groups combine to form water.

▶ Graphite embedded in a plastic is a composite that has found uses in sports equipment such as golf clubs, tennis rackets, and fishing rods. It is also being used to replace aluminum panels in aircraft skins. It is lighter, stronger, and for military aircraft it can be made to absorb radar.

PREPLANNING

▶ For Activity 14-2, you will need paper clips and plaster of paris. Pipe cleaners can be used by some students.

1 MOTIVATE

▶ **Demonstration:** In a large grocery sack, place 12-15 wire clothes hangers. Tell students that these hangers represent monomers. Shake the closed sack for 30 seconds. Reach in the sack and slowly pull a hanger out. Many of the monomers will now be attached, forming a polymer.

New Science Words

plastic
synthetic fiber
composite

Objectives

▶ Compare and contrast plastics and synthetic fibers.
▶ Describe a composite.

Plastics

Think how often you and your family use the telephone. How often have you accidentally dropped the receiver or knocked a telephone over? Did the phone still work? A telephone never seems to wear out. It lasts because most of its parts are made of durable plastics. The first synthetic plastic was made only about a century ago. You may be thinking that one hundred years is a long time. However, if you remember that alloys and ceramics have been around for thousands of years, you'll realize that plastics are really modern materials.

Recall from the last chapter that a polymer is a gigantic molecule formed from thousands of smaller organic molecules, such as hydrocarbons. Molecules that form polymers are called monomers. You are made of natural polymers, such as proteins and nucleic acids. Polymers that do not form naturally can be manufactured from organic compounds. These polymers are called synthetic polymers. A **plastic** is a polymer-based material that can be easily molded into various shapes. ❶

You are probably familiar with the rolls of plastic bags that you find in the produce section of supermarkets. These bags are made of polyethylene (pahl ee ETH uh leen), one of the world's most widely produced and used plastics. Polyethylene is used to make, among other things, food storage containers, bottles, and the bands used around beverage six-packs. This synthetic polymer

Figure 14-9. The versatility and ruggedness of plastics make them ideal for use in objects that receive a lot of rough handling.

OPTIONS

Meeting Different Ability Levels

For Section 14-3, use the following **Teacher Resource Masters** depending upon individual students' needs.

◆ **Study Guide Master** for all students.
● **Reinforcement Master** for students of average and above average ability levels.
▲ **Enrichment Master** for above average students.

Additional Teacher Resource Package masters are listed in any **PROGRAM RESOURCES** boxes that are in the section. The additional masters are appropriate for all students.

◆ **STUDY GUIDE** 60

STUDY GUIDE   Chapter 14
New Materials   Text Pages 362-368

In each of the following statements, a term has been scrambled. Unscramble the term and write it in the blank to the left.

polymer	1. A gigantic molecule formed from thousands of smaller organic molecules is called a *yplmeor.*
monomers	2. The molecules that form polymers are called *monomers.*
synthetic	3. Polymers that are made artificially in a laboratory are called *ihentceys* polymers.
plastic	4. A common material made from synthetic polymers is *claspit.*
ethene	5. Polyethylene is a polymer formed from monomers of *theene.*
fiber	6. A strand of a synthetic polymer is called a synthetic *berif.*
petroleum	7. Most of the raw materials used to make synthetic materials come from *ruelptom* products.
fiberglass	8. A glass-fiber composite used to make the hulls of boats is *bagrsfles.*
composite	9. A mixture of two materials made by embedding one material in the other is called a *stoipmoce.*
organic	10. Plastics are made from *granoic* compounds.

In the spaces below, list five products that you use every day that are made from plastics.

11. food wrap or food storage bags
12. telephones
13. food storage containers
14. pens, markers, push pins
15. computers, phonograph records, cassette storage containers

Answers will vary. Suggested answers are given. Accept all logical responses.

60

is made of monomers of ethene, an unsaturated hydrocarbon. The structural formula of ethene is shown to the right.

Basically, polyethylene is formed by breaking the double bonds of many ethene molecules and allowing the molecules to reform as a polymer. Part of the polymer of polyethylene is shown below.

Because so many different organic compounds can be used as monomers, there are many different plastics, as shown in Table 14-3.

Table 14-3

COMMON PLASTICS		
Name	**Polymer Structure**	**Uses**
Polypropylene		Rope, protective clothing, textiles, carpet
Polystyrene		Containers, boats, coolers, insulation, furniture, models
Polyvinyl chloride (PVC)		Rubber substitute, cable covering, tubing, rainwear, gaskets
Teflon (polytetrafluorethane)		Nonstick cookware surfaces
Saran (polyvinylidene chloride)		Clinging food wraps

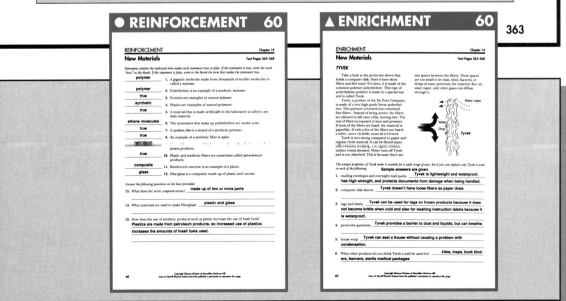

TYING TO PREVIOUS KNOWLEDGE: Students who have camped in a tent will recall that the bottom was probably a plastic called polypropylene. Most plastic wrap used in the kitchen is polyethylene. Vinyl is used to cover notebooks. List on the chalkboard the uses of plastic that students recall.

OBJECTIVES AND SCIENCE WORDS: Have students review the objectives and science words to become familiar with this section.

2 TEACH

Key Concepts are highlighted.

CONCEPT DEVELOPMENT

▶ Have a student give a brief report on the Bronze Age. Then ask the class if they believe they are living in the Plastic Age.

▶ Skin is composed mostly of proteins. A protein is a polymer. Ask the students if they think they are plastic wrapped. In a sense, they are. Skin is tough yet flexible. It is waterproof and provides a barrier against infection. It is also a mixture of polymers. Skin has many of the characteristics of a good plastic.

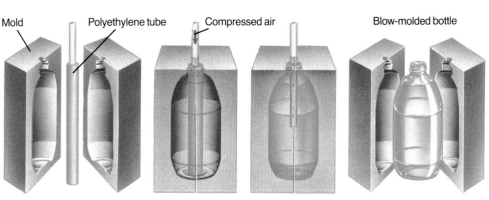

Mold   Polyethylene tube   Compressed air   Blow-molded bottle

Figure 14-10. The major use of high-density polyethylene (HDPE) is to make blow-molded products.

REVEALING MISCONCEPTIONS

▶ Many people believe that all plastics get soft and melt when heated. Many plastics do soften when heated. They are called thermoplastic materials. The chains of thermosetting polymers are cross-linked. Heating causes more cross-links to form and the plastic gets harder. See the Problem Solving feature on page 355.

CROSS CURRICULUM

▶ **Art:** Have students bring in different small items that are made from plastic. Arrange them using stiff wire and string to form a mobile. Hang the mobile from the ceiling under a sign that reads "New Materials."

TEACHER F.Y.I.

▶ Plastic 2-liter beverage bottles can now be recycled as can 1-gallon plastic milk jugs. The caps must be removed and the two different types of plastic separated. The recycled plastic can't be used again for food containers.

Connect to...
Physics

Answer: Originally, the volume of the tube is small and the compressed air pressure is high. As the volume of the tube increases, the pressure of the air decreases.

Connect to...
Physics

Explain how the process shown in Figure 14-10 illustrates Boyle's law.

Do you know that making plastic soft drink bottles is similar to blowing up a balloon? Refer to Figure 14-10 as you read how polyethylene bottles are manufactured. First, a tube of warm polyethylene is placed inside a bottle-shaped mold. Then the mold is closed, sealing the bottom of the tube. Next, compressed air is blown into the polyethylene tube; the tube expands and takes the shape of the mold. The mold is then opened and the bottle is removed.

Table 14-4

COMMON POLYMERS		
Name	**Structural Formula**	**Uses**
Dacron (a polyester)	$\cdots C - \bigcirc - C - OCH_2CH_2O - C - \bigcirc - C - OCH_2CH_2O \cdots$ (with $=O$ on each C)	Textiles, arterial grafts
Nylon 66	$\cdots C(CH_2)_4 - CN(CH_2)_6N - C(CH_2)_4C - N(CH_2)_6N \cdots$ (with $=O$ and H groups)	Tire cord, textiles, brush bristles, netting, carpet, athletic turf, sutures
Polyethylene	$\cdots CH_2 - CH_2 - CH_2 - CH_2 - CH_2 - CH_2 \cdots$	Tubing, prosthetic devices, packaging materials, kitchen utensils, paper coating
Orlon (polyacrylonitrile)	$\cdots C - C - C - C - C - C \cdots$ (with H and CN groups)	Textiles

364 USEFUL MATERIALS

OPTIONS

ASSESSMENT—ORAL

▶ **Some plastics have properties similar to those of rubber. What does this indicate about the chemical structure of rubber?** *Rubber is also a polymer.*

▶ **Why are synthetic fibers necessary in order to clothe the world's population?** *Natural fibers rely on agricultural processes. Land that will grow cotton and graze sheep is also needed to produce food. Oil wells don't require much land and can yield the raw materials needed to produce synthetic fibers.*

▶ **Silk is made by a caterpillar that eats the leaves of mulberry trees. Compare the cost of a man's silk tie to a polyester one. Why is there a price difference? Why are silk ties still preferred?** *The production of silk requires more labor, which is expensive. Silk is also in shorter supply than are synthetic fibers. However, silk usually gives a better appearance.*

Plastic Parts Instantly

All over the world, powerful computer systems are being used to create electronic, three-dimensional models of the products of tomorrow. These systems, called CAD systems, have greatly reduced the amount of time needed to determine the size and shape of new products. Once a new product is designed, the next step is the construction of a model that can be held in your hand. This model is called a prototype, and it is tested to be sure that it works as the designer intended.

Now a process invented by Charles W. Hull permits engineers to grow a prototype from liquid plastic, using the information from the CAD electronic model. Software slices the electronic model into a series of horizontal layers. A laser under computer control is directed at the surface of a vat of photosensitive plastic. Each pass of the laser

causes the plastic to harden. The hardened part sinks to the bottom of the vat, and the next laser pass adds another layer of hardened plastic. In this way the prototype actually grows from the bottom up. This technique, called stereolithography, should drastically reduce the time and expense required to bring many new products to market.

Think Critically: What properties make a material useful for building prototypes or models?

Think Critically: The properties will depend on the type of testing the prototype will undergo. The material used to make a prototype which is to be used only to evaluate shape needs only to be moldable. If the prototype is to be used to evaluate function, the material may need to be strong, durable, waterproof, or have other characteristics.

CONCEPT DEVELOPMENT

Cooperative Learning: Send an Expert Team to interview a fire prevention officer to determine if there is a danger in having curtains, drapes, carpeting, and upholstery made of synthetic fibers. Have students ask what gaseous products form when various fibers burn.

▶ Ask your students if they have observed the construction of a new house that was wrapped in a white paper-like material. This Kevlar wrap is used to help make the house draft-free. This will result in energy conservation.

▶ Students may be interested that today's army helmets are also made from lightweight Kevlar fibers.

Cooperative Learning: Send an Expert Team to a local carpet store to interview a salesperson about the different fibers used in carpet manufacture. Have them determine the advantages and disadvantages of the various carpet fibers.

The clothing you are wearing may be made of fabrics that have been woven from synthetic fibers. A **synthetic fiber** is a strand of a synthetic polymer. Some synthetic fibers have amazing properties. For example, a strand of a synthetic fiber called Kevlar is five times stronger than a similar strand of steel. It is so strong it is used to make bulletproof vests. Synthetic fibers are used to weave both indoor and indoor-outdoor carpeting, upholstery coverings, and other textiles. Today, the use of synthetic fibers is greater than that of natural fibers. Table 14-4 lists the names and polymer structures of several familiar synthetic fibers. Fabrics with new properties are made by weaving natural fibers, such as cotton and silk, with synthetic fibers. If you look at the label of a permanent-press shirt, you will see that the fabric is a mixture of natural and synthetic fibers.

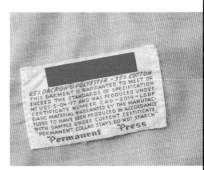

Figure 14-11. Wrinkle-resistant materials can be produced by combining synthetic fibers and natural fibers.

CROSS CURRICULUM

▶ **Art:** Have each student bring in a swatch of cloth made from synthetic fibers. Have the class decide on a picture they would like and draw a rough sketch on heavy card stock. "Paint" the picture by cutting and gluing the cloth over the rough sketch.

ENRICHMENT

▶ Have students investigate the monomers that go into the production of synthetic fibers such as Kodel, Acrilan, Dynel, and Mylar. Kodel is a copolymer of ethylene glycol and terephthalic acid. Acrilan is a polymer of acrylonitrile. Dynel is a copolymer of acrylonitrile and vinyl chloride. Mylar is a copolymer of ethylene glycol and terephthalic acid.

PROGRAM RESOURCES

From the **Teacher Resource Package** use:

Concept Mapping, page 33.

Science and Society, page 18, Bottle Bill.

Transparency Masters, pages 55-56, Production of Nylon.

Use **Color Transparency** number 28, Production of Nylon.

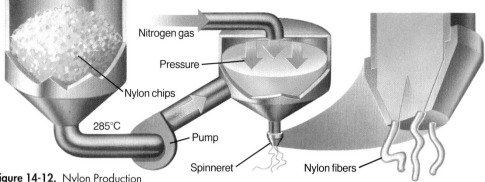

▶ A car body shop can be a source of a composite that has been removed from a collision-damaged fiberglass car body. Students can be shown how the epoxy and fiberglass mat has been used to form a car body panel. **CAUTION:** *Students should handle the broken material only while wearing gloves.*

▶ Graphite composites are being used to form panels on modern airplanes, such as the stealth fighter F117A.

▶ Ask a student who has a graphite composite golf club, tennis racket, or fishing rod to bring it to class and show the other students. Ask a track coach if you can show the class a fiberglass composite pole used in the pole vault event.

VideoDisc

STVS: Composite Materials, Disc 2, Side 1

STVS: Advanced Composites, Disc 2, Side 1

CHECK FOR UNDERSTANDING

Use the Mini Quiz to check for understanding.

MINI QUIZ

Use the Mini Quiz to check students' recall of chapter content.

1 **An easily molded material made from polymers is called a(n) _____ .** *plastic*

2 **A strand of synthetic polymer is called a(n) _____ .** *synthetic fiber*

3 **Most plastics and synthetic fibers are made from the raw materials _____ .** *petroleum and natural gas*

4 **When one material is embedded in another material, the mixture is called a(n) _____ .** *composite*

RETEACH

Have students make flash cards with names of modern materials on one side and examples listed in the textbook on the reverse side.

EXTENSION

For students who have mastered this section, use the **Reinforcement** and **Enrichment** masters or other OPTIONS provided.

Figure 14-12. Nylon Production

Figure 14-12 shows how nylon fibers are manufactured. Nylon chips are heated until they melt. The melted nylon is pumped into a high-pressure chamber. It is then forced through tiny openings of a nozzle called a spinneret. As it cools, the nylon forms long strands.

3 You may wonder where the raw materials—the hydrocarbons and organic compounds—used to produce plastics and synthetic fibers come from. Most of them are found in petroleum—crude oil—and in natural gas. Can you explain why plastics and synthetic fibers are sometimes called petrochemical products? As the production of plastics and synthetic fibers continues to increase, so will the demand for crude oil.

Composites

Have you ever seen a picture of a face made from cut-up photographs of famous people? These pictures are called composite pictures. The word *composite* means "made of two or more parts." Some materials are also composites.

Figure 14-13 shows a bridge being built of reinforced concrete. As you can see, the concrete has long steel rods

Figure 14-13. The steel "skeleton" adds strength and flexibility to the concrete used to build this bridge.

OPTIONS

INQUIRY QUESTIONS

▶ **Because fiberglass composites don't rust, why aren't they used instead of steel to make car bodies?** *Steel is cheaper and can be stamped into body panels. Composites must be molded.*

▶ **Plastics will last a long time and don't biodegrade in a landfill. Why have plastic bottles recently become more popular than the glass bottles that have been used for centuries?** *Plastics are lighter in weight, which reduces shipping costs, and they seldom* break in shipment. Some plastics can be recycled.

▶ **Synthetic fibers resist wrinkling, are colorfast, windproof, and wear resistant. Why is cotton so popular? Why is it blended with synthetic fibers such as polyester?** *Cotton allows fabrics to breathe. Some synthetics do not allow perspiration or air to pass through. Some synthetics feel hot in summer and cold in winter. The addition of cotton to the synthetic materials can help overcome these problems.*

Figure 14-14. The composite material used in this artificial limb makes it strong, yet light in weight.

running through it. These rods reinforce the concrete, giving it additional strength and support. Reinforced concrete is an example of a composite. A **composite** is a mixture of two materials, one embedded in the other.

Have you ever heard of cars with fiberglass bodies? These bodies are made of a glass-fiber composite that is a mixture of small threads, or fibers, of glass, embedded in a plastic. The structures of the fiberglass reinforce the plastic, making a strong, lightweight composite. A glass-fiber composite is an example of a ceramic embedded in a plastic. How would you describe reinforced concrete? Many different composites can be made using various metals, plastics, and ceramics. Figure 14-14 shows an example. In the future you may be driving a car and living in a house that are made almost entirely of composites.

SECTION REVIEW

1. Name several plastics and synthetic fibers.
2. Compare and contrast plastics and synthetic fibers.
3. Describe a composite.
4. **Apply:** What advantages would an automobile engine made of a metal-ceramic composite have compared to one made of an alloy?
5. **Connect to Life Science:** Many athletes now play on nylon-based artificial playing surfaces. What properties of plastic make this surface an advantage for the athletes?

☒**Observing and Inferring**

Look at the figures in this section. Describe a way to manufacture a roll of polyethylene bags. If you need help, refer to Observing and Inferring in the **Skill Handbook** on page 678.

Skill Builder

Figure 14-15. This familiar figure is a composite of the "potato" and whatever facial features are added to it.

Did You Know?

The organs a spider uses to spin the fibers for its web are called spinnerets. The manufacture of nylon fibers mimics this natural process.

ACTIVITY 14-2

OBJECTIVE: Design and carry out an experiment to show how a composite material will have properties of the utilized materials.

Time: two class periods separated by a day for drying

PROCESS SKILLS applied in this activity are **interpreting data, observing, measuring,** and **predicting**.

PREPARATION: To shorten lab time, the aluminum foil boxes could be prepared ahead of time. Assemble several common items, such as screening, pipe cleaners, paper clips, string, and popsicle sticks, to be used as embedding material.

Cooperative Learning: Have Science Investigation Teams divide the activity tasks into measuring, mixing, and constructing. Have a reader give instructions and monitor each task.

SAFETY

Caution students to have any means of comparing products approved by the teacher. Any striking of materials by a hammer should be done when the material is wrapped in a towel and any person nearby is wearing goggles.

THINKING CRITICALLY

Long, thin materials such as pipe cleaners or paper clips should add strength to the composite. Soda straws may make it lighter but weaker. Screening may cause it to resist crumbling. Try to get students to relate the desired property to a logical choice of embedding material.

TEACHING THE ACTIVITY

Refer to the Activity Worksheets for additional information and teaching strategies.

• If possible, try the plaster mix ahead of time so that you can tell students how long to wait before pouring it. The plaster should become thick enough to support the reinforcing materials but not so firm that it will not adhere.

• For best results, observe the 24-hour drying time.

ACTIVITY 14-2 DESIGNING AN EXPERIMENT
Compose a Composite

If you have ever seen a bridge or a large building under construction you may have noticed concrete structures with steel rods embedded in them. By designing these structures with this type of mixture, engineers are able to take advantage of properties of both concrete and steel. In this activity you will prepare a mixture of two materials, one embedded in the other, to create your own composite.

Getting Started

You will need to prepare two samples of plaster of paris in a special aluminum foil box. One sample can serve as a control to compare to the new composite you will make as you add other materials to the second plaster of paris sample.

Thinking Critically

Do you want the new composite to be stronger than plaster of paris? Do you want it to resist shattering or to be lighter? What types of materials will you embed in the plaster of paris in order to bring about new properties for your composite?

Materials

Your cooperative groups will have available for use:

- plaster of paris
- water
- measuring cup
- heavy-duty aluminum foil
- materials to embed in the plaster of paris, such as paper clips, soda straws, pipe cleaners
- hammer
- beaker
- paper towels

Try It!

1. Shape the aluminum foil into a large rectangle with sides about 3 cm high and a ridge down the center so that you have two equal-sized compartments. A recommended overall size is 20 cm x 25 cm x 3 cm.
2. Slowly add one cup of plaster of paris to 2/3 cup of water. Gently mix and allow to stand for approximately five minutes.
3. Stir the mixture, and add approximately 1/4 of it to each of the two compartments. Embed the material you have chosen in the plaster of paris in one half of the pan.

4. Wait 5 five minutes and pour the rest of the plaster of paris equally into both compartments. Allow both compartments to set for a day. Then tear away the aluminum foil frame.
5. Within your group, decide how you want to *compare* your new composite to the plaster of paris. **CAUTION:** *All tests must be approved by your teacher before you use them.*

Summing Up/Sharing Results

- Find out what materials and results other groups had with their new composites.
- How do you think the density of the composite *compares* to the density of plaster of paris?
- In what way is your composite similar to some concrete structures?

Going Further!

Predict what you think would happen if you doubled the amount of embedding material while holding the amount of plaster of paris constant.

SUMMING UP/SHARING RESULTS

The density of the composite will increase if the embedded material has a greater density than does plaster of paris. If the embedded material is light or causes air to be trapped, its presence will decrease density. Like reinforced concrete, plaster of paris is poured around another, strengthening material.

PROGRAM RESOURCES

From the **Teacher Resource Package** use:
Activity Worksheets, pages 112-113,
Activity 14-2: Compose a Composite.

GOING FURTHER!

Doubling the amount of material may be beneficial if it does not prevent the plaster of paris from adhering to the material.

Activity
ASSESSMENT

Performance: To further assess students' understanding of composites, see USING LAB SKILLS, Question 12, on page 370.

CHAPTER
REVIEW

SUMMARY

14-1: Materials with a Past
1. People have been making and using alloys and ceramics for thousands of years. Some common alloys include bronze, brass, amalgams, and various alloys of iron. Some common ceramics include structural ceramics, such as brick and tile, and various kinds of glass.
2. An alloy is a mixture of a metal with one or more other elements. Alloys exhibit metallic properties. Ceramics are composed of clay or claylike mixtures. Except for cermets—ceramic metals—ceramics generally have nonmetallic properties.

14-2: Science and Society: Recycling
1. There are two important reasons for recycling materials: preservation of the environment and conservation of natural resources.

2. State and local governments encourage recycling through educational programs and by passing laws requiring that certain materials be recycled.

14-3: New Materials
1. Plastics and synthetic fibers are materials made from synthetic polymers. Plastics can be produced in many forms, ranging from very thin films to thick slabs or blocks. Synthetic fibers are produced in thin strands that can be woven into fabrics.
2. A composite is a mixture of two materials, one embedded in the other. Reinforced concrete is an example of a composite.

KEY SCIENCE WORDS

a. alloy
b. amalgam
c. ceramic
d. cermet
e. composite
f. glass
g. ore
h. plastic
i. recycling
j. synthetic fiber

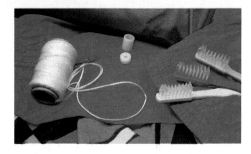

UNDERSTANDING VOCABULARY

Match each phrase with the correct term from the list of Key Science Words.

1. a strand of a synthetic polymer
2. ceramic with no regular crystal structure
3. mixture consisting of a metal and one or more other elements
4. made from dried clay or claylike mixtures
5. material made from polymers; can be easily molded
6. mined source of metals
7. mixture of one material embedded in another
8. recovering waste materials and reprocessing them for reuse
9. has properties of ceramics and alloys
10. alloy containing mercury

USEFUL MATERIALS **369**

OPTIONS

ASSESSMENT
To assess student understanding of material in this chapter, use the resources listed.

COOPERATIVE LEARNING
Consider using cooperative learning in the THINK AND WRITE CRITICALLY, APPLY, and MORE SKILL BUILDERS sections of the Chapter Review.

PROGRAM RESOURCES
From the **Teacher Resource Package** use:
Chapter Review, pages 31-32.
Chapter and Unit Tests, pages 88-91, Chapter Test.
Chapter and Unit Tests, pages 92-93, Unit Test.

CHAPTER
REVIEW

SUMMARY
Have students read the summary statements to review the major concepts of the chapter.

UNDERSTANDING VOCABULARY
1. j
2. f
3. a
4. c
5. h
6. g
7. e
8. i
9. d
10. b

ASSESSMENT
Portfolio
Encourage students to place in their portfolios one or two items of what they consider to be their best work. For each item, ask students to explain why that item was chosen and what they learned from it. Items might be selected from the following.
- Activity 14-1 observations and answers, p. 359
- You Decide responses, p. 361
- Skill Builder description and Assessment diagram, p. 367

Performance
Additional performance assessments may be found in *Performance Assessment* and *Science Integration Activities* that accompany **Merrill Physical Science.** Performance Task Assessment Lists and rubrics for evaluating these activities and other products generated throughout the chapter can be found in Glencoe's *Performance Assessment in Middle School Science.*

CHAPTER
REVIEW

CHECKING CONCEPTS

1. d	**6.** b
2. a	**7.** a
3. a	**8.** c
4. c	**9.** b
5. a	**10.** c

USING LAB SKILLS

ASSESSMENT

Use these alternate lab exercises to assess students' understanding of skills used in this chapter.

11. Students should observe the techniques that seem to produce the most successful alloys and specify those steps. For example, students may specify the length of time spent cleaning the penny, the distance the penny is held from the flame, or the time the penny is waved through the flame.

12. The embedded material would lessen the flexibility of the rubbery composite.

THINK AND WRITE CRITICALLY

13. The primary raw material is silicon dioxide, sand. It is abundant and inexpensive and the production process is relatively simple.

14. Preservation is keeping things as they are. Conservation is saving a resource by using less of it or by finding a substitute.

15. It takes less energy to produce glass from recycled materials than to produce it from raw materials.

16. Copper can be found in its elemental form in nature. Iron is found only in a combined state and must be separated chemically to be usable.

17. Steel is an alloy of a metal with a nonmetal, carbon. The other alloys are made from two or more metals.

CHAPTER
REVIEW

CHECKING CONCEPTS

Choose the word or phrase that completes the sentence.

1. The production of _____ is greater than that of any other alloy.
   a. amalgam   **c.** bronze
   b. brass   **d.** steel

2. Steel is an alloy of iron and _____.
   a. carbon   **c.** tin
   b. mercury   **d.** zinc

3. Structural ceramics contain silicon or _____.
   a. aluminum   **c.** copper
   b. carbon   **d.** lithium

4. A source of the materials used to make plastics is _____.
   a. clay   **c.** petroleum
   b. ore   **d.** synthetic fiber

5. The most commonly recycled metal is _____.
   a. aluminum   **c.** iron
   b. glass   **d.** paper

6. Brass and bronze both contain _____.
   a. mercury   **c.** tin
   b. copper   **d.** zinc

7. _____ alloys are very lightweight and strong.
   a. Aluminum-lithium   **c.** Copper-tin
   b. Copper-zinc   **d.** Iron-carbon

8. Most elements needed to make alloys are obtained from _____.
   a. amalgams   **c.** ores
   b. ceramics   **d.** recycling

9. Clay is used to make _____.
   a. alloys   **c.** ores
   b. ceramics   **d.** plastics

10. Most solid waste is _____.
   a. recycled
   b. in usable form
   c. deposited in landfills
   d. burned

USING LAB SKILLS

11. In Activity 14-1 on page 359, you learned that too little or too much heating would prevent the copper-zinc alloy from forming. How might you design a method for improving this part of the procedure?

12. The plaster of paris composite that you made in Activity 14-2 on page 370 was rigid after it dried. What properties would a composite have if the same material were embedded but a rubbery material was poured?

THINK AND WRITE CRITICALLY

Answer the following questions in your Journal using complete sentences.

13. Explain why most glass products are relatively inexpensive.

14. Explain the difference between preservation and conservation.

15. Explain why it is important to recycle glass when the raw materials for making it are so plentiful.

16. Iron bonds more readily with other elements than does copper. Why do you think copper was discovered so much earlier than iron was?

17. In what way is steel different from such alloys as brass, bronze, and most aluminum alloys?

18. Describe three ways you can conserve energy in your home.

19. List two reasons why you would choose to use recycled materials, even though other materials may cost less.

20. A lower carat gold has less gold in it than a higher carat gold. Why might you prefer a ring that is 10 carat gold over a ring that is 20 carat gold?

21. Explain how we contribute to air and water pollution when we don't recycle.

22. A synthetic fiber might be preferred over a natural fiber for use outdoors because it will not rot. Why might this property become a negative feature in the environment?

MORE SKILL BUILDERS

If you need help, refer to the Skill Handbook.

1. Comparing and Contrasting: Compare and contrast alloys and ceramics.

2. Measuring in SI: A bronze trophy has a mass of 952 grams. If the bronze is 85 percent copper, how many grams of tin are contained in the trophy?

3. Interpreting Data: Aluminum recycling saves 95 percent of the energy it takes to produce an aluminum product from ore. On the average, each American uses 320 aluminum beverage cans per year. If all 320 cans are recycled into other cans, how many new cans could be produced from ore for the same amount of energy used?

4. Recognizing Cause and Effect: Americans use 215 million aluminum cans per day. Compare the effects of recycling these cans to the effects of throwing them away.

5. Concept Mapping: Draw a network tree classifying matter, moving from the most general term to the most specific. Use the terms *compounds, elements, heterogeneous, heterogeneous mixtures, homogeneous, homogeneous mixtures, materials, solutions, substances.* Check (✔) the most specific term that describes an alloy and underline the most specific term that describes a composite.

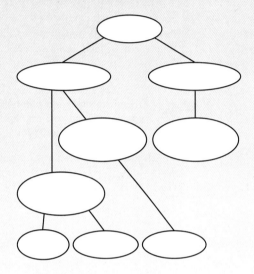

PROJECTS

1. Research gold, its alloys, and "carats." Find out several uses for gold and its alloys and what carat gold is used for each.

2. Make a poster of the floor plan of your school or an area of the school. On the floor plan, list locations where ceramics are used and the types of ceramics used there.

3. Research the production of silk fabric and compare it to production of synthetic fabrics such as nylon. Display samples of each.

USEFUL MATERIALS **371**

18. Answers will vary, but may include turning off lights, adjusting the thermostat, and not leaving hot water running.

19. Answers will vary, but may include the fact that using recycled materials conserves energy and resources. Also, the recycling process may produce less pollution, thereby preserving the environment.

20. The 10-carat ring will be less expensive, and less easily bent, worn away, or scratched.

21. Answers will vary, but may include the facts that more energy is used, wastes are produced, and unrecycled materials are discarded, thus contributing to land and water pollution.

22. Some synthetic fibers will not decompose and may be found in the environment thousands of years later.

MORE SKILL BUILDERS

1. Comparing and Contrasting: Both alloys and ceramics are mixtures designed to use the most favorable properties of their components. Alloys are usually mixtures of two or more metals. Ceramics are mixtures of nonmetals, or a nonmetal and a metal.

2. Measuring in SI: 143 grams

3. Interpreting Data: 16 cans

4. Recognizing Cause and Effect: Recycling the cans will conserve aluminum and the energy required to produce it. Recycling will also decrease the amount of solid waste discarded in landfills or as litter.

5. Concept Mapping:

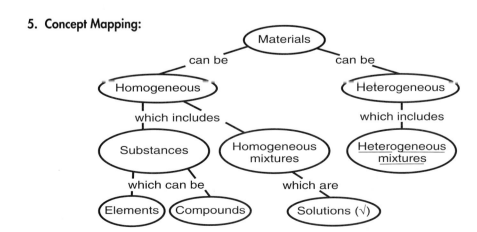

Objective

In this unit-ending feature, the unit topic, "Kinds of Substances," is extended to other disciplines. Students will see how different chemical substances affect other places around the world.

Motivate

Cooperative Learning: Assign one Connection to each group of students. Using the Expert Teams strategy, have each group research to find out more about the geographic location of the Connection—its climate, culture, flora and fauna, and ecological issues.

Teaching Tips

▶ Tell students to keep in mind the connection between chemical substances and their uses or effects as they are reading this feature.

▶ Ask students to brainstorm about new products and/or technologies that might exist in the future.

Wrap-Up

Conclude this lesson by having students discuss how the Connections presented here also affect other parts of Earth.

BIOLOGY

Background: The Providence system is set up in a greenhouse, with a series of vats containing swamp-like ecosystems. In marshes and swamps, sunlight bleaches some pollutants from water. Others are broken down by bacteria or are removed by plants such as cattails.

Discussion: Ask students to compare the organisms in the artificial wetland with those that would occur in a natural ecosystem.

Answer to Question: Organic matter and heavy metals would pollute any areas, either land or water, where they were released.

Extension: Have students research the Biosphere II plan for sewage treatment.

Kinds of Substances

In this unit, you studied about elements, compounds, and other useful substances. Now find out how these different kinds of substances are connected to other subjects and places around the world.

BIOLOGY

NATURE'S WATER FILTERS
Providence, Rhode Island
An artificial wetland, complete with bacteria, algae, plants, snails, and fish, can purify the sewage from 150 households. Bacteria digest organic matter, and plants can remove even nitrates and heavy metals. Why is it important that these substances be removed?

GEOLOGY

GREEN GEMS
Muzo, Columbia
Emeralds are crystals of beryl, colored green by chromium or vanadium. For as long as 1000 years, the mine at Muzo has produced the largest and best emeralds ever found. Where are some other places in the world where emeralds are mined?

GEOLOGY

Background: Colombia produces half of the billion dollars' worth of emeralds mined yearly in the world. Beryls are minerals composed of beryllium aluminum silicate. Only those that are deep green and transparent are emeralds.

Discussion: Discuss with students how modern chemical analysis has changed what is called an emerald. Before then, almost any green stone was called an emerald. Gemologists can often determine the mine site of an emerald by studying the emerald.

Answer to Question: Zambia, Brazil, Zimbabwe, and Pakistan are the other major producers of emeralds.

Extension: Have students find out how synthetic emeralds are manufactured.

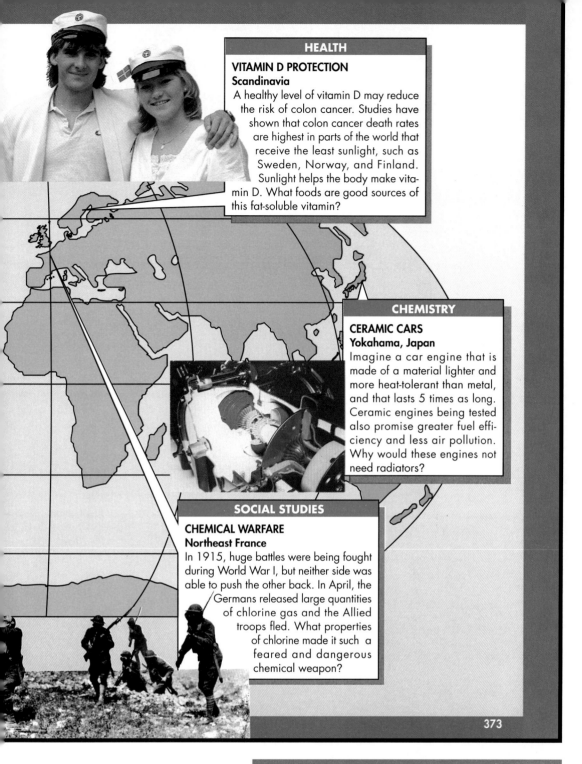

HEALTH

VITAMIN D PROTECTION
Scandinavia

A healthy level of vitamin D may reduce the risk of colon cancer. Studies have shown that colon cancer death rates are highest in parts of the world that receive the least sunlight, such as Sweden, Norway, and Finland. Sunlight helps the body make vitamin D. What foods are good sources of this fat-soluble vitamin?

CHEMISTRY

CERAMIC CARS
Yokahama, Japan

Imagine a car engine that is made of a material lighter and more heat-tolerant than metal, and that lasts 5 times as long. Ceramic engines being tested also promise greater fuel efficiency and less air pollution. Why would these engines not need radiators?

SOCIAL STUDIES

CHEMICAL WARFARE
Northeast France

In 1915, huge battles were being fought during World War I, but neither side was able to push the other back. In April, the Germans released large quantities of chlorine gas and the Allied troops fled. What properties of chlorine made it such a feared and dangerous chemical weapon?

373

SOCIAL STUDIES

Background: The use of chlorine gas was the first recorded use of poison gas in chemical warfare. Mustard gas ($C_4H_8Cl_2S$), an oily liquid which evaporates to a poison gas that causes blindness, burns, and death, was also used during World War I.

Discussion: By international agreement, the use of chemical weapons has been banned. However, not all countries have adhered to the ban.

Answer to Question: Chlorine is a poisonous gas that is heavier than air and settled in the trenches. It is very irritating to the nose, throat, and lungs.

Extension: Have students research the use of the chlorine compound 2,4,5-T, which was used as a chemical defoliant during the Vietnam war.

HEALTH

Background: Vitamin D is dissolved in and transported through the body in fat. It can be stored in fatty tissues, and toxic levels can build up if a person takes more than the recommended amount.

Discussion: Discuss with students why extra exposure to sunlight might not be the answer to the colon cancer risk. Point out that exposure to UV radiation from sunlight increases the risk for skin cancer.

Answer to Question: Fortified milk, liver, and fatty fish are good sources of vitamin D.

Extension: Ask students to find out other environmental and lifestyle risk factors for cancer.

CHEMISTRY

Background: One Japanese car company has test driven a ceramic-engine prototype car over 5000 kilometers at speeds up to 150 km/hour.

Discussion: Point out to students that one disadvantage of many ceramics is that they are brittle. Ask what problems this could cause in car engines.

Answer to Question: Ceramics can withstand temperatures that would melt metal engines, so a radiator, whose purpose is to cool an engine, is not needed.

Extension: Have students prepare reports on some of the elements used in ceramics: titanium, zirconium, aluminum, silicon, carbon, nitrogen, and oxygen.

FARMER

Background: Farmers may work on family farms, as tenant farmers who live and work on property owned by others, or as hired hands who live elsewhere.

Related Career	Education
Farm-equipment mechanic	technical school
Animal nutritionist	college degree
Aerial crop sprayer	technical school
Feed salesperson	high school

Career Issue: Many farmers are concerned about contamination of groundwater from agricultural runoff. Some people want to see the use of certain agricultural chemicals restricted or banned.

What do you think? Lead students in a discussion of their own attitudes about the use of farm chemicals. Reducing the use of fertilizers and pesticides might result in smaller crops and higher prices. Would they be willing to pay more for food to reduce chemical use on farms?

PHARMACIST

Background: Dispensing pharmacists work in drugstores, clinics, and hospitals. Other pharmacists work for pharmaceutical laboratories testing drugs for purity and strength.

Related Career	Education
Crime lab technician	technical school
Quality control technician	technical school
Biomedical engineer	college degree
Pharmaceutical technician	technical school

Career Issue: In most states, unless a physician specifies on a prescription that a brand name drug must be used, a generic drug may be substituted for a brand name. If a pharmacist must dispense the brand name drug, it is usually at a higher cost to the patient.

What do you think? Do students think doctors should be allowed to require the use of a brand name drug without the approval of the patient?

PHARMACIST

A *pharmacist* dispenses drugs and medicines prescribed by physicians and dentists. He or she also advises consumers on the uses and possible side effects of medicines—both prescription and nonprescription. A pharmacist must know about the chemical properties of drugs and their effects on the body.

If you're interested in becoming a pharmacist, you should take high school classes in biology, chemistry, and mathematics. Pharmacists attend college for four to six years. All states require a pharmacist to pass a licensing examination.

For Additional Information
Contact the American Pharmaceutical Association, 2215 Constitution Avenue NW, Washington, DC 20037.

FARMER

Because modern farming is so complex, a *farmer* needs business skills, as well as an understanding of and experience in methods and problems of farming. Different kinds of farming include dairy production, livestock production, crop production, orchards, and vineyards.

To be a farmer, you should be in good physical condition, enjoy working outdoors, and be interested in working with plants and animals. You also need a good background in biology, chemistry, mathematics, and good mechanical ability.

Many farmers receive on-the-job training while working with relatives or as hired hands. Some farmers take vocational classes to expand and update their knowledge. Others take 2- or 4-year college courses in agriculture.

For Additional Information
Contact the American Farm Bureau Federation, 225 Touhy Avenue, Park Ridge, Illinois 60068.

UNIT READINGS

▶Corrick, James A. *Recent Revolutions in Chemistry.* Danbury, CT: Watts, 1986.
▶"Elements Show They're Metal." *New Scientist,* April 9, 1987, pp. 32-35.
▶Ponte, Lowell. "Dawn of the New Stone Age." *Reader's Digest,* July, 1987, pp. 128-133.

374

UNIT READINGS

Background
▶ *Recent Revolutions in Chemistry* presents discoveries such as silicon chips and polymers in a clear, understandable way.
▶ "Elements Show They're Metal" describes some unusual properties of metals subjected to high temperatures and pressures.
▶ "Dawn of the New Stone Age" discusses the uses of new ceramic compounds.

More Readings
1. Ward, Fred. "Emeralds." *National Geographic.* July 1990, pp. 38-69. Describes the often dangerous world of emerald mining and buying.
2. Canby, Thomas Y. "Advanced Materials—Reshaping Our Lives." *National Geographic.* December 1989, pp. 746-781.

The Art of Pottery

The passage that follows discusses an ancient technique for making pottery and a woman, Margaret Tafoya, who uses the technique to create highly prized pieces.

How and where pottery originated remains unknown, but early pottery can be traced back for about 9000 years. At some point, it was discovered that when dried clay bowls were placed in a fire and heated, they became hard and retained their shape—they became pottery, the first ceramics. Pottery could hold liquids, such as oil or water, which baskets could not.

In the areas of North America where pottery making flourished, three basic techniques were used—coiling, molding, and coiling and molding. Most pots were made by coiling or by a combination of coiling and molding. Coiling is done by forming a clay ball into a flat disk to serve as a base. Additional clay balls are rolled out to form coils and placed on top of one another to form the walls of the pot. To make the surfaces of coiled pots smooth for polishing, carving, or painting, a material called slip is applied. Slip is made by mixing fine clay with water until it has the consistency of heavy cream. The pots are then polished with smooth, round polishing stones. The completed pots are fired in shallow pits or directly on the ground in fires of cedar wood. Potters can tell by the color of the fire when the pots are done.

Margaret Tafoya, a Pueblo potter from Santa Clara, New Mexico, uses the same methods to create her pottery that were used 1500 years ago by her Anasazi ancestors. She and other members of her family have dug clay from the same area for generations. She then shapes the clay, coil by coil, into a pot. The decorations she carves into her pots are symbols of the Santa Clara people. Her deeply carved redware and blackware are highly prized. She says the secret to the brilliant shine on her pottery is the polishing. She spends hours carefully rubbing her pots before firing them. The polishing stones she uses have been passed down from mother to daughter for generations.

In 1984, Margaret Tafoya was named a National Heritage Fellow by the National Endowment for the Arts. Since 1982 the Endowment has recognized, through its Folk Art Program, exceptional artists who have preserved their cultural and artistic traditions.

In Your Own Words

▶ Does a person have to be a painter or sculptor to be considered an artist? Write an essay supporting your position.

375

Biography: Margaret Tafoya is a member of the Tafoya-Naranjo family, known since the 1930s for their polished, carved, black and red pottery. Four generations of the family currently carry on the pottery-making tradition.

TEACHING STRATEGY——

Have students read through the article on pottery. Then have them respond to the discussion questions below.

Discussion Questions

1. **The designs for Margaret Tafoya's pottery are inspired by old myths of her people and include water serpents, buffalo horns, and bear paws. If you were going to make pottery, what kinds of designs would you use to represent your ethnic or cultural heritage?** *Allow students to describe symbols they would use and encourage them to explain the personal significance of the symbols.*

2. **Margaret Tafoya regards her polishing stones as her most valuable family heirlooms. Would you consider items such as these heirlooms? What items would be considered family heirlooms in your family?** *Family heirlooms are items that have special meaning and emotional attachment for family members. Margaret Tafoya's polishing stones have been used for generations to carry on the art of pottery. Family heirlooms that students could mention might include such things as items of furniture, books, old photo albums, or any other item that helps hold a family tradition or culture together.*

Classics

▶ Street, A. and Alexander, W. *Metals in the Service of Man.* New York, NY: Penguin, 1962.

Other Works

▶ Books and articles on Native American pottery include: Wormington, H.M. *The Story of Pueblo Pottery.* Denver, Colo: Denver Museum of Natural History. Museum Pictorial, No. 2, 1974. Fenstermarker, Gerald, B. "Iroquois Pottery." *Pennsylvania Archaeologist.* January 1973. Dockstader, Frederick. *Naked Clay: Unadorned Pottery of the American Indian.* New York, NY: Museum of the American Indian, 1972.

In Unit 5, students are introduced to broad categories of physical and chemical changes in matter. Common properties of solutions and their behaviors are discussed. Chemical changes in matter are categorized as chemical reactions that can be represented by chemical equations. Four broad classes of chemical reactions are discussed as well as the role of energy in determining chemical reactions. The unit concludes with a discussion of acids and bases.

CONTENTS

ADVANCE PREPARATION

Audiovisuals
▶ Show the filmstrip/cassette *Chemical Reactions,* Science Software.
▶ Show the filmstrip *All About Acids and Bases,* Science Software.

Field Trips and Speakers
▶ Arrange for a county extension agent to visit your class to discuss testing soil acidity and alkalinity.

376

OPTIONS

Cross Curriculum
Have students research how the shelf life of a food product is increased with preservatives. Have students research the two main types of preservatives: antimicrobials and antioxidants. Have them consider the economic and social benefits and also potential harm that food preservatives afford.

Science at Home
Cooperative Learning: Have groups of students begin collecting labels from empty containers of household materials that contain acids and bases and have safety statements and instructions for emergency antidotal procedures. Have students prepare a household alert bulletin board to describe dangers, proper uses, and first-aid procedures.

What's Happening Here?

What puts the sting in a fire ant's bite—and what in an aspirin takes the stinging out? Acids are responsible in both cases. The itching and burning from the ant's bite are caused by formic acid. The easing of pain, fever, and swelling that an aspirin provides is caused by acetylsalicylic acid. How do acid solutions react with other substances to cause such different effects? You'll learn more about solutions and chemical reactions in this unit.

UNIT CONTENTS

377

Multicultural Awareness

Pickling, a process of food preservation that depends upon the chemical process of fermentation and the prohibition of bacterial growth in a highly acidic solution, is found in the cuisine of many cultures. Have students research different pickling processes and prepare lists of how and what products are pickled in different cultures. You may want to enlist the aid of the cafeteria director to assemble pickled foods from various cultures for a tasting.

Inquiry Questions

Use the following questions to focus a discussion of acids and solutions.

▶ **Suppose you have to take a pill (prescribed by a doctor) which you can't swallow. You might want to dissolve it in water. What things can you do to make it dissolve more quickly or completely?** *Stir it into the water; warm the water; crush the tablet into smaller pieces.*

▶ **Vinegar, lemon juice, and tomato juice contain organic acids. What common taste do they share?** *They taste sour.*

INTRODUCING THE UNIT

What's Happening Here?

▶ Have students look at the photos and read the text. Ask them to tell you what's happening here. Point out to students that in this unit they will learn that acids and other groups of substances can be classified by their chemical properties. They will also learn what happens to substances during chemical reactions and how the products of chemical reactions can be predicted.

▶ **Background:** Formic acid and acetylsalicylic acid are organic acids. Their respective structural formulas are

$$\begin{array}{c} OH \\ | \\ H-C=O \end{array} \qquad \qquad \begin{array}{c} O \quad CH_3 \\ \\ O \\ | \\ C-OH \\ \| \\ O \end{array}$$

Formic acid destroys proteins and has deleterious effects similar to the methanol from which it is metabolized. Acetylsalicylic acid reduces pain by interfering with the production of hormones that affect the signals transmitted across the synapses of sensory nerves.

Previewing the Chapters

▶ Have students identify photographs in the chapters that indicate chemical changes have taken place.

▶ Have students identify photographs that show chemical reactions with which they are familiar.

Tying to Previous Knowledge

▶ Have students recall the structural formula of formic acid that they were asked to write in the Skill Builder from Section 13-2, on page 336. Draw the structure of acetylsalicylic acid on the chalkboard. Have them determine how many single and double bonds are in each compound.

▶ Use the **inquiry questions** in the OPTIONS box to discuss acid solutions.

CHAPTER SECTION	OBJECTIVES	ACTIVITIES
15-1 How Solutions Form (2 days)	1. **Classify** solutions into three types and **identify** their solutes and solvents. 2. **Explain** the dissolving process. 3. **Describe** the factors that affect the rates at which solids and gases dissolve in liquids.	**MINI-Lab:** *How does solute surface area affect dissolving?* p. 383
15-2 Oceans—The World's Largest Solution Science & Society (1 day)	1. **Explain** why an ocean is considered a solution. 2. **Compare** and **contrast** methods of desalination.	
15-3 Solubility and Concentration (2 days)	1. **Discuss** how solubility varies among different solutes and for the same solute at different temperatures. 2. **Demonstrate** an understanding of solution concentrations. 3. **Compare** and **contrast** a saturated, unsaturated, and supersaturated solution.	**Activity 15-1:** *Saturation Situation,* p. 394
15-4 Particles in Solution (2 days)	1. **Compare** and **contrast** the behavior of polar and non-polar substances in forming solutions. 2. **Relate** the processes of dissociation and ionization to solutions that conduct electricity. 3. **Explain** how the addition of solutes to solvents affects the freezing and boiling points of solutions.	**Activity 15-2:** *Boiling Points of Solutions,* p. 398
Chapter Review		

ACTIVITY MATERIALS

FIND OUT	ACTIVITIES		MINI-LABS
Page 379 1 paper or foam cup 1/3 c. clean sand 1/2 c. fine gravel 1 or 2 pieces of bar-becue charcoal crushed into powder clear, plastic cup dirty water	**15-1 Saturation Situation, p. 394** solute distilled water large test tube graduated cylinder test tube holder 2 hole stopper thermometer balance apron goggles hot plate copper stirrer	**15-2 Boiling Points of Solutions, p. 398** 400 mL distilled water Celsius thermometer ringstand 72 g table salt, NaCl laboratory burner 250-mL beaker	**How does solute sur-face area affect dis-solving? p. 383** 4 sugar cubes 2 100-mL beakers 2 stirring rods

CHAPTER FEATURES	TEACHER RESOURCE PACKAGE	OTHER RESOURCES
Problem Solving: *Derrick's Dilemma,* p. 384 **Skill Builder:** *Comparing and Contrasting,* p. 385	**Ability Level Worksheets** ◆ **Study Guide,** p. 61 ● **Reinforcement,** p. 61 ▲ **Enrichment,** p. 61 **Activity Worksheets,** pp. 5, 122 **Concept Mapping,** pp. 35, 36 **Science and Society,** p. 19 **Transparency Masters,** pp. 57, 58	**Color Transparency 29,** The Solution Process **Laboratory Manual 30,** Solutions
You Decide! p. 387	**Ability Level Worksheets** ◆ **Study Guide,** p. 62 ● **Reinforcement,** p. 62 ▲ **Enrichment,** p. 62	
Technology: *Replacing a Super Solvent,* p. 392 **Skill Builder:** *Making and Using Graphs,* p. 393	**Ability Level Worksheets** ◆ **Study Guide,** p. 63 ● **Reinforcement,** p. 63 ▲ **Enrichment,** p. 63 **Activity Worksheets,** pp. 5, 116, 117 **Cross-Curricular Connections,** p. 21	**Laboratory Manual 31,** Solubility **Science Integration Activity 15**
Skill Builder: *Concept Mapping,* p. 397	**Ability Level Worksheets** ◆ **Study Guide,** p. 64 ● **Reinforcement,** p. 64 ▲ **Enrichment,** p. 64 **Activity Worksheets,** pp. 118, 119 **Critical Thinking/Problem Solving,** p. 21 **Transparency Masters,** pp. 59, 60	**Color Transparency 30,** Dissociation and Ionization
Summary Think & Write Critically Key Science Words Apply Understanding Vocabulary More Skill Builders Checking Concepts Projects Using Lab Skills	**ASSESSMENT RESOURCES** **Chapter Review,** pp. 33, 34 **Chapter Test,** pp. 101-104 **Performance Assessment in Middle School Science**	**Chapter Review Software** **Test Bank** **Alternate Assessment** **Performance Assessment**

◆ Basic   ● Average   ▲ Advanced

ADDITIONAL MATERIALS

SOFTWARE	AUDIOVISUAL	BOOKS/MAGAZINES
Introduction to General Chemistry: Solutions, EduQuest. *Solubility,* EME. *Soluble, Programs for Learning Solutions,* Focus. *The Solution Process,* Queue. *Solutions,* Queue.	*Chemistry Matters,* Video, Coronet. *Mr. Wizard's World: Chemistry in the Kitchen,* video, Macmillan/McGraw-Hill School Division. *Solutions: Ionic and Molecular,* Video, Coronet. *Structure of Matter,* Video, AIT.	Cohen, I. Bernard. *Theory of Solutions & Stereo-Chemistry.* Salem, NH: Ayer Co. Pub. 1981. DeRenzo, D.J. *Solvents Safety Handbook.* Park Ridge, NJ: Noyes Press, 1986. Markham, Ursula. *Crystal Workbook: A Complete Guide to Working With Crystals.* New York: Sterling Pub., 1988.

THEME DEVELOPMENT: Systems and Interactions is a theme of this textbook that is clearly developed in Chapter 15. The interaction of solute and solvent is developed by discussing the dissolving process. The solute interacts with the solvent and changes the physical characteristics of the solvent.

CHAPTER OVERVIEW

▶ **Section 15-1:** The different types of solutions are described. The dissolving process is presented in detail as are the factors that affect the rate of dissolving.

▶ **Section 15-2: Science and Society:** Students discover that the ocean could become the world's source of fresh water.

▶ **Section 15-3:** Solubility is defined and developed in this section. Ways used to describe solution concentration are presented. Unsaturated, saturated, and supersaturated solutions are discussed.

▶ **Section 15-4:** The effect of solute and solvent polarity on solubility is presented in this section. Electrolytes are introduced and students learn that solutes have an effect on a solvent's boiling and freezing points.

CHAPTER VOCABULARY

solute	supersaturated
solvent	solution
desalination	dissociation
distillation	ionization
solubility	electrolyte
saturated	nonelectrolyte
solution	
unsaturated	
solution	

CHAPTER
15 Solutions

378

OPTIONS

For Your Gifted Students

Gifted students should find out how nonpolar solutes dissolve, be able to describe the equilibrium that exists between solute and solid in a saturated solution, and show how chemical theory explains Raoult's law. In addition, students could extend Activity 15-1 by obtaining more data and drawing a graph of solubility versus temperature. Activity 15-2 could be extended by using different salts and including freezing point.

For Your Mainstreamed Students

Students can observe what happens when soluble and insoluble substances in a liquid are filtered. They should stir table salt into 50 mL of water until no more salt will dissolve. Then they should add 5 mL of powdered chalk and stir. Have them line a funnel with filter paper and pour the liquid through quickly. They should observe the substance on the filter paper after it has dried. Have them evaporate the remaining liquid to dryness and observe the crystals that remain.

Did you know that people in the United States consume about 1.5 trillion liters of water daily from sources such as the Colorado River? Almost all of this water is put through filtration.

FIND OUT!

Do this activity to find out what things are removed from water in the filtering process.

Use a sharp pencil to poke ten holes in the bottom of a foam cup. Place 1 cm of fine gravel in the cup. Then add 3 cm of clean sand. Place 1 cm of powdered charcoal on top of the sand. Finally, place another layer of fine gravel on top of the charcoal. Now your *model* filtration system is ready.

Slowly pour about 100 mL of dirty water through the cup. Catch the water that passes through the filtration system in a clear plastic cup. How does the filtered water *compare* to the original water? **CAUTION:** *This water is not suitable to drink.*

Gearing Up
Previewing the Chapter
Use this outline to help you focus on important ideas in this chapter.

Section 15-1   How Solutions Form
► Types of Solutions
► The Dissolving Process
► Rate of Dissolving

Section 15-2   Science and Society
Oceans—The World's Largest Solution
► Can Oceans Be Used as Fresh Water Sources?

Section 15-3   Solubility and Concentration
► Solubility
► Concentration
► Limits of Solubility

Section 15-4   Particles in Solution
► Solvents and Solutes
► Solutions as Conductors
► Effects of Solute Particles

Previewing Science Skills
► In the Skill Builders, you will compare and contrast, make and use a graph, and use a concept map.
► In the Activities, you will measure, graph, calculate, and infer.
► In the MINI-Lab, you will observe and infer.

What's next?

You have shown that filtering dirty water removes some contaminants. You will learn why all of them can't be removed by filtration alone when you read the pages that follow.

379

INTRODUCING THE CHAPTER
Use the Find Out activity to introduce students to solutions. Inform students that they will be learning more about how substances dissolve to form solutions as they read the chapter.

FIND OUT!
Preparation: Before doing the activity, outside the building, place the charcoal in a cloth sack and pound with a hammer until it is a powder. You may choose to purchase activated charcoal used in aquarium filters.
Materials: one paper or foam cup, one-third cup clean sand, one-half cup fine gravel, one or two pieces of barbecue charcoal crushed into a powder, one clear, plastic cup, and dirty water for each group.
Teaching Tips
► Holes should be carefully punched so they are small. A straightened wire paper clip can also be used to punch holes.
► Students should observe that the filtered water is much clearer than the original water.
► After the students have used their filters to clear the muddy water, you can ask them if they think the filters could be used indefinitely. No. The sand and gravel can become clogged. The charcoal filter will become saturated with chemical contaminants.

Gearing Up
Have students study the Gearing Up feature to familiarize themselves with the chapter. Discuss the relationships of the topics in the outline.

What's Next?
Before beginning the first section, make sure students understand the connection between the Find Out activity and the topics to follow.

ASSESSMENT OPTIONS

PORTFOLIO
Refer to page 399 for suggested items that students might select for their portfolios.

PERFORMANCE ASSESSMENT
See page 399 for additional Performance Assessment options.
Process
Skill Builders, pp. 393, 397
MINI-Lab, p. 383
Activities 15-1, p. 394; 15-2, p. 398
Using Lab Skills, p. 400

CONTENT ASSESSMENT
Assessment—Oral, pp. 382, 385
Skill Builder, pp. 385
Section Reviews, pp. 385, 387, 393, 397
Chapter Review, pp. 399-401
Mini Quizzes, pp. 384, 390, 392, 397

GROUP ASSESSMENT
Opportunities for group assessment occur with Cooperative Learning Strategies and Flex Your Brain Activities.

PREPARATION

SECTION BACKGROUND

▶ Because there are three common states of matter, there are nine possible combinations of solvent-solute pairs. Not all possible combinations are presented in this introduction.

▶ Without stirring, the dissolving process slows as the solution reaches saturation around each piece of solute. Eventually the process reaches equilibrium as the number of particles leaving the surface of the solute equals the number of particles returning to the surface. Stirring brings a fresh supply of solvent near the solute.

▶ Most solids have positive enthalpies of solution, and are more soluble in hot water than in cold. Gases and some solids have negative enthalpies of solution and are more soluble in cold than in hot water.

▶ The mass of a gas that will dissolve in a liquid at a given temperature varies directly with the partial pressure of that gas. This is why solutions of gases in water such as soft drink must be maintained under pressure.

PREPLANNING

▶ To prepare for the MINI-Lab, obtain four sugar cubes per laboratory team.

1 MOTIVATE

▶ **Demonstration:** Place 20 g each of calcium acetate and potassium nitrate in separate, labeled beakers that contain 50 mL of water each. Stir, and observe that all the calcium acetate dissolves, but only part of the potassium nitrate dissolves. Then heat both beakers on a hot plate and stir occasionally. More potassium nitrate will dissolve while the calcium acetate will come out of solution.

New Science Words

solute
solvent

Objectives

▶ Classify solutions into three types and identify their solutes and solvents.
▶ Explain the dissolving process.
▶ Describe the factors that affect the rates at which solids and gases dissolve in liquids.

Types of Solutions

When you hear the word *solution,* you may think of a kind of liquid mixture, like salt water or soda. Both of these liquids are examples of solutions. But did you know that you also breathe a solution? Yes, air is a solution—and so is the sterling silver used to make fine jewelry. Solutions, then, can be gaseous or solid as well as liquid, as shown in Figure 15-1 and Figure 15-2. What makes all these mixtures solutions? Recall that a solution is a homogeneous mixture, in which the particles of the mixing substances are evenly distributed throughout.

There are three classes of solutions, as shown in Table 15-1: gaseous solutions, liquid solutions, and solid solutions. A gaseous solution is a mixture of two or more gases. A liquid solution results when a gas, liquid, or solid is dissolved in a liquid. A solid solution forms when a liquid and a solid or two or more solid substances are

Figure 15-1. Examples of Gaseous and Liquid Solutions

Table 15-1

COMPOSITION OF SOLUTIONS		
	Types of Solutions	**Examples**
Gaseous Solutions	gas + gas	air
Liquid Solutions	liquid + gas liquid + liquid liquid + solid	club soda vinegar sugar water
Solid Solutions	solid + liquid solid + solid	dental amalgam steel, brass

OPTIONS

Meeting Different Ability Levels

For Section 15-1, use the following **Teacher Resource Masters** depending upon individual students' needs.

◆ **Study Guide Master** for all students.
● **Reinforcement Master** for students of average and above average ability levels.
▲ **Enrichment Master** for above average students.

Additional Teacher Resource Package masters are listed in any **PROGRAM RESOURCES** boxes that are in the section. The additional masters are appropriate for all students.

♦ STUDY GUIDE 61

STUDY GUIDE — Chapter 15
How Solutions Form — Text Pages 380–385

melted, mixed, and cooled. Solid solutions containing metals are usually called alloys.

To describe a solution, you may say that one substance is dissolved in another. The substance being dissolved is the **solute.** The substance that dissolves the solute is the **solvent.** When a solid dissolves in a liquid, the solid is the solute and the liquid is the solvent. Thus, in salt water, sodium chloride is the solute, and water is the solvent. In a liquid-gas solution, the gas is the solute. In soda, carbon dioxide is the solute and water is the solvent.

Generally, the substance present in the largest amount is considered to be the solvent. Air is 78 percent nitrogen, 21 percent oxygen, less than 1 percent argon, and smaller amounts of other gases. Thus, nitrogen is the solvent. In the alloy sterling silver, made of 92.5 percent silver and 7.5 percent copper, silver is the solvent and copper is the solute.

The Dissolving Process

A good way to make lemonade is to prepare a solution of sugar in water before you add the lemon juice and ice. By what process do a solid and a liquid, such as sugar and water, form a solution? The dissolving of a solid in a liquid occurs at the surface of the solid. For water solutions, keep in mind two things you have learned about water. Like the particles of any liquid, water molecules are constantly moving. You also know that a water molecule is polar, which means it has a positive area and a negative area. Molecules of sugar are also polar.

Figure 15-3. To prepare a glass of lemonade, it helps to first dissolve the sugar in water.

Figure 15-2. These objects are made of solid solutions called alloys.

Connect to...
Earth Science

Bronze is an alloy that can be 90 percent copper and 10 percent tin. What metal is the solvent? What metal is the solute?

In air—a gaseous solution—which substance is the solvent?

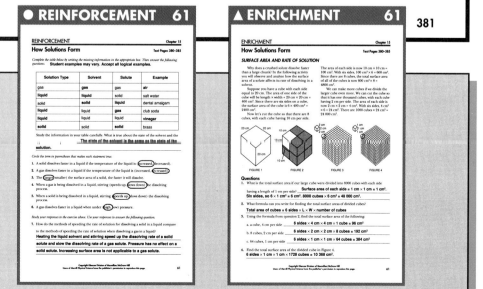

TYING TO PREVIOUS KNOWLEDGE: Have the students recall various solvents used around the house. Water is the most common, but paint thinner, alcohol, spot removers, and nail polish removers are also frequently used. Ask students to recall solutions found in the garage, basement, kitchen, or bathroom.

2 TEACH

Key Concepts are highlighted.

CONCEPT DEVELOPMENT

▶ **Demonstration:** To demonstrate the dissolving process, partially fill a petri dish with water and place it on the overhead projector. Place a crystal of potassium permanganate in the dish. Have students note the purple streamers as the water is stirred *gently.*

▶ The Motivate demonstration on page 380 makes use of the following solubility data per 100 mL water.

	0°C	100°C
Calcium acetate	37.4 g	29.7 g
Potassium nitrate	13.3 g	247.0 g

Potassium nitrate has a positive enthalpy of solution while calcium acetate has a negative enthalpy of solution.

▶ **Demonstration:** If students did not perform Activity 14-1 in which an alloy was formed, you may want to present it now as a demonstration. Point out that the brass that forms on the penny's surface is an alloy, a solution of a solid in a solid.

Connect to...
Earth Science

Answer: Copper is the solvent; tin is the solute.

REVEALING MISCONCEPTIONS

▶ There is a big difference between a liquid and a solution, but many people fail to see the difference and use the words interchangeably. Discuss the difference with your students. Also, whenever possible, reinforce the idea that it is possible to have solutions in solvents other than water.

CROSS CURRICULUM

▶ **Dietetics:** People who are trained in food preparation and nutrition know the economy of buying concentrates and diluting them to make the desired solutions. Shipping costs and fuel consumption are reduced when you add the water at the destination.

CONCEPT DEVELOPMENT

▶ **Demonstration:** To show the polarity of water, blow up a balloon and rub its surface with a wool cloth or fur. Turn on the water faucet so it delivers a thin stream. Bring the statically charged balloon near the stream and observe as the stream bends dramatically. Polar solvents attract and dissolve polar solutes.

TEACHER F.Y.I.

▶ The U.S. Navy recommends that divers using compressed air not dive below 38 meters. This recommendation is based on the fact that too much nitrogen and oxygen from the air will dissolve in the blood. This high concentration causes a type of intoxication called "rapture of the deep."

STUDENT TEXT QUESTION

▶ Page 382, paragraph 3: **What causes the particles in an alloy to be evenly spread out?** *The components are originally mixed as a liquid solution and the particles in a liquid move more freely than those of solid.*

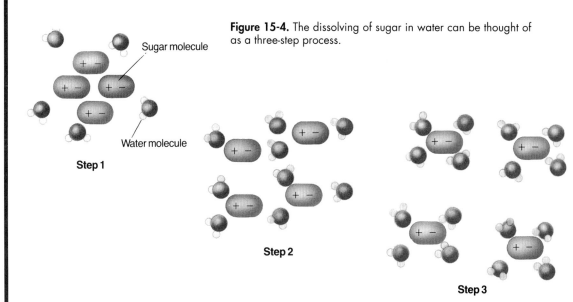

Figure 15-4. The dissolving of sugar in water can be thought of as a three-step process.

Sugar molecule

Water molecule

Step 1

Step 2

Step 3

When sugar dissolves in water, why are the water molecules attracted to the sugar molecules?

In Your JOURNAL

Imagine what the submicroscopic world of a solution might be like. **In your Journal,** write what happens to a sugar molecule as it goes from being part of a crystal until it is part of a solution.

Study Figure 15-4 and the following steps to see how a sugar crystal dissolves in water.

Step 1: The moving water molecules cluster around the sugar molecules. The negative areas of the water molecules are attracted to the positive areas of the sugar molecules.
Step 2: The water molecules pull the sugar molecules into solution.
Step 3: The moving water molecules spread the sugar molecules out equally throughout the solution.

The process repeats itself as layer after layer of sugar molecules move away from the crystal until all the molecules are evenly spread out. The same three steps occur when any polar or ionic compound dissolves in a polar liquid. A similar, but more difficult, process also occurs when a gas dissolves in a liquid.

You know from your study of fluids in Chapter 8 that particles of liquids and gases move much more freely than do the particles of solids. When gases dissolve in gases, or when liquids dissolve in liquids, this movement results in uniform distribution. Alloys are made by first melting and then mixing the components. What causes the particles in an alloy to be evenly spread out?

382 SOLUTIONS

OPTIONS

ASSESSMENT—ORAL

▶ **When a glass of iced tea has some undissolved sugar on the bottom, why doesn't it dissolve and the tea become sweeter?** *The solution becomes concentrated around the sugar. Thus there are fewer free water molecules near the crystals. Also, the cold temperature reduces molecular movement.*
▶ **An opened bottle of carbonated soft drink goes "flat" upon standing. How do you think this occurs?** *The dissolved gas molecules are in motion and move out of the solution and into the air. The gas molecules* are nonpolar and not strongly attracted to the solvent particles.

PROGRAM RESOURCES

From the **Teacher Resource Package** use:
  Science and Society, page 19, Iron in Cereal.
  Transparency Masters, pages 57-58, The Solution Process.
Use **Color Transparency** number 29, The Solution Process.

Rate of Dissolving

Think again about making a sugar solution for lemonade. When you add the sugar to the water, you stir it. Stirring a solution speeds up dissolving because it brings more fresh solvent in contact with more solute. The fresh solvent attracts the particles in the solute, causing the solid solute to move into solution faster.

A second way to speed the dissolving of a solid in a liquid is to grind large crystals into smaller ones. Suppose you had to use a 5-g crystal of rock candy, which is made of sugar, to sweeten your lemonade. If you put the crystal into a glassful of water, it might take two minutes to dissolve even with stirring. However, 5 g of powdered rock candy would dissolve in the same amount of water in a few seconds with stirring.

Why does powdering a crystal cause it to dissolve faster? Breaking the crystal into smaller pieces greatly increases its surface area, as you can see in Figure 15-5. Because dissolving takes place at the surface of the solid, increasing the surface area allows more solvent to come in contact with more solid solute. Thus, the speed of the solution process increases.

A third way to increase the rate at which most solids dissolve is to increase the temperature of a solvent. Think of making a sugar solution for lemonade. You can make the sugar dissolve faster by putting it in hot water instead of cold water. Increasing the temperature of a solvent speeds up the movement of its particles. This causes more solvent particles to bump into the solute. As a result, solute particles break loose from the surface faster.

(4)

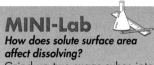

MINI-Lab
How does solute surface area affect dissolving?
Grind up two sugar cubes into granules. *Compare* the area covered by the granules to the outside surface area covered by the 12 sides of two sugar cubes. Place the granules and the cubes into separate 100-mL beakers of water, stir both evenly, and *compare* the times required to dissolve both. What do you *conclude* about dissolving rate and surface area?

Figure 15-5. As a crystal is broken down into smaller pieces, the total surface area of the crystal increases.

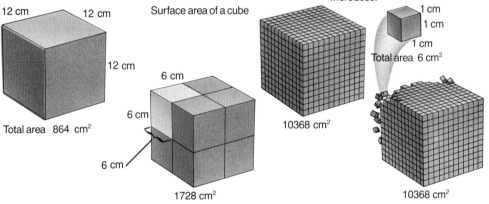

15-1 HOW SOLUTIONS FORM **383**

CHAPTER 15 **383**

Have students examine packages of powdered sugar at home before answering the questions.

Think Critically: The constants were the amount of sugar, amount of water, size of cup, and temperature of water. Packaged powdered sugar often contains cornstarch, which will not dissolve in cold water.

CONCEPT DEVELOPMENT

▶ Pressure has little effect on solutions unless the solute is a gas. At higher pressures, gas molecules are closer together (more concentrated) over the solvent and therefore enter solution more readily.

CHECK FOR UNDERSTANDING

Use the Mini Quiz to check for understanding.

MINI QUIZ

Use the Mini Quiz to check students' recall of chapter content.

1 **List five different types of solutions with an example of each.** *See Table 15-1 for possible answers.*

2 **What are two parts that make up a solution?** *solute and solvent*

3 **Polar solvents are able to dissolve which types of solute?** *polar and ionic*

4 **How can the speed of solvent particles be increased?** *increase the temperature*

RETEACH

▶ Make a list of factors that affect the rate of solution for different types of solutions.

EXTENSION

For students who have mastered this section, use the **Reinforcement** and **Enrichment** masters or other OPTIONS provided.

3 CLOSE

▶ Ask questions 1-2 and the **Apply** and **Connect to Life Science** questions in the Section Review.

PROBLEM SOLVING

Derrick's Dilemma

Derrick's teacher asked the students to think about the dissolving process. She asked them to think of ways to speed up the rate of dissolving a solid in a liquid.

Why does soda in an opened bottle bubble up when shaken?

Derrick knew that granulated sugar dissolves faster than sugar cubes. He hypothesized that powdered sugar would dissolve even faster than granulated sugar.

Derrick tested his hypothesis at home. He placed one level spoonful of powdered sugar in one cup and the same amount of granulated sugar in an identical cup. He added 250 mL of water at the same temperature to each cup. To his surprise, all the powdered sugar didn't dissolve. His mother suggested he read the ingredients on the powdered sugar package.

Think Critically: What four factors did Derrick keep constant in his experiment? How can you explain why all the powdered sugar did not dissolve?

How do you think these same factors will affect a gas-liquid solution? When you shake or stir an opened bottle of soda, it bubbles up and usually spills over—or squirts out. Did you ever wonder why? Stirring or shaking a solution of a gas in a liquid causes the gas to come out of solution faster. This happens because as you shake or stir the solution, more gas molecules are exposed to the surface. These molecules escape more freely. Shaking and stirring also increase the temperature of the solution slightly, which decreases the solubility of the gas.

How might you do the opposite—cause the gas to dissolve faster in the liquid? The answer is simple: cool the liquid solvent and increase the pressure of the gas. In a soda bottling plant, both of these things are done. The machinery cools the solution and keeps it under pressure.

OPTIONS

ENRICHMENT

▶ Have students look up the term *miscible* and explain what it means to say that two liquids are miscible. The liquids dissolve in each other in all proportions.

▶ Have students make clay cubes 10 cm on a side. Have them calculate the surface area of the six faces (600 cm²). Cut each cube into quarters, 5 cm on a side, and calculate the total surface area again. Each cube's area is 6 faces × 25 cm²/face = 150 cm². Therefore the total surface area is 8 cubes × 150 cm²/cube = 1200 cm². The surface

area doubles.

▶ Have students look up the term *effervescence* and describe the difference in effervescence when opening bottles of cold soda and warm soda. The effervescence is greater in the warm soda.

PROGRAM RESOURCES

From the **Teacher Resource Package** use:
Activity Worksheets, page 5, Flex Your Brain.

Figure 15-6. When bottles of soda are opened, more gas comes out of solution in the warm bottle than in the cold one.

Maybe you have noticed the difference between opening bottles of cold and warm soda, Figure 15-6. All gases are more soluble in cooler solvents. In Figure 15-7, an unopened bottle of soda has no visible bubbles. In the sealed bottle, increased pressure keeps the gas dissolved. When the bottle is opened, the pressure is reduced. Then the carbon dioxide comes out of solution quickly.

Figure 15-7. Reduced pressure inside an opened bottle of soda causes the gas to come out of solution.

SECTION REVIEW

1. What are the three types of solutions? Give an example of each type.
2. What are three ways to increase the rate of dissolving a solid in a liquid?
3. **Apply:** Amalgams, sometimes used in tooth fillings, are alloys of mercury with other metals. Is an amalgam a solution? Explain.
4. **Connect to Life Science:** Many fish aquariums have a device that bubbles air into the water. Why is it necessary to constantly bring air into the water?

☑ Comparing and Contrasting

Skill Builder

Compare and contrast the effects on the rate of dissolving (1) a solid in a liquid and (2) a gas in a liquid, when (a) the solution is cooled, (b) it is stirred, and (c) the pressure on it is lowered. If you need help, refer to Comparing and Contrasting in the **Skill Handbook** on page 679.

PREPARATION

SECTION BACKGROUND

▶ Point out to the class that many people around the world do not have pure water or enough water to drink. Many of these people cannot afford the energy costs to desalinate water.

1 MOTIVATE

▶ **Demonstration:** Distill some water that has food coloring added to it. If you do not have a cold water condenser, just pass the steam through glass tubing. The separation of clear and colored water is visible.

Science and WRITING

Have students research the extraction of metals from their salts once the salts have been isolated from seawater.

2 TEACH

Key Concepts are highlighted.

Connect to... Physics

Answer: A membrane that allows water, but not dissolved salts, to pass through is placed between samples of pure water and salt water. Pressure applied on the salt water side causes the water from the salt water to move through the membrane.

SCIENCE & SOCIETY **15-2** Oceans—The World's Largest Solution

New Science Words

desalination
distillation

Science and WRITING

Prepare a report for the class explaining how minerals are mined from the ocean.

Objectives

▶ Explain why an ocean is considered a solution.
▶ Compare and contrast methods of desalination.

Can Oceans Be Used as Fresh Water Sources?

About 97 percent of the water on Earth is in our salty oceans. Although the most abundant salt in the oceans is sodium chloride, the oceans also contain many other dissolved salts, such as magnesium salts and calcium salts. Thus, the oceans make up the world's largest solution. Do we need this solution as a source of fresh water?

The need for fresh water in the world is greater today than ever before. Several reasons contributing to an increased need for fresh water are:

1. Increase in the world's population,
2. High concentration of people living in selected areas,
3. Increase in the uses of fresh water,
4. Increase in the pollution of existing sources of fresh water, and
5. Development of areas where water has always been scarce.

To meet this need, scientists are turning to desalination. Any method that removes dissolved salts from ocean water to produce fresh water is called **desalination.**

In 1989, two billion gallons of fresh water were produced per day by more than 1500 desalination plants

386 SOLUTIONS

OPTIONS

Meeting Different Ability Levels

For Section 15-2, use the following **Teacher Resource Masters** depending upon individual students' needs.

◆ **Study Guide Master** for all students.

● **Reinforcement Master** for students of average and above average ability levels.

▲ **Enrichment Master** for above average students.

worldwide. The most common desalination methods used are distillation and freezing.

In **distillation,** water is evaporated from a solution, cooled, condensed, and collected as fresh water. The simplest and cheapest type of distillation uses a solar still. Heat from the sun evaporates the water. The water vapor condenses on the cover and runs into trays.

Another type of distillation is flash distillation. Flash distillation makes use of the fact that water boils at a much lower temperature in a vacuum or reduced-pressure chamber. In flash distillation, ocean water is pumped into a vacuum chamber where it starts to boil. The salt-free water vapor is collected and condensed to form fresh water.

As shown in Figure 15-8, the freeze method also can be used to desalinate water. When salt water is cooled sufficiently, the ice that forms is salt free. In the freeze method, ocean water enters a vacuum freezing chamber. The vapor produced is condensed directly to fresh water. The water that freezes is rinsed and then melted to form fresh water.

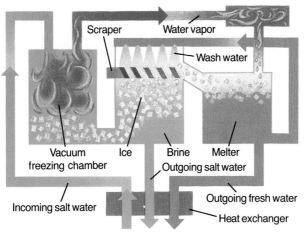

Figure 15-8. In the freeze process, ocean water is frozen. This ice is rinsed and then melted to produce salt-free water.

Connect to...

Physics

Another important method of desalination is reverse osmosis. Explain how this process can produce, on a small scale, fresh water from salt water.

SECTION REVIEW

1. Why are the oceans a solution?
2. Describe how distillation and freezing ocean water can be used to produce fresh water.
3. **Connect to Earth Science:** Icebergs float in ocean water. Neglecting the costs of towing an iceberg to warmer climates, why might icebergs be a source of fresh water?

You Decide!

Suppose that you were in charge of building a desalination plant in a desert area. Large amounts of ocean water could be brought to the area. Which desalination method would you use and why?

SCIENCE & SOCIETY

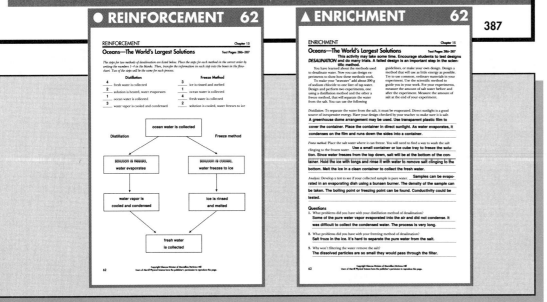

● **REINFORCEMENT** 62

▲ **ENRICHMENT** 62

387

REINFORCEMENT   Chapter 15

Oceans—The World's Largest Solutions   Text Pages 386–387

The steps for two methods of desalination are listed below. Place the steps for each method in the correct order by writing the numbers 1–4 in the blanks. Then, transfer the information in each step into the boxes in the flow-chart. Two of the steps will be the same for each process.

Distillation   **Freeze Method**

4 fresh water is collected   3 ice is rinsed and melted
2 solution is heated, water evaporates   4 ocean water is collected
1 ocean water is collected   1 fresh water is collected
3 water vapor is cooled and condensed   2 solution is cooled, water freezes to ice

ocean water is collected

Distillation   Freeze method

solution is heated,   solution is cooled,
water evaporates   water freezes to ice

water vapor is   ice is rinsed
cooled and condensed   and melted

fresh water
is collected

62   Copyright Glencoe Division of Macmillan/McGraw-Hill
        Users of Merrill Physical Science have the publisher's permission to reproduce this page.

ENRICHMENT   Chapter 15

Oceans—The World's Largest Solutions   Text Pages 386–387

DESALINATION This activity may take some time. Encourage students to test designs and do many trials. A failed design is an important step in the scientific method.

You have learned about the methods used to desalinate water. Now you can design experiments to show how these methods work. To make your "seawater" add about 200 g of sodium chloride to one liter of tap water. Design and perform two experiments, one using a distillation method and the other a freeze method, that will separate the water from the salt. You can use the following guidelines, or make your own design. Design a method that will use as little energy as possible. Try to use common, ordinary materials in your experiment. Use the scientific method to guide you in your work. For your experiments, measure the amount of salt water before and after the experiment. Measure the amount of salt at the end of your experiment.

Distillation: To separate the water from the salt, it must be evaporated. Direct sunlight is a good source of inexpensive energy. Have your design checked by your teacher to make sure it is safe. **A greenhouse dome arrangement may be used. Use transparent plastic film to cover the container. Place the container in direct sunlight. As water evaporates, it condenses on the film and runs down the sides into a container.**

Freeze method: Place the salt water where it can freeze. You will need to find a way to wash the salt clinging to the frozen water. **Use a small container or ice cube tray to freeze the solution. Since water freezes from the top down, salt will be at the bottom of the container. Hold the ice with tongs and rinse it with water to remove salt clinging to the bottom. Melt the ice in a clean container to collect the fresh water.**

Analysis: Develop a test to see if your collected sample is pure water. **Samples can be evaporated in an evaporating dish using a bunsen burner. The density of the sample can be taken. The boiling point or freezing point can be found. Conductivity could be tested.**

Questions
1. What problems did you have with your distillation method of desalination? **Some of the pure water vapor evaporated into the air and did not condense. It was difficult to collect the condensed water. The process is very long.**
2. What problems did you have with your freezing method of desalination? **Salt froze in the ice. It's hard to separate the pure water from the salt.**
3. Why won't filtering the water remove the salt? **The dissolved particles are so small they would pass through the filter.**

62   Copyright Glencoe Division of Macmillan/McGraw-Hill
        Users of Merrill Physical Science have the publisher's permission to reproduce this page.

CROSS CURRICULUM

▶**Literature:** Samuel T. Coleridge wrote in *The Rime of the Ancient Mariner* these words:
> Water, water, everywhere,
> And all the boards did shrink;
> Water, water, everywhere
> Nor any drop to drink.

Cooperative Learning: Ask Paired Partners to interpret the Coleridge poem using the knowledge gained in this section.

CHECK FOR UNDERSTANDING

Have students answer questions 1-2 and the **Connect to Earth Science** question in the Section Review.

RETEACH

Point out that the salts dissolved in ocean water do not evaporate easily. With that in mind, have students interpret the process of distillation stepwise and explain why it yields pure water.

EXTENSION

For students who have mastered this section, use the **Reinforcement** and **Enrichment** masters or other OPTIONS provided.

3 CLOSE

▶ Have students prepare a list of ways that society uses fresh water. Ask the students which uses would produce the greatest conservation if reduced.

SECTION REVIEW ANSWERS

1. There are many salts dissolved in the oceans.
2. In distillation, ocean water is evaporated and condensed, leaving salts behind. When salt water is frozen, the ice that forms is salt free and can be melted to yield fresh water.
3. Connect to Earth Science: When icebergs form, most of the salt in the ocean water is excluded.

YOU DECIDE!

Answers will vary. Make sure students can support their answers. They should consider the types of energy available in the area. Is there sunlight only or is there abundant electricity and/or fuel?

SECTION BACKGROUND

▶ Solubility differences can be used to separate a mixture of different substances. If a water solution of two salts is allowed to evaporate, the least soluble one at the temperature of evaporation will crystallize first.

▶ In science, more solutions are expressed in mass percentages than volume percentages.

▶ A saturated solution is in a state of equilibrium. The number of particles leaving the crystal surface (dissolving) is equal to the number returning to the surface (crystallizing).

▶ Supersaturation is possible because solids will not crystallize unless there is a suitable surface such as a crystal, upon which to start crystallization.

PREPLANNING

▶ To prepare for Activity 15-1, you will need to prepare a copper wire stirrer for each team.

▶ To save lab time and improve results, you may want to prepare the 9-gram samples of potassium bromide in test tubes.

▶ For the demonstration on page 392, prepare a supersaturated solution for each class by adding 50 to 75 g of sodium acetate trihydrate to a very clean 250-mL Erlenmeyer flask. Warm the flask on a hot plate until the crystals melt. Use a wash bottle filled with distilled water to rinse down the sides of the flask with about 8 mL of water. Gently swirl the flask to mix, then cover it and allow to cool.

1 MOTIVATE

▶ Show the students a bottle of contact lens solution. Read the ingredients and their concentrations. Ask them if concentration is important to their eye health. Too much salt or too little can cause damage to living tissue.

15-3 Solubility and Concentration

New Science Words

solubility
saturated solution
unsaturated solution
supersaturated solution

Objectives

▶ Discuss how solubility varies among different solutes and for the same solute at different temperatures.
▶ Demonstrate an understanding of solution concentrations.
▶ Compare and contrast a saturated, unsaturated, and supersaturated solution.

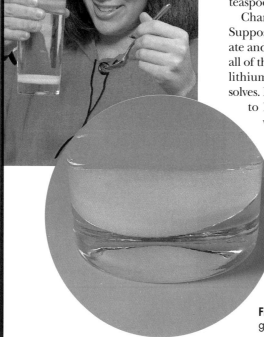

Solubility

Sugar, as you know, dissolves easily in water. Suppose you want to make super sweet lemonade. You stir two, three, four—or more—teaspoons of sugar into a cup of water, and it all dissolves. But eventually you add another teaspoon of sugar and it no longer dissolves, Figure 15-9.

Change the scene from your kitchen to a laboratory. Suppose now you measure out 1.3 g of lithium carbonate and add it to 100 g of water at 20°C. You observe that all of the lithium carbonate dissolves. But if you add more lithium carbonate to the same solution, none of it dissolves. However, you could add 34 g of potassium chloride to 100 g of water before no more will dissolve. You would have shown that the amount of these two substances that dissolves in 100 g of water at 20°C varies greatly.

Generally, the **solubility** of a substance is expressed as the maximum number of grams of the substance that will dissolve in 100 g of solvent at a certain temperature. Table 15-2 shows how the solubility of several substances varies at 20°C. For solutes that are gases, the pressure must also be given. Pressure affects the solubility of a gas.

Figure 15-9. The amount of sugar that can dissolve in a glass of water is limited.

OPTIONS

Meeting Different Ability Levels

For Section 15-3, use the following **Teacher Resource Masters** depending upon individual students' needs.

◆ **Study Guide Master** for all students.
● **Reinforcement Master** for students of average and above average ability levels.
▲ **Enrichment Master** for above average students.
Additional Teacher Resource Package masters are listed in any PROGRAM RESOURCES boxes are are in the section. The additional masters are appropriate for all students.

◆ STUDY GUIDE 63

STUDY GUIDE   Chapter 15
Solubility and Concentration   Text Pages 388-394

In the blank at the left, write the letter of the term or phrase that correctly completes each statement.

___ 1. The maximum number of grams of solute that will dissolve in 100 g of solvent at a certain temperature is the ____ of the solute.
   a. solubility   b. dilution

___ 2. Different substances have ____ solubilities.
   a. different   b. the same

___ 3. The concentration of a mixture of two or more liquids is expressed as a percentage by ____.
   a. mass   b. volume

___ 4. A solution that has dissolved all the solute it can hold at a given temperature is ____.
   a. unsaturated   b. saturated

___ 5. As the temperature of a liquid solvent increases, the amount of solid solute that can be dissolved in the solvent ____.
   a. increases   b. decreases

___ 6. Any solution that can hold more solute at a given temperature is ____.
   a. unsaturated   b. saturated

___ 7. Each time a saturated solution is heated to a higher temperature, it becomes ____.
   a. unsaturated   b. supersaturated

___ 8. A solution that contains more solute than a saturated one at a given temperature is ____.
   a. unsaturated   b. supersaturated

___ 9. Lines on a graph that show how much solute a solvent can hold at a given temperature are called ____.
   a. solution graphs   b. solubility curves

___ 10. The concentration of a solid solute in a liquid solvent is expressed as a percentage by ____.
   a. mass   b. volume

___ 11. A solution that has 4 g of KCl dissolved in 100 mL of water is ____ compared to a solution that has 50 g of KCl dissolved in 100 mL of water.
   a. dilute   b. concentrated

___ 12. One mL of water has a mass of ____.
   a. one gram   b. one kilogram

Table 15-2

SOLUBILITY OF SUBSTANCES IN WATER AT 20°C	
Solid Substances	**Solubility in g/100 g of Water**
Barium sulfate	0.00025
Lithium carbonate	1.3
Potassium chloride	34.0
Sodium nitrate	87.6
Lithium bromide	166.0
Sucrose (sugar)	203.9
Gaseous Substances*	
Hydrogen	0.00017
Oxygen	0.005
Carbon dioxide	0.16

*when pressure = 1 atmosphere

Concentration

Suppose you added one spoonful of lemon juice to a glass of water to make lemonade. Your friend decided to add four spoonfuls of lemon juice to a glass. You could say that your glass of lemonade is dilute. Your friend's glass of lemonade is concentrated. It would have more lemon flavor than yours. A concentrated solution is one in which there is a large amount of solute in the solvent. A dilute solution is one in which there is a small amount of solute in the solvent.

Concentrated and *dilute* are not precise terms. But there are ways to describe solution concentrations precisely. One of these ways is to state the percentage by volume of the solute. Do you ever have a fruit juice drink in a box with your lunch or for a snack? Next time you do, read the label to see how much actual juice you are getting. The percentage by volume of the cherry juice in the drink shown in Figure 15-11 is 10 percent cherry juice and about 90 percent water. Ten mL of cherry juice plus 90 mL of water makes 100 mL of cherry drink. Generally, if two or more liquids are being mixed, the concentration is often given in percentage

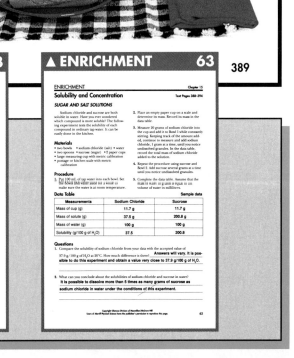

Figure 15-11. The concentrations of fruit juices are often given in percent by volume.

Barium sulfate is sometimes given to a patient before an X ray of the patient's intestines. Does barium sulfate have a high solubility or a low solubility? Besides its ability to absorb X rays, how is its solubility related to this medical use?

Dilute Solution

Concentrated Solution

Figure 15-10. The concentrated solution of lemonade contains more solute (lemon juice) than does the dilute solution.

389

TYING TO PREVIOUS KNOWLEDGE: Ask students to check at home to see if there is a very old jar of honey on a shelf. As the water slowly evaporates from the honey, sugar crystals begin to form and cause the honey to have a coarse texture. The solution has become saturated.

2 TEACH

Key Concepts are highlighted.

CONCEPT DEVELOPMENT

Cooperative Learning: Use the Science Investigation Group strategy. Provide teams with the chemicals to determine the solubility of an unknown substance by repeatedly adding 1 g samples to 100 mL of water at 20°C. When the solution is saturated, ask students to analyze their solubility data and determine the identity of their unknown. Use information from Tables 15-2, 15-3, and from reference books for other substances. Use only substances that are safe.

REVEALING MISCONCEPTIONS

▶ Many students believe that all concentrated acids are 100% acid. Have small labeled bottles of concentrated hydrochloric, nitric, and sulfuric acids on display. Have students read from the label the percentage of acid in each.

Connect to...
Life Science

Answer: Because of its low solubility, barium sulfate does not enter the bloodstream like other more soluble materials might.

CROSS CURRICULUM

▶ **Art:** Have students use solutions to produce artwork. Pour milk on a plate to a depth of 1/4 inch. Place small drops of food colorings at various points around the edge of the milk's surface.

CONCEPT DEVELOPMENT

▶ Prepare an overhead transparency or a chalkboard presentation of the example problem on page 390. Use it to go through this example in detail. Emphasize the problem-solving steps.
▶ Encourage students to bring calculators to class to solve the solution concentration problems.

PRACTICE PROBLEM ANSWER

1.0 L = 1000 mL
40 g/1000 mL = 0.040 g/mL
0.040 g/mL × 20 mL = 0.80 g NaOH

MINI QUIZ

Use the Mini Quiz to check students' recall of chapter content.

1 The maximum number of grams of a substance that will dissolve in 100 g of solvent at a specific temperature is known as the _____ of the substance. *solubility*

2 When there is a large amount of solute in the solvent, the solution is said to be _____ . *concentrated*

3 Use Table 15-2 to determine how much sucrose would dissolve in 100 g and in 50 g of water at 20°C. *204 g and 102 g*

4 The concentration of a solution of a solid in a liquid is usually expressed as a percentage by _____ . *mass*

5 A solution that contains all the solute it can hold at a given temperature is said to be _____ . *saturated*

PROGRAM RESOURCES

From the **Teacher Resource Package** use:

Cross-Curricular Connections, page 21, Analyzing Food Labels.

Science Integration Activity 15

Did You Know?

Floods have diluted the Great Salt Lake so much that you can sink in it now. In the past, it was so salty that sinking in it wasn't possible.

---

by volume, stated in number of milliliters of solute plus enough solvent to make 100 mL of solution.

You can express concentration of a solid dissolved in a liquid as percentage by mass. This is the mass in grams of solute plus enough solvent to make 100 g of solution. Because 1 mL of water has a mass of 1 g, you would mix 10 g of sodium chloride with 90 mL of water to make a 10 percent solution of sodium chloride.

You can also express concentration as mass of solute in a liter of solution. When a certain volume of solution is measured out, the number of grams of solute it contains can easily be calculated.

EXAMPLE PROBLEM: Calculating the Mass of Solute/Liter of Solution

Problem Statement:	A potassium chloride solution contains 88 g of KCl in 1.0 L of solution. How many grams of solute are in 50 mL of solution?
Problem-Solving Steps:	
1. Change 1.0 L to mL	1.0 L = 1000 mL
2. Figure out the number of g of solute in 1 mL of solution.	88 g/1000 mL = 0.088 g/mL
3. Use equation:	Mass of solute = concentration of 1 mL solution × volume of solution
Solution:	Mass = 0.088 g/mL × 50 mL = 4.4 g

PRACTICE PROBLEM

<u>Strategy Hint</u>: Divide 40.0 g by 1000 to find the mass of solute in 1 mL of solution.

1. Forty grams of lye (NaOH) were dissolved in enough water to make 1.0 L of solution. How many grams of lye would be in 20 mL of the solution?

Limits of Solubility

What is a saturated solution?

If you add 30.0 g of potassium chloride, KCl, to 100 g of water at 0°C, only 28 g will dissolve. You have a saturated solution because no more KCl can dissolve. A **saturated solution** is a solution that has dissolved all the solute it can hold at a given temperature. But if you heat the mixture to a higher temperature, more KCl can dissolve. As the temperature of the liquid solvent increases, the amount of solid that can dissolve also increases. Table 15-3 gives the amounts of a few solutes that can dissolve in water at different temperatures, forming saturated solutions.

390 SOLUTIONS

OPTIONS

INQUIRY QUESTIONS

▶ A sodium nitrate solution contains 40 g of NaNO₃ dissolved in 1.0 L of solution. How many grams of sodium nitrate can be recovered when 100 mL of solution is evaporated to dryness? *4 grams*
▶ Use Table 15-2 to determine how much sodium nitrate will dissolve in 1000 g of water at 20°C. *876 g*
▶ A 50.0-mL sample of salt solution is found to contain 0.040 g of sodium chloride. How much salt would be in 1.0 L of solution? *0.80 g*

ENRICHMENT

▶ "Oil and water do not mix" is a simplistic statement, but it generally means that organic solutes are dissolved by organic solvents and not by water. Ask a student to demonstrate for the class how best to clean a paint brush that has been used with a water-based latex paint and one that has an oil based paint in it. **CAUTION:** *Paint thinner is flammable. Never use gasoline as a substitute.*

Table 15-3

SOLUBILITY OF COMPOUNDS IN WATER AT VARIOUS TEMPERATURES

Compound	Formula	Solubility in g/100 g Water at the Temperature Indicated			
		0°C	20°C	60°C	100°C
Ammonium chloride	NH_4Cl	29.4	37.2	55.3	77.3
Barium hydroxide	$Ba(OH)_2$	1.67	3.89	20.94	101.40
Copper(II) sulfate	$CuSO_4$	23.1	32.0	61.8	114
Lead(II) chloride	$PbCl_2$	0.67	1.00	1.94	3.20
Potassium bromide	KBr	53.6	65.3	85.5	104
Potassium chloride	KCl	28.0	34.0	45.8	56.3
Potassium nitrate	KNO_3	13.9	31.6	109	245
Sodium acetate	$NaC_2H_3O_2$	36.2	46.4	139	170.15
Sodium chlorate	$NaClO_3$	79.6	95.9	137	204
Sodium chloride	$NaCl$	35.7	35.9	37.1	39.2
Sodium nitrate	$NaNO_3$	73.0	87.6	122	180
Sucrose (sugar)	$C_{12}H_{22}O_{11}$	179.2	203.9	287.3	487.2

Another way to picture the effect of higher temperatures on solubility is with line graphs, like those in Figure 15-12. The lines are called solubility curves. You can use the curves to figure out the amount of solute that will dissolve at any temperature given on the graph. For example, at 47°C, about 82 g of both KBr and KNO_3 form saturated solutions with 100 g of water. About how much NaCl will form a saturated solution with 100 g of water at the same temperature?

6 An **unsaturated solution** is any solution that can dissolve more solute at a given temperature. Each time a saturated solution is heated to a higher temperature, it may become unsaturated. The term *unsaturated* isn't precise. At 20°C, 37.2 g of NH_4Cl dissolved in 100 g water is a saturated solution. However, an unsaturated solution of NH_4Cl could be any amount less than 37.2 g in 100 g of water at 20°C.

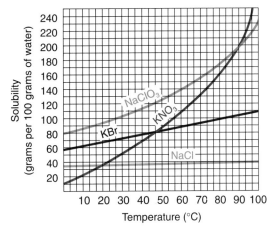

Figure 15-12. The solubilities of substances in water change with temperature.

CONCEPT DEVELOPMENT
▶ Quiz your students randomly about information on Table 15-3. For example, ask how many grams of potassium chloride will dissolve in 100 g of water at 60°C (45.8 g).
▶ **Demonstration:** Prepare 50 mL of a saturated solution of any substance from Table 15-3 except lead(II) chloride and barium hydroxide. Place a small amount of this solution in a petri dish on the overhead projector. Place a small amount of the same solution in a second petri dish and add water to make it unsaturated. Have a student drop a crystal of the salt into each petri dish and slowly stir both solutions. The class will observe the crystal dissolve in the unsaturated solution, but it will remain visible in the saturated solution.
▶ Emphasize to your students that the term *unsaturated* is not a precise indicator of how concentrated a solution is. *Concentrated* and *dilute* also do not convey any quantitative information about a solution.
▶ In class, place a seed crystal of sodium acetate on a watch glass. Slowly pour supersaturated solution on the crystal. The class will observe a stalagmite-like solid form on the glass as you pour. The crystals can be reused.

REVEALING MISCONCEPTIONS
▶ Most people believe that all solid solutes become more soluble in water as the temperature increases. Calcium acetate's solubility data show that this is a misconception. At 0°C, 37.4 g will dissolve in 100 mL of water while at 100°C only 29.7 g is soluble. The slope of the solubility graph for such a substance is negative.

STUDENT TEXT QUESTION
▶ Page 391, paragraph 1: **About how much NaCl will form a saturated solution with 100 g of water at 47°C?** *about 37 g*

MULTICULTURAL PERSPECTIVE

Sandbox Trees
Tall sandbox trees are found in the jungles of South and Central America. Their seed capsules were once used as boxes to hold sand for blotting ink. The trees, however, are dangerous. The bark of the tree is poisonous and is covered with short spines. The sap is acidic and will burn skin or cause blindness. The leaves, also poisonous, form a structure at the top of the trees that contains the seed capsules. Humans and animals can be injured when the seed capsules explode.

Nonetheless the sap becomes part of a very useful solution. The poisonous sap is mixed with sand so that it can be safely moved. It is thrown into areas of lakes and streams that have been dammed to form quiet pools. The sap goes into solution in the water and stuns any fish there. While the fish are stunned, people can gather all the fish they need for food. When they have collected all the fish they need, they remove the dams and water dilutes the sap so that the remaining fish recover completely.

For more information on replacing CFCs see "Atmosphere of Uncertainty" by Deborah Erickson, *Scientific American,* April 1990, pp. 77-78.

Think Critically: Answers will vary. Examples include shoe polish, car waxes, water-repellent products, and stain-resistant products.

CONCEPT DEVELOPMENT

▶ **Demonstration:** Drop one crystal of sodium acetate trihydrate into a previously prepared supersaturated solution of sodium acetate. Have students note changes in appearance and temperature.

CHECK FOR UNDERSTANDING

 FLEX Your Brain

Use the Flex Your Brain activity to have students explore SOLUBILITY.

ASSESSMENT

Portfolio: Use the Flex Your Brain activity to reinforce critical-thinking and problem-solving skills. In Step 2, students might list effects of temperature on solubility.

RETEACH

Use the Mini Quiz to reteach.

MINI QUIZ

Use the Mini Quiz to check students' recall of chapter content.

6 A solution that can dissolve more solute at a given temperature is said to be _____ . *unsaturated*

7 A solution that contains more solute than a saturated one has at a specific temperature is said to be _____ . *supersaturated*

8 If you add a solute crystal to an unsaturated solution, the crystal will _____ . *dissolve*

PROGRAM RESOURCES

From the **Teacher Resource Package** use:

Activity Worksheets, page 5, Flex Your Brain.

Use **Laboratory Manual 31,** Solubility.

Replacing a Super Solvent

Scientists the world over are involved in research to replace chlorofluorocarbons, often called CFCs. One of these compounds, named CFC-113, has been described as a super solvent. This compound doesn't bead up like water, so it can flow into all the tiny spaces on a printed circuit board to clean it up. This CFC has been used to clean sensitive equipment on the space shuttle and the electronic chips responsible for emission control in cars.

This super solvent has a serious drawback. Like other CFCs, it damages Earth's protective ozone layer, high in the atmosphere. As you will read in the next chapter, radiation from the sun splits off chlorine atoms from CFCs, and these atoms destroy ozone.

Thus, scientists need to develop solvents that can do the same jobs as CFCs but contain no chlorine. Recently, two new compounds called hydrochlorofluorocarbons, or HCFCs, have been tested. HCFCs work almost as well as the CFCs as solvents and cleaning agents, but they contain less chlorine. The HCFCs can be used until solvents containing no chlorine at all are available for use.

Think Critically: The inability of one substance to wet another is important in the development of many products. Provide some examples.

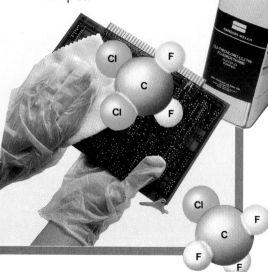

If you make a saturated solution of potassium nitrate at 100°C and then let it cool to 20°C, part of the solute separates from the solution. At the lower temperature, a saturated solution is formed with less solute. Most other saturated solutions behave in a similar way. But if you cool a saturated solution of sodium acetate from 100°C to 20°C, no solute comes out. This solution is supersaturated. A **supersaturated solution** contains more solute than a saturated one has at that temperature. This kind of solution is unstable. When a small crystal of the solute is added to a supersaturated solution, the excess solute quickly crystallizes out, as is shown in Figure 15-13.

OPTIONS

INQUIRY QUESTIONS

▶ **You have a test tube containing a clear solution of dissolved zinc chloride. You also have a crystal of zinc chloride. How can you determine if the solution is unsaturated, saturated, or supersaturated?** *Drop the crystal into the solution. If the crystal dissolves, the solution was unsaturated. If the crystal does not dissolve, the solution was saturated. If the solution crystallizes, it was supersaturated.*

▶ **A chemist has 50.0 g of sodium acetate and 100.0 g of water. When mixed hot then** cooled to 20°C, will the resulting solution be unsaturated, saturated, or supersaturated? Use Table 15-3. *supersaturated*

▶ **If the temperature of the solution described in the previous question is cooled to 0°C, how much solid will crystallize out of solution when a seed crystal is dropped into it?** *According to the table, 100 g water can dissolve 36.2 g of sodium acetate at 0°C. Therefore, 50.0 g -36.2 g = 13.8 g*

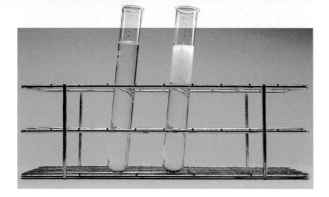

Figure 15-13. A supersaturated solution of sodium acetate (left) crystallizes out when a crystal of sodium acetate is added (right).

Suppose you add a solute crystal to a solution. If the crystal dissolves, the solution is unsaturated. If the crystal does not dissolve, the solution is saturated. And if excess solute comes out, the solution is supersaturated. How would you explain each of these possible results?

SECTION REVIEW

1. Do all solutes dissolve to the same extent in the same solvent? How do you know?
2. Using Table 15-3 on page 391, state the following: the mass of $NaNO_3$ that would have to be dissolved in 100 g of water to form a saturated, an unsaturated, and a supersaturated solution of $NaNO_3$ at 20°C.
3. **Apply:** By volume, an orange drink is 10 percent orange juice and 10 percent corn syrup. A 1500-mL can of the drink costs $0.95. A 1500-mL can of orange juice is $1.49, and 1500 mL of corn syrup is $1.69. How could you make orange drink? Is it cheaper to make or to buy?
4. **Connect to Earth Science:** Potassium chloride is used in some fertilizers. Using Table 15-2 on page 389, find out how many grams of potassium chloride could be dissolved in 250 mL of a water-based fertilizer.

☑ Making and Using Graphs

Using Table 15-3 on page 391, make a graph showing the solubility curves for $CuSO_4$ and $NaNO_3$. How would you make a saturated water solution of each substance at 80°C? If you need help, refer to Making and Using Graphs in the **Skill Handbook** on page 687.

Skill Builder ∿

EXTENSION

For students who have mastered this section, use the **Reinforcement** and **Enrichment** masters or other OPTIONS provided.

STUDENT TEXT QUESTION

▶ Page 393, paragraph 1: **How would you explain the behavior of a crystal in unsaturated, saturated, and supersaturated solutions?** *Unsaturated: The solvent can accept more solute. Saturated: The solvent cannot accept more solute. Supersaturated: The crystal provides a place for crystallization.*

3 CLOSE

▶ Ask questions 1-2 and the **Apply** and **Connect to Earth Science** questions in the Section Review.

SECTION REVIEW ANSWERS

1. No. The solubility data in Tables 15-2 and 15-3 shows wide variation.

2. saturated — 87.6 g; unsaturated — less than 87.6 g; supersaturated — more than 87.6 g

3. Apply: The simplest approach is to assume you will use all the orange juice and corn syrup plus eight 1500-mL cans of water. This makes 15 000 mL of orange drink for $3.18. Made this way, 1500 mL would cost $0.318 (rounded to $0.32). This is $0.95 − $0.32 = $0.63 cheaper to make than to buy.

4. Connect to Earth Science: 34 g KCl/100 g H_2O × 250 g H_2O = 85 g KCl.

Skill Builder
ASSESSMENT
Performance: To assess the accuracy of the graphs, ask students to determine from the graphs the temperatures at which only half of their reported saturation amounts would be dissolved. $NaNO_3$—about 0°C; $CuSO_4$—about 35°C.

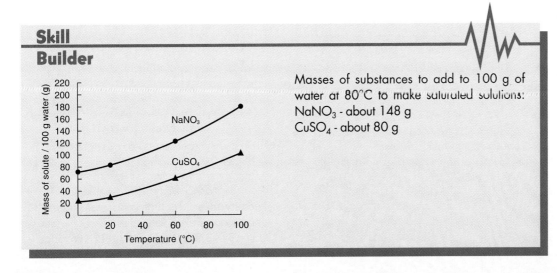

Skill Builder

Masses of substances to add to 100 g of water at 80°C to make saturated solutions:
$NaNO_3$ - about 148 g
$CuSO_4$ - about 80 g

ACTIVITY 15-1

OBJECTIVE: Compare the solubility of a solute at different temperatures.
Time: 45 minutes

PROCESS SKILLS applied in this activity are **measuring, calculating,** and **inferring.**

PREPARATION

Prepare massed samples of salts. See Teaching Tips for suggestions. Insert a thermometer into one hole of each stopper. Prepare and insert one wire stirrer per group as shown.

Cooperative Learning: You can save time by using the Science Investigation strategy with groups of six divided into three pairs. Each pair conducts the activity with one of the three water amounts.

SAFETY

Caution students to use a test-tube holder when handling hot test tubes and never stir with a thermometer. Lubricate thermometers with glycerin and wrap in a towel the part you are holding before inserting the thermometers into the stoppers.

THINKING CRITICALLY

At saturation, some amount of undissolved solute is present. By adding more solvent, the opportunity for attraction between solute and solvent particles increases, thereby increasing the amount of solute that would dissolve at that temperature.

TEACHING THE ACTIVITY

*Refer to the **Activity Worksheets** for additional information and teaching strategies.*
• Sample data is given for 9.0 g KBr.

mL H$_2$O	Saturation Temperature	g KBr per 100 g
10	68°C	90
12	41°C	75
14	24°C	64

Other suggestions are 6.5 g AlCl$_3$, 9.0 g Ba (OH)$_2$, and 10.0 g CuSO$_4$.

Two major factors to consider when you are dissolving a solute in water are temperature and the ratio of solute to solvent.

Getting Started
In this activity you will find out at what temperature the saturation point is reached. **CAUTION:** *Avoid touching hot materials. Handle any hot test tubes by using the test-tube holder.*

Thinking Critically
What clue can you see that indicates that a solute and solvent have formed a saturated solution? Why would increasing the amount of solvent change the saturation temperature?

Materials
Your cooperative group will use:
• large test tube
• thermometer inserted in a two-holed rubber stopper
• copper wire stirrer
• distilled water
• electric hot plate
• beaker
• 10-mL graduated cylinder
• test-tube holder
• solute

 Try It!

1. Turn the hot plate on. Pour tap water into the beaker until it is about half full, and place it on the hot plate to heat.
2. Obtain a solute sample from your teacher. *Make a data table* for your solute. Include the mass of solute, the volume of solvent, the saturation temperature, and the solubility at that temperature for each of the three readings.
3. *Measure* 10 mL of distilled water into your test tube. Then add your solute sample.
4. Place the stopper assembly into the test tube.
5. Place the test tube and stopper assembly into the boiling water bath. Stir the solution with the stirrer until the solute dissolves. Do not heat the solution any warmer than 80°C.
6. When the solute has dissolved, remove the assembly from the water bath and allow it to cool.

As soon as solute reappears in the solution, *record* the temperature as the saturation point.
7. Add 2 mL of distilled water to the solution in the test tube and repeat Steps 4–6.
8. Repeat step 7, and determine a third saturation temperature.

Summing Up/Sharing Results
• Use your data to find the solubility in 100 g of water at each saturation temperature.
• How did the saturation temperature change as you added more solvent?
• *Make a line graph* for the solubility, placing grams of solute per 100 g water on the y axis and temperature on the x axis.

Going Further!
In making hard candy, a solution of sugar in water is heated until a thick syrup forms. When the syrup is cooled, hard candy forms. Explain what happens in this process.

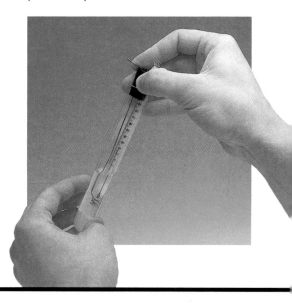

SUMMING UP/SHARING RESULTS
• Encourage students to use proportions for calculating solubilities. For example,

$$\frac{9.0 \text{ g KBr}}{14 \text{ g H}_2\text{O}} = \frac{x \text{ g KBr}}{100 \text{ g H}_2\text{O}}$$

$$x = 64 \text{ g KBr}$$

• Saturation temperatures decrease as the amount of solvent increases.
• Most graphs will be close to a straight line with a positive slope.

GOING FURTHER!
As the sugar solution cools, the solubility of sugar decreases. The sugar crystallizes from solution forming hard candy.

PROGRAM RESOURCES
From the **Teacher Resource Package** use:
Activity Worksheets, pages 116-117, Activity 15-1: Saturation Situation.

Activity ASSESSMENT
Performance: To further assess students' understanding of saturated solutions, see USING LAB SKILLS, Question 12, on page 400.

Particles in Solution 15-4

Objectives

▶ Compare and contrast the behavior of polar and nonpolar substances in forming solutions.
▶ Relate the processes of dissociation and ionization to solutions that conduct electricity.
▶ Explain how the addition of solutes to solvents affects the freezing and boiling points of solutions.

New Science Words

dissociation
ionization
electrolyte
nonelectrolyte

Solvents and Solutes

Why do you have to shake an oil and vinegar salad dressing, Figure 15-14, immediately before you use it? Oil and vinegar do not form a solution. Oil does not dissolve in vinegar, which is approximately 95 percent water.

Why does a substance dissolve in one solvent but not in another? Solvents that have nonpolar molecules dissolve solutes that have nonpolar molecules. Hexane dissolves grease because both substances have nonpolar molecules. Similarly, polar solvents dissolve polar solutes. Water is a polar solvent, and it dissolves sucrose, a polar solute. Polar solvents also dissolve ionic solutes, such as sodium chloride. A polar solvent won't normally dissolve a nonpolar solute. That's why oil, which is nonpolar, won't dissolve in vinegar, which is polar. In general, when predicting which solutes will dissolve in which solvents, remember the phrase, "like dissolves like."

Some substances form solutions with both polar and nonpolar solutes, because their molecules have a polar and a nonpolar end. Ethanol is such a molecule, Figure 15-15. The polar end dissolves polar substances, and the nonpolar end dissolves nonpolar substances. Thus, ethanol dissolves iodine, which is nonpolar, and water, which is polar.

Figure 15-14. Vinegar and oil don't form a solution. You can see oil drops in vinegar even when the mixture is shaken.

In Your JOURNAL

Polarity plays a major role in solubility. **In your Journal,** write a brief explanation of why some molecules are polar and some are not.

Figure 15-15. Ethanol, C_2H_5OH, has a polar –OH group at one end and a nonpolar –CH$_3$ group at the other end.

15-4   PARTICLES IN SOLUTION   **395**

PREPARATION

SECTION BACKGROUND

▶ In 1887, Arrhenius offered an explanation of why acids and bases conduct an electric current. These substances ionize in water to produce ions. He called the charged particles ions (wanderers).

1 MOTIVATE

▶ **Demonstration:** Clamp a large dill pickle on a ring stand. To release steam, poke a hole in the side of the pickle. Place a nail in each end of the pickle so that the points are about 1 to 2 cm apart. Using an electrical cord that has two alligator clips at one end, connect the clips to the nails. Plug the electric cord into any regular 110 volt outlet. **CAUTION:** *Do not touch any part of the setup while the cord is plugged in. Make sure the stand is not on a conductive surface and that students do not approach. Caution students not to try this procedure at home.* Turn off the lights and observe the pickle glow. Ask students to interpret the phenomenon. The pickling solution contains an electrolyte and conducts electricity.

In Your JOURNAL

Student entries should make reference to the uneven sharing of electrons in a covalent bond. Unless polar covalent bonds are symmetrical in a molecule, a polar molecule results.

Skill Builder

Compounds that dissolve in water
- conduct electricity
- do not conduct electricity

Electrolytes — Nonelectrolytes

type — type — type

Ionic compounds — Certain polar compounds — Other polar compounds

process — process

Dissociation — Ionization

This concept map goes with the Section Review on page 397.

Ask students why it is unwise to take a bath while an electric appliance is plugged into an outlet nearby. Ask them if they know why a person can be electrocuted. Most tap water contains enough dissolved salts to make it conductive.

2 TEACH

Key Concepts are highlighted.

CONCEPT DEVELOPMENT

▶ **Demonstration:** Using a conductivity checker, show the class that *distilled* water is a nonelectrolyte. Place the electrodes in a beaker of dry salt, NaCl, crystals to show no conduction. Then with the electrodes submerged in *distilled* water, slowly add salt to the water while stirring. The meter or light bulb will show increasing conductivity as the number of ions in solution increases. Use great caution if the apparatus uses line voltage.

Connect to...
Physics

Answer: Dry cell batteries do have a moist paste that allows electrolytes to move and conduct a current.

PROGRAM RESOURCES

From the **Teacher Resource Package** use:

Critical Thinking/Problem Solving, page 21, Denatured Alcohol.

Transparency Worksheets, pages 59-60, Dissociation and Ionization.

Use **Color Transparency** number 30, Dissociation and Ionization.

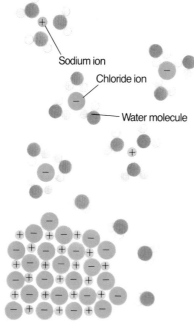

Figure 15-16. When sodium chloride dissolves in water, H₂O molecules surround, pull apart, and separate the Na⁺ and Cl⁻ ions.

Solutions as Conductors

Why should you never use a hair dryer when standing on a wet bathroom floor? You take such precautions because, as you may have discovered in a safer situation, you are an excellent conductor of electricity. Your body is about 70 percent water with many ionic compounds dissolved in it. Like the metals used to wire lamps and appliances, water solutions of ionic compounds and of some polar compounds conduct electricity.

As an ionic solid dissolves in water, the positive and negative ions are separated from one another. This process is called **dissociation.** Sodium chloride dissociates when it dissolves in water, as shown in Figure 15-16. When certain polar substances dissolve in water, the water pulls their molecules apart, forming ions. This process is called **ionization.** Hydrogen chloride ionizes in water, as shown in Figure 15-17 below. A substance that separates into ions or forms ions in a water solution is called an **electrolyte.** Thus, both NaCl, which dissociates, and HCl, which ionizes, are examples of electrolytes.

Pure water does not conduct electricity. If a water solution is a conductor, the solute must be an electrolyte. But many polar substances, such as sugar and alcohol, do not ionize when they dissolve in water. These solutions do not conduct electricity. A substance whose water solutions are nonconducting is a **nonelectrolyte.**

Figure 15-17. When hydrogen chloride dissolves in water, H₂O molecules surround and pull apart HCl molecules, forming the ions H₃O⁺ and Cl⁻.

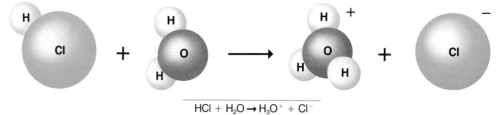

$$HCl + H_2O \rightarrow H_3O^+ + Cl^-$$

Effects of Solute Particles

Antifreeze that you may add to water in a car radiator makes freezing more difficult. Adding a solute to a solvent lowers the freezing point of the solvent. How much

OPTIONS

Meeting Different Ability Levels

For Section 15-4, use the following **Teacher Resource Masters** depending upon individual students' needs.

◆ **Study Guide Master** for all students.

● **Reinforcement Master** for students of average and above average ability levels.

▲ **Enrichment Master** for above average students.

Additional Teacher Resource Package masters are listed in any PROGRAM RESOURCES boxes that are in the section. The additional masters are appropriate for all students.

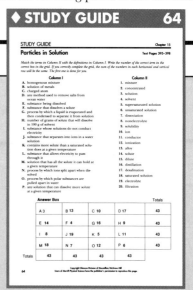

the freezing point goes down depends upon how many solute particles you add.

How does antifreeze work? As a pure solvent freezes, its particles organize themselves into an orderly pattern. Solute particles interfere with the formation of this pattern, preventing the solvent from freezing at its normal freezing point. To overcome this interference, a lower temperature is required to freeze the solvent.

Antifreeze also raises the boiling point of the water in a car radiator. As a result, the radiator does a better job of removing the heat from the engine. The amount that the boiling point is raised depends upon the number of solute particles present. The more solute present, the higher the boiling point becomes because the attraction between solute and solvent particles interferes with evaporation. Thus, more energy is needed to allow the solvent particles to evaporate. And the solution boils at a higher temperature.

As you can see, solutions such as antifreeze in water, fluids in your body, lemonade, and ocean water are part of your everyday life.

Why do particles of solute lower the freezing point of water?

EcoTip

Antifreeze has a sweet odor and taste, but is deadly to pets. If antifreeze leaks onto the driveway, wash it away immediately. Never pour antifreeze into street gutters.

Why do particles of solute raise the boiling point of water?

Connect to...
Physics

Read about the internal structure of a typical dry cell battery. Why is the term *dry cell* not exactly correct?

SECTION REVIEW

1. Explain why (a) water dissolves sugar, (b) water does not dissolve oil, and (c) benzene does dissolve oil.
2. What kinds of solute particles are present in water solutions of (a) electrolytes and (b) nonelectrolytes?
3. **Apply:** In very cold weather, people often put salt on ice that forms on sidewalks and driveways. The salt helps melt the ice, forming a saltwater solution. Explain why this solution may not refreeze.
4. **Connect to Life Science:** Many insects can survive extremely cold winter temperatures. Like humans, insects often have a lot of water in their bodies. What can you conclude about their body fluids?

✉ Concept Mapping

Draw a concept map to show the relationship among the following terms: *electrolytes, nonelectrolytes, dissociation, ionization, ionic compounds, certain polar compounds, other polar compounds*. If you need help, refer to Concept Mapping in the **Skill Handbook** on pages 684 and 685.

Skill Builder

CHECK FOR UNDERSTANDING
Use the Mini Quiz to check for understanding.

CHECK FOR UNDERSTANDING
Use the Mini Quiz to check for understanding.

MINI QUIZ

Use the Mini Quiz to check students' recall of chapter content.

1. **When an ionic solid dissolves in water, the separation process is called _____** . *dissociation*
2. **When a polar solute is pulled apart by water, the process is called _____** . *ionization*
3. **What happens to the freezing point of a solvent when a solute is added**? *It is lowered.*

RETEACH

▶ Have students look at and describe the processes taking place in the diagrams in Figures 15-16 and 15-17. Perform or repeat the conductivity demonstration on page 396.

EXTENSION

For students who have mastered this section, use the **Reinforcement** and **Enrichment** masters or other OPTIONS provided.

3 CLOSE

▶ Ask questions 1-2 and the **Apply** and **Connect to Life Science** questions in the Section Review.

SECTION REVIEW ANSWERS
1. a. Both are polar. b. Water is polar but oil is not. c. Both are nonpolar.
2. a. ions; b. molecules
3. **Apply:** The freezing point of the water from the melted ice is lowered by the presence of sodium and chloride ions from the salt. As long as the temperature does not drop lower than the new freezing point of the solution, the water will remain a liquid.
4. **Connect to Life Science:** The fluids must contain high concentrations of solute.

Skill Builder
ASSESSMENT
Oral: Have students use their concept maps to explain the demonstration on page 396.

Skill Builder is on page 395.

ACTIVITY 15-2
35 minutes

OBJECTIVE: Interpret data and draw conclusions regarding the effect of a solute on the boiling point of water.

PROCESS SKILLS applied in this activity:
▶ **Measuring** in Procedure Steps 2-5.
▶ **Graphing** in Procedure Step 6.

COOPERATIVE LEARNING
Use Science Investigation Groups. Have one student in a group measure out the additional NaCl needed while others handle heating. Students should work on graphs in groups.

TEACHING THE ACTIVITY

Alternate Materials: Other soluble ionic compounds, such as calcium chloride, will also raise the boiling point.

Troubleshooting: Be sure students have thermometer bulbs immersed when reading temperatures and that thermometers read clearly in a range above 100°C. The boiling temperature of water may be less than 100°C because atmospheric pressure is usually less than 1 atmosphere.

▶ The following is a graph using sample data. Students should obtain similar graphs.

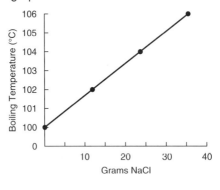

▶ It is possible to do the activity by adding successive 12-gram amounts of NaCl to the same beaker, but it will not give accurate results because of water loss.

▶ To save time, you could have students use level teaspoons (approximately 12 grams) of NaCl. It would be better, though, to reinforce science concepts by having them use a balance.

Boiling Points of Solutions

Adding small amounts of salt to water being boiled to cook pasta and adding antifreeze to a car's radiator have a common result. In each case, the boiling point of the water is now higher than that of pure water. Try this activity to see how much the boiling point of a solution can be changed.

Materials

- 400 mL distilled water
- thermometer
- ring stand
- 72 g table salt, NaCl
- laboratory burner
- 250-mL beaker

Procedure

1. Copy the data table and use it to *record your observations.*
2. Bring 100 mL of distilled water in a 250-mL beaker to a gentle boil. Record the temperature.
3. Dissolve 12 g of NaCl in 100 mL of distilled water. Bring this solution to a gentle boil and record its boiling point. **CAUTION:** *Always keep the thermometer away from the flame.*
4. Repeat Step 2, using 24 g of NaCl.
5. Repeat Step 2 again, using 36 g of NaCl.
6. Plot your results on a *graph* that shows boiling point on the vertical axis and grams of NaCl on the horizontal axis.

Data and Observations Sample Data

Grams of NaCl Solute	Boiling Point (°C)
0	~100
12	~102
24	~104
36	~106

Analyze

1. What difference is there between the boiling point of a pure solvent and that of a solution?
2. Instead of doubling the amount of NaCl in Step 4, what would have been the effect of doubling the amount of water?
3. What would be the result of using tap water instead of distilled water?

Conclude and Apply

4. In cooking, why does adding salt to water cause some foods to cook faster?
5. If you continued to add more salt, would you *predict* that your graph would continue in the same pattern or level off? Explain your prediction.

ANSWERS TO QUESTIONS

1. The boiling point of the solution is higher.
2. The boiling point would have gone down but would still be higher than the boiling point of pure water.
3. Most tap water contains dissolved salts, so its boiling point would be above 100°C.
4. The saltwater solution would boil at a little higher temperature.
5. The graph would continue until saturation was reached. Then it would level off because no more salt would dissolve.

PROGRAM RESOURCES

From the **Teacher Resource Package** use:
Activity Worksheets, pages 118-119, Activity 15-2: Boiling Points of Solutions.

Activity
ASSESSMENT
Performance: Have students use their graphs to predict the boiling point of a solution that contains 18 g of NaCl. *about 103°C*

CHAPTER
REVIEW

CHAPTER
REVIEW

SUMMARY

15-1: How Solutions Form
1. Solutions are classified into three types according to their final state: gaseous, liquid, and solid.
2. Dissolving occurs when constantly moving solvent molecules attract particles of solute and surround them with solvent.
3. Stirring, surface area, temperature, and pressure may affect the rate of dissolving.

15-2: Science and Society: Oceans— The World's Largest Solution
1. The oceans form the world's largest solution because they contain, in addition to dissolved sodium chloride, many other dissolved salts.
2. Methods being used to desalinate ocean water include distillation, flash distillation, and freezing followed by melting.

15-3: Solubility and Concentration
1. The solubility of substances varies among different solutes and for the same solute at different temperatures.
2. Two precise ways to express solution concentrations are (1) percentage by volume and (2) percentage by mass.
3. A solution may be saturated, unsaturated, or supersaturated.

15-4: Particles in Solution
1. Usually, among polar and nonpolar solvents and solutes, "like dissolves like."
2. Ionic compounds dissociate when dissolved in water, and some polar compounds ionize when dissolved in water.
3. Adding a solute to a solvent lowers its freezing point and raises its boiling point.

KEY SCIENCE WORDS

a. desalination
b. dissociation
c. distillation
d. electrolyte
e. ionization
f. nonelectrolyte
g. saturated solution
h. solubility
i. solute
j. solvent
k. supersaturated solution
l. unsaturated solution

UNDERSTANDING VOCABULARY

Match each phrase with the correct term from the list of Key Science Words.

1. a solution that can dissolve more solute at a given temperature
2. the substance being dissolved
3. has more solute than a saturated solution has at that temperature
4. exists as ions in a water solution
5. molecules are pulled apart into ions in solution
6. separation of negative and positive ions
7. the most solute in grams, that will dissolve in 100 g of solvent at a certain temperature
8. a solution that has dissolved all the solute it can hold at a given temperature
9. the substance that dissolves a solute
10. the general term for any method that removes salt from ocean water

SOLUTIONS **399**

CHAPTER
REVIEW

SUMMARY
Have students read the summary statements to review the major concepts of the chapter.

UNDERSTANDING VOCABULARY
1. l
2. i
3. k
4. d
5. e
6. b
7. h
8. g
9. j
10. a

ASSESSMENT
Portfolio
Encourage students to place in their portfolios one or two items of what they consider to be their best work. For each item, ask students to explain why that item was chosen and what they learned from it. Items might be selected from the following.
- Flex Your Brain, p. 385
- Cross Curriculum interpretation, p. 387
- Activity 15-1 results and answers, p. 394

Performance
Additional performance assessments may be found in *Performance Assessment* and *Science Integration Activities* that accompany **Merrill Physical Science.** Performance Task Assessment Lists and rubrics for evaluating these activities and other products generated throughout the chapter can be found in Glencoe's *Performance Assessment in Middle School Science.*

OPTIONS

ASSESSMENT
To assess student understanding of material in this chapter, use the resources listed.

COOPERATIVE LEARNING
Consider using cooperative learning in the THINK AND WRITE CRITICALLY, APPLY, and MORE SKILL BUILDERS sections of the Chapter Review.

PROGRAM RESOURCES
From the **Teacher Resource Package** use:
Chapter Review, pages 33-34.
Chapter and Unit Tests, pages 101-104, Chapter Test.

CHAPTER REVIEW

CHAPTER REVIEW

CHECKING CONCEPTS

1. d	6. b
2. a	7. b
3. b	8. a
4. d	9. b
5. a	10. c

USING LAB SKILLS

ASSESSMENT

Use these alternate lab exercises to assess students' understanding of skills used in this chapter.

11. The brand with smaller-sized pieces may have a faster dissolving rate because more surface area will be in contact with the ice to begin dissolving.

12. NaCl shows very little change in saturation levels over the temperature range used in the activity.

THINK AND WRITE CRITICALLY

13. The boiling point of salt is much higher than that of water. Salt is a strongly bonded ionic compound.

14. The negative ends of polar water molecules attract the positive copper ions at the surface of the solid and pull them into solution. The positive ends of water molecules attract the negative sulfate ions at the surface of the solid and pull them into solution.

15. There is no set amount of solute that makes a solution concentrated or dilute.

16. Answers may vary. One possibility is to add 25 mL of apple juice to 75 mL of water.

17. Solutions may be prepared using solvents other than water. For example, iodine dissolves in alcohol to produce a solution (tincture of iodine). Water also could be the solute in a solution. An example would be rubbing alcohol, which is 70 percent isopropanol.

CHECKING CONCEPTS

Choose the word or phrase that completes the sentence or answers the question.

1. Which of the following is not a solution?
   - **a.** a glass of soda
   - **b.** air in a SCUBA tank
   - **c.** bronze (an alloy)
   - **d.** muddy water

2. Solutions may not be _____.
   - **a.** colloidal
   - **b.** gaseous
   - **c.** liquid
   - **d.** solid

3. When iodine is dissolved in alcohol, the alcohol is the _____.
   - **a.** alloy
   - **b.** solvent
   - **c.** solution
   - **d.** solute

4. If a bronze alloy is 85 percent copper and 15 percent tin, tin is the _____.
   - **a.** alloy
   - **b.** solvent
   - **b.** solution
   - **d.** solute

5. Forty-nine mL of water has a mass of _____.
   - **a.** 49 g
   - **b.** 51 g
   - **c.** 100 g
   - **d.** 4900 g

6. A polar solvent will best dissolve _____.
   - **a.** any solute
   - **b.** a polar solute
   - **c.** a nonpolar solute
   - **d.** no solute

7. If a water solution conducts electricity, the solute must be a(n) _____.
   - **a.** gas
   - **b.** electrolyte
   - **c.** liquid
   - **d.** nonelectrolyte

8. In forming a water solution, an ionic compound undergoes _____.
   - **a.** dissociation
   - **b.** electrolysis
   - **c.** ionization
   - **d.** no change

9. A gas becomes more soluble in a liquid when you increase _____.
   - **a.** particle size
   - **b.** pressure
   - **c.** stirring
   - **d.** temperature

10. Solute may come out of a solution that is _____.
   - **a.** unsaturated
   - **b.** saturated
   - **c.** supersaturated
   - **d.** miscible

USING LAB SKILLS

11. Two brands of rock salt were purchased to sprinkle on icy sidewalks to help melt the ice. Use the results of the MINI-Lab on page 383 to explain why one brand began to melt the ice more quickly than the other brand did.

12. Examine Table 15-3 on page 391. Explain why common table salt would not have been a good choice to use as a solute in Activity 15-1 on page 394.

THINK AND WRITE CRITICALLY

Answer the following questions in your Journal using complete sentences.

13. As the first step of distillation, salt water is boiled and the water vaporizes. Why doesn't the salt also vaporize?

14. Explain what happens when copper(II) sulfate, $CuSO_4$, an ionic compound, dissolves in water.

15. Why are *concentrated* and *dilute* not exact terms?

16. Explain how you would make a 25 percent solution of apple juice.

17. Why is the statement "Water is the solvent in a solution" not always true?

APPLY

18. Explain why tetrachloroethene, a dry cleaning fluid, will dissolve grease and water will not.

19. Why might a tropical lake have more minerals dissolved in it than a lake in Minnesota?

20. Explain why salt will melt ice on a sidewalk.

21. Why might potatoes cook quicker in salt water than in unsalted water?

22. Explain why an unrefrigerated glass of soda will go "flat" quicker in hot weather.

MORE SKILL BUILDERS

If you need help, refer to the Skill Handbook.

1. **Comparing and Contrasting**: Compare and contrast the processes of ionization and dissociation.

2. **Hypothesizing:** You are stocking a pond in a tropical climate and a pond in a temperate climate with fish. Both ponds contain about the same amount of water. Based on the amount of oxygen dissolved in the water, to which pond would you be able to add more fish? Explain why.

3. **Interpreting Data:** The label on a bottle of rubbing alcohol might read "70% isopropanol by volume." Assuming the rest of the solution is water, what does this label tell you about the contents and preparation of the solution in the bottle?

4. **Measuring in SI:** 153 g of potassium nitrate have been dissolved in enough water to make 1.00 L of solution. You use a graduated cylin-

der to measure 80.0 mL of solution. What mass of potassium nitrate do you have in the 80.0-mL sample?

5. **Making and Using Tables:** Using the data in Table 15-3 on page 391, fill in the following table. Use the words *saturated*, *unsaturated*, and *supersaturated*.

Compound	g Dissolved in 100 g Water at 20°C	Type of Solution
$Ba(OH)_2$	2.96	
$CuSO_4$	32.0	
KCl	45.8	
KNO_3	31.6	
$NaClO_3$	79.6	

PROJECTS

1. Research crystal growing using saturated and supersaturated solutions. Grow several crystals and display them. Accompany the display with a report explaining what you did.

2. Do research on a titanium alloy. Report on its production, composition, and uses.

3. Visit a SCUBA shop. Find out about the composition of the gas used in the tanks. In terms of solution, report your findings.

APPLY

18. Tetrachloroethene and grease are both composed of nonpolar molecules. Water is polar and is not attracted to nonpolar grease molecules.

19. A tropical lake is likely to be warmer. Most solutes are more soluble in water at higher temperatures.

20. The salt dissociates into ions when it dissolves. The presence of these ions lowers the freezing point of water. Unless it is very cold, the dissolved salt will keep the water liquid.

21. The salted water boils at a slightly higher temperature than unsalted water because of the presence of dissolved ions. At the higher temperature, the potatoes cook more quickly.

22. The higher room temperature in hot weather causes decreased solubility of carbon dioxide gas in water. Thus, more of the gas comes out of solution more rapidly.

MORE SKILL BUILDERS

1. **Comparing and Contrasting:** Both processes result in ions in solution. Dissociation involves the separation of ions in an ionic compound. Ionization involves the pulling apart of polar molecules into ions.

2. **Hypothesizing:** In theory, more fish could live in the temperate climate. At the colder temperature, more oxygen would dissolve in the water.

3. **Interpreting and Using Data:** For every 100 mL of the rubbing alcohol, 70 mL are alcohol, and 30 mL are water. The rubbing alcohol was most likely prepared by combining the ingredients in this ratio.

4. **Measuring in SI:**
$$\frac{153 \text{ g } KNO_3}{1000 \text{ mL solution}} \times 80.0 \text{ mL solution}$$
$$= 12.2 \text{ g } KNO_3$$

5. **Making and Using Tables:**
$Ba(OH)_2$ — unsaturated
$CuSO_4$ — saturated
KCl — supersaturated
KNO_3 — saturated
$NaClO_3$ — unsaturated

16 Chemical Reactions

CHAPTER SECTION	OBJECTIVES	ACTIVITIES
16-1 Chemical Changes in Matter (2 days)	1. **Identify** reactants and products in a chemical reaction. 2. **Explain** how a chemical reaction satisfies the law of conservation of mass. 3. **Interpret** chemical equations.	**MINI-Lab:** *Does mass change in a reaction?* p. 405
16-2 The Hole in the Ozone Layer Science & Society (1 day)	1. **Describe** the role of the ozone layer in protecting life on Earth. 2. **Explain** the role of CFCs in the threat to the ozone layer.	
16-3 Chemical Equations (2 days)	1. **Explain** what is meant by a balanced chemical equation. 2. **Demonstrate** how to write balanced chemical equations.	**MINI-Lab:** *Must the sums of reactant and product coefficients be equal?* p. 412
16-4 Types of Chemical Reactions (2 days)	1. **Describe** four types of chemical reactions using their generalized formulas. 2. **Classify** various chemical reactions by type.	**Activity 16-1:** *Metal Activity*, p. 416
16-5 Energy and Chemical Reactions (2 days)	1. **Differentiate** between an exothermic reaction and an endothermic reaction. 2. **Describe** the effects of catalysts and inhibitors on the speed of chemical reactions.	**Activity 16-2:** *Catalyzed Reaction*, p. 420
Chapter Review		

ACTIVITY MATERIALS

FIND OUT	ACTIVITIES		MINI-LABS	
Page 403 2 darkened pennies table salt vinegar medicine dropper paper towel plastic wrap one dish per group	**16-1 Metal Activity, p. 416** 3 test tubes test tube stand small pieces of copper, Cu; zinc, Zn; and magnesium, Mg 15 mL dilute hydrochloric acid, HCl graduated cylinder wooden splint	**16-2 Catalyzed Reaction, p. 420** 3 medium-sized test tubes and stand 15 mL H_2O_2 graduated cylinder small plastic spoon manganese dioxide, MnO_2 wooden splint hot plate, sand beaker of hot water	**Does mass change in a reaction? p. 405** medicine dropper bottle dilute NaOH solution dilute $FeCl_3$ solution soap balance	**Must the sums of reactant and product coefficients be equal? p. 412** cards markers

CHAPTER FEATURES	TEACHER RESOURCE PACKAGE	OTHER RESOURCES
Problem Solving: *Metals and the Atmosphere,* p. 407 **Skill Builder:** *Recognizing Cause and Effect,* p. 407	**Ability Level Worksheets** ◆ **Study Guide,** p. 65 ● **Reinforcement,** p. 65 ▲ **Enrichment,** p. 65 **Activity Worksheets,** p. 130	**Laboratory Manual 32,** Conservation of Mass
You Decide! p. 409	**Ability Level Worksheets** ◆ **Study Guide,** p. 66 ● **Reinforcement,** p. 66 ▲ **Enrichment,** p. 66 **Concept Mapping,** pp. 37, 38 **Transparency Masters,** pp. 61, 62	**Color Transparency 31,** CFCs and Ozone **STVS:** Disc 2, Side 1
Skill Builder: *Observing and Inferring,* p. 412	**Ability Level Worksheets** ◆ **Study Guide,** p. 67 ● **Reinforcement,** p. 67 ▲ **Enrichment,** p. 67 **Activity Worksheets,** p. 131 **Cross-Curricular Connections,** p. 22 **Transparency Masters,** pp. 63, 64	**Color Transparency 32,** Chemical Equations **Laboratory Manual 33,** Reaction Rates and Temperature
Skill Builder: *Hypothesizing,* p. 415	**Ability Level Worksheets** ◆ **Study Guide,** p. 68 ● **Reinforcement,** p. 68 ▲ **Enrichment,** p. 68 **Activity Worksheets,** pp. 124, 125 **Critical Thinking/Problem Solving,** p. 22 **Science and Society,** p. 20 **Transparency Masters,** pp. 65, 66	**Color Transparency 33,** Types of Chemical Reactions **Laboratory Manual 34,** Chemical Reactions **STVS:** Disc 2, Side 1 **Science Integration Activity 16**
Technology: *Catalytic Converters,* p. 419 **Skill Builder:** *Concept Mapping,* p. 419	**Ability Level Worksheets** ◆ **Study Guide,** p. 69 ● **Reinforcement,** p. 69 ▲ **Enrichment,** p. 69 **Activity Worksheets,** pp. 126, 127	**STVS:** Disc 2, Side 1
Summary Think & Write Critically Key Science Words Apply Understanding Vocabulary More Skill Builders Checking Concepts Projects Using Lab Skills	**ASSESSMENT RESOURCES** **Chapter Review,** pp. 35, 36 **Chapter Test,** pp. 105-108 **Performance Assessment in** Middle School Science	**Chapter Review Software** **Test Bank** **Alternate Asessment** **Performance Assessment**

◆ **Basic**   ● **Average**   ▲ **Advanced**

ADDITIONAL MATERIALS

SOFTWARE	AUDIOVISUAL	BOOKS/MAGAZINES
Chemical Reactions, Queue *Chemistry: Balancing Equations,* MECC. *Combining the Elements,* Wm. K. Bradford Publishing Co. *How Matter Changes,* Queue. *Introduction to General Chemistry: Chemical Formulas and Equations,* EduQuest. *Reactions,* J and S Software.	*Catalysts and Catalytic Reactions,* Video, Lucerne Media. *Catalytic Reactions,* Video, Britannica. *Chemical Reactions,* Video, Britannica. *Chemical Energy,* Laserdisc, Churchill Media. *Decomposition and Synthesis,* Video, Lucerne Media. *Formulas and Equations,* Video, Coronet.	Baer, Michael. *Theory of Chemical Reaction Dynamics.* Boca Raton, FL: CRC Press, 1985. Compton, R.G. *Comprehensive Chemical Kinetics.* New York: Elsevier, 1988. Sykes, Peter. *A Guidebook to Mechanism in Organic Chemistry.* New York: Wiley, 1986.

THEME DEVELOPMENT: Patterns of change as a theme of the textbook is developed through a presentation of how chemical changes are classified and represented by balanced chemical equations.

CHAPTER OVERVIEW

▶ **Section 16-1:** The chemical equation is introduced as a way of representing chemical reactions in a way that demonstrates the law of conservation of mass.

▶ **Section 16-2: Science and Society:** This section describes how the ozone layer is affected by CFCs.

▶ **Section 16-3:** How to balance a chemical equation is presented in this section.

▶ **Section 16-4:** Four common types of chemical reactions are presented. This section demonstrates how chemists are able to predict products for a chemical reaction.

▶ **Section 16-5:** Energy as a product or reactant in a chemical change is discussed. Catalysts and inhibitors are introduced.

CHAPTER VOCABULARY

chemical reaction
reactants
products
coefficients
chlorofluorocarbons (CFCs)
balanced chemical equation
synthesis reaction
decomposition reaction
single displacement reaction
double displacement reaction
precipitate
endothermic reactions
exothermic reactions
catalyst
inhibitor

CHAPTER

16 Chemical Reactions

402

OPTIONS

For Your Gifted Students

Challenge students to balance the following equations. The equations are given here in balanced form. Rewrite them, leaving out the coefficients.

1. $2KNO_3 \rightarrow 2KNO_2 + O_2$
2. $2C_2H_6 + 7O_2 \rightarrow 4CO_2 + 6H_2O$
3. $2Na + 2H_2O \rightarrow 2NaOH + H_2$
4. $3O_2 + CS_2 \rightarrow CO_2 + 2SO_2$
5. $2KClO_3 \rightarrow 2KCl + 3O_2$
6. $C_4H_8 + 6O_2 \rightarrow 4CO_2 + 4H_2O$
7. $2C_5H_{10} + 15O_2 \rightarrow 10\,CO_2 + 10\,H_2O$

For Your Mainstreamed Students

Have students make a crossword puzzle of the key science words found at the end of the chapter. Definitions for the terms can be found within the chapter and used as clues. Computer programs that construct crossword puzzles are available. Your school may have one.

You may not realize it, but the Statue of Liberty is made of copper. Why is it green? Brand new pennies are bright and shiny. Older pennies are black and quite dull. Some very old pennies often have a green layer on them. What causes pennies and copper statues to lose their shiny surfaces and turn green?

FIND OUT!

Do this activity to find out why copper surfaces often turn green.

Obtain two dark copper pennies. Sprinkle some table salt on them. Drop about five or six drops of vinegar on the salt-covered pennies. *Observe* the pennies for about 20 minutes and then rinse them with water. How do the pennies look now?

Place one of the pennies in plastic wrap. Wrap the penny tightly to prevent its exposure to air. Set this penny aside. Place the other penny on a saucer. Add just enough water to the saucer so that the penny is not completely covered. Let this coin remain in the water overnight. *Observe* the pennies the next day. How do they compare? What caused the changes that you observed?

Gearing Up
Previewing the Chapter

Use this outline to help you focus on important ideas in this chapter.

Previewing Science Skills

▶ In the Skill Builders, you will recognize cause and effect, observe and infer, hypothesize, and make a concept map.
▶ In the Activities, you will observe, infer, and classify.
▶ In the MINI-Labs, you will observe and infer.

What's next?

You have seen what happens to a penny when it is exposed to air. You will learn more about this chemical change and others as you read the pages that follow.

403

ASSESSMENT OPTIONS

PORTFOLIO
Refer to page 421 for suggested items that students might select for their portfolios.

PERFORMANCE ASSESSMENT
See page 421 for additional Performance Assessment options.
Process
Skill Builder, p. 419
MINI-Labs, pp. 405, 412
Activity 16-1, p. 416; 16-2, p. 420
Using Lab Skills, p. 422

CONTENT ASSESSMENT
Assessment—Oral, pp. 406, 413
Skill Builders, pp. 407, 412, 415
Section Reviews, pp. 407, 409, 412, 415, 419
Chapter Review, pp. 421-423
Mini Quizzes, pp. 406, 411, 414, 418

GROUP ASSESSMENT
Opportunities for group assessment occur with Cooperative Learning Strategies and Flex Your Brain Activities.

INTRODUCING THE CHAPTER
Use the Find Out activity to introduce students to chemical reactions. Inform students that they will be learning more about kinds of chemical reactions and how to describe them as they read the chapter.

FIND OUT!
Preparation: Have students refer to the chapter opening photo of the Statue of Liberty as you discuss this activity. Have students bring in pennies from home.
Materials: two darkened pennies, table salt, vinegar, medicine dropper, paper towel, plastic wrap, one dish per group
Teaching Tips
▶ This activity works well at home.
▶ The patina coating on the Statue of Liberty is basic copper(II) carbonate, $CuCO_3 \cdot 3Cu(OH)_2$, which is called brochantite. This protective patina has preserved the original copper skin. Only about four percent has been eroded so far, but acid rain can increase the rate of erosion.
▶ For copper to turn green, it must oxidize and then be exposed to water and sulfur compounds in air that has a relative humidity of at least 75 percent. This process is very slow.

Gearing Up
Have students study the Gearing Up feature to familiarize themselves with the chapter. Discuss the relationships of the topics in the outline.

What's Next?
Before beginning the first section, make sure students understand the connection between the Find Out activity and the topics to follow.

VideoDisc
STVS: Fire-Resistant Clothing, Disc 2, Side 1

PREPARATION

SECTION BACKGROUND

▶ The symbols used to indicate the state of matter have changed recently in scientific literature. The (s) for solid has been replaced with (cr) for crystalline solid. If the material is not crystalline, it is not a true solid, and the symbol (amor) for amorphous is used.

Connect to... Earth Science

Answer: Acid rain may decompose some of the green copper carbonate and leave behind a darker copper oxide.

1 MOTIVATE

▶ **Demonstration:** Prepare a soap solution by adding 160 mL of water to a 400-mL beaker, with 25 mL of liquid detergent and 5 mL of glycerine. In a separate beaker, dissolve 5 g of sucrose in 60 mL of water. Gently mix the two solutions. Connect one end of a length of rubber tubing to the gas outlet and the other end to a small funnel. Invert the funnel into the beaker of soap mixture. Make a bubble using the gas. Darken the room. Dislodge bubbles by turning the funnel sideways and gently shaking. As the bubble rises, ignite it with a burning candle taped to a meterstick. **CAUTION:** *Be sure there are no flammable materials nearby.*

TYING TO PREVIOUS KNOWLEDGE:

Remind students of the indications that a chemical change has occurred: color change, evolution of gas, heat, light, formation of a precipitate, production of electric current.

STUDENT TEXT QUESTION

▶ Page 404, paragraph 3: **What are the reactants and products in photosynthesis?** *reactants—carbon dioxide and water; products—sugar and oxygen*

New Science Words

chemical reaction
reactants
products
coefficients

Objectives

▶ Identify reactants and products in a chemical reaction.
▶ Explain how a chemical reaction satisfies the law of conservation of mass.
▶ Interpret chemical equations.

Connect to... Earth Science

Some darkening of the Statue of Liberty may be due to an increase in what environmental problem?

Figure 16-1. Antoine Lavoisier used precise balances to perform experiments that led to the law of conversation of mass.

Reactants and Products

In Chapter 9 you learned about chemical changes. These changes are taking place all around you and even inside your body. One of the most important chemical changes on Earth is photosynthesis. During photosynthesis plants use sunlight, carbon dioxide, and water to make sugar and oxygen. Another important chemical change takes place in the cells in your body. This change combines sugar and oxygen to produce energy, carbon dioxide, and water.

A **chemical reaction** is a well-defined example of a chemical change. In a chemical reaction, one or more substances are changed to new substances. The substances that are about to react are called **reactants.** The new substances produced are called **products.** This relationship can be written as follows:

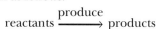

$$\text{reactants} \xrightarrow{\text{produce}} \text{products}$$

What are the reactants and products in the photosynthesis reaction described above?

Conservation of Mass

In the early 1700s, scientists wondered what happened to the masses of the reactants and products in a chemical reaction. The French chemist Antoine Lavoisier performed many experiments to find out. In one experiment, Lavoisier placed a carefully measured amount of solid

OPTIONS

Meeting Different Ability Levels

For Section 16-1, use the following **Teacher Resource Masters** depending upon individual students' needs.

◆ **Study Guide Master** for all students.
● **Reinforcement Master** for students of average and above average ability levels.
▲ **Enrichment Master** for above average students.

Additional Teacher Resource Package masters are listed in any **PROGRAM RESOURCES** boxes that are in the section. The additional masters are appropriate for all students.

◆ **STUDY GUIDE** 65

mercury(II) oxide into a sealed flask. When he heated this flask, oxygen gas and liquid mercury were produced:

solid mercury(II) oxide plus heat produces oxygen gas plus liquid mercury

Lavoisier found that the mass of the oxygen gas and the mercury produced was equal to the mass of the mercury(II) oxide that he started with:

mercury(II) oxide produces oxygen plus mercury
10.0 g   =   0.7 g   +   9.3 g

This and other experiments allowed Lavoisier to state the law of conservation of mass: in a chemical reaction matter is not created or destroyed but is conserved. In Chapter 9, you read how this law applies to chemical changes. For a chemical reaction in which all of the reactants change to products, this law means that the starting mass of the reactants equals the final mass of the products. The law of conservation of mass must be satisfied when describing a chemical reaction.

Describing Chemical Reactions

If you wanted to describe the chemical reaction shown in Figure 16-2, it might look something like this:

solid lead(II) nitrate, dissolved in water, plus
solid potassium iodide, dissolved in water, produce
solid lead(II) iodide plus potassium nitrate,
dissolved in water

This series of words is rather long and cumbersome. But, all information in this expression is important. The

Figure 16-2. The beakers contain solutions of lead(II) nitrate and potassium iodide (a). When these solutions are mixed, a bright yellow solid forms (b). The yellow solid, lead(II) iodide, settles to the bottom of the beaker. The liquid in the beaker is a potassium nitrate solution (c).

a

b

c

MINI-Lab
Does mass change in a reaction?
From your teacher, obtain solutions of the two reactants, $FeCl_3$ and NaOH—the $FeCl_3$ in a dropper plugged with soap and screwed into a bottle of NaOH. Determine the mass of the assembly. Then squeeze the dropper so that the plug is forced out. What do you *observe* as the reactants mix? Again determine the mass of the assembly, which now contains the products of the reaction—$Fe(OH)_3$ and NaCl. Was there a change in mass? What law does this procedure illustrate?

MINI-Lab
Materials: medicine dropper, bottle, dilute NaOH solution, dilute $FeCl_3$ solution, soap, balance
Teaching Tips
► Pre-assemble the apparatus.
► To make the needed solutions, dissolve 4 g NaOH in 100 mL H_2O and dissolve 8 g $FeCl_3$ in 100 mL H_2O. **CAUTION:** *These substances are corrosive. Be sure students do not touch the reactants.*
► Fill the dropper with $FeCl_3$ solution, and gently push the tip into a bar of soap so that a small plug of soap remains in the tip.
► Wipe the outside of the dropper before inserting it into the bottle.
Results: Mixing the solutions gives a brown precipitate of $Fe(OH)_3$.
Answers to Questions
Students should find no change in mass. This activity demonstrates the law of conservation of mass.

MINI-Lab
ASSESSMENT
Content: To further assess students' understanding of this reaction, see USING LAB SKILLS, Question 11, on page 422.

2 TEACH

Key Concepts are highlighted.

PROGRAM RESOURCES
From the **Teacher Resource Package** use:

Activity Worksheets, page 130, MINI-Lab: Does mass change in a reaction?

Use **Laboratory Manual 32,** Conservation of Mass.

Demonstration: To easily illustrate the law of conservation of mass, burn a piece of magnesium ribbon in a darkened room. Use tongs to hold the piece of burning ribbon inside a can so the students cannot see the flame directly. This is the same reaction that occurs in some flashbulbs. Determine the mass of a flashbulb on the balance. Fire the flashbulb. Show that the magnesium has oxidized inside the bulb, but there has been no change in mass.

CHECK FOR UNDERSTANDING

Use the Mini Quiz to check for understanding.

MINI QUIZ

Use the Mini Quiz to check students' recall of chapter content.

① **A chemical reaction begins with substances called _____ .** *reactants*

② **The new substances produced in a chemical reaction are called _____ .** *products*

③ **If you begin with 12.5 g of reactants that completely react, what mass of products can you expect to form?** *12.5 g*

④ **Numbers used in a chemical equation to represent the relative amounts of substances taking part in a reaction are called _____ .** *coefficients*

RETEACH

Demonstration: On the chalkboard, write the equation for a reaction of vinegar and baking soda. Show the reaction and discuss the evidence that a chemical change is taking place. Label the reactants and products. Point out that if the gas were collected, you could show that mass was conserved.

$NaHCO_3(cr) + CH_3COOH(aq)$
$NaCH_3COO(aq) + H_2O(l) + CO_2(g)$

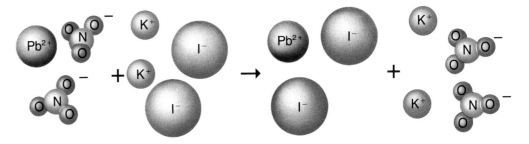

Figure 16-3. One unit of $Pb(NO_3)_2$ reacts with two units of KI to produce one unit of PbI_2 plus two units of KNO_3.

In Your JOURNAL

A balanced chemical equation tells the story of a chemical reaction. **In your Journal,** write the story of the chemical equation shown in Figure 16-3.

What is a chemical equation?

Table 16-1

SYMBOLS USED IN CHEMICAL EQUATIONS	
Symbol	**Meaning**
→	produces or forms
+	plus
(cr)	solid
(l)	liquid
(g)	gas
(aq)	aqueous, a solid is dissolved in water
heat →	the reactants are heated
light →	the reactants are exposed to light
elect. →	an electric current is applied to the reactants

same is true of descriptions of most chemical reactions—many words are needed to state all the important information. So scientists have developed a shorthand method to describe chemical reactions. A chemical equation is an expression that describes a chemical reaction using chemical formulas and other symbols. In Chapter 11, you learned how to use chemical symbols and formulas. Some of the other symbols used in chemical equations are listed in Table 16-1.

What would the chemical equation for the reaction in Figure 16-2 look like?

$$Pb(NO_3)_2(aq) + 2KI(aq) \rightarrow PbI_2(cr) + 2KNO_3(aq)$$

The symbols to the right of the formulas are (*cr*) for crystalline solid and (*aq*) for aqueous, which means dissolved in water.

What do the numbers to the left of the formulas for reactants and products mean? Remember that the law of conservation of mass states that matter is neither created nor destroyed during chemical reactions. Atoms are rearranged but never lost or destroyed. These numbers, called **coefficients,** represent the relative amounts of substances taking part in a reaction. They show you what change is taking place inside the reaction flask. For example, in the above reaction one unit of $Pb(NO_3)_2$ reacts with two units of KI to produce one unit of PbI_2 and two units of KNO_3. Figure 16-3 will help you visualize this reaction.

You don't always have to analyze the reaction mixture to find out what the coefficients in a chemical reaction are. In the next section you will find out how to choose coefficients for a chemical equation.

OPTIONS

PROBLEM SOLVING

Metals and the Atmosphere

When metals are exposed to air, they often corrode. Rusting is one type of corrosion. Rust is hydrated iron(III) oxide.

Aluminum also reacts with oxygen in the air to form aluminum oxide. Unlike rust, which crumbles and exposes more iron to the air, aluminum oxide adheres to the aluminum surface on which it forms, protecting the aluminum underneath.

Copper is another metal that corrodes when exposed to air. When copper corrodes, a green coating called basic copper sulfate is formed. You may have seen this type of corrosion on the Statue of Liberty.

Think Critically: Identify the reactants and products in the corrosion of iron. When the Statue of Liberty was restored, the green coating was not removed. Why?

SECTION REVIEW

1. Identify the reactants and the products in the following chemical equation
$$2B(cr) + 3I_2(g) \rightarrow 2BI_3(cr)$$
2. What is the name and state of matter of each substance in the following reaction?
$$4Al(cr) + 3O_2(g) \rightarrow 2Al_2O_3(cr)$$
3. **Apply:** When making soap, if 890 g of fat react totally with 120 g of sodium hydroxide, 92 g of glycerin are formed. How many grams of soap must be formed to satisfy the law of conservation of mass?
4. **Connect to Life Science:** Identify the reactants and the products in the body cell reaction described on page 404.

☑ Recognizing Cause and Effect

Lavoisier heated mercury(II) oxide in a sealed flask. Explain the effect on Lavoisier's conclusions about the law of conservation of mass if he had used an open flask. If you need help, refer to Recognizing Cause and Effect in the **Skill Handbook** on page 679.

Skill Builder

EXTENSION

For students who have mastered this section, use the **Reinforcement** and **Enrichment** masters or other OPTIONS provided.

 PROBLEM SOLVING

Think Critically
corrosion of iron—reactants: iron and oxygen; product: hydrated iron(III) oxide
corrosion of aluminum—reactants: aluminum and oxygen; product: aluminum oxide
The coating was not removed because it protects the copper from

3 CLOSE

▶ Ask questions 1 and 2 and the **Apply** and **Connect to Life Science** questions in the Section Review.

SECTION REVIEW ANSWERS

1. reactants—B and I_2; product—BI_3
2. Al—aluminum, solid; O_2—oxygen, gas; Al_2O_3—aluminum oxide, solid
3. **Apply:** 918 g of soap
4. **Connect to Life Science:** Reactants: O_2, $C_6H_{12}O_6$
Products: CO_2, H_2O

Skill Builder

Any gas produced could escape, making the apparent mass of the products less than the mass of the reactants.

Skill Builder
ASSESSMENT
Oral: Have students explain the importance of a closed system when collecting and measuring reactants and products.

ENRICHMENT
▶ Corrosion of iron results in the need for expensive repairs. Iron reacts with oxygen in the presence of water. Give several students small pieces of different metals to moisten and leave outside. Copper, zinc, lead, aluminum, iron, magnesium, and galvanized iron could be used. Have students discuss the application of their observations to the solution of industry's oxidation problem. One side of the metal sheets could be coated with polyurethane varnish to illustrate how coatings are used to retard oxidation.

MULTICULTURAL PERSPECTIVE

The Sky Is Falling, Or Is It?
Punta Arenas, Chile is a town of 115 000 that happens to be located under an ozone hole for part of the year. In Punta Arenas, reproductive patterns have been changing in local plants and animals. Plants are turning yellow, burned by the high levels of ultraviolet radiation. The vision of some rabbits has become poor. The people worry about the possible effects of radiation on human inhabitants: skin cancer, cataracts, a weakened immune system.

PREPARATION

SECTION BACKGROUND

▶ Some ultraviolet energy has a devastating effect on the DNA molecules that control the function of living cells of many microorganisms.

1 MOTIVATE

▶ **Demonstration:** In a darkened room, use an ultraviolet lamp to show how some chemicals glow when exposed to ultraviolet light. Boxes of detergent are often printed with fluorescent inks. Discuss how ultraviolet light differs from visible light.

2 TEACH

Key Concepts are highlighted.

CONCEPT DEVELOPMENT

▶ Bring an old can of auto air-conditioner refrigerant to class to show the students. Read the list of ingredients.

PROGRAM RESOURCES

From the **Teacher Resource Package** use:

Activity Worksheets, page 5, Flex Your Brain.

Concept Mapping, pages 37-38.

Transparency Masters, pages 61-62, CFCs and Ozone.

Use **Color Transparency** number 31, CFCs and Ozone.

 **16-2** # The Hole in the Ozone Layer

New Science Words

chlorofluorocarbons (CFCs)

Objectives

▶ Describe the role of the ozone layer in protecting life on Earth.
▶ Explain the role of CFCs in the threat to the ozone layer.

How Do CFCs Affect Ozone?

Have you heard that a decrease of ozone in Earth's atmosphere has led to an increase in skin cancer? That is probably so, but it is only the beginning. Far more serious might be widespread damage to crops or destruction of life in the oceans. Normally, the ozone layer absorbs much of the ultraviolet (UV) radiation from the sun. UV radiation is invisible, high-energy waves that can harm living things.

Ozone, remember, consists of O_3 molecules. Ozone can form from ordinary oxygen, O_2, under certain conditions. Near the ground, ozone is a major pollutant in smog produced from automobile exhausts. Even in minute amounts, the ozone in smog irritates the eyes and makes breathing difficult.

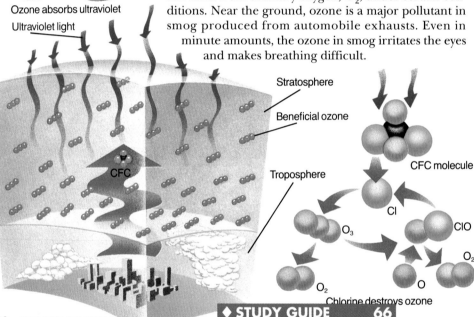

Ozone absorbs ultraviolet

Ultraviolet light

Stratosphere

Beneficial ozone

Troposphere

CFC

CFC molecule

Cl

ClO

O_3

O_2

O_2

O

Chlorine destroys ozone

OPTIONS

Meeting Different Ability Levels

For Section 16-2, use the following **Teacher Resource Masters** depending upon individual students' needs.

◆ **Study Guide Master** for all students.
● **Reinforcement Master** for students of average and above average ability levels.
▲ **Enrichment Master** for above average students.

Additional Teacher Resource Package masters are listed in any PROGRAM RESOURCES boxes that are in the section. The additional masters are appropriate for all students.

◆ **STUDY GUIDE** 66

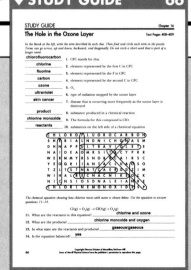

However, scientists have become concerned about the loss of more than three percent of the ozone in Earth's atmosphere. Satellite photos of Antarctica, like the one to the right, show that every year the hole in the ozone layer gets bigger. Less ozone in the stratosphere means more UV radiation can reach Earth.

Scientists have gathered evidence that ozone destruction is largely due to compounds called **chlorofluorocarbons (CFCs)**, a group of compounds of chlorine, fluorine, and carbon. Some CFCs are used in refrigeration. When CFCs are released into the air, they move into the upper atmosphere. There, UV radiation causes the CFCs to break down and release atoms of chlorine. When a chlorine atom destroys an ozone molecule, chlorine monoxide and oxygen form:

$$Cl(g) + O_3(g) \rightarrow ClO(g) + O_2(g)$$

The chlorine monoxide, ClO, then breaks apart, setting free the chlorine atom, which repeats the process. In this way, a single chlorine atom can destroy thousands of ozone molecules. The governments of 25 countries hope to totally stop the use of CFCs by the year 2000. But CFCs already in the atmosphere may continue to destroy the ozone for hundreds of years.

SECTION REVIEW

1. Why is the ozone layer in the atmosphere important?
2. Write an equation to show how a chlorine atom from a CFC destroys ozone.
3. **Connect to Earth Science:** What layer of Earth's atmosphere is closest to Earth's surface? In what layer of the atmosphere is most atmospheric ozone found?

You Decide!

Many businesses are calling for CFC recycling programs to prevent the CFCs from getting into the atmosphere. Will recycling solve the problem?

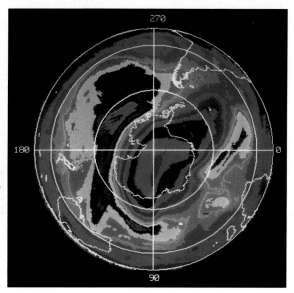

Figure 16-4. The colors in this satellite photo indicate how much ozone is present. Red shows the greatest amount of ozone; black indicates the least.

Connect to...
Physics

What is the range of wavelengths of light that are classified as ultraviolet?

SCIENCE & SOCIETY

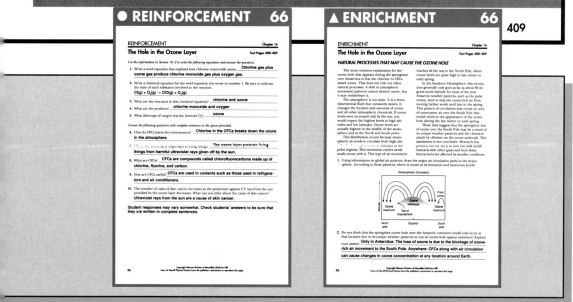

● **REINFORCEMENT** 66

▲ **ENRICHMENT** 66

CHECK FOR UNDERSTANDING
Ask questions 1 and 2 and the **Connect to Earth Science** question in the Section Review.

RETEACH
Have students draw molecules to represent the reaction in which ozone is destroyed. All bonds are covalent.

EXTENSION
For students who have mastered this section, use the **Reinforcement** and **Enrichment** masters or other OPTIONS provided.

3 CLOSE

❓ FLEX Your Brain

Use the Flex Your Brain activity to have students explore THE OZONE HOLE.

ASSESSMENT
Portfolio: Use the Flex Your Brain activity to reinforce critical-thinking and problem-solving skills. In Step 2, students might list what is harming the ozone layer.

Connect to...
Physics

Answer: 50-380 nanometers

SECTION REVIEW ANSWERS
1. It shields living things on Earth from harmful UV radiation from the sun.
2. $Cl(g) + O_3(g) \rightarrow ClO(g) + O_2(g)$
3. Connect to Earth Science: troposphere; stratosphere

YOU DECIDE!
SCIENCE & SOCIETY

Opinions will vary. Students may say that recycling would help only if it goes on indefinitely. They could consider whether it is possible for recycling to compensate for leaks.

VideoDisc

STVS: Hole in the Ozone, Disc 2, Side 1

PREPARATION

SECTION BACKGROUND

▶ Coefficients are used to balance an equation; subscripts are never changed. To change a subscript is to change the identity of a substance.

▶ A balanced chemical equation accurately represents what actually happens in a chemical reaction. The relative amounts of each substance are shown in the equation. The law of conservation of mass is observed in a balanced chemical equation not just as a formality, but because reacting substances follow this law.

1 MOTIVATE

▶ Representing balanced chemical equations can best be done using models. If you do not have commercial kits, substitute candy gum drops and toothpicks.

▶ To model the reaction on page 410, give each student four red, four white, and two black gum drops. The white ones represent silver atoms; the red ones represent hydrogen atoms; the black ones represent sulfur atoms.

▶ Have students draw an arrow on a sheet of paper. Ask them to place their models on the paper to show the balanced equation that appears at the top of page 411.

TYING TO PREVIOUS
KNOWLEDGE: Give students a simple addition problem followed by a simple multiplication problem. Inform the class that if they got both problems correct, they have the math skills needed to balance equations.

New Science Words

balanced chemical equation

Objectives

▶ Explain what is meant by a balanced chemical equation.
▶ Demonstrate how to write balanced chemical equations.

Table 16-2

ATOMS IN UNBALANCED EQUATION		
Kind of Atom	Number of Atoms $Ag + H_2S \rightarrow Ag_2S + H_2$	
Ag	1	2
H	2	2
S	1	1

Checking for Balance

Where does the tarnish on silver come from? As you read in Chapter 11, tarnish is silver sulfide, Ag_2S. It forms when sulfur-containing compounds in the air or food react with the silver. Suppose you write this chemical equation for tarnishing:

$$Ag(cr) + H_2S(g) \rightarrow Ag_2S(cr) + H_2(g)$$

Now, examine the equation. Remember that matter is never created or destroyed in a chemical reaction. Notice that one silver atom appears in the reactants, Ag + H_2S. However, two silver atoms appear in the products, Ag_2S + H_2. As you know, one silver atom can't just become two. The equation must be balanced so it shows a true picture of what takes place in the reaction. A **balanced chemical equation** has the same number of atoms of each element on both sides of the equation. To find out if this equation is balanced, make a chart like that shown in Table 16-2.

The number of hydrogen and the number of sulfur atoms are balanced. However, there are two silver atoms on the right side of the equation and only one on the left side. This equation isn't balanced. Never change subscripts of a correct formula to balance an equation. Instead, place whole number coefficients to the left of the formulas of the reactants and products so that there are equal numbers of silver atoms on both sides of the equation. If no number is written, the coefficient is one.

Choosing Coefficients

How do you find out which coefficients to use to balance an equation? This decision is a trial-and-error process. With practice, the process becomes simple to perform.

OPTIONS

Meeting Different Ability Levels

For Section 16-3, use the following **Teacher Resource Masters** depending upon individual students' needs.

◆ **Study Guide Master** for all students.

● **Reinforcement Master** for students of average and above average ability levels.

▲ **Enrichment Master** for above average students.

Additional Teacher Resource Package masters are listed in any PROGRAM RESOURCES boxes that are in the section. The additional masters are appropriate for all students.

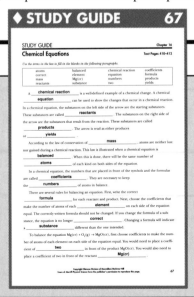

In the chemical equation for tarnishing, you found that both the sulfur atoms and the hydrogen atoms were already balanced. Putting a coefficient before those formulas that contain these atoms is not necessary at this time. So, look at the formulas containing silver atoms: Ag and Ag_2S. There are two atoms of silver on the right side and only one on the left side. If you put a coefficient of two before Ag, the equation is balanced, as shown in Table 16-3.

$$2Ag(cr) + H_2S(g) \rightarrow Ag_2S(cr) + H_2(g)$$

❸ Writing Balanced Chemical Equations

When a piece of magnesium ribbon burns in a flask of oxygen, a white powder called magnesium oxide is formed. To write a balanced chemical equation for this and most other reactions, follow these four steps:

Step 1 Describe the reaction in words, putting the reactants on the left side and the products on the right side.

magnesium plus oxygen produces magnesium oxide

Step 2 Write a chemical equation for the reaction using formulas and symbols. Review how to write formulas for compounds in Section 11-4. The formulas for elements are generally just their symbols. However, as you read in Chapter 12, some elements ordinarily exist as diatomic molecules as shown in Table 16-4. Oxygen is a diatomic molecule.

$$Mg(cr) + O_2(g) \rightarrow MgO(cr)$$

Step 3 Check the equation for atom balance. Set up a chart like Table 16-5 to help you.

The magnesium atoms are balanced, but the oxygen atoms are not. Therefore, this equation isn't balanced.

Step 4 Choose coefficients that balance the equation. Remember, never change subscripts of a correct formula to balance an equation. Try putting a coefficient of two before MgO to balance the oxygen.

$$Mg(cr) + O_2(g) \rightarrow 2MgO(cr)$$

Now there are two Mg atoms on the right side and only one on the left side. So a coefficient of two is needed before Mg also.

$$2Mg(cr) + O_2(g) \rightarrow 2MgO(cr)$$

Table 16-6 indicates that the equation is now balanced.

Table 16-3

ATOMS IN BALANCED EQUATION

Kind of Atom	Number of Atoms $2Ag + H_2S \rightarrow Ag_2S + H_2$	
Ag	2	2
H	2	2
S	1	1

Table 16-4

DIATOMIC MOLECULES

Name	Formula
Hydrogen	H_2
Oxygen	O_2
Nitrogen	N_2
Fluorine	F_2
Chlorine	Cl_2
Bromine	Br_2
Iodine	I_2

Table 16-5

ATOMS IN UNBALANCED EQUATION

Kind of Atom	Number of Atoms $Mg + O_2 \rightarrow MgO$	
Mg	1	1
O	2	1

Table 16-6

ATOMS IN BALANCED EQUATION

Kind of Atom	Number of Atoms $2Mg + O_2 \rightarrow 2MgO$	
Mg	2	2
O	2	2

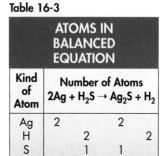

2 TEACH

Key Concepts are highlighted.

CONCEPT DEVELOPMENT

▶ Here are some helpful hints to give students to help them learn to balance equations.

1. Treat a polyatomic ion as a unit if it is not changed during a reaction.

2. If an element appears in more than one compound on the same side of the equation, leave that element until the last to balance.

3. If there is an even number of atoms of an element on one side of the equation and an odd number on the other, place a coefficient of 2 in front of the compound containing an odd number of atoms.

CHECK FOR UNDERSTANDING

Use the Mini Quiz to check for understanding.

MINI QUIZ

Use the Mini Quiz to check students' recall of chapter content.

❶ **A _____ chemical equation has the same number and kinds of atoms on each side.** *balanced*

❷ **The number placed in front of a chemical formula to balance an equation is called a(n) _____ .** *coefficient*

❸ **Balance the equation $NaBr + Cl_2 \rightarrow NaCl + Br_2$.** *$2NaBr + Cl_2 \rightarrow 2NaCl + Br_2$*

❹ **Balance the equation $Al(OH)_3 + CO_2 \rightarrow Al(HCO_3)_3$.** *$Al(OH)_3 + 3CO_2 \rightarrow Al(HCO_3)_3$*

RETEACH

Use gum drops and toothpicks or magnet-backed poster board "atoms" to build models of the molecules in equations to be balanced.

EXTENSION

For students who have mastered this section, use the **Reinforcement** and **Enrichment** masters or other OPTIONS provided.

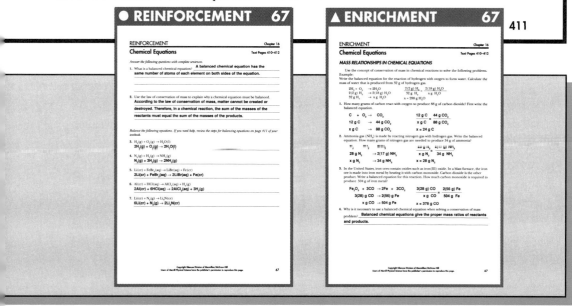

● REINFORCEMENT 67

▲ ENRICHMENT 67

411

MINI-Lab

Materials: cards, markers

Teaching Tips

▶Represent the teams as the combined formula, G₂F₂C. In this form, the equation is analogous to a chemical equation.

Answers to Questions

▶Coefficients represent only numbers of units (teams, ions, molecules). Each unit contains a specific number of components.

▶It shows that particles can come together to make a unit having different properties.

MINI-Lab

ASSESSMENT

Performance: Have students use their team equation to illustrate the law of conservation of mass.

---

3 CLOSE

▶ Ask questions 1 and 2 and the **Apply** and the **Connect to Earth Science** questions in the Section Review.

SECTION REVIEW ANSWERS

1. to accurately show what takes place in a reaction and to show that mass is conserved

2. (a) $2Cu(cr) + S(cr) \rightarrow Cu_2S(cr)$
(b) $2Na(cr) + 2H_2O(l) \rightarrow$
$2NaOH(aq) + H_2(g)$

3. Apply: $4Fe(cr) + 3O_2(g) \rightarrow$
$2Fe_2O_3(cr)$

4. Connect to Earth Science:
$CaCO_3(cr) + 2HCl(aq) \rightarrow CO_2 +$
$CaCl_2 + H_2O$

Skill Builder

$Ca(NO_3)_2(aq) + Na_2CO_3(aq) \rightarrow$
$2NaNO_3(aq) + CaCO_3(cr)$
The $CaCO_3$ precipitates as a white solid.

Skill Builder

ASSESSMENT

Performance: Have students use their balanced chemical equation and the periodic table on pages 258-259 to illustrate the law of conservation of mass.

Table 16-7

Kind of Atom	Number of Atoms $AgNO_3 + NaCl \rightarrow AgCl + NaNO_3$	
Ag	1	1
N	1	1
O	3	3
Na	1	1
Cl	1	1

ATOMS IN AgCl FORMATION

MINI-Lab

Must the sums of reactant and product coefficients be equal?
Obtain a marked card from your teacher. With others in the class, assemble the cards to represent a basketball team. Written as a chemical equation, the result would appear as: 2 guards + 2 forwards + 1 center = 1 team. **Hypothesize** as to why the sums of the coefficients on each side of the equation aren't equal. How is this equation like a typical chemical equation?

Skill Builder

Work through the following example.

When a silver nitrate solution is mixed with a sodium chloride solution, a white, insoluble solid is formed. This solid is silver chloride. The sodium nitrate formed remains in solution. Write a balanced equation for this reaction.

Step 1 Describe the reaction in words:
aqueous silver nitrate plus aqueous sodium chloride produces solid silver chloride plus aqueous sodium nitrate

Step 2 Write the chemical equation:
$AgNO_3(aq) + NaCl(aq) \rightarrow AgCl(cr) + NaNO_3(aq)$

Step 3 Check the equation for balance:
There are already equal numbers of each element on both sides of the equation. This equation is balanced.

Step 4 Choose coefficients:
This equation is balanced, so no coefficients other than one are needed.

SECTION REVIEW

1. What are two reasons for balancing equations for chemical reactions?
2. Write balanced chemical equations for the following reactions: (a) copper metal plus sulfur produces solid copper(I) sulfide, (b) sodium metal plus water produces aqueous sodium hydroxide plus hydrogen gas.
3. **Apply:** Rust is formed when iron is exposed to oxygen in the air. Assume rust is iron (III) oxide. Write a balanced equation for this reaction.
4. **Connect to Earth Science:** One way to test for carbonate ores is to add dilute acid to the sample and test for production of carbon dioxide gas. Balance the following equation. $CaCO_3(cr) + HCl(aq) \rightarrow CO_2(g) + CaCl_2(cr) + H_2O(l)$

☑ **Observing and Inferring**

Hard water contains ions of calcium, magnesium, and/or iron. When Na_2CO_3 is added to hard water, it is softened because these ions are removed as a white solid. For Mg, this reaction may occur:
$MgCl_2(aq) + Na_2CO_3(aq) \rightarrow MgCO_3(cr) + 2NaCl(aq)$
Write a balanced equation showing how water containing $Ca(NO_3)_2$ could be softened. If you need help, refer to Observing and Inferring in the **Skill Handbook** on page 678.

OPTIONS

INQUIRY QUESTIONS

▶ To purify air in space vehicles, lithium peroxide, Li_2O_2, is reacted with waste CO_2 to form Li_2CO_3 and O_2. Write a balanced equation. $2Li_2O_2 (cr) + 2CO_2(g) \rightarrow 2Li_2CO_3(cr) + O_2(g)$

▶ Ammonium nitrate, NH_4NO_3, an important fertilizer, is produced by treating nitric acid, HNO_3, with ammonia gas, NH_3. Write a balanced equation. $NH_3(g) + HNO_3(l) \rightarrow NH_4NO_3(cr)$

PROGRAM RESOURCES

From the **Teacher Resource Package** use:
Activity Worksheets, page 131, MINI-Lab: Must the sums of reactant and product coefficients be equal?
Cross-Curricular Connections, page 22, Writing Chemical Equations.
Transparency Masters, pages 63-64, Chemical Equations.
Use **Color Transparency** number 32, Chemical Equations.
Use **Laboratory Manual 33,** Reaction Rates and Temperature.

Types of Chemical Reactions

Objectives

▶ Describe four types of chemical reactions using their generalized formulas.

▶ Classify various chemical reactions by type.

Classifying Chemical Reactions

There are hundreds of kinds of chemical reactions. Rather than try to memorize them, it is easier to group reactions by their similarities. You can learn a great deal about a reaction by comparing it to others in its group.

The system of classification is based upon the way the atoms rearrange themselves in a chemical reaction. Most reactions are either synthesis, decomposition, single displacement, or double displacement reactions.

Synthesis Reactions

One of the easiest reaction types to recognize is a synthesis reaction. In a **synthesis reaction,** two or more substances combine to form another substance. The generalized formula for this reaction type is:

$$A + B \rightarrow AB$$

The reaction in which hydrogen burns in oxygen to form water is an example of a synthesis reaction:

$$2H_2(g) + O_2(g) \rightarrow 2H_2O(g)$$

This reaction between hydrogen and oxygen occurs between two elements. One type of rocket fuel is hydrogen, which burns explosively in oxygen when the rocket is fired.

Sulfuric acid is one of the most important manufactured chemicals. The final step in making sulfuric acid is a synthesis reaction between two compounds, sulfur trioxide and water:

$$SO_3(g) + H_2O(l) \rightarrow H_2SO_4(aq)$$

New Science Words

synthesis reaction
decomposition reaction
single displacement reaction
double displacement reaction
precipitate

Connect to... Life Science

Both plants and animals can form proteins. What type of compounds are the basic units in proteins? Which of the four major types of reactions forms proteins?

Did You Know?

The novocaine that dentists use to deaden pain is a stable, easy-to-synthesize isomer of cocaine with few side effects.

What type of reaction is the burning of hydrogen in oxygen?

SECTION 16-4

PREPARATION

SECTION BACKGROUND

▶ Chemists are able to predict the products of decomposition reactions because the reactions often follow known patterns. For example, some metal carbonates produce metal oxides and carbon dioxide gas. Some metal chlorates yield metal chlorides and oxygen gas. Some metal hydroxides decompose into metal oxides and water.

PREPLANNING

▶ To prepare for Activity 16-1, safely dilute hydrochloric acid by adding concentrated acid to water and prepare the small pieces of metal.

1 MOTIVATE

▶ **Demonstration:** A decomposition reaction that can be easily performed is the decomposition of sugar. Place some sucrose in a test tube and heat it until it burns. Carbon remains. Water vapor and carbon dioxide gas are released. Compare this reaction to what happens when sugar is digested and then metabolized in a living cell.

Connect to... Life Science

Answer: amino acids; synthesis

VideoDisc

STVS: Straw as Feed, Disc 2, Side 1

ASSESSMENT—ORAL

▶ Two components of smog are NO and NO_2. When NO_2 is exposed to sunlight it forms NO and O atoms. What type of reaction is this? *decomposition*

▶ A lab technician was estimating the amount of material needed for the production of sulfuric acid. The technician used the equation $SO_2 + O_2 \rightarrow SO_3$. What type of equation is it and why was the technician unable to correctly estimate the amounts of chemicals needed? *The reaction is synthesis. The equation is not balanced.*

PROGRAM RESOURCES

From the **Teacher Resource Package** use:
Critical Thinking/Problem Solving, page 22, Metal Corrosion.
Science and Society, page 20, Fuel Cells.
Transparency Masters, pages 65-66, Types of Chemical Reactions.
Use **Color Transparency** number 33, Types of Chemical Reactions.
Use **Laboratory Manual 34,** Chemical Reactions.

2 TEACH

Key Concepts are highlighted.

CONCEPT DEVELOPMENT

▶ **Demonstration:** A single displacement reaction can be shown by placing a piece of mossy zinc metal in dilute sulfuric acid. Hydrogen gas is produced along with zinc sulfate, which remains dissolved in the water. **CAUTION:** *Acid is corrosive. Hydrogen gas is flammable.*

REVEALING MISCONCEPTIONS

▶ Students often confuse elements in their pure form with elements in compounds. For example, students believe that copper in copper sulfate is the same as copper metal. Both use the symbol Cu. Point out that one form is an ion, whereas the other form is an uncharged atom.

CROSS CURRICULUM

▶ **Language Arts:** Have students look up the word *decompose* in a dictionary. Have them write a paragraph relating decomposition reactions to a possible solution to the problem of solid waste disposal caused by the closing of landfills.

CHECK FOR UNDERSTANDING

Use the Mini Quiz to check for understanding.

MINI QUIZ

Use the Mini Quiz to check students' recall of chapter content.

1️⃣ **What type of reaction occurs when two substances combine to form one?** *synthesis*

2️⃣ **What type of reaction occurs when one substance breaks down into two?** *decomposition*

3️⃣ **An insoluble solid that forms from a reaction in a solution is a(n)** _____ . *precipitate*

Figure 16-5. Because sulfuric acid is used to manufacture so many different products, more of it is produced than any other chemical.

Figure 16-6. Copper in a wire replaces silver in silver nitrate, forming a blue solution of a copper nitrate. The silver forms on the wire.

OPTIONS

Meeting Different Ability Levels

For Section 16-4, use the following **Teacher Resource Masters** depending upon individual students' needs.

◆ **Study Guide Master** for all students.

● **Reinforcement Master** for students of average and above average ability levels.

▲ **Enrichment Master** for above average students.

Additional Teacher Resource Package masters are listed in any PROGRAM RESOURCES boxes that are in the section. The additional masters are appropriate for all students.

In the next chapter you will learn more about the importance of sulfuric acid and other acids.

Decomposition Reactions

The opposite of a synthesis reaction is a decomposition reaction. The drawing below illustrates this relationship.

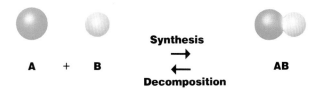

In a **decomposition reaction,** one substance breaks down, or decomposes, into two or more simpler substances. The generalized formula for this type of reaction is:

$$AB \rightarrow A + B$$

Most decomposition reactions require the use of heat, light, or electricity. The decomposition of water by an electric current produces hydrogen and oxygen.

$$2H_2O(l) \xrightarrow[\text{current}]{\text{electric}} 2H_2(g) + O_2(g)$$

Displacement Reactions

A **single displacement reaction** occurs when one element replaces another in a compound. There are two generalized formulas for this type of reaction.

In the first case, A replaces B as follows:

$$A + BC \rightarrow AC + B$$

In the second case D replaces C as follows:

$$D + BC \rightarrow BD + C$$

In Figure 16-5, a copper wire is put into a solution of silver nitrate. Because copper is a more active metal than silver, it replaces the silver, forming a blue copper(II) nitrate solution. The silver forms as an insoluble solid.

If a zinc strip is put into a copper(II) nitrate solution, solid copper forms.

$$Zn(cr) + Cu(NO_3)_2(aq) \rightarrow Zn(NO_3)_2(aq) + Cu(cr)$$

Zinc replaced the copper, so zinc must be a more chemically active metal than copper, as shown in Table 16-8.

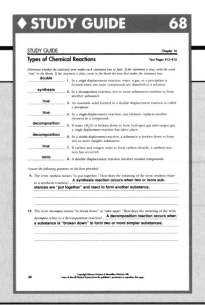

◆ **STUDY GUIDE** 68

A **double displacement reaction** takes place if a precipitate, water, or a gas forms when two ionic compounds in solution are combined. A **precipitate** is an insoluble compound formed during this type of reaction. In a double displacement reaction, the positive ion of one compound replaces the positive ion of the other compound to form two new compounds. The generalized formula for this type of reaction is:

$$AB + CD \rightarrow AD + CB$$

The reaction of silver nitrate with sodium chloride is an example of this type of reaction. A precipitate—silver chloride—is formed. The chemical equation is:

$$AgNO_3(aq) + NaCl(aq) \rightarrow AgCl(cr) + NaNO_3(aq)$$

You have seen just a few examples of chemical reactions classified into types. Many more reactions of each type occur around you.

SECTION REVIEW

1. Classify the following reactions by type:
   (a) $2KClO_3(cr) \rightarrow 2KCl(cr) + 3O_2(g)$
   (b) $CaBr_2(aq) + Na_2CO_3(aq) \rightarrow CaCO_3(cr) + 2NaBr(aq)$
   (c) $Zn(cr) + S(cr) \rightarrow ZnS(cr)$
   (d) $2Li(cr) + FeBr_2(aq) \rightarrow 2LiBr(aq) + Fe(cr)$
2. **Apply:** The copper bottoms of some cooking pans turn black after being used. The copper reacts with oxygen forming black copper(II) oxide. Write a balanced chemical equation for this reaction.
3. **Connect to Earth Science:** One method used to obtain gold from its ore involves forming a gold compound, then recovering the gold by using zinc. Balance the following equation and identify the reaction type.
   $Au(CN)_2{}^-(aq) + Zn(cr) \rightarrow Au(cr) + Zn(CN)_4{}^{2-}$

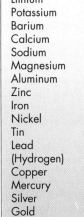

Table 16-8

ACTIVITY SERIES OF METALS

Lithium	**Most active**
Potassium	
Barium	
Calcium	
Sodium	
Magnesium	
Aluminum	
Zinc	
Iron	
Nickel	
Tin	
Lead	
(Hydrogen)	
Copper	
Mercury	
Silver	
Gold	**Least active**

☒ Hypothesizing

Group 1 metals replace hydrogen in water in reactions that are often very violent. A sample equation for one reaction is: $2K(cr) + 2HOH(l) \rightarrow 2KOH(aq) + H_2(g)$.

Use Table 16-8 to help you hypothesize about why these metals are often stored in kerosene. If you need help, refer to Hypothesizing in the **Skill Handbook** on page 682.

Skill Builder

● REINFORCEMENT 68   ▲ ENRICHMENT 68

RETEACH

Students usually learn to balance equations and classify reactions only through drill and practice. Provide additional equations to balance and classify. Most introductory chemistry texts and problem-solving books are good sources.

EXTENSION

For students who have mastered this section, use the **Reinforcement** and **Enrichment** masters or other OPTIONS provided.

3 CLOSE

▶ Ask question 1 and the **Apply** and **Connect to Earth Science** questions in the Section Review.

SECTION REVIEW ANSWERS

1. (a) decomposition; (b) double displacement; (c) synthesis; (d) single displacement

2. Apply: $2Cu(cr) + O_2(g) \rightarrow 2CuO(cr)$

3. Connect to Earth Science: $2Au(CN)_2^-(aq) + Zn(cr) \rightarrow 2Au(cr) + Zn(CN)_4^{2-}(aq)$; single displacement

Skill Builder

Evidence that these metals are very active is their position near the top of the activity series. Because they are very active, Group 1 metals will react with water vapor and oxygen in the air. Therefore they must not come in contact with air.

Skill Builder
ASSESSMENT

Oral: Have students explain why it might be useful to write water as HOH in a chemical equation.

ACTIVITY 16-1

OBJECTIVE: Design and carry out an experiment to show how to analyze and compare reaction results.

Time: 45 minutes; to shorten time, the hydrochloric acid could be premeasured and poured into test tubes for students.

PROCESS SKILLS applied in this activity are **observing, measuring, comparing,** and **inferring.**

PREPARATION
Dilute (0.1M) HCl may be prepared by adding 9 mL of concentrated HCl to 1 L of distilled water. **CAUTION:** *Avoid fumes of and direct contact with HCl.* Assemble small, identified samples of magnesium, zinc, copper, lead, aluminum, tin, and silver for testing.

Cooperative Learning: Use the Science Investigation Group strategy in teams of three. Have each student demonstrate one of the tests to the others and then pool resources to draw conclusions and answer questions.

SAFETY
Caution students to be careful around HCl. Avoid skin contact and fumes. Immediately wash any affected area with water. Wear goggles and aprons at all times. Do not allow students to test for the presence of hydrogen.

THINKING CRITICALLY
If an oxide forms, students may be comparing the reactivity of the oxide, not the metal, with the acid. The metal could be cleaned with sandpaper immediately before adding the sample to the acid.

TEACHING THE ACTIVITY
*Refer to the **Activity Worksheets** for additional information and teaching strategies.*
Troubleshooting: If the zinc is old, there may be no immediate reaction visible. Warming the tube between hands or in warm water may help.

DESIGNING AN EXPERIMENT
Metal Activity

One way to determine which of two substances is more chemically active is to place each of the substances in contact with another substance. The results can then be compared. Try this activity to investigate the ability of some metals to react with an acid.

Getting Started
Think about the description of a single displacement reaction. What may be used as evidence that the reaction has taken place? What factors would need to be controlled?

Thinking Critically
Some metals will react with oxygen in the air to form an oxide coating on their surface. If you were *comparing* the activity of some metals, how would an oxide coating on one of the samples affect your results? How could you prevent this?

Materials
Your cooperative group will use:
- test tubes, all the same size
- test-tube rack
- 5 mL of dilute hydrochloric acid, HCl, for each metal to be tested
- 10-mL graduated cylinder
- wooden splint
- metal samples

CAUTION: *Handle HCl with care. Report any spills immediately.*

Try It!
---

1. Choose several samples of different metals. Be sure each sample is labeled so that the metal is identified. You will test each for its ability to react with dilute HCl.

2. For each metal to be tested, measure 5 mL of dilute HCl into a test tube.
3. Make a data table in which to *record your observations* for each of the metals.
4. Carefully add a metal sample to each test tube that contains HCl.
5. Test for the presence of hydrogen gas by asking your teacher to collect a small amount of any gas produced and to test it with a burning splint.
6. Rank the metals you tested, least active to most active, based on the amount of hydrogen gas produced when reacted with HCl.

Summing Up/Sharing Results
- *Compare* your list with those of other groups and make a class activity list of all metals that were tested.
- Write balanced chemical equations for these reactions between metals and hydrochloric acid.

Going Further!
What could you do to make your comparisons more exact?

SUMMING UP/SHARING RESULTS
- Have students compare their classroom list to the activity list on page 415.
- Chemical equations should reflect that any metal more active than hydrogen would displace hydrogen from the acid. Metals less active than hydrogen would not react with the acid.

GOING FURTHER!
Accept any reasonable answers. One possible answer would be to make the metal samples of uniform size.

Activity
ASSESSMENT
Performance: To further assess students' understanding of activity, see USING LAB SKILLS, Question 12, on page 422.

PROGRAM RESOURCES
From the **Teacher Resource Package** use: **Activity Worksheets,** pages 124-125, Activity 16-1: Metal Activity.

Energy and Chemical Reactions 16-5

Objectives

▶ Differentiate between an exothermic reaction and an endothermic reaction.
▶ Describe the effects of catalysts and inhibitors on the speed of chemical reactions.

New Science Words

endothermic reactions
exothermic reactions
catalyst
inhibitor

Energy Changes in Chemical Reactions

Did you ever watch the explosion of dynamite? An explosion results from a very rapid chemical reaction. In all chemical reactions, energy is either released or absorbed. This energy can take many forms. It might be in the form of heat, light, sound, or even electricity. The explosion of dynamite produces heat, light, and sound energy as shown in the photo.

Where does the energy to be released or absorbed come from? When most chemical reactions take place, some chemical bonds in the reactants must be broken. To break chemical bonds, energy must be provided. In order for products to be produced, new bonds must be formed. Bond formation releases energy.

Endothermic Reactions

Sometimes, more energy is required to break bonds than to form new ones in a chemical reaction. In these reactions, called **endothermic reactions,** energy must be provided for the reaction to take place.

When some endothermic reactions proceed, so much heat is absorbed that their containers feel cold to the touch. In other endothermic reactions, so little heat is absorbed that you would need a thermometer to determine that a temperature change has occurred.

An endothermic reaction is frequently used to obtain a metal from its ore. For example, aluminum metal is

Connect to...
Life Science

Read about ADP and ATP. These important biological compounds help supply the energy needed to run many reactions in your body. Which molecule, ADP or ATP, stores more energy?

16-5 ENERGY AND CHEMICAL REACTIONS **417**

SECTION 16-5

PREPARATION

SECTION BACKGROUND

▶ Exothermic reactions generally take place spontaneously. Endothermic reactions are generally not spontaneous.
▶ A system in nature tends to go from a state of higher energy to a state of lower energy.
▶ Most heterogeneous catalysts work by adsorbing one of the reactants on the catalyst's surface.

PREPLANNING

▶ For Activity 16-2, obtain sand and manganese dioxide.

1 MOTIVATE

Ask your students to describe how they feel when they have a fever. Ask them why the body gets hot. Guide the students' thinking toward the making and breaking of chemical bonds with the associated release of energy. Some of this energy is released in the form of heat, which raises the body temperature.

VideoDisc

STVS: Grain-Dust Explosions, Disc 2, Side 1

Connect to...
Life Science

Answer: ATP

Skill Builder

This is the answer to the Skill Builder on page 419.

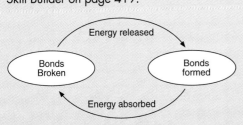

Skill Builder
ASSESSMENT
Oral: Have students explain what is happening in terms of bonding if a reaction in a solution in a beaker makes the beaker feel cold.

2 TEACH

Key Concepts are highlighted.

CONCEPT DEVELOPMENT

▶ **Demonstration:** To show the effect of a catalyst, dissolve 25 g of potassium sodium tartrate in 300 mL of very hot water in a 600-mL beaker. Then add 100 mL of six percent hydrogen peroxide to the beaker and heat to 85°C. Nothing happens until 3 grams of cobalt chloride, the catalyst, are added and stirred. The beaker may overflow, so place it on a tray.

CHECK FOR UNDERSTANDING

Use the Mini Quiz to check for understanding.

MINI QUIZ

Use the Mini Quiz to check students' recall of chapter content.

1 When more energy is required to break bonds than is released in forming bonds, the reaction will be _____ . *endothermic*

2 If energy is given off, a reaction is said to be _____ . *exothermic*

3 How does a catalyst affect the rate of a chemical reaction? *increases it*

4 A catalyst in a living organism is called a(n) _____ . *enzyme*

5 How does an inhibitor affect the rate of a chemical reaction? *decreases it*

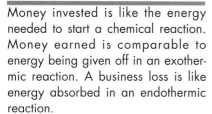

In Your JOURNAL

Money invested is like the energy needed to start a chemical reaction. Money earned is comparable to energy being given off in an exothermic reaction. A business loss is like energy absorbed in an endothermic reaction.

Figure 16-7. The refining of ores to produce useful metals frequently involves an endothermic reaction.

obtained by passing an electric current through molten aluminum ore.

$$2Al_2O_3 \overset{\text{electrical}}{\underset{\text{energy}}{\rightarrow}} 6Al + 3O_2$$

In this case, electrical energy, not thermal energy, provides the energy needed to keep the reaction going.

Figure 16-8. The burning of wood is an example of an exothermic reaction. Energy is released in the form of heat and light.

In Your JOURNAL

In your Journal, explain how the profit or loss in an investment or business deal is like the loss or gain of energy in a chemical reaction.

How do enzymes affect reactions in living organisms?

Exothermic Reactions

In many chemical reactions, less energy is required to break old bonds than is released when new bonds form. In these reactions, called **exothermic reactions,** some **2** form of energy is given off by the reaction. In many instances, the heat given off may cause the reaction mixture to feel hot.

The burning of wood and the explosion of dynamite are exothermic reactions. They are exothermic because they give off energy as the reaction proceeds. Rusting is also exothermic, but the reaction proceeds so slowly that it is difficult to detect any temperature change.

Catalysts and Inhibitors

Some reactions are too slow to be useful. To speed up these reactions you can add a catalyst. A **catalyst** is a sub- **3** stance that speeds up a chemical reaction without itself being permanently changed. When you add a catalyst to a reaction, you end up with the same amount of the catalyst that you started with.

Certain proteins known as enzymes act as catalysts in living organisms. Enzymes allow reactions to occur at **4** faster rates and lower temperatures than would otherwise be possible. Without these enzymes, life as we know it would not be possible.

Some reactions need to be slowed down. The food preservatives BHT and BHA slow down the spoilage of certain foods. BHT and BHA are inhibitors. Any substance that slows down a reaction is called an **inhibitor.** **5**

Using catalysts and inhibitors are just a few of the ways scientists control chemical reactions.

418 CHEMICAL REACTIONS

OPTIONS

Meeting Different Ability Levels

For Section 16-5, use the following **Teacher Resource Masters** depending upon individual students' needs.

◆ **Study Guide Master** for all students.

● **Reinforcement Master** for students of average and above average ability levels.

▲ **Enrichment Master** for above average students.

Additional Teacher Resource Package masters are listed in any **PROGRAM RESOURCES** boxes that are in the section. The additional masters are appropriate for all students.

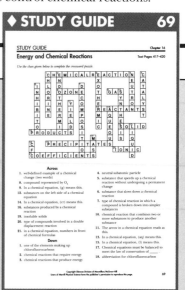

TECHNOLOGY

Catalytic Converters

The exhaust systems of cars today are equipped with catalytic converters that use rhodium and platinum as the catalysts. These catalysts speed up reactions of three types of toxic compounds given off by cars. Catalytic converters change unburned hydrocarbons, carbon monoxide, and nitrogen oxides into harmless compounds.

Two types of reactions are catalyzed. In one type of reaction, oxygen is added. Adding oxygen converts carbon monoxide to carbon dioxide, and unburned hydrocarbons to carbon dioxide and water. In the other type of reaction, oxygen is removed. Removing oxygen converts nitrogen oxides to nitrogen.

Think Critically: Why is it not necessary to add more rhodium and platinum to a catalytic converter as these substances are used?

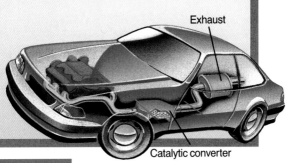

Exhaust

Catalytic converter

TECHNOLOGY

For more information on catalytic converters, read "They Forgot More Chemistry Than I Ever Knew" by Dennis Simanaitis, *Road and Track*, May 1985, page 154.

Think Critically: Rhodium and platinum are catalysts and are therefore not consumed.

RETEACH

Discuss how homes are heated, cars are fueled, and cooking is done. Have students identify where exothermic chemical reactions play a role.

EXTENSION

For students who have mastered this section, use the **Reinforcement** and **Enrichment** masters or other OPTIONS provided.

SECTION REVIEW

1. What is the difference between exothermic and endothermic reactions?
2. Oxygen is produced when potassium chlorate is heated. What is true about manganese dioxide if it is a catalyst for this reaction?
3. **Apply:** Suppose you wanted to develop a product for warming people's hands at outdoor winter events. Would you choose an exothermic reaction or an endothermic reaction to use in your device? Why?
4. **Connect to Life Science:** Chymotrypsin is an enzyme that helps humans digest protein. In what two ways does this enzyme help your body digest protein?

3 CLOSE

▶ Ask questions 1 and 2 and the **Apply** and **Connect to Life Science** questions in the Section Review.

SECTION REVIEW ANSWERS

1. An exothermic reaction releases energy. An endothermic reaction absorbs energy.

2. The MnO_2 would not be used up in the reaction.

3. Apply: You would choose an exothermic reaction so that the heat given off could be used to warm cold hands.

4. Connect to Life Science: Protein digests faster and at body temperature.

Note: Skill Builder answer is on page 417.

☑ Concept Mapping

Construct a concept map to show the relationship between energy and bond formation and bond breakage. If you need help, refer to Concept Mapping in the **Skill Handbook** on pages 684 and 685.

Skill Builder

● **REINFORCEMENT** 69   ▲ **ENRICHMENT** 69

ACTIVITY 16-2
30 minutes

OBJECTIVE: Operationally define a catalyst and **observe** its action.

PROCESS SKILLS applied in this activity:
▶ **Observing** in Procedure Step 3.
▶ **Inferring** in Analyze Questions 3, 4, and 5.
▶ **Operationally defining** in Conclude and Apply Question 6.

TEACHING THE ACTIVITY

Troubleshooting: Students should have the glowing splint ready when the MnO_2 is placed in the peroxide solution. Demonstrate the technique for students. Hydrogen peroxide must be freshly opened.
▶ Blood or small pieces of raw liver contain an enzyme that catalyzes the breakdown of H_2O_2. Save some blood from a beef roast and demonstrate its catalytic activity to students by substituting it for MnO_2.
▶ Repeat the activity as a demonstration by using larger test tubes and larger quantities.
▶ Ordinary 3 percent H_2O_2 available from drugstores should work well if it is fresh.

PROGRAM RESOURCES

From the **Teacher Resource Package** use:

Activity Worksheets, pages 126-127, Activity 16-2: Catalyzed Reaction.

A balanced chemical equation provides much information about a chemical reaction, but it doesn't tell you about the rate of the reaction. Temperature, concentration, and physical state may all affect the rate of reaction. In this activity, you will investigate the role of another influencing factor—a catalyst.

Materials
- 3 medium-sized test tubes
- test-tube stand
- 15 mL hydrogen peroxide, H_2O_2
- graduated cylinder
- small plastic spoon
- sand
- manganese dioxide, MnO_2
- wooden splint
- hot plate
- beaker of hot water

CAUTION: *Hydrogen peroxide can irritate skin and eyes. Wear goggles and apron.*

Procedure
1. Set three test tubes in a test-tube stand. Pour 5 mL of hydrogen peroxide into each tube.
2. Place about 1/4 spoonful of sand in tube 2 and the same amount of manganese dioxide in tube 3.
3. In the presence of some substances that act as catalysts, H_2O_2 decomposes rapidly, producing oxygen gas, O_2. A glowing splint placed in O_2 will relight. Test the gas produced in any of the tubes as follows. Light a wooden splint, blow out the flame, and insert the glowing splint into the tube.
4. Place all three tubes in a beaker of hot water. Heat on a hot plate until all the remaining H_2O_2 is driven away and there is no liquid left in the tubes.

Analyze
1. What changes did you *observe* when the solids were added to the tubes?
2. In which tube was oxygen produced rapidly, and how do you know?

3. Which substance, sand or manganese dioxide, caused the rapid production of gas from the hydrogen peroxide?
4. How did you identify the gas produced?
5. What remained in each tube after the hydrogen peroxide was driven away?

Conclude and Apply
6. What are two characteristics common to catalysts? Which substance in this activity has both characteristics?
7. The word *catalyst* has uses beyond chemistry. If a person who is added to a basketball team acts as a catalyst, what effect is that person likely to have on the team?

ANSWERS TO QUESTIONS

1. tube with H_2O_2 and sand—no change; tube with H_2O_2 and MnO_2—rapid bubbling
2. Oxygen was produced rapidly in the tube containing H_2O_2 and MnO_2. Bubbles appear and the glowing splint test for oxygen was positive.
3. MnO_2
4. The glowing splint burst into flame.
5. tube with H_2O_2 alone—nothing; tube with H_2O_2 and sand—sand; tube with H_2O_2 and MnO_2—MnO_2
6. A catalyst speeds up a chemical reaction.

A catalyst is not permanently changed by a reaction; MnO_2.
7. The person energizes the team and causes the team to be more active than it would normally be.

Activity
ASSESSMENT
Portfolio: Have students define the term *control.* Then, using examples from the activity, have them write out the role of the control in helping make conclusions in an experiment.

SUMMARY

16-1: Chemical Changes in Matter
1. In a chemical reaction, the reactants are changed into the products, which are different substances.
2. According to the law of conservation of mass, the mass of the reactants in a chemical reaction equals the mass of the products.
3. A chemical equation is a shorthand way of describing a chemical reaction using symbols, coefficients, and formulas.

16-2: Science and Society: The Hole in the Ozone Layer
1. The ozone layer helps protect life on Earth by absorbing much of the ultraviolet radiation from the sun.
2. In the upper atmosphere, CFCs release atoms of chlorine that destroy ozone molecules.

16-3: Chemical Equations
1. A balanced chemical equation has the same number of atoms of each element on both sides of the equation.
2. The final step in the process of balancing a chemical equation is the choice of the correct coefficients.

16-4: Types of Chemical Reactions
1. Generalized formulas are used to describe four reaction types—synthesis, decomposition, single displacement, and double displacement.
2. Many specific chemical reactions can be classified as one of four types.

16-5: Energy and Chemical Reactions
1. In an exothermic reaction, energy is released; in an endothermic reaction, energy is absorbed.
2. A catalyst increases the speed of a chemical reaction; an inhibitor decreases the speed of a chemical reaction.

KEY SCIENCE WORDS

a. balanced chemical equation
b. catalyst
c. chemical reaction
d. chlorofluorocarbon (CFC)
e. coefficient
f. decomposition reaction
g. double displacement reaction
h. endothermic reaction
i. exothermic reaction
j. inhibitor
k. precipitate
l. product
m. reactant
n. single displacement reaction
o. synthesis reaction

UNDERSTANDING VOCABULARY

Match each phrase with the correct term from the list of Key Science Words.

1. energy is given off
2. has same number of atoms on both sides
3. energy is absorbed
4. an element replaces another in a compound
5. slows down a reaction rate
6. substance breaks down into simpler substances
7. two ionic compounds react to form a precipitate, water, or a gas
8. two or more substances combine
9. compound that contains chlorine, fluorine, and carbon
10. well-defined example of chemical change

CHEMICAL REACTIONS **421**

SUMMARY

Have students read the summary statements to review the major concepts of the chapter.

UNDERSTANDING VOCABULARY

1.	i	6.	f
2.	a	7.	g
3.	h	8.	o
4.	n	9.	d
5.	j	10.	c

ASSESSMENT
Portfolio
Encourage students to place in their portfolios one or two items of what they consider to be their best work. For each item, ask students to explain why that item was chosen and what they learned from it. Items might be selected from the following.
- Skill Builder explanation, p. 407
- Flex Your Brain, p. 409
- Activity 16-1 observations and answers, p. 416

Performance
Additional performance assessments may be found in *Performance Assessment* and *Science Integration Activities* that accompany **Merrill Physical Science.** Performance Task Assessment Lists and rubrics for evaluating these activities and other products generated throughout the chapter can be found in Glencoe's *Performance Assessment in Middle School Science.*

OPTIONS

ASSESSMENT
To assess student understanding of material in this chapter, use the resources listed.

COOPERATIVE LEARNING
Consider using cooperative learning in the THINK AND WRITE CRITICALLY, APPLY, and MORE SKILL BUILDERS sections of the Chapter Review.

PROGRAM RESOURCES
From the **Teacher Resource Package** use:
Chapter Review, pages 35-36.
Chapter and Unit Tests, pages 105-108, Chapter Test.

CHAPTER

REVIEW

CHECKING CONCEPTS

1. d	6. a
2. b	7. c
3. a	8. d
4. a	9. b
5. c	10. c

USING LAB SKILLS

ASSESSMENT

Use these alternate lab exercises to assess students' understanding of skills used in this chapter.

11. The products of this double displacement reaction are NaCl and $Fe(OH)_3$. There is the same number of each type of atom on each side of the equation, which shows that mass was conserved.

12. The first two equations show that A is more active than B, so A would replace B in a compound. Also, in a compound, A will have an oxidation number of 2+, and B will have an oxidation number of 1+.

$A(cr) + 2BCl(aq) \rightarrow ACl_2(aq) + 2B(cr)$

THINK AND WRITE CRITICALLY

13. Equations will vary, but for all equations, the number of atoms of each element in the reactants must equal the number of atoms of each element in the products.

14. Zinc will replace copper in $Cu(NO_3)_2$ because zinc is the more active metal. Copper metal will form. No reaction will occur in the other case.

15. $PbSO_4(cr)$

16. Changing subscripts changes the identity of a substance.

17. $2CuO(cr) \rightarrow 2Cu(cr) + O_2(g)$

CHECKING CONCEPTS

Choose the word or phrase that completes the sentence.

1. An example of a chemical reaction is _____.
  a. bending   **c.** melting
  b. evaporation   **d.** photosynthesis

2. Lavoisier's experiments gave examples of the law of _____.
  a. chemical reaction
  b. conservation of mass
  c. coefficients
  d. gravity

3. An element that is more _____ will replace another element in a compound.
  a. active   **c.** inhibiting
  b. catalytic   **d.** soluble

4. In the expression $4Ca(NO_3)_2$, the 4 is a _____.
  a. coefficient   **c.** subscript
  b. formula   **d.** symbol

5. BHA is an example of a(n) _____.
  a. catalyst   **c.** inhibitor
  b. formula   **d.** CFC

6. If a substance is dissolved in water, _____ follows its formula in an equation.
  a. (aq)   **c.** (g)
  b. (cr)   **d.** (l)

7. In tarnishing, Ag_2S is a(n) _____.
  a. catalyst   **c.** product
  b. inhibitor   **d.** reactant

8. In the burning of hydrogen, O_2 is a(n) _____.
  a. catalyst   **c.** product
  b. inhibitor   **d.** reactant

9. _____ is an allotrope of oxygen, O_2, that absorbs UV radiation.
  a. H_2 **b.** O_3 **c.** Cl   **d.** Cl_2

10. If a substance is a solid, _____, follows its formula in an equation.
  a. (l)   **b.** (g)   **c.** (cr)   **d.** (aq)

USING LAB SKILLS

11. In the MINI-Lab on page 405, the reactants were $FeCl_3$ and NaOH. Name the products. Which type of reaction is this reaction? How would balancing the equation show the law of conservation of mass?

12. In Activity 16-1 on page 416, a chemically active metal replaced a less active metal in a compound. Use the following two equations to complete and balance the third equation. The symbols A and B represent metals.

$A(cr) + 2HCl(aq) \rightarrow ACl_2(aq) + H_2(g)$
$B(cr) + HCl(aq) \rightarrow$ no reaction
$A(cr) + BCl(aq) \rightarrow ?$

THINK AND WRITE CRITICALLY

Answer the following questions in your Journal using complete sentences.

13. Write a balanced chemical equation and use it to explain the law of conservation of mass.

14. If Zn is placed in a solution of $Cu(NO_3)_2$, and Cu is placed in a $Zn(NO_3)_2$ solution, what reaction takes place? Explain.

15. $PbCl_2$ and Li_2SO_4 react to form LiCl and what other substance?

16. Why should subscripts not be changed to balance an equation?

17. Write a balanced equation for the decomposition of copper(II) oxide.

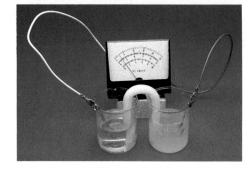

18. Chromium is produced by reacting its oxide with aluminum. If 76 g of Cr_2O_3 and 27 g of Al react to form 51 g of Al_2O_3 how many grams of Cr are formed?
19. Propane, $C_3H_8(g)$, burns in oxygen to form carbon dioxide and water vapor. Write a balanced equation for burning propane.
20. $Cl(g) + O_3(g) \rightarrow ClO(g) + O_2(g)$ plays a role in ozone destruction. What is the source of the monatomic chlorine, Cl, in this reaction?
21. In one reaction of a catalytic converter, nitrogen(II) oxide reacts with hydrogen to form ammonia and water vapor. Write a balanced equation for this reaction.
22. If lye, NaOH, is put in water, the solution gets hot. What kind of energy process is this?

MORE SKILL BUILDERS

If you need help, refer to the Skill Handbook.

1. **Observing and Inferring:** What belongs in the parentheses in the following double displacement reaction?

   $BaCl_2(aq) + K_2CO_3(aq) \rightarrow BaCO_3(\ ) + 2KCl(aq)$

2. **Recognizing Cause and Effect:** Sucrose, table sugar, is a disaccharide. This means that sucrose is composed of two simple sugars chemically bonded together. Sucrose can be separated by digestion or by heating it in an aqueous sulfuric acid solution. Find out what products are formed by breaking up sucrose. What role does the acid play?

3. **Interpreting Data:** When 46 g of sodium were exposed to dry air, 62 g of sodium oxide formed over a period of time. How many grams of oxygen from the air were used?

4. **Outlining:** Make an outline with the general heading "Chemical Reactions." Include the

four types of reactions, with a description and example of each.

5. **Concept Mapping:** The arrow in a chemical equation tells the reaction direction. Some reactions are reversible, because they don't go in only one direction. Sometimes the bond formed is weak, and a product breaks apart as it's formed. A double arrow used in the equation indicates this reaction. Fill in the cycle, using the words *product(s)* and *reactant(s)*. In the blanks in the center, fill in the formulas for the substances appearing in the reversible reaction:

$$H_2(g) + I_2(g) \rightleftarrows 2HI(g)$$

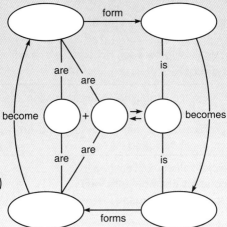

PROJECTS

1. Research common chemical reactions that occur safely in your home. Demonstrate one of these reactions. Tell what type of reaction it is and how it is used. Write a balanced equation for the reaction.
2. Investigate the label on a package of cold cuts. Research as many of the chemicals added as possible. Is anything added as an inhibitor? Report on your findings.

CHEMICAL REACTIONS **423**

18. $76 \text{ g } Cr_2O_3 + 27 \text{ g } Al = 51 \text{ g } Al_2O_3 + X \text{ g } Cr$
   mass of Cr = 52 g
19. $C_3H_8(g) + 5O_2(g) \rightarrow 3CO_2(g) + 4H_2O(g)$
20. decomposition of ClO and CFCs
21. $2NO(g) + 5H_2(g) \rightarrow 2NH_3(g) + 2H_2O(g)$
22. exothermic

MORE SKILL BUILDERS

1. **Observing and Inferring:** The symbol *cr* would be used. A precipitate must be formed.
2. **Recognizing Cause and Effect:** The simple sugars glucose and fructose are formed. The acid is a catalyst.
3. **Interpreting Data:** $46 \text{ g } Na + X \text{ g } O_2 = 62 \text{ g } Na_2O$
   mass of O_2 = 16 g
4. **Outlining:** Sample outline:
   I. Chemical reactions
     A. Synthesis
       1. Two or more substances react to form another substance.
       2. Example: $2H_2(g) + O_2(g) \rightarrow 2H_2O(g)$
     B. Decomposition
       1. A substance breaks down into other substances.
       2. Example: $2HI(g) \rightarrow H_2(g) + I_2(g)$
     C. Single displacement
       1. One element replaces another in a compound.
       2. Example: $Zn(cr) + 2AgNO_3(aq) \rightarrow 2Ag(cr) + Zn(NO_3)_2(aq)$
     D. Double displacement
       1. Takes place when two ionic compounds combine and water, a gas, or a precipitate is formed.
       2. Example: $NaCl(aq) + AgNO_3(aq) \rightarrow AgCl(cr) + NaNO_3(aq)$

5. **Concept Mapping:**

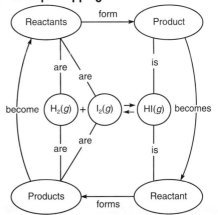

CHAPTER SECTION	OBJECTIVES	ACTIVITIES
17-1 Acids and Bases (2 days)	1. **Define** acid and base. 2. **Describe** the characteristic properties of acids and bases. 3. **List** the names, formulas, and uses of some common acids and bases. 4. **Relate** the processes of ionization and dissociation to the formation of acids and bases.	**MINI-Lab:** Do acids and bases conduct an electric current? p. 428
17-2 Strength of Acids and Bases (2 days)	1. **Explain** what determines the strength of an acid or a base. 2. **Differentiate** strength and concentration. 3. **Define** pH. 4. **Describe** the relationship between pH and the strength of an acid or a base.	**Activity 17-1:** Strong and Weak Acids, p. 437
17-3 Acid Rain Science & Society (1 day)	1. **Describe** the factors contributing to the formation of acid rain. 2. **Discuss** the problems acid rain is causing and how these problems might be solved.	
17-4 Acids, Bases, and Salts (2 days)	1. **Describe** a neutralization reaction. 2. **Explain** what a salt is and how salts form. 3. **Differentiate** soaps and detergents. 4. **Explain** how esters are made and what they are used for.	**Activity 17-2:** Be a Soda Scientist, p. 446
Chapter Review		

ACTIVITY MATERIALS

FIND OUT	ACTIVITIES		MINI-LABS
Page 425 soda water marble chips balance filter paper funnel heat lamp or portable hair dryer	**17-1 Strong and Weak Acids, p. 437** typing paper (22 cm × 28 cm), marked with rectangles thick cardboard (22 cm × 28 cm), marked with rectangles scissors 2 test tubes 2 medicine droppers graduated cylinder dilute hydrochloric acid (HCl) dilute acetic acid (CH_3COOH)	pH paper timer, with second hand **17-2 Be a Soda Scientist, p. 446** 2 test tubes 2 medicine droppers graduated cylinder carbonated beverage, colorless, 2 types dilute sodium hydroxide (NaOH) phenolphthalein indicator, 1%	**Do acids and bases conduct an electric current? p. 428** conductivity tester orange juice cleaner containing ammonia small jars or beakers

CHAPTER FEATURES	TEACHER RESOURCE PACKAGE	OTHER RESOURCES
Technology: *Book Decay,* p. 429 **Skill Builder:** *Comparing and Contrasting,* p. 433	**Ability Level Worksheets** ◆ *Study Guide,* p. 70 ● *Reinforcement,* p. 70 ▲ *Enrichment,* p. 70 **Activity Worksheets,** pp. 5, 139 **Concept Mapping,** pp. 39, 40 **Transparency Masters,** pp. 67, 68	**Color Transparency 34,** Acids in Solutions **STVS:** Disc 4, Side 2
Skill Builder: *Concept Mapping,* p. 436	**Ability Level Worksheets** ◆ *Study Guide,* p. 71 ● *Reinforcement,* p. 71 ▲ *Enrichment,* p. 71 **Activity Worksheets,** pp. 133, 134 **Critical Thinking/Problem Solving,** p. 23 **Transparency Masters,** pp. 69, 70	**Color Transparency 35,** The pH Scale **Laboratory Manual 35,** Acids, Bases, and Indicators **Science Integration Activity 17**
You Decide! p. 439	**Ability Level Worksheets** ◆ *Study Guide,* p. 72 ● *Reinforcement,* p. 72 ▲ *Enrichment,* p. 72	**STVS:** Disc 6, Side 2
Problem Solving: *Julio's Experiment,* p. 441 **Skill Builder:** *Interpreting Data,* p. 445	**Ability Level Worksheets** ◆ *Study Guide,* p. 73 ● *Reinforcement,* p. 73 ▲ *Enrichment,* p. 73 **Activity Worksheets,** pp. 5, 135, 136 **Cross-Curricular Connections,** p. 23 **Science and Society,** p. 21 **Technology,** pp. 15, 16	**Laboratory Manual 36,** Acid Rain **STVS:** Disc 2, Side 2
Summary Think & Write Critically Key Science Words Apply Understanding Vocabulary More Skill Builders Checking Concepts Projects Using Lab Skills	**ASSESSMENT RESOURCES** **Chapter Review,** pp. 37, 38 **Chapter Test,** pp. 109-112 **Unit Test,** pp. 113, 114 **Performance Assessment in** Middle School Science	**Chapter Review Software** **Test Bank** **Alternate Assessment** **Performance Assessment**

◆ Basic   ● Average   ▲ Advanced

ADDITIONAL MATERIALS

SOFTWARE	AUDIOVISUAL	BOOKS/MAGAZINES
Acid Rain, Diversified Educational Enterprises, Inc. *Acid-Base Theories,* Queue. *Acids and Bases,* J and S Software. *Acids and Bases,* Queue. *Introduction to General Chemistry: pH, Acids, and Bases in Water;* EduQuest.	*The Acid Assault,* Video, Journal Films. *Acid Rain, Video,* Film Fair Communications. *Acid Rain,* Video, AIT. *Acid Rain: No Simple Solution,* Video, Insight Media. *Acids,* Laserdisc, Journal Films. *Acids and Bases,* Video, Britannica. *Acids, Bases, and Salts,* Video, Coronet. *Handling Dangerous Chemicals: Acids,* Video, Coronet. *Handling Dangerous Chemicals: Bases,* Video, Coronet.	Gutnik, Martin J. *Experiments That Explore: Acid Rain.* Brookfield, CT: Millbrook Press, 1992. Stewart. *How to Understand Acid-Base: A Quantitative Acid Base Primer for Biology and Medicine.* NY: Elsevier Science Publishing Co., Inc., 1981. Turck, Mary. *Acid Rain.* NY: Crestwood House, 1990.

17

ACIDS, BASES, AND SALTS

THEME DEVELOPMENT: Systems and interactions as a theme of the textbook are developed through a presentation of the Arrhenius system of acids and bases. The interactions that occur between an acid and base to produce a salt and the corrosive interactions between an acid and other substances are developed in the chapter.

CHAPTER OVERVIEW

▶ **Section 17-1:** Acids and bases are defined in this section. Their properties are described and explained according to the theories of ionization and dissociation. Common acids and bases are named.

▶ **Section 17-2:** This section explains what determines acid or base strength. The concept of pH and how it relates to the strength of an acidic or basic solution is developed in detail.

▶ **Section 17-3: Science and Society:** Probable causes of acid rain are presented along with possible solutions to this environmental problem.

▶ **Section 17-4:** This section describes how a salt is formed in a neutralization reaction. The section also introduces the student to a saponification reaction and explains the difference between a soap and a detergent.

CHAPTER VOCABULARY

acid	pH
indicator	acid rain
dehydrating agent	plankton
pickling	neutralization
base	salt
hydronium ion	titration
strong acid	soaps
weak acid	saponification
strong base	detergents
weak base	ester

424

OPTIONS

For Your Gifted Students

▶ Students can do research to determine where in the U.S. and Canada there are indications of forest or wildlife damage as a result of acid rain. They can also research the level of damage at different altitudes. Have students draw a map of North America. The map can be color coded to indicate areas of dense population, industrialization, forest damage, and wildlife damage, including damage to bodies of water.

For Your Mainstreamed Students

▶ Special effort should be made to have mainstreamed students perform or assist in Activity 17-2. Some students could carry out their own titrations of vinegar, lemon juice, and orange juice to compare the acidity with that of carbonated beverages. Mainstreamed students might like to perform the suggested extension of this activity in which they compare the acidity of different brands and types of beverages.

Do you know what is causing this marble statue to deteriorate at an alarming rate?

FIND OUT!

Do this simple activity to find out how a solution can change a rock.

Marble is mostly calcite, $CaCO_3$, a mineral found in many rocks. Normal rainwater does not have much effect on calcite. However, in places where there is a lot of air pollution, certain chemical pollutants dissolve in rainwater and change its chemical makeup. This rainwater-pollutant solution reacts with calcite, causing it to weaken and eventually crumble.

Let's simulate this reaction. Mass about 5.0 g of marble chips and place them in a beaker. Next add about 50 mL of soda water, which is similar in some ways to the rainwater-pollutant solution. *Observe* the mixture for several minutes. Then stir the mixture vigorously and let it sit until it

stops moving. Pour the mixture through a filter paper. Dry the remaining marble chips and mass them again. Has their mass changed? How do your conclusions relate to acid rain?

Gearing Up
Previewing the Chapter

Use this outline to help you focus on important ideas in the chapter.

Section 17-1   Acids and Bases
▶ Properties of Acids
▶ Common Acids
▶ Properties of Bases
▶ Common Bases
▶ Solutions of Acids and Bases

Section 17-2   Strength of Acids and Bases
▶ Strong and Weak Acids and Bases
▶ pH of a Solution

Section 17-3   Science and Society
Acid Rain
▶ What Is Acid Rain?

Section 17-4   Acids, Bases, and Salts
▶ Neutralization
▶ Salts
▶ Titration
▶ Soaps and Detergents
▶ Organic Acids and Esters

Previewing Science Skills
▶ In the **Skill Builders,** you will compare and contrast, make a concept map, and interpret data.
▶ In the **Activities,** you will use models, hypothesize, measure, observe, and infer.
▶ In the **MINI-Lab,** you will observe and infer.

What's next?

You have seen that contact with some solutions can produce a change in a mineral. Now find out what kinds of solutions produce such changes.

425

PREPARATION

SECTION BACKGROUND
▶ This text limits the discussion of acids and bases to the Arrhenius theory. The theories proposed by Bronsted, Lowry, and Lewis build on the Arrhenius theory and extend the definitions of acids and bases.
▶ Binary acids contain only two elements. Their names end in -ic acid:. The names of the salts of these acids end in the suffix -ide.
▶ Ternary acids contain hydrogen, oxygen, and one other element. Names of oxy-acids end in suffix -ic or -ous, and those of their salts end in -ate and -ite.

PREPLANNING
▶ To prepare for the MINI-Lab on page 428, obtain a conductivity tester, orange juice, and ammonia cleaner.

1 MOTIVATE

▶ **Demonstration:** To establish a need to know more about acids, bases, and salts, prepare two solutions. The acid solution is made by adding 0.6 mL of concentrated (18M) sulfuric acid to 99.4 mL of water. Add 10 mL of this solution to 90 mL of water to prepare a 0.01M acid solution. Separately prepare a base solution by adding 0.32 g of $Ba(OH)_2 \cdot 8H_2O$ to 100 mL of water. This gives a 0.01M solution.

Add the 0.01M sulfuric acid solution to the beaker of a conductivity apparatus so that the beaker is half-filled with acid. Place the electrodes in the beaker. While stirring the solution, add the 0.01M $Ba(OH)_2$ solution dropwise. Have students observe both the salt formation and the decreasing conductivity as fewer ions are present in the solution. Barium sulfate is insoluble.

17-1 Acids and Bases

New Science Words
acid
indicator
dehydrating agent
pickling
base
hydronium ion

Objectives
▶ Define *acid* and *base*.
▶ Describe the characteristic properties of acids and bases.
▶ List the names, formulas, and uses of some common acids and bases.
▶ Relate the processes of ionization and dissociation to the formation of acids and bases.

Figure 17-1. The indicator methyl red turns red in the presence of an acid.

Properties of Acids

What comes to mind when you hear the word *acid*? Do you think about something that has a sour taste? Do you think of a substance that can burn your skin, or even burn a hole through a piece of metal? Although many acids are not strong enough to burn through metal, or even burn your skin, these characteristics are, indeed, properties of some acids.

Acids make up a very important group of compounds. All of these compounds contain hydrogen. When an acid is dissolved in water, some of the hydrogen is released as hydrogen ions (H^+). Thus, an **acid** is a substance that produces hydrogen ions (H^+) in solution. It is the presence of the H^+ ions that gives acids their characteristic properties. A brief description of these acidic properties follows.

Acids taste sour. The familiar sour taste of such foods as citrus fruits and tomatoes is due to the presence of acids. *However, taste should **NEVER** be used to test for the presence of acids.* Some acids can produce painful burns and damage to tissues.

Acids are electrolytes. Because they always contain some ions, acid solutions conduct electricity.

Acids are corrosive. Some acids react strongly with certain metals, seeming to "eat away" the metals as metallic compounds and hydrogen gas are produced.

Acids react with certain compounds, called indicators, to produce a predictable change in color. An **indicator** is an organic compound that changes color in an acid or a base.

◆ **STUDY GUIDE** 70

STUDY GUIDE   Chapter 17
Acids and Bases   Text Pages 426–433

Use the words in the box to fill in the blanks in the paragraphs below.

corrosive	bitter	hydroxide ions
sour	electrolytes	metals
slippery	hydrogen ions	electricity

An acid is a substance that produces ___hydrogen ions___ in solution. Acids taste ___sour___. Some acids can produce painful burns and damage tissues. Since acid solutions conduct ___electricity___, acids are electrolytes. Since acids seemingly "eat away" certain ___metals___; acids are corrosive.

A base is a substance that produces ___hydroxide ions___ in solution. In solution, bases feel ___slippery___ and have a ___bitter___ taste. Like acids, strong bases are ___corrosive___ and can produce painful burns. Bases are also ___electrolytes___.

Circle the term or phrase in parentheses that makes each statement true.
1. A substance that produces hydrogen ions in solution is (an acid, a base).
2. The familiar sour taste of citrus fruits and tomatoes is caused by the presence of (acids, bases) in these foods.
3. A substance that can remove water from materials is a (fertilizer, dehydrating agent).
4. The process by which oxides and other impurities are removed from metal surfaces by dipping the metals in hydrochloric acid is called (pickling, hydrating).
5. A substance that produces hydroxide ions in solution is (an acid, a base).
6. A hydrogen ion is indicated by (H+, OH−).
7. The notation for a hydroxide ion is (OH−, OH+).
8. An organic compound that changes color in an acid or a base is (an indicator, alcohol).
9. The ion formed by the bonding of a hydrogen ion to a water molecule is called a (hydroxyl group, hydronium ion).
10. The formula for a hydronium ion is (H₃O+, OH−).

70

Copyright Glencoe Division of Macmillan/McGraw-Hill
Users of Merrill Physical Science have the publisher's permission to reproduce this page.

OPTIONS

Meeting Different Ability Levels
For Section 17-1, use the following **Teacher Resource Masters** depending upon individual students' needs.
◆ **Study Guide Master** for all students.
● **Reinforcement Master** for students of average and above average ability levels.
▲ **Enrichment Master** for above average students.
Additional Teacher Resource Package masters are listed in any PROGRAM RESOURCES boxes that are in the section. The additional masters are appropriate for all students.

Common Acids

Many familiar items that you use every day contain acids. Acids are components of many foods. The gastric juices in your stomach contain acid that helps to break down food during digestion. Car batteries, some flashlight batteries, and some household cleaners also contain acids. Table 17-1 gives the names and formulas of a few common acids and tells where they are found.

In addition to these acids that you come in contact with every day, certain acids are vital to industry. The four most important industrial acids are sulfuric acid, phosphoric acid, nitric acid, and hydrochloric acid.

Sulfuric acid, H_2SO_4, is the most widely used chemical in the world. Almost 30 billion kilograms of this acid are produced in the United States annually. More than half of this acid is used by industries in this country. The rest is exported.

Sulfuric acid is a thick, oily liquid. Because of its use in automobile storage batteries, sulfuric acid is sometimes called battery acid. Most sulfuric acid produced is

❸

Did You Know?

In the 8th century, a mixture of nitric acid and hydrochloric acid was known as *aqua regia*, meaning "kingly water," because it was able to dissolve gold.

Table 17-1

SOME COMMON ACIDS		
Name	Formula	Where Found
Acetic acid	CH_3COOH	Vinegar
Acetylsalicylic acid	$HOOC-C_6H_4-OOCCH_3$	Aspirin
Ascorbic acid (vitamin C)	$H_2C_6H_6O_6$	Citrus fruits, tomatoes, vegetables
Boric acid	H_3BO_3	Eyewash solutions
Carbonic acid	H_2CO_3	Carbonated drinks
Hydrochloric acid	HCl	Gastric juices in stomach
Nitric acid	HNO_3	Making fertilizers, explosives (TNT)
Phosphoric acid	H_3PO_4	Making detergents, fertilizers
Sulfuric acid	H_2SO_4	Car batteries, making fertilizers

2 TEACH

Key Concepts are highlighted.

CONCEPT DEVELOPMENT

▶ Students will retain information that they have experienced. Each of the properties of acids can be easily demonstrated.

▶ **Demonstration:** Acids taste sour. Cut a lemon into thin slices and then cut the slices into smaller pieces. Distribute these to each student to taste.

▶ **Demonstration:** Acids are electrolytes. Materials to make a lemon or potato clock are available from commercial science suppliers. Cu/Zn electrodes connected to a digital clock are placed 1 cm apart in a lemon, and the clock operates. A voltmeter can be used to show that the electrodes in a lemon do produce voltage.

▶ **Demonstration:** Acids are corrosive. Place a piece of magnesium ribbon in a petri dish on the overhead projector. Add dilute HCl dropwise to the metal. The class will be able to see the hydrogen gas being evolved. Try the demonstration with warm lemon juice.

▶ **Demonstration:** Acids cause indicators to change color. Place a few milliliters of water containing universal indicator in a petri dish on the overhead projector. Add vinegar to the petri dish dropwise. The color changes will be visible to the entire class. Blue litmus paper can also be used.

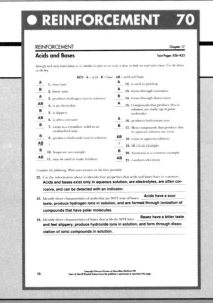
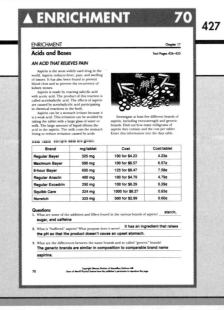
427

Figure 17-2. Sulfuric acid reacts with the hydrogen and oxygen in sugar, removing them as water and leaving only carbon.

used in the manufacture of fertilizer. It is also used in petroleum refining, steel manufacture, and in the production of plastics, drugs, dyes, and other acids.

Another important use for sulfuric acid is as a dehydrating agent. A **dehydrating agent** is a substance that can remove water from materials. As Figure 17-2 illustrates, organic compounds can be dehydrated by removing hydrogen and oxygen in the form of water from the compounds, leaving only carbon. When sulfuric acid comes in contact with human tissue, this dehydrating action produces painful burns.

Phosphoric acid, H_3PO_4, is another acid important to industry in the United States. Eighty percent of the phosphoric acid produced is used to make fertilizers.

Dilute phosphoric acid has a slightly sour but pleasant taste and is used in soft drinks. It is also used to make phosphates, which are added to detergents to enhance their cleaning power. Unfortunately, these phosphates can cause pollution problems in lakes and streams.

Nitric acid, HNO_3, is best known for its use in making explosives. However, like sulfuric and phosphoric acids, most of the nitric acid produced is used in the manufacture of fertilizers. Concentrated nitric acid is a colorless liquid. When exposed to light, the acid slowly changes to a yellow liquid. This change in color occurs because some of the nitric acid decomposes into nitrogen dioxide, NO_2, which is a brownish gas. Nitric acid can cause serious burns on human skin. Contact with light-colored skin causes yellow stains. This yellow color is a test for protein.

What is a dehydrating agent?

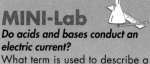

MINI-Lab

Do acids and bases conduct an electric current?
What term is used to describe a substance that, when dissolved in water, conducts an electric current? Carefully place the electrodes of a conductivity tester into a glass of orange juice. *Observe* the results. What acids are present in orange juice? (**CAUTION:** *Do not taste the juice.*) Try the same conductivity procedure with an ammonia cleaner. **CAUTION:** *Do not inhale ammonia fumes.* Did this solution conduct electricity? What base is present in the cleaner? What are the most important ions formed in aqueous solutions of acids? Of bases?

428 ACIDS, BASES, AND SALTS

OPTIONS

Hydrogen chloride, HCl, is a colorless gas. When this gas is dissolved in water, hydrochloric acid is formed. Both HCl fumes and the ions that form in solution can harm human tissue.

Hydrochloric acid, when used in industry to clean surfaces of materials, is commonly called muriatic acid. Large quantities of the acid are used by the steel industry for pickling. **Pickling** is a process in which oxides and other impurities are removed from metal surfaces by dipping the metals in hydrochloric acid.

⑤

Figure 17-3. Pickling removes impurities from metal surfaces.

T E C H N O L O G Y

Book Decay

New technologies often bring new problems. When paper made from flax or cotton was replaced by paper made from wood fiber, the life expectancy of the paper was severely reduced. Paper made from wood fiber must be treated with sizing. When this paper is exposed to heat and humidity, the sizing reacts to form an acid. The acid then decomposes the wood fiber in the paper. If the acid is not neutralized or removed, the paper will last only about 50 years.

The Library of Congress currently contains 16 million books and manuscripts that are in danger of acid decay. Several technologies are being developed to remove acid from paper. One involves vacuum drying the books and adding a magnesium compound to neutralize the acid. A second method dips books in a mixture of Freon and magnesium oxide. The most exotic technique exposes the books to diethylzinc (DEZ) gas for neutralization. DEZ, however,

is explosive, making the process hard to engineer. Recently, manufacturers have started to produce paper that is alkaline and, therefore, more durable.

Think Critically: What could be done to reduce the rate of paper deterioration while scientists search for an efficient and inexpensive neutralization technique?

17-1   ACIDS AND BASES   **429**

► The river Rio Vinagre, in the volcanic area of Mexico, contains 0.11% sulfuric acid and 0.095% hydrochloric acid. The pH of the water is 2, hence the name.

CONCEPT DEVELOPMENT

► **Demonstration:** Test a wet bar of soap with litmus paper to show the class that it is basic. Have students wash their hands with the soap and feel how slippery it is when wet. Ask how many students have slipped in the tub or shower. Ask how they can prevent falls and continue to use soap in the shower.

► Have students bring in samples of toothpaste. Test each with litmus paper to determine if it is basic. Soap is present in some toothpastes.

► **Demonstration:** Use a conductivity checker to show students that basic solutions, such as soapy water, conduct electricity due to the presence of ions.

► **Demonstration:** Metal oxides react with water to form basic solutions. Burn a few centimeters of magnesium ribbon. **CAUTION:** *Do not look directly at the bright light.* Place the white powder, MgO, in a test tube and add a milliliter of water. Heat to near boiling. Test the resulting $Mg(OH)_2$ with an indicator such as litmus.

► After the above demonstration, remind students that lime, CaO, is used in cement mixes. The dust can settle on skin and react with perspiration to form $Ca(OH)_2$, which can result in chemical burns.

CROSS CURRICULUM

► **Language Arts:** The old name for sulfuric acid was oil of vitriol. Have students use a dictionary to look up *vitriol* and *vitriolic*. Ask them to use *vitriolic* in a sentence.

EcoTip

Many detergents and household cleaners contain phosphates that pollute lakes, streams, and groundwater when released in wastewater. Read labels carefully and select cleansing agents that do not contain phosphates.

What properties do acids and bases have in common?

Figure 17-4. Many household materials contain bases.

There are several methods for making phosphoric, nitric, and hydrochloric acids. But one general method can be used to make all three acids. This method involves reacting concentrated sulfuric acid with a compound containing the negative ion of the desired acid.

$$Ca_3(PO_4)_2(cr) + 3H_2SO_4(aq) \rightarrow 2H_3PO_4(aq) + 3CaSO_4(cr)$$
$$NaNO_3(cr) + H_2SO_4(aq) \rightarrow HNO_3(g) + NaHSO_4(aq)$$
$$NaCl(cr) + H_2SO_4(aq) \rightarrow HCl(g) + NaHSO_4(aq)$$

Properties of Bases

Like acids, bases are an important group of chemical compounds. Although acids and bases seem to have some features in common, the two groups are actually quite different.

A **base** is a substance that produces hydroxide ions (OH^-) in solution. Does this OH combination look familiar? You may recall from Chapter 13 that an alcohol has a hydroxyl group, $-OH$, as part of its molecule. This hydroxyl group is not an ion and should not be confused with the OH^- ions that are present in all bases. Because alcohols do not produce OH^- ions, alcohols are not classified as bases.

The hydroxide ions present in all basic solutions are negative ions, whereas the hydrogen ions present in acidic solutions are positive ions. This difference in charge accounts for some of the differences between acids and bases.

In the pure, undissolved state, most bases are crystalline solids. In solution, bases feel slippery and have a bitter taste. Like acids, strong bases are corrosive, and contact with the skin may result in severe burns and tissue damage. *Therefore, taste and touch should **NEVER** be used to test for the presence of a base.* Basic solutions are electrolytes. This property is due to the presence of ions in the solutions. Finally, bases react with indicators to produce predictable changes in color.

430 ACIDS, BASES, AND SALTS

OPTIONS

INQUIRY QUESTIONS

► **Why do your eyes burn when you get shampoo in them?** *One reason is that the shampoo may contain a base, which irritates the eyes.*

► **Write an equation to show how calcium hydroxide breaks apart in solution to form ions.** $Ca(OH)_2(cr) \rightarrow Ca^{2+}(aq) + 2OH^-(aq)$

Common Bases

Many household products contain bases. Most soaps, for example, contain bases, which explains their bitter taste and slippery feel. Table 17-2 contains the names and formulas of some common bases and tells how the bases are used.

Table 17-2

COMMON BASES AND THEIR USES		
Name	**Formula**	**Uses**
Aluminum hydroxide	$Al(OH)_3$	Deodorant, antacid
Calcium hydroxide	$Ca(OH)_2$	Leather production, manufacture of mortar and plaster
Magnesium hydroxide	$Mg(OH)_2$	Laxative, antacid
Sodium hydroxide	NaOH	Drain cleaner, soap making

Although you won't find it listed in the table, the most widely used base is ammonia, NH_3. Pure ammonia is a colorless gas with a very distinctive, irritating odor. It can be extremely irritating to nasal passages and lungs if it is inhaled. When ammonia gas is dissolved in water, some of its molecules react with water molecules, forming ammonium ions (NH_4^+) and hydroxide ions.

$$NH_3(g) + H_2O(l) \rightarrow NH_4^+(aq) + OH^-(aq)$$

The solution containing ammonium ions and hydroxide ions is called ammonia water. Dilute ammonia water is an excellent household cleaning agent. Ammonia is also used as a fertilizer and in the production of rayon, nylon, and nitric acid.

Another widely used base is calcium hydroxide, $Ca(OH)_2$. Commonly called caustic lime, this base is a white crystalline powder that is only slightly soluble in water. Calcium hydroxide is used in the production of mortar and plaster and to "sweeten" acidic soils.

Sodium hydroxide, NaOH, is a strong, very corrosive base. This compound, commonly called lye, dissolves readily in water in an extremely exothermic process. Sodium hydroxide reacts with such organic materials as oils and fats to produce soap and glycerine. This property enables it to be an effective oven cleaner and drain cleaner.

Figure 17-5. Ammonia is an important ingredient of these products.

17-1 ACIDS AND BASES **431**

Use the Mini Quiz to check for understanding.

MINI QUIZ

Use the Mini Quiz to check students' recall of chapter content.

6 What do scientists call a substance that produces hydroxide ions in a water solution? *a base*

7 Give the name and formula for the ions that form when ammonia gas reacts with water. *ammonium, NH_4^+, and hydroxide, OH^-, ions*

8 What is the symbol and charge of a hydronium ion? *H_3O^+*

9 When an ionic compound is pulled apart by the solvent, the process is called _____ . *dissociation*

RETEACH

Demonstration: In a fume hood, add a small piece of copper wire to 2 mL of 6M nitric acid in a test tube fitted with a one-hole rubber stopper and delivery tube. Collect the dense gas by upward displacement of air in a small bottle that contains 8 mL of water that has universal indicator added. Close the bottle and shake the water as you observe the color change. Ask students to explain what has happened to cause the color change. You can relate this to acid rain, which is presented in Section 17-3.

EXTENSION

For students who have mastered this section, use the **Reinforcement** and **Enrichment** masters or other OPTIONS provided.

Figure 17-6. When an acid dissolves in water, hydrogen ions from the acid combine with water molecules to produce hydronium ions.

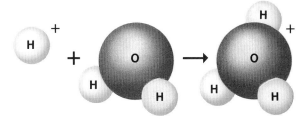

What is a hydronium ion?

Solutions of Acids and Bases

Substances such as HCl, HNO_3, and H_2SO_4 are often referred to as acids. But it is actually their ability to produce H^+ ions in water solutions that classifies them as acids. This ionization process is shown in Figure 17-7, using HCl as an example. When a polar molecule, such as HCl, is dissolved in water, the negatively charged area of nearby water molecules attracts the positively charged area of the polar molecule. The H^+ is removed from the polar molecule and a **hydronium ion,** H_3O^+ is formed, as is shown in Figure 17-6. Thus, *acid* describes any compound that can be ionized in water to form hydronium ions.

When an organic acid ionizes, the H at the end of the —COOH group combines with water to form the hydronium ion.

Compounds that can form hydroxide ions, OH^-, in solution are classified as bases. If you examine Table 17-2 closely, you would find that each substance listed contains OH within its formula. Except for ammonia, inorganic compounds that produce bases in aqueous solution are ionic compounds. That is, they are already made up of

Figure 17-7. When hydrogen chloride gas dissolves in water, it ionizes to produce hydronium ions and chloride ions.

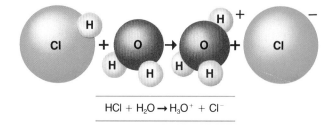

$$HCl + H_2O \rightarrow H_3O^+ + Cl^-$$

OPTIONS

ASSESSMENT—ORAL

▶ **What ion is responsible for acidic properties?** *hydrogen ion or hydronium ion*

▶ **What ion is responsible for basic properties?** *hydroxide ion*

▶ **An organic acid is classified as a carboxylic acid and contains the –COOH group. Acetic acid has the formula CH_3COOH. Which of the four hydrogens present in the formula is responsible for the acidic properties?** *The hydrogen in the –COOH group.*

ENRICHMENT

▶ Have a student use a dictionary to determine how *aqua regia* is prepared and how it is used. It is a mixture of nitric and hydrochloric acids that will dissolve gold or platinum.

▶ Have students collect and bring to class newspaper and magazine articles that deal with acids or bases. They may bring in articles on a toxic waste site, an acid spill on the highway, the economic importance of acids and bases, or the industrial or other practical uses of acids and bases.

ions. As the equation below shows, when such a compound dissolves, the ions dissociate, or pull apart, and exist as individual ions in solution. These substances release OH^- ions in water. If a solution contains more OH^- ions than H_3O^+ ions, it is referred to as a basic solution.

$$NaOH(cr) \xrightarrow{H_2O} Na^+(aq) + OH^-(aq)$$

Ammonia is a polar compound. In solution, ionization takes place when the ammonia molecule attracts a hydrogen atom from a water molecule, as shown in Figure 17-8.

The next time you use any of the products described in this section, stop and think for a minute. Think about what properties the product has and why it has them.

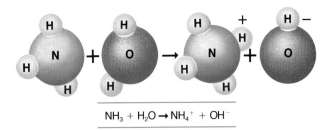

$$NH_3 + H_2O \rightarrow NH_4^+ + OH^-$$

SECTION REVIEW

1. Why are acids and bases electrolytes?
2. Name three important acids and three important bases and describe some uses of each.
3. **Apply:** When you are stung by a bee or a wasp, the insect injects formic acid, HCOOH, into your body. What kind of acid is formic acid? How do you know? Write an equation showing how formic acid ionizes.
4. **Connect to Earth Science:** Malachite, $CuCO_3 \cdot Cu(OH_2)$, is a common copper ore. Would this compound act as an acid or a base in solution? Explain your answer.

☑ Comparing and Contrasting

List as many ways as you can think of that acids and bases are similar. Make a second list of the ways in which they are different. If you need help, refer to Comparing and Contrasting in the **Skill Handbook** on page 679.

Skill Builder

Amino acid molecules have properties of both acids and bases. Copy the following structure of glycine and circle and label the parts that give the molecule its acidic and basic properties.

Figure 17-8. Even though ammonia is not a hydroxide, it reacts with water to produce some OH^- ions.

Connect to...
Life Science

Answer:

3 CLOSE

? FLEX Your Brain

Use the Flex Your Brain activity to have students explore ACIDS and BASES.

ASSESSMENT

Portfolio: Use the Flex Your Brain activity to reinforce critical-thinking and problem-solving skills. In Step 2, students might list different properties of acids and bases.

▶ Ask questions 1-2 and the **Apply** and **Connect to Earth Science** questions.

SECTION REVIEW ANSWERS

1. Acids and bases are electrolytes because they produce ions in solution. As a result, the solutions conduct electric currents.

2. Responses may vary, but should include the acids and bases discussed in this section. Accept all reasonable responses.

3. Apply: The carboxyl, –COOH, group indicates that formic acid is an organic acid.

$HCOOH + H_2O \rightarrow HCOO^- + H_3O^+$

4. Connect to Earth Science: The presence of OH in the formula indicates that malachite is a base.

Skill Builder

Similarities: corrosive, produce ions in solution, are electrolytes, cause color changes in indicators
Differences: taste, feel, reactions, acids produce H^+ ions, bases produce OH^- ions

---

PROGRAM RESOURCES

From the **Teacher Resource Package** use:
Activity Worksheets, page 5, Flex Your Brain.
Concept Mapping, pages 39-40.
Transparency Masters, pages 67-68, Acids in Solution.
Use **Color Transparency** number 34, Acids in Solution.

Skill Builder
ASSESSMENT
Oral: Have students use their lists to predict the properties of hydrofluoric acid.

PREPARATION

SECTION BACKGROUND

▶ The binary acids HCl, HBr, and HI are strong; all other binary acids and HCN are weak.

▶ Ternary acids contain oxygen. Strong ternary acids include HNO_3, H_2SO_4, and $HClO_4$. Examples of weak ternary acids are $HClO$ and H_2CO_3.

▶ Polyprotic acids are those that have more than one ionizable hydrogen. Examples are H_2SO_4 and H_3PO_4.

▶ Hydroxides of Group 1 and 2 metals (except beryllium and magnesium) are strong bases. All others are weak.

1 MOTIVATE

▶ **Demonstration:** Place two petri dishes, each containing a small piece of magnesium ribbon, on an overhead projector. Place several drops of 1M HCl on one piece of Mg and a similar amount of vinegar on the other Mg piece. Students will see that the action of a strong acid contrasts greatly with that of a weak acid.

PROGRAM RESOURCES

From the **Teacher Resource Package** use:

Critical Thinking/Problem Solving, page 23, Is Acid Rain a Threat?

Transparency Masters, pages 69-70, The pH Scale.

Science Integration Activity 17

Use **Color Transparency** number 35, The pH Scale.

Use **Laboratory Manual 35,** Acids, Bases, and Indicators.

New Science Words

strong acid
weak acid
strong base
weak base
pH

Objectives

▶ Explain what determines the strength of an acid or a base.
▶ Differentiate strength and concentration.
▶ Define *pH*.
▶ Describe the relationship between pH and the strength of an acid or a base.

Strong and Weak Acids and Bases

You have learned that all acids have certain properties in common. Yet, some acids are safe enough to swallow or put in your eyes, whereas other acids destroy human tissue and corrode metal. Obviously, all acids are not alike. Some acids are stronger than others. The same is true of bases. Table 17-3 lists some strong and weak acids and bases.

The strength of an acid or base depends on how completely a compound is pulled apart to form ions when dissolved in water. An acid that ionizes almost completely in solution is a **strong acid.** Conversely, an acid that only ❶ partly ionizes in solution is a **weak acid.**

Look at the equations for the ionization of hydrochloric acid, a strong acid, and acetic acid, a weak acid.

$$HCl(g) + H_2O(l) \rightarrow H_3O^+(aq) + Cl^-(aq)$$

$$CH_3COOH(l) + H_2O(l) \rightleftarrows H_3O^+(aq) + CH_3COO^-(aq)$$

In the equation for the formation of hydrochloric acid, note that no HCl molecules are present in solution. All of the HCl ionizes, and the H^+ ions produced combine with water to form H_3O^+ ions. In the equation for acetic acid, the double arrow indicates that not all of the CH_3COOH molecules ionize. Many of the molecules remain intact in solution. Thus, only a few H^+ ions are produced to form H_3O^+ ions.

Remember that many bases are ionic compounds that dissociate to produce individual ions when they dissolve. ❷ A **strong base** dissociates completely in solution. The com-

How do strong acids differ from weak acids?

Figure 17-9. H_2SO_4 is a strong acid; CH_3COOH is a weak acid.

434 ACIDS, BASES, AND SALTS

OPTIONS

Meeting Different Ability Levels

For Section 17-2, use the following **Teacher Resource Masters** depending upon individual students' needs.

◆ **Study Guide Master** for all students.

● **Reinforcement Master** for students of average and above average ability levels.

▲ **Enrichment Master** for above average students.

Additional Teacher Resource Package masters are listed in any PROGRAM RESOURCES boxes that are in the section. The additional masters are appropriate for all students.

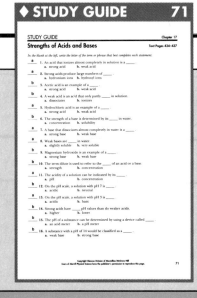

mon strong bases are the ionic hydroxides LiOH, NaOH, KOH, Ca(OH)$_2$, Sr(OH)$_2$, and Ba(OH)$_2$. The first three of these bases are soluble in water; the last three are only moderately soluble. A moderately soluble base can still be a strong base because all of the compound that does dissolve exists in the form of ions.

The following equations show the dissociation of sodium hydroxide, a strong base, and the ionization of ammonia, a weak base.

$$NaOH(cr) \rightarrow Na^+(aq) + OH^-(aq)$$

$$NH_3(aq) + H_2O(l) \rightleftarrows NH_4^+(aq) + OH^-(aq)$$

Whereas all of the NaOH has broken up into ions, most of the ammonia is in the form of NH$_3$. Because little ammonia is in the form of ions, ammonia is a **weak base.**

Often, the *strength* of an acid or base is confused with its *concentration*. As you learned in Chapter 15, *dilute* and *concentrated* are terms used to indicate the concentration of a solution. The concentration of an acid or base refers to the amount of acid or base dissolved in solution. It is possible to have dilute concentrations of strong acids or bases and concentrated solutions of weak acids or bases. *Strong* or *weak* refers to the ease with which an acid or base forms ions in solution.

pH of a Solution

If you have a pool or keep tropical fish, you know that the pH of the water must be controlled. **pH** is a measure of the concentration of hydronium ions in a solution. It indicates acidity. To determine pH, a scale ranging from 0 to 14 has been devised, as shown in the diagram below.

Table 17-3

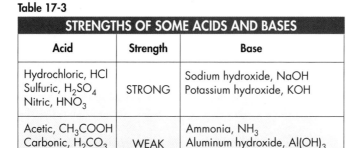

STRENGTHS OF SOME ACIDS AND BASES		
Acid	**Strength**	**Base**
Hydrochloric, HCl Sulfuric, H$_2$SO$_4$ Nitric, HNO$_3$	STRONG	Sodium hydroxide, NaOH Potassium hydroxide, KOH
Acetic, CH$_3$COOH Carbonic, H$_2$CO$_3$ Boric, H$_3$BO$_3$	WEAK	Ammonia, NH$_3$ Aluminum hydroxide, Al(OH)$_3$ Iron(III) hydroxide, Fe(OH)$_3$

In your Journal, write a short paragraph that explains how an acidic solution can be both weak and concentrated.

Did You Know?

The pH of human blood is approximately 7.4. The lungs, kidneys, and circulatory system help to maintain that basic level.

The aromas of many fish are caused by compounds called amines. If the pH of a dilute solution of an amine is 11.4, is the amine an acid or a base?

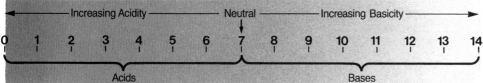

Acids — Neutral — Bases

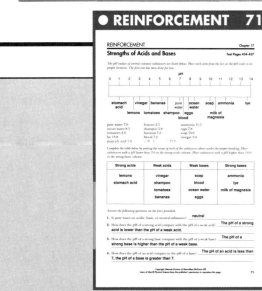

● REINFORCEMENT 71

▲ ENRICHMENT 71

435

In Your JOURNAL

Student responses should include that there could be a relatively large amount of solute dissolved in solution, yet a small percentage of it ionized.

2 TEACH

Key Concepts are highlighted.

CONCEPT DEVELOPMENT

▶ **Demonstration:** Conductivity apparatus can be used to show the relative ion concentrations that determine acid or base strength. Prepare four solutions of acetic acid to be tested. Conductivity is directly related to the concentration of ions in solution. This demonstration will help students see that the percent of ionization varies with concentration.

Sample Acetic Acid Concentrations	Percent of Ionization
6.0M	0.2%
1.0M	0.4%
0.1M	1.3%
0.01M	4.2%

The greater ratio of water molecules to acid molecules in the more dilute solution helps to ionize the CH$_3$COOH molecules.

Answer: a base

CHECK FOR UNDERSTANDING

Use the Mini Quiz to check for understanding.

MINI QUIZ

Use the Mini Quiz to check students' recall of chapter content.

1 An acid that ionizes almost completely in solution is a(n) _____ . *strong acid*

2 A strong base dissociates in solution to produce a large number of _____ ions. *hydroxide*

3 A solution with a pH of 11 is classified as a(n) _____ . *base*

RETEACH

Have each student look at the food labels in a pantry or refrigerator and record two items that contain a weak acid.

EXTENSION

For students who have mastered this section, use the **Reinforcement** and **Enrichment** masters or other OPTIONS provided.

3 CLOSE

▶ Ask questions 1-2 and the **Apply** and **Connect to Life Science** questions.

SECTION REVIEW ANSWERS

1. The strength of an acid depends on the number of hydronium ions present in solution—the greater the number, the stronger the acid. For bases, the same principle holds, except that the ions in solution are hydroxide ions.

2. A strong acid can be made dilute by adding a small amount of acid to a large amount of water. Examples may include dilution of any strong acid, such as HCl, H_2SO_4, or HNO_3.

3. Apply: Rainwater is slightly acidic; soda water is moderately acidic; drain cleaner is strongly basic; seawater is moderately basic; pure water is neutral.

4. Connect to Life Science: A pH of 1.5 is more acidic and would require more base to neutralize it.

Skill Builder
ASSESSMENT

Performance: List several common materials and their pH values on the chalkboard. Have students classify each material as an acidic, a basic, or a neutral solution.

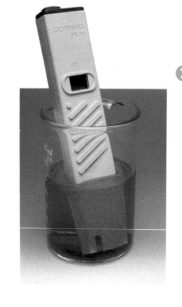

Figure 17-10. When matched with a color chart, the color of the pH paper will show that the solution being tested is a base.

As the diagram on page 435 shows, solutions with a pH lower than 7 are acidic. The lower the value, the more acidic the solution. Solutions with pH greater than 7 are basic, and the higher the pH, the more basic the solution. A solution with a pH of exactly 7 is neutral—neither acidic nor basic. Pure water has a pH of 7.

Strong acids will have lower pH values—be more acidic—than weak acids of the same concentration. This is because strong acids ionize more completely, thus forming larger numbers of H_3O^+ ions. Similarly, strong bases, which contain large numbers of OH^- ions, will have higher pH values than weak bases of the same concentration.

A pH meter can be used to determine the pH of a solution. This meter is operated by immersing the electrodes in the solution to be tested and reading the dial. Small, battery-operated pH meters with digital readouts make measuring the pH of materials convenient.

If a pH meter is not available, a universal indicator or pH paper can be used. Both of these undergo a color change in the presence of H_3O^+ ions and OH^- ions in solution. The final color of the solution or the pH paper is matched with colors in a chart to find the pH, as shown in Figure 17-10.

SECTION REVIEW

1. What determines the strength of an acid? A base?
2. How can you make a dilute solution of a strong acid? Include an example as part of your explanation.
3. **Apply:** What does the pH of each of the solutions indicate about the solution? Rainwater, 5.8; soda water, 3.0; drain cleaner, 14.0; seawater, 8.9; pure water, 7.0.
4. **Connect to Life Science:** Stomach acid is a solution of HCl. If an antacid were used, which would require more antacid, stomach contents with a pH of 1.5 or an equal volume with a pH of 2.0? Explain your answer.

Skill Builder

☑ Concept Mapping

Make a concept map of pH values. Start with three boxes labeled acidic, neutral, and basic and indicate the pH range of each box. Below each box, give some examples of solutions that belong in each pH range. If you need help, refer to Concept Mapping in the **Skill Handbook** on pages 684 and 685.

436 ACIDS, BASES, AND SALTS

Skill Builder

Concept maps will vary. A sample is given here.

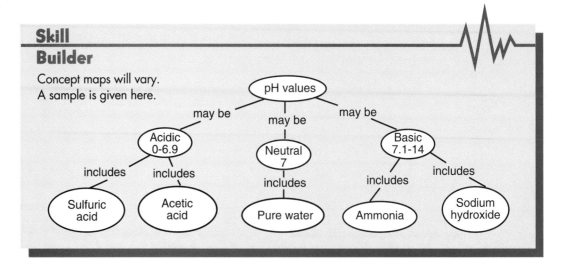

Strong and Weak Acids

   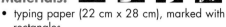

When you read about the behavior of things as small as molecules, it is difficult to visualize what causes the behavior. This activity will help you visualize the ease of ionization of two acids.

Materials:

- typing paper (22 cm x 28 cm), marked with rectangles
- thick cardboard (22 cm x 28 cm), marked with rectangles
- scissors
- test tubes (2)
- medicine droppers (2)
- graduated cylinder
- dilute hydrochloric acid (HCl)
- dilute acetic acid (CH₃COOH)
- pH paper
- timer, with second hand

Procedure

1. *Prepare a data table* like the one shown.
2. Make sure your paper and cardboard are marked with equal numbers of rectangles. Mark every other rectangle with a plus sign (+) to represent hydronium ions. Then mark the blank rectangles with a minus sign (−) to represent negative ions.
3. Using scissors, cut the typing paper into as many of its individual rectangles as possible in ten seconds.

4. Repeat Step 3 with the piece of cardboard.
5. Obtain 2 mL each of dilute HCl and dilute CH₃COOH in test tubes. **CAUTION:** *Handle these acids with care. Avoid contact with the skin or clothing. Report any spills to your teacher immediately.*
6. Using a different dropper for each acid, add two drops of each to separate strips of pH paper. Determine their respective pH values and record them in the data table.

Data and Observations   Sample Data

8-12 **ions removed from typing paper**	1 **pH of HCl solution**
4-6 **ions removed from cardboard**	2 **pH of acetic acid solution**

Analyze

1. Which was easier to "separate" into ions, the typing paper or the cardboard?
2. Which acid separated into ions most easily? How do you know?

Conclude and Apply

3. Which acid is stronger, HCl or CH₃COOH? How do you know?
4. Which represents the stronger acid, the typing paper or the cardboard? Explain your answer.
5. Which has the stronger bonds between fibers, the typing paper or the cardboard? Explain your answer.
6. Which acids have stronger bonds within their molecules, strong acids or weak acids? Explain your answer.

17-2   STRENGTH OF ACIDS AND BASES   **437**

OBJECTIVE: Distinguish between weak and strong acids by **comparing** ease of ionization.

PROCESS SKILLS applied in this activity:
▶ **Using models** in Conclude and Apply Questions 4 and 5.
▶ **Hypothesizing** in Conclude and Apply Question 6.

COOPERATIVE LEARNING
The Paired Partner strategy should work well in this activity. Pairs should divide up the manipulative tasks and work together to interpret data and answer questions.

TEACHING THE ACTIVITY
Troubleshooting: Caution students to cut at a steady pace and not to rush.
▶ To emphasize the difference in the separation of paper ions versus the cardboard ions, make a chalkboard data table for the entire class and have each team record its results.
▶ To save time, have the rectangles marked on the paper and cardboard before class.
▶ Use 0.1*M* concentrations of HCl and CH₃COOH. You may wish to have 2-mL samples of each solution available for students.
▶ To prepare 0.1*M* acetic acid, dilute 5.9 mL of concentrated (17*M*, glacial) acetic acid to 1.0 L with distilled water.
▶ To prepare 0.1*M* hydrochloric acid, dilute 8.4 mL of concentrated (12*M*) hydrochloric acid to 1.0 L with distilled water.
▶ Although a time factor is used in the cutting of paper and cardboard ions, the actual ionization of acids in water is not time-dependent. A more precise model might have equal amounts of force attempting to pull apart paper ions and the cardboard ions.

PROGRAM RESOURCES

From the **Teacher Resource Package** use:
Activity Worksheets, pages 133-134, Activity 17-1: Strong and Weak Acids.

ANSWERS TO QUESTIONS

1. The ions on the typing paper were easier to separate.
2. The HCl separated more easily. It had a lower pH, indicating a greater concentration of H₃O⁺ ions.
3. The HCl is the stronger acid. The acids were of the same concentration, but HCl was more ionized, as shown by its lower pH.
4. The typing paper represented the stronger acid. It separated more readily.
5. The cardboard was more strongly bonded because it was more difficult to separate.

6. Weak acids are more strongly bonded. The attractions of water molecules do not cause them to break into ions as readily as do strong acids.

Activity
ASSESSMENT
Performance: To further assess students' understanding of acid strength, see USING LAB SKILLS, Question 11, on page 448.

 **17-3 Acid Rain**

PREPARATION

SECTION BACKGROUND

▶ Acid rain harms living organisms. As the acidity of lake water increases, metal ions such as aluminum dissolve from the rocky lake bed. The presence of these metals interferes with the reproductive cycle of some fish.

1 MOTIVATE

▶**Demonstration:** In a fume hood, ignite a pea-sized piece of sulfur in a deflagrating spoon. Lower it into a wide-mouth gas collecting bottle that contains 25 mL of water. Cover the bottle with a glass plate until the sulfur flame is smothered. Remove the spoon, stopper, and shake. Test the solution with universal indicator or litmus. The solution will be acidic.

TYING TO PREVIOUS KNOWLEDGE: Have students recall and discuss where they have observed marble or limestone objects that show the effects of weathering.

2 TEACH

Key Concepts are highlighted.

CONCEPT DEVELOPMENT

Cooperative Learning: Have Expert Teams research photochemical smog. The library will have information on California air quality. This state has taken a lead role in improving the quality of air that citizens breathe.

New Science Words

acid rain
plankton

Objectives

▶ Describe the factors contributing to the formation of acid rain.
▶ Discuss the problems acid rain is causing and how these problems might be solved.

What Is Acid Rain?

Fish populations in lakes are being reduced. The surfaces of sculptures and buildings are wearing away. What is the cause of these and certain other problems? The answer could be acid rain. The term *acid rain* was first used in 1872 by Angus Smith. Smith wrote a book about polluted air and rain near large cities in England. In the 1970s, people first started to regard acid rain as a serious problem in the United States and Canada. Now acid rain seems to be a problem in all industrialized countries.

Normal rain has a pH of 5.6 due to the reaction of carbon dioxide gas with rainwater to form carbonic acid.

$$CO_2(g) + H_2O(l) \rightarrow H_2CO_3(aq)$$

Carbonic acid is weak. Thus, the typical levels of carbon dioxide in the air do not contribute very much to the problem of acid rain.

Any form of precipitation having a pH lower than 5.6 is called **acid rain.** The model that scientists use to describe the formation of acid rain suggests that oxides of sulfur and nitrogen in the atmosphere react with rainwater to form acids. These oxides are released when fossil fuels are burned and can combine with rainwater to produce strong acids such as sulfuric acid and nitric acid. Although these acids are quite dilute in rainwater, they can harm the environment. The problem worsens in densely populated industrial regions where large quantities of gasoline and high-sulfur fuels are burned.

When acid rain falls to Earth, the soil and water become increasingly acidic. Among the first organisms to suffer are plankton. **Plankton** are tiny aquatic plants and animals.

Figure 17-11. This tree shows the effects of acid rain.

438   ACIDS, BASES, AND SALTS

OPTIONS

Meeting Different Ability Levels

For Section 17-3, use the following **Teacher Resource Masters** depending upon individual students' needs.

◆ **Study Guide Master** for all students.
● **Reinforcement Master** for students of average and above average ability levels.
▲ **Enrichment Master** for above average students.

◆ **STUDY GUIDE**   **72**

STUDY GUIDE   Chapter 17

Acid Rain   Text Pages 438-439

Use the clues to identify the missing terms in the puzzle. When you have completed the puzzle, you will discover a term spelled vertically in the black boxes. Write the term in the space provided below the puzzle. Then, write the definition for the term.

```
1.              C A R B O N I C
2. S U L F U R I C
3.          F O S S I L F U E L S
4.          O X I D E S
5.          M A R B L E
6.          P L A N K T O N
7.          N I T R I C
8. L I M E S T O N E
```

Clues
1. The acid formed when carbon dioxide gas mixes with rainwater is ____ acid.
2. The acid formed when sulfur oxides mix with rainwater is ____ acid.
3. Oxides are released into the air when these are burned.
4. Compounds of this type may form acid rain when they react with rainwater.
5. material commonly used in statues that weathers rapidly because of acid rain
6. tiny aquatic plants and animals
7. The acid formed when nitrogen oxides mix with water is ____ acid.
8. building material that weathers rapidly due to acid rain

Term: acid rain
Definition: any form of precipitation having a pH lower than 5.6

72

These organisms form the base of the food chain for small fish. When the plankton die, the fish that depend on them as a food source soon die also.

Acid rain also has harmful effects on soil and land plants. As acid rain moves through the soil, it dissolves important mineral nutrients and carries them away. Plants deprived of these nutrients will not grow at a normal rate. Crops and forests are damaged.

Acid rain also causes rapid weathering of buildings and statues made of limestone and marble. For example, the Parthenon in Greece has survived for more than 2000 years. Today, it is rapidly being destroyed by acid rain.

Connect to... Earth Science

Volcanic eruptions also release sulfur oxides into the atmosphere. Write the balanced chemical equation for the reaction of SO_3 and water to form sulfuric acid.

Figure 17-12. The deterioration of this building is due to the chemical reaction of acid rain with calcite, the principal mineral in marble and limestone.

SECTION REVIEW

1. What is the main cause of acid rain?
2. What are the effects of acid rain?
3. **Connect to Earth Science:** Limestone is mostly calcium carbonate, $CaCO_3$. Write the balanced chemical equation for the reaction of nitric acid, HNO_3, from acid rain, with limestone. CO_2 and water are two of the products.

You Decide!

Assume you live in an area whose main industry is mining high-sulfur coal. The coal is burned by the local power company. A law is passed requiring this company to reduce its sulfur dioxide emissions. Plant owners can buy low-sulfur coal from a neighboring state and keep the same electric rates. Or they can use local coal and increase electric rates ten percent to cover the costs of removing sulfur and sulfur compounds. Which choice would you support?

439

CHECK FOR UNDERSTANDING
Ask questions 1-2 and the **Connect to Earth Science** question.

RETEACH
Is a damaged environment easily repaired? Ask students to discuss how technology's impact can be minimized.

EXTENSION
For students who have mastered this section, use the **Reinforcement** and **Enrichment** masters or other OPTIONS provided.

Connect to... Earth Science

Answer:
$SO_3(g) + H_2O(l) \rightarrow H_2SO_4(aq)$

3 CLOSE

▶ Ask students to discuss the role of economics in finding a solution. The Clean Air Act will be expensive.

SECTION REVIEW ANSWERS
1. The main cause of acid rain is the reaction of rainwater with oxides released into the air by the burning of fossil fuels.
2. Acid rain is harmful to plants and animals and causes rapid deterioration of many stone structures.
3. **Connect to Earth Science:** $CaCO_3(cr) + 2HNO_3(aq) \rightarrow CO_2(g) + H_2O(l) + Ca(NO_3)_2(aq)$

YOU DECIDE!

Student responses may vary, but the most reasonable response is probably (2), raising rates. This choice would result in cleaner air and the continuing operation of the local coal mines, the major economic base of the community.

VideoDisc
STVS: Fish and Acid Rain, Disc 6, Side 2

PREPARATION

SECTION BACKGROUND

▶ When an alcohol reacts with either an organic acid or an organic acid anhydride, an ester is formed. This type of reaction is called esterification.

▶ An ester can be split into an alcohol and carboxylic acid by the addition of water, called hydrolysis.

▶ If a metallic base is used instead of water, the metal salt of the carboxylic acid is obtained, not the acid. This process is called saponification. Soap is a metal salt of a fatty acid. The natural fat or oil is an ester.

PREPLANNING

▶ To prepare for Activity 17-2, purchase clear carbonated beverages. Prepare a 0.20M NaOH solution.

1 MOTIVATE

▶ Use the chemical equations shown below to introduce students to neutralization reactions that are important to keeping them healthy. Human blood is buffered primarily by HCO_3^-, the hydrogen carbonate ion. This ion can react with excess acid or base in the blood to help maintain the pH at 7.4. The reaction with excess hydronium ions from acid is $HCO_3^- + H_3O^+ \rightarrow H_2CO_3 + H_2O$. When the H_2CO_3 reaches the lungs it decomposes into CO_2 and water vapor. The reaction with excess hydroxide ions from base is $HCO_3^- + OH^- \rightarrow H_2O + CO_3^{2-}$.

VideoDisc

STVS: Treating Acid Lakes, Disc 2, Side 2

New Science Words

neutralization
salt
titration
soaps
saponification
detergents
ester

What is neutralization?

Did You Know?

A 500-million-dollar, ten-year study of acid rain was completed in 1990. The study concluded with a 15 000-page report indicating that scientists on both sides of the controversy had overstated their cases.

Objectives

▶ Describe a neutralization reaction.
▶ Explain what a salt is and how salts form.
▶ Differentiate soaps and detergents.
▶ Explain how esters are made and what they are used for.

Neutralization

You have probably seen television commercials for antacids that describe how effectively these products neutralize excess stomach acid. Would the pH of such a product be higher or lower than 7? If you answered higher, you are correct. Only a base can neutralize the effects of an acid.

Neutralization is a chemical reaction between an acid and a base. During a neutralization reaction, hydronium ions from the acid combine with hydroxide ions from the base to produce water.

$$H_3O^+(aq) + OH^-(aq) \rightarrow 2H_2O(l)$$

As the reactive hydronium and hydroxide ions are removed from the solution, the acidic and basic properties of the reactants are cancelled, or neutralized.

The equation above accounts for only half of the ions present in the solution. What happens to the remaining ions? They react to form a salt. A **salt** is a compound formed when the negative ions from an acid combine with the positive ions from a base.

Neutralization reactions are ionic. The following equations show what happens to all of the ions during a neutralization reaction:

$$HCl(aq) + NaOH(aq) \rightarrow$$
$$H_3O^+(aq) + Cl^-(aq) + Na^+(aq) + OH^-(aq)$$

Water Formation: $H_3O^+(aq) + OH^-(aq) \rightarrow 2H_2O(l)$

Salt Formation: $Na^+(aq) + Cl^-(aq) \rightarrow NaCl(cr)*$

*Note: The formation of crystalline NaCl occurs only if the water is removed by boiling or evaporation.

OPTIONS

Meeting Different Ability Levels

For Section 17-4, use the following **Teacher Resource Masters** depending upon individual students' needs.

◆ **Study Guide Master** for all students.

● **Reinforcement Master** for students of average and above average ability levels.

▲ **Enrichment Master** for above average students.

Additional Teacher Resource Package masters are listed in any **PROGRAM RESOURCES** boxes that are in the section. The additional masters are appropriate for all students.

◆ STUDY GUIDE 73

STUDY GUIDE   Chapter 17
Acids, Bases, and Salts   Text Pages 440-446

Solve the following crossword puzzle by using the clues provided.

Across
1. process of making soap
4. compound formed when the negative ions from an acid combine with the positive ions from a base
7. process in which a solution of known concentration is used to determine the concentration of another solution
8. measure of the acidity of a substance
10. NH_4^+ stands for the ____ ion.
11. organic salt with a structure similar to that of soap
12. organic compound formed by the reaction of an organic acid and an alcohol
13. softening agent in hand creams

Down
1. chemical name for table salt (2 words)
2. In an equation, (cr) means this.
3. chemical reaction between an acid and a base
5. substance that produces H^+ ions in solution
6. organic salt made by reacting fats or oils with sodium hydroxide or potassium hydroxide
9. one of the products of a neutralization reaction

PROBLEM SOLVING

Julio's Experiment

Julio went to the doctor with stomach pains. The doctor told Julio that he had excess stomach acid and advised him to purchase an over-the-counter antacid and take it according to the directions on the package.

Julio wants to determine the best antacid to use. He thinks the best antacid will neutralize the greatest amount of hydrochloric acid.

He went to the drugstore and purchased several antacids that he had seen advertised on television. His science instructor said he would allow Julio to conduct his experiment during study hall and advised Julio to use bromothymol blue as his indicator because it turns pale green at pH 7. What was Julio's hypothesis?

Think Critically: How could Julio design an experiment to determine which antacid is most effective in neutralizing stomach acid?

Salts

Many substances that you come in contact with every day are salts. Of course, the most familiar salt is sodium chloride—common table salt. Table 17-4 on page 442 contains information about some common salts. As the table shows, most salts are composed of a metal and a nonmetal other than oxygen, or a metal and a polyatomic ion. Ammonium salts contain the polyatomic ammonium ion, NH_4^+, rather than a metal. Salts also form when acids react with metals. Hydrogen gas is released during such reactions.

$$Acid + Metal \rightarrow Salt + Hydrogen$$

$$H_2SO_4(aq) + Zn(cr) \rightarrow ZnSO_4(aq) + H_2(g)$$

$$6HCl(aq) + 2Fe(cr) \rightarrow 2FeCl_3(aq) + 3H_2(g)$$

Reactions between metals and acids are replacement reactions in which the metal displaces hydrogen from the acid and replaces it.

How do salts form?

Connect to...
Life Science

Potassium iodide, KI, is added to table salt to help prevent thyroid gland problems. Predict what acid and base would react to form the salt KI.

● **REINFORCEMENT 73**

▲ **ENRICHMENT 73**

(reinforcement worksheet)

REINFORCEMENT   Chapter 17

Acids, Bases, and Salts   Text Pages 440–446

Use the equation below to answer questions 1–6.

$$HCl(aq) + NaOH(aq) \rightarrow H_2O(l) + NaCl(cr)$$

1. What type of reaction is shown? **neutralization**
2. What are the products of this reaction? **water (H_2O) and sodium chloride (NaCl)**
3. What are the reactants? **HCl (an acid) and NaOH (a base)**
4. a. Which of the reactants shown is a base? **NaOH**
   b. How do you know? **It has an OH⁻ ion in its formula.**
5. a. Which of the reactants is an acid? **HCl**
   b. What is the name of the acid? **hydrochloric acid**
   c. Is the acid a strong acid or a weak acid? **a strong acid**
6. What kind of compound is NaCl? **a salt**

Identify the type of substance that is most likely to be formed by each reaction described below. Use the terms soap, salt, ester, and ester.

   salt   7. hydrochloric acid and a base

   ester   8. an organic acid and an alcohol

   soap   9. sodium hydroxide and a fat

   ester   10. acetic acid and methyl alcohol

   soap   11. potassium hydroxide and oil

   salt   12. an acid and ammonia

Answer the following questions on the lines provided.

13. How does a soap made from sodium hydroxide differ from a soap made from potassium hydroxide? **A soap made from sodium hydroxide is a solid. A soap made from potassium hydroxide is a liquid.**

14. Why are most laundry products detergents instead of soaps? **Detergents do not react with hard water to form precipitates the way soaps do.**

15. What is an observable characteristic of an ester? **Most esters have an odor.**

(enrichment worksheet)

ENRICHMENT   Chapter 17

Acids, Bases, and Salts   Text Pages 440–446

MIXING TO EMULSIFY AND TO NEUTRALIZE

Detergent emulsifies fat or grease. The grease is emulsified when it no longer remains at the surface of the water, but is dispersed into smaller globules. The following experiment examines how well a detergent emulsifies fat or grease.

Materials
• vegetable oil or lard   • spoon
• warm water   • detergent
• clear drinking glass

Procedure
1. Measure one teaspoon of vegetable oil or lard into warm water in a clear drinking glass.
2. Carefully add 1 mL of detergent and stir.
3. Continue to add detergent 1 mL at a time while stirring until the vegetable oil or lard is dispersed into the water.

Questions
1. How many milliliters of detergent were required to completely disperse the vegetable oil or lard? **Answers will vary depending on the detergent used.**
2. Is the action of the detergent on the vegetable oil or lard an example of a physical or chemical change? Explain. **It is a physical change. The oil dispersed in the water is a colloid. Neither the oil nor the water is chemically changed.**

Predict the products of the following neutralization reactions and balance each equation.

1. HCl + NaOH →
   HCl + NaOH → NaCl + H₂O
2. HI + Mg(OH)₂ →
   2HI + Mg(OH)₂ → MgI₂ + 2H₂O
3. H₂SO₄ + KOH →
   H₂SO₄ + 2KOH → K₂SO₄ + 2H₂O
4. HBr + Al(OH)₃ →
   3HBr + Al(OH)₃ → AlBr₃ + 3H₂O
5. H₃PO₄ + Ca(OH)₂ →
   2H₃PO₄ + 3Ca(OH)₂ → Ca₃(PO₄)₂ + 6H₂O

441

PROBLEM SOLVING

Answers to Questions: Julio's hypothesis was that the best antacid would be the one that neutralized the most hydrochloric acid.

Think Critically: Julio could add each antacid to equal quantities of dilute hydrochloric acid containing bromothymol blue. The most effective antacid would be the one that changed the color of the acid solution pale green using the smallest amount of antacid. **CAUTION:** *The one that neutralizes the most acid may cause irritation.*

TYING TO PREVIOUS KNOWLEDGE: Ask students if they have ever taken something to relieve stomach discomfort. Stomach remedies contain a base to neutralize the hydrochloric acid. Magnesium and calcium hydroxides are common bases used.

Connect to...
Life Science

Answer: HI and KOH

2 TEACH

Key Concepts are highlighted.

CONCEPT DEVELOPMENT

▶ **Demonstration:** Dissolve two tablets of a common stomach acid remedy in warm water. Add a few drops of universal indicator. Slowly add a few drops of dilute 0.1M HCl to the beaker with stirring. As you continue to add acid, the base is neutralized and the indicator changes color. Use this demonstration to introduce the ideas of neutralization and endpoints.

▶ Slowly evaporate the solution from the above demonstration in a warm oven overnight. The students will be able to observe the salt formed by the reaction of the acid and base.

CHAPTER 17   **441**

▶ When an acid reacts with a base, a salt and water are the products. Because the term *neutralization* is applied to the reaction of an acid with a base, many people think that the resulting salt solution always has a neutral pH of 7. This is true when the acid and base are both strong or when weak bases neutralize weak acids. When a strong acid neutralizes a weak base, the salt solution has an acidic pH. When a strong base neutralizes a weak acid, the salt solution has a basic pH. This happens because some salts may react further with surrounding water molecules.

CONCEPT DEVELOPMENT

▶ **Demonstration:** Use medicine droppers to show students that equal volumes of strong acid and strong base of the same concentration produce a neutral solution. Use an overhead projector and a small beaker. Place 50 drops of 0.1M HCl and a drop of universal indicator in the beaker. Then slowly add, with swirling, 50 drops of 0.1M NaOH. Have students match the final color with the chart that comes with universal indicator.

TEACHER F.Y.I.

▶ Alkaloids are naturally occurring bases that contain nitrogen. Like ammonia, the nitrogen base in these substances attracts hydrogen from water, leaving hydroxide ions. This results in a basic solution. Some alkaloids are listed below.

Quinine—found in cinchona bark; used to treat malaria

Morphine—narcotic found in opium poppy flower; used to relieve pain

Caffeine—a stimulant found in coffee beans and tea leaves

Nicotine—a stimulant found in tobacco leaves

Mescaline—a hallucinogen found in peyote cactus

Table 17-4

	SOME COMMON SALTS		
Name	Formula	Common Name	Uses
Sodium chloride	NaCl	Salt	Food preparation; manufacture of chemicals
Sodium hydrogen carbonate	NaHCO$_3$	Sodium bicarbonate (baking soda)	Food preparation; in fire extinguishers
Calcium carbonate	CaCO$_3$	Calcite (chalk)	Manufacture of paint and rubber tires
Potassium nitrate	KNO$_3$	Saltpeter	In fertilizers; manufacture of explosives
Potassium carbonate	K$_2$CO$_3$	Potash	Manufacture of soap and glass
Sodium phosphate	Na$_3$PO$_4$	TSP	In detergents
Ammonium chloride	NH$_4$Cl	Sal ammoniac	In dry cells

Figure 17-13. The apparatus is set up to perform a titration of a base.

Titration

It is sometimes necessary to find the concentration of an acidic or basic solution. This can be accomplished by titration. **Titration** is the process in which a solution of known concentration is used to determine the concentration of another solution. Most titrations involve acid-base neutralizations.

In a titration, a solution of known concentration, called the standard solution, is added to a solution of unknown concentration to which an indicator has been added. If the solution of unknown concentration is a base, a standard acid solution is used. If the unknown is an acid, a standard basic solution is used.

As an example, assume that you need to find the concentration of an acid solution. First, you would add a few drops of phenolphthalein (feen ul THAYL een) indicator to a carefully measured amount of this solution. Phenolphthalein is colorless in an acid, but is pink in a base.

A standard base solution is carefully added to this acid. At some point, one drop of the base just begins to turn the acid solution pink. This is known as the endpoint of the titration. Just enough standard solution has been added to neutralize the acid. The volume of the base used to neutralize the known volume of acid is determined, and the concentration of the acid can be calculated.

442 ACIDS, BASES, AND SALTS

OPTIONS

ASSESSMENT—ORAL

▶ **There are four areas of taste found on the tongue—sweet, sour, salty, and bitter. Which three relate to the words in the title of Section 17-4?** *acids—sour, bases—bitter, some salts—salty*

▶ **In one or two sentences, describe the process in which a base neutralizes an acid.** *The hydronium ion from the acid and the hydroxide ion from the base unite to form water, while the other ions form a salt.*

▶ **What is the purpose of performing a titration?** *to determine the concentration of an unknown solution*

▶ **What is an endpoint in a titration experiment?** *point at which just enough acid has been added to react with the base to produce color change in an indicator*

Soaps and Detergents

⑤ **Soaps** are organic salts. Soaps are made by reacting fats or oils with sodium hydroxide or potassium hydroxide. One formula for soap made using sodium hydroxide is $C_{17}H_{35}COONa$. The structural formula for this soap is provided below.

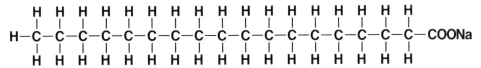

A soap made using potassium hydroxide might have the formula $C_{15}H_{31}COOK$. Below is the structural formula for this soap.

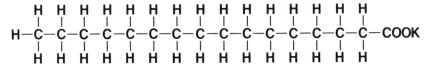

Sodium hydroxide produces solid soaps. Potassium hydroxide makes liquid soaps. Another product of this reaction is glycerin, which is a softening agent in hand creams.

⑥ The process of making soap is called **saponification.** Soaps increase the cleaning action of water. When soap is put into water, it ionizes as follows:

$$C_{17}H_{35}COONa(cr) \rightarrow C_{17}H_{35}COO^-(aq) + Na^+(aq)$$

The negative ion consists of two parts: an ionic head and a long, nonpolar hydrocarbon tail. Remember that grease is composed of hydrocarbon molecules. These molecules are similar in structure to the long hydrocarbon tail of the soap molecule.

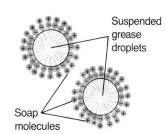

Figure 17-14. Soap removes grease by breaking it up into tiny droplets.

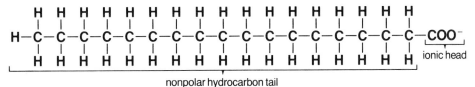

When you use soap to wash your hands, the nonpolar hydrocarbon tail dissolves any fat or grease that may be on them. The ionic head dissolves in the water and carries the dirt away.

CONCEPT DEVELOPMENT

▶ **Demonstration:** Show students how soap is made by placing 25 grams of solid vegetable shortening in a 250-mL beaker. Add 10 mL of ethanol and 5 mL of 6M NaOH (6 g NaOH in 25 mL water). Heat the mixture using a hot plate and stir for 15 minutes. **CAUTION:** *Ethanol is flammable.* A small piece of colored crayon can be added to make colored soap. Cool the mixture in an ice water bath. Add 25 mL of water and 25 mL of saturated NaCl solution. The soap will appear as curds. Collect the soap by filtering it through cheesecloth and pressing it into an evaporating dish to mold it. Allow the soap to dry and harden for several days.

▶ **Demonstration:** To show an effect of soap, pour 3.5 percent butterfat milk one-half centimeter deep in a petri dish. Place a drop each of four different food colors in four different areas of the milk. Dip a toothpick into liquid dish detergent and then touch the surface of the milk in the center of the petri dish. Hold the toothpick in the milk, but don't touch the bottom of the dish. The detergent affects the fat in the milk to produce a colorful mixing.

MINI QUIZ

Use the Mini Quiz to check students' recall of chapter content.

① **What reaction occurs when an acid reacts with a base to produce water and a salt?** *neutralization*

② **When negative ions from an acid combine with positive ions from a base, what is produced?** *a salt*

③ **When an active metal reacts with an acid, what gas is evolved?** *hydrogen*

④ **What name is used to describe a solution of known concentration?** *standard solution*

⑤ **When a fatty acid reacts with an inorganic base, what organic salt is produced?** *soap*

⑥ **The process of making soap is called _____ .** *saponification*

CONCEPT DEVELOPMENT

▶ **Demonstration:** Esters can be prepared by placing 6 mL of each reactant into a test tube with 5 drops of concentrated sulfuric acid. **CAUTION:** *Sulfuric acid is corrosive, and alcohols are flammable.* Heat the test tube in a warm water bath. Pineapple smell can be created by reacting butyric acid with ethanol, apples by reacting acetic acid with ethanol, and wintergreen by reacting salicylic acid and methanol.

MINI QUIZ

Use the Mini Quiz to check students' recall of chapter content.

7 What do scientists call an organic salt that has a structure similar to that of soap? *detergent*

8 Which ions in hard water react with soap to form a precipitate known as soap scum? *Ca, Mg, and Fe ions*

9 What forms when an organic acid reacts with an alcohol? *an ester*

10 What do esters contribute to flowers, fruits, and many foods? *flavors and odors*

In Your JOURNAL

Entries should reflect how soap's polar and nonpolar ends enable unlike substances, such as water and grease, to be brought together.

CHECK FOR UNDERSTANDING

▶ Ask questions 1-2 and the **Apply** and **Connect to Life Science** questions.

RETEACH

Use models or magnet-backed paper "atoms" to demonstrate the ionization of acids and the dissociation of bases in water solution. Use the resulting ion models to show what takes place in a neutralization reaction.

EXTENSION

For students who have mastered this section, use the **Reinforcement** and **Enrichment** masters or other OPTIONS provided.

Detergents are organic salts having structures similar to those of soaps. The most common detergent in use today has the following structural formula: **7**

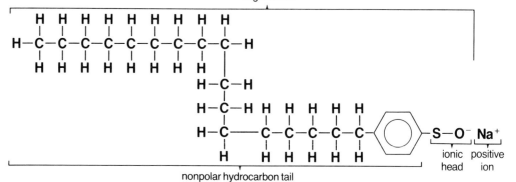
negative ion
ionic head
positive ion
nonpolar hydrocarbon tail

Like soap, the negative ions of detergents have a nonpolar hydrocarbon tail and an ionic head. Detergents also enhance the cleaning action of water.

When soap is used in hard water, it forms soap scum. Hard water contains ions of calcium, magnesium, and iron that react with the soap to form a precipitate. Detergents do not form this scum. Therefore, most laundry products are detergents, not soaps. **8**

Organic Acids and Esters

An **ester** is an organic compound formed by the reaction of an organic acid with an alcohol. The reaction needs a compound that will catalyze the formation of a molecule of water from the organic acid and alcohol. Concentrated sulfuric acid, a powerful dehydrating agent must be present for the organic reaction to take place. Figure 17-15 shows the reaction of acetic acid and methyl alcohol to produce an ester—methyl acetate—and water. **9**

Esters are responsible for the many wonderful odors and flavors of flowers, fruits, and other foods. Sometimes esters are added to gelatin desserts or candy to give the characteristic flavors of strawberry, banana, or apple. **10**

In Your JOURNAL

In political and labor disputes, a mediator is often called in to bring opposing sides together. **In your Journal,** explain how soap could be thought of as a mediator for grease cleaning.

What is an ester?

Figure 17-15. The structural equation below shows the formation of an ester, methyl acetate, by the reaction of an organic acid and an alcohol.

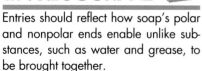
acetic acid   +   methanol   ⇌   methyl acetate (an ester)   +   H₂O water

444 ACIDS, BASES, AND SALTS

OPTIONS

INQUIRY QUESTIONS

▶ Complete and balance the following acid-base reaction:

$$LiOH + HBr \rightarrow$$
$$LiOH + HBr \rightarrow LiBr + H_2O$$

▶ Antacid tablets are advertised for an upset stomach. How would you classify magnesium hydroxide, which is present in some antacids? Why would antacids help calm the stomach? *It is a base. The stomach normally contains acid. Sometimes too much acid is produced. Bases neutralize acids.*

▶ If 20 drops of a solution of HCl exactly neutralize 10 drops of a solution of NaOH, what can be said about the concentrations of the two solutions? *The HCl solution is half as concentrated as the NaOH solution.*

▶ Complete and balance the following equation to show the products that form when barium hydroxide neutralizes perchloric acid.

$$Ba(OH)_2 + 2HClO_4 \rightarrow$$
$$Ba(OH)_2 + 2HClO_4 \rightarrow Ba(ClO_4)_2 + 2H_2O$$
barium perchlorate and water

Synthetic fibers known as polyesters are made from an organic acid that has two –COOH groups and an alcohol that has two –OH groups. Because the two compounds form long chains with the ester linkage, a polymer results.

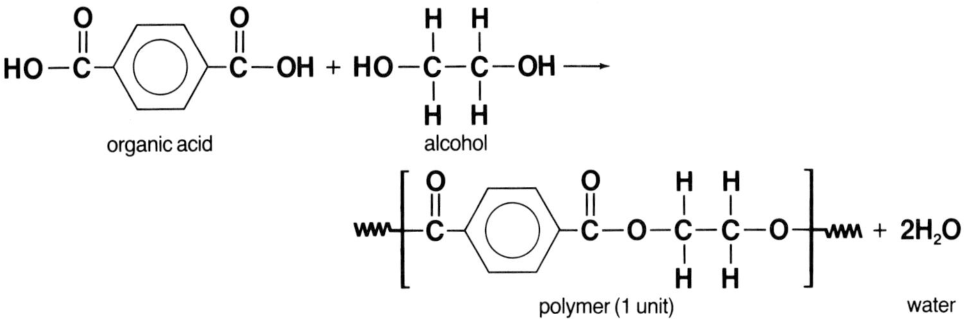

SECTION REVIEW

1. What is a neutralization reaction? What are the products of such reactions?
2. When doing laundry, what advantage does using a detergent have over using a soap?
3. **Apply:** Give the names and formulas of the salt that will form in these neutralizations:
   a. hydrochloric acid and ammonium hydroxide
   b. nitric acid and potassium hydroxide
   c. carbonic acid and aluminum hydroxide
4. **Connect to Life Science:** Use the reaction shown in Figure 17-15 as a model to predict what acid and alcohol molecules combine to form the ester shown below that gives the aroma to bananas.

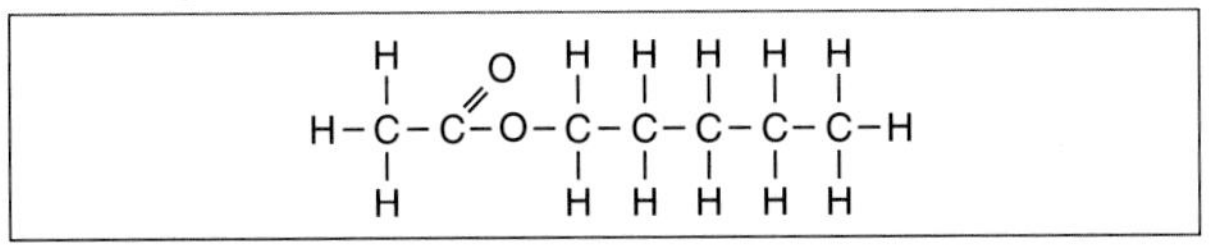

Interpreting Data

Skill Builder

Three salts — calcium sulfate, sodium chloride, and potassium nitrate — were obtained in reactions of the acid-base pairs shown here. Match each salt with the acid-base pair that produced it. If you need help, refer to Interpreting Data in the **Skill Handbook** on page 683.

HCl + NaOH HNO_3 + KOH $H_2SO_4 + Ca(OH)_2$

3 CLOSE

FLEX Your Brain

Use the Flex Your Brain activity to have students explore REACTIONS OF ACIDS AND BASES.

ASSESSMENT

Portfolio: Use the Flex Your Brain activity to reinforce critical-thinking and problem-solving skills. In Step 2, students might list possible products of these reactions.

SECTION REVIEW ANSWERS

1. Neutralization is a reaction between an acid and a base; the products are a salt and water.
2. Unlike soaps, detergents do not react with minerals in hard water to produce scum.
3. Apply: a. ammonium chloride, NH_4Cl; b. potassium nitrate, KNO_3; c. aluminum carbonate, $Al_2(CO_3)_3$
4. Connect to Life Science: acetic acid, CH_3COOH, and pentanol, $C_5H_{11}OH$

Skill Builder

calcium sulfate from H_2SO_4 + $Ca(OH)_2$; sodium chloride from HCl + NaOH; potassium nitrate from KOH + HNO_3

ENRICHMENT

▶ Have an interested student make a list of plants that grow best in your area in acid soils. What methods do local experts suggest to make a soil more acidic or basic?

▶ Exhibit samples of liquid drain cleaners that are used at home. Prepare a mixture of dog or cat hair and solid cooking oil. Place the "clog" in a small beaker and add drain cleaner. **CAUTION:** *Be sure students use gloves, aprons, and eye protection.* Record observations each hour and at 24 hours. Which is the most effective drain cleaner?

Skill Builder

ASSESSMENT

Performance: Ask students to predict the formula of the salt formed when H_2SO_4 and $Al(OH)_3$ react. $Al_2(SO_4)_3$

PROGRAM RESOURCES

From the **Teacher Resource Package** use:

Activity Worksheets, page 5, Flex Your Brain.

ACTIVITY 17-2

OBJECTIVE:
Design and carry out an **experiment** to show that a neutralization reaction can be used to find the level of acidity in a solution.
Time: one class period

PROCESS SKILLS
applied in this activity are **observing, comparing, measuring,** and **inferring.**

PREPARATION
To prepare 0.2 M NaOH solution, dissolve 8.0 g of NaOH pellets in enough water to make 1.0 L of solution. **CAUTION:** *Sodium hydroxide is caustic. Do not touch the pellets or the solution.* Be sure the carbonated beverages are all freshly opened so that escape of CO_2 does not affect the acidity.

Cooperative Learning: Divide the class into Science Investigation Teams.

SAFETY
Caution students to avoid all contact with the NaOH solution. Do not allow students to drink the beverages.

THINKING CRITICALLY
Variables to control include freshness, volume, and temperature of the beverages. Colored beverages would mask the color of the indicator.

TEACHING THE ACTIVITY
*Refer to the **Activity Worksheets** for additional information and teaching strategies.*
• If small Erlenmeyer flasks are available, they will work better than test tubes.
• Be sure students mix the contents well after each drop of NaOH is added. If not mixed, the acid may be neutralized in the top of the tube, giving a false result.
• The pink color can best be seen if the test tubes are held against a piece of white paper.
• Be sure to try the activity ahead of time to make sure that the two beverages chosen have a measurable difference in acidity.
• For most carbonated beverages, approximately 5 mL of beverage requires 15-25 drops of NaOH solution.

DESIGNING AN EXPERIMENT
Be a Soda Scientist

Most carbonated drinks contain dilute solutions of carbonic and phosphoric acids. Do all such beverages contain the same amount of these acids?

Getting Started
You know that bases neutralize acids. Therefore, you could use a neutralization reaction as a method of comparing acid levels in solutions. In this activity, the acid solutions will be colorless carbonated soft drinks. You will neutralize the acid in these beverages with an NaOH solution. **CAUTION:** *NaOH is caustic and should not contact your skin.*

Thinking Critically
If you want to *compare* the acidity level in two different carbonated soft drinks, what variables will you want to control? Why must the beverages be colorless?

Materials
Your cooperative group will use:
• 2 different colorless carbonated soft drinks
• 2 test tubes
• graduated cylinder
• 2 droppers
• phenolphthalein indicator, 1%
• dilute sodium hydroxide, NaOH, solution

Try It!

1. *Prepare a data table* like the one shown.
2. Measure equal amounts of colorless carbonated beverages into test tubes.

Data and Observations Sample Data

	Beverage 1	Beverage 2
Number of drops of NaOH solution needed	15	21

3. Add 2 drops of 1% phenolphthalein indicator to each of your beverage samples.
4. Add the NaOH solution, drop by drop, until a permanent faint pink color indicates that the acid is neutralized. Carefully swirl the test tube after each drop is added. *Record* in your data table the number of drops of NaOH used.

Summing Up/Sharing Results
• Did your samples require different amounts of NaOH for neutralization? Which sample is more acidic?
• Phenolphthalein changes from colorless to pink at a pH of 8. Explain why the indicator was colorless in the soft drink but became pink as the base was added.

Going Further!
Write out the balanced chemical equation for the reaction between NaOH and carbonic acid, H_2CO_3. If additional water were added to the NaOH solution, how would it affect the number of drops required for neutralization?

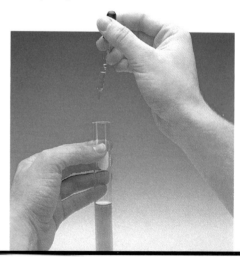

SUMMING UP/SHARING RESULTS
• The sample that required the most NaOH for neutralization is the most acidic.
• A pH of 8 indicates a slightly basic solution. The indicator was colorless in the beverage because the beverage was acidic and thus had a pH less than 7.

PROGRAM RESOURCES
From the **Teacher Resource Package** use:
Activity Worksheets, pages 135-136, Activity 17-2: Be a Soda Scientist.

GOING FURTHER!
$$2NaOH + H_2CO_3 \rightarrow Na_2CO_3 + 2H_2O$$
If additional water were added to the NaOH solution, more drops would be required for neutralization.

Activity
ASSESSMENT
Content: To further assess students' understanding of neutralization, see USING LAB SKILLS, Question 12, on page 448.

SUMMARY

17-1: Acids and Bases

1. An acid is a substance that produces hydrogen ions (H^+) in solution. A base produces hydroxide ions (OH^-) in solution.
2. Properties of acids and bases are due, in part, to the presence of H^+ and OH^- ions.
3. Common acids include hydrochloric acid, sulfuric acid, nitric acid, and phosphoric acid. Common bases include sodium hydroxide, calcium hydroxide, and ammonia.
4. Acidic solutions form when certain polar compounds ionize as they dissolve in water. Except for ammonia, basic solutions form when certain ionic compounds dissociate upon dissolving in water.

17-2: Strength of Acids and Bases

1. The strength of an acid or base is determined by how easily it forms ions when in solution.
2. Strength and concentration are not the same thing. Concentration involves the relative amounts of solvent and solute in a solution.
3. pH is a measure of the hydronium ion concentration of a solution.

4. For acidic solutions of equal concentration, the stronger the acid, the lower its pH; for basic solutions of equal concentration, the stronger the base, the higher the pH.

17-3: Science and Society: Acid Rain

1. Acid rain is produced when substances in the air react with rainwater to make it acidic. Acid rain production is increased by the release of certain oxides into the air when fossil fuels are burned.
2. Acid rain is harmful to plants and animals and increases the rate of weathering.

17-4: Acids, Bases, and Salts

1. In a neutralization reaction, the H_3O^+ ions from an acid react with the OH^- ions from a base to produce water molecules. The products of neutralization are a salt plus water.
2. Salts form when the negative ions from an acid combine with the positive ions from a base.
3. Soaps and detergents are organic salts. Unlike soaps, detergents do not react with compounds in hard water to form scum deposits.
4. Esters are organic compounds formed by the reaction of an organic acid and an alcohol.

KEY SCIENCE WORDS

a. acid
b. acid rain
c. base
d. dehydrating agent
e. detergent
f. ester
g. hydronium ion
h. indicator
i. neutralization
j. pH
k. pickling
l. plankton
m. salt
n. saponification
o. soap
p. strong acid
q. strong base
r. titration
s. weak acid
t. weak base

UNDERSTANDING VOCABULARY

Match each phrase with the correct term from the list of Key Science Words.

1. a hydrogen ion bonded to a water molecule
2. a reaction between an acid and a base
3. acid that ionizes completely in solution
4. base that partly dissociates in solution
5. can remove water from materials
6. formed when negative ions from an acid combine with positive ions from a base
7. process that removes impurities from metal surfaces
8. expresses the concentration of H_3O^+ ions
9. any solution that has a pH less than 7
10. the process of making soap

ACIDS, BASES, AND SALTS **447**

CHAPTER
REVIEW

SUMMARY

Have students read the summary statements to review the major concepts of the chapter.

UNDERSTANDING VOCABULARY

1. g	6. m
2. i	7. k
3. p	8. j
4. t	9. a
5 d	10. n

ASSESSMENT
Portfolio

Encourage students to place in their portfolios one or two items of what they consider to be their best work. For each item, ask students to explain why that item was chosen and what they learned from it. Items might be selected from the following.

- For Your Gifted Students map, p. 424
- Flex Your Brain, p. 433
- Activity 17-1 results and answers, p. 437

Performance

Additional performance assessments may be found in *Performance Assessment* and *Science Integration Activities* that accompany **Merrill Physical Science.** Performance Task Assessment Lists and rubrics for evaluating these activities and other products generated throughout the chapter can be found in Glencoe's *Performance Assessment in Middle School Science.*

OPTIONS

ASSESSMENT

To assess student understanding of material in this chapter, use the resources listed.

COOPERATIVE LEARNING

Consider using cooperative learning in the THINK AND WRITE CRITICALLY, APPLY, and MORE SKILL BUILDERS sections of the Chapter Review.

PROGRAM RESOURCES

From the **Teacher Resource Package** use:
Chapter Review, pages 37-38.
Chapter and Unit Tests, pages 109-112, Chapter Test.
Chapter and Unit Tests, pages 113-114, Unit Test.

CHAPTER
REVIEW

CHECKING CONCEPTS

1. a	6. a
2. a	7. c
3. b	8. b
4. d	9. d
5. a	10. c

USING LAB SKILLS

ASSESSMENT

Use these alternate lab exercises to assess students' understanding of skills used in this chapter.

11. It would have a strong attraction.
12. The basic NaOH solution is more concentrated.

THINK AND WRITE CRITICALLY

13. HCl ionizes, forming H$^+$ and Cl$^-$ ions.
14. In alcohol, OH forms the hydroxyl group, which is not ionized. In a base, OH forms the hydroxide ion, OH$^-$.
15. In water, ammonia molecules react with water molecules, producing ammonium ions and hydroxide ions.
16. A concentrated acid contains more solute and less water than does a dilute acid. The terms have nothing to do with how much an acid dissociates in water, which is the measure of its strength.
17. Ashes were used as the source of hydroxide ions. These ashes were mixed with animal fat to make soap.

CHAPTER
REVIEW

CHECKING CONCEPTS

Choose the word or phrase that completes the sentence.

1. HF reacts strongly with metals; CH$_3$COOH does not. HF is more _____.
   a. acidic   c. soluble
   b. basic   d. sour

2. Sulfuric acid is also known as _____.
   a. battery acid   c. stomach acid
   b. citric acid   d. vinegar

3. Most sulfuric acid is used to produce _____.
   a. batteries   c. petroleum products
   b. fertilizer   d. plastics

4. _____ is used to make phosphoric, nitric, and hydrochloric acids.
   a. Dehydration   c. Pickling
   b. A base   d. Sulfuric acid

5. The most widely used base is _____.
   a. ammonia   c. lye
   b. caustic lime   d. milk of magnesia

6. Carrots have a pH of 5.0, so carrots are _____.
   a. acidic   c. neutral
   b. basic   d. an indicator

7. Pure water has a pH of _____.
   a. 0   c. 7
   b. 5.2   d. 14

8. Certain materials can act as indicators because they change _____.
   a. acidity   c. concentration
   b. color   d. taste

9. KBr is an example of a(n) _____.
   a. acid   c. indicator
   b. base   d. salt

10. You might use a solution of _____ to titrate an oxalic acid solution.
    a. HBr   c. NaOH
    b. Ca(NO$_3$)$_2$ d. NH$_4$Cl

USING LAB SKILLS

11. Think about how you represented strong and weak acids in Activity 17-1 on page 437. If an acid is described as weak, would its negative ions have a strong or a weak attraction for any hydronium ions in solution?

12. In Activity 17-2 on page 446, you neutralized an unknown acid solution with a basic solution. If you found that 1 mL of the NaOH would neutralize 5 mL of the carbonated beverage, which is more concentrated, the acid or the base?

THINK AND WRITE CRITICALLY

Answer the following questions in your Journal using complete sentences.

13. When hydrogen chloride, HCl, is dissolved in water to form hydrochloric acid, what happens to the HCl?

14. Explain how the hydroxide ion differs from the –OH group in an alcohol.

15. Why is ammonia considered a base, even though it contains no hydroxide ions?

16. Explain why a concentrated acid is not necessarily a strong acid.

17. Ashes from a wood fire are basic. Explain how early settlers used this fact when making soap.

18. Explain why you should never use taste to test for an acid, even though acetic, citric, and dilute phosphoric acids are in things you eat and drink.
19. How would the pH of a dilute solution of HCl compare with the pH of a concentrated solution of the same acid? Explain.
20. Acid rain containing sulfuric acid, H_2SO_4, will react with iron objects. What products will result from this reaction?
21. Chalk, $CaCO_3$, is a salt. What acid and what base react to form this salt?
22. Suppose you have hard water in your home. Would you use a soap or a detergent for washing your clothes and dishes? Explain your answer.

MORE SKILL BUILDERS

If you need help, refer to the Skill Handbook.

1. **Making and Using Tables:** Make a table that lists the chemical and physical properties of acids and bases.
2. **Recognizing Cause and Effect:** Complete the following table by describing the cause and effect of each change listed in the left-hand column.

Process	Cause	Effect
Saponification		
Esterification		
Acid rain		
Neutralization		
Corrosion		

3. **Comparing and Contrasting:** Compare and contrast the reactions that would be produced by pouring sulfuric acid on a piece of paper and burning a marshmallow.
4. **Observing and Inferring:** You have equal volumes of three colorless liquids, A, B, and C. You add several drops of phenolphthalein to each liquid. A and B remain colorless, but C turns pink. Next you add some of liquid C to liquid A and the pink color disappears. You add the rest of C to liquid B and the mixture remains pink. What can you infer about each of these liquids? Which liquid probably has a pH of 7?
5. **Interpreting Data:** A soil test indicates that the pH of the soil in a field is 4.8. To neutralize the soil, would you add a substance containing H_3PO_4 or one containing $Ca(OH)_2$? Explain your answer.

PROJECTS

1. Make a display and write a report on common household acids and bases, how they are used, and cautions to be taken.
2. Do research to find out how acids are used in making fertilizer. Name several acids and tell why each is needed and how their proportions may vary from fertilizer to fertilizer. Conduct an investigation by growing seedlings using different fertilizers. Describe your results in a report.

ACIDS, BASES, AND SALTS **449**

18. Acids that you eat are weak. Strong acids can cause severe burns.
19. The pH of the concentrated solution would be lower (more acidic) than that of the dilute solution. In the dilute solution, the hydronium ions are less concentrated than in the concentrated solution.
20. hydrogen gas and iron(II) sulfate
21. calcium hydroxide, $Ca(OH)_2$, and carbonic acid, H_2CO_3
22. You would use a detergent because a detergent will not react with minerals in the water to form a scum (precipitate).

MORE SKILL BUILDERS

1. **Making and Using Tables:** Tables may vary, but should resemble the following.

	Physical Properties	Chemical Properties
Acid	sour taste, electrolyte	corrosive, reacts with indicators, forms H_3O^+ in solution
Base	bitter taste, feels slippery, electrolyte	corrosive, reacts with indicators, forms OH^- in solution

2. **Recognizing Cause and Effect:** See table at bottom of page.
3. **Comparing and Contrasting:** Both processes involve dehydration of an organic material, removing the water and leaving only carbon. Thus, both final products are dark in appearance. They differ in that acid is used as a dehydrating agent on the paper, and heat drives off the water in the marshmallow.
4. **Comparing and Contrasting:** Liquid C is a base because it turns phenolphthalein pink. Liquids A and B are not bases. Liquid A is an acid because it turns the pink base solution colorless. Liquid B is probably not acid and is most likely to have a pH of 7.
5. **Interpreting Data:** You would use $Ca(OH)_2$. The soil has a pH of 4.8, indicating that it is acidic. To neutralize this acidic soil, a base should be added.

Answer to More Skill Builders, number 2.

Process	Cause	Effect
Saponification	NaOH or KOH and fat react	soap and glycerine formed
Esterification	organic acid and alcohol react	ester and water formed
Acid rain formation	pollutants from burning fossil fuels react with water in air	destruction of life, soil, metal, minerals, buildings
Neutralization	acid and base react	salt and water formed
Corrosion	metal reacts with a corrosive agent	metal forms a compound and loses strength

Objective

In this unit-ending feature, the unit topic, "Interactions of Matter," is extended into other disciplines. Students will see how interactions of matter are occurring around the planet.

Motivate

Cooperative Learning: Assign one Connection to each group of students. Using the Expert Teams strategy, have each group find out more about the geographical location of the Connection—its climate, culture, flora and fauna, and ecological issues.

Teaching Tips

▶ Ask students to describe the kind of interaction of matter that is occurring in each Connection.

Wrap-Up

Conclude this lesson by having students predict other places besides the ones shown here where similar interactions of matter might occur.

METEOROLOGY

Background: Great Salt Lake is the remnant of Lake Bonneville, formed 16 000 years ago during the last glacial period. The lake now covers an area about the size of Delaware.

Discussion: Discuss how varying weather conditions affect this lake. Ask students to hypothesize what weather conditions might have lead to the lake's lowest level, reached in 1963. Ask how the lake's salinity would have been affected.

Answer to Question: More water would enter the lake, but less water would evaporate so the salinity would probably decrease.

Extension: Have students use salt and water to make salt solutions that represent the maximum and minimum concentrations of Great Salt Lake.

UNIT 5
GLOBAL CONNECTIONS

Interactions of Matter

In this unit, you studied how matter interacts in solutions, chemical reactions, and acids and bases. Now find out how the interactions of matter are connected to other subjects and places around the world.

120°   60°

60°

BIOLOGY

CREATING AN ACID LAKE
Ontario, Canada
For five years, scientists added sulfuric acid to a lake to lower its pH and to observe what happened to organisms in the lake. When they stopped adding acid, microbes in the mud were able to start neutralizing the acid. Why do you think the scientists did this experiment?

METEOROLOGY

INLAND OCEAN
Great Salt Lake, Utah
Spring runoff brings in about 2 million tons of dissolved minerals, while the summer sun evaporates water, accounting for the Great Salt Lake's salinity. Since 1843, the depth of the lake has ranged between 7.3 and 13.7 meters and the salinity ranged from 20% to 6%. How would wet winters and cool, cloudy summers affect the salinity of the lake?

GEOLOGY

CAVE FORMATION
Carlsbad Caverns, New Mexico
Over 200 million years ago, corals built a reef in a sea. As the area was raised above sea level, acidic groundwater entered cracks in the reef and dissolved limestone, forming caverns. Water containing dissolved minerals continued to drip into the caverns. As the water evaporated, mineral deposits formed stalactites and stalagmites. How do stalactites and stalagmites differ?

450

GEOLOGY

Background: About 95% of Carlsbad's formations are now dry, and very little cave building is occurring. The area above ground is now desert. Cave temperatures remain fairly constant year round.

Discussion: Discuss the chemistry of cave formation. Tell students that when carbon dioxide dissolves in water, weak carbonic acid forms. The acid reacts with limestone (calcium carbonate) to form calcium hydrogen carbonate, which dissolves in the water.

Answer to Question: Stalactites form as water with dissolved minerals drips down from cavern ceilings. Stalagmites form from the ground up as water drips down stalactites to end up on the cavern floor.

Extension: Have students use dilute HCl to observe how acidic water can dissolve limestone.

HISTORY

ANTISEPTIC SURGERY
London, England

In 1865, surgeon Joseph Lister began to use carbolic acid solutions to clean surgical instruments and the hands of hospital workers. The death rate of patients after surgery dropped dramatically. Why did this happen?

0°

SOCIAL STUDIES

GUNPOWDER
People's Republic of China

Chinese books dating back to 1044 give the directions for making gunpowder. The Mongols took the discovery to Europe. The Europeans developed ways to use gunpowder as a weapon. Find out what chemicals make up gunpowder.

451

HISTORY

Background: Lister had learned about Pasteur's germ theory of disease. He hypothesized that deaths occurring after surgery might be caused by germ infections. He also realized the germs could be coming from the doctors' hands or their instruments, so he used carbolic acid in an attempt to kill the germs.

Discussion: Discuss the importance of Lister's discovery. Point out that before this, patients often died even though their surgery was successful.

Answer to Question: Carbolic acid acts as an antiseptic and kills germs that cause infections.

Extension: Have students research other antiseptics and their chemical makeup.

BIOLOGY

Background: Researchers at Canada's Experimental Lakes Area sacrificed a lake in Ontario to see if ecosystems in seemingly lifeless lakes damaged by acid rain could be brought back. As they lowered the pH from 6.5 to 5.1, fish stopped reproducing and other organisms died off. As the pH rose to 5.4, fish started reproducing again, but all species did not return to the lake.

Discussion: Discuss what scientists hoped to learn from the experiment. Ask students to discuss the advantages of using a real lake for the experiment rather than a laboratory.

Answer to Question: Scientists hoped to find out if the lake would recover and if populations of organisms would return to the lake.

Extension: Have students find out about other research being done on lakes damaged by acid rain.

SOCIAL STUDIES

Background: Evidence indicates that the Chinese had invented gunpowder by the year 250, but used it primarily for fireworks. It was not extensively used in warfare until it reached Europe.

Discussion: Discuss how knowledge of gunpowder led to the development of cannons. Ask students to discuss how this invention changed warfare in Europe.

Answer to Question: The chemicals in gunpowder are saltpeter, KNO_3; charcoal; and sulfur.

Extension: Have students research the development of cordite, the explosive that replaced gunpowder on the battlefield.

CAREERS

PAINT ANALYST

Background: Paint analysts work for companies that manufacture paints. In addition to developing different colors, many paint analysts work on the development of specialty paints, such as marine paints and mildew-resistant paints.

Related Career	Education
Art restorer	graduate degree
Automotive painter	high school
Painter	high school
Lithographic artist	technical school

Career Issue: Some specialty paints, such as those designed to protect boat hulls from marine organisms and those designed to protect objects from mildew, contain chemical additives that some people worry about. They think these paints can harm the environment.

What do you think? Have students discuss of the pros and cons of using chemical additives in certain paints.

WATER-TREATMENT PLANT TECHNICIAN

Background: Water treatment technicians may work in industrial plants, municipal plants, or state and federal centers. Because water treatment is a 24-hour-a-day operation, technicians work different shifts.

Related Career	Education
Hydrologist	college degree
Water-treatment plant operator	high school
Agricultural technician	technical school
Instrumentation technician	technical school

Career Issue: In some areas, municipal wells have had to be closed down because of contamination from agricultural chemicals, industrial pollutants, or chemicals used on icy roads.

What do you think? Lead students in a discussion about their attitudes toward groundwater pollution. How do they think this problem should be dealt with? What role should water-treatment technicians play?

WATER TREATMENT TECHNICIAN

A *water treatment technician* works wherever there is a possibility of water contamination. The technician collects and prepares water samples for laboratory examination.

Some technicians test drinking-water supplies from municipal water plants or wells to make sure the water is safe to use and drink. They add chemicals, such as chlorine or fluorides to the water supply. Other technicians work in waste-water plants, making sure the waste is clean enough to be released back into the environment.

If you're interested in becoming a water treatment technician, you should take high school classes in chemistry, mathematics, and biology. Because some technicians in smaller communities also perform maintenance duties, such as repairing pumps, you should also have mechanical aptitude. Most technicians complete a two-year course at a technical school.

For Additional Information
Contact the National Environmental Training Association, 2930 E. Camelback Road, Suite 185, Phoenix, AZ 85016.

UNIT READINGS

▶ Cobb, Vicki. *Chemically Active!* Philadelphia: Lippincott, 1985.
▶ Mohnen, Volker A. "The Challenge of Acid Rain." *Scientific American,* August 1988, pp. 30-38.
▶ Whyman, Dathryn. *Chemical Changes,* Danbury, CT: Gloucester, 1986.

452

CAREERS

PAINT ANALYST

Paint analysts develop new colors of paints. They mix together basic colors to create hundreds of different colors. You have probably seen these on paint chips in paint or hardware stores. Once you have selected the color you want, a worker at the store mixes the paint according to directions that were provided by the paint analyst.

If you're interested in becoming a paint analyst, you should have good color vision and artistic skills. High school classes in art and chemistry are also helpful. Although some paint analysts receive on-the-job training, most have college degrees in chemistry.

For Additional Information
Contact the American Chemical Society, 1155 16th Street NW, Washington, DC 20036.

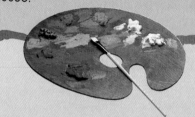

UNIT READINGS

Background
▶ *Chemically Active!* describes how to make solutions and how to separate mixtures.
▶ "The Challenge of Acid Rain" discusses advancements that help provide solutions to the acid rain problem.
▶ *Chemical Changes* illustrates some basic principles of science.

More Readings
1. Zubrowski, Bernie. *Messing Around with Baking Chemistry.* Boston, MA: Little, 1980. Presents experiments to explore what happens when batter and dough turn into cake and bread.
2. Walters, Derek. *Chemistry.* New York, NY: Watts, 1982. Easy experiments that highlight the applications of chemistry to everyday life.
3. Atkins, P.W. *Molecules.* New York, NY: Scientific American Library, 1987. Essays about interesting molecules.

Snow

by Ruth Kirk

The passage that follows gives Ruth Kirk's perspective on the use of salt for snow control on roads.

Tests show salt damage as far as one hundred feet from the edge of pavement. It harms soil structure and by upsetting osmotic balance causes water to be drawn out of plants' roots instead of into them. (The flow is toward the greater salt concentration, which normally is in the root sap.) Gardeners at Arlington National Cemetery have reported the loss of privet hedges and bluegrass lawns because of salt, and at Walter Reed Hospital street maples and parking lot hemlocks have died because of salt-laden snow piled up outside curbing where its melt seeped into the ground. In New Hampshire, Massachusetts, Vermont, and Connecticut, tests of afflicted and dying trees indicate excess sodium in leaf tissue and a high total salt concentration in sap. Maples seem the most affected, sugar maples more so than red maples. The New Hampshire tests noted damage along state roads, which are salted, but not along roads of the same area where de-icing salts are not used.

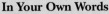

Animals and human life suffers too. The death of pheasants, pigeons, quail and rabbits have been traced to salt poisoning in the Madison, Wisconsin, region. Deer drawn to roads to lick salt have been struck by cars. Dog owners protest damage to pets' feet. Doctors in several areas of high winter salt use recommend the purchase of distilled water by patients with congestive heart failure, certain kidney problems, or hypertension, and for many pregnant women. Widespread contamination of municipal wells has become commonplace and a few communities have been forced to close water supplies that had served for generations. Some of the trouble comes from snow scraped off streets and roads and dumped into rivers, lakes, and ponds; some is from seepage through the soil. Improper storage causes a high proportion of the problem. Salt piles should rest on an impermeable footing and be covered as protection from rain and snow, but often no effort at containment is made.

In Your Own Words

▶ Write an informative essay on the importance of finding alternatives to snow control, based on Ruth Kirk's writings.

Classics

▶ Asimov, Isaac. *Asimov on Chemistry.* New York NY: Doubleday, 1974. A collection of essays on chemistry written between 1958 and 1965 for magazines.

Other Works

▶ Other books and articles that include information on snow removal techniques include: "Water Pollution and Associated Effects from Street Salting." Environmental Protection Technology Series. Environmental Protection Agency R2-73-257. Washington, D.C., May 1973.

▶ Stamps, David. "The Real Price of Road Salt." *National Wildlife.* December-January 1989.

Source: Ruth Kirk, *Snow,* New York: William Morrow and Company, 1978.
Biography: Ruth Kirk is well known for nature writings. Her previous magazine articles and books have dealt with subjects ranging from desert and rain forest ecology to archaeology. In researching this book, she studied hundreds of scientific reports, talked with experts, and traveled extensively.

TEACHING STRATEGY

▶ Have students read through the passage by Ruth Kirk. The have them respond to the discussion questions below.

Discussion Questions

1. **From the passage given here, how does Ruth Kirk describe the damage to plant and animal life caused by the use of road salts?** *Kirk refers to plant life, such as trees and grasses, as being killed by the salt "upsetting the osmotic balance," causing "water to be drawn out of plants' roots instead of into them." Birds and small mammals have been poisoned by salt; deer have been killed by vehicles when they lick salt from the roads; and salt injures dogs' feet.*

2. **Do research to learn more about what nonbiological damage results from salting roads and highways. If you live in an area where it snows, but salt is not used, find out how snow on highways is treated and why salt is not used.** *Automobile magazines, general-interest magazines, and consumer publications are good sources. Encourage students to research this topic using Reader's Guide to Periodical Literature. Students may find out about damage to metal structures, deterioration of concrete, and damage to automobiles themselves. In areas that have snow but do not use salt, road crews may spread sand, stone, or cinders, or may simply rely on plowing. In some communities, salt may be outlawed. Students may be surprised to learn that salt may not be used because the climate is too cold for it to be effective.*

In Unit 6, students are introduced to wave phenomena. The properties and behavior of transverse mechanical waves are discussed and related to those of longitudinal waves. The various properties of sound are explained by its wave characteristics. Light is then introduced to demonstrate the wave characteristics of electromagnetic waves. The unit closes by having students explore optics and optical instruments.

CONTENTS

ADVANCE PREPARATION

Activities
▶ **Activity 18-2, page 471,** requires plastic pipe (2 1/2" to 4") that can be obtained in hardware or plumbing supply stores.

Audiovisuals
▶ Show the video *Mr. Wizard's World: Sound Instruments,* Macmillan/McGraw-Hill School Division.
▶ Show the video *Noise Pollution,* LCA.
▶ Show the film *Color From Light,* Churchill Films.
▶ Show the film *Light and Lenses,* Journal Films, Inc.

454

OPTIONS

Cross Curriculum

Cooperative Learning: Assign students to groups and have them keep journals indicating when terms related to the unit are used or discussed in classes other than science. Have them note the class, the circumstance, and if the term was used the same way. At the end of the unit, have students in each group compile their journals and discuss their findings with the class.

Science at Home

Have students list the titles of songs that they have heard on radio, TV, or recordings, or have read on the covers of recordings, albums, or sheet music that contain colors. Have them conjecture on how color is used to portray or affect a mood.

What's Happening Here?

What colors would you choose to show hot and cold? Why do we think of "red hot" and "cool blue"? This color-enhanced satellite photo of the Atlantic Ocean uses red for hot and blue for cold. The orange-red area is the Gulf Stream, a major warm-water current. Satellites detect warm water by measuring waves of electromagnetic radiation. Although we think of red as hot and blue as cool, you'll discover that blue light actually has more energy than red. In this unit, you'll learn about how your experience of heat, light, color, sound, and music depends on waves.

UNIT CONTENTS

455

Multicultural Awareness

Have interested students research the cultural differences in the symbolic use of color. Students might be interested in surveying the use of color in flags of nations around the world.

Inquiry Questions

▶**What part of the satellite detects the infrared radiation?** *The radiation is detected by photosensitive instruments mounted on the bottom of the satellite.*

▶**What human body organ detects infrared radiation?** *skin*

▶**What organ detects light?** *eye*

▶**What was the energy source of the infrared radiation when this picture was taken?** *water*

▶**What would be the energy source if the satellite took a picture using visible light?** *sun*

INTRODUCING THE UNIT

What's Happening Here?

▶ Have students look at the photos and read the text. Ask them to tell you what's happening here. Point out to students that in this unit they will learn how all electromagnetic energy, such as infrared radiation and visible light, and detectors of electromagnetic energy, such as the satellite's sensors and the human eye, have common characteristics.

▶**Background:** The computer-enhanced image can be considered a thermograph or temperature picture of the area. All matter radiates thermal energy in the form of electromagnetic waves called infrared radiation. The frequency of the infrared radiation is precisely related to the temperature of the material from which it is radiated. The satellite detects the different frequencies of infrared radiation and relays the data to ground stations, where computers process the data to produce colored images. The colors used to enhance the image are chosen for psychological effect.

Previewing the Chapters

▶ Have students find and identify the photographs in the chapters that show (1) what noise and musical sounds look like; *Figure 18-9, page 473*, (2) an unappetizing picture of broccoli; *Figure 19-10b, page 494*, (3) something that they listen to that also makes colors; *Figure 19-19, page 505*, (4) an application of a laser *Figure 20-18, page 531.*

Tying to Previous Knowledge

▶ Have students recall other types of thermal energy transfer in matter.

▶ Use the **Inquiry Questions** in the OPTIONS box to investigate light.

CHAPTER
18 Waves and Sound

CHAPTER SECTION	OBJECTIVES	ACTIVITIES
18-1 Wave Characteristics (2 days)	1. **Sketch** a transverse wave and **identify** its characteristics. 2. **Discuss** the relationship between the frequency and wavelength in a transverse wave. 3. **Using** the relationship between wavelength, frequency, and velocity, find one variable when two are given.	**Activity 18-1:** *Making Waves,* p. 463
18-2 The Nature of Sound (2 days)	1. **Describe** the transmission of sound through a medium. 2. **Recognize** the relationships between intensity and loudness and frequency and pitch. 3. **Illustrate** the Doppler effect with a practical example.	**MINI-Lab:** *How is sound different when it travels through solids?* p. 466
18-3 Noise Pollution Science & Society (1 day)	1. **Analyze** the role of noise as one type of pollution. 2. **Suggest** three ways noise pollution can be reduced.	
18-4 Musical Sounds (2 days)	1. **Distinguish** music and noise. 2. **Describe** why different instruments produce sounds of different quality. 3. **Explain** two types of wave interference.	**MINI-Lab:** *How can hearing loss change the sounds you hear?* p. 475 **Activity 18-2:** *Frequency of Sound Waves,* p. 478
Chapter Review		

ACTIVITY MATERIALS

FIND OUT	ACTIVITIES		MINI-LABS	
Page 457 1 soda pop bottle water	**18-1 Making Waves, p. 463** small Slinky stopwatch	**18-2 Frequency of Sound Waves, p. 478** plastic pipe rubber band metric ruler	**How is sound different when it travels through solids? p. 466** 1.5 m string metal objects	**How can hearing loss change the sounds you hear? p. 475** radio heavy pads

CHAPTER FEATURES	TEACHER RESOURCE PACKAGE	OTHER RESOURCES
Skill Builder: *Comparing and Contrasting,* p. 462	**Ability Level Worksheets** ◆ **Study Guide,** p. 74 ● **Reinforcement,** p. 74 ▲ **Enrichment,** p. 74 **Concept Mapping,** pp. 41, 42 **Science and Society,** p. 22 **Activity Worksheets,** pp. 5, 141, 142 **Transparency Masters,** pp. 71, 72	**Color Transparency 36,** Wave Motion **Laboratory Manual 37,** Velocity of a Wave **STVS:** Disc 1, Side 1 **Science Integration Activity 18**
Technology: *Window on the Deep?* p. 467 **Skill Builder:** *Concept Mapping,* p. 470	**Ability Level Worksheets** ◆ **Study Guide,** p. 75 ● **Reinforcement,** p. 75 ▲ **Enrichment,** p. 75 **Activity Worksheets,** p. 147 **Transparency Masters,** pp. 73, 74	**Color Transparency 37,** The Decibel Scale **Laboratory Manual 38,** Sound Waves and Pitch **STVS:** Disc 3, Side 2; Disc 1, Side 1
You Decide! p. 473	**Ability Level Worksheets** ◆ **Study Guide,** p. 76 ● **Reinforcement,** p. 76 ▲ **Enrichment,** p. 76	
Problem Solving: *The Piano that Played Itself,* p. 474 **Skill Builder:** *Recognizing Cause and Effect,* p. 477	**Ability Level Worksheets** ◆ **Study Guide,** p. 77 ● **Reinforcement,** p. 77 ▲ **Enrichment,** p. 77 **Critical Thinking/Problem Solving,** p. 24 **Cross-Curricular Connections,** p. 24 **Activity Worksheets,** pp. 143, 144, 148	**STVS:** Disc 1, Side 2
Summary Think & Write Critically Key Science Words Apply Understanding Vocabulary More Skill Builders Checking Concepts Projects Using Lab Skills	**ASSESSMENT RESOURCES** **Chapter Review,** pp. 39, 40 **Chapter Test,** pp. 122-125 **Performance Assessment in Middle School Science**	**Chapter Review Software** **Test Bank** **Performance Assessment** **Alternate Assessment**

◆ **Basic**   ● **Average**   ▲ **Advanced**

ADDITIONAL MATERIALS

SOFTWARE	AUDIOVISUAL	BOOKS/MAGAZINES
Heat, Light, and Sound, Queue. *Learning All About Heat and Sound,* Queue. *Sound,* Queue. *Sound and Light,* Queue. *Sound, J and S Software.* *Sound,* Cross Educational Software. *Wave Motion,* Queue.	*Hearing and Sound,* Laserdisc, Journal Films. *Learning About Sound,* Video, Britannica. *The Secret Life of the Radio Set,* Video, Lucerne Media. *Sound, Energy, and Wave Motion;* Video, Coronet. *Sound,* Video, AIT. *Sound, Acoustics, and Recording:* Video, Coronet. *Sound Science: You Can Do It!,* Video, Britannica. *Standing Waves and the Principle of Superposition,* Video, Insight Media.	Darling, David. *Sounds Interesting: The Science of Acoustics.* NY: Dillon Press, 1991. Lampton, Christopher F. *Sound: More Than What You Hear.* Hillsdale, NJ: Enslow, 1992. Parker, Steve. *Singing a Song: How You Sing, Speak, and Make Sounds.* NY: Watts, 1992. Wood, Robert W. *Physics for Kids: 49 Easy Experiments with Acoustics.* Blue Ridge Summit, PA: Tab, 1990.

THEME DEVELOPMENT: Energy is one of the main themes of this chapter, as waves are rhythmic disturbances that carry energy. Emphasize how the amplification of waves increases the energy. Use examples to show both kinds of waves carrying energy.

CHAPTER OVERVIEW

▶ **Section 18-1:** This section introduces transverse waves. The parts of a wave are identified, and the relationship among frequency, wavelength, and velocity is discussed.

▶ **Section 18-2:** Compressional waves are explained. The differences between frequency and pitch and intensity and loudness are examined. A discussion of the Doppler effect concludes this section.

▶ **Section 18-3: Science and Society:** Noise pollution, its control, and its effects on the human ear are explored. The You Decide feature asks students to determine if skateboarders violate noise pollution codes.

▶ **Section 18-4:** This section contrasts music and noise. Musical quality and interference are illustrated.

CHAPTER VOCABULARY

waves	intensity
medium	loudness
transverse wave	noise
crests	pollution
troughs	music
wavelength	noise
amplitude	resonance
frequency	quality
compressional	interference
wave	reverberation
pitch	acoustics

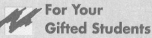

456

OPTIONS

For Your Gifted Students

▶ Have students research the speeds of light and sound in different media, make a bar graph for each, and make a hypothesis about how the density of matter affects both light and sound.

▶ Have students determine the ratio of the speed of light and the speed of sound in air at a specific temperature.

For Your Mainstreamed Students

▶ Play a radio in the classroom at a comfortable level of volume. Place different objects in front of the radio to determine how well they absorb sound. Objects you could try might include a balloon, a pillow, a book, and some paper. Rank the items you tested in order of how well they absorbed sound. Discuss the types of materials that could be used to soundproof buildings.

Have you ever played a musical instrument? Perhaps you plucked the strings on a guitar, or made music by blowing air into a harmonica or a clarinet. Did you know you can even make music with a soda pop bottle?

FIND OUT!

Do this simple activity to find out how you can make music with a soda pop bottle.

You need a clean, empty soda pop bottle. First, place the empty bottle just below your lower lip so it touches your lip lightly. Take a big breath and blow a steady stream of air across the top of the bottle. Did you hear a musical tone? Fill the bottle halfway with water and blow across the bottle again. Did it sound lower or higher than the first tone you made? Pour some water out of the bottle. How do you expect the tone to sound now? It should be lower. *Experiment* and try to play a song with several other soda pop bottles with different water levels. Try it!

Gearing Up
Previewing the Chapter

Use this outline to help you focus on important ideas in this chapter.

Previewing Science Skills

► In the Skill Builders, you will make a concept map, determine cause and effect, and compare and contrast.
► In the Activities, you will observe, measure, and define operationally.
► In the MINI-Labs, you will observe, interpret, and compare.

What's next?

Now that you know how to make music with a soda pop bottle, you will learn how sound waves are made. You will also find out how changing the length of the air column in the bottle affects the musical tone.

457

INTRODUCING THE CHAPTER
Use the Find Out activity to introduce students to musical pitches. Explain that as they read the chapter they will be learning what sound is and why each sound is unique.

FIND OUT!
Preparation: Several days before you begin this chapter, have students bring in clean, empty soda pop or juice bottles. Save these bottles to use in future activities.

Materials: one soda pop bottle for every three students; a container of water or access to a sink for each group

Cooperative Learning: Use the Science Investigation strategy in groups of three. Have one student describe and record the sounds heard, the second student adjust the water level, and the third student blow across the bottle.

Teaching Tips
► The cooperative learning suggestion above encourages student communication and raises the level of excitement.
► The bottles should be washed thoroughly after each use.
► The water level in the bottle during each test could be measured and recorded so students can infer the relationship between water level and sound.
► Have the class try to play a song.

Gearing Up
Have students study the Gearing Up section to familiarize themselves with the chapter. Discuss the relationships of the topics in the outline.

What's Next?
Before beginning the first section, make sure students understand the connection between the Find Out activity and the topics to follow.

ASSESSMENT OPTIONS

PORTFOLIO
Refer to page 479 for suggested items that students might select for their portfolios.

PERFORMANCE ASSESSMENT
See page 479 for additional Performance Assessment options.
Process
Skill Builders, pp. 462
MINI-Labs, pp. 466, 475
Activities 18-1, p. 463; 18-2, p. 478
Using Lab Skills, p. 480

CONTENT ASSESSMENT
Assessment—Oral, pp. 466, 469, 476
Skill Builders, pp. 470, 477
Section Reviews, pp. 462, 470, 472, 477
Chapter Review, pp. 479-481
Mini Quizzes, pp. 460, 470, 476

GROUP ASSESSMENT
Opportunities for group assessment occur with Cooperative Learning Strategies and Flex Your Brain Activities.

PREPARATION

SECTION BACKGROUND

▶ Although students sometimes name water waves as examples of transverse waves, these waves are actually a distinct kind of wave called a surface wave. In addition to moving up and down, the water molecules also move in circles.

▶ Earthquakes under the ocean floor can cause giant tidal waves called tsunamis. They move at speeds up to 800 km/h in deep waters, and wave height can exceed that of a 20-story building.

▶ One hertz is one cycle per second.

PREPLANNING

▶ Obtain a class set of small Slinkys for Activity 18-1.

1 MOTIVATE

▶ Place a table tennis ball in a wide pan of water about halfway between the center and the edge of the pan. When the water is still, drop a rock into the pan. The wave moves, but the ball has no horizontal motion. Compare the motion of the wave to that of the energy.

▶ Have the class make a wave like those that spectators make at ball games. Join hands in a circle and emphasize that there must be a certain rhythm to each wave. Experiment with how many ways you can change the appearance of the wave (wavelength, frequency, amplitude, speed).

In Your JOURNAL

Students may group waves into categories such as waves you can or cannot see and waves that do or do not require a medium in which to travel.

V i d e o D i s c

STVS: Seismic Simulator, Disc 1, Side 1

18-1 Wave Characteristics

New Science Words

waves
medium
transverse wave
crests
troughs
wavelength
amplitude
frequency

Objectives

▶ Sketch a transverse wave and identify its characteristics.
▶ Discuss the relationship between the frequency and wavelength in a transverse wave.
▶ Using the relationship between wavelength, frequency, and velocity, find one variable when two are given.

Transverse Waves

What examples come to mind when you think of waves? What do you think water waves, microwaves, sound waves, and radio waves have in common with each other? These and all other types of waves transfer energy from one place to another. In this lesson, you will read about some of the characteristics of waves.

Water waves are probably the easiest type of wave to visualize. If you've been in a boat on a lake, you know that approaching waves bump against the boat but do not carry the boat along with them as they pass. The boat mostly moves up and down as the waves pass by. Only energy carried by the waves moves forward.

Waves are rhythmic disturbances that carry energy ❶ through matter or space. Water waves transfer energy through the water. Earthquakes transfer energy in powerful shock waves that travel through Earth. Both types of waves travel through a **medium,** a material through which a wave can transfer energy. This medium may be a solid, a liquid, a gas, or a combination of these. Radio waves and light waves, however, are types of waves that can travel without a medium.

Two types of wave motion can carry energy. In one type, a **transverse wave,** the medium moves at right angles to the direction the wave travels. Figure 18-2 shows how you can make transverse waves by shaking the end of a rope up and down while your friend holds one end. The other type of wave motion will be described in the discussion of compressional waves in the next lesson.

Figure 18-1. The energy of a water wave does work on anything in its path.

What are waves?

In Your JOURNAL

In your Journal, make a list of as many examples of waves as you can think of. Suggest how you might categorize them and rearrange your list into those categories.

458 WAVES AND SOUND

OPTIONS

Meeting Different Ability Levels

For Section 18-1, use the following **Teacher Resource Masters** depending upon individual students' needs.

◆ **Study Guide Master** for all students.
● **Reinforcement Master** for students of average and above average ability levels.
▲ **Enrichment Master** for above average students.

Additional Teacher Resource Package masters are listed in any **PROGRAM RESOURCES** boxes that are in the section. The additional masters are appropriate for all students.

◆ STUDY GUIDE   74

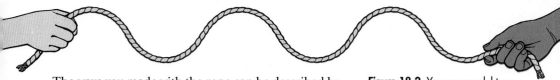

The wave you made with the rope can be described by its characteristics. When you snapped the rope up and down, you may have noticed that high points and low points formed. The highest points of a wave are called the **crests,** and the lowest points are called the **troughs.** Waves are measured by their wavelength. **Wavelength** is the distance between a point on one wave and the identical point on the next wave, such as from crest to crest, or trough to trough. The wavelength between two crests is labeled on Figure 18-3. How could you measure the wavelength on other parts of the wave?

Ocean or lake waves can be described by how high they appear above the normal water level. **Amplitude** is the distance from the crest (or trough) of a wave to the rest position of the medium, as shown in Figure 18-3. The amplitude corresponds to the amount of energy carried by the wave. Waves that carry great amounts of energy have large heights or amplitudes, and waves that carry less energy have smaller amplitudes.

Figure 18-2. You can model transverse waves with a rope.

What are the high points and low points of a wave called?

Connect to... Earth Science

Earthquakes and volcanic activity under the ocean floor can cause giant tidal waves. Find out what these waves are called and why they are so dangerous.

Figure 18-3. Parts of a Transverse Wave

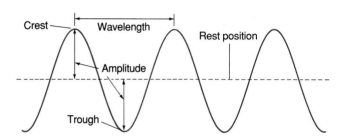

Wave Frequency

Do you know the frequency of your favorite radio station? When you tune your radio to a station, you are actually looking for waves of a certain frequency. The **frequency** of a wave is the number of wave crests that pass one place each second. Frequency is expressed in hertz (Hz). One hertz is the same as one wave per second.

TYING TO PREVIOUS KNOWLEDGE: Review the idea of energy introduced in Chapter 5. Ask students if they ever made waves in the bathtub. Ask what you have to do to make a wave. (You must move your body to put energy into the water.)

OBJECTIVES AND SCIENCE WORDS: Have students review the objectives and science words to become familiar with this section.

2 TEACH

Key Concepts are highlighted.

CONCEPT DEVELOPMENT

▶ To reinforce the comprehension of the major features of a transverse wave, let students demonstrate how amplitude, wavelength, and frequency can be varied by making waves on a rope or Slinky.

STUDENT TEXT QUESTION

▶ Page 459, paragraph 1: **How could you measure the wavelength on other parts of the wave?** *You can measure wavelength from any part on one wave to the same part of the next wave (crest to crest, trough to trough, and so on).*

Connect to... Earth Science

Answer: These waves are called tsunamis and carry extremely large amounts of energy. As the water becomes shallower near shore, the wave height can exceed that of a 20-story building.

CONCEPT DEVELOPMENT

▶ Demonstrate frequency by beating a pencil on your desk with a steady rhythm. Change the frequency and ask students to explain what has changed (the time intervals between taps and the number of taps per second).

▶ This is a good opportunity to emphasize that frequency and wavelength are inversely proportional if wave speed remains constant.

CROSS CURRICULUM

▶ **Math:** Students have learned that as frequency decreases, the wavelength increases if the speed of the wave is constant. Ask them what the relationship between wavelength and frequency is called (inversely proportional).

CHECK FOR UNDERSTANDING

Use the Mini Quiz to check for understanding.

MINI QUIZ

Use the Mini Quiz to check students' recall of chapter content.

1 **What do waves transfer?** *energy*

2 **In what unit is frequency usually expressed?** *Hertz*

3 **What happens to the wavelength if the frequency increases?** *It decreases.*

4 **The highest points of a wave are called _____ .** *crests*

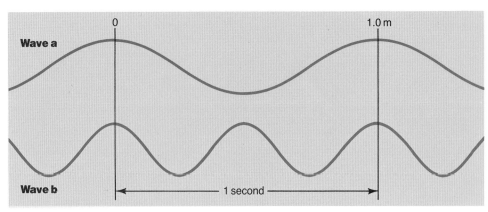

Figure 18-4. Wave a has a longer wavelength and a lower frequency than wave b. Both waves are traveling at the same speed.

What happens to the wavelength of a wave as the frequency increases?

How do you increase the frequency of a wave? To do this with a rope, simply move the rope up and down faster to create more crests per second. As the frequency increases, the wavelength becomes shorter because the speed of the wave remains constant. In other words, as the frequency increases, the wavelength decreases. Using a rope, you can demonstrate this principle as shown in Figure 18-4. This relationship between wavelength and frequency will be discussed further in the next section and in Chapter 19.

Wave Velocity

Sometimes you may want to know how fast a wave is traveling. For example, earthquakes below the ocean can produce giant tidal waves. You would want to know how soon a tidal wave would reach you and if you needed to seek shelter. Wave velocity, v, describes how fast the wave moves forward.

Wave velocity can be determined by multiplying the wavelength and frequency as shown below. Wavelength is represented by the Greek letter lambda, λ. If you know any two variables in the following equation, you can find the remaining unknown variable.

$$\text{velocity} = \text{wavelength} \times \text{frequency}$$
$$v = \lambda \times f$$

The following examples show how you can use this equation to solve for the unknown variable.

Did You Know?

Lightning flashes move at speeds up to 140 000 km/s and last about 0.003 s, with temperatures of about 30 000°C (or 5 times the temperature on the surface of the sun).

OPTIONS

INQUIRY QUESTIONS

▶ **What other two variables would you need to know to find the wavelength of a water wave?** *velocity and frequency* **What formula would you use?** $\lambda = v/f$

▶ **Could you find the frequency of a wave if you knew how fast it was traveling and the distance from trough to trough?** *yes* **Explain your answer mathematically.** *frequency = velocity/wavelength*

PROGRAM RESOURCES

From the **Teacher Resource Package** use:
Science Integration Activity 18
Use **Laboratory Manual 37,** Velocity of a Wave.

EXAMPLE PROBLEM: Calculating the Velocity of a Wave

Problem Statement: A wave is generated in a wave pool at a water amusement park. The wavelength is 3.2 m. The frequency of the wave is 0.60 Hz. What is the velocity of the wave?

Known Information:

Strategy Hint: Another way to express Hertz is 1/second, therefore, m × 1/s = m/s.

wavelength, λ = 3.2 m
frequency, f = 0.60 Hz

Unknown Information: velocity (v)

Equation to Use: $v = \lambda \times f$

Solution: $v = \lambda \times f$ = 3.2 m × 0.60 Hz = 1.92 m/s

PRACTICE PROBLEM

Strategy Hint: Make sure all units correspond.

1. A wave moving along a rope has a wavelength of 1.2 m and a frequency of 4.5 Hz. How fast is the wave traveling along the rope?

EXAMPLE PROBLEM: Calculating the Frequency of a Wave

Problem Statement: Earthquakes can produce three types of waves. One of these is a transverse wave called an S wave. A typical S wave travels at 5000 m/s. Its wavelength is about 417 m. What is its frequency?

Known Information:

Strategy Hint: Remember, Hz = 1/s, so m/s ÷ m = 1/s = 1 Hz

velocity, v = 5000 m/s
wavelength, λ = 417 m

Unknown Information: frequency (f)

Equation to Use: $v = \lambda \times f$

Solution: $v = \lambda \times f$, so $f = v/\lambda$
= (5000 m/s)/(417 m) = 12 Hz

PRACTICE PROBLEM

Strategy Hint: What formula do you use to find frequency?

1. A tuning fork produces a sound wave with a wavelength of 0.20 m and a velocity of 25.6 m/s. What is the frequency of the tuning fork?

18-1   WAVE CHARACTERISTICS   **461**

INQUIRY QUESTIONS

▶ **Three waves with frequencies of 1 Hz, 3 Hz, and 9 Hz travel at the same speed. Rank these waves in order of decreasing wavelength.** _1 Hz, 3 Hz, 9 Hz. As the frequency increases, the wavelength decreases._

▶ **What happens to the wavelength and frequency of a wave if its velocity increases?** _The wavelength, the frequency, or both must increase._

RETEACH

Give students a piece of string about two feet long. Instruct them to form the string into the shape of a transverse wave. Count the number of waves and measure the average wavelength. Now change the wave so it has a greater amplitude; then change it again so it has shorter wavelengths. **What happens to the frequency?** _It increases._

EXTENSION

For students who have mastered this section, use the **Reinforcement** and **Enrichment** masters or other OPTIONS provided.

PRACTICE PROBLEM ANSWER
Calculating the Velocity of a Wave
1. wavelength, λ = 1.2 m
   frequency, f = 4.5 Hz
   $v = \lambda \times f$ = 1.2 m × 4.5 Hz
   = 5.4 m/s

PRACTICE PROBLEM ANSWER
Calculating the Frequency of a Wave
1. velocity, v = 25.6 m/s
   wavelength, λ = 0.20 m
   $f = v/\lambda$ = (25.6 m/s)/(0.20 m)
   = 128 Hz

3 CLOSE

▶ Use the Slinky again to review transverse wave characteristics. Let the students try to make other kinds of rhythmic disturbances with the Slinky. Some of them are likely to discover compressional waves. Have them demonstrate these for the class as the next topic of study.

▶ Ask questions 1-3 and the **Apply** and **Connect to Earth Science** questions in the Section Review.

CHAPTER 18   **461**

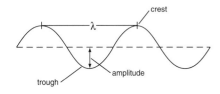

FLEX Your Brain

Use the Flex Your Brain activity to have students explore WAVE CHARACTERISTICS.

ASSESSMENT
Portfolio: Use the Flex Your Brain activity to reinforce critical-thinking and problem-solving skills. In Step 2, students might list experiences at an ocean or amusement park, going to a concert, or noise in their neighborhoods.

SECTION REVIEW ANSWERS
1.

2. The wavelength decreases as the frequency increases, and the wavelength increases as the frequency decreases.
3. $v = \lambda \times f$, so $\lambda = v/f = (4.0$ m/s$) \div (3.5$ Hz$) = 1.14$ m
4. **Apply:** Because both travel at the same speed, the lowest frequency station, 101.9 MHz, sends out waves with longer wavelengths.
5. **Connect to Earth Science:** Pendulums oscillate back and forth between high and low points, as do transverse waves.

Skill Builder

Amplitude depends on energy; wavelength would be measured in meters; and frequency depends on the number of waves.

Skill Builder
ASSESSMENT
Performance: Have students use a Slinky to determine which of the three variables compared in this Skill Builder cannot be directly controlled when shaking the Slinky to create a transverse wave. *Wavelength can only be controlled indirectly by changing the frequency.*

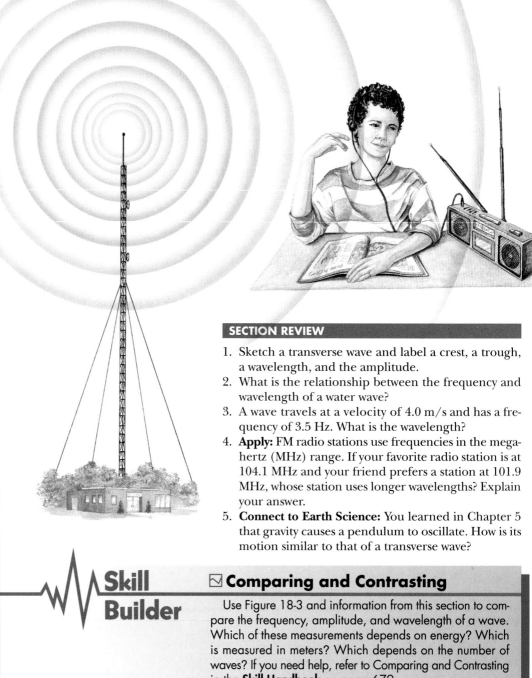

SECTION REVIEW

1. Sketch a transverse wave and label a crest, a trough, a wavelength, and the amplitude.
2. What is the relationship between the frequency and wavelength of a water wave?
3. A wave travels at a velocity of 4.0 m/s and has a frequency of 3.5 Hz. What is the wavelength?
4. **Apply:** FM radio stations use frequencies in the megahertz (MHz) range. If your favorite radio station is at 104.1 MHz and your friend prefers a station at 101.9 MHz, whose station uses longer wavelengths? Explain your answer.
5. **Connect to Earth Science:** You learned in Chapter 5 that gravity causes a pendulum to oscillate. How is its motion similar to that of a transverse wave?

Skill Builder

☑ Comparing and Contrasting

Use Figure 18-3 and information from this section to compare the frequency, amplitude, and wavelength of a wave. Which of these measurements depends on energy? Which is measured in meters? Which depends on the number of waves? If you need help, refer to Comparing and Contrasting in the **Skill Handbook** on page 679.

462 WAVES AND SOUND

OPTIONS

PROGRAM RESOURCES
From the **Teacher Resource Package** use:
Concept Mapping, pages 41-42.
Science and Society, page 22, Wave Energy and Shoreline Erosion.
Activity Worksheets, page 5, Flex Your Brain.
Transparency Masters, pages 71-72, Wave Motion.
Use **Color Transparency** number 36, Wave Motion.

ACTIVITY 18-1

DESIGNING AN EXPERIMENT
Making Waves

All waves must carry energy from one place to another. In this activity, you will create waves in a Slinky. Which wave quantities can you directly influence?

Getting Started
You will be investigating transverse waves using Slinkys. Do not twist or stretch the Slinkys.

Thinking Critically
What determines the amplitude of a transverse wave on a Slinky? What do you think happens to a transverse wave when it hits an unmovable barrier?

Materials
Your cooperative group will use a Slinky.

Try It!

1. Two people in your group should be seated on a smooth floor with the Slinky on the floor and stretched between you. One person will be the wave maker and the other will hold the other end as still as possible.
2. The wave maker should abruptly shake the end of the spring horizontally about a foot to create a single transverse wave pulse. *Record your observations.* Consider its shape, speed, and what happens when it hits the fixed end of the spring. Find other ways of creating a transverse wave.

Summing Up/Sharing Results
- What happens when the wave hits the fixed boundary?
- Why does the wave eventually seem to disappear?

Going Further!
Design at least one Slinky experiment that is not described in the Try It! section. *Describe* your question, *conduct your experiment,* and *record your observations.*

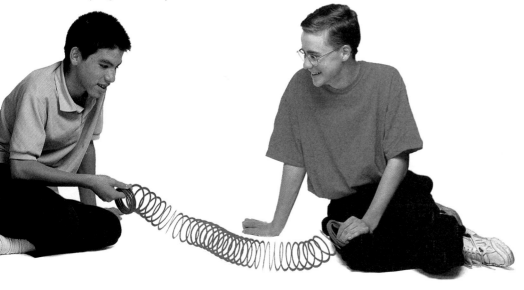

18-1 WAVE CHARACTERISTICS **463**

OBJECTIVE:
Use Slinkys and rope or string to investigate some of the properties and behaviors of transverse waves. **Time:** one class period

PROCESS SKILLS applied in this activity include **observing, inferring,** and **hypothesizing.**

PREPARATION
Cooperative Learning: Use the Science Investigation strategy in groups of three or four. Two students at a time can hold the spring while the other one or two record observations. Have groups repeat observations after exchanging roles.

THINKING CRITICALLY
The energy of a wave determines its amplitude. When a wave hits a fixed barrier, some energy will be absorbed, and the wave will be reflected.

TEACHING THE ACTIVITY
*Refer to the **Activity Worksheets** for additional information and teaching strategies.*
- Remind the students not to overstretch the coiled springs. The small coiled springs sold in toy stores work very well. To avoid having tangled coils, it is wise to have a box or sack for each spring.
- You also might have groups attempt the activity using tightly pulled ropes instead of coiled springs, but ropes do not hold the energy of the wave as well.

GOING FURTHER!
Answers will vary. Students may try sending waves toward each other on the same side (constructive interference) or on opposite sides (destructive interference). Students may create standing waves. Some may discover how to make compressional waves, which are discussed in the next section.

PROGRAM RESOURCES

From the **Teacher Resource Package** use:
Activity Worksheets, pages 141-142, Activity 18-1: Making Waves.

Activity
ASSESSMENT
Performance: Have students sketch a series of diagrams to show what happens to a single transverse wave as it travels along the spring, hits a fixed barrier, and returns to its point of origin.

SUMMING UP/SHARING RESULTS
Shaking the spring vertically will also create a transverse wave, but the energy dissipates more rapidly. When the wave hits the fixed boundary, the wave is reflected back with smaller amplitude in an inverted position. The energy of the wave is absorbed by the floor and the barriers. The behavior of a wave as it passes across the boundary of two mediums depends on the nature of the mediums and the direction.

18-2 The Nature of Sound

PREPARATION

SECTION BACKGROUND

▶ The speed of sound in air is called Mach 1. A common reference value for Mach 1 at a 12-km altitude is 1056 km/h. Altitude and air temperature affect this value.

▶ When an object exceeds the speed of sound, a sonic boom is produced. A sonic boom is a sharp crack that is heard by listeners as the shock waves that follow a supersonic object reach their ears. Captain Chuck Yeager first broke the sound barrier in 1947.

▶ The speed of sound waves depends on the temperature and elasticity of the matter in the medium. Atoms are usually close together in solids. As a result, solids transmit sound faster than air. Hunters of herd animals often put their ears to the ground to determine where the animals are.

▶ A person with a cold often loses his or her voice due to swollen vocal cords that can't vibrate enough to produce sound.

1 MOTIVATE

▶ Begin class by pretending to speak. Mouth the words you want to say, but make no sound until students are curious. Then begin speaking normally. Ask them to explain what produces sound when you speak. Ask how your voice travels to their ears.

▶ Begin class by playing a current song on a tape player. Ask the students what produces the sound and what actually changes when the volume is turned up. Ask if they could listen to this song on the moon.

V i d e o D i s c

STVS: Mapping with a Rifle, Disc 3, Side 2

STVS: Detecting Flaws in Machine Parts, Disc 1, Side 1

New Science Words

compressional wave
pitch
intensity
loudness

Objectives

▶ Describe the transmission of sound through a medium.
▶ Recognize the relationships between intensity and loudness and frequency and pitch.
▶ Illustrate the Doppler effect with a practical example.

Compressional Waves

Think of all the sounds you've heard since you awoke this morning. Did you hear a blaring alarm, honking horns, human voices, or lockers slamming? Your ears allow you to recognize these different sounds, but do you know what they all have in common? These sounds are all produced by the vibrations of objects. For example, your voice is produced by the vibrations of your own vocal cords. The energy produced by these vibrations is carried to your friend's ears by sound waves.

The waves discussed in the last section were described as transverse waves because the matter moved at right angles to the direction the wave was traveling. You could produce this type of wave in a rope or spring by moving one end from side to side or up and down. Sound waves carry energy by a different type of wave motion. You can model sound waves with a coil spring. If you hold one end of a spring, squeeze the coils together, and then release the coils while holding the end of the spring, you will produce a compressional wave. Matter vibrates in the same direction as the wave travels in a **compressional wave.** Figure 18-5 shows how the compressional wave you made should look.

Figure 18-5. You can demonstrate how compressional waves form with a spring.

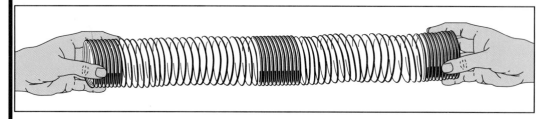

OPTIONS

Meeting Different Ability Levels

For Section 18-2, use the following **Teacher Resource Masters** depending upon individual students' needs.

◆ **Study Guide Master** for all students.
● **Reinforcement Master** for students of average and above average ability levels.
▲ **Enrichment Master** for above average students.

Additional Teacher Resource Package masters are listed in any PROGRAM RESOURCES boxes that are in the section. The additional masters are appropriate for all students.

◆ **STUDY GUIDE** 75

STUDY GUIDE   Chapter 18
The Nature of Sound   Text Pages 464–471

Match the items in Column II with the phrases in Column I. Write the letter of the correct item on the blank to the left of each phrase in Column I.

	Column I		Column II
q	1. sounds move fastest in these media	a.	amplitude
e	2. apparent change in pitch of a sound caused by the motion of the object making the sound	b.	compression
h	3. sounds with frequencies too low for the human ear to hear	c.	compressional waves
b	4. area of a sound wave where particles are squeezed close together	d.	crests
i	5. human perception of loudness	e.	Doppler effect
n	6. condition of a medium that affects the speed at which a sound wave travels	f.	frequency
s	7. produce sounds	g.	gases
c	8. matter vibrates in the same direction as these waves travel	h.	infrasonic
t	9. vibrate when you talk	i.	intensity
k	10. unit of sound intensity	j.	liquids
m	11. area of a sound wave where particles are less dense	k.	decibel
r	12. frequencies too high-pitched for the human ear to hear	l.	pitch
l	13. the highness or lowness of a sound	m.	rarefaction
u	14. distance between two side by side compressions of the same wave	n.	temperature
f	15. number of compressions that pass each place each second	o.	solids
		p.	troughs
		q.	solids
		s.	ultrasonic
		t.	vocal cords
		u.	wavelength

75

Notice that as the wave moves, some of the coils are squeezed together just as you squeezed the ones on the end of the spring. This crowded area is called a compression. The compressed area then expands, spreading the coils apart, creating a less dense area. This less dense area of the wave is called a rarefaction. Does the whole spring move forward? Tie a piece of string on one of the coils and observe its motion. The string moves back and forth with the coils. Therefore, the matter in the medium does not move forward with the wave. Instead, the wave carries only the energy forward.

Recall that transverse waves have wavelengths, frequencies, amplitudes, and velocities. Compressional waves also have these characteristics. A wavelength in a compressional wave is made of one compression and one rarefaction as shown in Figure 18-7. Notice that one wavelength is the distance between two compressions or two rarefactions of the same wave. The frequency is the number of compressions that pass a place each second. If you could repeatedly squeeze and release the end of the spring two times each second, you would produce a wave with a frequency of 2 Hz. The amount of compression is like the amplitude of the transverse wave, and it depends on the energy content of the wave. Think about what you would do to increase the amount of compression in the coil spring. You would have to squeeze harder, and you would be putting more energy into the wave.

Media and the Speed of Sound

Perhaps while you were making compressional waves on a spring, you spoke to your friend. The vibrations generated by your vocal cords produced compressional waves that traveled through the air to your friend. This process is very similar to what you saw when you made compressional waves on a spring. Your voice causes compressions and rarefactions among the particles in the air.

Figure 18-6. The sound of this porpoise's voice travels slower in air than it does in water.

Your ear collects sound waves. Write a brief paragraph describing how compressional waves generated by a human voice reach your brain as a nerve signal.

Figure 18-7. The spring vibrates back and forth, but the energy of this compressional wave moves forward.

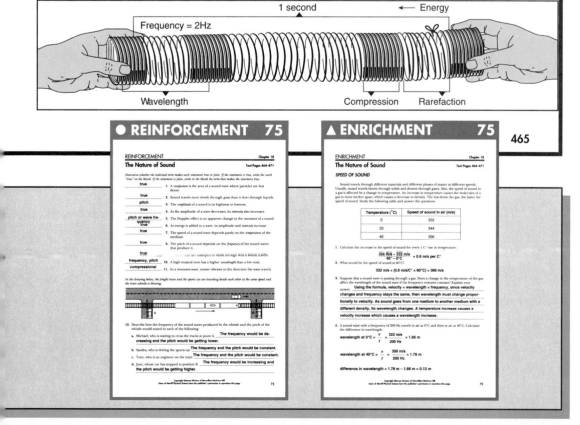

1 second — Energy
Frequency = 2Hz
Wavelength   Compression   Rarefaction

465

TYING TO PREVIOUS KNOWLEDGE: Ask students what they have to do to sing a tune. (They know they must make their voice go higher and lower.) Explain that in this lesson they will find out what *higher* and *lower* really mean.

2 TEACH

Key Concepts are highlighted.

CONCEPT DEVELOPMENT

▶ It is very helpful to use a coil spring to actually do the exercises mentioned in the student text. The compressions and rarefactions can be easily identified. Have a student sketch a compressional wave on the board and identify how frequency and wavelength are measured.

▶ Students get excited when discussing space. When discussing the requirement for a medium for sound travel, ask them whether they could talk to each other on the moon. Because there is no atmosphere, this wouldn't be possible without the aid of electronic equipment.

Answer: The eardrum vibrates causing the three bones of the middle ear to vibrate. The bones transfer the energy to the liquid in the inner ear where the vibration is converted to nerve signals. These signals travel to the brain via the auditory nerve.

The speed of light is 300 000 000 m/s, so the light gets there virtually instantaneously. The speed of sound is about 344 m/s, so the timed speed will be 0.6 s faster than the real speed.

CONCEPT DEVELOPMENT

▶ Have students place their hands gently over their throats and sing the musical scale, "do re mi fa so la ti do." Ask what they feel. (They should be able to tell that their vocal cords vibrate differently as they go up the scale.) Use this demonstration to introduce pitch.

MINI-Lab

▶ Use about 1.5 meters of string per student.

▶ Try a variety of metal objects—ring stand rods make excellent bell-like sounds. Wire coat hangers make gong-like sounds. Curtain rods, metal tools, dinner knives, and forks could be tested. Oven racks give impressive results.

▶ **Answer:** Low energy, low frequency sounds are not easily heard through air but travel well through the string, giving the objects sounds similar to large bells.

MINI-Lab
ASSESSMENT

Content: Ask students why the sound travels better through the string than the air.

Science and MATH

The timer at a track meet starts the watch when he hears the sound of the gun rather than when he sees the smoke. If the gun is 200 m away from him, how much faster or slower would the recorded time be than the actual time?

MINI-Lab

How is sound different when it travels through solids?
Tie a metal object to the center of a piece of string. Wrap each of the two ends of the string around one finger on each hand. Place the fingers holding the string in your ears. Let the object swing until it bumps against the edge of a chair or table and listen to the sound. *Compare* this to the sound you hear from the object when your fingers are not in your ears. Which frequencies, high or low, seem to travel best through the string? What kinds of objects produce the most surprising sounds?

What is pitch?

The speed of sound waves depends on the medium through which the waves travel and the temperature of this medium. Air is the most common medium you hear sound waves through, but sound waves can be transmitted through any type of matter. Liquids and solids are even better conductors of sound than air is because the individual particles in a liquid or solid are much closer together than the particles in air, making the transmission of energy easier. Can sound be transmitted if there is no matter to form a medium? Astronauts on the moon would find it impossible to talk to each other without the aid of modern electronic communication systems. Because the moon has no atmosphere, there is no air to compress and expand and thus transmit sound from one place to another.

The temperature of the medium is also an important factor in determining the speed of sound waves. As the temperature of a substance increases, the molecules move faster and, therefore, collide more frequently. This increase in molecular collisions transfers more energy in a shorter amount of time. This allows the sound waves to be transmitted faster. Sound travels through air at 344 m/s if the temperature is 20°C, but at only 332 m/s when the temperature is 0°C.

The speed of sound is much slower than the speed of light. Have you ever tried to guess how far away a lightning bolt is by counting the time interval between when you see a lightning flash and when you hear the thunder? Have you seen fireworks explode in the sky before you heard the boom? You see the light before you hear the sound because light waves travel through air about one million times faster than sound waves.

Frequency and Pitch

If you have ever taken a music class, you are probably familiar with the scale "do re mi fa so la ti do." As you sing this scale, your voice starts low and becomes higher with each note. You hear a change in pitch. **Pitch** is the highness or lowness of a sound. The pitch you hear depends on the frequency of the sound waves. The higher the frequency is, the higher the pitch is, and the lower the frequency is, the lower the pitch is. A healthy human ear can hear sound frequencies from about 20 Hz to 20 000 Hz.

OPTIONS

ASSESSMENT—ORAL

▶ If you are watching a space movie and two starfighters are firing weapons at each other in space, what sound effects should you hear? *Nothing — sound waves don't travel in a vacuum.*

▶ How can you increase the speed of sound waves in a substance? *Increase the temperature or density of the substance.*

PROGRAM RESOURCES

From the **Teacher Resource Package** use:
Activity Worksheets, page 147, MINI-Lab: How is sound different when it travels through solids?

As people age, they often have more trouble hearing high frequencies.

Most people can't hear sound frequencies above 20 000 Hz, which are called ultrasonic waves. Bats, however, can detect frequencies as high as 100 000 Hz. Ultrasonic waves are used in sonar as well as in medical diagnosis and treatment. Sonar, or sound navigation ranging, is a method of using sound waves to estimate the size, shape, and depth of underwater objects. Infrasonic, or subsonic, waves have frequencies below 20 Hz. These are produced by sources such as heavy machinery and thunder. Although you probably can't hear them, you may have sensed these sound waves as a disturbing rumble inside of your body.

Science and WRITING

You have just formed a new company, Ultrasonics Unlimited. Develop an advertisement for a product that uses this energy.

Science and WRITING

An encyclopedia will describe many uses including scientific (oceanographic exploration and sonar), industrial (cleaning, flaw detection, and welding), medical (diagnosis, treatment, and sanitization), residential (burglar and pest control), and others.

TECHNOLOGY

For more information on the use of low frequency sonar to find underwater treasures see "Deep Quest" by Abe Dane, *Popular Mechanics*, Jan. 1990, pp. 56-59.

Think Critically: Scientists might be able to map the features of the ocean floor with great accuracy. They may also be able to locate biological organisms with this system.

TEACHER F.Y.I.

▶ The frequencies of the human voice range from about 250 to 2000 Hz in a normal conversation.

TECHNOLOGY

Window on the Deep?

Over 130 years ago, a side-wheel steamer, the *Central America*, disappeared in a hurricane off the coast of South Carolina. In its hold lay three tons of newly minted gold coins and bars worth over 50 million dollars in today's market. In 1987 the application of a sophisticated new sonar technology opened a window on the deep for a group of scientifically trained treasure hunters. The group found the wreck of the *Central America* and her rich cargo under more than 2800 m of water.

The treasure hunters used a low frequency sonar system to conduct their search. It could scan a 3-mile-wide section of ocean in a single pass. Signals from the sonar were processed by a computer which displayed images on its screen. When set to a narrower focus, the sonar can spot an object as small as 25 cm at a depth of 7000 m. This method of merging computer and sonar technologies can revolutionize the ways scientists investigate the oceans.

Think Critically: In what other ways do you think these technologies can help scientists study the ocean?

INQUIRY QUESTIONS

▶ **How can you sense sounds you can't hear?** *Sound waves are caused by vibrations in matter, and they carry energy from these vibrations through a medium. You might feel the energy of the sound waves in your body tissues without it stimulating your eardrums.*

CONCEPT DEVELOPMENT

▶ Play a radio and adjust the volume knob to introduce the idea of loudness and intensity. Have students identify the wave property that changes with volume (a change in amplitude).

▶ Have the students brainstorm a list of common sounds. Write this list on the chalkboard. Next, have the students look at Table 18-1 and decide where each item in their list should be placed on the table.

In Your JOURNAL

Answers will vary, but check to see that the estimated decibel levels are reasonable. Students will need to realize decibels are not a linear measure. Decibels are a logarithmic measure. Note that the levels given assume a conversational distance.

Did You Know?

Prolonged noise above 150 dB can cause permanent deafness. The roar of racing cars can be 125 dB; amplified music, 130 dB; and some toy guns, 170 dB.

In Your JOURNAL

In your Journal, make a list of some specific sounds you have heard in the last 24 hours. List them from loudest to quietest. Use Table 18-1 to predict the intensity level of those sounds.

Intensity and Loudness

Have you ever been told to turn down your stereo? If so, you probably adjusted the volume. The music still had the same notes, so the frequencies didn't change, but the amplitude of each sound wave was reduced. The **intensity** of a sound wave depends on the amount of energy in each wave. This, in turn, corresponds to the wave's amplitude. Intensity of a sound wave increases as its amplitude increases.

Loudness is the human perception of sound intensity. The higher the intensity and amplitude, the louder the sound. People vary in sensitivity to different frequencies. What seems loud to one person may not seem loud to you. The intensity level of a sound is measured in units called decibels, abbreviated dB. On this scale, the faintest sound that can be heard by most humans is 0 dB. Sounds with intensity levels above 120 dB may cause pain and permanent hearing loss. Sounds at this intensity level occur during some rock concerts. Table 18-1 shows some familiar sounds and their intensity levels in dB.

Table 18-1

DECIBEL SCALE

Loudness in Decibels

- 160
- Jet plane taking off (150)
- 140
- 120
- Chain saw (115)
- Power mower (100) — 100
- Noisy restaurant (80) — 80
- Vacuum cleaner (75)
- 60
- Average home (50)
- 40
- Purring cat (25)
- Rustling leaves (20) — 20
- Whisper (15)
- 0 Faintest sound that can be heard (0)

OPTIONS

INQUIRY QUESTIONS

▶ What happens to the loudness, intensity, amplitude, and energy of sound waves when you turn up the volume on a radio? *All will increase.*

▶ How would you describe the relationship between loudness, intensity, amplitude, and energy in a sound wave? *When one increases, the others increase, too.*

PROGRAM RESOURCES

From the **Teacher Resource Package** use:

Transparency Masters, pages 73-74, The Decibel Scale.

Use **Color Transparency** number 37, The Decibel Scale.

Use **Laboratory Manual 38,** Sound Waves and Pitch.

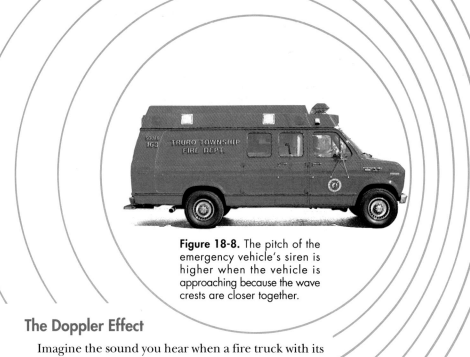

Figure 18-8. The pitch of the emergency vehicle's siren is higher when the vehicle is approaching because the wave crests are closer together.

The Doppler Effect

Imagine the sound you hear when a fire truck with its siren on rapidly approaches and then passes you. As the truck is moving toward you, the pitch of the siren sounds higher than it would if the truck were not moving. Each wave crest forms an expanding circle around the spot where it started (see crests A and B in Figure 18-8). By the time crest B left the siren, the truck had moved forward causing crest B to be closer to crest A in front of the truck. The result is a higher frequency and pitch in front of the moving truck. This change in wave frequency due to a moving wave source is called the Doppler effect. ④ You can also see from Figure 18-8 that the frequency is lower in the area behind the moving truck.

What would you expect would happen if you were moving past a stationary sound source? Suppose you were riding a school bus and passed by a building with a ringing alarm bell. The pitch would sound higher as you approached the building and lower as you rode away from it. The Doppler effect is observed when the source of sound is moving relative to the observer.

Think again of the alarm clock that woke you up this

When can the Doppler effect be observed?

CONCEPT DEVELOPMENT

▶ **Demonstration:** Cut a small door in the side of a Nerf ball. Place a piezo-electric buzzer connected to a battery inside the ball. Throw the ball from the front to the back of the room. The increased and decreased pitches caused by the Doppler effect should be audible.

CROSS CURRICULUM

▶ **History:** Have students research the first sonic boom. (See note in Section Background on page 464.)

CHECK FOR UNDERSTANDING

Ask your students if they would hear an alarm clock on the moon. There is no air on the moon for the compressional wave to travel through.

RETEACH

Model an alarm clock ringing on the moon. Place a ringing alarm clock under a bell jar on the pad of a vacuum pump. Ask what happens as you begin to pump the air out of the jar. (The ringing gets quieter.) Ask what happens as you slowly let air back into the jar. (The ringing returns to normal loudness.)

EXTENSION

For students who have mastered this section, use the **Reinforcement** and **Enrichment** masters or other OPTIONS provided.

ASSESSMENT—ORAL

▶ Suppose you were riding the same school bus described in paragraph 2 and you approached a fire truck that was parked beside an intersection. Explain how the pitch of the fire truck's siren would change if the school bus approached the intersection, stopped for a red light, and then drove on. *As the bus approaches the fire truck, the pitch of the siren would be higher than normal because the sound waves would have an increased frequency. As the bus stopped,* the pitch would lower to normal. As the bus pulled away, the pitch of the siren would fall because the sound waves reaching your ears would have decreased in frequency.

▶ If you observed a speeding fire truck with a blaring siren, and you were not a passenger on that fire truck, is there any way you could NOT observe the Doppler effect? *Only if you were moving at the same speed and in the same direction as the fire truck.*

1 A change in the pitch of a sound is caused by a change in _____. *frequency*

2 The amount of energy in a sound wave determines its _____. *intensity, amplitude, loudness*

3 Can sound travel through empty space? *No, it must have a medium through which it can travel.*

4 The change in wave frequency due to a moving wave source is the _____. *Doppler effect*

3 CLOSE

▶ Make two different sounds for your class. Have students explain how the sound is created and is transferred, which sound has the greater pitch, and which sound has the greater intensity.

▶ Ask questions 1-3 and the **Apply** and **Connect to Life Science** questions in the Section Review.

SECTION REVIEW ANSWERS

1. compressional waves; in the same direction the waves move, by colliding particles

2. Sound waves move faster at higher temperatures.

3. No; there is no matter in space; compressional waves don't transfer energy in a vacuum.

4. Apply: Intensity, amplitude, and loudness change.

5. Connect to Life Science: The bat is flying toward the prey; the prey is flying toward the bat; or both are flying toward each other.

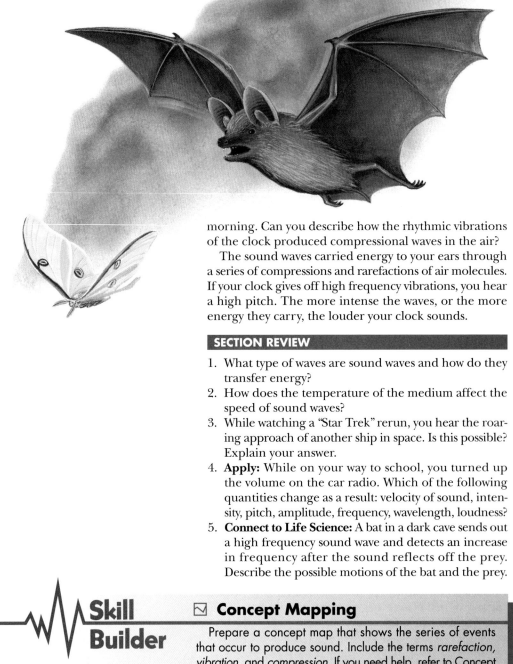

morning. Can you describe how the rhythmic vibrations of the clock produced compressional waves in the air?

The sound waves carried energy to your ears through a series of compressions and rarefactions of air molecules. If your clock gives off high frequency vibrations, you hear a high pitch. The more intense the waves, or the more energy they carry, the louder your clock sounds.

SECTION REVIEW

1. What type of waves are sound waves and how do they transfer energy?
2. How does the temperature of the medium affect the speed of sound waves?
3. While watching a "Star Trek" rerun, you hear the roaring approach of another ship in space. Is this possible? Explain your answer.
4. **Apply:** While on your way to school, you turned up the volume on the car radio. Which of the following quantities change as a result: velocity of sound, intensity, pitch, amplitude, frequency, wavelength, loudness?
5. **Connect to Life Science:** A bat in a dark cave sends out a high frequency sound wave and detects an increase in frequency after the sound reflects off the prey. Describe the possible motions of the bat and the prey.

Skill Builder

☒ Concept Mapping

Prepare a concept map that shows the series of events that occur to produce sound. Include the terms *rarefaction*, *vibration*, and *compression*. If you need help, refer to Concept Mapping in the **Skill Handbook** on pages 684 and 685.

Skill Builder

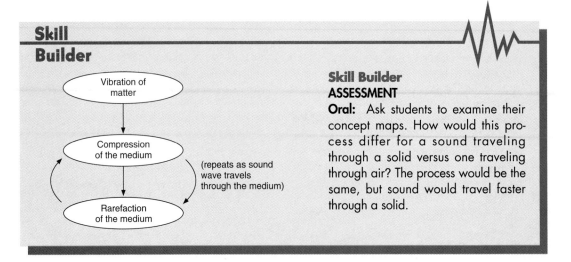

Vibration of matter

↓

Compression of the medium

↓

Rarefaction of the medium

(repeats as sound wave travels through the medium)

Skill Builder
ASSESSMENT
Oral: Ask students to examine their concept maps. How would this process differ for a sound traveling through a solid versus one traveling through air? The process would be the same, but sound would travel faster through a solid.

Noise Pollution

Objectives

▶ Analyze the role of noise as one type of pollution.
▶ Suggest three ways noise pollution can be reduced.

New Science Words

noise pollution

What Is Noise Pollution?

Are you aware that you can be fined for littering on a highway or in a public place? Littering is one of the most obvious types of pollution. There are other types of pollution which may not seem so obvious. One of these is noise pollution. **Noise pollution** includes sounds that are loud, annoying, or harmful to the ear. These sounds can come from sources such as a jackhammer, a jet engine, or highly amplified music. Noise pollution is becoming a problem that sometimes requires legal intervention because it can be harmful in several ways. Recall the way in which sound waves transfer energy through compressions and rarefactions. If the intensity of the sound waves is high enough, the energy carried can actually shatter windows and crack plaster. However, most laws that govern sound levels were created because loud sounds can damage the human ear.

When sound waves reach the human ear, the vibrations pass through its various parts. Extremely intense vibrations can rupture the eardrum, but loudness-related hearing loss usually develops gradually. Your brain perceives sound when the auditory nerve carries a nerve impulse to the brain. This nerve is composed of many tiny nerve fibers surrounded by a fluid inside your ear. Hearing loss can occur when intense compressional waves traveling through the fluid destroy these nerve fibers. Loud sounds in the frequency range of 4000 to 20 000 Hz cause most of the damage to these nerve fibers. Amplified music, motorcycles, and machinery are sources of sound in this frequency range that often cause hearing loss.

In Your JOURNAL

In your Journal, make a list of examples of noise pollution you have observed in the last week. Write a paragraph describing which were most annoying. Did you create any of these situations?

Connect to...
Chemistry

Have you noticed any sound-insulating materials in use in your school or community? Describe the properties these materials are likely to have.

◆ **STUDY GUIDE** 76

471

OPTIONS

Meeting Different Ability Levels

For Section 18-3, use the following **Teacher Resource Masters** depending upon individual students' needs.

◆ **Study Guide Master** for all students.
● **Reinforcement Master** for students of average and above average ability levels.
▲ **Enrichment Master** for above average students.

STUDY GUIDE   Chapter 18
Noise Pollution   Text Pages 472-473

Use the terms in the box to correctly complete each statement.

amplified	ear plugs	gradually	noise pollution
barriers	fibers	intensity	permanent
eardrums	frequency	legal	vibrations

1. Extremely intense sound can rupture the _____ **eardrums**
2. _____ **Amplified** music can be a source of noise pollution.
3. Noise pollution can cause _____ **permanent** damage to the ears.
4. Sound _____ **vibrations** pass through the various parts of the ear.
5. Loudness-related hearing loss usually develops _____ **gradually** .
6. Sometimes it requires _____ **legal** intervention to control noise pollution.
7. Hearing loss occurs when nerve _____ **fibers** are destroyed.
8. Most hearing loss is caused by sounds in the _____ **frequency** range of 4000 to 20 000 Hz.
9. _____ **Ear plugs** can be used to help protect your ears from noise pollution.
10. Sound waves of great _____ **intensity** can shatter windows and crack plaster.
11. _____ **Noise pollution** includes sounds that are loud or annoying.
12. Building high _____ **barriers** along the sides of highways helps to reduce noise pollution in residential areas.

76

PREPARATION

SECTION BACKGROUND

▶ The Occupational Safety and Health Administration (OSHA) regulations require that workers exposed to sound intensities greater than 85 dB be provided with ear protection and have annual hearing exams.

1 MOTIVATE

▶ Have students make a list of sounds that really annoy them or make them uncomfortable. Ask where these sounds are encountered.

TYING TO PREVIOUS KNOWLEDGE:

Have the students recall that sound waves are capable of vibrating objects, including the eardrum. If the vibrations are too intense, damage to the ear can occur.

2 TEACH

Key Concepts are highlighted.

CONCEPT DEVELOPMENT

▶ Borrow a model or large diagram of the human ear. Describe the function of the ear and show where damage can occur.

CROSS CURRICULUM

▶ **Language Arts:** Have students use the periodicals in the library to find an article describing a noise pollution situation. Have them critique the article and explain whether they agree with the author's position.

Connect to...
Chemistry

The gym, cafeteria, and music rooms may be insulated. Materials are usually soft, porous, or fibrous so they absorb, rather than reflect sound.

3 CLOSE

Can you suggest how the amount of noise pollution could be decreased? One way would be to reduce the intensities of the sound waves from sources that cause noise pollution. Some scientists and engineers work on making quieter machinery and cars. Another way to reduce noise exposure is to insulate the loud areas with sound barriers. Giant walls are built along the sides of highways to keep some of the sound from reaching residential areas. You can also put the sound barriers over your own ears by wearing ear protection.

Think about the other kinds of pollution you are familiar with, such as littering, water pollution, and thermal pollution. Rank your list from the most serious pollution problem to the least serious problem. Where does noise pollution rank? Can you explain your reasoning?

SECTION REVIEW

1. What is noise pollution?
2. How can loud sounds damage your hearing?
3. List at least two things that can be done to reduce the harmful effects of noise pollution.
4. **Connect to Earth Science:** Traffic noise is a major source of noise pollution. How could automobiles be designed to reduce this noise?

SCIENCE & SOCIETY

You Decide!

Sometimes a noise can be irritating without being harmful. In one community, some teens built a large skateboarding ramp in the front yard of a house. Their neighbors have complained to the city officials about the ongoing noise the skating makes. The city officials have determined that the sound levels don't exceed the maximum intensities allowed in the city ordinance. Can this still be considered noise pollution? How might this problem be solved?

472

Musical Sounds

Objectives

▶ Distinguish music and noise.
▶ Describe why different instruments produce sounds of different quality.
▶ Explain two types of wave interference.

What Is Music?

Has anyone ever commented that the music you were listening to sounded like a jumble of noise? Both music and noise are caused by vibrations, but there are some important differences. You can easily make a noise by just speaking a word or tapping a pencil on a desk, but it takes some deliberate actions to create music. Of course, you may be able to create music with your voice or your pencil if you try. **Music** is created using specific pitches and sound quality and by following a regular pattern. The most common kind of sound is **noise,** which has no set pattern and no definite pitch. Figure 18-9 shows a comparison of noise and music patterns.

A stringed musical instrument, such as a guitar, generates a sound when you pluck a string. Because the ends of the string are fastened, the waves created reflect back and forth between the ends. This causes the string to vibrate at its natural frequency. Most objects have a natural frequency of vibration.

What kind of sound would be produced if you held a guitar string tightly between your hands while a friend plucked it? It would be much quieter than if the string were fixed on a guitar because the guitar frame and the air inside the instrument absorb energy from the vibrating string. The vibration of the guitar and the air inside it is called a forced vibration, and this makes the sound of the string louder.

If the sound that reaches an object is at the same frequency as the natural frequency of the object, the object will begin to vibrate at this frequency. This type of vibration is called **resonance.**

New Science Words

music
noise
resonance
quality
interference
reverberation
acoustics

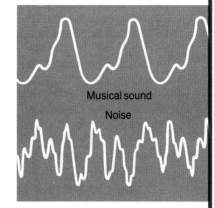

Musical sound

Noise

Figure 18-9. Music follows a pattern; noise does not.

How do music and noise differ?

◆ STUDY GUIDE   77

473

STUDY GUIDE   Chapter 18
Musical Sounds   Text Pages 476-478

Unscramble each group of letters to make a word used in the textbook. Write the word in the space provided and then find the word in the word square. Words may be spelled forward, backward, up, or down.

scale	1. casel	has eight notes
quality	2. tyaquil	describes the difference between two sounds having the same pitch
reverberation	3. breevanoitrre	effect produced by many reflections of sound
resonance	4. sneeracon	produced when an instrument vibrates
acoustics	5. scoutacis	the study of sound
interference	6. ferrincneeie	ability of two or more waves to combine and form a new wave
beats	7. sebat	variations of sound intensity
fundamental	8. menalfantad	tone produced by one vibration of a string
music	9. crims	sounds that follow a regular pattern
octave	10. voceat	frequency range of the musical scale
overtones	11. stoorenso	produced by vibrations that are multiples of the fundamental frequency
noise	12. isone	has no set pattern or definite pitch

Copyright Glencoe Division of Macmillan/McGraw-Hill
Users of Merrill Physical Science have the publisher's permission to reproduce this page.   77

SECTION 18-4

PROBLEM SOLVING

The group could sing a note at a different frequency.
Think Critically: The singing voices created compressional waves at the same frequency as the natural frequency of the piano string, causing the piano string to resonate. No; if Alan hadn't released the strings, they wouldn't have been free to vibrate.

TYING TO PREVIOUS KNOWLEDGE:

Students have taken music at some point in their education. Ask what kinds of things the choir teacher looks for when directing a choir. Answers may include pitch and a specific rhythm. This should introduce music as related to physics.

OBJECTIVES AND SCIENCE WORDS:

Have students review the objectives and science words to become familiar with this section.

2 TEACH

Key Concepts are highlighted.

CONCEPT DEVELOPMENT

▶ If you have students who can play musical instruments, use actual demonstrations whenever possible in this section.

▶ Pluck a guitar string. Use a strobe light to show the standing wave vibrating on the string.

▶ **Demonstration:** Obtain two tuning forks of the same frequency mounted on a hollow box. Strike one with a rubber object. The other one should begin vibrating as the sound waves of the first tuning fork strike it. Use this demonstration to illustrate forced vibrations and resonance.

▶ Large symphonies produce a more intense sound than that of unamplified small bands. Have students use physics terms to explain why three cellos playing together sound louder than one. If the cellos are playing the same note at the same time, their compressions overlap to form a wave of greater amplitude and intensity. Thus, the music sounds louder.

474 CHAPTER 18

P R O B L E M   S O L V I N G

The Piano That Played Itself

Alan had started piano lessons in elementary school. After many years of practice, he became a member of a local rock band.

One afternoon as he was practicing for a gig, several friends stopped by. He decided to use the piano to play a trick on them. He said, "I bet this piano can play itself. I won't even touch a key." Ralph voiced everyone's reaction when he replied, "No way."

First, Alan pushed a pedal that released all the strings in the piano and left them free to vibrate. Then he asked his friends to join in as he sang a note. When everyone stopped singing, they heard the same note coming from the piano. How could the group cause a different note to come from the piano?

Think Critically: How did the piano play the note? Would this trick have worked if Alan hadn't released the piano strings? Explain why or why not.

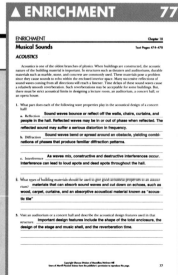

In Your JOURNAL

Several famous singers, such as Ella Fitzgerald and Enrico Caruso, have repeatedly broken crystal glasses by loudly singing a note at a specific frequency. **In your Journal,** write your speculations on how this happens.

Define sound quality.

Musical Sounds

If you were to play a note of the same pitch and loudness on a flute and on a piano, the sound wouldn't be the same. These instruments have a different quality of sound. This quality does not refer to how good or bad the instrument sounds. Sound **quality** describes the differences among sounds of the same pitch and loudness. All sounds are produced by vibrations of matter, but most objects vibrate at more than one frequency. Distinct sounds from musical instruments are produced by different combinations of these wave frequencies.

Imagine producing a tone by plucking a guitar string. The tone produced when the string vibrates along its entire length is called the fundamental frequency. At the same time, each half of the string can vibrate on its own.

This produces the first overtone. Its frequency is twice the fundamental frequency. Overtones have frequencies that are multiples of the fundamental frequency. The intensity and number of overtones vary with each instrument to form a distinct quality of sound. Figure 18-10 illustrates the fundamental frequency and the first three overtones.

Music is written and played based on a musical scale of eight notes. Each note has a characteristic frequency, and all eight notes span a frequency range called an octave. The highest note in an octave has exactly twice the frequency of the lowest note in that octave.

Did You Know?

The housefly hums at a pitch equivalent to the middle octave F on the piano.

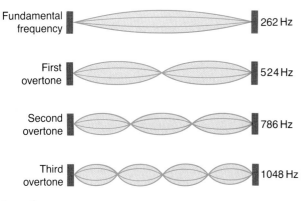

Fundamental frequency	262 Hz
First overtone	524 Hz
Second overtone	786 Hz
Third overtone	1048 Hz

Figure 18-10. This diagram illustrates some of the ways a guitar string can vibrate to produce overtones.

Interference

In a band performance you may have heard several instruments playing the same notes at the same time. What is the purpose of having more than one instrument creating the same sound? The waves are combining to form a new wave. **Interference** is the ability of two or more waves to combine and form a new wave. Because the musicians are simultaneously playing the same note, their compressions overlap to form a greater compression. As a result, the music sounds much louder. Constructive interference occurs when the compressions of different waves arrive at the same place at the same time.

Sometimes the compression of one wave will arrive with the rarefaction of another wave. They cancel each other, resulting in a decrease in loudness. This is an example of destructive interference.

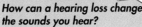
MINI-Lab
How can a hearing loss change the sounds you hear?
To simulate a hearing loss, tune a radio to a news or talk station. Turn the volume down to the lowest level you can hear and understand. Turn the bass to maximum and the treble to minimum. If the radio does not have these controls, mask out the higher frequency sounds with heavy pads over your ears. *Observe* which voices are harder to understand, men's or women's. What letter sounds are more difficult to hear, vowels or consonants? How could you help a person with a hearing loss understand what you say?

18-4 MUSICAL SOUNDS **475**

MINI-Lab
Materials: one radio for not more than six students
▶Work might be best done at home by individuals. Each listener needs two pads of several layers of cloth or small pillows to muffle sound.
Alternate Materials: A small radio or small speaker could be enclosed in a pad of cloth.
▶**Answers:** Most hearing losses are in the higher frequencies of the speech range.
Most affected are women's voices and consonant sounds.
People with hearing losses should be spoken to face on, at a steady, unrushed pace with a slight emphasis on consonant sounds.

MINI-Lab
ASSESSMENT
Performance: Have students find out how these results would be affected if the bass were minimized and the treble maximized.

CROSS CURRICULUM
▶**Music:** Group students in threes and have each group select an instrument. Each group should investigate what vibrates, discover how to produce a change in pitch, and decide to which family of instruments its instrument belongs. Have groups share their findings with the class.

In Your JOURNAL

The frequency of the singer's voice matches the natural frequency of the glass, causing it to resonate. If the glass vibrates intensely enough, it will shatter.

OPTIONS

INQUIRY QUESTIONS
▶If the frequency of the first note of a scale—C—is 262 Hz, what is the frequency of the next C note up the scale? *524 Hz*
▶What is the frequency of the C note one octave below the original C? *131 Hz*

PROGRAM RESOURCES
From the **Teacher Resource Package** use:
Activity Worksheets, page 148, MINI Lab: How can a hearing loss change the sounds you hear?

Use the Mini Quiz to check for understanding.

Use the Mini Quiz to check students' recall of chapter content.

1 Two different instruments that play at the same pitch and loudness may have different _____ . *qualities*

2 What is sound with no set pattern and no definite pitch? *noise*

3 _____ occurs when two or more waves combine to form a new wave. *interference*

4 _____ is caused when the same sound reaches the same place at several different times. *reverberation*

RETEACH

 **Cooperative Learning:** Use the Study Buddies strategy and have each group complete a written analysis of one of the illustrations (Figures 18-9, 18-10, or 18-11) in this section. Have each group prepare a written explanation of the concept the diagram is representing, including definitions of terms.

EXTENSION

For students who have mastered this section, use the **Reinforcement** and **Enrichment** masters or other OPTIONS provided.

Connect to...
Life Science

Answer: Sounds from many directions can cause complicated interference. The sound waves from your friend will combine with those from many others, making all sounds less clear.

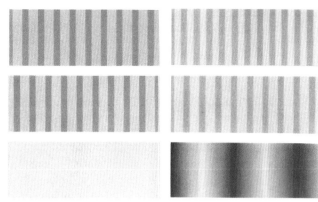

a. Reinforcement   b. Cancellation   c. Beats

Figure 18-11. In (a) the sound compressions reinforce and produce a louder sound. In (b) compressions and rarefactions combine to cancel the sound waves. In (c) two different frequencies produce loud and soft beats.

What are beats?

If a tuning fork with a frequency corresponding to middle C is used to tune a piano, the piano frequency of middle C should blend perfectly with the tuning fork. If the piano produces a slightly different frequency than middle C, the compressions from the fork can't continue to arrive at the same time as the compressions from the piano. The musician will hear variations of sound intensity called beats. The sum of the amplitudes of the waves causes the loudness to regularly rise and fall. Have you ever heard two flutes play the same note when they weren't properly tuned? You could clearly hear the beats until the musicians correctly adjusted their instruments. The beats slowed and then stopped when the flutes were tuned. Figure 18-11 shows a comparison of the types of sound wave interference.

Acoustics

At a concert or a school assembly where a speaker sound system is used, someone usually speaks into the microphone to test the system. Sometimes you hear the sound linger for a couple of seconds. Perhaps you hear echoes of the sound. The sound reaches your ears at different times because it has been reflected off different walls and objects around you. This effect produced by **4** many reflections of sound is called **reverberation.**

Concert halls and theaters are designed by scientists and engineers who specialize in **acoustics,** the study of sound. You will often see carpets and draperies lining the walls of concert halls. Soft, porous materials and certain

OPTIONS

ASSESSMENT—ORAL
▶ At the beginning of a concert, you sometimes see the orchestra conductor listening to several instruments as they play the same note. What is the conductor listening for? *The conductor is listening for beats that will indicate the instruments are out of tune and are causing destructive interference in the sound waves.*

PROGRAM RESOURCES
From the **Teacher Resource Package** use:
Critical Thinking/Problem Solving, page 24, DAT Recorder.
Cross-Curricular Connections, page 24, Synthesizer.

▶ Listen to a tape of a symphony or a popular hit. Identify examples of the ideas introduced in this section. For example, how many kinds of music qualities can you hear? Why is this music rather than noise? What part vibrates in each instrument to make a sound?

▶ Ask questions 1-3 and the **Apply** and the **Connect to Life Science** questions in the Section Review.

SECTION REVIEW ANSWERS

1. Music has definite pitches and a rhythmic pattern; noise has irregular patterns and random pitches.

2. Instruments differ in their sound qualities.

3. Compressions overlap, arrive together, and amplify sound in constructive interference; in destructive interference, cancellation occurs when compressions and rarefactions overlap.

4. Apply: If the glass is vibrated by the compressional waves and resonates at the same frequency, it might shatter.

5. Connect to Life Science: Your vocal chords have natural frequencies and overtones that give them a unique quality, as do the sound organs of the animals. So, it is difficult to imitate animal noises.

room shapes can reduce excess reverberation. Acoustic scientists also work on understanding human hearing and speaking processes.

SECTION REVIEW

1. Compare and contrast music and noise.
2. If you were to close your eyes and listen to middle C played both on a flute and on a cello, what musical property would enable you to distinguish one instrument from the other?
3. Explain the difference between constructive and destructive interference.
4. **Apply:** Intense high-frequency sound can actually cause glass to shatter. What might be happening to the glass that causes it to break?
5. **Connect to Life Science:** Use physics terms to describe why it is difficult for humans to imitate animal noises.

It can be difficult to converse in a crowded room. Explain why it might be hard to distinguish the words from a nearby friend in such a situation.

☑ Recognizing Cause and Effect

What is the effect when sound waves interact by constructive interference? Describe the cause and effect sequence for destructive interference. If you need help, refer to Recognizing Cause and Effect in the **Skill Handbook** on page 679.

Skill Builder

Constructive interference causes an increase in amplitude, intensity, and loudness of the sound heard. Destructive interference is caused when a compression arrives along with a rarefaction, causing a decrease in sound intensity. As a result, less sound is heard.

18-4   MUSICAL SOUNDS   **477**

ENRICHMENT

▶ Have students investigate the architecture and design of some of the famous theaters, amphitheaters, and concert halls around the world. Have them identify ways that the engineers and architects designed and built these structures to improve sound quality.

Skill Builder
ASSESSMENT

Oral: Ask students to explain why there are sometimes spots in auditoriums where little sound is heard. Which type of interference might explain this?

ACTIVITY 18-2
30 minutes

OBJECTIVE: Compare wavelength and frequency to the size of an object producing sound.

PROCESS SKILLS applied in this activity:
▶ **Observing** in Procedure Steps 3, 4, and 6.
▶ **Measuring** in Procedure Step 1 and Analyze Question 3.
▶ **Using Numbers** in Analyze Questions 1 and 2.
▶ **Defining Operationally** in Conclude and Apply Question 1.

COOPERATIVE LEARNING
If you have enough materials, use the Paired Partner strategy. Students should trade equipment with other teams.

TEACHING THE ACTIVITY

Alternate Materials: Any kind of hard-walled pipe will work. Rolled paper will absorb sound without resonating.

Troubleshooting: Students can hear the resonant frequency of the pipe by tapping the open end with a pencil.

▶ Use PVC pipe sold in home supply or hardware stores. For best results, use thin-walled pipe of 1-inch diameter or more. Pipe can easily be cut with a hacksaw. Cut into various lengths from 20 cm to 1 meter. Mark each pipe with an identifying number.

▶ The pipe produces its fundamental frequency regardless of the frequency of the rubber band. But overtones of the fundamental can be heard as slightly louder sounds when the rubber band hits those frequencies.

▶ If a pitch-pipe, tuning fork, or musical instrument is available, have students try to match the sound of the pipe to a note of known pitch and frequency.

PROGRAM RESOURCES
From the **Teacher Resource Package** use:

Activity Worksheets, pages 143-144, Activity 18-2: Frequency of Sound Waves.

ACTIVITY 18-2

Frequency of Sound Waves

Sounds originate with a vibration. Sometimes this vibration also causes nearby objects to vibrate, or resonate, at the same frequency. Many musical instruments make use of a column of air that vibrates at a certain frequency. How is pitch controlled in instruments such as trumpets? By closing and opening specific valves, the length of the air column, the wavelength, and the frequency are changed. Can you find the wavelength and frequency of the sound made in an open-ended pipe?

Materials
- plastic pipe
- rubber band
- metric ruler

Procedure
1. *Measure* the length of the pipe and record it on the data table.
2. Stretch a rubber band across the open end of the pipe and hold it firmly in place as shown. **CAUTION:** *Be careful not to release your grip on the ends of the rubber band.*
3. Hold the rubber band close to your ear and pluck it.
4. Listen for a *double* note.
5. Slowly relax the tightness of the rubber band. Listen for one part of the double note to change and the other part to remain the same.
6. Continue to adjust the tightness until you hear only one note.
7. Exchange pipes with another group and repeat the experiment.

Data and Observations Sample Data

Sound Frequencies Produced by Open Pipes		
Length of pipe	Length of wave	Frequency of sound
0.2 m	0.4 m	855 Hz
0.5 m	1.0 m	342 Hz

Analyze
1. The wavelength you obtained in Step 6 is twice the length of the pipe. *Calculate* the wavelength.

2. Assume the velocity of sound to be 34 400 cm/s. Use the equation

    frequency = velocity/wavelength

    to calculate the frequency of the note.

3. What were the wavelength and frequency of the sound waves in the second pipe?

Conclude and Apply
4. How does the length of a pipe compare with the frequency and wavelength of the sound it can make?
5. A pipe organ uses pipes of different lengths to produce various notes. What other musical instruments use lengths of pipe to produce musical notes?

ANSWERS TO QUESTIONS
1. longest wavelength = 2 × pipe length (Example) 2 × 20 cm = 40 cm
2. Example:
    $$\frac{34\ 400\ cm/s}{40\ cm} = 860\ Hz$$
3. Answers will vary. Wavelength will increase and frequency decrease as the pipes become longer.
4. The longer the pipe, the longer the wavelength and the lower its frequency.

5. All horns and woodwinds as well as the human voice use a vibrating air column. A xylophone uses open pipes to amplify the sound of the vibrating bars.

Activity ASSESSMENT
Performance: Have students predict how six pipes of different lengths should be arranged from highest to lowest pitch. Then, have them test their predictions.

CHAPTER

REVIEW

SUMMARY

18-1: Wave Characteristics

1. In a transverse wave, the medium moves at right angles to the direction the wave travels. Transverse wave characteristics include crests, troughs, wavelength, and amplitude.
2. If the speed of a wave remains constant, as the frequency increases, the wavelength decreases, and vice versa.
3. The velocity of a wave is equal to its wavelength multiplied by its frequency.

18-2: The Nature of Sound

1. Sound begins as a vibration that is transferred through a medium in a series of compressions and rarefactions of the matter in the medium, called compressional waves.
2. The pitch of a sound becomes higher as the frequency increases, and lower as the frequency decreases. Both amplitude and intensity increase as energy is added to a wave. Loudness is the human perception of sound intensity.
3. The Doppler effect is an apparent change of frequency and pitch of a sound as a result

of either the observer or the sound source or both moving with respect to each other, such as a fire truck siren.

18-3: Science and Society: Noise Pollution

1. Noise pollution includes sounds that are loud, annoying, or harmful to the ear.
2. Noise pollution can be reduced by producing less noise, building barriers, or by using protective wear over the ears.

18-4: Musical Sounds

1. Music is created using specific pitches, sound quality, and a pattern. Noise has no definite pitch or set pattern.
2. Each musical instrument has its own unique sound quality. Sound quality describes the differences among sounds of the same pitch and loudness.
3. Interference is the ability of two or more waves to combine constructively or destructively and form a new wave.

KEY SCIENCE WORDS

a. acoustics
b. amplitude
c. compressional wave
d. crests
e. frequency
f. intensity
g. interference
h. loudness
i. medium
j. music

k. noise
l. noise pollution
m. pitch
n. quality
o. resonance
p. reverberation
q. transverse wave
r. troughs
s. wavelength
t. waves

UNDERSTANDING VOCABULARY

Match each phrase with the correct term from the list of Key Science Words.

1. distance between identical points on two waves
2. sounds that are loud, annoying, or harmful
3. the study of sound
4. matter vibrates in the same direction as the wave travels
5. the highness or lowness of a sound
6. material through which a wave travels
7. expressed in Hertz
8. the highest points of a transverse wave
9. distance from the rest position of a medium to the trough or crest of a wave
10. human perception of sound intensity

WAVES AND SOUND   **479**

SUMMARY

Have students read the summary statements to review the major concepts of the chapter.

UNDERSTANDING VOCABULARY

1. s	**6.** i
2. l	**7.** e
3. a	**8.** d
4. c	**9.** b
5. m	**10.** h

ASSESSMENT
Portfolio

Encourage students to place in their portfolios one or two items of what they consider to be their best work. For each item, ask students to explain why that item was chosen and what they learned from it. Items might be selected from the following.

• Practice Problem calculations, p. 461
• Connect to Life Science answer, p. 465
• Activity 18-2 results and answers, p. 478

Performance

Additional performance assessments may be found in *Performance Assessment* and *Science Integration Activities* that accompany **Merrill Physical Science.** Performance Task Assessment Lists and rubrics for evaluating these activities and other products generated throughout the chapter can be found in Glencoe's *Performance Assessment in Middle School Science.*

OPTIONS

ASSESSMENT

To assess student understanding of material in this chapter, use the resources listed.

COOPERATIVE LEARNING
Consider using cooperative learning in the THINK AND WRITE CRITICALLY, APPLY, and more SKILL BUILDERS sections of the Chapter Review.

PROGRAM RESOURCES

From the **Teacher Resource Package** use:
Chapter Review, pages 39-40.
Chapter and Unit Tests, pages 122-125, Chapter Test.

CHECKING CONCEPTS

1. b	**6.** d
2. a	**7.** a
3. b	**8.** b
4. d	**9.** a
5. c	**10.** c

USING LAB SKILLS

ASSESSMENT

Use the alternate lab exercises to assess students' understandings of the skills used in this chapter.

11.

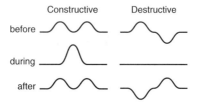

	Constructive	Destructive
before		
during		
after		

12. Cardboard is less elastic than PVC pipe, so it absorbs sound and does not resonate as much as the PVC pipe.

THINK AND WRITE CRITICALLY

13. In a transverse wave, amplitude is the distance between the rest position of the medium and the crest or trough; frequency is the number of crests that pass a point in one second; and wavelength is the distance between two consecutive crests or troughs. In a compressional wave, amplitude is the amount of compression of the medium's particles; frequency is the number of compressions that pass a point in one second; and wavelength is the distance between two consecutive compressions or rarefactions.

14. All three occur when two waves meet. In constructive interference, waves of equal frequency meet crest-to-crest so that their amplitudes add up and loudness increases. In destructive interference, waves of equal frequency meet crest-to-trough so that their amplitudes cancel one another and loudness decreases. Beats are formed when waves of different frequencies meet, resulting in alternating periods of loudness (constructive interference) and softness (destructive interference).

CHECKING CONCEPTS

Choose the word or phrase that completes the sentence.

1. Waves carry _____ forward.
- **a.** matter
- **b.** energy
- **c.** matter and energy
- **d.** the medium

2. A wave that carries a large amount of energy will always have a _____.
- **a.** large amplitude
- **b.** small amplitude
- **c.** high frequency
- **d.** short wavelength

3. A sound with a low pitch always has a low _____.
- **a.** amplitude
- **b.** frequency
- **c.** wavelength
- **d.** wave velocity

4. As _____, sound intensity decreases.
- **a.** wave velocity decreases
- **b.** wavelength decreases
- **c.** quality decreases
- **d.** amplitude decreases

5. Sounds with the same pitch and loudness may differ in _____.
- **a.** frequency
- **b.** amplitude
- **c.** quality
- **d.** wavelength

6. Sound cannot travel through _____.
- **a.** solids
- **b.** liquids
- **c.** gases
- **d.** empty space

7. Variations in the loudness of sound that are caused by wave interference are called _____.
- **a.** beats
- **b.** standing waves
- **c.** reverberations
- **d.** forced vibrations

8. _____ is shown when a window pane vibrates at the same frequency as a thunderclap.
- **a.** The Doppler effect
- **b.** Resonance
- **c.** Reverberation
- **d.** Destructive interference

9. Wave frequency is measured in _____.
- **a.** hertz
- **b.** decibels
- **c.** meters
- **d.** meters/second

10. When a sound source moves away from you, the sound's _____.
- **a.** velocity decreases
- **b.** loudness increases
- **c.** pitch decreases
- **d.** frequency increases

USING LAB SKILLS

11. In Activity 18-1 on page 463, you observed some of the behaviors of transverse waves on a Slinky. Use the Slinky to create constructive and destructive interference by sending waves toward each other. Sketch the spring before, during, and after the waves overlap.

12. Try to use an empty cardboard paper towel roll to repeat the procedure used in Activity 18-2 on page 478 to find the tube's natural frequency. Do you hear as clear a sound? Explain why or why not.

THINK AND WRITE CRITICALLY

Answer the following questions in your Journal using complete sentences.

13. Describe how amplitude, frequency, and wavelength are determined in transverse and compressional waves.

14. What do constructive interference, destructive interference, and the formation of beats have in common? How are they different?

15. Explain how different combinations of wave frequencies make a guitar and a trumpet sound different even when the same note is played.

16. In what ways can noise pollution be reduced?

17. Why does the ringing of an alarm clock enclosed in an airtight container become softer as the air is drawn out of the container?

---

15. A note played on a musical instrument is associated with a fundamental frequency. Whole number multiples of this frequency produce overtones. Each instrument has a different number of overtones for a given note. This produces distinct sound qualities that make the instruments sound different from one another.

16. Noise pollution can be reduced by reducing the intensity of the sound waves at the source, or by using soundproof barriers.

17. Compressional waves need a medium to be transferred. As the density of the medium decreases, less energy is carried by the waves.

18. A wave has a wavelength of 6 m and a wave velocity of 420 m/s. What is its frequency?
19. A bus driver is rounding a curve approaching a railroad crossing. She hears a train's whistle and then hears the whistle's pitch become lower. What assumptions can she make about what she will see when she rounds the curve and looks at the crossing?
20. When a little boy blows a dog whistle, his dog comes, even though the boy can't hear the whistle. Explain why the boy can't hear the whistle, but his dog can.
21. An earthquake beneath the middle of the Pacific Ocean produces a tidal wave that hits a remote island. Is the water that hits the island the same water that was above the earthquake? Explain.

MORE SKILL BUILDERS

If you need help, refer to the Skill Handbook.

1. **Hypothesizing:** Sound travels slower in air at high altitudes than at low altitudes. State a hypothesis to explain this observation.
2. **Observing and Inferring:** Infer the effect of increasing wave velocity on the wavelength of a compressional wave that has a constant frequency.
3. **Interpreting Scientific Illustrations:** Look at the two transverse waves in Figure 18-4 on page 460. Compare the frequencies, wavelengths, amplitudes, and energies of these waves. Draw another wave that has twice the frequency and energy of the bottom wave.
4. **Making and Using Graphs:** Construct a bar graph to analyze the following data. Order the substances from most to least dense. Does this graph indicate any differences in the speed of each substance's particles?

Substance	Speed of Sound 25°C
air	343 m/s
brick	3650 m/s
cork	500 m/s
water	1498 m/s
steel	5200 m/s

5. **Making and Using Tables:** You have started a lawn mowing business during summer vacation. Your family's power lawn mower has a sound level of 100 decibels. Using the table below, determine how many hours a day you can safely work mowing lawns. If you want to work longer hours, what can you do to protect your hearing? If your family purchases a new lawn mower with a sound level of 95 dB, how will your business be affected?

OSHA RECOMMENDED NOISE EXPOSURE LIMITS	
Sound Level (decibels)	**Time Permitted (hours per day)**
90	8
95	4
100	2
105	1
110	0.5

PROJECTS

1. Research the uses of sonar and of ultrasonic waves in medicine. Prepare a written report.
2. Using materials you have at home, make a musical instrument. Play your instrument for your classmates and explain how you can change the pitch of your instrument.

18. Given: wavelength = 6 m
    velocity = 420 m/s

Unknown: frequency
Equation: $v = \lambda \times f$

Solution: 420 m/s = 6 m × f

$$f = \frac{420 \text{ m/s}}{6 \text{ m}} = 70 \text{ Hz}$$

19. She can assume that she will see that the engine of the train has passed the crossing because the drop in the pitch of the whistle indicates that the engine is moving away from her.
20. The dog whistle must have had a frequency outside of the range of human hearing.
21. No. Waves transfer energy, not the matter in the media through which they move. The water that hits the shore was already near the shore.

MORE SKILL BUILDERS

1. **Hypothesizing:** Two possible hypotheses are:
a. Air particles are farther apart at high altitudes.
b. Air temperature is lower at high altitudes, and the slower moving particles do not transfer sound as quickly.
The latter hypothesis is correct.
2. **Observing and Inferring:** The equation relating velocity, wavelength, and frequency is: $v = \lambda \times f$. If frequency does not change, then wavelength increases with velocity.
3. **Interpreting Scientific Illustrations:** Wave *a* has a longer wavelength and lower frequency. Both have the same amplitude and transfer the same amount of energy.

4. Making and Using Graphs:

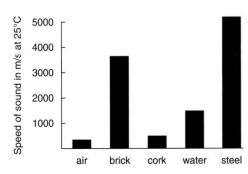

The temperature is constant, so the differences in sound velocity must be due to density. Sound travels faster in more dense substances, so in order from most to least dense are: steel, brick, water, cork, air. The graph does not indicate any differences in particle speed.

5. Making and Using Tables: You can safely work two hours using a 100 dB lawn mower. You should wear earplugs or some other hearing protection device. You can work twice as long.

CHAPTER SECTION	OBJECTIVES	ACTIVITIES
19-1 Electromagnetic Radiation (2 days)	1. **Contrast** electromagnetic waves with other kinds of waves. 2. **Describe** the arrangement of electromagnetic waves on the electromagnetic spectrum. 3. **Explain** at least one application of each type of electromagnetic wave.	**MINI-Lab:** *Is fluorescent light hot?* p. 490
19-2 Light and Color (2 days)	1. **Describe** the differences among opaque, transparent, and translucent materials. 2. **Explain** how you see color. 3. **Describe** the difference between light color and pigment color.	**Activity 19-1:** *Spectrum Inspection,* p. 497
19-3 Battle of the Bulbs Science & Society (1 day)	1. **Explain** how incandescent and fluorescent bulbs work. 2. **Analyze** the advantages and disadvantages of different light sources.	
19-4 Wave Properties of Light (2 days)	1. **State** and **give an example** of the law of reflection. 2. **Explain** how refraction is used to separate the colors of the spectrum in white light. 3. **Describe** how diffraction and interference patterns demonstrate the wave behavior of light.	**Activity 19-2:** *Make a Light Bender,* p. 506
Chapter Review		

ACTIVITY MATERIALS

FIND OUT	ACTIVITIES		MINI-LABS
Page 483 objects in room	**19-1 Spectrum Inspection, p. 497** diffraction grating power supply with rheostat clear, tubular light bulb socket colored pencils (red, yellow, and blue)	**19-2 Make a Light Bender, p. 506** light source pencil clear rectangular container water notebook paper clay	**Is fluorescent light hot? p. 490** incandescent light fluorescent light, same wattage as above styrofoam cup plastic food wrap thermometer

CHAPTER FEATURES	TEACHER RESOURCE PACKAGE	OTHER RESOURCES
Skill Builder: *Outlining,* p. 491	**Ability Level Worksheets** ◆ **Study Guide,** p. 78 ● **Reinforcement,** p. 78 ▲ **Enrichment,** p. 78 **Concept Mapping,** pp. 43, 44 **Science and Society,** p. 23 **Activity Worksheets,** p. 156 **Transparency Masters,** pp. 75, 76	**Color Transparency 38,** The Electromagnetic Spectrum **Laboratory Manual 39,** Light Intensity **Laboratory Manual 40,** Producing a Spectrum **STVS:** Disc 1, Side 1
Problem Solving: *Color in the Sunday Comics,* p. 496 **Skill Builder:** *Concept Mapping,* p. 496	**Ability Level Worksheets** ◆ **Study Guide,** p. 79 ● **Reinforcement,** p. 79 ▲ **Enrichment,** p. 79 **Cross-Curricular Connections,** p. 25 **Activity Worksheets,** pp. 5, 150, 151	**Science Integration Activity 19**
You Decide! p. 499	**Ability Level Worksheets** ◆ **Study Guide,** p. 80 ● **Reinforcement,** p. 80 ▲ **Enrichment,** p. 80	**STVS:** Disc 1, Side 1
Technology: *Holograms—The Key to 3-D,* p. 504 **Skill Builder:** *Observing and Inferring,* p. 505	**Ability Level Worksheets** ◆ **Study Guide,** p. 81 ● **Reinforcement,** p. 81 ▲ **Enrichment,** p. 81 **Critical Thinking/Problem Solving,** p. 25 **Activity Worksheets,** pp. 152, 153 **Transparency Masters,** pp. 77, 78	**Color Transparency 39,** Wave Interference **STVS:** Disc 1, Side 2
Summary Think & Write Critically Key Science Words Apply Understanding Vocabulary More Skill Builders Checking Concepts Projects Using Lab Skills	**ASSESSMENT RESOURCES** **Chapter Review,** pp. 41, 42 **Chapter Test,** pp. 126-129 **Performance Assessment in Middle School Science**	**Chapter Review Software** **Test Bank** **Alternate Assessment** **Performance Assessment**

◆ **Basic**   ● **Average**   ▲ **Advanced**

ADDITIONAL MATERIALS

SOFTWARE	AUDIOVISUAL	BOOKS/MAGAZINES
Diffraction, Sunburst. *Heat, Light, and Sound;* Queue. *Introduction to Light,* Queue. *Learning All About Light and Lasers,* Queue. *Light,* EME Corp. *PSL Light Experiments,* EduQuest. *Sound and Light,* Queue. *Theory Formation: Reflections and Patterns,* EduQuest.	*Color and Light: An Introduction ,* Video, Coronet. *How to Bend Light,* Video, Britannica. *Light, Color, and the Visible Spectrum,* Video, Coronet. *Light and Color: What Color Is An Apple At Night?,* Video, AIT. *Light and the Electromagnetic Spectrum,* Video, Coronet. *Light,* Video, AIT. *Light and Color,* Video, Britannica. *Light Science: You Can Do It!,* Video, Britannica. *Light Energy,* Laserdisc, Churchill Media. *Properties of Light,* Video, AIT.	Gardner, Robert. *Experimenting With Light.* NY: Watts, 1991. Gardner, Robert. *Investigate and Discover Light.* Englewood Cliffs, NJ: Messner, 1991. Ward, Alan. *Experimenting with light and Illusions.* NY: Chelsea House, 1990.

THEME DEVELOPMENT: Electromagnetic radiation is energy, the major theme of this chapter. Help students make connections using applications of radiation they are already familiar with. Stress that light and other types of radiation are actually forms of energy.

CHAPTER OVERVIEW

▶ **Section 19-1:** This section introduces the electromagnetic spectrum and discusses each type of radiation with familiar examples.

▶ **Section 19-2:** The spectrum of light is used to explain colors and the difference between transparent and opaque objects is discussed. Pigments are explained.

▶ **Section 19-3: Science and Society:** The differences between incandescent and fluorescent bulbs are explored. Students are encouraged to make informed decisions as energy-conscious consumers.

▶ **Section 19-4:** Reflection and refraction are discussed. Diffraction and interference patterns are investigated.

CHAPTER VOCABULARY

radiation	opaque materials
electromagnetic	transparent
spectrum	materials
photons	translucent
radio waves	materials
modulation	incandescent light
microwaves	fluorescent light
infrared radiation	reflection
visible radiation	refraction
ultraviolet	diffraction
radiation	diffraction
X rays	grating
gamma rays	

CHAPTER
19 Light

482

OPTIONS

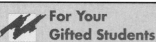

For Your Gifted Students

▶ Have students fold different colors of construction paper or fabric to form sleeves. They should insert a thermometer into each sleeve, place it 25 cm from a light source, and record the temperature after 10 minutes. They should repeat the procedure with several colors, compare the results, and explain their findings to the class.

▶ Have students investigate the particle-wave theories of light.

For Your Mainstreamed Students

A student can observe refraction by placing a coin in the bottom of an empty cup and lowering his or her head so the coin is just hidden from sight by the edge of the cup. As the student maintains this line of sight, have another student slowly pour water into the cup. The coin should come into view. Use Figure 19-17 to explain this.

Color is a very important part of our lives. How would you describe things around you without using color?

FIND OUT!

Do the following activity to find out how it feels not to use color.

Get together with a partner. Each of you should pick an object and form a clear picture of it in your own mind. Next, one of you should close your eyes while the other describes his or her object as completely as possible without using colors. Can you guess what it is? Switch roles and try it again. Why is it so difficult to *describe* or identify objects without the use of colors? You depend on light and color to *observe* and describe everything in the world around you, from the food you eat to the clothes you wear.

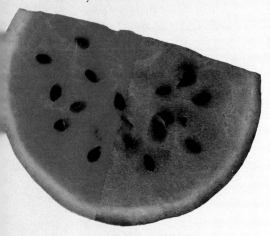

Gearing Up
Previewing the Chapter

Use this outline to help you focus on important ideas in this chapter.

Section 19-1   Electromagnetic Radiation
▶ The Electromagnetic Spectrum
▶ Radio Waves
▶ Infrared Radiation
▶ Visible Radiation
▶ Ultraviolet Radiation
▶ X Rays and Gamma Rays

Section 19-2   Light and Color
▶ Light and Matter
▶ Colors
▶ Pigments

Section 19-3   Science and Society
Battle of the Bulbs
▶ Do Light Bulbs Make a Difference?

Section 19-4   Wave Properties of Light
▶ Reflection
▶ Refraction
▶ Diffraction and Interference

Previewing Science Skills

▶ In the Skill Builders, you will outline, make a concept map, and observe and infer.
▶ In the Activities, you will observe, hypothesize, compare, and infer.
▶ In the MINI-Lab, you will observe, interpret, and measure.

What's next?

Now that you have thought about how much you depend on light and color to see and describe objects around you, learn why objects have colors. Learn about the characteristics of light, and how they affect the color you see.

483

Use the Find Out activity to introduce the students to the idea of color. Explain that they'll be investigating how light and color are related.

FIND OUT!

Preparation: Place a few colorful objects or posters around the room so students have a variety of objects to describe.

Cooperative Learning: Use the Paired Partners strategy. After doing the activity once, they should switch roles.

Teaching Tips
▶ Have one person in each group turn toward the back of the room. Put a colorful object in front of the room. Have the partner describe it without color. Keep score of correct guesses and find out which group has the highest score.

Gearing Up

Have students study the Gearing Up section to familiarize themselves with the chapter. Discuss the relationships of the topics in the outline.

What's Next?

Before beginning the first section, make sure students understand the connection between the Find Out activity and the topics to follow.

ASSESSMENT OPTIONS

PORTFOLIO
Refer to page 507 for suggested items that students might select for their portfolios.

PERFORMANCE ASSESSMENT
See page 507 for additional Performance Assessment options.
Process
Skill Builders, pp. 496, 505
MINI-Lab, p. 490
Activities 19-1, p. 497; 19-2, p. 506
Using Lab Skills, p. 508

CONTENT ASSESSMENT
Assessment—Oral, pp. 486, 489, 494, 502
Skill Builder, p. 491
Section Reviews, pp. 491, 496, 499, 505
Chapter Review, pp. 507-509
Mini Quizzes, pp. 494, 504

GROUP ASSESSMENT
Opportunities for group assessment occur with Cooperative Learning Strategies and Flex Your Brain Activities.

SECTION BACKGROUND

▶ Scientists now agree that light has both particle and wave nature, but there is a rich scientific history leading to this idea. In the fifth century B.C., Socrates and Plato thought light was made of streams of light emitted by the eye. Followers of Pythagoras thought luminous objects emitted light particles. Newton formed a particle theory of light at the same time Huygens concluded it was a wave. Einstein's theory of light as particles called photons was published in an explanation of the photoelectric effect in 1905.

▶ The photoelectric effect is the ejection of electrons from certain photosensitive metals when photons of light are absorbed by an electron in the material. The photon must have enough energy for the electron to escape from the metal. This is evidence for the particle, or quantum, theory of light.

▶ Electromagnetic radiation is energy emitted from vibrating electric charges in the form of transverse waves. These waves are composed of an electric field and a magnetic field oscillating at right angles to each other.

PREPLANNING

▶ To prepare for the MINI-Lab, obtain an incandescent bulb and a fluorescent bulb of the same wattage, a thermometer, a polystyrene cup, and some plastic wrap.

VideoDisc

STVS: Infrared Observatory, Disc 1, Side 1

STVS: Video Astronomy, Disc 1, Side 1

19-1 Electromagnetic Radiation

New Science Words

radiation
electromagnetic spectrum
photons
radio waves
modulation
microwaves
infrared radiation
visible radiation
ultraviolet radiation
X rays
gamma rays

Objectives

▶ Contrast electromagnetic waves with other kinds of waves.
▶ Describe the arrangement of electromagnetic waves on the electromagnetic spectrum.
▶ Explain at least one application of each type of electromagnetic wave.

The Electromagnetic Spectrum

Do you listen to the radio, watch television, play video games, or cook with a microwave oven? These devices all make use of different kinds of electromagnetic waves. Light, radio waves, and microwaves are all examples of electromagnetic waves.

Electromagnetic waves are transverse waves produced by the motion of electrically charged particles. We often call these waves *electromagnetic radiation* because they radiate from the particles. The transfer of energy by electromagnetic waves is called **radiation.** One way these waves differ from those you learned about in Chapter 18 is that electromagnetic waves do not need a medium to transfer energy. They can travel through a vacuum—empty space—at a speed of 300 000 km/sec. These waves travel slower when they pass through any type of matter, but they still travel very fast compared to sound or water waves.

All electromagnetic waves travel at the same speed in each particular medium, but their frequencies and wavelengths may vary. The shorter the wavelength of a wave, the higher its frequency. Electromagnetic waves are classified from low frequency, long wavelength radio waves to high frequency, short wavelength gamma rays according to their wavelengths on the **electromagnetic spectrum** (see Figure 19-2).

Figure 19-1. Electromagnetic waves travel at the same speed but at different wavelengths and frequencies.

OPTIONS

Meeting Different Ability Levels

For Section 19-1, use the following **Teacher Resource Masters** depending upon individual students' needs.

◆ **Study Guide Master** for all students.
● **Reinforcement Master** for students of average and above average ability levels.
▲ **Enrichment Master** for above average students.

Additional Teacher Resource Package masters are listed in any PROGRAM RESOURCES boxes that are in the section. The additional masters are appropriate for all students.

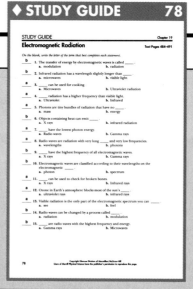

Scientists have observed that radiation not only carries energy, but also has momentum. This suggests that electromagnetic radiation has particle-like behavior. In 1905, Albert Einstein suggested that light is composed of tiny particles. These tiny, massless bundles of radiation are called **photons.** The photons with the highest energy correspond to light with the highest frequency. Very high energy photons can actually damage matter, such as the cells in your body.

Radio Waves

When you tune your radio to a station, you are adjusting it to respond to radio waves of a certain wavelength. Even though radio waves are all around you right now, you can't feel them. **Radio waves** are the kind of electromagnetic radiation with very long wavelength and very low frequency. Thus, radio waves have the lowest photon energy. Locate radio waves on the electromagnetic spectrum in Figure 19-2.

Figure 19-2. All electromagnetic waves are classified by their wavelengths on the electromagnetic spectrum.

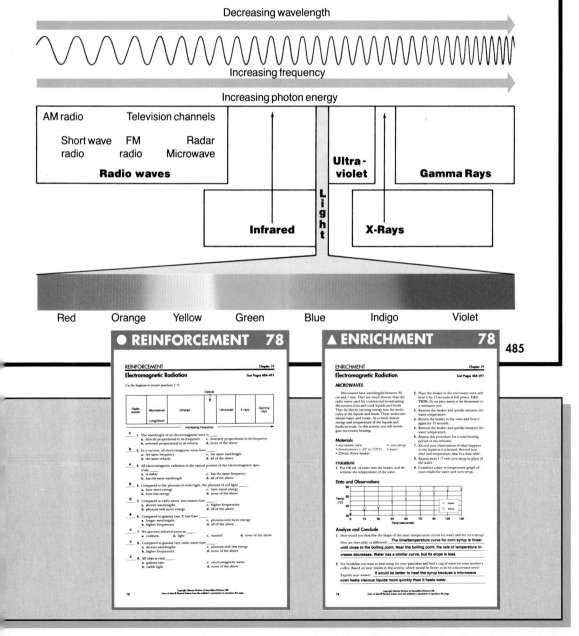

Did You Know?

If the sun quit shining in the past eight minutes, you wouldn't know it yet because it takes that long for light from the sun to reach Earth.

Describe the wavelength and frequency of radio waves.

In Your JOURNAL

After reading this section on radio waves, write a paragraph **in your Journal** explaining whether or not you can hear radio waves. Give plenty of evidence for your answer.

1 MOTIVATE

► Ask the students how they can prove that electromagnetic radiation is all around them. You could demonstrate by turning on a radio.

► Make the classroom as dark as possible. Pose an interesting question. If you can't see colors in the dark, are the objects still colored? This might make students wonder how light helps us see color.

TYING TO PREVIOUS KNOWLEDGE: Emphasize that, like sound waves and water waves, electromagnetic waves carry energy. This energy can be used to do work. Ask them what happens if you move a solar-powered calculator away from any light.

OBJECTIVES AND SCIENCE WORDS: Have students review the objectives and science words to become familiar with this section.

2 TEACH

Key Concepts are highlighted.

In Your JOURNAL

You don't hear radio waves; you hear the sound waves produced by the receiver that collects the radio waves.

PROGRAM RESOURCES

From the **Teacher Resource Package** use:

Transparency Masters, pages 75-76, The Electromagnetic Spectrum.

Use **Color Transparency,** number 38, The Electromagnetic Spectrum

▶ Radio waves were first modulated by clicking them on and off in Morse Code.

CONCEPT DEVELOPMENT

▶ Bring a radio to class and have students tune it to AM and FM stations. Stress that radios are tuned in by the frequency of the carrier wave. List their favorite stations on the chalkboard in order of increasing frequency. Explain the difference between AM and FM. *AM* is an abbreviation for amplitude modulation. In this process, the amplitude of the radio wave increases or decreases with the sound. *FM,* or frequency modulation, is a process where the frequency of the radio wave increases or decreases with the sound.

▶ **Demonstration**: Illustrate the cooking pattern in a microwave oven. Saturate a paper towel in a concentrated solution of cobalt chloride. Place it on an empty cardboard box to elevate it several cm. Cook on high in 15-second intervals until you see areas of the towel dry and turn blue. Use this demonstration to show why it is important to rotate food while cooking it in a microwave.

In addition to radio communications, radio waves are used in television, cellular telephones, and cordless telephones. How is your voice transmitted by radio waves on a cordless telephone? The sound waves produced by your voice are changed to electrical currents that represent your speech patterns and pitches. These signals are used to vary either the amplitudes or frequencies of radio waves that are transmitted from the handset to the base. This process of varying radio waves is called **modulation**. Besides your voice, light images, computer information, and music can also be used to modulate radio waves.

The radio waves of the highest frequency and energy are called **microwaves.** They are used in communications, but you are probably most familiar with microwaves for their speedy cooking abilities. Have you ever popped popcorn in a microwave oven? Do you wonder how the kernels pop so quickly? Microwaves carry energy inside the popcorn to the molecules of water, causing them to vibrate faster and rotate. As a result, the kinetic energy and temperature of the molecules increases, the water inside the popcorn kernel turns to steam, and the kernel explodes due to the increased pressure. Materials such as glass, paper, and some plastics are used in microwave ovens because the microwaves pass through them easily and little energy is wasted in heating the container.

486   LIGHT

OPTIONS

ASSESSMENT—ORAL

▶ If microwaves are really high frequency radio waves, how would the wavelengths of microwaves compare to those of radio waves? *Microwaves are radio waves with short wavelengths.*

PROGRAM RESOURCES

From the **Teacher Resource Package** use:
Concept Mapping, pages 43-44.
Use **Laboratory Manual 39**, Light Intensity.

Infrared Radiation

Have you ever napped in a comfortable lawn chair on a hot summer day? Even with your eyes closed, could you feel when clouds moved in front of the sun? When the sunlight wasn't blocked by the clouds, you may have felt its warmth on your skin. This warm feeling is caused by the infrared radiation from the sun. **Infrared radiation** has a wavelength slightly longer than light, as you can see by its location on the electromagnetic spectrum. Your skin feels warm because it is absorbing some of the infrared radiation from the sun. This causes the molecules in your skin to vibrate more, increasing their kinetic energy and temperature.

Warmer objects, such as your body, give off more infrared radiation than do cooler objects. Some parts of your body are warmer than others and, as a result, give off more infrared radiation. Measurement of the body's emission of infrared radiation helps doctors make some medical diagnoses. A thermogram, such as the one shown in Figure 19-3b, can be produced by measuring the infrared radiation given off by different body parts. Tumors can sometimes be detected in a thermogram because they are warmer than the healthy tissue around them.

People using infrared-sensitive binoculars can see humans and animals in complete darkness. These binoculars can detect the infrared waves given off by warm bodies. Some home security systems are designed to

What objects give off infrared radiation?

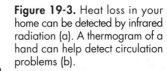

Figure 19-3. Heat loss in your home can be detected by infrared radiation (a). A thermogram of a hand can help detect circulation problems (b).

a

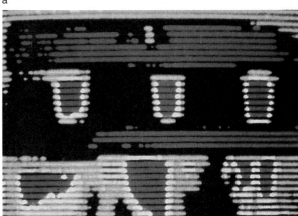

b

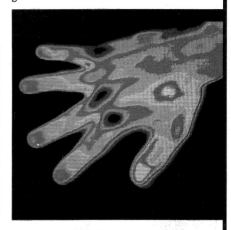

▶ An unknown material can be identified by passing infrared radiation through it. The molecules that make up the unknown substance will absorb specific wavelengths of the infrared radiation. After the infrared radiation has passed through the unknown material, the molecules can be identified by the missing wavelengths.

MULTICULTURAL PERSPECTIVE

Pride of the Nations

Christiaan Huygens was a Dutch physicist and astronomer who lived about the same time as Isaac Newton and who demonstrated that the momentum and kinetic energy of a system are conserved—laws on which modern physicists depend. It is now clear that Huygens was a skilled physicist. However, when he proposed a wave theory for the structure of light that conflicted with Newton's idea of light's being made of particles, his skills and insights were questioned. Because Huygens was not English (and was not Newton), his wave theory was ignored for almost a century in England, which was the major center of science in Europe. It took another English physicist, Thomas Young, an acknowledged genius, to propose a wave theory that was accepted. Even so, in spite of experimental evidence that showed Young was correct, efforts to fully verify his theory were thwarted in England. The work to overturn Newton's particle theory had to be done in France by Arago and Fresnel. Ironically, neither the wave theory nor the particle theory is completely correct, but a combination of the two. Newton himself had proposed ideas along those lines that were ignored by his later supporters in favor of a simpler theory.

INQUIRY QUESTIONS

▶ **Compare the speed, frequency, and wavelengths of the types of electromagnetic radiation we have discussed so far.**

(a) All forms of electromagnetic radiation travel at the same speed, the speed of light, in the same medium.

(b) in order of decreasing frequency: infrared radiation, microwaves, radio waves

(c) in order of decreasing wavelengths: radio waves, microwaves, infrared radiation

▶ Emphasize that light is only a very small part of the entire electromagnetic spectrum. We are most familiar with it because we can see it. It differs from other forms of electromagnetic radiation in wavelength and frequency range. Light and all other forms of electromagnetic radiation travel at the same speed, $c = 2.9979 \times 10^8$ m/s.

REVEALING MISCONCEPTIONS

▶ Many people think infrared radiation is visible because infrared heat lamps give off a reddish glow. Because infrared radiation is just a little longer in wavelength than that of red light in the visible spectrum, some wavelengths of red light are produced by the filament of the lamp.

STUDENT TEXT QUESTION

▶ Page 488, paragraph 1: **Can you think of any other uses of this form of radiant energy?** Animals use infrared radiation to locate prey; molecules in an unknown material can be identified using infrared radiation.

Connect to...
Chemistry

Answer: Oxygen is also produced during photosynthesis.

Figure 19-4. You may have seen infrared lamps, like these, in restaurants, keeping food warm until it is served.

What are some uses of infrared radiation?

Connect to...
Chemistry

In photosynthesis, chlorophyll in green plants absorbs sunlight to provide energy for chemical reactions that produce carbohydrates. In addition to providing food for plants, this reaction has another product that is important to humans. Find out what this product is.

detect objects giving off infrared radiation and to respond by activating a light or an alarm.

Because infrared radiation raises the temperature of matter, it can be used to warm and dry objects. Infrared lamps are used in some restaurants to keep cooked food hot until it is served. Some auto paint shops use infrared radiation to dry car finishes. Can you think of any other uses of this form of radiant energy?

Visible Radiation

Visible radiation, or light, is the only part of the electromagnetic spectrum you can see. Can you find visible radiation on the electromagnetic spectrum diagram in Figure 19-2? Notice it covers a very small range of the spectrum compared to the other types of radiation.

Hot objects, such as the sun, radiate a great deal of electromagnetic energy. Some of this energy may be in the range of the electromagnetic spectrum that is visible to humans.

Light can stimulate chemical reactions. It provides the energy for the process of photosynthesis in which green plants make their own food through a series of chemical reactions. Light also stimulates chemical reactions in your eyes that allow you to see. As you learned in Chapter 16, light can also stimulate decomposition reactions of materials such as hydrogen peroxide.

OPTIONS

INQUIRY QUESTIONS

▶ **Which would indicate more heat—a blue flame or a yellow?** *The blue flame. The color blue indicates a higher frequency, and therefore more photon energy than the color yellow. Recall that heat is a form of energy.*

Ultraviolet Radiation

Why do you wear sunglasses or use sunscreen when you're in the sunlight for several hours? These two products are designed to protect you from large doses of ultraviolet radiation. Where is ultraviolet radiation located with respect to light on the electromagnetic spectrum in Figure 19-2? **Ultraviolet radiation** has a higher frequency than light, so its photons are more energetic and have greater penetrating power. Exposure to ultraviolet radiation enables the skin cells to produce vitamin D, which is needed for healthy bones and teeth. However, overexposure to ultraviolet radiation kills healthy cells. Prolonged and frequent overexposure can lead to sagging, dry skin, and even skin cancer. For this reason, it is important to use a sunscreen regularly if you spend a lot of time outdoors. Sunscreens absorb many of the ultraviolet rays before they penetrate your skin.

Earth's atmosphere has a natural filter, ozone, that blocks most of the sun's ultraviolet rays. Ozone is a form of oxygen where three oxygen atoms combine to make each ozone molecule. A reduction in the amount of ozone in Earth's atmosphere results in an increase in the ultraviolet radiation reaching Earth's surface. Some chemicals can break down ozone molecules. Use of some spray-can propellants and refrigerants containing these chemicals may be breaking down this layer, so use of these compounds should be limited. (See *Science & Society*, Section 16-2.)

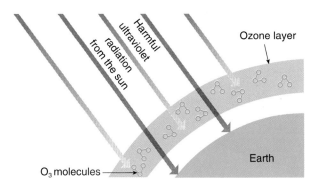

Figure 19-5. A layer of ozone molecules in Earth's atmosphere blocks most of the sun's ultraviolet rays.

19-1   ELECTROMAGNETIC RADIATION   **489**

MINI-Lab
Teaching Tips

▶ **CAUTION**: *The bulbs may be hot. Students should not allow the cup or the window to touch them.*

▶ The heat collector will reach its heat capacity when it absorbs heat as fast as it radiates heat. Therefore, the temperature increase is a rough measure of the rate at which heat flows through the window.

▶ **Answer:** The student will discover more heat flows from the incandescent light.

MINI-Lab
ASSESSMENT

Oral: Ask students which of the two bulbs would give off high levels of infrared radiation. *the incandescent bulb*

CROSS CURRICULUM

▶ **Medical Science:** Obtain some old X rays from a doctor's or dentist's office and view them. For reinforcement, ask students why only bony tissue is visible. Point out that when having X rays taken, patients usually wear protective lead aprons to cover body parts not being viewed.

CHECK FOR UNDERSTANDING

To find out if the students can distinguish the various types of radiation, ask them to answer these questions.

Which type of radiation

(a) would you use to identify a fluorescent mineral? *ultraviolet*

(b) allows you to listen to the radio? *radio waves*

(c) is used in cancer therapy? *gamma*

(d) keeps food warm in restaurants? *infrared*

RETEACH

Cooperative Learning: Divide the class into seven groups. Present each group with a sign of one of the seven types of radiation. Give them about ten minutes to become experts on their topic, finding out the relative penetrating power and several applications. Have one speaker from each group carry their sign as they line up from the longest to shortest wavelength and make a short presentation.

MINI-Lab

Is fluorescent light hot?

Use an incandescent light and a fluorescent light of identical wattage. Make a heat collector by covering the top of a plastic foam cup with a plastic food wrap window. Push a thermometer through the side of the cup. Hold the window of the tester one centimeter from each light for two minutes. *Measure* the temperature change inside the "heat collector" for exposure to each bulb. What was the temperature change inside the cup for each bulb? Which bulb appears to give off more heat?

Because ultraviolet rays can penetrate cells, they can be used to kill germs in food and in hospitals. Some minerals become fluorescent when exposed to ultraviolet light. Fluorescence occurs when a material absorbs ultraviolet radiation and changes some of the radiation into light.

X Rays and Gamma Rays

If you ever had a bad fall, you probably had to have an X ray taken to check for broken bones. **X rays** have a shorter wavelength and higher frequency than ultraviolet radiation. X-ray photons carry higher energy and have a greater penetrating power than any of the forms of electromagnetic radiation discussed so far. This higher energy allows X rays to travel through some types of matter, such as your skin and muscles. When X rays hit a more dense material, such as bone, they are absorbed. If you saw the X ray photograph of your broken bone, it probably looked similar to the one in Figure 19-6. An X-ray photograph is a negative; thus, the bones appear much brighter than the surrounding tissues because they absorb most of the X rays.

Gamma rays have the highest frequency and are the most penetrating of all the electromagnetic waves, so they are located at the opposite end of the electromagnetic spectrum from radio waves. Gamma rays are emitted from the nuclei of radioactive atoms and Earth receives some gamma radiation from space. Concentrated gamma rays are very destructive to human cells and can be used to kill cancerous cells. People who undergo gamma radiation therapy for cancer frequently suffer side effects from the therapy because healthy cells are damaged, as well.

Doctors and technicians who give gamma radiation therapy or take X-ray pictures protect themselves from this penetrating radiation by standing behind lead shields. These shields absorb the high energy photons. Excess exposure to X rays and gamma radiation is much more harmful to your body than overexposure to ultraviolet radiation.

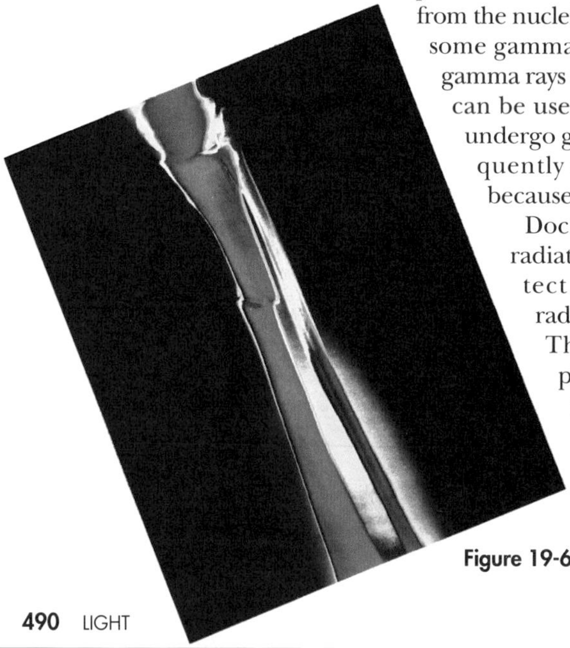

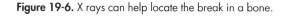

Figure 19-6. X rays can help locate the break in a bone.

PROGRAM RESOURCES

From the **Teacher Resource Package** use:

Activity Worksheets, page 156, MINI-Lab: Is fluorescent light hot?

Science and Society, page 23, Food Irradiation.

Use **Laboratory Manual 14,** Producing a Spectrum.

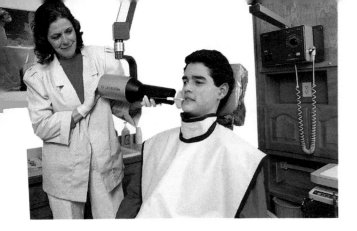

vignette edge

Figure 19-7. Exposure to X rays and gamma radiation can be harmful to patients if they don't use protective measures. Medical personnel usually leave the room before activating X-ray equipment.

Think of all the uses of the waves of the electromagnetic spectrum that you read about in this section. Can you think of some uses that weren't mentioned? In the next section, you will learn more about the visible part of the spectrum, *light*.

SECTION REVIEW

1. Describe at least three ways electromagnetic waves differ from sound waves.
2. Arrange the following waves in order of decreasing wavelength: radio waves, gamma rays, ultraviolet rays, light, infrared radiation.
3. Explain how X rays can be used to photograph your bones.
4. How do microwaves cook food?
5. **Apply:** If someone told you that you were being exposed to radio waves and gamma radiation, which would you be more concerned about? Explain your choice.
6. **Connect to Life Science:** Explain why you can detect light with your eyes, but you cannot detect any kind of electromagnetic radiation by hearing it.

☑ Outlining

Outline the major types of electromagnetic radiation discussed in this section. Treating X rays and gamma radiation together, include at least one use for each type listed. If you need more help, refer to Outlining in the **Skill Handbook** on page 677.

Skill Builder

19-1 ELECTROMAGNETIC RADIATION **491**

Skill Builder

I. Radio waves
 A. radio and television communications
 B. cellular and cordless telephones
II. Infrared radiation
 A. medical diagnoses
 B. warming food
III. Visible radiation
 A. stimulates chemical reactions
 B. helps you see color
IV. Ultraviolet radiation
 A. helps skin make vitamin D
 B. kills germs in food processing
V. X rays and gamma rays
 A. examine bones
 B. cancer therapy

---

3 CLOSE

▶ Ask students to locate where light is found on the electromagnetic spectrum. Emphasize that it is a very small range of the whole spectrum, but it is of special interest to us because we can see it. The next section will focus on light and color.

▶ Ask questions 1-4 and the **Apply** and **Connect to Life Science** questions in the Section Review.

SECTION REVIEW ANSWERS

1. Electromagnetic waves don't need a medium to transfer energy. They are all transverse waves, and they travel much faster than sound waves through air.

2. radio, infrared, light, ultraviolet, gamma

3. X rays can easily penetrate skin and muscle tissues, but are absorbed by bones. Those X rays that are not absorbed expose the photographic film. Those X rays that are absorbed by the bones create a shadow of the bones on the photographic film.

4. Energy from the microwaves is absorbed by food molecules, making these molecules vibrate faster and rotate. The temperature of the food increases with the kinetic energy of the molecules.

5. Apply: Gamma rays; they carry more energy and are more penetrating.

6. Connect to Life Science: Light causes chemical reactions in your eyes that allow you to see. Electromagnetic radiation is not a mechanical wave, so there is not a force to vibrate the eardrum.

Skill Builder
ASSESSMENT
Oral: Ask students to look at their list of uses for each type of electromagnetic radiation. Discuss which type of radiation is least likely to affect or be detected by the human body and why.

PREPARATION

SECTION BACKGROUND

▶ Materials that are transparent to light are not necessarily transparent to other types of radiation. For example, glass is not transparent to ultraviolet radiation. This explains why you do not get a sunburn from light that has passed through a window.

▶ Determining the real color of something is difficult because color depends on the wavelengths of light produced by the source. People complain of looking "washed out" in fluorescent lights. This happens because fluorescent lamps produce light concentrated in wavelengths near the blue end of the spectrum. Hence, blue colors in skin stand out more than the reddish colors under fluorescent bulbs.

1 MOTIVATE

▶ **Demonstration:** Begin by convincing students that there is more than one color in white light. Aim an overhead projector toward a white screen. Narrow the light path by passing it through a slit and then aim the light beam through a prism. You should be able to project the spectrum on the wall. Remember that refraction isn't discussed until later in the chapter.

▶ Bring in three white or colorless objects. Make sure one is opaque, one is transparent, and the other is translucent. Have students describe, as specifically as they can, the different ways light behaves when it shines on the objects.

19-2 Light and Color

New Science Words

opaque materials
transparent materials
translucent materials

Objectives

▶ Describe the differences among opaque, transparent, and translucent materials.
▶ Explain how you see color.
▶ Describe the difference between light color and pigment color.

Light and Matter

Have you ever been asleep in a dark room when someone suddenly opened the curtains and bright light came bursting into the room? You probably groaned as your eyes adjusted to the light. As you looked around, you could clearly see all the objects in the room and their colors. When no light was in the room, your eyes couldn't distinguish those objects or their colors. What you see depends on the amount and color of light the objects you are looking at are reflecting or absorbing. In order for you to see an object, it must reflect at least a little bit of light.

The type of matter in an object determines the amount of light it absorbs and reflects. For example, the curtains at the window kept the room dark when they were completely closed. The curtains are opaque. **Opaque materials**  absorb or reflect all light and you cannot see objects through them. When the curtains were opened, bright sunlight came shining through the glass window panes. Most glass windows are transparent. **Transparent materials** allow light to pass through and you can clearly see objects through them. Other materials, such as frosted glass and wax paper, allow light to pass through but you cannot clearly see objects through them. These materials are **translucent materials.**

Figure 19-8. The vase and the lenses in the glasses are transparent, some flower petals are translucent, but most of the flowers are opaque.

OPTIONS

Meeting Different Ability Levels

For Section 19-2, use the following **Teacher Resource Masters** depending upon individual students' needs.

◆ **Study Guide Master** for all students.

● **Reinforcement Master** for students of average and above average ability levels.

▲ **Enrichment Master** for above average students.

Additional Teacher Resource Package masters are listed in any **PROGRAM RESOURCES** boxes that are in the section. The additional masters are appropriate for all students.

◆ STUDY GUIDE   79

STUDY GUIDE   Chapter 19
Light and Color   Text Pages 492-497

Use the words in the box to fill in the blanks.

| translucent | primary | opaque | black | transmits | colors |
| white | cone | absorbs | | transparent | reflect |

For you to see an object, it must __reflect__ light. A material through which nearly all light passes is __transparent__. A material that you cannot see through clearly is __translucent__. __Opaque__ objects cannot be seen through. __White__ light is a mixture of all visible wavelengths of light. __Black__ objects absorb all colors and reflect little light. Red, blue, and green are the three __primary__ colors of light. They can be mixed to produce any color.

The retina contains __cone__ cells that detect certain signals of light. When the brain responds to these signals, we see __colors__.

One way of producing color is by the use of a __filter__, a transparent object that __absorbs__ some colors and allows others to pass through. The color of the filter is the same as the color of light it __transmits__.

Use the words in the box to fill in the blanks.

| cyan | filter | pigment | additive |
| subtractive | black | reflected | |

A colored material that absorbs certain colors and reflects others is a __pigment__.

To mix and make any color, it is necessary to have only three primary pigment colors—magenta, yellow, and __cyan__. Light color is determined by the wavelength of light transmitted through a __filter__. Pigment color is determined by the wavelength of light __reflected__ from pigment particles.

Because primary light colors combine to produce white light, they are called __additive__ colors. If all primary pigments are added equally, the result will be __black__. Because black results from the absence of reflected light, the primary pigment colors are called __subtractive__ colors.

Copyright Glencoe Division of Macmillan/McGraw-Hill
Users of *Merrill Physical Science* have the publisher's permission to reproduce this page.   79

Colors

Have you ever wondered why your blue jeans look blue or why grass looks green? What do you suppose your blue jeans and grass have in common? They are both opaque materials, either absorbing or reflecting nearly all of the light that strikes them. When struck by white light, which is actually a blend of a spectrum of colors, your blue jeans reflect blue light back to your eyes and absorb all of the other colors. What color of light do you think a blade of grass reflects? White objects appear white because they reflect all colors of light in the visible spectrum. The colors present in white light, arranged in order of decreasing wavelengths, are red, orange, yellow, green, blue, indigo, and violet. Objects that appear black absorb all colors of light and reflect little or no light back to your eye. Why do you think colorful objects appear to be black in a dark room?

What would this white page look like if you placed a colored, transparent plastic sheet over it? The paper would appear the same color as the plastic. The plastic sheet is a filter. A filter is a transparent material that transmits one or more colors of light, but absorbs all others. The color of a filter is the same as the color of light it transmits. What happens when you look at colored objects through colored filters? In white light, broccoli looks green because it reflects only the green light in the white

Figure 19-9. The colors of the flags depend on the wavelengths they absorb and reflect.

Why do some objects appear black?

In Your JOURNAL

If you were going to spend several hours outside on a hot, sunny day, would it be more sensible to wear a white shirt or a black shirt? **In your Journal,** write an explanation for your answer.

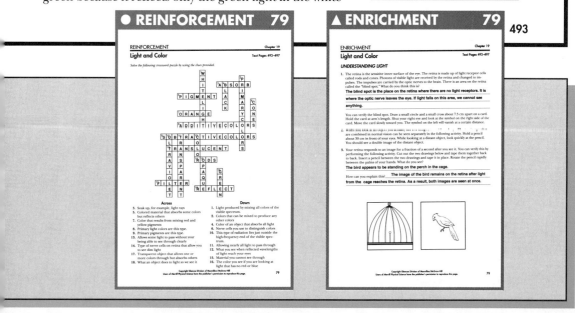

STUDENT TEXT QUESTIONS

▶ Page 493, paragraph 1: **What color of light do you think a blade of grass reflects?** *A blade of grass reflects green light.*

▶ Page 493, paragraph 1: **Why do you think colorful objects appear to be black in a nearly dark room?** *Colorful objects appear to be black in a nearly dark room because there is so little light for them to reflect.*

TYING TO PREVIOUS KNOWLEDGE:
Ask students to describe sunlight. They will probably use the phrase *white light.* Point out that if you can see it, then it is part of the visible spectrum. This, in turn is a part of the electromagnetic spectrum, as they read in the last section.

OBJECTIVES AND SCIENCE WORDS:
Have students review the objectives and science words to become familiar with this section.

In Your JOURNAL

A white shirt would keep you cooler because white materials reflect all visible wavelengths. A black shirt would absorb all visible wavelengths, as well as some infrared, and the absorbed energy would make you feel warmer.

2 TEACH

Key Concepts are highlighted.

REVEALING MISCONCEPTIONS

▶ Ask students if they can name the three primary light colors. They may name the primary pigment colors instead. (Children learn red, yellow, and blue.) From their art education, they may have a working knowledge of color. Emphasize that the primary pigment colors are different from the primary light colors. We will investigate what makes things look green, blue, and red.

493

Figure 19-10. The broccoli appears green when viewed through a green filter (a) and black when viewed through a red filter (b).

CONCEPT DEVELOPMENT

▶ **Demonstration:** Obtain sheets of red, blue, and green transparency film. Cut a 10-cm circle of each color. Place these on the overhead projector and shine combinations of these primary colors on a white screen to make other colors. Demonstrate how red and green overlap to make yellow, red and blue make magenta, and green and blue make cyan.

▶ Show how the demonstration above relates to Figure 19-11.

▶ Colored overhead transparencies can be used as light filters. They can be stacked easily in different combinations. Colored slides can also be used.

STUDENT TEXT QUESTION:

▶ Page 494, paragraph 1: **Why does [the broccoli] appear this way?** *Broccoli can appear to be very dark, almost black, when viewed through a red filter. The red filter absorbs green light, so none of the green light reflected by the broccoli passes through the filter to your eyes.*

CROSS CURRICULUM

▶ **Theater Arts:** Make a trip to the stage in the school auditorium or theater, if one is available. Find out what kind of colored lighting is used to illuminate the stage. Investigate the special effects that can be created with lighting.

CHECK FOR UNDERSTANDING

Use the Mini Quiz to check for understanding.

MINI QUIZ

Use the Mini Quiz to check students' recall of chapter content.

1 _____ objects reflect or absorb nearly all light. *Opaque*

2 The three primary light colors are _____ . *red, blue, and green*

3 The three primary pigment colors are _____ . *yellow, magenta (red) and cyan (blue)*

4 The three primary pigment colors mixed together form _____ . *black*

---

light striking it. It absorbs light of all other colors. If you look at the broccoli through a green filter, the broccoli still looks green because the filter transmits the reflected green light. Figure 19-10b shows how the broccoli looks when you look at it through a red filter. Why does it appear this way?

② Red, green, and blue light are the primary colors of light. They can be mixed in different amounts to produce any color of light. Figure 19-11 shows how all three primary colors form white light.

How do you actually see colors? First, light enters your eye and is focused on the retina, which is made up of two main types of nerve cells. When these nerve cells, the rods and cones, absorb light, they send signals to your brain. The rods allow you to see dim light because they are more sensitive than the cones. The cones allow you to distinguish colors. There are three types of cones, each of which absorbs a different range of wavelengths. "Red" cones absorb mostly red and yellow, "green" cones absorb mostly yellow and green, and "blue" cones absorb mostly blue and violet.

What happens when you look at pure yellow light, such as the yellow part of the rainbow? Both your red and green cones respond, and your brain interprets the combined signal as yellow. Your brain would get the same signal if a mixture of red light and green light reached your eye. Again, your red and green cones would respond, and you would see yellow light because your brain can't perceive the difference.

Figure 19-11. White light is produced when the three primary colors of light are mixed.

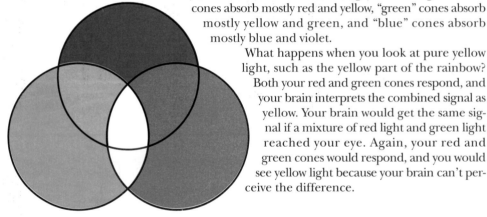

OPTIONS

ASSESSMENT—ORAL

▶ Some people are color-blind, and as a result, can't distinguish the colors red and green. Based on the discussion of cones above, what can you infer about this disorder? *Color-blind people either don't have both red and green cones, or these cones are not properly stimulated by certain wavelengths of light, or if the cones exist, and are stimulated, the proper message doesn't reach the brain.*

▶ How is a colored light bulb like a filter? *The color of the glass on the outside of the bulb is the same color as the light it transmits. The colored glass absorbs other colors from white light given off by the filament.*

PROGRAM RESOURCES

From the **Teacher Resource Package** use:
Cross-Curricular Connections, page 25, Psychology of Light and Color.
Science Integration Activity 19

You see white light when a mixture of all visible wavelengths of light enter your eye because all of your cones are stimulated. If a mixture of red, green, and blue light, the primary colors, reaches your eye, you would also see white light.

Pigments

A pigment is a colored material that absorbs some colors and reflects others. Pigments are used by artists to make various colors of paints. Paint pigments are usually made of powdered insoluble chemicals such as titanium (IV) oxide, a bright white pigment, and lead (II) chromate, used in painting yellow lines on highways. Few people have exactly the same skin color because the amount of pigmentation in the skin varies.

You can make any pigment color by mixing different amounts of the three primary pigments—yellow, magenta, and cyan. A primary pigment's color depends on the color of light it reflects. For example, in white light the yellow pigment appears yellow because it reflects red and green light but absorbs blue light. The color of a mixture of two primary pigments is determined by the primary colors of light that both pigments can reflect.

Look at Figure 19-12. Its center appears black because the three blended primary pigments absorb all the primary colors of light. Note that the primary colors of light combine to produce white light; they are called additive colors. But the primary pigment colors combine to produce black. Because black results from the absence of reflected light, the primary pigments are called subtractive colors.

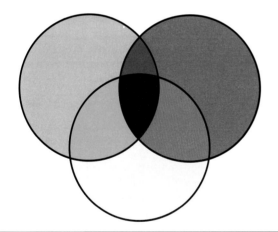

What is a pigment?

Connect to...
Earth Science

Minerals can be classified by a variety of techniques, such as testing the hardness or observing the crystal structure. They can also be grouped by their *luster*. Find out what the luster of a mineral is.

Science and READING

Advertisers write their ads to appeal to a certain audience. Look through magazines and newspapers to see if you can find different kinds of ads for some of the everyday products mentioned in this chapter. Then, write an ad of your own.

Figure 19-12. The three primary colors of pigment appear black when they are mixed.

19-2 LIGHT AND COLOR **495**

Connect to...
Earth Science

Answer: Luster describes how the surface of the material appears due to the way it reflects light. Some types of luster are metallic, vitreous (glassy), resinous (like plastic), pearly, silky, and dull.

RETEACH

Cooperative Learning: Obtain some spot plates and some primary pigment paints from the art department. Have students work in groups and combine small amounts of various combinations of pigments to make other colors. For each color, have them describe which colors are reflected and which are absorbed. Be sure they mix all three primary pigments to produce black. Point out that black pigment absorbs all light and reflects none.

EXTENSION

For students who have mastered this section, use the **Reinforcement** and **Enrichment** masters or other OPTIONS provided.

Science and READING

Readers of *Popular Science* look for more specific and technical information than readers of *People,* where the ads may be more "image" oriented.

3 CLOSE

▶ Ask questions 1-4 and the **Apply** and **Connect to Life Science** questions in the Section Review.

? FLEX Your Brain

Use the Flex Your Brain activity to have students explore COLORS.

ASSESSMENT

Portfolio: Use the Flex Your Brain activity to reinforce critical-thinking and problem-solving skills. In Step 2, students might list how colors change when seen through sunglasses, the colors they like and dislike, and how colors change when the weather changes.

Think Critically: A mixture of cyan and yellow dots makes the grass appear green. Cyan reflects blue and green and absorbs red; yellow reflects green and red and absorbs blue. Green is the only color reflected by both cyan and yellow ink.

SECTION REVIEW ANSWERS

1. Transparent materials, such as a glass window, transmit all light so objects can be seen clearly. Opaque objects, like a wall, absorb or reflect all light. Translucent materials, such as waxed paper, allow light through, but objects can't be clearly seen.

2. red reflected, all others absorbed

3. Blue light is a part of the electromagnetic spectrum; blue pigment is a substance that reflects blue light and absorbs all the other colors.

4. Apply: Light enters your eye and is focused on the retina, which sends signals to your brain. The red, green, and blue cones enable the brain to interpret colors.

5. Connect to Life Science: The lens of your eye is transparent, your fingernail is translucent, your skin is slightly translucent, and your teeth are opaque.

 # PROBLEM SOLVING

Color in the Sunday Comics

Becky looked forward to Sunday mornings because she liked to read the comics in the Sunday newspaper. One morning, as she was reading the comics, she wondered how color was produced in them. She decided to take a closer look, so she dug through her closet and located a hand lens.

She remembered from science class that the primary colors of pigments were magenta, cyan, and yellow. First, she examined the primary colors in the comics. The red areas were made of magenta dots, the blue areas of cyan dots, and the yellow areas of yellow dots. Next, she examined the other colors in the comics. She saw that an illustration of an orange school bus was made up of a mixture of magenta and yellow dots and one of a purple box was composed of a mixture of magenta and cyan dots. In the next cartoon frame, she examined a field of green grass.

Think Critically: What color dots do you think she found? How can you explain the reflection of green?

SECTION REVIEW

1. Contrast opaque, transparent, and translucent materials. Give at least one example of each.
2. If white light shines on a red shirt, what colors are reflected and what colors are absorbed?
3. What is the difference between blue light and blue pigment?
4. **Apply:** Explain how your eye sees color.
5. **Connect to Life Science:** Consider the following parts of your anatomy: the lens of your eye, a fingernail, your skin, and a tooth. Decide whether each of these is opaque, transparent, or translucent. Explain.

Skill Builder

☑ Concept Mapping

Design a concept map to show the chain of events that must happen for you to see a blue object. Work with a partner. If you need help, refer to Concept Mapping in the **Skill Handbook** on pages 684 and 685.

Skill Builder

Light strikes blue object
↓
Blue light reflected; other colors absorbed
↓
Blue light strikes cones and rods on retina
↓
Cones sensitive to blue absorb the light
↓
Cones send the signal to brain

Skill Builder
ASSESSMENT
Performance: Ask students to draw a similar concept map for seeing a white object. Have them explain any differences.

ACTIVITY 19-1
DESIGNING AN EXPERIMENT
Spectrum Inspection

Have you ever used a dimmer switch to turn down the brightness of a light gradually? Are all of the same wavelengths present at all settings of a dimmer switch? The following activity will help you find out.

Getting Started
In this activity you will use a diffraction grating to separate the colors of light produced by a light bulb at different levels of brightness. **CAUTION:** *Do not touch the bulb or the diffraction grating.*

Hypothesizing
Which colors of the visible spectrum have the highest frequency? The highest energy? Write a **hypothesis** describing which colors will be produced by the light source and how they will be affected by reducing its brightness and temperature.

Materials
Your cooperative group will use:
• diffraction grating
• power supply with rheostat (dimmer switch)
• clear, tubular light bulb and socket
• colored pencils (red, yellow, and blue)

Try It!

1. With the light bulb in an upright position, adjust the light to its brightest setting.

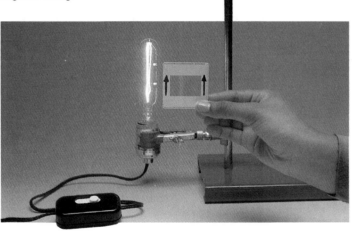

2. Look toward the light through the diffraction grating. Draw the color spectrum you see to the right and left of the bulb.

3. Slowly turn down the power supply to dim the light. Draw the color spectrum you see through the diffraction grating. Make sure all group members observe and draw the spectrum.

Summing Up/Sharing Results
• How did your two spectra differ?
• What can you *infer* about the connection between color, frequency, and the temperature of the light source?

Going Further!
Recall your original spectrum from your bulb on the highest setting. Would you expect to find the same spectrum if you used a different kind of bulb, such as a colored light bulb, neon light, or fluorescent bulb? Try it and see.

19-2   LIGHT AND COLOR   **497**

SUMMING UP/ SHARING RESULTS
As the light dims, the blue end of the spectrum becomes less visible and the red appears more prominent. As the brightness and temperature of the light decrease, the blue colors decrease. High temperatures cause high frequencies of light, corresponding to blue colors, to be given off.

GOING FURTHER!
No. The spectrum will vary with the nature of its light source and its temperature.

Activity
ASSESSMENT
Oral: Ask students to discuss whether long or short wavelengths of light will be most prevalent in a very bright and hot white light or in a dim and relatively cool white light.

PROGRAM RESOURCES
From the **Teacher Resource Package** use:
Activity Worksheets, pages 150-151, Activity 19-1: Spectrum Inspection.

OBJECTIVE: Use a diffraction grating to **identify** the color spectrum of a light source and r**elate** the frequency of the colors in the spectrum to the temperature of the light source.
Time: one class period

PROCESS SKILLS applied in this activity are **observing, interpreting,** and **inferring.**

PREPARATION
Be sure to have some alternate light sources available for the Going Further activity.

Cooperative Learning: Use the Science Investigation strategy in groups of three or four. Emphasize that all students should view the spectra and make their own observations.

SAFETY
Be sure to check the cords and rheostats to make sure they are intact. Caution students about the possible hot temperatures of the bulb.

HYPOTHESIZING
The blue and purple colors have the highest frequency and the highest energy. Because the bulb produces white light, the spectrum should show a full range of colors (red, orange, yellow, green, blue, indigo, and violet). If you dim the light source, reducing its temperature, the blue end of the spectrum will be reduced.

TEACHING THE ACTIVITY
*Refer to the **Activity Worksheets** for additional information and teaching strategies.*

• Use a clear, bright lamp like the one shown in the photo. Try the activity ahead of time to ensure that the lamp is bright enough to give a full spectrum and to determine where the blue portion of the spectrum begins to disappear.
• The spectra can be seen most clearly in a dark room.

PREPARATION

SECTION BACKGROUND
▶ Standard 60–75-watt incandescent bulbs can be replaced by 18-watt compact fluorescent bulbs. They use about 90 percent less electricity to produce the same amount of light.

1 MOTIVATE

▶ Classroom lights are usually fluorescent bulbs. Ask your students how these differ in appearance from those in lamps at home.

TYING TO PREVIOUS KNOWLEDGE:
Ask students what a light bulb feels like after it has been on. It feels warm. Incandescent light is produced by heat, and fluorescent bulbs produce heat as a by-product.

2 TEACH

Key Concepts are highlighted.

CONCEPT DEVELOPMENT
▶ Emphasize that phosphors are fluorescent materials that give off light when struck with ultraviolet radiation. Make sure students do not confuse this with the element phoshor*us*.

Connect to...
Chemistry

Answer: Tungsten (atomic number 74) is a hard, heavy, gray, metallic element. It is often added to steel to improve its strength and can also be found in surgical instruments and solar energy devices.

VideoDisc
STVS: Synchrotron; Disc 1, Side 1

New Science Words

incandescent light
fluorescent light

Objectives

▶ Explain how incandescent and fluorescent bulbs work.
▶ Analyze the advantages and disadvantages of different light sources.

Connect to...
Chemistry

Tungsten, used in making the filament in incandescent bulbs, has the highest melting point of all metals. Find out at least one other property and one other use of tungsten.

Do Light Bulbs Make a Difference?

Are you using light from a light bulb to illuminate this page as you read it? Have you ever thought about what actually produces this light?

If you touch a light bulb after it has been on for a while, it may feel hot. **Incandescent light** is produced by heat. If you look into an unlit incandescent light bulb, you will see a thin wire called a filament. It is usually made of the element tungsten. When you turn on the light, electricity flows through the filament and causes it to heat up. When it gets hot, tungsten gives off light. Over half of the energy given off by incandescent bulbs is heat.

Fluorescent lighting is an alternative to incandescent lighting. A fluorescent bulb is filled with gas at a low pressure. The inner side of the bulb is coated with phosphors, fluorescent materials that give off light when they absorb ultraviolet radiation. When the electricity is turned on, electrons collide with the gas molecules in the bulb to make them give off ultraviolet radiation. You can't see the ultraviolet radiation, but the phosphors absorb it and glow to give off light.

A **fluorescent light** produces light without excessive loss of energy due to heat. These bulbs use as little as one-fifth the energy of ordinary incandescent bulbs. This energy difference can save you from $25 to $60 over the life of the fluorescent bulb.

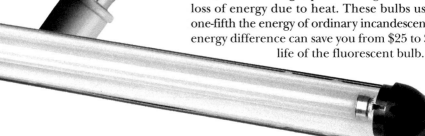

498 LIGHT

OPTIONS

Meeting Different Ability Levels
For Section 19-3, use the following **Teacher Resource Masters** depending upon individual students' needs.
◆ **Study Guide Master** for all students.
● **Reinforcement Master** for students of average and above average ability levels.
▲ **Enrichment Master** for above average students.
Additional Teacher Resource Package masters are listed in any PROGRAM RESOURCES boxes that are in the section. The additional masters are appropriate for all students.

◆ STUDY GUIDE 80

STUDY GUIDE   Chapter 19
Battle of the Bulbs   Text Pages 498–499

Determine whether the italicized term makes each statement true or false. If the statement is true, write the word "true" in the blank. If the statement is false, write in the blank the term that makes the statement true.

true	1. Incandescent light is produced by *heat*.
tungsten	2. An incandescent bulb contains a filament of *platinum*.
ultraviolet	3. *Infrared* light causes phosphors to give off visible light.
1/5	4. A fluorescent light uses *5 times* as much energy as an incandescent bulb.
low	5. A fluorescent bulb is filled with gas at a *high* pressure.
more	6. *Less* than half of the energy given off by incandescent bulbs is heat.
phosphorus	7. The inner wall of a fluorescent bulb is coated with *potassium*.
20%	8. About *10%* of all electricity consumed in the United States is used for lighting.
visible	9. When the filament in an incandescent lamp gets hot, it gives off *ultraviolet* light.
true	10. A fluorescent bulb is *more* efficient than an incandescent bulb.
true	11. An incandescent bulb contains a thin wire called a *filament*.
absorbs	12. In a fluorescent bulb, phosphorus *reflects* ultraviolet radiation.

80   Copyright Glencoe Division of Macmillan/McGraw-Hill
                      Users of Merrill Physical Science have the publisher's permission to reproduce this page.

The electricity used by a light bulb has been generated at a power plant. Whenever you turn on a light at home or at school, the electric company measures the amount of energy that the light bulb uses while it is on. The electric company then charges a fee for the energy used. By turning a light off when you leave a room, you are saving money as well as electricity.

About 20 percent of all electricity consumed in the United States is used for lighting. A great deal of this energy is wasted by lighting unoccupied rooms and using inefficient lighting sources. How efficient is the lighting in your home? You can find out.

SECTION REVIEW

1. Explain how light is produced in an ordinary incandescent bulb.
2. What are the advantages and disadvantages of using a fluorescent bulb instead of an incandescent bulb?
3. **Connect to Earth Science:** Other than saving you money, why is it important that you conserve electricity? Where does the energy in this electricity come from?

You Decide!

You are at the store to purchase a new study lamp. The fluorescent and incandescent lamps cost about the same, but the fluorescent bulb costs about ten times as much as the incandescent bulb. The fluorescent bulb is also guaranteed to last ten times longer than the incandescent bulb. Which would you buy? Explain your reasoning.

● **REINFORCEMENT** 80   ▲ **ENRICHMENT** 80

499

Ask students to answer these questions: **What light is produced by heat?** *incandescent* **What happens when ultraviolet radiation strikes phosphors?** *They fluoresce.*

RETEACH

Have students diagram and label the parts of an incandescent light and a fluorescent light, and write captions as if these were diagrams in a book.

EXTENSION

For students who have mastered this section, use the **Reinforcement** and **Enrichment** masters or other OPTIONS provided.

3 CLOSE

▶ Ask questions 1-2 and the **Connect to Earth Science** question in the Section Review.

SECTION REVIEW ANSWERS

1. The tungsten filament inside the bulb heats up as electricity passes through it, giving off light.

2. advantages—more energy efficient, more economical to use; disadvantages—more costly to purchase

3. Connect to Earth Science: Most ways of generating electricity impact our environment. Energy sources such as fossil fuels and nuclear energy cause pollution. Even hydroelectric plants can upset ecosystems.

YOU DECIDE!

Note that although the fluorescent bulb is more expensive, it lasts much longer and uses as little as 20 percent of the energy to produce the same amount of light as an incandescent bulb.

PREPARATION

SECTION BACKGROUND

► Light that falls on a rough surface is reflected in many directions. This phenomenon is called diffuse reflection. You see most objects by diffuse reflection of light. Otherwise you would always see your own reflection in objects.

► The ratio of the speed of light in a vacuum to the speed of light in another material is the index of refraction. The higher this value is, the slower light travels through the other material.

► Did you know that you actually can see the sun a few minutes before the sun rises above and after the sun falls below the horizon? Light entering Earth's atmosphere changes speeds due to the change in density, producing the index of refraction of 1.0003. The light rays from the sun are bent, causing the sun to appear higher in the sky than it is.

► Christian Huygens is usually considered the originator of the wave theory of light, which he published in 1690. Huygen's principle states that each wave front is actually composed of many smaller wave fronts or a new source of disturbance. Using this model, diffraction and interference are easier to understand.

PREPLANNING

► Get a light source and a clear container for Activity 19-2.

VideoDisc

STVS: Laser Identification of Fibers; Disc 1, Side 2

New Science Words

reflection
refraction
diffraction
diffraction grating

Objectives

► State and give an example of the law of reflection.
► Explain how refraction is used to separate the colors of the spectrum in white light.
► Describe how diffraction and interference patterns demonstrate the wave behavior of light.

Figure 19-13. You can't see a clear image reflected from an uneven surface such as this one.

EcoTip

Turn out lights in your home when they are not needed. Exchange 100 watt bulbs with 60 watt bulbs to save energy in areas that do not require bright light.

Reflection

Just before you left for school this morning you might have glanced in a mirror one last time to check your appearance. In order for you to see your reflection in the mirror, light had to reflect off you, hit the mirror, and be reflected off the mirror into your eye. **Reflection** occurs when a wave strikes an object and bounces off.

Reflection occurs with all types of waves: electromagnetic waves, sound waves, and water waves. Look at the light beam striking a mirror in Figure 19-14. The beam striking the mirror is called the incident beam. The beam that bounces off the mirror is called the reflected beam.

Notice that in Figure 19-14 a line is drawn perpendicular to the surface of the mirror. This line is called the *normal*. The angle formed by the incident beam and the normal is the angle of incidence, labeled *i*. The angle formed by the reflected beam and the normal is the angle of reflection, labeled *r*. The law of reflection states that the angle of incidence is equal to the angle of reflection. Any reflected light, whether it is reflected from a mirror, a piece of foil, or the moon, follows the law of reflection.

If you took a smooth piece of aluminum foil and looked into it, you would see a slightly distorted image of yourself. What if you crumpled up the foil and then unfolded it again? What would you see? The creases in the foil create an uneven surface. You can't see an image of your-

OPTIONS

Meeting Different Ability Levels

For Section 19-4, use the following **Teacher Resource Masters** depending upon individual student' needs.

◆ **Study Guide Master** for all students.
● **Reinforcement Master** for students of average and above average ability levels.
▲ **Enrichment Master** for above average students.

Additional Teacher Resource Package masters are listed in any PROGRAM RESOURCES boxes that are in the section. The additional masters are appropriate for all students.

◆ **STUDY GUIDE** 81

STUDY GUIDE — Chapter 19
Wave Properties of Light — Text Pages 500–506
Use the words in the box to fill in the blanks.

| incident | equal | reflection | incidence | reflected | normal | reflection |

When a wave strikes an object and bounces off, ___reflection___ occurs. Waves that strike an object are called ___incident___ waves. Waves that bounce off are called ___reflected___ waves. A perpendicular line drawn from where the incident wave strikes is called the ___normal___. The angle between the incident wave and the normal is the angle of ___incidence___. The angle between a reflected wave and a normal is the angle of ___reflection___. In reflection, the angles will be ___equal___.

Label the diagram of a refracted light wave. Use the terms incident wave, angle of incidence, refracted wave, and normal to fill in the blanks. One term is used twice.

Angle of Incidence — Normal — Incident wave — Glass — Refracted wave — Normal

Use the words in the box to fill in the blanks.

| interference | light | diffraction | slits | dark | colors | diffraction grating |

The bending of light around corners is ___diffraction___. Diffraction results in light and ___dark___ areas on the edge of a shadow. Light or sound waves can meet, causing ___interference___. If light is passed through narrow ___slits___, the light waves will interfere, forming dark and ___light___ bands. When white light is passed through a ___diffraction grating___, white light is separated into ___colors___.

81

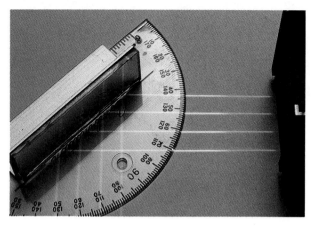

self because the reflected light is scattered in different directions. Smooth surfaces reflect light in one direction, but rough surfaces scatter light in many directions.

Refraction

Stick your finger at an angle halfway into a glass of water and look at it through the side of the glass. Do you notice anything bizarre? Your finger appears to be bent or even split into two pieces once it enters the water. This happens because light waves bend when they move from air to water, because the speed of light changes when light waves move from one medium to another.

Refraction is the bending of waves caused by a change in their speed. The amount of bending that occurs depends on the speed of light in both materials. The greater the difference between the speeds of light in two media, the more the light is bent as it passes at an angle from one medium to another. When light is passing into a material that will slow it down, the light is refracted (bent) toward an imaginary line drawn perpendicularly through the surface of the medium at the point where the wave strikes the surface. This imaginary line is called the normal. The angle between the normal and the ray entering the medium is called the angle of incidence. The angle between the normal and the ray after it has entered the medium is called the angle of refraction. When light passes into a material in which light travels faster, it will be refracted (bent) away from the normal.

Figure 19-14. The light beam striking the mirror is the incident beam and the one bouncing off is the reflected beam. Note that the angles of incidence and reflection are the same.

Figure 19-15. The handle of the net looks bent because the light waves are refracted as they change speed when they pass from the water to the air.

● REINFORCEMENT 81

▲ ENRICHMENT 81

501

REINFORCEMENT Chapter 19
Wave Properties of Light Text Pages 500–506

Fill in the blanks in this diagram of a light wave hitting a smooth, shiny surface.

FIGURE 1
normal
angle of incidence   angle of reflection
incident wave   reflected wave

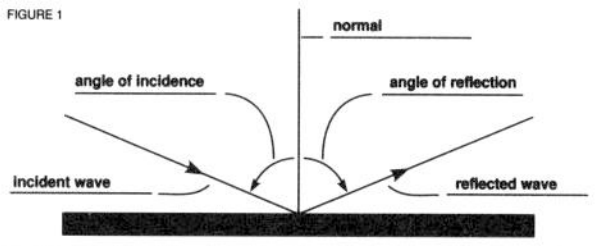

Figure 2 is a sketch of Tanya's fish tank as she looks at it from one of the corners. It appears to Tanya that there are two fish in the tank. However, she knows she has only one fish. Explain why two fish are seen and draw a ray diagram to show what happens. (Hint: The aquarium glass refracts light rays.)

FIGURE 2
F₁ F F₂

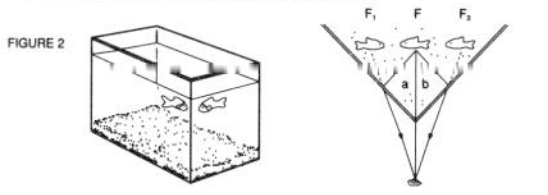

Light rays a and b from the fish, F, are refracted producing two images that appear to come from F₁ and F₂.

On the blank, write the letter of the term that best completes each of the following statements.

c 1. The interference of light shows the ___ behavior of light.
    a. particle   b. translucent   c. wave   d. refraction
b 2. The bending of light around corners is called ___.
    a. refraction   b. diffraction   c. interference   d. reflection
a 3. A(n) ___ is used to separate the colors of white light.
    a. diffraction grating   c. photon
    b. electromagnetic spectrum   d. modulation

Copyright Glencoe Division of Macmillan/McGraw-Hill
Users of Merrill Physical Science have the publisher's permission to reproduce this page.   81

ENRICHMENT Chapter 19
Wave Properties of Light Text Pages 500–506

LIGHT THEORY AND EVERYDAY PHENOMENA

Use the library to find information to explain the following phenomena.

1. What is a rainbow? _A rainbow forms when the sun is behind you and there are water droplets in the air in front of you. When sunlight strikes the water droplets, the light is bent, or refracted, to form the colors of the spectrum. The refracted light is reflected by the water droplets. We see a rainbow when the angle of reflected rays with the sun's rays is between 40°24' and 42°18'. Each color of the rainbow is a certain angle in this range. Violet will be at the bottom of the band of colors since it is refracted the most. Red will be at the top since it is refracted the least._

2. Why are sunrises and sunsets sometimes red? _When the sun is low in the sky, light rays pass through more atmosphere, dust particles, and water droplets than when the sun is high in the sky. Short wavelengths of light such as blue are scattered more than the longer wavelengths of light such as red and orange. As a result, more of the orange and red reach our eyes by the time it reaches us._

3. What causes eyes to be blue and brown? _When a baby is born, its eyes are blue. Actually a baby's eyes do not have any color. The blue is due to the scattering of light. When white light enters the iris, muscle tissue scatters it. The reds pass through, but the scattered blue light is reflected. This makes the baby's eyes appear blue. As the baby gets older, brown pigment forms on the back part of the iris. If this pigment is dark and heavy, the person has brown eyes; the scattered blue light is not apparent. When the layer of pigment is lighter, the color that results is a mixture of brown and the scattered blue. Since the amount of pigment varies from person to person, eye color varies greatly._

4. Look at the side of a compact disc that is read by the laser during playing. What do you see? _colored bands of light_

5. Explain your observation. _The compact disc is etched with many pits. The pits act much like diffraction gratings and diffracted light waves are reflected._

Copyright Glencoe Division of Macmillan/McGraw-Hill
Users of Merrill Physical Science have the publisher's permission to reproduce this page.   81

1 MOTIVATE

▶ Ask students if they have ever seen a mirage, or wavering images above hot ground. What is it? Sometimes images of nearby objects appear inverted. A mirage occurs when a layer of hot air lies right above the ground. Light can move through hot air faster than through the colder air above. This causes a bending of light rays, and refracted images of objects can be seen.

▶ Shine a light on a compact disc and look at the colors reflected. Where does the color come from? The different wavelengths and colors of white light are separated by diffraction in the grooves in the disc.

REVEALING MISCONCEPTIONS

▶ Many people think that seeing a mirage on an extremely hot day is caused by mental confusion resulting from the heat. In most cases, there is a valid scientific explanation for it. See the explanation in the Motivate section.

TYING TO PREVIOUS KNOWLEDGE: Ask students how the underwater portions of their bodies look when they are in a swimming pool. They probably will say that they look shorter and distorted. This is because the speed of light in water is different than the speed of light in air, causing light to refract and distort the image.

OBJECTIVES AND SCIENCE WORDS: Have students review the objectives and science words to become familiar with this section.

2 TEACH

Key Concepts are highlighted.

CONCEPT DEVELOPMENT

▶ When discussing reflection, give the students some foil and mirrors and ask them to describe how their images differ in each one. Discuss the explanation given in the text.

Cooperative Learning: Use the Paired Partners strategy. Obtain a shoe box and cut out one of the narrow sides. Tape a maze from a coloring book on the bottom, inside the box and near the cut-out end. Attach a mirror inside the box to the other narrow end. Cut a hole in the top of the box big enough to allow a student to see the reflection of the maze, but small enough so the top will cover the maze itself. Have several students try to draw a path through the maze while looking at the reflection. Discuss why this is difficult.

▶ **Demonstration:** Show that waves can be diffracted. Set up a "pond" in a large pan. Put a barrier in the pan. Drop a stone in the pan and watch how the waves bend around the barrier. If you have a wave generator, use it instead.

▶ To help students remember the colors of the spectrum from longest to shortest wavelength, use the fictitious character ROY G. BIV as a memory device. The name corresponds to the colors of the rainbow: red, orange, yellow, green, blue, indigo, violet.

STUDENT TEXT QUESTION

▶ Page 502, paragraph 1: **Which color of light would you expect to bend the least?** *Because red light has the longest wavelength, it would bend the least.*

a

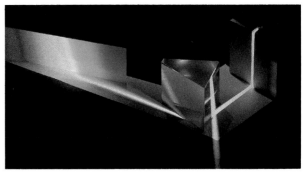

b

Figure 19-16. A prism is an angular transparent object (a). White light is refracted into the colors of the visible spectrum as it passes through a prism (b).

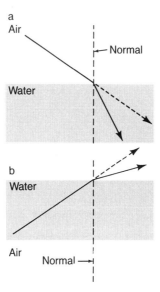

a
Air

Normal

Water

b
Water

Air

Normal

Figure 19-17. Light slows down and refracts toward the normal as it passes into a more dense medium (a), and light speeds up and bends away from the normal as it passes into a less dense medium (b).

The amount of refraction also depends on the wavelength of the light. In the visible spectrum, the wavelengths of light vary from the longer red waves to the shorter violet waves. Figure 19-16 shows what happens when white light passes through a prism. The triangular prism refracts the light twice, once when it enters the prism and again when it leaves the prism and reenters the air. Because the shorter wavelengths of light are refracted more than the longer wavelengths, violet light is bent the most. Which color of light would you expect to bend the least? As a result of this varied refraction, the different colors are separated as they emerge from the prism.

Does the light leaving a prism remind you of a rainbow? If the sun shines during a rain shower, you might see a rainbow. Like prisms, rain droplets also refract light. The refraction of the different wavelengths can cause white light from the sun to separate into the individual colors of the visible spectrum. Isaac Newton recognized that white light actually includes all of the seven colors of the rainbow. In order of decreasing wavelength, the colors you should see in the rainbow are red, orange, yellow, green, blue, indigo, and violet—the same order as the colors of the electromagnetic spectrum. Have you noticed that the reddish colors are always on top and the bluish colors are always on the bottom of a rainbow?

Diffraction and Interference

Have you heard bells or music played by vendors selling ice cream as they drive their trucks through your neigh-

ASSESSMENT—ORAL

▶ **What makes stars twinkle?** *Light traveling through the atmosphere is refracted by varying amounts because the density and composition of the atmosphere along its path varies. Some light from a star is refracted away from our line of sight because the atmosphere changes in density and composition. This causes the star to appear to turn on and off, or jump around.*

▶ **List the colors of light in order of most to least diffraction.** *violet, indigo, blue, green, yellow, orange, red*

▶ **If you walked toward an open door and music were playing inside the room, you would hear the music before you reached the doorway. How is this possible?** *Sound waves diffract, or bend around barriers. The sound waves of the music bend outward as they pass through the door. They also reflect off surfaces, obeying the law of reflection.*

TECHNOLOGY

Holograms—The Key to 3-D

A hologram is a vivid three-dimensional image that appears to float in space. As you walk around a hologram you see the image from a slightly different angle.

Holograms are produced by illuminating the object you wish to make an image of with light from a laser. Laser light reflected from the object shines on photographic film simultaneously with light from a second laser of the same wavelength. The pattern created on the photographic film produces a hologram image when laser light shines through it.

A hologram conveys more information to your eye than a conventional two-dimensional photograph by controlling both the intensity and direction of the light that departs from the image. As a result, these vivid three-dimensional objects are very difficult to copy. For this reason, holographic images are used on credit cards and on the labels of some clothing to help prevent counterfeiting. Scientists are working on ways of displaying computer information on a three-dimensional screen. How would you like to play video games in 3-D?

Think Critically: What are some situations where a three-dimensional image or display would be a significant advantage over a two-dimensional image?

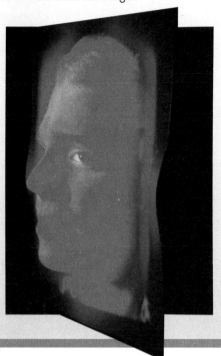

borhood? Or maybe you have heard cars drive by your home with blasting stereos. You can hear these sounds even when buildings or hills separate you from the source. This happens because sound waves can bend around corners to reach you. **Diffraction** is the bending of waves around a barrier. In the 1600s, an Italian physicist, Francesco Grimaldi, observed light and dark areas on the edge of a shadow. If you observe the shadow formed when light passes through an open door, you'll notice no clearly defined boundary between light and dark. Instead, you

Whales are capable of making sounds that can be detected for miles. Explain which wave properties might help these sounds travel through the ocean so efficiently.

TECHNOLOGY

▶ Trace the history of attempts to produce 3-D images in books, at the movies, and on TV.

▶ For more information on 3-D images, see Rennie, John. "Move Over, Mr. Spock." *Scientific American.* July 1990, pages 89-92.

Think Critically: A three-dimensional display would be advantageous in situations such as air traffic control, automobile design, architecture, etc.

CONCEPT DEVELOPMENT

▶ Pass diffraction gratings around. Explain that there are many slits to let light pass through. Look through one while looking at a light source—what do you see? You see the colors of the spectrum because the different wavelengths of light are separated by diffraction.

CROSS CURRICULUM

▶ **Language Arts:** Have students write a fictitious, creative short story explaining why the sky is blue. Then have them research and write the factual reason that the sky appears blue.

Answer: The waves can be reflected off the bottom or the surface of the ocean. When barriers, such as reefs, are encountered, the waves can diffract around them. Refraction plays a role when there are significant changes in temperature between layers of water.

INQUIRY QUESTIONS

▶ **As you are walking toward the door, which sounds would you expect to hear first, low frequency or high frequency?** *Explain your reasoning. You would hear the low frequency sounds first because they have longer wavelengths, therefore, they are easier to diffract than the shorter wavelengths of high frequency sounds*

PROGRAM RESOURCES

From the **Teacher Resource Package** use:

Transparency Masters, pages 77-78, Wave Interference.

Use **Color Transparency,** number 39, Wave Interference.

Use the Mini Quiz to check for understanding.

MINI QUIZ

Use the Mini Quiz to check students' recall of chapter content.

1 _____ occurs when waves bend due to a change in their speed. *Refraction*

2 A line drawn perpendicular to the surface of a barrier is the _____ . *normal*

3 _____ is the bending of waves around a barrier. *Diffraction*

4 _____ is caused when light waves overlap each other. *Wave interference*

RETEACH

Give each pair of students a cup of water and a round washer. Drop the washer in the cup. Try to put a pen or pencil through the hole in the washer. Have students explain why it is difficult to hit the hole directly. The light reflected from the washer bends away from the normal as it emerges from the water. Because the light ray that reaches your eye is bent, the washer appears higher in the water than it actually is.

EXTENSION

For students who have mastered this section, use the **Reinforcement** and **Enrichment** masters or other OPTIONS provided.

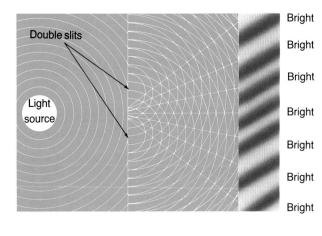

Figure 19-18. Wave interference demonstrates how light behaves like waves.

What waves can be diffracted?

will see a gradual transition. Grimaldi explained this phenomenon by suggesting that light could be bent around the edges of barriers.

Electromagnetic waves, sound waves, and water waves can all be diffracted. You can see water waves bend around you as you swim. Sand bars are formed along shorelines as water that is carrying sand is diffracted by some obstruction in the water. The pattern of the waves changes as the waves are diffracted. Diffraction is important in the transfer of radio waves. Longer wavelengths, such as those used by AM radio stations, are easier to diffract than short FM waves. That is why AM reception is often better than FM reception around tall buildings and hills.

4 Recall from Section 18-4 that sound waves can interfere with each other to form constructive and destructive interference. In the early 1800s, Thomas Young, an English scientist, expanded the diffraction theory Grimaldi had developed. In a famous experiment, he passed light of a uniform wavelength through a narrow slit. The new diffraction pattern of the light waves then passed through a barrier with two slits. You can see the results, wave interference, in Figure 19-18. The wave crests are shown by the semicircles. The light from these slits was projected on a screen. Young observed light bands where two crests or two troughs combined, and dark areas where a crest and a trough crossed paths. This experiment shows how light behaves as a wave. Only waves exhibit interference; particles do not.

You know that one way to separate colors of white light is by refraction in a prism. Colors can also be separated by interference using many slits. A **diffraction grating** is a piece of glass or plastic made up of many parallel slits. Diffraction gratings commonly have as many as 12 000 slits per centimeter. When white light shines through a diffraction grating, the colors are separated. Reflective materials can be ruled with closely spaced grooves to produce diffraction patterns. For example, shiny bumper stickers sometimes diffract light into a wide array of colors. You can also see the dazzling results of simple diffraction gratings by looking at the reflection of light provided from the grooves in a compact disc.

Recall that throughout this chapter, we have referred to light as both waves and particles. That is because, as you have read in this lesson, light demonstrates properties of both waves and particles. What are the wave properties of light? What properties of light support the particle theory?

Figure 19-19. Compact discs can produce diffraction patterns.

SECTION REVIEW

1. Explain the law of reflection.
2. When light moves from air into glass at an angle, is the light refracted toward or away from the normal?
3. Explain how you could use a prism to separate the colors of the spectrum from white light.
4. **Apply:** Scientists say that light has both particle and wave properties. Explain why observations of diffraction and interference patterns conflict with the idea that light consists of particles.
5. **Connect to Chemistry:** Some substances can be classified by measuring a change in the angle of a beam of light as it enters the substance. Which property of waves makes this possible? Explain.

☑ Observing and Inferring

Imagine you are on the shore of a large lake and see waves moving toward you from the center of the lake. However, the waves pass by a boat dock and move toward you at a slightly different angle afterwards. What would you infer is happening? If you need help, refer to Observing and Inferring in the **Skill Handbook** on page 678.

Skill Builder

▶ Page 505, paragraph 2: **What are the wave properties of light?** *reflection, refraction, diffraction, interference*
▶ Page 505, paragraph 2: **What properties of light support the particle theory?** *evidence of the existence of photons and measurements of their momentum; cell damage caused by high energy radiation*

3 CLOSE

Ask questions 1-3 and the **Apply** and the **Connect to Chemistry** questions in the Section Review.

SECTION REVIEW ANSWERS

1. The angle of incidence equals the angle of reflection.
2. Toward; light moves more slowly in glass.
3. A prism refracts light twice. The shortest wavelengths are refracted the most and the longest wavelengths are refracted the least.
4. Apply: Light spreads out as it passes through a diffraction grating; this behavior is characteristic of waves, not particles. Light waves interfere with each other, causing the light and dark bands observed when light passes through a diffraction grating. Particles, like waves, will reflect, but they cannot interfere. Diffraction supports the wave theory of light.
5. Connect to Chemistry: Light refracts (bends) as it passes into the unknown material due to a change in speed.

Skill Builder
The boat dock is acting as a barrier and causing the wave front to bend as it tries to move around it. This changes the direction of the approaching wave.

OPTIONS

ENRICHMENT
▶ Have students investigate and describe the phenomenon that causes the spectrum of colors to be seen in soap bubbles.

Skill Builder
ASSESSMENT
Performance: Have students test their inference by building a small model of this situation in a shallow pan. Ask them to sketch what they see as a wave encounters a barrier, such as a wood block.

ACTIVITY 19-2

40 minutes

OBJECTIVE: Predict how light reflects and refracts.

PROCESS SKILLS applied in this activity:
▶ **Observing** in Analyze Question 1.
▶ **Experimenting** in Analyze Question 2.
▶ **Predicting** in Conclude and Apply Question 4.

COOPERATIVE LEARNING
Students can work in teams of not more than three. Up to four teams can share the same light source.

TEACHING THE ACTIVITY

Troubleshooting: The light should be taped down so it can't be moved during the experiment.
• Use a clear rectangular container. Size: 5 to 8 cm across and at least 3 cm deep. A clear glass baking dish can be used if you can't find a plastic box. Boxes with curved surfaces can be used for follow-up.
• The pencil **must** stand straight up. Use the edge of the container to check.
• Measurement of angles between rays and normals is not necessary for observation and description of the general effect.

PROGRAM RESOURCES

From the **Teacher Resource Package** use:

Activity Worksheets, pages 152-153, Activity 19-2: Make a Light Bender.

Activity
ASSESSMENT

Oral: Ask students if they would expect the same results if a different clear liquid, such as alcohol or mineral oil, were in the box. You may wish to have them try this.

Make a Light Bender

Can you recall seeing your reflection in the surface of a lake or other body of water? You can see your image because some of the light that reflects off your face also strikes the water's surface and reflects into your eyes. However, you don't see a clear, color image because much of the light enters the water rather than being reflected. Would a person under the surface see a clear image of you?

Materials

• light source
• pencil
• clear rectangular container
• water
• notebook paper
• clay

Procedure

1. Fill the container with water and place it on a sheet of notebook paper.
2. Outline the container on the paper.
3. Stand the pencil on end in the clay and place it on the paper in front of the container.
4. Place the lamp in an upright position near the paper and turn it on.
5. Adjust the position of the paper and the pencil so the pencil's shadow on the paper goes completely through the container.
6. Draw lines on the shadow where it enters and leaves the container. Draw a line on the shadow that reflects from the surface of the container.
7. Move the container. Connect the lines to show the shadow through the container.

Analyze

1. Draw a reference line (normal) at right angles through the outline of the container at the point where the shadow touches its surface. As the shadow enters the container, does it refract toward the reference line or away from it? What happens when the shadow leaves the other side of the container?
2. Alter the experiment by changing the angle between the reference line and the shadow. What happens to the reflected and refracted shadows?

Conclude and Apply

3. *Compare* the angles of reflection and refraction for light striking the flat surface of the container.
4. Would the angles of reflection or refraction change in Question 3 if the surface of the container were curved? *Explain* your answer.

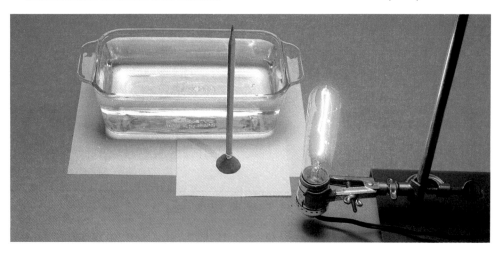

506   LIGHT

ANSWERS TO QUESTIONS

1. The shadow refracts toward the reference line when it enters the box and refracts away when it leaves.

2. The angles of the refracted and reflected rays increase when the angle of the incoming shadow is increased. Students might also notice that the intensity of the reflected ray increases as the incident angle increases.

3. Light rays *refract* to make smaller angles inside water than outside, but rays always *reflect* with the same angle as the incoming ray.

4. The statement is true for curved surfaces. For groups of rays the images are distorted with curved surfaces.

SUMMARY

19-1: Electromagnetic Radiation
1. Electromagnetic waves differ from other types of waves because they do not need a medium to transfer energy.
2. Electromagnetic waves are arranged on the electromagnetic spectrum by their wavelength and frequency.
3. Radio waves and microwaves are used in communications. Infrared radiation is used to detect tumors. Light is produced by light bulbs. Ultraviolet radiation causes fluorescent bulbs to glow. X rays aid medical diagnosis. Gamma rays can be used to destroy cancer cells.

19-2: Light and Color
1. You can't see through opaque materials. You can see clearly through transparent materials and unclearly through translucent materials.
2. You see color when light is reflected off objects and into your eye. Inside your eyes, cones respond to certain wavelengths.
3. The three primary colors of light can be mixed to form all other colors. The color of pigments is determined by the colors they reflect.

19-3: Science and Society: Battle of the Bulbs
1. Incandescent bulbs produce light by heating a tungsten filament until it glows brightly. Fluorescent bulbs give off light when ultraviolet radiation produced inside the bulb causes a fluorescent coating inside the bulb to glow.
2. Although expensive to purchase, fluorescent bulbs waste less energy, last longer, and cost much less to use than incandescent bulbs.

19-4: Wave Properties of Light
1. The law of reflection states that the angle of incidence is equal to the angle of reflection. You can observe this by examining the reflection of an object in a mirror.
2. White light can be separated into the colors of the visible spectrum because each wavelength refracts at a different angle as it passes into a medium.
3. Diffraction and interference show wave patterns of light by showing that light waves bend around a barrier and can cancel each other.

KEY SCIENCE WORDS

a. **diffraction**
b. **diffraction grating**
c. **electromagnetic spectrum**
d. **fluorescent light**
e. **gamma rays**
f. **incandescent light**
g. **infrared radiation**
h. **microwaves**
i. **modulation**
j. **opaque material**
k. **photon**
l. **radiation**
m. **radio waves**
n. **reflection**
o. **refraction**
p. **translucent material**
q. **transparent material**
r. **ultraviolet radiation**
s. **visible radiation**
t. **X rays**

UNDERSTANDING VOCABULARY

Match each phrase with the correct term from the list of Key Science Words.

1. energy transfer by electromagnetic waves
2. bundle of radiation with no mass
3. electromagnetic radiation that is felt as heat
4. object that can't be seen through
5. light produced by heat
6. occurs when a wave strikes an object and then bounces off
7. the bending of waves around a barrier
8. contains many parallel slits that can separate white light into colors
9. highest frequency electromagnetic waves
10. radio waves with the greatest energy

OPTIONS

ASSESSMENT
To assess student understanding of material in this chapter, use the resources listed.

👥 COOPERATIVE LEARNING
Consider using cooperative learning in the THINK AND WRITE CRITICALLY, APPLY, and MORE SKILL BUILDERS sections of the Chapter Review.

PROGRAM RESOURCES
From the **Teacher Resource Package** use:
Chapter Review, pages 41-42.
Chapter and Unit Tests, pages 126-129.

CHAPTER

REVIEW

SUMMARY
Have the students read the summary statements to review the major concepts of the chapter.

UNDERSTANDING VOCABULARY

1. l	**6.** n
2. k	**7.** a
3. g	**8.** b
4. j	**9.** e
5. f	**10.** h

ASSESSMENT
Portfolio
Encourage students to place in their portfolios one or two items of what they consider to be their best work. For each item, ask students to explain why that item was chosen and what they learned from it. Items might be selected from the following.
- MINI-Lab data and conclusions, p. 480
- the answer to Section Review question 1, p. 496
- the answer to Section Review question 4, p. 505

Performance
Additional performance assessments may be found in *Performance Assessment* and *Science Integration Activities* that accompany **Merrill Physical Science.** Performance Task Assessment Lists and rubrics for evaluating these activities and other products generated throughout the chapter can be found in Glencoe's *Performance Assessment in Middle School Science.*

CHAPTER REVIEW

CHAPTER REVIEW

CHECKING CONCEPTS

1. d		**6.** b	
2. a		**7.** c	
3. a		**8.** d	
4. a		**9.** a	
5. b		**10.** c	

USING LAB SKILLS

ASSESSMENT

Use these alternate lab exercises to assess students' understanding of the skills used in this chapter.

11. Incandescent bulbs make objects appear more red or orange, and part of their heat is due to waves in the infrared part of the spectrum. Fluorescent bulbs make objects appear bluish, so they emit fewer waves at the red end of the spectrum.

12. Both angles inside the box are the same and both angles in the air are the same. The angle of the shadow entering the pan is the same as the angle leaving the pan.

THINK AND WRITE CRITICALLY

13. Sound waves can be converted to electrical signals that correspond to the sound's characteristic patterns. These electrical signals can then be used to modulate, or vary, either the amplitude or frequency of a radio wave. This process is utilized in radio and television transmissions, cellular telephones, and cordless telephones.

14. Light color is determined by the wavelength of light transmitted while pigment color is determined by the color of light reflected.

15. Light reflects off a white wall or a mirror because of the law of reflection. Both the wall and mirror reflect all frequencies of light. Light reflected off a wall is scattered because the surface is rough and light reflected off a mirror is not scattered.

16. Rainbows are produced when white light from the sun passes through large droplets of water suspended in the atmosphere after a heavy rain. The water droplets act like prisms, *refract-*

CHECKING CONCEPTS

Choose the word or phrase that completes the sentence.

1. Electromagnetic waves are different from other types of waves in that they do not _____.
   a. have amplitude   **c.** transfer energy
   b. have frequency   **d.** need a medium

2. When light passes through matter, it ____.
   a. slows down
   b. speeds up
   c. travels at 300 000 km/sec
   d. travels at the speed of sound

3. A contact lens is _____.
   a. transparent   **c.** opaque
   b. translucent   **d.** square

4. Electromagnetic waves with the longest wavelengths are _____.
   a. radio waves   **c.** X rays
   b. visible light   **d.** gamma rays

5. The process of changing the frequency or amplitude of radio waves in order to send a signal is _____.
   a. diffraction   **c.** reflection
   b. modulation   **d.** refraction

6. When food molecules absorb microwaves, they vibrate faster and their _____.
   a. kinetic energy decreases
   b. kinetic energy increases
   c. temperature decreases
   d. temperature remains constant

7. Your body gives off _____.
   a. radio waves   **c.** infrared radiation
   b. visible light   **d.** ultraviolet radiation

8. Fluorescent bulbs glow when the phosphors inside absorb _____.
   a. microwaves   **c.** infrared radiation
   b. gamma rays   **d.** ultraviolet radiation

9. X rays are best absorbed by _____.
   a. bone   **c.** muscle
   b. hair   **d.** skin

10. Objects that partially scatter light that passes through them are called _____.
   a. reflective   **c.** translucent
   b. opaque   **d.** transparent

USING LAB SKILLS

11. In the MINI-Lab on page 490, you used a heat collector to compare the heat given off by incandescent and fluorescent bulbs. Observe a colorful object under both lights. Does it appear the same color? Which light has more waves in the red end of the spectrum?

12. Repeat Activity 19-2 on page 506. Measure the angle of incidence and the angle of refraction as the shadow enters and leaves the container. Show the angles on the diagram. What do you notice?

THINK AND WRITE CRITICALLY

Answer the following questions in your Journal using complete sentences.

13. Explain how sound waves are converted to radio waves. Give some examples.

14. What is the difference between light color and pigment color?

---

ing light of different wavelengths and separating colors into the visible spectrum.

17. Light has been modeled as both a particle and a wave. Albert Einstein postulated that light is transmitted as tiny packets of energy called photons. Light can also be diffracted to show interference patterns. This suggests that light behaves as a wave. Light's wave-like behavior was studied by Francesco Grimaldi and Thomas Young.

APPLY

18. Blue light has a higher frequency than red light, so its particles carry more energy.

The hotter an object is, the more energy it gives off.

19. A blue filter will transmit the blue light reflected from the shirt, and the shirt will appear blue. Because the red and green filters each absorb blue light, blue light reflected from the shirt will be absorbed by either filter, and the shirt will appear black.

20. blue filter: blue cones; red filter: red cones; green filter: none

21. Violet changes speed the most since it is bent the most by a prism and the greater the difference in the speed of light in two different media, the more it is refracted.

15. How is the reflection of light off a white wall similar to the reflection of light off a mirror? How is it different?

16. Explain which property of light helps produce a rainbow.

17. Describe the two models of light and note some of the scientists who studied both models.

APPLY

18. Heated objects often give off light of a particular color. Explain why an object that glows blue is hotter than one that glows red.

19. How would a blue shirt appear if a blue filter were placed in front of it? A red filter? A green filter?

20. What color cones in your eye would transmit signals to your brain as you looked at a purple shirt through each of the three filters described in Question 19?

21. Which color of light changes speed the most when it passes through a prism? Explain.

22. Explain why you can hear a fire engine coming around a street corner, but cannot see it.

MORE SKILL BUILDERS

If you need help, refer to the Skill Handbook.

1. **Sequencing:** List the types of radiation in the electromagnetic spectrum in order of decreasing penetrating power. Use Figure 19-2, the electromagnetic spectrum, as a reference.

2. **Making and Using Tables:** Construct a table to show the applications of each type of electromagnetic wave. Which type would an electronics engineer be most interested in? A doctor?

3. **Observing and Inferring:** Most mammals, such as dogs and cats, can't see colors. Infer how a cat's eye might be different from your eye.

4. **Concept Mapping:** Use the blank concept map below to show the five steps in the production of fluorescent light.

Initiating Step

```
┌─────────────────────────────┐
│                             │
└─────────────────────────────┘
              ↓
┌─────────────────────────────┐
│                             │
└─────────────────────────────┘
              ↓
┌─────────────────────────────┐
│                             │
└─────────────────────────────┘
              ↓
┌─────────────────────────────┐
│                             │
└─────────────────────────────┘
              ↓
```

Final Outcome

```
┌─────────────────────────────┐
│                             │
└─────────────────────────────┘
```

5. **Outlining:** Make an outline of Section 19-4. Be sure to include the four wave properties of light and at least one example of how each can be observed.

PROJECTS

1. Make a scrapbook of newspaper and magazine articles describing the dangers of ultraviolet radiation and how this harmful radiation is absorbed by Earth's ozone layer. Write a short summary of each article.

2. Make a poster to show how the three primary pigments are combined to produce common colors such as blue, red, yellow, green, purple, brown, and black.

22. Waves with greater wavelengths are diffracted more easily than waves with shorter wavelengths. Sound has a much longer wavelength than light. Sound is therefore bent much more easily around a street corner than light.

MORE SKILL BUILDERS

1. **Sequencing:** Penetrating power is directly related to wave energy which is, in turn, directly related to wave frequency. Therefore, the order of decreasing penetrating power of electromagnetic waves is the same as the order of decreasing frequency: gamma rays, X rays, ultraviolet radiation, light, infrared radiation, microwaves, radio waves.

2. **Making and Using Tables:** A possible table is shown below, left. An electronics engineer would be most interested in radio waves, microwaves, and light, while a doctor would be more interested in infrared radiation, X rays, or gamma rays.

3. **Observing and Inferring:** The best inference would be that a cat's eye does not have the cone nerve cells that are in the human eye.

4. **Concept Mapping:** Possible steps might be, in order: Turn on the light switch. Electrons collide with gas molecules in the bulb. Gas molecules give off ultraviolet radiation. Phosphors coated on the inside of the bulb absorb the ultraviolet radiation. Phosphors give off light.

5. **Outlining:** The main topics in the outline should be reflection, refraction, diffraction, and interference. At least one example should be listed under each main topic.

Type of Radiation	Applications
Radio waves	Radio and TV transmissions, cordless telephones
Microwave	Cooking
Infrared radiation	Thermograms to detect tumors
Light	Solar-powered calculators, etc.
Ultraviolet radiation	Fluorescent lights, to kill germs
X rays	Medical diagnoses
Gamma rays	Cancer treatment

20 Mirrors and Lenses

CHAPTER SECTION	OBJECTIVES	ACTIVITIES
20-1 The Optics of Mirrors (2 days)	1. **Explain** how an image is formed in two types of mirrors. 2. **Identify** examples and uses of plane, concave, and convex mirrors.	**Activity 20-1:** *Reflections of Reflections,* p. 517
20-2 The Optics of Lenses (2 days)	1. **Describe** the types of images formed with convex and concave lenses. 2. **Cite examples** of how these lenses are used. 3. **Explain** how lenses are used to correct vision.	**MINI-Lab:** *Can lenses be made of liquids?* p. 520
20-3 Optical Instruments (2 days)	1. **Compare** refracting and reflecting telescopes. 2. **Explain** how a camera creates an image.	**MINI-Lab:** *What do telescopes see?* p. 523
20-4 The Hubble Space Telescope **Science & Society** (1 day)	1. **Describe** the development and goals of the Hubble Space Telescope. 2. **Evaluate** the need for a space telescope.	
20-5 Applications of Light (2 days)	1. **Describe** polarized light and the uses of polarizing filters. 2. **Explain** how a laser produces coherent light and how it differs from incoherent light. 3. **Apply** the concept of total internal reflection to the uses of optical fibers.	**Activity 20-2:** *What's Behind Those Shades?* p. 534
Chapter Review		

ACTIVITY MATERIALS

FIND OUT	ACTIVITIES		MINI-LABS	
Page 511 metal spoons flat mirrors	**20-1 Reflections of Reflections, p. 517** 2 plane mirrors cellophane tape masking tape protractor paper clip	**20-2 What's Behind Those Shades?** **p. 534** 2 polarizing filters light source objects with flat, hard surfaces masking tape	**Can lenses be made of liquids? p. 520** plastic bowl plastic wrap small objects tape knife or scalpel	**What do telescopes see? p. 523** 2 pieces of aluminum foil needle light bulb

CHAPTER FEATURES	TEACHER RESOURCE PACKAGE	OTHER RESOURCES
Problem Solving: *Mirrors on the New Car,* p. 516 **Skill Builder:** *Recognizing Cause and Effect,* p. 516	**Ability Level Worksheets** ◆ **Study Guide,** p. 82 ● **Reinforcement,** p. 82 ▲ **Enrichment,** p. 82 **Activity Worksheets,** pp. 158, 159 **Concept Mapping,** pp. 45, 46 **Transparency Masters,** pp. 79, 80	**Color Transparency 40,** Optics of Concave Mirrors **Laboratory Manual 41,** Reflection of Light **Laboratory Manual 42,** Magnifying Power
Skill Builder: *Concept Mapping,* p. 521	**Ability Level Worksheets** ◆ **Study Guide,** p. 83 ● **Reinforcement,** p. 83 ▲ **Enrichment,** p. 83 **Activity Worksheets,** pp. 5, 164 **Science and Society,** p. 24 **Transparency Masters,** pp. 81, 82	**Color Transparency 41,** Vision Corrections **STVS:** Disc 1, Side 1
Skill Builder: *Hypothesizing,* p. 525	**Ability Level Worksheets** ◆ **Study Guide,** p. 84 ● **Reinforcement,** p. 84 ▲ **Enrichment,** p. 84 **Activity Worksheets,** p. 165 **Cross-Curricular Connections,** p. 26 **Critical Thinking/Problem Solving,** p. 26	**STVS:** Disc 1, Side 2 **Science Integration Activity 20**
You Decide! p. 527	**Ability Level Worksheets** ◆ **Study Guide,** p. 85 ● **Reinforcement,** p. 85 ▲ **Enrichment,** p. 85	**STVS:** Disc 3, Side 1
Technology: *The Light Scalpel,* p. 533 **Skill Builder:** *Sequencing,* p. 533	**Ability Level Worksheets** ◆ **Study Guide,** p. 86 ● **Reinforcement,** p. 86 ▲ **Enrichment,** p. 86 **Activity Worksheets,** pp. 160, 161 **Technology,** pp. 17, 18	**STVS:** Disc 1, Side 1
Summary Think & Write Critically Key Science Words Apply Understanding Vocabulary More Skill Builders Checking Concepts Projects Using Lab Skills	**ASSESSMENT RESOURCES** **Chapter Review,** pp. 43, 44 **Chapter Test,** pp. 130-133 **Unit Test,** pp. 134, 135 **Performance Assessment in Middle School Science**	**Chapter Review Software** **Test Bank** **Alternate Assessment** **Performance Assessment**

◆ **Basic**   ● **Average**   ▲ **Advanced**

ADDITIONAL MATERIALS		
SOFTWARE	**AUDIOVISUAL**	**BOOKS/MAGAZINES**
General Physics Series, Volume 8: Optics, Cross Educational Software. *Lasers,* Queue. *Mirrors and Lenses,* Queue. *Reflection and Refraction,* Queue.	*Lasers: An Introduction,* Video, Coronet. *Light and Images,* Video, Coronet.	Aust, Siegfried. *Lenses! Take a Closer Look.* Minneapolis: Lerner, 1991. Darling, David. *Making Light Work: The Science of Optics.* NY: Dillon Press, 1991. Manly, Peter L. *Unusual Telescopes.* NY: Cambridge University Press, 1992.

THEME DEVELOPMENT: This chapter discusses the principles and applications of geometric optics. Systems and interactions are a major theme of this chapter. Light interacts with mirrors and lenses to produce images. Mirrors and lenses allow us to take pictures, view distant stars and planets, and perform surgery using lasers and fiber optics.

CHAPTER OVERVIEW

▶ **Section 20-1:** This section introduces the optics of plane, concave, and convex mirrors. Methods of using the focal point to find virtual and real images from reflections are illustrated.

▶ **Section 20-2:** Concave and convex lenses are discussed, as well as how they affect vision.

▶ **Section 20-3:** This section explains the optics of telescopes, microscopes, and cameras.

▶ **Section 20-4: Science and Society:** NASA's Hubble Space Telescope project is presented, and students are asked to think about the relative importance of answering questions about the universe.

▶ **Section 20-5:** Technological applications of light are discussed. Polarized light, lasers, and fiber optics are highlighted.

CHAPTER VOCABULARY

plane mirror	reflecting telescope
virtual image	microscope
concave mirror	wide-angle lenses
focal point	telephoto lenses
focal length	polarized light
real image	lasers
convex mirror	coherent light
convex lenses	incoherent light
concave lenses	total internal
refracting	reflection
telescope	optical fibers

CHAPTER
20 Mirrors and Lenses

510

OPTIONS

⚡ For Your Gifted Students

▶ Have students cut a strip of graph paper and hold it partially immersed in a bottle of water. Have them observe the strip, comparing the spacing between the lines both vertically and horizontally to the paper outside the water. Have students relate any observable differences to the curvature of the bottle. Students may repeat these examinations using bottles of different curvatures.

⚡ For Your Mainstreamed Students

▶ Have students trace the shape of a convex lens on a sheet of narrowly lined paper then focus the lens over the outline. They will compare the number of spaces seen through the lens with the number of spaces in the shape. For example, if there are eight spaces in the shape to two through the lens, the lens magnifies four times (4×).

Have you ever seen a magnified or distorted reflection of yourself? What kinds of objects cause this reflection?

FIND OUT!

Do the following activity to find out how light reflecting off surfaces of different shapes can produce different images.

Obtain a flat mirror and a shiny metal spoon. *Observe* your reflection in the flat mirror. What do you see? Is the reflection the same size as your face? Is it right side up? Now look at your image in the back of the spoon. Move the spoon close to your face and then far away. How does the image change? Turn the spoon over and look into the inside of the spoon. Move it back and forth. *Compare* and *contrast* the images produced by these three shiny surfaces.

Previewing Science Skills

► In the Skill Builders, you will recognize cause and effect, make a concept map, hypothesize, and sequence.
► In the Activities, you will observe, measure, predict, and infer.
► In the MINI-Labs, you will hypothesize, infer, and measure.

What's next?

You've seen how your reflection can change, depending on the shape of and distance to the mirror you are looking into. As you read the next section, you'll find out how images are formed in three types of mirrors.

511

INTRODUCING THE CHAPTER
Use the Find Out activity to introduce students to images produced by reflection. Inform students that they will investigate how the shape of mirrors and lenses affects the kind of image produced.

FIND OUT!
Preparation: Gather enough shiny spoons and flat mirrors for every two people in your class. You might be able to borrow some from the school cafeteria.

Materials: spoons, flat mirrors

Cooperative Learning: Use the Paired Partners strategy for this activity. One student can look into the spoon while the other person records observations about the image for each position of the spoon. Have them change roles.

Teaching Tips
► Display a large concave and a large convex mirror and have students compare each part of the spoon to the mirrors. Have them view their images in the mirrors and find similarities between their images in the mirrors and those in the spoon.

Gearing Up
Have students study the Gearing Up section to familiarize themselves with the chapter. Discuss the relationships of the topics in the outline.

What's Next?
Before beginning the first section, make sure students understand the connection between the Find Out activity and the topics to follow.

ASSESSMENT OPTIONS

PORTFOLIO
Refer to page 535 for suggested items that students might select for their portfolios.

PERFORMANCE ASSESSMENT
See page 535 for additional Performance Assessment options.
Process
Skill Builders, pp. 521, 533
MINI-Labs, pp. 520, 523
Activities 20-1, p. 517; 20-2, p. 534
Using Lab Skills, p. 536

CONTENT ASSESSMENT
Assessment—Oral, pp. 514, 524, 530
Skill Builders, pp. 516, 525
Section Reviews, pp. 516, 521, 525, 527, 533
Chapter Review, pp. 535-537
Mini Quizzes, pp. 514, 521, 524, 532

GROUP ASSESSMENT
Opportunities for group assessment occur with Cooperative Learning Strategies and Flex Your Brain Activities.

PREPARATION

SECTION BACKGROUND

▶ Principles of reflection and refraction are consistent with the wave model of light. However, the analysis of images formed by mirrors and lenses is based on the ray model of light, which assumes that light travels in straight-line paths called rays. We assume light travels from objects to our eyes in straight paths.

▶ A defect present in spherical mirrors is called spherical aberration. This occurs when rays come to an imperfect focus at the focal point. The larger the mirror, the more blurred the image is likely to be. For this reason, mirrors in astronomical telescopes must be finely ground and calibrated. Spherical mirrors would form a sphere if the surface were extended. The focal length is equal to half the radius of the sphere.

PREPLANNING

▶ Gather a few full-sized mirrors, smaller makeup mirrors, and a collection of concave and convex lenses to use in demonstrations.

1 MOTIVATE

▶ Bring a door-sized, plane mirror to class. Have one student hold the mirror. Stand with your nose against the side of the mirror, so that half your body is in front and half your body is in back. Now pick up your leg and flap your arms as if flying. Students looking into the mirror will see you "fly."

▶ Discuss other optical illusions and magic tricks that are produced with mirrors.

▶ Ask students if they have ever been in a store and thought it was much larger due to a reflection.

20-1 The Optics of Mirrors

New Science Words

plane mirror
virtual image
concave mirror
focal point
focal length
real image
convex mirror

Objectives

▶ Explain how an image is formed in two types of mirrors.
▶ Identify examples and uses of plane, concave, and convex mirrors.

Plane Mirrors

Recall the wave properties of light from Chapter 19—reflection, refraction, and diffraction. In this chapter, you will examine the properties of reflection and refraction more closely. First, you will read about how mirrors reflect light and lenses refract light to form images. Next you will study some of the practical applications of these concepts.

Now, close your eyes and picture your own face. How do you know what you look like? You have seen your reflection. In what objects have you seen your reflection? The most obvious answer is a mirror, but you probably have seen your reflection in windows and pieces of aluminum foil also. Any smooth object that reflects light to form an image is a mirror.

You are probably used to seeing your image in a **plane mirror,** one with a flat surface. What do you see when you stand in front of the mirror and look directly into it? Your reflection is upright and appears to be the same size as you. Figure 20-1 shows how your image is formed by a plane mirror, which is a piece of glass with a reflective coating on the front or the back. Light is reflected off you toward the mirror, which reflects the light back to your eyes.

The image appears to be behind the mirror because you perceive the reflected light as coming from somewhere beyond the mirror. (See Figure 20-1.) However, light rays do not exist *behind* the mirror; it is opaque. Because the image only *seems* to be behind the plane mirror, it is called a virtual image. A **virtual image** is an image in which no light rays pass through the image. The virtual image formed by a plane mirror is erect and appears as far behind the mirror as the object is in front of it. **1**

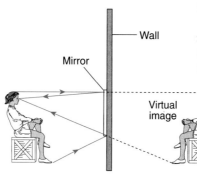

Figure 20-1. A plane mirror forms an upright, virtual image. Study the diagram to see why the rays the person sees appear to come from the opposite side of the mirror.

Labels: Wall, Mirror, Virtual image

OPTIONS

Meeting Different Ability Levels

For Section 20-1, use the following **Teacher Resource Masters** depending upon individual students' needs.

◆ **Study Guide Master** for all students.

● **Reinforcement Master** for students of average and above average ability levels.

▲ **Enrichment Master** for above average students.

Additional Teacher Resource Package masters are listed in any **PROGRAM RESOURCES** boxes that are in the section. The additional masters are appropriate for all students.

◆ STUDY GUIDE 82

STUDY GUIDE   Chapter 20
The Optics of Mirrors   Text Pages 512-517

Use the terms in the list below to fill in the blanks in the paragraphs about mirrors.

reversed	smooth	eyes	concave	focal	smaller
reflect	behind	ray	convex	optical	upside down
virtual	plane	length	real	spread	upright

Mirrors can be formed by almost any ____**smooth**____ surface. Flat mirrors made from glass with a reflective coating on the back surface are called ____**plane**____ mirrors. To see your face in a mirror, light has to ____**reflect**____ off your face. This light goes to the mirror and is reflected toward your ____**eyes**____ . The image you see will be ____**reversed**____ from left to right. To explain this requires the use of a ____**ray**____ model. The image will appear to come from ____**behind**____ the mirror. Since there is nothing behind the mirror, this image is called a ____**virtual**____ image.

Mirrors that have a curve like the bowl of a spoon are called ____**concave**____ mirrors. A straight line going through the center of a mirror is called the ____**optical**____ axis. Beams of light parallel to this axis will strike a concave mirror and be reflected to pass through a point on the optical axis called the ____**focal**____ point. The distance from the center of the mirror to the focal point is called the focal ____**length**____ . When a concave mirror is used to reflect light from an object that is placed farther from the mirror than the focal point, the image formed will be a ____**real**____ image. The image will be enlarged and ____**upside down**____ . If the object is placed between the focal point and the mirror, an image is seen that is enlarged in size, ____**upright**____ , and seems to be ____**behind**____ the mirror. Because the image appears to be behind the mirror, it cannot be projected onto a screen as a real image and is therefore called a ____**virtual**____ image.

A type of mirror like the back of a spoon is called a ____**convex**____ mirror. The rays that are reflected from this mirror are always ____**spread**____ out. When this happens, the image will appear to be behind the mirror and be upright but ____**smaller**____ than the original object.

82   Copyright Glencoe Division of Macmillan/McGraw-Hill
                  Users of Merrill Physical Science have the publisher's permission to reproduce this page.

Concave Mirrors

Mirrors are not always flat. If the surface of a mirror is curved inward, like the inside of a spoon, it is a **concave mirror.** Look for your reflection in the bowl of a shiny spoon. Concave mirrors form images differently than plane mirrors do. The way an image is formed depends on the position of the object in front of the mirror. Figure 20-2 shows one way an image can be formed in a concave mirror. The straight line drawn through the center of the mirror is the optical axis. Light rays parallel to the optical axis are all reflected to pass through one point on the optical axis, called the **focal point.** The distance from the center of the mirror to the focal point is called the **focal length.**

Suppose that the distance from the object to the mirror is a little greater than the focal length, as in Figure 20-2. You can locate the top of the image by following the two red rays. One ray is drawn from the top through the focal point to the mirror. All rays that pass through the focal point on the way to the mirror are reflected parallel to the optical axis. A second ray is drawn from the top parallel to the optical axis. This ray is reflected through the focal point. The point where the two red rays meet is the top of the reflected image. Using the same method, rays from the bottom of the object (the blue rays in Figure 20-2) locate the bottom of the image. The image is real, enlarged, and upside down. This is a **real image** because the rays of light really meet at the image, so you could hold a screen there and see it. Recall that light does not pass through a virtual image.

Connect to... Life Science

In biology, *convergence* refers to the tendency of different organisms to have some common characteristics when living in the same conditions. Concave mirrors are also said to *converge* light. From these uses, can you deduce a general definition of *converge?* Explain.

What is the focal length?

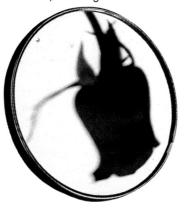

Figure 20-2. When the distance from the object to the concave mirror is a little greater than the focal length, you see an enlarged, inverted, real image.

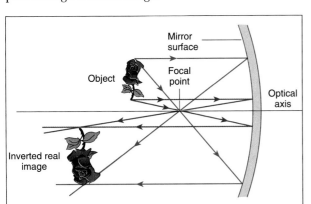

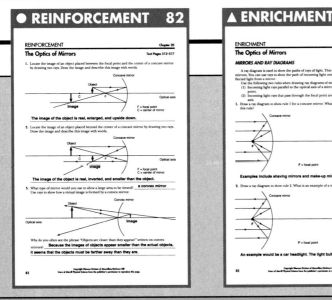
TYING TO PREVIOUS KNOWLEDGE:
Recall the law of reflection in the last chapter and the difference between looking in smooth and crumpled aluminum foil. In this section, the law of reflection will be applied to common types of mirrors.

2 TEACH

Key Concepts are highlighted.

Cooperative Learning: Ask students how large the mirror must be in order to see a full view of one's body. Place students in Paired Partners and have them make a prediction. Have students stand about one meter in front of a tall plane mirror; the partner should place a piece of tape where the other sees his or her head and another where he or she sees his or her feet. Compare your height to the distance between the pieces of tape. The distance between the tape should be half your height.

▶ Use the above setup to investigate the effect of distance from the mirror on image height. After marking the image with pieces of tape, take a few steps back and again mark the position of your head and feet in the mirror. Students will be surprised to find that although the image looks smaller from their point of view, the image height in the mirror is still the same. Beyond a certain distance, the size of the mirror needed does not depend on one's distance from the mirror.

Connect to... Life Science

Answer: An appropriate definition from these contexts would be "to come together."

CONCEPT DEVELOPMENT

▶ Take apart a flashlight and look at the concave mirror surrounding the light bulb. Ask students to explain the placement of the bulb in front of the mirror. The concave mirror reflects the light from the bulb in nearly parallel rays to form a beam of light because the bulb is placed at the focal point.

MINI QUIZ

Use the Mini Quiz to check students' recall of chapter content.

1 **A _____ forms an upright, virtual image.** *plane mirror*

2 **A _____ is curved like the inside of a spoon.** *concave mirror*

3 **What image do you see if you place the object at the focal point of a concave mirror?** *no image*

REVEALING MISCONCEPTIONS

▶ Clarify what materials are used in making common mirrors reflective. The process of making a mirror is often called silvering. However, common mirrors are made with aluminum rather than silver. Ask students why this is so. Silver's high cost makes it impractical for widespread use.

CROSS CURRICULUM

▶ **Psychology:** Have students investigate the use of two-way mirrors. A two-way mirror acts as a mirror from the inside, and as a tinted window from the outside. They are often used to secretly observe animals or people (for example, in criminal investigations). Is this use of technology an invasion of privacy?

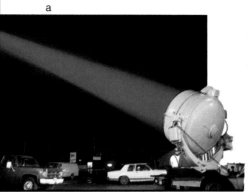
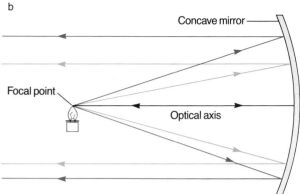

Figure 20-3. A beam of light forms (a) when a light is placed at the focal point of a concave mirror (b).

Figure 20-4. The image of the rosebud is magnified (a) when the rosebud is placed between the focal point and the surface of a concave mirror (b).

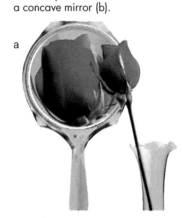
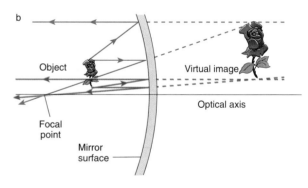

514 MIRRORS AND LENSES

What if you placed an object at the focal point of the concave mirror? Figure 20-3 shows that if the object is at the focal point, the mirror reflects all light rays parallel to the optical axis. No image can be seen because the rays do not converge. So, a light placed at the focal point is reflected in a beam. Devices such as car headlights, flashlights, and spotlights use this technique to create a concentrated light beam of nearly parallel rays. The rays aren't exactly parallel because not all of the light bulb can be exactly at the focal point.

What if you placed an object between the mirror and the focal point? You can find the top of the image using two rays from the top of the object. (See Figure 20-4b.) One ray is drawn as if it comes through the focal point and is reflected parallel to the optical axis. The second ray leaves the object parallel to the optical axis and reflects through the focal point. These rays never meet to form a real image. Instead, they appear to come from a single

OPTIONS

ASSESSMENT—ORAL

▶ **Suppose you wanted to buy a shaving or makeup mirror. What kind would you buy? Explain your choice?** *A concave mirror because its image is magnified.*

▶ **Assume you bought a concave mirror to use to apply makeup, but it reflected an image of your face that was upside down. Is the mirror faulty and should you return it to the store?** *No, you need to stand closer to the mirror so your face is between the focal point and the mirror.*

INQUIRY QUESTION

▶ **Why don't convex mirrors form real images?** *Light rays have to converge to form a real image, and convex mirrors only diverge light rays.*

PROGRAM RESOURCES

From the **Teacher Resource Package** use:

Transparency Masters, pages 79-80, Optics of Concave Mirrors.
Use **Color Transparency** number 40, Optics of Concave Mirrors.
Use **Laboratory Manual 41,** Reflection of Light.

point behind the mirror. You can use rays from the bottom of the object to locate the bottom of the upright, enlarged, and virtual image. Hand mirrors that magnify reflections use this technique. The effect can also be seen when the bowl of a shiny spoon is placed close to your face.

Convex Mirrors

Have you ever seen a large mirror mounted above the aisles in a store? This type of mirror that curves outward is called a **convex mirror.** Figure 20-5 shows how convex mirrors produce an image. The reflected rays never meet, so the image is always virtual, upright, and smaller than the actual object.

Because convex mirrors spread out the reflected light, they allow large areas to be viewed. In addition to increasing the field of view in places like grocery stores and factories, convex mirrors can widen the view of traffic that can be seen in rear or side-view mirrors of automobiles. Your perception of distance can be distorted, however, because objects are always closer than they appear in a convex mirror. Some mirrors that are on automobiles warn the driver that distances and sizes as seen in the mirror are not realistic.

So far, you have read about three ways that light can be reflected to form images. Can you recall the three types of mirrors and describe the images that each mirror produces? In Section 20-2, you will find out the ways in which light can be refracted to form images.

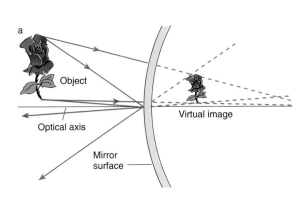

In Your JOURNAL

In your Journal, make a list of all the mirrors you might see during an average day. Describe what each is used for and try to identify each one as plane, concave, or convex.

What kind of image does a convex mirror form?

Figure 20-5. A convex mirror diverges reflected rays (a) to form a virtual image that is always upright and smaller than the object (b).

b

CHECK FOR UNDERSTANDING
Ask students to draw a ray diagram that represents looking into a makeup or shaving mirror. They should draw the face between the mirror and the focal point. Have them find the image. The image is enlarged, upright, and virtual (behind the mirror). Refer to Figure 20-4. They should use rays from the top and bottom of the face.

RETEACH
Guide the students through the solution to the problem in the Problem Solving feature.

EXTENSION
For students who have mastered this section, use the **Reinforcement** and **Enrichment** masters or other OPTIONS provided.

In Your JOURNAL

Suggest students consider their homes, autos, school surroundings, stores, etc.

3 CLOSE

▶ Ask questions 1-3 and the **Apply** and **Connect to Chemistry** questions in the Section Review.
▶ Have students make a list of as many situations as possible where mirrors are used. Divide the lists into the three types of mirrors studied here: plane, concave, and convex. Try to specify in each case the type of image produced: real or virtual, enlarged or smaller, and upright or inverted.

MULTICULTURAL PERSPECTIVE

Arabian Lights

One of the greatest early physicists was an Arabian scientist named Abu 'Ali al-Hassan ibn al-Hagthan, better known in the West as al-Hazen. Born in Basra, he lived from 965 to 1038, and his book, *The Optical Thesaurus,* was unsurpassed until Johannes Kepler's work, 600 years later. Among the contributions he made was the theory that vision is based on light coming from a source and being reflected from an object. Another achievement was the development of the *camera obscura,* which we know as a pinhole camera. Although he was very knowledgeable in science, he was not necessarily wise with people. At one point al-Hazen made a promise to control the flooding of the Nile to the mad Caliph of Egypt, al-Hakim. When he failed, al-Hazen had to pretend he was mad, as well, to escape death. The pretense had to go on for many years until the Caliph died.

PROBLEM SOLVING

Joel's image in the plane mirror was virtual, upright, and the same size as his face. Joel's image in the convex mirror was virtual, upright, and smaller than his face.

Think Critically: Convex mirrors give drivers a wider view of the road. They are stamped with the warning so that drivers do not misjudge the distance of the car behind them.

SECTION REVIEW ANSWERS

1. enlarged, upside down, and real
2. Convex mirrors are used to provide a wide view because they can form images that are smaller than the object.
3. plane mirrors—flat; concave mirrors—curved inward; convex mirrors—curved outward
4. **Apply:** Use a concave mirror to form a real image since the object is so far beyond the focal point. It converges the light so the image can be viewed.
5. **Connect to Chemistry:** Chemists can be sure they are looking straight at the needle by putting the needle directly between their eyes and its reflection. If they see the reflection, they know they are looking at the needle from the side and will record an incorrect reading.

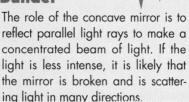

Skill Builder

The role of the concave mirror is to reflect parallel light rays to make a concentrated beam of light. If the light is less intense, it is likely that the mirror is broken and is scattering light in many directions.

Skill Builder
ASSESSMENT

Oral: Ask students what the beam of a flashlight would look like if there were no mirror in it at all. Note that it would function like an ordinary light bulb, and the light shining into the flashlight would not be used.

PROBLEM SOLVING

Mirrors on the New Car

When Joel and his father went to pick up their new car, Joel's father disappeared with the salesman to complete the paperwork. So, Joel decided to give the new car

a quick once-over. He noticed that the mirror on the passenger side had a warning stating "OBJECTS IN MIRROR ARE CLOSER THAN THEY APPEAR." He thought that was strange and looked at the driver's side mirror. It didn't have the warning. Joel compared his image in both mirrors and decided the mirror on the driver's side was a plane mirror and the mirror on the passenger side was a convex mirror. Describe the images Joel saw in the two mirrors.

Think Critically: Explain why convex mirrors are sometimes used as outside rear-view mirrors on cars. Why are they stamped with a warning?

Figure 20-6. A Meter

SECTION REVIEW

1. Describe the image formed by a concave mirror when the object is between one and two focal lengths.
2. What are convex mirrors used for? Explain.
3. Contrast the differences between the surfaces of plane, concave, and convex mirrors.
4. **Apply:** What kind of mirror would you use to focus light entering a telescope? Explain.
5. **Connect to Chemistry:** Some measuring instruments used in chemistry have a plane mirror behind the needle. (See Figure 20-6.) How does this help a chemist make correct measurements?

Skill Builder ☑ **Recognizing Cause and Effect**

Suppose you drop a flashlight that has a concave mirror in it. When you turn the flashlight on, you notice the light is less intense than it was before you dropped it. What may have happened? If you need help, refer to Recognizing Cause and Effect in the **Skill Handbook** on page 679.

OPTIONS

PROGRAM RESOURCES
From the **Teacher Resource Package** use:
  Concept Mapping, page 45.
Use **Laboratory Manual 42,** Magnifying Power.

ENRICHMENT
▶ Have students find out how large mirrors are made for telescopes so as to create a smooth finish on the mirror's surface.

Reflections of Reflections

You have probably looked at your face in a mirror sometime today, but have you seen a reflected image of the back of you head? If so, you most likely looked into a mirror held at an angle in front of your face into a mirror directly behind you. You actually saw a reflection of the original reflection of the back of your head. Can you create multiple reflections of another object?

Materials

- 2 plane mirrors
- cellophane tape
- masking tape
- protractor
- paper clip

Procedure

1. Lay the two mirrors side by side and tape them together so they will open and close. Label them *R* and *L* as shown.
2. Place the mirrors on a sheet of paper and, using the protractor, close the mirrors to an angle of 72°. Mark the position of the *R* mirror on the paper.
3. Bend one leg of a paper clip up 90° and place it close to the front of the *R* mirror.
4. Count the number of images of the paper clip you see in the *R* and *L* mirrors. Don't move the clip.
5. Count the images as you slowly open the mirrors to 90° and then to 120°, keeping the paper clip close to the *R* mirror.
6. *Make a data table* to record the number of images you can see in the *R* and *L* mirrors when they are at 72°, 90°, and 120°.

Analyze

1. How is the number of paper clip images affected by increasing the angle between the mirrors?
2. The mirror arrangement creates an image of a complete circle divided into wedges by the mirrors. How many wedges did you *observe* with the 72°, 90°, and 120° angles?

Conclude and Apply

3. Considering that there are 360° in a circle, how many wedges of space should be formed by each of the mirror angles? Does this agree with your answer in Question 2 above?
4. What angle would divide a circle into six wedges? **Hypothesize** how many images would be produced.
5. Which is the better predictor of the number of paper clip images that can be seen—the number of mirror images or the number of space segments?

Data and Observations   Sample Data

Angle of Mirrors	Number of Paper Clip Images	
	R	L
72°	2	2
90°	2	1
120°	1	1

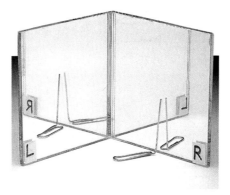

OBJECTIVE: Predict image formation by plane mirrors.

PROCESS SKILLS applied in this activity:
▶ **Measuring** in Procedure Steps 2, 3, and 5.
▶ **Predicting** in Conclude and Apply Questions 4 and 5.
▶ **Inferring** in Analyze Question 2 and Conclude and Apply Question 3.

COOPERATIVE LEARNING
Arrange students in Problem Solving Teams.

TEACHING THE ACTIVITY

▶ Use rectangular mirrors at least 5 cm across. Thin glass is better. Mirror tiles (hardware store) can be cut to size but sharp edges must be ground or taped.
▶ Place a protractor on a copy machine and make lab worksheets upon which students can measure the appropriate angles.

PROGRAM RESOURCES

From the **Teacher Resource Package** use:

Activity Worksheets, pages 158-159, Activity 20-1: Reflections of Reflections.

Activity
ASSESSMENT
Performance: Have students face two mirrors angled at 45° to each other. How many images of their face do they see? What about smaller angles? Larger angles? Have them explain their results.

ANSWERS TO QUESTIONS

1. The number of paper clip images in the mirrors is reduced as the angle between the mirrors increases.

2. 72° – five wedges
90° – four wedges
120° – three wedges

3. Each number divides evenly into 360. As a result, the 360° space around the axis of the mirror pair is divided into five, four, and three equal segments.

4. The angle producing six segments is 360/6 = 60 degrees. Five images will be produced.

5. The number of mirror images is the number of paper clip images. This number is one less than the number of segments.

PREPARATION

SECTION BACKGROUND

▶ Note that in both concave and convex lenses, the greatest bending of light rays occurs near the edges of the lens. Near the edges, the angle between the two glass surfaces is greater, and more total refraction occurs. Light is refracted twice when passing through a lens, once entering and once leaving. At the point in the center of the lens, the glass sides are parallel to each other and the light ray passes straight through.

▶ Lenses are already somewhat familiar because so many people wear eyeglasses. Eyeglasses were used as early as the thirteenth century, and gems were used even earlier as natural magnifying glasses by the Greeks and Arabs.

1 MOTIVATE

▶ Ask students how their eyes focus on both near and faraway objects. The lens in your eye is flexible and can change shape.

VideoDisc

STVS: Laser Eye Surgery, Disc 1, Side 1

20-2 The Optics of Lenses

New Science Words

convex lenses
concave lenses

Objectives

▶ Describe the types of images formed with convex and concave lenses.
▶ Cite examples of how these lenses are used.
▶ Explain how lenses are used to correct vision.

Did You Know?

The fastest camera, built for laser research, registers images at the rate of 33 million per second.

Convex Lenses

Do you wear glasses or contact lenses? If so, you use lenses to improve your ability to see. Like curved mirrors, lenses are described as convex or concave, depending on their shape.

Convex lenses are thicker in the middle than at the edges. Light rays approaching the lens parallel to the optical axis are refracted toward the center of the lens. They converge at the focal point, so they are capable of forming real images that can be projected on a screen.

The amount of refraction depends on the change in the speed of light as it passes through a material and the shape of the object. Thick lenses with very curved surfaces bend light a great deal more than thin ones with less curved surfaces. The focal length of the thick convex lens in Figure 20-7 is shorter than that of the thin

Figure 20-7. A thick convex lens bends light more than a thin convex lens. Notice that the focal length is shorter for the thick lens.

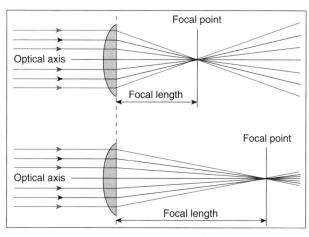

OPTIONS

Meeting Different Ability Levels

For Section 20-2, use the following **Teacher Resource Masters** depending upon individual students' needs.

◆ **Study Guide Master** for all students.
● **Reinforcement Master** for students of average and above average ability levels.
▲ **Enrichment Master** for above average students.

Additional Teacher Resource Package masters are listed in any **PROGRAM RESOURCES** boxes that are in the section. The additional masters are appropriate for all students.

◆ STUDY GUIDE 83

STUDY GUIDE — Chapter 20
The Optics of Lenses — Text Pages 518–521

Use the terms in the list below to fill in the blanks in the paragraphs about lenses.

concave	longer	larger	curved	convex	length	clearly
object	thick	shape	lens	retina	lens	
refracting	inverted	muscles	virtual	cornea	astigmatism	

Lenses are made of transparent material and have a __curved__ surface. A convex lens has thin edges and a __thick__ middle. Another type of lens is thicker at the edge than the middle and is called a __concave__ lens. All lenses work by __refracting__ light. Parallel rays of light are refracted toward each other and brought to a focal point in a __convex__ lens. Light is refracted both when it enters and leaves a __lens__. The amount of refraction depends on the change of the speed of light as it passes through a material and on the __shape__ of the lens. In a convex lens, the type of image formed depends on the position of the __object__ and the focal length of the lens. When the object is more than twice the focal length from the lens, the real image is smaller than the object and __inverted__. If the object is between one and two focal lengths, the image is __larger__ than the object and inverted. When the object is between the lens and the focal point, the image is larger and upright but is a __virtual__ image. Concave lenses are not able to produce real images and are used with convex lenses to create a __longer__ focal length.

The light we see enters our eyes through the transparent covering of the eye called the __cornea__. The light then passes through the pupil and converges on the back part of the eye called the __retina__. Images are properly focused on the retina by the convex lens in the eye, which is controlled by eye __muscles__. To focus images of distant objects, a longer focal __length__ is needed. To do this, the muscles relax, allowing the lens to be __less__ convex. People are farsighted when they can see things far away __clearly__ but have fuzzy vision at close range. To correct this problem, a __convex__ lens is used. A __concave__ lens is used to correct the vision of a nearsighted person. An eye problem caused by an unevenly curved cornea is __astigmatism__.

83

---

convex lens. Convex lenses are capable of producing many kinds of images, both real and virtual, upright, inverted, enlarged, or smaller. The type of image formed depends on the position of the object and also on the focal length of the lens.

Have you ever photographed a faraway object? If so, it's likely the object was more than two focal lengths from the lens. If you follow the light paths in Figure 20-8a, you'll notice that the real image is smaller than the object, and inverted. The lens in your eye forms images in the same way that a camera forms images.

If an object is between one and two focal lengths from the lens, as in Figure 20-8b, the real image is inverted and larger than the object. This is the method used to project a movie from a small film to the large screen of the theater or from an overhead projector to a screen in your classroom. Can you think of other examples in which producing a larger or an inverted image is desired?

Have you ever used a magnifying glass to closely examine an object? A magnifying glass is a convex lens, so you must hold it less than one focal length from the object. The light rays can't converge and an enlarged, upright, and virtual image is formed. Look at the position of the image in Figure 20-8c. Notice the object seems larger and farther away than it really is.

Concave Lenses

Concave lenses are thinner in the middle and thicker at the edges. As is shown in Figure 20-9, light passing through a concave lens bends toward the edges. The rays diverge and never form a real image. The image is virtual, upright, and smaller than the actual object. The image formed by a concave lens is similar to the image produced by a convex mirror because they both diverge light to form virtual images.

Concave lenses are usually used in combination with other lenses. They can be used with convex lenses in telescopes and cameras to spread out incoming light and extend the focal length so you can see a clear image of a faraway object. Concave lenses are also used to correct nearsighted vision.

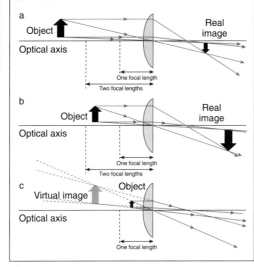

Figure 20-8. The image formed by a convex lens depends on the location of the object in relation to the focal length of the lens.

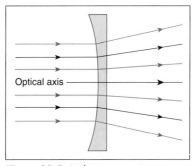

Figure 20-9. Light rays passing through a concave lens diverge and form a virtual image.

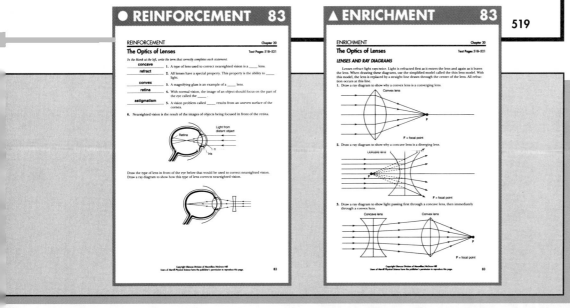

519

OBJECTIVES AND SCIENCE WORDS: Have students review the objectives and science words to become familiar with this section.

2 TEACH

Key Concepts are highlighted.

CONCEPT DEVELOPMENT

▶ Distribute some convex lenses of varying focal lengths to your class. Show students how to find the focal length of a lens by focusing the clearest possible image of an overhead light on a white piece of paper (held by a partner) and measuring the distance from the paper to the lens.

▶ Following the previous suggestion and a discussion of the kinds of images formed by convex lenses, pass out some concave lenses. Tell students to find the focal lengths of the concave lenses. They will not be able to focus the image because these lenses diverge light to form only virtual images.

▶ Ask local eye doctors if they will donate old eyeglass lenses or come to your class to demonstrate simple vision tests.

CROSS CURRICULUM

▶ **Language Arts:** Have students write a paper about how convex and concave lenses are manufactured for use in eyeglasses and optical instruments.

STUDENT TEXT QUESTION

▶ Page 519, paragraph 3: **Can you think of other examples in which producing a larger or an inverted image is desired?** *the microscope*

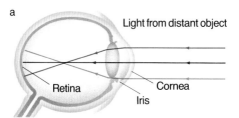
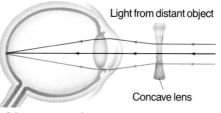
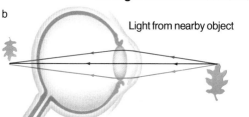
MINI-Lab

Teaching Tips

▶ Demonstrate safe procedures for using a sharp object.

▶ A margarine container makes a good holder. Cut the hole with a pocket knife or scalpel.

▶ The window must be stretched tight and have no wrinkles.

▶ The water drop forms a convex lens. Too large a drop will lose its curvature and too small a drop is hard to look through.

▶ Holding the drop close to the print will form a virtual image; magnified and upright. Holding the drop farther away will form a real image; small and upside down.

Answers to Questions

▶ The drop forms a convex lens.

▶ It can make two kinds of images if you adjust the focal length.

MINI-Lab
ASSESSMENT

Oral: Ask students what properties a material would need to be used in a lens. What do glass, plastic, and water have in common?

CHECK FOR UNDERSTANDING

Present the following situation to your class: **Keisha can read what is written on the chalkboard but has trouble reading her text. What is the cause of her vision problem and what kind of lens could correct it?** *She is farsighted, and the image focuses behind the retina (the eyeball is too short or the cornea is too flat). Correct this problem with a convex lens.*

RETEACH

Compare eyeglasses that correct near-sightedness and farsightedness. Have students examine near and far objects through each type of lens and explain how each lens corrects vision problems.

EXTENSION

For students who have mastered this section, use the **Reinforcement** and **Enrichment** masters or other OPTIONS provided.

Figure 20-10. Some vision problems can easily be corrected with concave and convex lenses.

MINI-Lab

Can lenses be made of liquids?
Design a water-drop lens holder by cutting a round hole in the bottom of a plastic bowl. Make the hole about 2 cm across. Stretch a piece of plastic wrap over the hole and tape it in place. Put a drop of water on the plastic window and look at this print through the drop. *Observe* some small objects. What kind of lens does the drop form? How can your lens make two kinds of images?

Lenses and Vision

What determines how well you can "see" the words on this page? Your ability to focus on these words depends on the way your eye is designed. Light enters your eye through the transparent covering of your eye, the cornea. The light then passes through an opening called the pupil. The colored part of your eye, the iris, adjusts the pupil size to control how much light can pass through a convex lens behind the pupil. The light then converges to ➌ form an inverted image on your retina. The lens in your eye is soft, and flexible muscles in your eye can change its shape. When you look at a distant object, you need a longer focal length, so your eye muscles adjust your lens to a less convex shape. When you focus on a nearby object, the eye muscles increase the curvature of the lens.

If you have healthy vision, you should be able to see objects clearly from a focal length of about 25 cm or more. Many people need their vision corrected. To have normal vision, the image of an object should focus on the retina inside your eye. A nearsighted person has difficulty seeing distant objects clearly. The eyeball is too long or the cornea bulges out, focusing the image in front of the retina. Figure 20-10a illustrates how concave lenses correct this problem by diverging the light rays before they enter the eye.

PROGRAM RESOURCES

From the **Teacher Resource Package** use:

Activity Worksheets, page164, MINI-Lab: Can lenses be made of liquids?

Activity Worksheets, page 5, Flex Your Brain

Science and Society, page 24, A New Vision.

Transparency Masters, pages 81-82, Vision Corrections.

Use **Color Transparency** number 41, Vision Corrections.

Farsighted people can see faraway objects, but they can't focus clearly on nearby objects. Their eyeballs are either too short, or their corneas are too flat to allow the rays to converge on the retina. As a result, the image is focused behind the retina. Figure 20-10b shows how this condition can be corrected.

Another vision problem is blurry vision from astigmatism caused when the surface of the cornea is curved unevenly. Corrective lenses for this condition have an uneven curvature as well.

There are currently several ways to correct poor vision caused by lens problems in the eye. Artificial lenses in the form of eyeglasses or contacts can be worn to refract light before it enters the eye, so the light will focus on the retina. As a result, the wearer will see clear images. Contact lenses are actually worn over the cornea. In some cases, another way to correct the lens in the eye is by using surgical lasers to reshape the cornea.

Can you recall what all lenses have in common? They all refract light that passes through them. Convex lenses refract light toward the center of the lens, and concave lenses refract light away from the center of the lens. As you read the next section, you'll see how these two kinds of lenses are used in cameras, microscopes, and telescopes.

SECTION REVIEW

1. Distinguish between the characteristics of convex and concave lenses.
2. When using a slide projector, why must the slides be inserted in the projector upside down?
3. What type of lens would you use to examine a tiny spider on your desk?
4. **Apply:** If you have difficulty reading the chalkboard from the back row, what is most likely your vision problem? How could it be corrected?
5. **Connect to Life Science:** Why must the lens in your eye be convex, rather than concave? Explain.

What do all lenses have in common?

By middle age, the muscles controlling the shape of the lens do not function properly for many people, and they need help focusing on both near and far objects. Describe a common correction for this problem.

✉ Concept Mapping

Mirrors and lenses are the simplest optical devices. Design a network tree concept map to show some uses for each shape of mirror and lens. If you need help, refer to Concept Mapping in the **Skill Handbook** on pages 684 and 685.

Skill Builder

Skill Builder

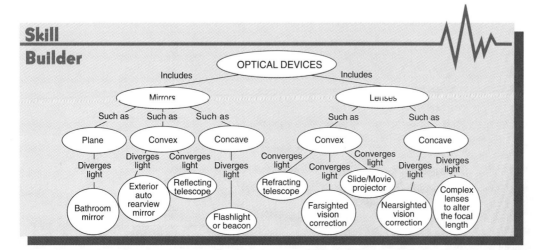

SECTION BACKGROUND

▶ Galileo did not invent the telescope, but he was among the first to use it in monitoring the heavens. For example, he discovered sunspots, some moons of Jupiter, and the phases of Venus.

▶ The total magnification of a simple microscope is the product of the magnifications produced by each of the two lenses. Note that the eyepiece lens is called the ocular.

PREPLANNING

▶ If your school does not have a telescope, try to borrow one for demonstrations. Bring in a microscope and several cameras.

1 MOTIVATE

▶ Have students examine the close-up photo of the moon's surface on the left page and compare it to the photo of the moon as it would look to the unaided eye. Discuss the ways in which optical devices, such as telescopes and cameras, have helped form our view of the world around us.

TYING TO PREVIOUS

KNOWLEDGE: Ask students if they have ever taken a blurry picture with a camera. Have them suggest why this might have happened. The function of a camera will be discussed in this section.

20-3 Optical Instruments

New Science Words

refracting telescope
reflecting telescope
microscope
wide-angle lenses
telephoto lenses

Objectives

▶ Compare refracting and reflecting telescopes.
▶ Explain how a camera creates an image.

Telescopes

There are many uses for lenses and mirrors. They are important components in optical instruments—devices that are designed to aid the human eye in making observations. In this section you'll read about three common optical instruments that you may be familiar with. The first of these is the telescope.

Have you ever looked at the moon through a telescope? It appears to be very different from the moon you see when you glance at the night sky. With a good telescope, you should be able to clearly see the craters and other features on the moon's surface. Telescopes are designed to magnify objects that are very far away. Much of the information we have today about the moon, the planets, our galaxy, and other galaxies has been gathered by viewing these celestial bodies through telescopes.

Early telescopes, like those used today, were built from lenses and mirrors. Around the year 1600, lensmakers in Holland constructed a telescope to view distant objects. In 1609, Galileo built and used his own telescope to discover the moons of Jupiter, the phases of Venus, and some details of the Milky Way galaxy. Today, scientists use several kinds of telescopes with many design improvements.

Figure 20-11. The moon can be seen in greater detail when viewed through a telescope, as in the lower photo.

522 MIRRORS AND LENSES

OPTIONS

Meeting Different Ability Levels

For Section 20-3, use the following **Teacher Resource Masters** depending upon individual students' needs.

◆ **Study Guide Master** for all students.
● **Reinforcement Master** for students of average and above average ability levels.
▲ **Enrichment Master** for above average students.

Additional Teacher Resource Package masters are listed in any **PROGRAM RESOURCES** boxes that are in the section. The additional masters are appropriate for all students.

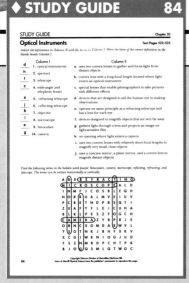

◆ **STUDY GUIDE** 84

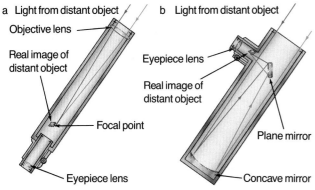

a Light from distant object   b Light from distant object

Objective lens

Real image of
distant object

Eyepiece lens

Real image of
distant object

Focal point

Plane mirror

Eyepiece lens

Concave mirror

Figure 20-12. A refracting telescope (a) and a reflecting
telescope (b) magnify the images
of distant objects.

One common telescope is the **refracting telescope.** A
simple refracting telescope uses two convex lenses to gather and focus light from distant objects. Figure 20-12a is
a diagram of a refracting telescope. Notice how light
enters the telescope through a convex lens with a long
focal length. This lens is called the objective lens. The
real image formed by this lens is magnified by a second
convex lens, called the eyepiece, with a shorter focal
length. What you view through the eyepiece is an
enlarged, virtual image of the real image. The image you
see is also inverted.

There are several problems with refracting telescopes
that may make another type of telescope more desirable
to use. The objective lens must be quite large to allow
enough light in to form a bright image. These heavy glass
lenses are hard to make and quite costly. Their own weight
can cause them to sag and distort the image. As a result,
most large telescopes are reflecting telescopes. A **reflecting telescope** uses a concave mirror, a plane mirror, and
a convex lens to magnify distant objects. Figure 20-12b
shows how light enters the telescope and is reflected by the
concave mirror onto a plane mirror inside the telescope.
The plane mirror reflects the rays to form an inverted
real image in the telescope. The convex lens in the eyepiece then magnifies this image. The eyepiece can be
replaced by a camera to photograph the real image.

Sometimes you might want to view distant objects so
they appear upright. Imagine trying to watch a baseball
game through binoculars if the image were upside down.
Binoculars work on the same principle as a refracting
telescope, except there are two sets of lenses—one for
each eye.

MINI-Lab

What do telescopes see?
Use a needle to punch two closely
spaced holes in a piece of aluminum foil. Have a friend hold it in
front of a light bulb. Move away
from the light bulb until you can
barely distinguish both holes. Make
a tiny hole in a second piece of foil.
Make two slightly larger holes in
the second piece of foil. Hold the
foil close to your eye and look
through each hole at the two
"stars." *Compare* and *contrast* the
images of the "stars" as seen
through each of the three holes.

Connect to...
Chemistry

The reflective coating on many mirrors used in telescopes is made of
a valuable metallic element. This
same element is found in the light-
sensitive compounds used in
photographic film. What are the
name, chemical symbol, and atomic number of this element?

523

Key Concepts are highlighted.

CONCEPT DEVELOPMENT

▶ Obtain two convex lenses with short focal lengths. Mount them on a meterstick and focus them so that you see an enlarged image of a small, close-up object such as the print in this book. This is a simple microscope.

▶ If possible, obtain a telescope and microscope to dismantle in class to show students where the lenses are.

CROSS CURRICULUM

▶ **Art:** Find a book on photography and investigate what variables in a camera can be controlled to gain the desired effects in a photograph. Look up aperture, shutter speed, wide-angle and telephoto lenses, and flashes.

CHECK FOR UNDERSTANDING

Use the Mini Quiz to check for understanding.

MINI QUIZ

Use the Mini Quiz to check students' recall of chapter content.

1 **A telescope that contains a concave mirror, a plane mirror, and a convex lens is called a(n) _____ telescope.** *reflecting*

2 **What optical instrument could you make to magnify close objects too small to see with the unaided eye?** *microscope*

3 **What kind of lens would you use if you wanted to photograph a person with his or her surroundings?** *a wide-angle lens*

RETEACH

Point to a somewhat distant object that can be seen separately from its surroundings. Tell students to imagine they are taking two photos of the same object, one with a wide-angle lens and one with a telephoto lens. Have them sketch what they might see with each lens. **Which lens has a longer focal length?** *telephoto lens*

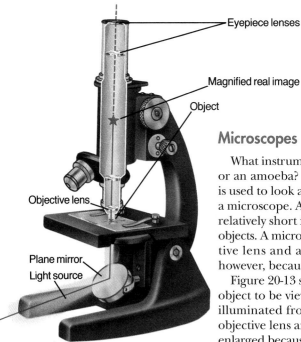

Figure 20-13. A microscope contains two convex lenses so it can magnify very small objects.

Did You Know?

The most powerful microscope is the IBM 1981 scanning tunneling microscope with the magnifying ability of 100 million X. This instrument resolves down to 1/100 the diameter of an atom and the tip of its probe is a single atom.

A third lens or a pair of reflecting prisms has been added to binoculars to invert the upside-down image so it appears upright. Terrestrial telescopes, such as those used for bird watching, are also designed to produce an upright image.

Microscopes

What instrument would you use to look at a cell, a hair, or an amoeba? You wouldn't use a telescope because it is used to look at faraway objects. Instead, you would use a microscope. A **microscope** uses two convex lenses with relatively short focal lengths to magnify very small, close objects. A microscope, like a telescope, has both an objective lens and an eyepiece. It is designed differently, however, because the objects viewed are not far away.

Figure 20-13 shows the operation of a microscope. The object to be viewed is placed on a transparent slide and illuminated from below. The light travels through the objective lens and a real, enlarged image is formed. It is enlarged because the object is between one and two focal lengths from the lens. The real image is magnified again by the eyepiece to create a virtual, enlarged image. This results in an image up to several hundred times larger than the actual object.

Cameras

Do you keep a photograph album with your favorite pictures? Have you ever wondered how these pictures were made? Of course, they were made with a camera, but have you ever wondered how a camera transfers an image onto film? A camera gathers light through a lens and projects an image on light-sensitive film.

When you take a picture with a camera, the light reflected off the subject enters an opening in the camera called the aperture. A shutter on the aperture opens to allow light to enter the camera.

The light passes through the lens of the camera, which focuses the image on the photographic film. The image is real, inverted, and smaller than the actual object. The size of the image depends on the focal length of the lens and how close the lens is to the film.

524 MIRRORS AND LENSES

OPTIONS

ASSESSMENT—ORAL

▶ **What happens inside a camera when you focus a picture?** *You are adjusting the focal length, or the distance between the film and the lens.*

▶ **What type of lens would you expect to find in a camera and why?** *A convex lens, because a concave lens can't focus light rays to form a real image.*

ENRICHMENT

▶ Have students use a kit or use cardboard tubes, lenses, and clay to build their own telescopes.

▶ Have students find out what a pinhole camera is. Have them build one of these cameras and take a picture with it.

Suppose you and a friend photograph the same object at the same distance, but with different types of cameras. Your picture would look different from that of your friend if the cameras had different lenses. Some lenses have short focal lengths that produce a relatively small image of the object but include much of its surroundings. These lenses are called **wide-angle lenses,** and they must be placed close to the film to focus the image with their short focal length. **Telephoto lenses** have longer focal lengths and are located farther from the film than wide-angle lenses. Telephoto lenses are easy to recognize because they protrude out from the camera to increase the distance between the lens and the film. The image seems enlarged and the object seems closer than it actually is. These lenses are preferred when photographing people's faces from a distance.

Telescopes, microscopes, and cameras are just a few examples of instruments that contain mirrors and lenses and help you to make observations. What are some other types of optical instruments? See how many you can name.

Figure 20-14. The upper photo was taken with a wide-angle lens, and the lower photo was taken with a telephoto lens.

SECTION REVIEW

1. Compare and contrast reflecting and refracting telescopes.
2. If you wanted to photograph a single rose on a rosebush, what kind of lens would you use? Explain why you chose this lens.
3. Microscopes and refracting telescopes both use two sets of convex lenses. How can they be used for different purposes?
4. **Apply:** Which optical instrument—a telescope, a microscope, or a camera—forms images in a way most like your eye? Explain.
5. **Connect to Earth Science:** Why are some maps of the moon upside down?

☒ **Hypothesizing**

You've noticed that all the objects in a photograph you've taken are blurry. Use your knowledge of lenses and focal lengths to form a hypothesis that could explain why the photo was blurred. If you need help, refer to Hypothesizing in the **Skill Handbook** on page 682.

Skill Builder

20-3 OPTICAL INSTRUMENTS **525**

Skill Builder
ASSESSMENT
Oral: Ask students what the photographer would need to do to fix this problem. Many cameras have focusing mechanisms that move the lens closer to or farther from the film.

EXTENSION
For students who have mastered this section, use the **Reinforcement** and **Enrichment** masters or other OPTIONS provided.

3 CLOSE

▶ Ask questions 1-3 and the **Apply** and **Connect to Earth Science** questions in the Section Review.
▶ Bring in a pair of binoculars. They work on the same principle as refracting telescopes, somewhat like having a mini-telescope for each eye. But unlike a telescope, the image is upright. What might make it upright? A third convex lens or pair of reflecting prisms is used to once again invert the image.

SECTION REVIEW ANSWERS

1. Reflecting telescopes form images with a concave mirror, a plane mirror, and a convex lens. Refracting telescopes use two convex lenses. Both form virtual, inverted images.
2. Telephoto lens—it has a longer focal length and allows a certain object to be enlarged while omitting most surroundings.
3. Objects viewed with a telescope are very distant from the lens. Objects viewed with a microscope are between one and two focal lengths from the lens.
4. Apply: The camera—the camera and the eye adjust so they will focus on near and far objects; both control the amount of light that enters; and both form real, inverted images.
5. Connect to Earth Science: Telescopes produce inverted virtual images. The maps are upside down so they look like the image seen through the telescope.

Skill
Builder
A reasonable hypothesis would be that the lens was too close or too far away from the film. To form a clear image, the film must be at the focal point of the lens.

PREPARATION

SECTION BACKGROUND

▶ NASA has a teacher resource center that will provide free Hubble Space Telescope materials.

▶ Have students research the significant error that was found shortly after launching.

1 MOTIVATE

▶ Display photos of the Hubble Space Telescope in your classroom.

TYING TO PREVIOUS KNOWLEDGE:

Ask students if they have ever tried to retrieve a coin from a swimming pool. The light is refracted by the water and shifts as the water moves, so the image of the coin is distorted. Convection in the atmosphere does the same thing to light reaching us from distant stars.

V i d e o D i s c

STVS: Flying Observatory, Disc 3, Side 1

2 TEACH

Key Concepts are highlighted.

CONCEPT DEVELOPMENT

▶ Draw a line 2.4 m long to show students how large the diameter of the primary mirror is. The large size allows the telescope to capture more light so that faint, distant stars can be observed. These stars could not be seen from Earth's surface.

Connect to...
Earth Science

Answer: Solar energy is collected and converted using solar panels.

SCIENCE & SOCIETY 20-4 The Hubble Space Telescope

Objectives

▶ Describe the development and goals of the Hubble Space Telescope.
▶ Evaluate the need for a space telescope.

Connect to...
Earth Science

The Hubble Space Telescope should be able to collect information for many years. What source of energy is used to move its parts?

Is It Worth It?

Imagine trying to read a sign from the bottom of a swimming pool. The water distorts your view of objects beyond the water. In a similar way, Earth's atmosphere blurs our view of many stars, planets, and other objects in space. Not even powerful telescopes positioned at high elevations can allow us to see distant objects clearly. On April 20, 1990, the National Aeronautics and Space Administration (NASA) launched the Hubble Space Telescope. The telescope has produced images sharper than powerful telescopes on Earth by allowing us to view the planets, stars, and distant galaxies from an orbit beyond Earth's atmosphere. It is designed to detect infrared and ultraviolet light in space that is usually blocked by Earth's atmosphere.

The Hubble Space Telescope was placed into an orbit almost 600 kilometers above Earth by the space shuttle *Discovery*. The 13 m, 11 300 kg telescope is named after Edwin P. Hubble, who is famous for his observations of many other galaxies beyond the Milky Way and for finding evidence that the universe appears to be expanding.

Look at the diagram of the Hubble Space Telescope on the opposite page. The solar panels provide electrical power to the system. A 2.4 m primary and a smaller secondary mirror collect and focus light to form an image. Various instruments on the telescope interpret the data and communicate it to scientists on Earth.

OPTIONS

Meeting Different Ability Levels

For Section 20-4, use the following **Teacher Resource Masters** depending upon individual students' needs.

◆ **Study Guide Master** for all students.

● **Reinforcement Master** for students of average and above average ability levels.

▲ **Enrichment Master** for above average students.

Additional Teacher Resource Package masters are listed in any PROGRAM RESOURCES boxes that are in the section. The additional masters are appropriate for all students.

STUDY GUIDE 85

STUDY GUIDE Chapter 20
The Hubble Space Telescope Text Pages 526–527

Determine whether the italicized term makes each statement true or false. If the statement is true, write the word "true" in the blank. If the statement is false, write in the blank the term that makes the statement true.

true	1. The Hubble Space Telescope is named after *Edwin P. Hubble*, an astronomer.
atmosphere	2. Our view of outer space from the surface of Earth is blurred by Earth's *oceans*.
ultraviolet	3. The Hubble Space Telescope is designed to detect infrared and *visible* light in space that usually cannot be detected by telescopes at Earth's surface.
solar panels	4. Electrical power is supplied to the telescope's system by the *electric company*.
Aeronautics	5. NASA is the abbreviation for the National *Airways* and Space Administration.
600	6. The Hubble Space Telescope is in an orbit about *100* kilometers above Earth.
billion	7. The final cost of the Hubble Space Telescope project is about 2 *million* dollars.
true	8. The Hubble Space Telescope was launched by *NASA* on April 20, 1990.
ten	9. The Hubble Space Telescope produces images that are *five* times sharper than powerful telescopes on Earth.
expanding	10. The universe appears to be *contracting*.

Answer the following question on the lines below. Use complete sentences.

11. What do scientists hope to learn by using the Hubble Space Telescope? What would you like to study in outer space? Why?
   Scientists hope to learn how the universe began and whether there are inhabited planets circling distant stars. Accept all reasonable responses for students' preferences for study in outer space.

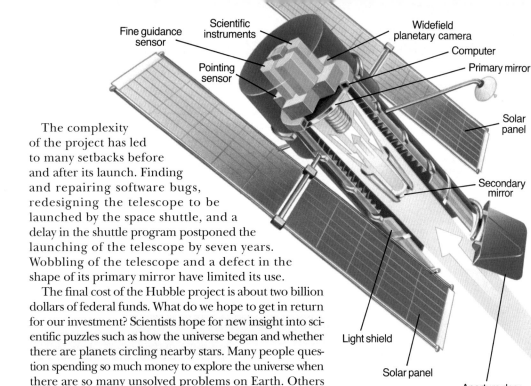

Fine guidance sensor
Scientific instruments
Pointing sensor
Widefield planetary camera
Computer
Primary mirror
Solar panel
Secondary mirror
Light shield
Solar panel
Aperture door

The complexity of the project has led to many setbacks before and after its launch. Finding and repairing software bugs, redesigning the telescope to be launched by the space shuttle, and a delay in the shuttle program postponed the launching of the telescope by seven years. Wobbling of the telescope and a defect in the shape of its primary mirror have limited its use.

The final cost of the Hubble project is about two billion dollars of federal funds. What do we hope to get in return for our investment? Scientists hope for new insight into scientific puzzles such as how the universe began and whether there are planets circling nearby stars. Many people question spending so much money to explore the universe when there are so many unsolved problems on Earth. Others point to many problems that have been solved with knowledge gained through science. What do you think?

SECTION REVIEW

1. Explain whether the Hubble Telescope is designed more like a refracting or reflecting telescope.
2. What knowledge do we hope to gain from the Hubble Space Telescope?
3. **Connect to Earth Science:** Why can an orbiting telescope form clearer images than one on Earth?

You Decide!

How would you decide between spending money to try to solve problems on Earth and spending it to expand our knowledge of the universe? You may want to consider how successful we have been at solving our problems and the success of science programs. Also, consider the cost if our problems continue and what we might not have if science had not found new information.

SCIENCE & SOCIETY

● REINFORCEMENT 85

REINFORCEMENT   Chapter 20
The Hubble Space Telescope   Text Pages 526–527

Write a paragraph describing the Hubble Space Telescope. Use the following terms in your paragraph.

distortion   Hubble   primary mirror
images   galaxies   secondary mirror
orbit   universe   computer software
infrared   expanding   investigation
ultraviolet   solar panels

Accept all reasonable paragraphs.

Describe the problems and setbacks faced in launching the Hubble Space Telescope into orbit. Use the following terms in your description.

late   software   redesign   delay   testing

Accept all reasonable paragraphs.

Copyright Glencoe Division of Macmillan/McGraw-Hill
Users of Merrill Physical Science have the publisher's permission to reproduce this page.   85

▲ ENRICHMENT 85

ENRICHMENT   Chapter 20
The Hubble Space Telescope   Text Pages 526–527

ATMOSPHERIC REFRACTION

Light rays are bent, or refracted, when they move from one medium to another medium. Therefore, light entering Earth's atmosphere from space is refracted. This refraction of light causes images viewed from telescopes to be blurry. Orbiting satellites, such as the Hubble Space Telescope, are designed to work outside Earth's atmosphere. This allows a clearer view of distant objects.

1. Why are ground-based telescopes built on high mountains away from large cities? **The atmosphere at high altitudes is thinner and clearer. Light from cities can interfere with starlight.**

2. Because of atmospheric refraction, you can see the sun in the evening for several minutes after it is really below the horizon. In the morning you can see it for several minutes before it is actually above the horizon. Draw a simple diagram to show it.

Apparent direction to the sun
Light from the sun
Earth

3. How would the sun look from a planet with a very thick and dense, but still transparent, atmosphere? **The sun would seem to be flattened in the vertical direction. Light from the bottom edge would be more strongly refracted than light from the top edge.**

4. Locations of stars and planets are measured using altitude (degrees above the horizon) and azimuth (compass direction). What errors are possible when making measurements of star and planet locations? **Refraction causes light to be bent. The measurements will be off by the angle of refraction of the light.**

Copyright Glencoe Division of Macmillan/McGraw-Hill
Users of Merrill Physical Science have the publisher's permission to reproduce this page.   85

527

CHECK FOR UNDERSTANDING
Ask questions 1-2 and the **Connect to Earth Science** question in the Section Review.

RETEACH
Reinforce the idea that the Hubble Space Telescope needs to be above Earth's atmosphere by using a circle to represent Earth and a circle of shaded chalk to represent the atmosphere.

EXTENSION
For students who have mastered this section, use the **Reinforcement** and **Enrichment** masters.

3 CLOSE

▶ After discussing the benefits and drawbacks of operating the Hubble Space Telescope, ask some students to explain their point of view.

SECTION REVIEW ANSWERS
1. It is designed most like a reflecting telescope because the main optical devices are mirrors.
2. unsolved questions about the universe—such as how it began, or if there is life on other planets
3. Connect to Earth Science: Telescopes on Earth form images distorted by Earth's nonuniform atmosphere.

YOU DECIDE!

SCIENCE & SOCIETY
Answers will vary. Make sure students can support their answers.

PREPARATION

SECTION BACKGROUND

▶ Lasers are available in a variety of colors; the wavelength and color of light emitted depends on the materials in the laser. The most common one is probably the helium-neon laser, which explains why so many people imagine lasers as a red beam of light.

▶ Laser stands for **L**ight **A**mplification by **S**timulated **E**mission of **R**adiation. In contrast with the spontaneous release of light during a flame test of an element, the atoms in a laser remain unexcited until struck by a photon of light emitted by another atom.

▶ In most light sources, the electrons are vibrating in infinitely many directions and light is emitted in every imaginable plane. Use polarization to support the fact that light waves are transverse, not longitudinal like sound.

PREPLANNING

▶ If you don't have a laser, arrange to borrow one from a nearby high school, university, or business.

1 MOTIVATE

▶ Walk into class wearing a pair of sunglasses or 3-D glasses. Ask students why you might want to wear them. Note that polarized sunglasses are more expensive and far more effective at cutting glare. This is a good lead-in to a discussion of polarized light.

Science and WRITING

This is a good time to discuss advertising image versus reality as it relates to a wide variety of products. Science can make us better consumers also.

20-5 Applications of Light

New Science Words

polarized light
lasers
coherent light
incoherent light
total internal reflection
optical fibers

Objectives

▶ Describe polarized light and the uses of polarizing filters.
▶ Explain how a laser produces coherent light and how it differs from incoherent light.
▶ Apply the concept of total internal reflection to the uses of optical fibers.

Science and WRITING

Write an article for your school newspaper answering the question that's on everyone's mind—which sunglasses are best? Do a preference poll among your classmates. Check the claims in the ads and see what research magazines, such as *Consumer Reports*, have to say.

Polarized Light

Have you ever purchased a new pair of sunglasses? Did you notice that some of them had a sticker on them that said *polarized*? What makes them different?

Recall modeling a transverse wave on a rope in Chapter 18. You could make the waves vibrate in any direction—horizontal, vertical, or anywhere in between. Most light sources, such as incandescent lamps and the sun, emit light that vibrates in many directions. If this light passes through a special filter, called a polarizing filter, the light becomes polarized. In **polarized light**, the transverse waves ❶ vibrate in only one plane. A polarizing filter contains molecules that act like parallel slits to allow only those light waves vibrating in one direction to pass through. If a second polarizing filter is aligned so its molecules are oriented at right angles to the first filter, very little light passes through. (See Figure 20-15(a).)

Figure 20-15. Very little light passes through two polarized filters that are aligned at right angles to each other (a). A polarizing filter is used in the left photo (b) to reduce glare.

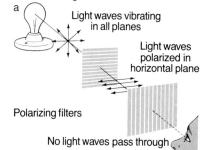

OPTIONS

Meeting Different Ability Levels

For Section 20-5, use the following **Teacher Resource Masters** depending upon individual students' needs.

◆ **Study Guide Master** for all students.

● **Reinforcement Master** for students of average and above average ability levels.

▲ **Enrichment Master** for above average students.

Additional Teacher Resource Package masters are listed in any **PROGRAM RESOURCES** boxes that are in the section. The additional masters are appropriate for all students.

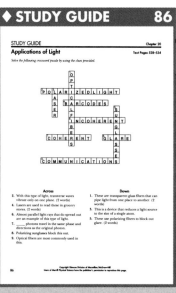

◆ STUDY GUIDE 86

STUDY GUIDE
Applications of Light

Light reflected from horizontal surfaces, such as a lake or a car's hood, is partially polarized horizontally and is called glare. Polarizing sunglasses are made with vertically polarizing filters to block out most of the glare while allowing vertically polarized light through. Polarizing filters can also be placed over camera lenses to reduce glare when taking pictures.

Have you ever watched a 3-D movie? Did you wear special glasses to see the effects? The characters probably seemed to be right in front of you. One kind of three dimensional (3-D) glasses uses polarizing filters. The filter in front of one eye is aligned vertically and the other filter is aligned horizontally. The movie is shown through two projectors, one with a horizontally polarizing filter and the other with a vertically polarizing filter. As a result, your right eye sees a slightly different picture than is seen by your left eye. This creates the impression of depth, or three dimensions.

Next time you shop for sunglasses, you will know that some are polarized to reduce glare and others are not. What kind do you think you would prefer?

Lasers

The narrow beams of light that zip across the stage and through the auditorium during a rock concert are produced by **lasers.** Beams of laser light do not spread out because laser light is coherent. **Coherent light** is elec-

Figure 20-16. Polarizing filters are often used by photographers to reduce glare.

529

TYING TO PREVIOUS KNOWLEDGE: Recall from Chapter 19 that light can be modeled as a transverse wave. Ask students to show how they would model a transverse wave (a wave on a rope). This conceptual understanding is important to the three new applications of light in this section.

OBJECTIVES AND SCIENCE WORDS: Have students review the objectives and science words to become familiar with this section.

2 TEACH

Key Concepts are highlighted.

CONCEPT DEVELOPMENT
► Have a laser behind your desk. When you turn it on, tell students they must find the position of the laser beam. They will be disappointed to find only a small dot on the wall. How are laser beams visible in the pictures and laser shows students may have seen? Scatter some chalk dust in the air to make the laser light visible. Discuss how the laser light must be reflected off a particle into your eye for you to see the beam.

V i d e o D i s c
STVS: Ultraviolet Laser, Disc 1, Side 1

● **REINFORCEMENT** 86

REINFORCEMENT   Chapter 20

Applications of Light   Text Pages 528–534

Use two or three sentences to respond to the following questions.

1. Why are sunglasses with polarized lenses often worn by people driving long distances? ___ Light that is reflected from a horizontal surface, such as a highway, is partially polarized horizontally. This annoying reflection is called glare. Polarizing sunglasses are made with vertically polarizing filters. They block out most of the glare while allowing vertically polarized light to pass through.

2. What is laser light? ___ Laser light is a beam of coherent photons, which are photons traveling in the same phase and in the same direction.

3. Laser light has many practical uses. Briefly describe its use in the following areas.
   a. retail stores and grocery stores ___ Lasers are used to read bar codes.
   b. home entertainment systems ___ Lasers are used to play discs in music systems.
   c. medicine ___ Lasers are used to cut through body tissues, to reduce bleeding by sealing off blood vessels, and for eye surgery including cataract removal.
   d. industry ___ Lasers can be used to cut and weld materials.
   e. surveying ___ Lasers can be used to measure great distances.
   f. astronomy ___ Lasers have been used to measure the moon's orbit, and also to measure the distance from Earth to the moon.
   g. communications ___ Lasers provide a coherent light source for fiber-optic communications.

4. What are optical fibers? What are some of their major uses? ___ Optical fibers are transparent glass fibers that can pipe light from one place to another. Optical fibers are used in communications where one optical fiber can carry thousands of phone conversations at the same time. In medicine, physicians can use fibers to examine body parts that would otherwise be very difficult to reach and examine visually.

86   Copyright Glencoe Division of Macmillan/McGraw-Hill

Users of Merrill Physical Science have the publisher's permission to reproduce this page.

▲ **ENRICHMENT** 86

ENRICHMENT   Chapter 20

Applications of Light   Text Pages 528–534

OPTICAL FIBERS

Optical fibers are used to transmit information through telephone lines. As light passes from one medium to another, it is refracted. Reflection is used in optical fibers to produce total internal reflection of light rays. The following activity will help you observe total internal reflection.

and cut a hole in the tube to expose the flashlight switch.

5. Set up the plastic dishpan as shown in Figure 2. Darken the room and turn on the flashlight. Remove the tape covering the holes in the metal cap. Tilt the tube so that the water pours out of the large opening into the dishpan.

Materials
- tall narrow jar with metal screw cap
- several sheets of dark-colored paper
- punch-type can opener
- large plastic dishpan
- water   • tape
- flashlight   • scissors

Procedure
1. Punch two holes in the metal cap. One hole should be about 2 cm in diameter. The other hole should be much smaller. Put the holes on opposite edges of the cap.
2. Add water to the jar until it is about 4/5 full. Screw the cap on tightly. Cover the holes in the cap with tape while you finish making the model. Be sure the outside of the jar is dry.
3. Refer to Figure 1. Put the bottom of the jar on top of the flashlight so that the light will shine through the jar when the flashlight is turned on. Tape the flashlight securely to the jar. Use as little tape as possible.

FIGURE 2.

Observe and Conclude
1. What did you observe as the water poured out? ___ The light was reflected inside the stream of water. The light bends with the stream of water.
2. How can you explain your observation? ___ The stream of water reflects the light beam and keeps it inside the water.
3. How does your model compare to an optical fiber? ___ The water is like the glass fiber. The light beam is reflected internally and passes down the stream of water in the model. Similarly, light is reflected internally in a glass fiber and bends with the fiber.

FIGURE 1.

4. Note where the flashlight switch is located. Make a tube by wrapping several sheets of dark-colored paper around the jar and the flashlight. Tape the paper tube together

86   Copyright Glencoe Division of Macmillan/McGraw-Hill

Users of Merrill Physical Science have the publisher's permission to reproduce this page.

CONCEPT DEVELOPMENT

▶ Use two Polaroid filters to illustrate Figures 20-15,16. Place one filter on the overhead projector and then slowly rotate the second one over it. Ask students to identify when the filters are parallel (when it is light) and when they are perpendicular (when it is dark).

▶ Use the same setup as above, but put a piece of stretched plastic wrap or pieces of cut-up storage bags between the filters. Rotate the second filter over it again. You should see an array of continually changing colors and brightness. The chains of molecules in the plastic are rearranged when stretched, and this produces the polarization of light of different wavelengths.

▶ After talking about the function of a laser and the coherent nature of laser light, give a small laser show of your own. Have a student clap erasers together to give you a continual source of particles in the air. Show diffraction through a thin slit, through a Fresnel lens, and take the opportunity to review refraction and reflection.

Science and READING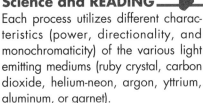

Each process utilizes different characteristics (power, directionality, and monochromaticity) of the various light emitting mediums (ruby crystal, carbon dioxide, helium-neon, argon, yttrium, aluminum, or garnet).

TEACHER F.Y.I.

▶ The stimulated emissions that produce laser light are similar to the phenomenon that produces flame tests. As a result, the color of laser light depends on the nature of the materials used to produce it.

In Your JOURNAL

Answers may include surgery, surveying, welding, weapons, etc.

tromagnetic energy of only one wavelength that travels with its crests and troughs aligned. The beam does not spread out because all the waves travel in the same direction. Light from an ordinary light bulb is incoherent. **Incoherent light** may contain more than one wavelength, and its electromagnetic waves do not travel in the same direction, causing the beam to spread out.

Photons in a beam of coherent light are identical, travel in the same direction, and can be produced by a laser. A laser's light begins when a photon is spontaneously emitted from an atom. This photon is reflected between two facing mirrors at opposite ends of the laser, one of which is partially coated to allow some light to pass through. If the emitted photon travels perpendicular to one of the mirrors it will be reflected between them many times, stimulating other atoms to emit identical photons, as well. The continual production of photons traveling perpendicularly to the mirror by *other* photons produces a coherent beam of laser light.

Lasers can be made with many different materials, including gases, liquids, and solids. One of the most common is the helium-neon laser, which produces a beam of red light. A mixture of helium and neon gases sealed in a tube with mirrors at both ends is excited by a flashtube (as shown in Figure 20-17). The excited atoms then lose their excess energy by emitting photons.

Figure 20-17. A laser produces a coherent beam of visible light of the same wavelength.

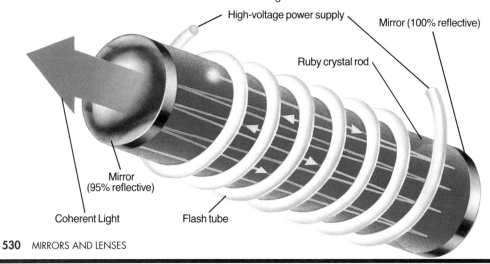

High-voltage power supply

Mirror (100% reflective)

Ruby crystal rod

Mirror (95% reflective)

Coherent Light

Flash tube

OPTIONS

ASSESSMENT—ORAL

▶ **Does polarized light support the wave theory of light or the particle theory of light?** *the wave theory, because it is discussed as being transverse waves vibrating on only one plane*

▶ **Would laser light support the wave theory of light or the particle theory of light?** *It supports both theories because coherency depends on light's wave properties, and generating the light is based on light's particle properties.*

All lasers are very inefficient. No more than one percent of the electrical energy that is used by the laser is converted to light energy. Despite this inefficiency, lasers have many unique properties that make them useful. The beam of the laser is narrow and focused. It also does not spread out as it travels over long distances.

Laser light has many applications, such as reading the bar codes on packages or maintaining high sound quality from compact discs by not scratching the discs' surfaces. Surgeons use lasers in place of scalpels to cut cleanly through body tissues. The energy from the laser seals off some blood vessels in the incision to reduce bleeding. Lasers are routinely used to remove cataracts and repair the retina in the eye. Powerful lasers are used for cutting and welding materials in industry. Surveyors and builders use lasers for measuring and leveling. Lasers aimed at the moon allow us to measure the moon's orbit with great accuracy. Lasers also provide a coherent light source for fiber-optic communications.

Optical Fibers

Did you ever dangle your legs from the side of a swimming pool and watch your feet disappear as you raised them in the water? The disappearance of your feet is an example of total internal reflection. **Total internal reflection** occurs when light striking a surface between two materials reflects totally back into the first material. As you know, to see your feet in the pool, light reflecting from your feet must reach your eyes. As you raise your feet in the pool, the light reflecting from your feet strikes the surface between the water and the air and reflects back into the water. Your feet seem to disappear because light reflecting from your

Figure 20-18. There are many practical uses for laser light.

Connect to...
Chemistry

A helium-neon laser contains a mixture of 15 percent He and 15 percent Ne. Where are these gases located on the periodic table? Would you be concerned about them reacting chemically in the laser? Explain.

What materials can lasers be made from?

Figure 20-19. Total internal reflection causes gems to sparkle.

20-5   APPLICATIONS OF LIGHT   **531**

Use the Mini Quiz to check for understanding.

MINI QUIZ

Use the Mini Quiz to check students' recall of chapter content.

1 **How does polarized light differ from ordinary light?** *The waves all vibrate in one plane.*

2 **List three applications of lasers.** *read grocery bar codes, compact disc players, surgery, cutting and welding, fiber optic communications*

3 **A(n) _____ is a transparent glass fiber that pipes light from one place to another.** *optical fiber*

RETEACH

To reinforce the idea of coherent light, first have everyone in the class clap their own individual rhythm. It sounds scattered and jumbled. Now have everyone clap on the number as you count "one and two and three and...." The sound is "coherent" or together and more intense.

EXTENSION

For students who have mastered this section, use the **Reinforcement** and **Enrichment** masters or other OPTIONS provided.

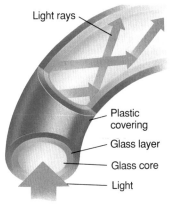

Figure 20-20. An optical fiber is designed to reflect light so that it is piped through the fiber without leaving it, except at the ends.

Light rays
Plastic covering
Glass layer
Glass core
Light

Figure 20-21. Just one of these optical fibers can carry thousands of phone conversations at the same time.

feet never reaches your eyes. Total internal reflection depends on the speed of light in the two materials and the angle at which the light strikes the surface. The speed of light in the first material must be less than it is in the second. Also, the angle at which the light strikes the surface of the first material must be large.

Total internal reflection makes light transmission in optical fibers possible. **Optical fibers** are transparent glass fibers that can pipe light from one place to another. As shown in Figure 20-20, light entering one end of the fiber is continuously reflected from the sides of the fiber until it emerges from the other end. Very little light is lost or absorbed in optical fibers.

Optical fibers are most commonly used in communications. Telephone conversations, television programs, and computer information can be used to modulate light beams into optical signals. The signals are transmitted by a laser through the optical fibers with far less loss of signal than if similar electric signals were transmitted though copper wires. Because of total internal reflection, signals can't leak from one fiber to another and interfere with other messages. As a result, the signal is clearly transmitted. One optical fiber can carry thousands of phone conversations at the same time because the signals can be produced quite rapidly and travel at high speeds through the fiber.

Optical fibers are also used to explore the inside of the human body. One bundle of fibers transmits light, while the other carries the reflected light back to the doctor. Plants have also been shown to use the same principles used in optical fibers to transport light to cells that use light energy.

532 MIRRORS AND LENSES

OPTIONS

ENRICHMENT

▶ Have students investigate the use of polarized optical fibers in communications.

▶ Have students find out how law enforcement agencies are using lasers and fiber optics to detect the smuggling of illegal drugs.

TECHNOLOGY

The Light Scalpel

Optical fibers piping laser energy deep inside the human body are replacing some surgical procedures. The effect of the laser on human tissue depends on the wavelength and intensity of the laser light and the color of the tissue. By varying the wavelength and intensity of a laser, a particular kind of tissue can be targeted.

Low-power lasers are used to seal soft tissue and to treat ulcers in the stomach, intestine, and colon. Many other surgical applications, however, require high-power lasers. One of the most exciting applications would be in the treatment of cardiovascular diseases. An optical fiber-conducted laser may be used to deliver pulses of high-power laser light to clear a blocked artery.

Think Critically: What problems might arise in using a high-power laser to clear an artery of an obstruction?

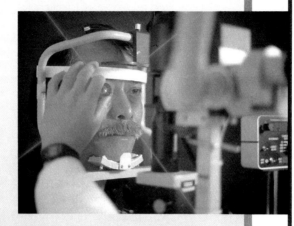

SECTION REVIEW

1. What is polarized light?
2. Distinguish between coherent and incoherent light.
3. Explain how an optical fiber transmits light.
4. **Apply:** Which of the following materials could possibly be substituted for the glass in an optical fiber: clear plastic, wood, or water? Explain your answer.
5. **Connect to Earth Science:** Geologists and surveyors often use lasers for aligning equipment, measuring, and mapping. Explain why.

✉ Sequencing

Sequence the events that occur in a laser in order to produce coherent light. Begin with the emission of a photon from an atom. If you need help, refer to Sequencing in the **Skill Handbook** on page 676.

Skill Builder
〰

Skill Builder
〰

1. emission of a photon from an atom
2. photon bounces back and forth between two mirrors
3. photon stimulates other atoms to emit photons that must move in the same phase and direction as the original photon
4. Photons of coherent light escape from the mirror at the end of the laser.
5. Coherent light travels with very little spreading out.

Skill Builder
ASSESSMENT
Performance: Ask students to add beginning steps to their sequences detailing the role of the flashtube. They should note that (a) the flashtube emits bright light and (b) this energy is absorbed by some atoms.

---

3 CLOSE

▶ Discuss the medical applications of lasers and optical fibers. Lasers are used for precise cutting and cauterization of blood vessels. Optical fibers are inserted into small incisions inside the body. Light travels down one set of fibers, is reflected, and returns up another set of fibers to produce an image on a computer screen. Together, they revolutionize many kinds of surgery because the required incision is so small.

▶ Have the students make a card file of the various types of lasers. This file should include the wavelength of light produced by the laser and its current applications. Relate the wavelength of light to energy.

▶ If the technology is accessible, put this information into a database. Use the database to arrange the lasers from the most powerful to the least powerful.

▶ Ask questions 1-3 and the **Apply** and **Connect to Earth Science** questions in the Section Review.

SECTION REVIEW ANSWERS

1. All light waves vibrate in the same plane.

2. Coherent, or laser light, has a single wavelength and travels with its crests and troughs aligned. This means in phase. Most light contains many wavelengths and is incoherent.

3. The light undergoes total internal reflection as it strikes the inside of the glass tube.

4. Apply: Plastic would work because it is transparent. Water is also transparent, and would work, but is impractical to use because it is a liquid. Wood is opaque and wouldn't transmit light.

5. Connect to Earth Science: Because coherent light travels in straight paths, it can be used to find the direct path between two points.

TECHNOLOGY

▶**Reference:** Katzir, Abraham. "Optical Fibers in Medicine." *Scientific American.* May 1989, pp. 120-125.

Think Critically: The wall of the artery might absorb enough energy to be damaged.

OBJECTIVE: **Investigate** the effects of polarizing filters and **relate** these observations to practical applications of polarized light.
Time: one class period

PROCESS SKILLS applied in this activity are **experimenting, observing,** and **inferring.**

PREPARATION

Polarized light filters can be cut into small pieces, but keep edges in line with the direction of polarization.

Cooperative Learning: Students can work in teams of 2-4, depending on your supply of polarizing filters.

SAFETY

Remind students not to look directly at the sun, even through a polarizing filter.

THINKING CRITICALLY

Glare from the ground is horizontally polarized. Polarizing filters in sunglasses should be oriented vertically to filter out the glare.

TEACHING THE ACTIVITY

*Refer to the **Activity Worksheets** for additional information and teaching strategies.*

• To create the glare, use blocks of polished or painted wood or plastic. Do not use either dull or mirrored surfaces.
• Try to have several pairs of polarizing sunglasses available for students.

PROGRAM RESOURCES

From the **Teacher Resource Package** use:

Activity Worksheets, pages 160-161, Activity 20-2: What's Behind Those Shades?

Imagine being near a swimming pool or lake on a bright, sunny day. You would likely be squinting because some sunlight is reflected from the water's surface rather than being absorbed. How would regular or polarizing sunglasses affect this glare?

Getting Started

In this activity, you will *investigate* the effects of polarizing filters and *relate* your observations to some practical uses of these filters. Be sure not to look directly at the sun at any time.

Thinking Critically

In what plane is glare from the ground polarized? How should the polarizing filters in sunglasses be oriented?

Materials

Your cooperative group will use:
• two polarizing filters • masking tape
• light source • objects with flat, hard surfaces

 Try It!

1. Hold both filters together and look through them. Rotate one filter while holding the other still. When the maximum light can be seen, mark the top and bottom edges of both filters "X" and the side edges "Y".

2. Find a way to block nearly all light using the two polarizing filters.
3. Hold an object with a flat surface horizontally and reflect light from its surface. Look at the reflection through one filter and rotate it until the glare disappears. Repeat this with a vertical surface.

Summing Up/Sharing Results

• *Estimate* how many degrees you must turn one filter relative to the other to change light passing through from brightest to darkest.
• When the glare from the horizontal surface disappears, which edge of the rotated filter is up?
• Is this also true for glare from the vertical surface?

Going Further!

Light from the portion of the sky which is 90° from the sun is polarized. Look through the filter at this part of the sky and rotate the filter to make the sky darken. If there are clouds in the sky, how do they appear as the filter darkens the sky?

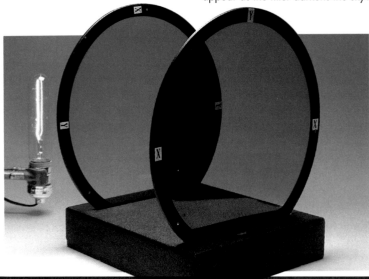

SUMMING UP/SHARING RESULTS

• The filter must be turned 90°.
• In the horizontal and vertical glare questions, if "X" is the answer to part one, then "Y" is the answer to part two, and vice versa.

GOING FURTHER!

Although the sky darkens as the filter is turned, clouds do not change.

Activity
ASSESSMENT

Oral: Ask students if polarizing sunglasses would work as well if they were turned sideways? Upside down? Have them explain using observations from this activity.

SUMMARY

20-1: The Optics of Mirrors
1. Plane mirrors and convex mirrors produce virtual images. Concave mirrors produce real images.
2. Plane mirrors are used in bathroom mirrors, concave mirrors are used to create flashlight beams and magnify images, and rearview mirrors and shoplifting mirrors are convex.

20-2: The Optics of Lenses
1. Convex lenses form real images; concave lenses form virtual images.
2. Convex lenses converge light rays and can form images on a screen. Concave lenses diverge light rays and are often used in combination with other lenses.
3. Corrective lenses can be used to focus images on the retina. Farsighted people must wear convex lenses, and nearsighted persons must wear concave lenses.

20-3: Optical Instruments
1. A refracting telescope uses convex lenses to magnify distant objects; a reflecting telescope uses concave and plane mirrors and a convex lens to magnify distant objects.

2. Light passing through the lens of a camera is focused on photographic film inside the camera. The image on the film is real, inverted, and smaller than the object being photographed.

20-4: Science and Society: The Hubble Space Telescope
1. By avoiding atmospheric distortion, the Hubble Space Telescope produces sharper images than telescopes on Earth. In addition, it can detect infrared and ultraviolet radiation.
2. Scientists hope space telescopes will lead to new information about the universe.

20-5: Applications of Light
1. Polarized light consists of transverse waves that only vibrate along one plane. Polarized filters block light waves that aren't vibrating in the same plane as the filter.
2. A laser produces coherent light by emitting a beam of photons that travel in the same phase and direction. Light that spreads out from its source is incoherent.
3. Optical fibers can pipe light rays because the fibers are made of a material that allows the light rays to reflect totally inside the fibers.

KEY SCIENCE WORDS

a. **coherent light**
b. **concave lens**
c. **concave mirror**
d. **convex lens**
e. **convex mirror**
f. **focal length**
g. **focal point**
h. **incoherent light**
i. **laser**
j. **microscope**
k. **optical fiber**
l. **plane mirror**
m. **polarized light**
n. **real image**
o. **reflecting telescope**
p. **refracting telescope**
q. **telephoto lens**
r. **total internal reflection**
s. **virtual image**
t. **wide-angle lens**

UNDERSTANDING VOCABULARY

Match each phrase with the correct term from the list of Key Science Words.

1. mirror with a flat surface
2. image that cannot be projected onto a screen
3. image formed where light rays actually meet
4. curved mirror that diverges reflected light
5. lens that converges light at its focal point
6. a telescope that uses two convex lenses
7. an instrument used to study very small objects
8. light waves that vibrate in only one plane
9. light produced by lasers
10. often used to transmit telephone signals

MIRRORS AND LENSES **535**

CHAPTER
REVIEW

SUMMARY
Have students read the Summary statements to review the major concepts of the chapter.

UNDERSTANDING VOCABULARY

1.	l	6.	p
2.	s	7.	j
3.	n	8.	m
4.	e	9.	a
5.	d	10.	k

ASSESSMENT
Portfolio
Encourage students to place in their portfolios one or two items of what they consider to be their best work. For each item, ask students to explain why that item was chosen and what they learned from it. Items might be selected from the following.
- Skill Builder hypothesis, p. 525
- You Decide! response, p. 527
- Activity 20-2 answers and results, p. 534

Performance
Additional performance assessments may be found in *Performance Assessment* and *Science Integration Activities* that accompany **Merrill Physical Science.** Performance Task Assessment Lists and rubrics for evaluating these activities and other products generated throughout the chapter can be found in Glencoe's *Performance Assessment in Middle School Science.*

OPTIONS

ASSESSMENT
To assess student understanding of the material in this chapter, use the resources listed.

COOPERATIVE LEARNING
Consider using Cooperative Learning in the THINK AND WRITE CRITICALLY, APPLY, and MORE SKILL BUILDERS sections of the Chapter Review.

PROGRAM RESOURCES
From the **Teacher Resource Package** use:
Chapter Review, pages 43-44.
Chapter and Unit Tests, pages 130-133, Chapter Test.
Chapter and Unit Tests, pages 134-135, Unit Test.

1. c	**6.** c
2. b	**7.** b
3. c	**8.** d
4. c	**9.** d
5. b	**10.** c

USING LAB SKILLS

ASSESSMENT

Use these alternate lab exercises to assess students' understanding of the skills used in this chapter.

11. If the drop is too small, it will not magnify a large enough area to be useful. If it is too large, it will not be concave enough to magnify. A medium-sized drop works best.

12. The polarizing filter must be oriented so people wearing polarized glasses can see the time.

THINK AND WRITE CRITICALLY

13. Light rays parallel to the optical axis are reflected through the mirror's focal point. Light rays approaching through the focal point of a concave mirror are reflected parallel to the optical axis.

14. to give us more information and to answer some unsolved questions about the universe by avoiding atmospheric distortion

15. In convex lenses, light is refracted towards the center of the lens and converges at the focal point of the lens, hence, the name converging lens. In contrast, light is refracted towards the edges of concave lenses therefore it diverges away from the lens' focal point. Concave lenses are thus called diverging lenses.

16. Both are used to magnify objects. However, telescopes are used to magnify very large objects that are quite far away, while microscopes magnify very small objects that are close at hand. The refracting telescope is built according to the same principles as the microscope.

17. A photon is emitted from an atom and reflected between two mirrors at

---

Choose the word or phrase that completes the sentence.

1. Images formed by plane mirrors are not _____.
   a. upright
   c. enlarged
   b. reversed
   d. virtual

2. An object that reflects light and curves inward is called a _____.
   a. plane mirror
   c. convex mirror
   b. concave mirror
   d. concave lens

3. Mirrors that can magnify a reflection are _____.
   a. convex
   c. concave
   b. plane
   d. transparent

4. The light bulb in a headlight, flashlight, or spotlight is placed at the focal point of a _____.
   a. concave lens
   c. concave mirror
   b. convex lens
   d. convex mirror

5. Lenses form images by _____.
   a. reflecting light
   c. diffracting light
   b. refracting light
   d. interfering with light

6. A concave lens bends light towards its _____.
   a. optical axis
   c. edges
   b. center
   d. focal point

7. Farsighted people must wear _____.
   a. flat lenses
   b. convex lenses
   c. concave lenses
   d. unevenly curved lenses

8. Reflecting telescopes don't contain a _____.
   a. plane mirror
   c. convex lens
   b. concave mirror
   d. concave lens

9. Some sunglasses and 3-D glasses use _____.
   a. concave lenses
   c. telephoto lenses
   b. convex lenses
   d. polarizing filters

10. Lasers are often used in _____.
   a. cooking food
   c. surgery
   b. traffic control
   d. headlights

USING LAB SKILLS

11. Review the MINI-Lab on page 520. You can also make a liquid magnifying lens by placing a drop of water directly onto a page of text covered by plastic. Compare the magnifying properties of small, medium, and large drops. Which size is most effective and why?

12. In Activity 20-2 on page 534, you observed the effect of polarizing filters. Liquid Crystal Displays (LCDs) in digital watches and calculators have polarizing filters. Why does it matter which way a digital watch's polarizing filter is oriented?

THINK AND WRITE CRITICALLY

Answer the following questions in your Journal using complete sentences.

13. Describe how a concave mirror reflects light rays that approach it parallel to its optical axis. How does such a mirror reflect approaching light rays that pass through its focal point?

14. Why was the Hubble Space Telescope built?

15. Convex lenses are often called converging lenses while concave lenses are often called diverging lenses. Explain these different names by describing how each type of lens refracts light.

16. Compare and contrast the uses of telescopes and microscopes. Which type of telescope is built most like a microscope?

17. Explain how a laser produces coherent light.

---

the ends of the laser. This photon excites other atoms within the laser and they emit photons, as well. Some of the photons penetrate one of the mirrors and leave the end of the laser in a fine stream of coherent light.

APPLY

18. If the object the audience was looking at were really an image in a concave mirror, the magician could make this image disappear by moving the object to the focal point of the mirror where no image is formed.

19. It would produce an enlarged, upright, virtual image that can't be projected onto a screen.

20. a convex lens

21 No. The convex mirror would produce a virtual image that cannot be magnified by the eyepiece.

22. A wide angle lens; wide-angle lenses are easier to use and can be used in many different and more common situations.

APPLY

18. Magicians often make objects disappear by using trick mirrors. How might a magician seem to make an object disappear by using a concave mirror?

19. What would happen if a movie projector's lens were less than one focal length from the film?

20. If you were an optician, what type of lens would you prescribe for a patient who can't focus clearly on close objects?

21. Would a reflecting telescope work properly if its concave mirror were replaced by a convex mirror? Explain.

22. You only have enough money to buy one lens for your camera. What type of lens would be most useful? Explain.

MORE SKILL BUILDERS

If you need help, refer to the Skill Handbook.

1. **Outlining:** Summarize in an outline the different types of images formed by plane, concave, and convex mirrors.

2. **Observing and Inferring:** Infer the effects of a hard, rigid eye lens on human vision. Would this make the eye more or less like a simple camera?

3. **Recognizing Cause and Effect:** Distinguish and describe the causes and effects of the following vision problems: nearsightedness, farsightedness, and astigmatism.

4. **Hypothesizing:** Rough, uncut diamonds lack the sparkle of diamonds that have been cut by a gem cutter. Propose a hypothesis to explain this observation.

5. **Concept Mapping:** Below is a concept map summarizing characteristics of coherent and incoherent light. Use the following terms to complete the map (terms may be used more than once): *wavelength(s), frequency(ies), color(s), sun, lasers, coherent light, incoherent light.*

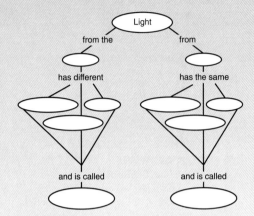

PROJECTS

1. Write a report tracing the development of the telescope from the time of Galileo to the Hubble Space Telescope.

2. Investigate the types of mirrors used in funhouses. Explain how these mirrors give distorted images and report your findings to the class.

MIRRORS AND LENSES **537**

1. **Outlining:** *Mirror Images*
   I. Plane mirrors (for all object distances)
      A. virtual
      B. upright
      C. same size as object
      D. reversed
      E. image distance equals object distance
   II. Concave Mirrors
      A. Object distance: less than one focal length
         1. virtual
         2. upright
         3. larger than object
      B. Object distance: focal length
         1. no image
      C. Object distance: more than one focal length but less than two focal lengths
         1. real
         2. inverted
         3. larger
   III. Convex Mirrors
      A. virtual
      B. upright
      C. smaller than object

2. **Observing and Inferring:** A hard, rigid eye lens would have a fixed focal length. This means that the image of an object could only be focused on the retina when the object is a specific distance from the eye. Such an eye would be more like a simple camera which has a lens of fixed focal length.

3. **Recognizing Cause and Effect:** *Nearsightedness—cause:* an abnormally long eyeball or bulging cornea. *effect:* light from a distant object is focused in front of the retina. *Farsightedness—cause:* abnormally short eyeball or flattened cornea. *effect:* light from nearby objects is focused behind the retina. *Astigmatism—cause:* unevenly curved cornea. *effect:* all light is poorly focused on the retina.

5. **Concept Mapping:** Student maps will vary. Sample map follows.

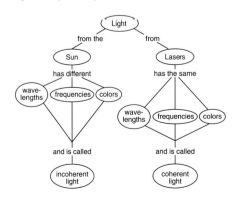

4. **Hypothesizing:** One possible hypothesis might be: Cutting diamonds in specific ways gives them inner surfaces that refracted light can strike at angles large enough to produce total internal reflection and thus the diamond sparkles.

Objective

In this unit-ending feature, the unit topic, "Waves, Light, and Sound," is extended into other disciplines. Students will see how waves, light, and sound affect events around the planet.

Motivate

Cooperative Learning: Assign one Connection to each group of students. Using the Expert Teams strategy, have each group research to find out more about the geographic location of the Connection—its climate, culture, flora and fauna, and ecological issues.

Teaching Tips

▶ Tell students to keep in mind the connection between waves and each event described in this feature.

▶ Ask students to explain any differences in the kinds of waves involved in the different Connections.

Wrap-Up

Conclude this lesson by having students predict how new knowledge about waves, light, and sound might affect their future lives.

GEOLOGY

Background: The October 17th earthquake registered 7.1 on the Richter scale and was felt across a million square kilometers. Structures built on mud, sand, or fill collapsed as seismic waves turned the soil and groundwater into a quicksand-like "soup."

Discussion: Discuss the accuracy of earthquake predictions. Ask students to discuss the benefits of being able to accurately predict where and when earthquakes will happen.

Answer to Question: Earthquake waves were amplified by the soft fill material where the Marina district had expanded into San Francisco Bay. L-waves travel along Earth's surface and cause the most damage.

Extension: Have students research the 1988 Armenian and 1985 Mexico City earthquakes.

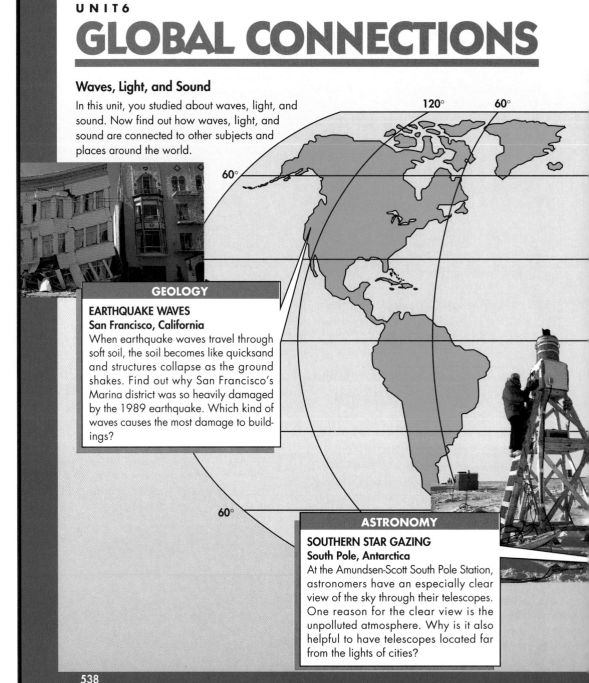

UNIT 6
GLOBAL CONNECTIONS

Waves, Light, and Sound

In this unit, you studied about waves, light, and sound. Now find out how waves, light, and sound are connected to other subjects and places around the world.

GEOLOGY

EARTHQUAKE WAVES
San Francisco, California
When earthquake waves travel through soft soil, the soil becomes like quicksand and structures collapse as the ground shakes. Find out why San Francisco's Marina district was so heavily damaged by the 1989 earthquake. Which kind of waves causes the most damage to buildings?

ASTRONOMY

SOUTHERN STAR GAZING
South Pole, Antarctica
At the Amundsen-Scott South Pole Station, astronomers have an especially clear view of the sky through their telescopes. One reason for the clear view is the unpolluted atmosphere. Why is it also helpful to have telescopes located far from the lights of cities?

538

ASTRONOMY

Background: The moving layers of Earth's atmosphere interfere with astronomers' views of celestial objects. For this reason, telescopes are usually located where the atmosphere is the least dense.

Discussion: Discuss with students why many telescopes are located high on mountains where the air is less dense. Ask students to describe how the view from the South Pole telescope would differ from the view from those in the United States.

Answer to Question: Lights from cities make it more difficult to see faint objects in the sky.

Extension: Have students find out why astronomers were so anxious to have the Hubble Space Telescope launched.

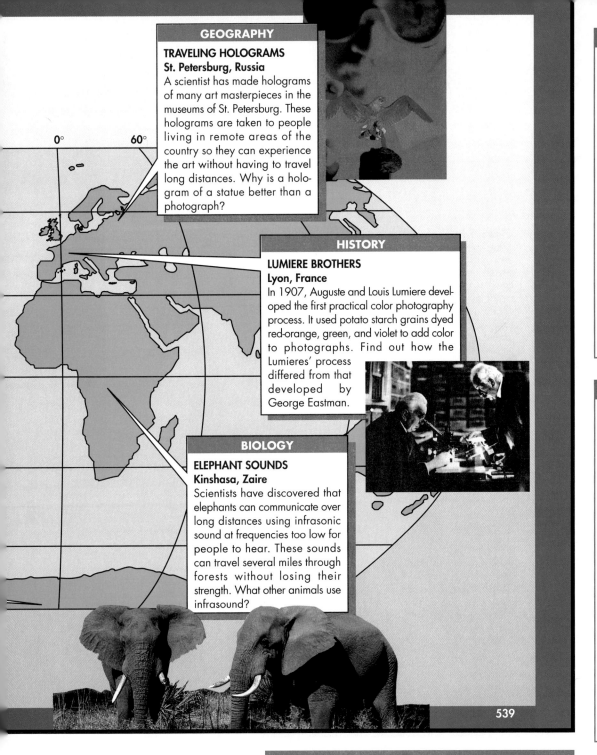

GEOGRAPHY

TRAVELING HOLOGRAMS
St. Petersburg, Russia

A scientist has made holograms of many art masterpieces in the museums of St. Petersburg. These holograms are taken to people living in remote areas of the country so they can experience the art without having to travel long distances. Why is a hologram of a statue better than a photograph?

HISTORY

LUMIERE BROTHERS
Lyon, France

In 1907, Auguste and Louis Lumiere developed the first practical color photography process. It used potato starch grains dyed red-orange, green, and violet to add color to photographs. Find out how the Lumieres' process differed from that developed by George Eastman.

BIOLOGY

ELEPHANT SOUNDS
Kinshasa, Zaire

Scientists have discovered that elephants can communicate over long distances using infrasonic sound at frequencies too low for people to hear. These sounds can travel several miles through forests without losing their strength. What other animals use infrasound?

539

BIOLOGY

Background: An elephant makes infrasonic sounds by vibrating a spot on its forehead. The spot, near the nasal openings, flutters at frequencies between 14 and 24 hertz. Infrasonic sounds travel much farther than high-frequency sounds.

Discussion: Discuss with students how using infrasonic calls would help keep a group of elephants together while traveling through a dense forest.

Answer to Question: Some types of birds, including pigeons, can hear infrasonic waves. Fin whales also produce infrasonic calls.

Extension: Have students research how different species of bats use ultrasonic sounds.

HISTORY

Background: The Lumieres' starch grains were coated with light-sensitive chemicals, which filtered colors as light passed through. The developed plate produced a negative that was exposed to light and redeveloped. The result was a transparency with specks of color that formed a full-color image.

Discussion: Discuss with students how the development of color photography might have changed people's ideas about the world around them.

Answer to Question: Kodachrome film, from George Eastman's Kodak labs, uses dyes of cyan, magenta, and yellow which were introduced layer by layer during processing.

Extension: Have students research information on color blindness.

GEOGRAPHY

Background: Holograms are 3-dimensional pictures that are produced by the use of laser light. However, lasers are not needed to view all holograms.

Discussion: Discuss with students how holograms differ from photographs. Ask them if they have seen holograms on credit cards, magazine covers, or cereal boxes.

Answer to Question: Because a statue is a 3-dimensional object, a hologram shows it better than a photograph.

Extension: Have students examine with a hand lens the holograms on the March 1984, November 1985, or December 1988 covers of *National Geographic*.

OPTICAL MECHANIC

Background: Optical mechanics may work in factories where cameras and binoculars are manufactured or in centers where eyeglasses and contact lenses are made.

Related Career	Education
Optician	technical school
Optometrist	college degree
Ophthalmologist	medical school
Laser technician	college degree

Career Issue: Recently people have become concerned about problems with extended-wear contact lenses. Some ophthalmologists and optometrists are advising patients against these products because of potential eye damage.

What do you think? Lead students in a discussion of their own attitudes about contact lenses, particularly the extended-wear type. What are the advantages and disadvantages for wearers?

PHOTOGRAPHER

Background: Many photographers are self-employed. Some specialize in portrait photography; others specialize in advertising photography or nature photography. Some photographers work for newspapers and magazines and many companies have staff photographers, as well.

Related Career	Education
Film technician	high school
Retouch artist	technical school
Food stylist	technical school
Cinematographer	college degree

Career Issue: Computer technology now allows photographic images to be manipulated to add or delete items or people from pictures or to combine images from several photographs. Some people are concerned about the ethics of altering photographs, particularly if it occurs in newspapers or news magazines.

What do you think? Lead students in a discussion of how they feel about alteration of photographs. Can they

OPTICAL MECHANIC

An *optical mechanic* uses special equipment to grind and polish lenses. Some optical mechanics make lenses for cameras and binoculars, while others make lenses for eyeglasses. Each pair of eyeglass lenses is made according to a prescription written by an optometrist or ophthalmologist. The optical mechanic makes sure each lens is correctly ground and then fits it into the eyeglass frames.

Most optical mechanics receive on-the-job training for about three years. If you're interested in becoming an optical mechanic, you should take courses in biology and physics.

For Additional Information

Contact the Optical Laboratories Association, 11096-B Lee Highway, Unit 102, Fairfax City, Virginia 22030.

PHOTOGRAPHER

A *photographer* uses light meters, lights, and cameras to take photographs. Some photographers work in commercial studios, photographing products or people. Others work for magazines or newspapers. Many photographers are self-employed.

A person interested in photography should have good color vision and artistic skills. High school classes in art, chemistry, and physics are helpful. If you're interested in becoming a photographer, there are several options for training. He or she can work as an assistant and receive on-the-job training for two or three years, or attend an art school or college that offers special programs in photography. A photographer who wants to specialize in medical or scientific subjects needs additional college classes in science.

For Additional Information

Contact the Professional Photographers of America, Inc., 1090 Executive Way, Des Plaines, Illinois 60018.

UNIT READINGS

▶Heckman, Philip. *The Magic of Holography.* New York: Atheneum, 1986.
▶Ward, Alan. *Experimenting With Light and Illusions.* London, England: Batsford, 1985.
▶Wolkomir, Richard and Joyce. "When Animals Sound Off." *National Wildlife,* April - May 1990, pp. 48-50.

always believe what they see in a photograph?

UNIT READINGS

Background

▶ *The Magic of Holography* describes how holography is used today and how it might be used in the future.

▶ *Experimenting with Light and Illusions* contains experiments that illustrate the nature of light and illusions.

▶ "When Animals Sound Off" describes the various ways different animals use sound.

More Readings

1. Filson, Brent. *Exploring with Lasers.* New York, NY: Messner, 1984. This book describes how lasers operate and how they are used.

2. Proujan, C. "Looking Through 'Walls.'" *Scholastic Science World.* October 5, 1984, p. 11. A brief look at X rays.

SCIENCE
& ART

Alma Woodsey Thomas — Color Field Painter

Alma Thomas was an African American artist who achieved prominence in the mainstream art community. She worked in the modern tradition of Color Field painting.

She was born in 1892 in Columbus, Georgia. Because her aunts were teachers, she decided at an early age that teaching could be her way to a better life, too. Her family moved to Washington, D.C., in 1907. In 1924, she was the first graduate of the new art department at Howard University.

She taught art in the Washington, D.C., schools for 35 years. During that time, she earned an M.A. at Teachers College of Columbia University. During her teaching years, she exhibited realistic paintings in shows of African American artists. But in the 1950s, she took painting classes at American University and became interested in color and abstract art.

By 1959, her paintings had become abstract. By 1964, she had discovered a way to create an image through small dabs of paint laid edge to edge across the painting's surface. In *Iris, Tulips, Jonquils, and Crocuses,* the color bands move vertically and horizontally across the canvas to represent a breeze moving over a sunlit spring garden. In *Autumn Leaves Fluttering in the Wind,* shown below, rust-colored patches move in patterns like those of swirling autumn leaves. The spaces between the patches show glimpses of colors that represent the sky and the land.

Thomas's paintings are mosaics of color that she said, "represent my communion with nature." She wrote, "Color is life. Light reveals to us the spirit and living soul of the world through colors."

In Your Own Words
▶ Alma Thomas wrote that she was "intrigued with the changing colors of nature as the seasons progress." Describe how you would paint a natural scene using the Color Field painting style.

Classics
▶ Bob Thomas, ed. *Directors in Action.* New York, NY: Bobbs-Merrill Company, Inc., 1973. Describes the work of a variety of film directors who translate movie scripts into films.

Biography: Alma Woodsey Thomas (1892-1978) was the first African American woman to have a solo exhibition at the Whitney Museum of American Art (1972). During her years of teaching she was an important force in the Washington arts scene. She organized clubs and art lectures for her students, established art galleries in the public schools, and helped found the Barnett-Aden Gallery, one of the first galleries in Washington devoted to modern art.

TEACHING STRATEGY
Have students read through the passage about Alma Thomas. Then have them respond to the discussion questions below.

Discussion Questions
1. **From the information in the article on Alma Thomas, how do you think she felt about the use of color in paintings?** *She used mosaics of color patches to convey abstract images of nature. She said that color is life and the spirit of the world is revealed in colors.*
2. **Compare the technique used by Alma Thomas to the technique used by artists who work with stained glass. How are they alike and how do they differ?** *Both Thomas and stained-glass artists use small areas of color to create a larger image. The colors seen in a painting are seen by light reflected from the canvas and the colors seen in stained-glass art are seen as light is transmitted through the glass.*

Other Works
▶ Other Color Field works by Alma Thomas include *Wind and Crepe Myrtle Concerto* (1973), *New Galaxy* (1970), and *Flowers at Jefferson Memorial* (1970).

In Unit 7, students are first introduced to electricity and magnetism and how they are related. The world of micro-electronics is then discussed. Radio-activity is introduced with emphasis given to its application. The unit ends with a discussion of energy consump-tion, alternative energy sources, and the role of energy conservation.

CONTENTS

ADVANCE PREPARATION

Audiovisuals
▶ Show the film *Electrostatic Charges and Forces*, Coronet.
▶ Show the video *Learning About Magnetism*, EBEC.

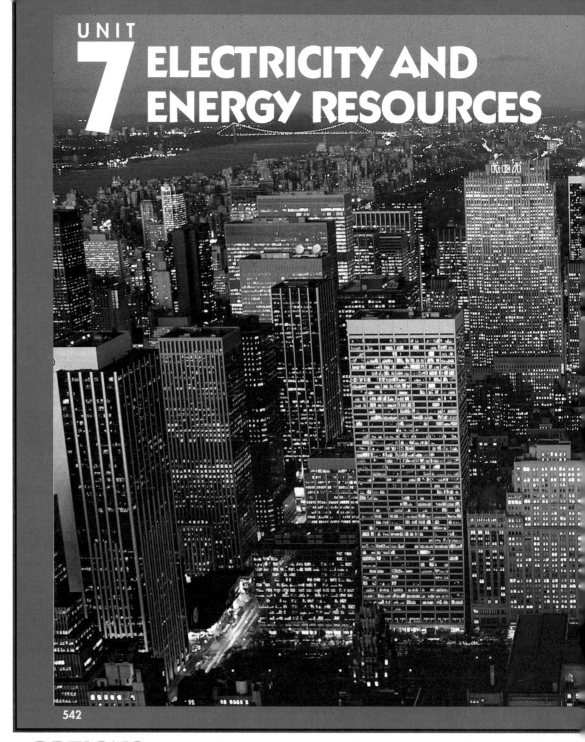

UNIT

7 ELECTRICITY AND ENERGY RESOURCES

542

OPTIONS

Cross Curriculum
Have students keep logs of the ways that electrical energy is used in their classes. At the end of the unit, have students volunteer suggestions that might be used to conserve electrical energy.

Science at Home
Cooperative Learning: Have groups of students monitor TV and newspapers for coverage of problems concerning the pro-cessing and storing of radioactive wastes.
▶ Have students keep daily logs of their elec-trical energy uses. Have them note the device or appliance used, its function, if it is battery-operated or not, and how long it was used. Have them calculate or approximate their personal electrical energy consumption by using tables of appliance power-rating sup-plied by most utility companies.

What's Happening Here?

When the sun goes down, New York City's lights go on. New York City generates electricity for lighting by burning fossil fuels, harnessing water power, and controlling nuclear reactions. What does it mean to "generate" electricity? How do solar collectors like the ones shown below generate electricity? Why is it important to develop alternatives to fossil fuels? In this power-packed unit, you'll learn the answers to these questions. You'll also learn about magnetism, nuclear reactions, and computers.

UNIT CONTENTS

543

Multicultural Awareness

Have interested students research how peoples of various cultures have adapted their lifestyles to the consumption of limited sources of fossil fuels or the exploitation of alternative energy sources.

Inquiry Questions

Use the following questions to focus a discussion of electricity and its uses.
▶ **What is the most apparent way that electricity is being used in this picture?** lighting
▶ **How else do you suppose electricity is being used in these buildings?** *Accept all reasonable answers. heating, cooling, office cleaning equipment, elevators, computers, movie projectors*
▶ **Would these uses change during the year?** *Accept all reasonable answers. Air conditioning would be heavier during the summer.*

INTRODUCING THE UNIT

What's Happening Here?
▶ Have students look at the photos and read the text. Ask them to tell you what's happening here. Point out to students that in this unit they will learn what electrical energy is; how it is converted to light, heat, and other forms of energy; and how other forms of energy are converted into electrical energy.
▶ **Background:** About 70% of the electricity produced in the United States is produced by the burning of fossil fuels, 20% from nuclear fission, and 10% from moving water. Lighting accounts for the smallest fraction of electricity's use. Most electricity is used for heating, cooling, and operating industrial machinery. In most cases, electricity is produced by generators that convert mechanical energy into electrical energy. However, in solar cells, electricity is produced by silicon wafers that convert radiant energy into electrical energy.

Previewing the Chapters
▶ Have students use the photographs in the unit to identify a household device that (1) uses both electrical energy and nuclear energy; *smoke detector, Figure 24-12, page 620,* (2) converts electrical energy into radiant energy; *light bulb or electric heater, Figure 21-6, page 555,* (3) converts electrical energy into sound; *radio, page 599,* (4) converts electrical energy into mechanical energy; *drill, Figure 22-8, page 580.*

Tying to Previous Knowledge
▶ Have students brainstorm lists of electrical appliances and devices. Then have them categorize the appliance or device as to its major function, such as heating, cooling, lighting, motion, etc. Have them conjecture which category probably accounts for their greatest personal use of electrical energy.
▶ Have students discuss energy uses and energy sources that they are now familiar with. Ask them to discuss what they perceive as energy conservation and how it can be accomplished.
▶ Use the **inquiry questions** in the OPTIONS box to focus on the topic of electricity.

CHAPTER SECTION	OBJECTIVES	ACTIVITIES
21-1 Electric Charge (1 day)	1. **Describe** the effects of static electricity. 2. **Distinguish** between conductors and insulators. 3. **Recognize** the presence of charge in an electroscope.	**MINI-Lab:** *Can static charge move things?* p. 548
21-2 Lightning—Its Causes and Effects Science & Society (1 day)	1. **Explain** the occurrence of lightning in terms of induction and static discharge. 2. **Evaluate** the positive and negative aspects of lightning-induced forest fires.	
21-3 Electric Current (2 days)	1. **Describe** how potential energy of an electron changes as it moves through a simple circuit. 2. **Explain** how a dry cell is a source of electricity. 3. **Conceptually** and **mathematically relate** potential difference, resistance, and current.	**Activity 21-1:** *Modeling Ohm's Law,* p. 559
21-4 Electrical Circuits (2 days)	1. **Sketch** a series and a parallel circuit, and **list** applications of each type of circuit. 2. **Recognize** the function of circuit breakers and fuses.	**Activity 21-2:** *Electric Circuits,* p. 564
21-5 Electrical Power and Energy (2 days)	1. **Explain** and **calculate** electric power. 2. **Calculate** the amount of electrical energy in kilowatt-hours.	**MINI-Lab:** *How much power operates an electric toy?* p. 567
Chapter Review		

ACTIVITY MATERIALS

FIND OUT	ACTIVITIES		MINI-LABS	
Page 545 tissue paper plastic rulers	**21-1 Modeling Ohm's Law, p. 559** plastic funnel ring stand with ring 1 m rubber tubing meterstick 2 250-mL beakers stopwatch or clock	**21-2 Electric Circuits, p. 564** aluminum foil cellophane tape scissors 3 lights with sockets 6 paper clips battery (6 or 9 volt)	**Can static charge move things? p. 547** plastic food wrap cotton cloth paper hole punch aluminum foil	**How much power operates an electric toy? p. 567** milliammeter 3 wires with small alligator clips strips of aluminum foil electric toy with battery tape or rubber bands

CHAPTER FEATURES	TEACHER RESOURCE PACKAGE	OTHER RESOURCES
Problem Solving: *How Can Birds Perch on Power Lines?* p. 548 **Skill Builder:** *Observing and Inferring,* p. 549	**Ability Level Worksheets** ◆ **Study Guide,** p. 87 ● **Reinforcement,** p. 87 ▲ **Enrichment,** p. 87 **MINI-Lab Worksheet,** p. 173	**STVS:** Disc 1, Side 1
You Decide! p. 551	**Ability Level Worksheets** ◆ **Study Guide,** p. 88 ● **Reinforcement,** p. 88 ▲ **Enrichment,** p. 88 **Concept Mapping,** pp. 47, 48	**STVS:** Disc 1, Side 1
Technology: *Shake and Bake Superconductors,* p. 556 **Skill Builder:** *Making and Using Tables,* p. 558	**Ability Level Worksheets** ◆ **Study Guide,** p. 89 ● **Reinforcement,** p. 89 ▲ **Enrichment,** p. 89 **Activity Worksheets,** pp. 5, 167, 168 **Critical Thinking/Problem Solving,** p. 27 **Science and Society,** p. 25	**Laboratory Manual 43,** Wet Cell Battery **STVS:** Disc 2, Side 2 **Science Integration Activity 21**
Skill Builder: *Hypothesizing,* p. 563	**Ability Level Worksheets** ◆ **Study Guide,** p. 90 ● **Reinforcement,** p. 90 ▲ **Enrichment,** p. 90 **Activity Worksheet,** pp. 169, 170 **Transparency Masters,** pp. 83-86	**Color Transparency 42,** Series & Parallel Circuits **Color Transparency 43,** Household Circuits **Laboratory Manual 44,** Simple Circuits
	Ability Level Worksheets ◆ **Study Guide,** p. 91 ● **Reinforcement,** p. 91 ▲ **Enrichment,** p. 91 **MINI-Lab Worksheet,** p. 174 **Cross-Curricular Connections,** p. 27	
Summary Think & Write Critically Key Science Words Apply Understanding Vocabulary More Skill Builders Checking Concepts Projects Using Lab Skills	**ASSESSMENT RESOURCES** **Chapter Review,** pp. 45, 46 **Chapter Test,** pp. 143-146 **Performance Assessment in Middle School Science**	**Chapter Review Software** **Test Bank** **Alternate Assessment** **Performance Assessment**

◆ **Basic**   ● **Average**   ▲ **Advanced**

ADDITIONAL MATERIALS

SOFTWARE	AUDIOVISUAL	BOOKS/MAGAZINES
Alternating Current Circuits, Queue. *Batteries and Bulbs,* EduQuest. *Build a Circuit,* Sunburst. *Electric Instrument,* Queue. *Electric Circuits,* Queue. *Electricity,* J and S Software. *Learning All About Electricity and Magnetism,* Queue. *MMV Electricity,* Queue. *Safe and Sure With Electricity,* Queue.	*Basic Electricity,* Video, Insight Media. *Electric Currents and Circuits,* Video, Coronet. *Electrical Energy,* Laserdisc, Churchill Media. *Electrical Circuits: You Can Do It!,* Video, Britannica. *Electricity,* Video, AIT. *Energy: Working for Us,* Video, Lucerne Media.	Clemence, John, and Janet Clemence. *Electricity.* Ada, OK: Garrett Educational, 1991. Ford, R.A. *Homemade Lightning: Creative Experiments in Electricity.* Blue Ridge Summit, PA: Tab, 1991. Schaffer, Larry E. *Taking Charge: An Introduction to Electricity.* Washington, DC: National Science Teachers Association, 1992.

THEME DEVELOPMENT: This chapter introduces the basic science and applications of electricity. Energy is developed as a major theme of this chapter. Emphasize conservation of energy. Electricity is a convenient way to deliver energy, but it is often changed to other forms such as light and mechanical energy as we use it.

CHAPTER OVERVIEW

▶ **Section 21-1:** This section investigates the causes and effects of static electricity, the behavior of conductors and insulators, and the use of an electroscope.

▶ **Section 21-2: Science and Society:** The science behind lightning is explained and followed by a discussion of lightning-induced forest fires. The You Decide question asks whether natural fires should be allowed to burn.

▶ **Section 21-3:** Electric currents are introduced and explained. Resistance, current, and potential difference are related conceptually and mathematically.

▶ **Section 21-4:** This section illustrates series, parallel, and complex circuits through diagrams and examples.

▶ **Section 21-5:** Electrical power and energy are distinguished, and calculations of power and energy are included.

CHAPTER VOCABULARY

static	dry cell
electricity	wet cell
electric field	resistance
conductor	Ohm's law
insulator	series circuit
electroscope	parallel
lightning rod	circuit
potential difference	electrical
circuit	power
current	kilowatt-hour

544

OPTIONS

✗ For Your Gifted Students

Have students investigate conductors and insulators. First, they can brainstorm ways to test a list of objects and predict the results. Students should design and make a circuit tester to test the objects. They can make a chart to show which items are conductors and which are insulators.

✗ For Your Mainstreamed Students

Have students place several pieces of newspaper on a wooden board. They can take various objects (plastic wrap, wool, foil, and so on) and then rub the paper with them. They should then lift the sheet of newspaper from the wood. If an electrical charge was produced, the paper will be attracted to the wood.

Throughout the day you see examples of electricity and its uses. All of us have come to depend on electricity on a daily basis. Electricity provides us with entertainment, transportation, and convenience. So where does electricity come from? What is it? How does it affect matter?

FIND OUT!

Do this simple activity to find out how matter can be affected by electric charges.

Get a thin plastic ruler. Tear some tissue paper into tiny pieces less than 1 cm² and scatter them on your desk top. Rub the plastic ruler briskly across your hair several times and slowly lower it near the paper. *Observe* what happens. Touch the ruler with your other hand and lower it to the paper again. What happens now?

Gearing Up
Previewing the Chapter
Use this outline to help you focus on important ideas in this chapter.

Section 21-1   Electric Charge
► Static Electricity
► Conductors and Insulators
► The Electroscope

Section 21-2   Science and Society
Lightning—Its Causes and Effects
► Should Lightning-Induced Forest Fires Be Left to Burn?

Section 21-3   Electric Current
► Flowing Electrons
► Batteries
► Resistance
► Ohm's Law

Section 21-4   Electrical Circuits
► Series Circuits
► Parallel Circuits
► Household Circuits

Section 21-5   Electrical Power and Energy
► Electrical Power
► Electrical Energy

Previewing Science Skills
► In the **Skill Builders,** you will observe and infer, hypothesize, and make a concept map.
► In the **Activities,** you will measure in SI, predict, and formulate models.
► In the **MINI-Labs,** you will observe, hypothesize, and interpret data.

What's next?

Now you may wonder what electric charges are and where they come from? As you read on, you will find out more about electric charges and electricity.

545

PREPARATION

SECTION BACKGROUND
▶ Benjamin Franklin arbitrarily named the two types of electric charge *positive* and *negative*.

PREPLANNING
▶ Try to obtain access to a Van de Graaff generator and several electroscopes for demonstration purposes.

1 MOTIVATE

▶ Obtain a copy of the 1990 hit song "Opposites Attract" by Paula Abdul. Ask students what the main phrase of the song means and how it might apply to this chapter.

TYING TO PREVIOUS KNOWLEDGE:
Ask students what sometimes happens when they take clothes out of the dryer. They may mention static cling and that they can hear it crackle. Explain that this is caused by the discharge of static electricity, the topic of this section.

VideoDisc

STVS: Diseased Cells and Lasers; Disc 1, Side 1

CROSS CURRICULUM
▶ **Language Arts:** Have students use a dictionary to find the origin of the word *electricity*. It comes from the Greek *elektron*, which is petrified tree resin, or amber. When amber is rubbed with a piece of cloth, it will attract small particles of paper or leaves.

21-1 Electric Charge

New Science Words
static electricity
electric field
conductor
insulator
electroscope

Objectives
▶ Describe the effects of static electricity.
▶ Distinguish between conductors and insulators.
▶ Recognize the presence of charge in an electroscope.

Static Electricity

Have you ever walked across a carpeted floor and been shocked by a spark as you reached out to touch something? If you immediately touched the object a second time, you might have felt a very small spark or none at all. If you shuffled your feet on the carpet again, you might have felt a larger spark again. What caused this startling and sometimes painful phenomenon?

When your feet rubbed on the carpet, some of the atoms in the carpet were disturbed. Recall from Chapter 10 that atoms contain protons, neutrons, and electrons. Neutrons have no charge, protons are positively charged, and electrons are negatively charged. An atom is electrically neutral if it has an equal number of protons and electrons. Sometimes electrons are not held tightly in the atom. For example, as you walked on the carpet some electrons that were loosely held by the atoms rubbed from the carpet onto your shoes. As a result, your shoes gained electrons, and they were no longer neutral, but instead had a negative charge. The carpet lost electrons, leaving it positively charged. The excess electrons, stored in your body, gave you an overall negative electric charge. This is an example of static electricity. **Static electricity** is the accumulation of electric charges on an object. Can you think of any other examples of static electricity?

Have you noticed how a sock will sometimes cling to your shirt when removed from the dryer? Electrons can be rubbed off some clothes while they are tumbling around inside the dryer. Clothes that gain electrons become negatively charged, whereas those that lose electrons become positively charged. Clothes with opposite charges cling together, but clothes with the same charge

Figure 21-1. When charges are brought together, opposite charges attract and like charges repel.

Opposite charges attract

Like charges repel

Like charges repel

546 ELECTRICITY

OPTIONS

Meeting Different Ability Levels

For Section 21-1, use the following **Teacher Resource Masters** depending upon individual students' needs.
◆ **Study Guide Master** for all students.
● **Reinforcement Master** for students of average and above average ability levels.
▲ **Enrichment Master** for above average students.
Additional Teacher Resource Package masters are listed in any PROGRAM RESOURCES that are in the section. The additional masters are appropriate for all students.

repel each other. Electrically charged objects obey the following rule: opposite charges attract, and like charges repel.

Charged objects can cause electrons to rearrange their position on a neutral object. For example, suppose you charge a balloon by rubbing it with a cloth. If you bring the negatively charged balloon near your sleeve, the extra electrons on the balloon will repel the electrons in the sleeve. The electrons near the surface will move away from the balloon, leaving a positively charged area on the surface of the sleeve. As a result, the negatively charged balloon will attract the positively charged area of the sleeve. The rearrangement of electrons on a neutral object caused by a nearby charged object is called charging by induction.

How can an electron exert a force on a particle that is some distance away? It does this by setting up an **electric field** in space. This electric field exerts a force on anything that has an electric charge. The electric field is strongest near the electron and becomes weaker as the distance from the electron increases.

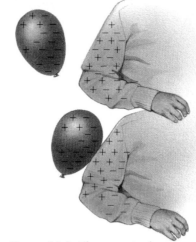

Figure 21-2. The negatively charged balloon induces a positively charged area in the sleeve by repelling its electrons.

Conductors and Insulators

You now know you can build up a negative charge by walking across a carpet. Suppose you then could touch either a wooden door or a metal doorknob. Which one would you prefer to touch? If your choice was the metal doorknob, be prepared to feel a spark.

When you put your finger near the doorknob, the electric field between your finger and the knob became so strong that it pulled electrons out of molecules in the air. These molecules became positively charged ions. Movement of these ions and the electrons created the spark you saw and felt.

The electrons can move through your body to the metal doorknob because both your body and the metal are conductors. A **conductor** is a material that allows electrons to move easily through it. Metals such as copper and silver are made of atoms that don't hold their electrons tightly, so electrons can move easily through materials made up of these kinds of atoms. For this reason, electric wires are usually made of copper, a good conductor. Silver wire also conducts electricity very well, but silver is much more expensive than copper.

MINI-Lab
Can static charge move things?
Get a piece of plastic food wrap, about 30 cm by 30 cm. Lay it on a tabletop and smooth it down flat with a cotton cloth. Use a paper punch to make round chips of aluminum foil. Put the foil chips in a pile in the center of the plastic wrap. Lift the plastic wrap slowly from the table and observe the response of the aluminum. *Observe* how the aluminum chips react to the plastic. How do they react to each other? Would paper chips respond the same way? How would you summarize the behavior of electrically charged objects?

547

2 TEACH

Key Concepts are highlighted.

CONCEPT DEVELOPMENT

▶ When discussing static discharges, reinforce the idea that only electrons move from one object to another to cause overall positive and negative charges in the objects.

MINI QUIZ

Use the Mini Quiz to check students' recall of chapter content.

① **The buildup of charges on an object is called _____ .** *static electricity*

② **Electrons move easily through materials called _____ and do not move easily through materials called _____ .** *conductors, insulators*

③ **What is the region around the balloon where you notice electric forces acting on other particles called?** *electric field*

MINI-Lab

Materials: plastic wrap, cotton cloth, paper punch, aluminum foil

Teaching Tips

▶ Pull back the plastic wrap *slowly*.

▶ Overhead projector film can be used in place of food wrap.

▶ **Answers:** The chips do not respond until the plastic is lifted because charging the plastic by rubbing induces an opposite charge in the tabletop. Chips that fly off received the plastic's charge by *conduction*. Those that stick have an opposite charge by *induction*.

▶ Most chips repel each other because they have the same charge.

▶ Paper chips respond the same.

▶ Like charges repel and unlike charges attract.

MINI-Lab
ASSESSMENT

Content: Have students explain charging by friction, conduction, and induction.

► The chimpanzee was injured when the electric current passed from the wire through his body and the aluminum ladder to the ground.
Think Critically: The sparrows are not injured sitting on the power lines because they are too small to touch two wires, or one wire and the ground at the same time. In other words, they are not grounded.

STUDENT TEXT QUESTION

► Page 548, paragraph 1: **Would you expect static discharge to occur if you touched the wooden door instead of the metal doorknob?** *no*

CHECK FOR UNDERSTANDING

► Instruct the class to watch while you touch a charged electroscope with your finger. The leaves fall to neutral position. Your finger and body act as a ground to absorb or donate electrons to remove the charge in the electroscope. Have students write a short explanation of this at their desks and ask for volunteers to share their ideas.

► Ask questions 1-2 and the **Apply** and **Connect to Chemistry** questions in the Section Review.

Connect to...
Earth Science

Answer: Earth has an enormous supply of positive and negative charges. Excess electrons are attracted by positive particles and do not change the overall charge of Earth significantly.

 P R O B L E M   S O L V I N G

How Can Birds Perch on Power Lines?

As Maria was watching television one evening, she saw an advertisement on the dangers of electric power lines. The advertisement showed a man climbing an aluminum ladder to saw off some tree branches near some power lines. Near the top of the ladder, he reached for the branches and the ladder began to wobble. Unbalanced, he reached out toward the power lines for support.

Just before he grasped the power lines, the man turned into a chimpanzee and the television screen went blank. A message then appeared on the screen warning people not to monkey around with power lines.

The next day, Maria noticed several sparrows perching on a high voltage power line. She thought about the advertisement she had seen on television and wondered how the birds could safely perch on a power line. Explain why the advertisement inferred that the man was injured by electric current when he grabbed the power lines.

Think Critically: How could the sparrows perch on the power line without getting injured?

Connect to...
Earth Science

Why is Earth used to ground objects? Where do the grounded charges go?

What covers the metal wires in cords attached to telephones and other household appliances? They are usually coated with some type of plastic, an insulating material. An **insulator** is a material that doesn't allow electrons to move through it easily. In addition to plastic, wood, rubber, and glass are good insulators. Would you expect static discharge to occur if you touched the wooden door instead of the metal doorknob?

The largest object you touch is Earth. Earth contains a large supply of electrons and functions as a conductor of electricity. It is sometimes desirable to provide a path for the static discharge to reach Earth. An object connected to Earth, or the ground, by a good conductor is said to be grounded. Look around you. Do you see anything that might act as a path to the ground? Plumbing fixtures, such as metal faucets, sinks, and pipes, often provide a convenient ground connection.

548 ELECTRICITY

OPTIONS

INQUIRY QUESTIONS

► If electric charges cause the attraction between socks in your dryer, do you think this electricity could be used to run your portable tape player? Why or why not? *No. The movement, or discharge, of electricity happens rapidly and does not continue. It could not be used as a continuous supply of energy.*

ENRICHMENT

► Have interested students investigate Coulomb's law, the relationship between the electric force, charge, and distance between two charged objects. Coulomb's law is an inverse square law similar to Newton's law of gravitation.

The Electroscope

The presence of electric charges can be detected by an **electroscope.** An electroscope is made of two thin metal leaves attached to a metal rod with a knob at the top. The leaves are allowed to swing freely from the metal rod. When the device is not charged, the leaves hang straight down.

Suppose a negatively charged balloon touches the knob. Because the metal is a good conductor, electrons travel down the rod into the leaves. Both leaves become negatively charged as they gain electrons. Because the leaves have similar charges, they repel each other.

If a glass rod is rubbed with silk, electrons leave the glass rod and build up on the silk. The glass rod becomes positively charged. When the positively charged glass rod is touched to the metal knob, electrons are conducted out of the metal leaves and onto the rod. The leaves repel each other because each leaf becomes positively charged as it loses electrons.

Can you think of any other effects of static electricity you have seen? Can you explain them in terms of like or opposite charges? How do objects become charged, and what happens when they discharge?

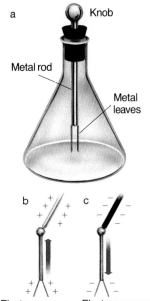

Figure 21-3. Notice the position of the leaves on the electroscope when they are uncharged (a), positively charged (b), and negatively charged (c).

SECTION REVIEW

1. What is static electricity?
2. Distinguish between electrical conductors and insulators and give an example of each.
3. **Apply:** Assume you have already charged an electroscope with a positively charged glass rod. Hypothesize what would happen if you touched the knob again with another positively charged object.
4. **Connect to Chemistry:** Explain why metals are typically much better conductors than nonmetals.

☑ Observing and Inferring

Suppose that you observe the individual hairs on your arm rise up when a balloon is placed near them. Using the concept of induction and the rules of electricity, what could you infer about the cause of this phenomenon? If you need help, refer to Observing and Inferring in the **Skill Handbook** on page 678.

Skill Builder

PROGRAM RESOURCES

From the **Teacher Resource Package** use:
Activity Worksheets, page 173, MINI Lab: Can static charge move things?

Skill Builder
ASSESSMENT
Oral: Ask students if the arm has a net charge in this case. Discuss the difference between a net charge and separation of charges.

RETEACH

Carefully demonstrate the function of the electroscope again, using a diagram to show positive and negative areas. Have a student rub a glass rod with silk, so the electrons leave the glass rod and build up on the silk. Touch the electroscope with the glass rod. **Why do the leaves split apart?** *Electrons flow from the leaves into the glass rod. The leaves are positive and repel each other.*

EXTENSION

For students who have mastered this section, use the **Reinforcement** and **Enrichment** masters or other OPTIONS provided.

3 CLOSE

▶ Charge up a Van de Graaff generator. Slowly approach the dome with a lit match. The match will go out. Have students work in pairs to offer an explanation for this phenomenon. The oxygen atoms in the flame are ionized and are attracted or repelled by the generator, creating a wind that blows out the match.

SECTION REVIEW ANSWERS

1. the accumulation of electric charges on an object.
2. A conductor is a material that allows electrons to move easily through it, such as copper and silver. An insulator is a material that doesn't allow electrons to pass easily through it, such as plastic, wood, rubber, and glass.
3. Apply: The leaves might spread farther apart.
4. Connect to Chemistry: Atoms in metals hold electrons loosely. They can easily move through the material.

Skill Builder
The attraction between the balloon and the hairs on your arm was caused by opposite charges. The negatively charged balloon induced a positive charge on the surface of your arm by repelling electrons.

PREPARATION

SECTION BACKGROUND
▶ A bolt of lightning is so high in energy and happens so fast that it can have 3 750 000 000 kW of power. The surrounding air temperature can rise by 30 000°C.

PREPLANNING:
▶ Try to obtain a Wimshurst machine for the Reteach demonstration.

1 MOTIVATE

▶ Ask students how they think most forest fires are started. They will say careless campers, smokers, and perhaps lightning. Ask them to think of a good reason why a park ranger might decide to let a lightning-induced fire burn.

VideoDisc
STVS: Lightning; Disc 1, Side 1

2 TEACH

Key Concepts are highlighted.

CONCEPT DEVELOPMENT
▶ Draw a diagram on the chalkboard showing how a negative area in a cloud can induce a positive charge near Earth's surface. After the discharge, the cloud and Earth's surface are neutral again.

Connect to...
Chemistry

Answer: In ionization, enough energy is added to an atom to remove one or more electrons from it.

 **21-2** # Lightning—Its Causes and Effects

New Science Words

lightning rod

Objectives

▶ Explain the occurrence of lightning in terms of induction and static discharge.
▶ Evaluate the positive and negative aspects of lightning-induced forest fires.

Should Lightning-Induced Forest Fires Be Left to Burn?

Have you ever seen lightning strike Earth? Lightning is actually a very large discharge of static electricity. The air currents in a cloud can build up areas of positive and negative charges, just as scuffing your feet on a carpet builds opposite charges in you and the carpet. If the bottom portion of a cloud has a negative charge, it can induce a positive charge on Earth's surface. As the difference in charge increases, electrons may be attracted toward the positively charged ground. A lightning bolt occurs when many electrons are transferred at the same time. Each lightning bolt that strikes Earth may carry several billion billion electrons!

Much of the lightning you see doesn't strike Earth's surface. Electrons can also move through lightning bolts from the negative area of one cloud to the positive area of another cloud. The electrical energy in a lightning bolt ionizes atoms in the atmosphere and produces great amounts of heat. The heat causes the air in the bolt's path to expand very rapidly, producing thunder. Have you ever tried to time the difference between the flash of light and the loud crack of thunder in a thunderstorm? Because sound travels much slower than light, you see the lightning flash before you hear the crack or rumble of the thunder.

The sudden discharge of so much electricity can be quite dangerous. Lightning strikes Earth many times

550 ELECTRICITY

OPTIONS

Meeting Different Ability Levels
For Section 21-2, use the following **Teacher Resource Masters** depending upon individual students' needs.
◆ **Study Guide Master** for all students.
● **Reinforcement Master** for students of average and above average ability levels.
▲ **Enrichment Master** for above average students.
Additional Teacher Resource Package masters are listed in any PROGRAM RESOURCES boxes that are in the section. The additional masters are appropriate for all students.

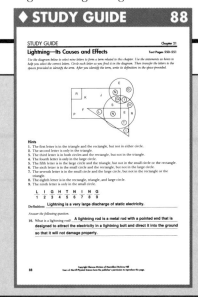

◆ **STUDY GUIDE** **88**

each day. If it strikes a populated area, it can cause power outages, fires, or even injury or loss of life. One way to prevent lightning damage is to provide a path for the electrons to travel to the ground. Many buildings have lightning rods. A **lightning rod** is a pointed metal rod that extends above the highest part of a structure with a cable that connects the rod to the ground. Lightning will strike the rod and the electric current will be carried harmlessly to the ground.

Lightning is also responsible for an important cycle in Earth's forests. You have probably seen news reports about huge forest fires burning out of control in dry regions. Many of these fires were started by lightning. Often, the flames creep along the ground and don't destroy large healthy trees. In order to protect the beauty of our national parks and wilderness areas, these fires were promptly extinguished. However, it became evident to ecologists that nature's cycle of growth and renewal might not be consistent with the human version of natural beauty. Therefore, laws were passed in the 1970s to allow fires started by lightning to burn naturally unless they threaten people or private property.

Many people were upset in 1989 when one-third of Yellowstone National Park was burned. However, suppressing fires can allow dead debris to accumulate in the forest, and increase the risk of a rapidly spreading natural fire. Perhaps protecting the forest by putting out fires from lightning doesn't preserve a forest as well as allowing nature to take its course.

Connect to... Chemistry

Lightning ionizes oxygen in the atmosphere and leads to the formation of ozone, O_3. Describe the process of ionization.

SECTION REVIEW

1. How are lightning and thunder produced?
2. What is the purpose of a lightning rod?
3. **Connect to Life Science:** Describe the possible effects of a forest fire on animal life in the vicinity of the fire.

You Decide!

Suppose a lightning storm has started a large fire in Yosemite National Park in California. Should it be allowed to burn along its natural course, or should it be put out to preserve areas for human and wildlife use? Would your decision be different if the fire were caused by careless campers?

SCIENCE & SOCIETY

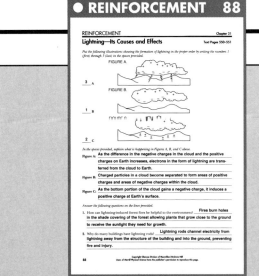

551

CHECK FOR UNDERSTANDING
Ask students to diagram how an ordinary TV antenna might function as a lightning rod. If lightning does strike, it would be drawn through the antenna and to the ground.

RETEACH
Use a Wimshurst machine to show how charge leaks off a metal point to avoid a large discharge of electricity. Small spheres can hold only small amounts of charge before discharging, so a large charge cannot build up. This is the reason lightning rods and antennas have small metal spheres on their tips.

EXTENSION
For students who have mastered this section, use the **Reinforcement** and **Enrichment** masters or other OPTIONS provided.

3 CLOSE

▶ Ask questions 1-2 and the **Connect to Life Science** question in the Section Review.
▶ Use the You Decide question to analyze the controversial question of natural forest fires.

SECTION REVIEW ANSWERS

1. Lightning is a static discharge between negative areas and positive areas. Thunder is produced by the rapid expansion of air due to the heat of the discharge.

2. A lightning rod acts as a ground.

3. Connect to Life Science: Animals might be killed by the fire. They could escape to nearby unburned areas, but this could change the natural balance of animal life in those areas. Also, if animals survive the fire itself, the food supply could become a problem.

SCIENCE & SOCIETY

YOU DECIDE!

Answers will vary. You might divide the class into groups to debate this issue.

PREPARATION

SECTION BACKGROUND

▶ In 1800, an Italian physicist named Alessandro Volta observed that two metals connected by a conducting liquid produced a continuous transfer of electrons. This phenomenon was different from the rapid static discharge observed by Ben Franklin. This moving electric charge was later called an electric current.

1 MOTIVATE

▶ Obtain a fresh lemon, new penny, and a silver dime (before 1965). Attach an alligator clip to each coin and insert the coins about 2 cm apart into the lemon. Use the leads from the coins to connect a piezoelectric buzzer to complete the circuit. Ask students what makes the buzzer go off.

VideoDisc
STVS: Battery Science; Disc 2, Side 2

New Science Words

potential difference
circuit
current
dry cell
wet cell
resistance
Ohm's law

Objectives

▶ Describe how the potential energy of an electron changes as it moves through a simple circuit.
▶ Explain how a dry cell is a source of electricity.
▶ Conceptually and mathematically relate potential difference, resistance, and current.

Flowing Electrons

You read in Section 21-1 that if you touch a conductor after building up a negative charge in your body, electrons will move from you to the conductor. Could you light a bulb in this manner? Probably not, because the static discharge occurs for an instant and then stops. The bulb needs a continuous flow of electrons to stay lit. Why does the static discharge stop so suddenly?

Recall from Chapter 5 that heat flows from objects with higher temperatures to objects with lower temperatures. Heat ceases to flow when the temperatures of the objects become the same. Similarly, a negatively charged object has electrons with more potential energy to move and do work than those of an uncharged object. This difference in potential energy causes the electrons to flow from places of higher potential energy to those with lower potential energy. In a static discharge, the potentials quickly become equal and electron flow stops.

The potential energy difference per unit of charge is called the electrical potential. The difference in potential between two different places is the **potential difference.** Potential difference is measured in volts, (V). Potential difference, often called voltage, is measured by a voltmeter. The voltage doesn't depend on the number of electrons flowing, but on a comparison of the energy carried by electrons at different points.

How can you get electrons to flow through a lamp continuously? You must connect it in an electric circuit. A **circuit** is a closed path through which electrons can flow. Because the lamp is part of a circuit, there is a potential

How does the electric potential energy of a negatively charged object compare to that of an uncharged object?

OPTIONS

Meeting Different Ability Levels

For Section 21-3, use the following **Teacher Resource Masters** depending upon individual students' needs.

◆ **Study Guide Master** for all students.
● **Reinforcement Master** for students of average and above average ability levels.
▲ **Enrichment Master** for above average students.

Additional Teacher Resource Package masters are listed in any PROGRAM RESOURCES that are in the section. The additional masters are appropriate for all students.

◆ **STUDY GUIDE** 89

STUDY GUIDE — Chapter 21
Electric Current — Text Pages 552–559

In the blank at the left, write the letter of the term that best completes each statement.

b 1. Voltage is a measure of the ____ between two places.
   a. resistance potential   b. potential difference
b 2. A closed path through which electrons can flow is ____.
   a. voltage   b. a circuit
a 3. Potential difference is measured in ____.
   a. volts   b. amperes
a 4. The flow of electrons through a wire or any conductor is called ____.
   a. current   b. a circuit
b 5. Because has a potential difference between the positive and negative terminals, a ____ can act as an electron pump.
   a. voltmeter   b. dry cell
a 6. A car battery is an example of a ____.
   a. wet cell   b. dry cell
b 7. The tendency for a material to oppose the flow of electrons is called ____.
   a. voltage   b. resistance
b 8. Resistance is measured in units called ____.
   a. volts   b. ohms
b 9. Current is measured in ____.
   a. volts   b. amperes
a 10. The equation I = V/R mathematically expresses ____.
   a. Ohm's law   b. current law
a 11. The symbol Ω means ____.
   a. ohm   b. ampere
b 12. In the equation I = V/R, I stands for ____.
   a. potential difference   b. current
b 13. In the equation I = V/R, V stands for ____.
   a. potential difference   b. current
a 14. Thin wires have a ____ resistance to electron flow than do thicker wires.
   a. greater   b. lesser
b 15. Potential difference is measured with ____.
   a. an electroscope   b. a voltmeter

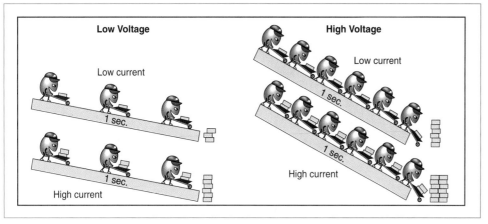

Low Voltage	High Voltage
Low current	Low current
1 sec.	1 sec.
	1 sec.
1 sec.	High current
High current	

Figure 21-4. The amount of energy delivered each second in a circuit, or the rate of electron flow, depends on the number of electrons and how much energy each electron carries.

difference across it. If the lamp is turned on, electrons will move through it causing it to produce light. The electrons will continue to flow in the circuit as long as there is a potential difference and the path of the flowing electrons is unbroken.

The flow of electrons through a wire or any conductor is called **current.** The amount of electric current depends on the number of electrons passing a point in a given time. The current in a circuit is measured in amperes (A). One ampere is one coulomb of charge flowing past a point in one second. One coulomb is the charge carried by 6.24 billion billion electrons. Current is measured with an ammeter.

In order to keep the current moving through a circuit, there must be a device that maintains a potential difference. One common source of potential difference is a battery. Unlike a static discharge from your finger to a doorknob, a battery can light a lamp by maintaining a potential difference in the circuit.

What is current?

What keeps current moving through a circuit?

Batteries

Have you ever noticed how a tape begins to drag in a portable tape player after using it for several hours? Perhaps you decided the batteries were dead and replaced them. Do you know why batteries are required to operate your tape player?

You probably have the option of plugging your tape player into a wall outlet or using batteries to supply the

OBJECTIVES AND SCIENCE WORDS: Have students review the objectives and science words to become familiar with this section.

2 TEACH

Key Concepts are highlighted.

CONCEPT DEVELOPMENT

▶ Have a stereo music box in front of the room. Ask students what you need to make the stereo work. They will say plug it in or use batteries. **What do batteries and the wall outlet have in common?** *They both supply electric current to the stereo.*

▶ Use Figure 21-4 to explain potential difference and current in a way that is easier for the students to understand. Have them brainstorm some analogies that could represent the same idea.

● **REINFORCEMENT** 89

▲ **ENRICHMENT** 89

CONCEPT DEVELOPMENT

▶ Obtain a flashlight battery and take it to the shop room. Have it cut lengthwise to reveal the carbon rod, zinc case, and electrolyte paste inside. Some of these chemicals are corrosive, so seal the two halves in a plastic bag to pass around to the class.

REVEALING MISCONCEPTIONS

▶ People commonly refer to single dry cells as batteries. Technically, a battery is actually more than one dry cell or wet cell connected in series. Most devices use more than one cell to supply electric power, so *battery-operated* is a correct term.

Science and READING

Accidents involving car batteries have become more frequent and serious in recent years. Point out the precautions and the steps to be followed in jump starting a dead car battery. These should be listed in the owner's manual.

MULTICULTURAL PERSPECTIVE

A Powerful Pioneer

In 1918, the Edison Pioneers was formed to honor some of the people who worked with Thomas Edison as the "creators of the electric industry." One member was the son of a freed slave. Lewis H. Latimer was born in 1848 in Massachusetts, taught himself to be a draftsman when he was a teenager, and convinced a businessman to hire him. The office Latimer worked in was near a school where Alexander Graham Bell was developing a device so his deaf, mute wife could hear him. Latimer prepared the drawings that Bell needed to patent the telephone. In 1879, Latimer was hired by the United States Electric Lighting Company where he invented and patented the first carbon filament electric lamp and invented an inexpensive way to produce the filaments. In 1883, he joined Edison, and in 1890 he published the first textbook on electrical lighting.

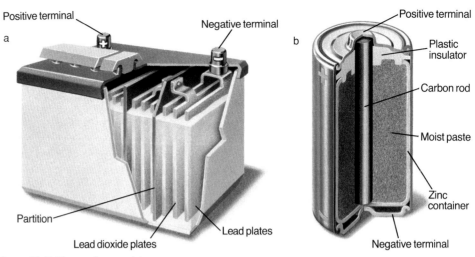

Figure 21-5. The car battery (a) is a series of wet cells, and the dry cell (b) can be connected in series with other dry cells to form a larger battery.

Science and READING

Read an automobile owner's manual to see if it explains how to "jump start" a car with a discharged battery. Explain this process to your classmates.

energy it needs to operate. If you want to take the tape player outside, you will have to use dry cell batteries. Look at the dry cell shown in Figure 21-5b. Can you locate the positive and negative terminals of the dry cell in the diagram? They are located at opposite ends. Notice that the zinc container of the dry cell contains a moist chemical paste with a solid carbon rod suspended in the middle. The carbon rod forms the positive terminal of the dry cell, and the zinc container forms the negative terminal. A **dry cell** can act as an electron pump because it has a potential difference between the positive and negative terminals. ❷

When the two terminals of the battery are connected in a circuit, electrons are released from the carbon rod as a chemical reaction occurs between the zinc and the chemical paste. The carbon rod becomes positive, forming the positive (+) terminal of the battery. Extra electrons accumulate on the zinc, making it negative (-). The potential difference between these two terminals causes current to flow through the closed circuit. As long as the chemical reaction continues, electrons are pumped from the negative terminal to the positive terminal of the dry cell. Two or more cells can be connected together to produce a higher voltage. How many dry cells does your tape player or camera require?

Another way to operate your tape player is by plugging it into a wall socket. The potential difference between

OPTIONS

ASSESSMENT—ORAL

▶ **How is a dry cell (or battery) similar to a wall socket?** *They both provide potential difference to cause a current.*

▶ **Why do some electrical devices require more than one battery?** *Multiple cells create the higher voltage (and current) needed to operate the device.*

two holes in a wall socket is usually 120 V. The electricity coming out of the wall socket is provided by an electric generator, instead of a battery.

Batteries can also be wet cells. A **wet cell** contains two connected plates made of different metals or metallic compounds in an electrolyte solution. One of the most common wet cell batteries is a car battery. Most car batteries contain a series of wet cells made up of lead and lead dioxide plates in a sulfuric acid solution, as shown in Figure 21-5a. As a chemical reaction occurs between the lead and the sulfuric acid inside the battery, electrons move from the lead plates through the conductor to the lead dioxide plates. As a result, a negative terminal with an excess of electrons and a positive terminal with a shortage of electrons form. This potential difference produces a current in the circuit between the battery and various parts of the car. Can you think of any other situations where wet cell batteries are used?

Resistance

One function of the car battery mentioned earlier is to light various light bulbs in the car's electric circuits. Do you know what makes a light bulb glow? Look at the light bulb in Figure 21-6. Part of the circuit through the bulb contains a filament. As a current flows through the filament, electrical energy is converted by the filament into light and heat. The current loses electrical energy as it moves through the filament because the filament, as do most materials, resists the flow of electrons.

 Resistance is the tendency for a material to oppose the flow of electrons. With the exception of a few substances that become superconductors at very low temperatures, all conductors have some resistance. The amount of resistance varies with each conductor. Resistance is measured in ohms (Ω).

Figure 21-6. The light bulb and the heater glow and give off heat as current moves through them because they each have a high resistance to the flow of electrons.

How does a car battery maintain a potential difference in a circuit?

Connect to... Chemistry

In a car battery, also called a lead storage battery, the following chemical reaction occurs: $Pb + PbO_2 + H_2SO_4 \rightarrow PbSO_4 + H_2O$. Use coefficients to balance this equation.

CONCEPT DEVELOPMENT

▶ Usually, the resistance of conductors increases with increasing temperature because the atoms are moving more. In carbon, however, the electrons are separated from their atoms at high temperature. As a result, electric current is increased and resistance is decreased.

▶ Wet appliances are a hazard because ions in normal tap water make the electrical resistance lower. If your hand contacts the appliance near a wet switch, the low resistance allows a high current to pass through your body.

STUDENT TEXT QUESTION

▶ Page 555, paragraph 2: **Can you think of any other situations where wet cell batteries are used?** boats

? FLEX Your Brain

Use the Flex Your Brain activity to have students explore BATTERIES.

ASSESSMENT

Portfolio: Use the Flex Your Brain activity to reinforce critical-thinking and problem-solving skills. In Step 2, students might list kinds of batteries they use, how long a battery lasts, or differences in sizes and shapes of batteries.

Connect to... Chemistry

Answer:
$Pb(cr) + PbO_2(cr) + 2H_2SO_4\ (aq) \rightarrow 2PbSO_4(cr) + H_2O(l)$

PROGRAM RESOURCES

From the **Teacher Resource Package** use:

Critical Thinking/Problem Solving, page 27, Are Electric Cars Practical?

Science and Society, page 25, Electricity and Safety.

Activity Worksheets, page 5, Flex Your Brain.

Science Integration Activity 21

Use **Laboratory Manual 43,** Wet Cell Battery.

CONCEPT DEVELOPMENT

▶ **Demonstration:** Set up a wet cell and show that it produces a current by connecting it to an ammeter. There are a number of wet cells possible; a simple one consists of copper metal in a copper sulfate solution connected to zinc in a zinc chloride solution. Connect the two electrodes through an ammeter and place a salt bridge between the beakers of the two solutions. A salt bridge can be made by filling a U-shaped tube with a salt solution and loosely plugging both ends with cotton.

▶ Purchase a two-potato clock from Edmund Scientific Co. You can power a digital clock from two potatoes.

▶ Punch three holes in a vertical line in the side of a coffee can, evenly spaced from the bottom to the top. Fill it with water and observe how the water comes out of the holes. The bottom hole shoots water the farthest, because it is under the most pressure. Draw an analogy between this and the fact that when the potential difference is large (electrical pressure), the current is also large (assuming resistance is the same).

CROSS CURRICULUM

▶ **Biology:** Have students find out why *Torpedo nobiliana* is commonly called the electric eel. **How does it produce its electrical current?** *Because its numerous cell membranes are connected in parallel, it can produce a 1-A current at 600 V.*

TECHNOLOGY

To find out more about shake and bake superconductors, see Maranto, Gina. "Superconductivity: Hype Vs. Reality." *Discover.* August 1987, pp 22-32.
Think Critically: The superconductors require low temperatures, and the power used for refrigeration would count toward the total power loss.

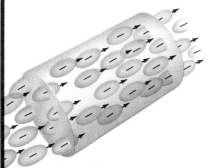

Figure 21-7. A short, thick piece of wire has less resistance than a long, thin piece of wire.

Copper is an excellent conductor; it has low resistance to the flow of electrons. Copper is used in household wiring because very little electrical energy is converted to thermal energy as current passes through the wires. In contrast, tungsten wire glows white-hot as current passes through it. Tungsten's high resistance to current makes it very suitable for use as filaments in light bulbs.

The size of wires also affects their resistance. Figure 21-7 illustrates how electrons have more room to travel through thick wires than thin wires. In wires of the same

TECHNOLOGY

Shake and Bake Superconductors

Mix together some oxides of lanthanum, barium, and copper, grind them up, and bake them in a furnace with some oxygen and, presto, you have made your own superconductor. After you cool your superconductor to its critical temperature, it will offer very little resistance and produce very little heat as electrons flow through it. The first superconductors were cooled to temperatures near absolute zero (–273°C) to achieve these results. However, your "shake and bake" compound will become superconductive at a comparatively warm –178°C. In other words, your superconductor can be cooled easier and with less expense than the first superconductors.

The future of these new superconductive materials is promising and challenging. First, however, we must find ways to fashion these brittle superconducting materials into wires and thin films. The rewards of

solving these problems are tremendous. For example, high powered electric cars, magnetically levitated trains, super fast computers, and extremely efficient power transmission might become realities.

Think Critically: Even though superconductive materials lose very little energy as heat, a power transmission system using these new superconductors would not be energy-loss free. Where would these energy losses occur?

OPTIONS

ENRICHMENT

▶ Have students find out why it is desirable to have resistors in some circuits, even though they don't appear to do any work (light a bulb, turn a motor, and so on).

INQUIRY QUESTIONS

▶ **Form a hypothesis to explain why the resistance of a conductor usually increases with temperature.** *Atoms have more kinetic energy at higher temperatures, and this motion creates more resistance to the flow of the charge.*

Figure 21-8. As the height of the hose increases, the potential difference increases and water flows at a faster rate. Electrons also flow at a faster rate when the potential difference in a circuit is increased.

length and material, thinner wires have greater resistance to electron flow. Likewise, if the diameters of two wires of the same material are the same, the longer wire offers a greater resistance. In most conductors, the resistance also increases as the temperature increases.

Ohm's Law

When you try to understand the relationship between voltage, current, and resistance, it is helpful to think of the way water behaves in a pipe. If one end of the pipe is higher than the other, there is a difference in the potential energy of the water due to gravity, and pressure at the nozzle increases. This causes a stream, or current, of water to flow. If the height difference increases, the current increases. In a similar way, a greater potential difference in a circuit also causes the electric current to increase. Also, just as the walls and any obstructions in the pipe resist the flow of water, atoms in a wire resist the flow of electricity. As a result, the current in a circuit depends on both the voltage and the resistance.

George Simon Ohm, a German physicist, found experimentally that the current in a metal conductor is directly proportional to the potential difference across its ends and inversely proportional to the resistance. This is expressed mathematically in the equation called **Ohm's law:**

Potential difference = current × resistance

$$V \text{ (volts)} = I \text{ (amperes)} \times R \text{ (ohms)}$$

④

21-3 ELECTRIC CURRENT **557**

Did You Know?

The highest synthetic potential difference ever achieved was more than 30 million volts.

1. $I = \dfrac{V}{R} = \dfrac{12\ V}{20\ \Omega} = 0.6\ A$

$I = \dfrac{6\ V}{20\ \Omega} = 0.3\ A$

2. $R = \dfrac{V}{I} = \dfrac{120\ V}{1.5\ A} = 80\ \Omega$

3 CLOSE

▶ Set up a simple circuit by connecting a dry cell (or power source), a variable resistor, and a small light bulb. Have students explain what happens to the current and potential difference as you vary the resistance.

▶ Explain that there are two main ways parts of a circuit can be connected, and these will be discussed in the next section.

SECTION REVIEW ANSWERS

1. A circuit has continuous current provided by a voltage source. A static discharge happens very rapidly. Both are caused by potential difference.

2. A chemical reaction causes a negative charge on the zinc terminal and a positive charge on the carbon rod. This creates a potential difference and causes a current.

3. $V = IR = (0.3A)(25\ \Omega) = 7.5\ V$

4. Apply: The current is halved. It has no effect on the current.

5. Connect to Chemistry: Because copper is an excellent conductor, you would expect tungsten to have a higher resistance. The tungsten filament gives off heat and light because resistance converts some electrical energy to thermal energy and electromagnetic radiation.

EXAMPLE PROBLEM: Calculating Current

Problem Statement:
Strategy Hint: Make sure the decimal is correctly placed.

A light bulb with a resistance of 160 Ω is plugged into a 120-V outlet. What is the current flowing through the bulb?

Known Information:
resistance, $R = 160\ \Omega$
voltage, $V = 120\ V$

Unknown Information:
current (I)

Equation to Use:
$I = V/R$

Solution:
$I = V/R = 120\ V/160\ \Omega = 0.75\ A$

PRACTICE PROBLEMS

Strategy Hint: Your answer will be in amperes.

1. Find the current flowing through a 20-Ω wire connected to a 12-V battery. What if it were connected to a 6-V battery?

Strategy Hint: Your answer will be in ohms. Use $R = V/I$.

2. The current flowing through a lamp is 1.5 A. It is plugged into a 120-V outlet. What is the resistance of the lamp?

SECTION REVIEW

1. How does a current traveling through a circuit differ from the static discharge?
2. Briefly describe how a carbon-zinc dry cell supplies electricity for your tape player.
3. Calculate the potential difference across a 25-Ω resistor if a 0.3-A current is flowing through it.
4. **Apply:** How is the current in a circuit affected if the resistance is doubled? What if both the voltage and resistance are doubled?
5. **Connect to Chemistry:** Which would you expect to have higher resistance—the copper wire in the cord of a lamp or the tungsten filament in the lamp's bulb? What observable evidence supports your conclusion?

Skill Builder

☑ Making and Using Tables

Suppose you individually connect three copper wires of unequal length to a 1.5-V dry cell and an ammeter. The following currents were obtained: wire 1, 1.2 A; wire 2, 1.4 A; wire 3, 1.1 A. Make a table showing current (given) and resistance (use Ohm's law). If you need help, refer to Making and Using Tables in the **Skill Handbook** on page 686.

Skill Builder

Students should use the equation, $R = V/I$, to calculate the resistance needed to complete the table for each of the three wires.

Wire	Current (A)	Resistance (Ω)
1	1.2A	1.3 Ω
2	1.4A	1.1 Ω
3	1.1A	1.4 Ω

Skill Builder
ASSESSMENT
Performance: Have students use the data in their table to predict the relative lengths (longest, medium length, shortest) of the wires. Record this in a fourth column. The length is directly proportional to resistance, so the higher the resistance, the longer the wire.

Modeling Ohm's Law

After several hours of use, batteries may go dead. What has changed in the batteries? For the batteries to cause a current in your stereo, there must be a potential difference across the ends of the batteries. In this activity, you will use gravitational potential energy and water to model potential difference and current in an electric circuit.

Materials
- plastic funnel
- ring stand with ring
- rubber tubing (1 m)
- meterstick
- 2 beakers (250 mL)
- stopwatch or clock

Procedure
1. *Create a data table* like the one below.
2. Assemble the apparatus as shown. Place the funnel as high as possible.
3. *Measure* the height from the top of the funnel to the outlet end of the rubber tubing, in meters. *Record* your data on the table.
4. Pour 200 mL water into the funnel fast enough to keep it full, but not overflowing.
5. *Measure* the time for 0.10 L water to flow into the lower beaker, and *record* it.
6. Repeat Steps 2 through 4 at least three more times, lowering the funnel for each trial.

Data and Observations Sample Data

Trial	Height (m)	Time (s)	Rate (L/s)
1	0.60	10	0.010
2	0.50	12	0.0083
3	0.40	15	0.0067

Analyze
1. Gravity causing water to move can be compared to voltage causing electrons to move. Which trial can represent a circuit with the highest voltage?
2. The rate (L/sec) of flow of water from the tubing can be compared to current. Which trial can represent the highest current?
3. If voltage is increased, what happens to current?

Conclude and Apply
4. According to Ohm's law, what should happen to the current if the voltage stays the same but the resistance is reduced?
5. If a long tube has more resistance, what should happen to the rate of flow of water if the tube is shorter?

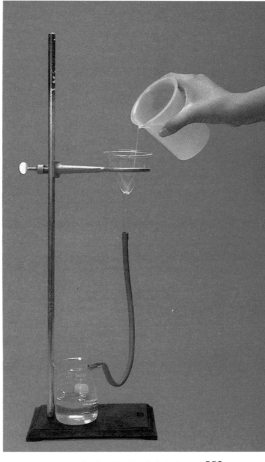

21-3 ELECTRIC CURRENT **559**

OBJECTIVE: Produce and operate a water analogy of an electric circuit.

PROCESS SKILLS applied in this activity:
▶ **Measuring** in Procedure Steps 3-6.
▶ **Predicting** in Conclude and Apply Questions 4 and 5.
▶ **Experimenting** in Conclude and Apply Question 5.
▶ **Formulating Models** in Analyze Questions 1 and 2.

COOPERATIVE LEARNING
Three to four students can be assigned to each Science Investigation Group. Assign individual tasks such as timer, pourer, recorder, and measurer.

TEACHING THE ACTIVITY
▶ The water should be poured fast enough to keep the funnel full. The timer should measure the flow into the lower beaker.
▶ The tube outlet should be kept at a constant height for all trials.
▶ A second tube with a length of 0.5 m can be provided for further experimentation.
▶ Students may need help calculating the rate.
▶ The actual rates of flow depend on the diameter of the tubing.

PROGRAM RESOURCES
From the **Teacher Resource Package** use:
  Activity Worksheets, pages 167-168, Activity 21-1: Modeling Ohm's Law.

Activity
ASSESSMENT
Oral: This activity uses an analogy between electrical potential energy and gravitational potential energy. Ask students to explain the real differences between these two quantities.

ANSWERS TO QUESTIONS
1. The highest funnel position represents the greatest voltage. (The most *work* done on a quantity of water is similar to the most work done on a quantity of electrons.)
2. The greatest amount of water flowing per second occurs when the funnel is at its highest position. The quantity of water flowing per second compares to the quantity of electrons flowing per second (current).
3. A greater voltage in a circuit produces a greater current.
4. According to Ohm's law, if the voltage remains the same, the current will increase as the resistance is decreased.
5. A shorter tube offers less resistance, resulting in higher rate of water flow.

PREPARATION

SECTION BACKGROUND

▶ In studying and teaching circuits, keep in mind that resistance, potential, and current are related by Ohm's law, $V=IR$. Normally, R is constant. If you increase the potential, current will increase, and, if you decrease potential, current will decrease.

PREPLANNING

▶ Gather the materials needed for Activity 21-2 and the Motivate Demonstration below.

1 MOTIVATE

▶ **Demonstration:** Try to have several small objects with electrical circuits, partially taken apart, in the room for students to examine. You might display a small radio, a flashlight, and/or a telephone.

STUDENT TEXT QUESTION

▶ Page 560, paragraph 2: **When this happens, does the dryer still operate?** *no*

Science and WRITING ✏️

Any home safety manual should have a list of problems caused by these electrical circuits. Examples might be overheating, fires, or electrical shock.

21-4 Electrical Circuits

New Science Words

series circuit
parallel circuits

Objectives

▶ Sketch a series and a parallel circuit, and list applications of each type of circuit.
▶ Recognize the function of circuit breakers and fuses.

Science and WRITING ✏️

With two other students, brainstorm a list of possible home safety problems caused by faulty or improperly used electrical circuits.

Series Circuits

Look around you. How many electrical devices, such as lights, alarm clocks, stereos, and televisions, do you see that are plugged into wall outlets? These devices all rely on a source of electrical energy and wires to complete an electrical circuit. Most circuits include a voltage source, a conductor, and one or more devices that use the electricity to do work.

Consider, for example, a circuit that includes an electric hair dryer. The dryer must be plugged into a wall outlet to receive current. The dryer and the circuit in the house both contain conducting wires to carry the current. A generator at a power plant produces a potential difference in the circuit, causing the electrons to move. The hair dryer turns the electricity into thermal and mechanical energy to do work. When you unplug the hair dryer, or turn off its switch, you are opening the circuit and breaking the path of the current. When this happens, does the dryer still operate?

Figure 21-9. There is only one path for electrons to follow in a series circuit.

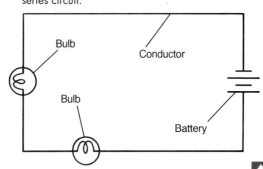

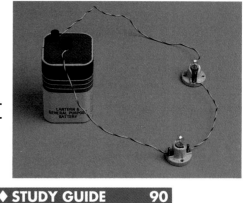

OPTIONS

Meeting Different Ability Levels

For Section 21-4, use the following **Teacher Resource Masters** depending upon individual students' needs.

◆ **Study Guide Master** for all students.
● **Reinforcement Master** for students of average and above average ability levels.
▲ **Enrichment Master** for above average students.

Additional Teacher Resource Package masters are listed in any PROGRAM RESOURCES that are in the section. The additional masters are appropriate for all students.

◆ **STUDY GUIDE** 90

STUDY GUIDE Chapter 21
Electrical Circuits Text Pages 560–564

Use the clues below to identify the term described by each statement. Write the term in the blank to the left. Then, find and circle each term in the hidden word puzzle. Terms can go across, up and down, backward, or diagonally.

series circuit	1. circuit that has only one path
parallel circuit	2. circuit that has more than one path
wire	3. In a circuit diagram, the symbol ⟶ means ____.
switch	4. In a circuit diagram, the symbol ⟶ means ____.
light bulb	5. In a circuit diagram, the symbol means ____.
voltage	6. Another term for potential difference is ____.
ohm	7. The symbol Ω stands for ____.
dry cell	8. A flashlight battery is an example of a ____.
voltmeter	9. Potential difference can be measured with a ____.
resistance	10. tendency for a material to oppose the flow of electrons
coulomb	11. unit that means 6.24 billion billion electrons
amperes	12. units used to measure the rate of electron flow

There are several kinds of circuits. One kind of circuit is called a series circuit. Some holiday lights are wired together in a series circuit. In a **series circuit**, the current has only one path it can travel along. Look at the diagram of the series circuit in Figure 21-9. If you have ever decorated a window or a tree with a string of lights, you may have had the frustrating experience of trying to find one burned out bulb. How can one faulty bulb cause the whole string to be out? Because the parts of a series circuit are wired one after another, the amount of current is the same through every part. When any part of a series circuit is disconnected, no current can flow through the circuit. This is called an "open" circuit. The electrons require a closed path or they won't move at all. Does this explain how a broken bulb can ruin a whole string of lights?

Figure 21-10 shows the symbols used in diagramming electric circuits. Notice that the switch must be closed for the circuit to be continuous.

Parallel Circuits

What would happen if your home was wired in series and you turned off a light? All other lights and appliances in your home would go out too! Fortunately, houses are wired in parallel. **Parallel circuits** contain separate branches for current to move through. Look at the parallel circuit in Figure 21-11. The current splits up to flow through the different branches. More current flows through the paths of lowest resistance. Because all branches connect the same two points of the circuit, the potential difference is the same in each branch.

Connect to... Earth Science

Rivers sometimes form different branches that separate and then rejoin, possibly making an island. Write a paragraph describing which kind of circuit this is most like and why.

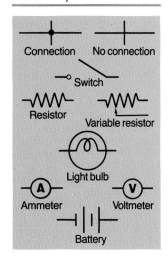

Figure 21-10. A circuit diagram is very easy to draw when you use these symbols.

Figure 21-11. There is more than one path for current to follow in a parallel circuit; the current can follow any of the branches.

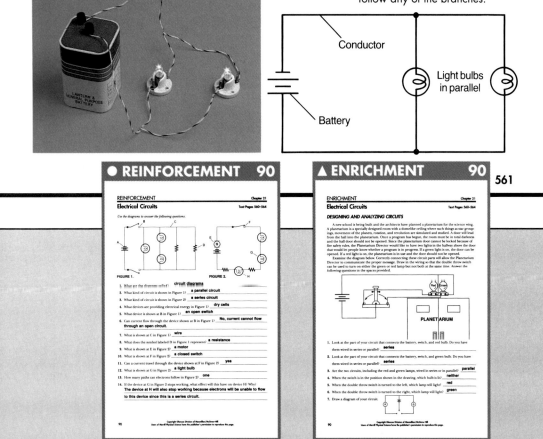

Conductor

Light bulbs in parallel

Battery

561

TYING TO PREVIOUS KNOWLEDGE: Point out that in the last section, students learned about how the resistance, voltage, and current are related. This section will apply those terms to circuits in real devices.

OBJECTIVES AND SCIENCE WORDS: Have students review the objectives and science words to become familiar with this section.

TEACHER F.Y.I.

▶ In a series circuit, the total resistance is equal to the sum of the individual resistances. $R(total) = R(1) + R(2) + ...$ The potential difference across any resistance is equal to the current times that specific resistance.

▶ In a parallel circuit, the total resistance can be calculated by the following equation. $1/R(total) = 1/R(1) + 1/R(2) + ...$ The total resistance is less than any single resistance in a parallel circuit.

2 TEACH

Key Concepts are highlighted.

CONCEPT DEVELOPMENT

▶ Emphasize that electrons move in all parts of a circuit simultaneously. Electrons in the circuit outside the battery lose energy as they move through devices in the circuit that convert electrical energy into other forms of energy, such as light, heat, and mechanical energy. Within the battery, electrons gain energy produced by chemical reactions. The battery converts chemical energy to electrical energy.

Connect to... Earth Science

Answer: This would be analogous to a parallel circuit. The change in potential energy is the same in both branches, and the branches rejoin with the same current as before the split.

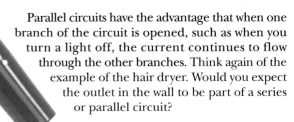

CHECK FOR UNDERSTANDING

What will happen when one lamp in a simple series circuit is disconnected? *Current ceases in the entire circuit.* **What will happen when one lamp on a parallel branch of a circuit is disconnected?** *Current stops in the broken branch, but continues in other parts of the circuit.*

RETEACH

Demonstration: Set up a simple series circuit with a battery and a couple of small light bulbs. You might want to connect ammeters in two different places to show that the current is the same everywhere in the circuit. Now disconnect one lamp to show that the entire circuit is broken. Do the same for a parallel circuit, showing that the current is not the same everywhere in a parallel circuit. Disconnect a lamp to show only that branch is affected. The broken branch no longer carries current, thus altering the current elsewhere in the parallel circuit.

EXTENSION

For students who have mastered this section, use the **Reinforcement** and **Enrichment** masters or other OPTIONS provided.

STUDENT TEXT QUESTION

▶ Page 562, paragraph 1: **Would you expect it to be part of a series or parallel circuit?** *parallel*

CROSS CURRICULUM

▶ **Electrical Engineering:** Contact a local building contractor to find out how the wiring on new buildings is done. Try to obtain a blueprint of the electrical plan and try to identify the major parts.

CONCEPT DEVELOPMENT

▶ **Demonstration:** Obtain a fuse and a circuit breaker from an electrical or hardware store. Let students examine each device. Then set up a demonstration circuit you can use to first blow the fuse and then cause the circuit breaker to open.

In Your JOURNAL

Verify that students are using proper symbols and are drawing parallel and series circuits in reasonable ways.

In Your JOURNAL

In your Journal, draw a circuit diagram of your bedroom or another room. Show all lights or appliances and consider whether they behave as if wired in series or parallel. Would you like to have two or more devices controlled by the same switch?

Figure 21-12. A household circuit is a complex combination of parallel circuits.

Parallel circuits have the advantage that when one branch of the circuit is opened, such as when you turn a light off, the current continues to flow through the other branches. Think again of the example of the hair dryer. Would you expect the outlet in the wall to be part of a series or parallel circuit?

Household Circuits

Try to count how many different things in your home require electricity. You don't see the wires because most of them are hidden behind the walls, ceilings, and floors. This wiring is composed mostly of a combination of parallel circuits connected in a very organized and logical network. Electrical current enters your home from overhead or underground wires. Figure 21-12 shows how electrical current passes through a meter to monitor your energy use. The main switch and circuit breaker box serve as a sort of electrical headquarters for your home. Parallel circuits branch out from the breaker box to wall sockets, major appliances, and lights.

Many appliances can draw current from the same circuit, so protection against overheating must be built in to prevent fires. Either a fuse or a circuit breaker is wired between every parallel circuit and the main switch box as a safety device.

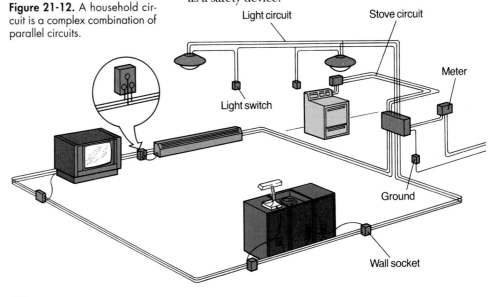

OPTIONS

ASSESSMENT—ORAL

▶ **Imagine a circuit containing two lamps connected in series. What would happen to the brightness of each lamp if two more lamps were added?** *The resistance would increase, and the current would decrease. The intensity, or brightness, of the lamps would decrease.*

▶ **Why does an entire light bulb fail to light if the filament is broken?** *There is only one path for the current to follow. Breaking the filament is like opening a switch; there is no current in the bulb.*

PROGRAM RESOURCES

From the **Teacher Resource Package** use:

Transparency Masters, pages 83-84, Series and Parallel Circuits.

Transparency Masters, pages 85-86, Household Circuits.

Use **Color Transparency** number 42, Series and Parallel Circuits.

Use **Color Transparency** number 43, Household Circuits.

Use **Laboratory Manual 44,** Simple Circuits.

What does it mean to say somebody has "blown a fuse"? Usually it refers to somebody losing his or her temper. This expression comes from the function of an electrical fuse, which contains a small piece of metal that melts if the current heats the circuit wire too much. When it melts, it causes a break in the circuit and prevents more current from flowing through the overloaded circuit. To fix this, you must replace the damaged fuse with a new one rated for the same amount of current as the original fuse was rated.

A circuit breaker is another guard against overheating a wire. A circuit breaker contains a piece of metal that bends when it gets hot. The bending causes a switch to open the circuit, preventing the flow of more current. Circuit breakers can usually be reset by flipping the switch. Before you reset a circuit breaker or replace a blown fuse, you should unplug some of the appliances from the overloaded circuit.

Figure 21-13. The circuit breaker (above) and fuses (below) prevent circuits from overheating.

SECTION REVIEW

1. Use circuit diagram symbols to draw a series circuit containing a battery, an open switch, a resistor, and a light bulb.
2. Use symbols to draw a parallel circuit with a battery and two resistors wired in parallel.
3. Compare and contrast fuses and circuit breakers. Which is easier to use?
4. **Apply:** Explain why buildings are wired in parallel instead of series circuits.
5. **Connect to Chemistry:** Pennies are made of copper and are excellent conductors of heat and electricity. Explain why you should **never** replace a blown fuse with a penny.

☑ Hypothesizing

Skill Builder

You are walking by a sign made of lighted bulbs. One of the lights begins to flicker and goes out. All other bulbs are still lit. Use your knowledge of circuits to form a hypothesis to explain why only one bulb went out instead of the entire sign. If you need help, refer to Hypothesizing in the **Skill Handbook** on page 682.

Use the Mini Quiz to check students' recall of chapter content.

1 **What is a series circuit?** *a circuit where the current has only one path to travel*
2 **The current splits up to move through separate branches in a(n) _____ circuit.** *parallel*
3 **What kind of circuit is used in most of your home wiring?** *parallel circuit*
4 **What are two devices that can keep a circuit from overheating?** *fuse, circuit breaker*

---

3 CLOSE

▶ Ask questions 1-3 and the **Apply** and the **Connect to Chemistry** questions in the Section Review.

SECTION REVIEW ANSWERS

1.

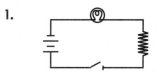

2.

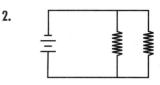

3. Both break overloaded circuits. Fuses melt and must be replaced. Circuit breakers bend to flip a switch that can be easily reset. Circuit breakers are easier to use.

4. Apply: Buildings are wired in parallel so opening one part of the circuit does not affect the other parts.

5. Connect to Chemistry: The copper penny would allow too much current in the circuit, and this could cause a fire.

Skill Builder

If one bulb went out and the others are still lit, there must be current in all other bulbs. The burnt-out bulb must have been connected in parallel, so current only stopped in one branch.

ENRICHMENT

▶ Have students investigate other electrical components commonly found in electrical circuits (see Chapter 23). Resistors, capacitors, and diodes have unique appearances and functions.

Skill Builder
ASSESSMENT
Performance: Have students design and carry out an experiment with a voltage source to test their hypothesis.

ACTIVITY 21-2

OBJECTIVE: Students will construct, test, and compare working examples of some electric circuits.
Time: one class period

PROCESS SKILLS applied in this activity are **communicating, experimenting,** and **hypothesizing.**

PREPARATION

Have the tape and aluminum foil available and demonstate how to make the conductors. If you are concerned about the overheating, substitute insulated wire for the aluminum foil.

Cooperative Learning: Use the Science Investigation strategy in groups of two or three.

SAFETY

Do not use a battery with a potential difference greater than 9-V. Caution students about the possible hot temperatures of the connecting wires and bulb. In the Going Further activity, emphasize that they should not leave the foil connector on for more than two seconds.

HYPOTHESIZING

If a bulb is removed from a series circuit, the lights will all go out. In a parallel circuit, the remaining bulbs will still be lit. Students may predict either the series or parallel circuit will shine brighter.

TEACHING THE ACTIVITY

*Refer to the **Activity Worksheets** for additional information and teaching strategies.*

• For economical, low-voltage bulbs, cut apart a string of mini-lights for Christmas trees and strip about 1-cm of plastic coating from the ends of the wires.
• Be sure all students are involved with manipulating the circuits.
• Wire from lights can be twisted onto small paper clips to make connectors, but students may also connect the circuit without using clips.

ACTIVITY 21-2 · DESIGNING AN EXPERIMENT
Electric Circuits

Imagine what your home would be like if it were wired in series. In order for your alarm clock to wake you up in the morning, your lights and anything else that used electricity would have to be on. Fortunately, most outlets in homes are wired on separate branches of the main circuit. Can you design simple circuits that have specific behaviors and uses?

Getting Started

In this activity you will *investigate* the behaviors of series and parallel circuits. **CAUTION:** *The parts of the circuits can become quite hot. Do not leave the battery connected for more than a few seconds at a time.*

Hypothesizing

Predict what will happen if a bulb is removed from each of the types of circuits. Also write a **hypothesis** predicting in which circuit the lights will shine the brightest.

Materials

Your cooperative group will use:
• aluminum foil
• cellophane foil
• scissors
• 3 lights with sockets
• 6 paper clips
• battery (6 or 9 volt)

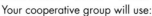
Try It!

1. On a piece of paper, draw a large series circuit of three lights and a battery as shown. Draw a parallel circuit with the same parts.

2. Make conducting wires by taping a 30-cm piece of cellophane tape to a sheet of aluminum foil and folding the foil over twice to cover the tape. Cut these to any length that works in your design.
3. Design several experiments you would like to try with each type of circuit. Be sure to look ahead to the Summing Up questions for some ideas.

Summing Up/Sharing Results

• Write down your conclusions about your **hypotheses.**

Going Further!

• Where in the parallel circuit would you place a switch to control all three lights? To control only one light? Try it.

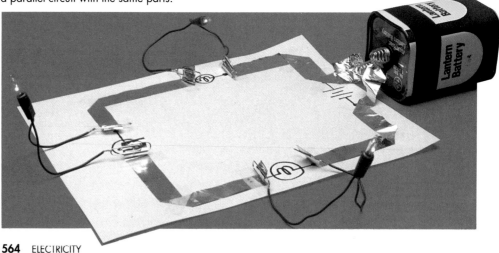

SUMMING UP/ SHARING RESULTS

In a series circuit, current cannot continue if the path is broken. In a parallel circuit, the current can still move through the other intact branches. Lights shine the brightest in the parallel circuit.

PROGRAM RESOURCES
From the **Teacher Resource Package** use: **Activity Worksheets,** pages 169-170, Activity 21-2: Electric Circuits.

GOING FURTHER!

A switch next to the battery will turn out all lights, and a switch next to one light will turn out only that light.

ACTIVITY
ASSESSMENT

Oral: Ask students to discuss why houses and buildings are wired in parallel and not in series. In addition to having to use appliances one at a time, the current in a series home would be too low to even operate light bulbs.

Electrical Power and Energy

21-5

Objectives
▶ Explain and calculate electric power.
▶ Calculate the amount of electrical energy in kilowatt-hours.

New Science Words
electrical power
kilowatt-hour

Electrical Power

What do you think of when you hear the word *power?* It has many different meanings. Earlier, in Chapter 7, you read that power is the rate at which work is done. Electricity can do work for us. Electrical energy is easily converted to other types of energy. For example, the blades of a fan can rotate and cool you as electrical energy is changed into mechanical energy. An iron changes electrical energy into heat. **Electrical power** is the rate at which electrical energy is converted to another form of energy.

How does electrical energy do work?

Table 21-1

ENERGY USED BY HOME APPLIANCES			
Appliance	Time of Usage (hours/day)	Power Usage (watts)	Energy Usage (kWh/day)
Hair dryer, blower	0.25	1000	0.25
Microwave oven	0.5	1450	0.73
Radio/record player	2.5	109	0.27
Range (oven)	1	2600	2.60
Refrigerator/freezer (15 cu ft, frostless)	24	615	14.76
Television (color)	3.25	200	0.65
Electric toothbrush	0.08	7	0.0006
100-watt light bulb	6	100	0.60
40-watt fluorescent light bulb	1	40	0.04

① **In Your JOURNAL**

In your Journal, make a list of the home appliances you plug into wall outlets and use daily. Which appliance uses electricity at the fastest rate? Which is responsible for the greatest energy usage each day?

OPTIONS

INQUIRY QUESTIONS
▶ **How are mechanical power and electrical power similar?** *They are both the rate at which a certain kind of work is done.*
▶ **Compute the number of watts in 6.5 kilowatts.**
$$6.5 \, kW \times \frac{1000 \, W}{1 \, kW} = 6500 \, W$$

SECTION 21-5

PREPARATION

SECTION BACKGROUND
▶ Electricity must often be transmitted many miles to reach people. There is some power loss during this transmission. However, it can be minimized if the electricity is transmitted at high voltages. The voltage in electric power lines may be as high as 700 kV (700 000 V).

PREPLANNING
▶ Find some sample electric bills, or ask students to bring in some from home.

1 MOTIVATE

▶ Ask students to get their parents' permission to bring in a copy of an old electric bill to use in class. Start by calculating a class average monthly bill and note that some people may be on an even monthly payment schedule. Use the bill to determine the cost of electrical energy in your area.

TYING TO PREVIOUS KNOWLEDGE:
Recall earlier definitions of work and power. Point out that, as a charge moves through a circuit, it does work. Electrical work is done as it is changed into another form of energy, such as mechanical or heat energy. The rate at which this occurs is electrical power.

OBJECTIVES AND SCIENCE WORDS:
Have students review the objectives and science words to become familiar with this section.

In Your JOURNAL

Note that the highest power rating may not be associated with the appliance that uses the most energy per day. This is due to the amount of time each appliance is in operation.

CHAPTER 21   **565**

CONCEPT DEVELOPMENT

▶ Bring in some advertisements for microwave ovens, hair dryers, and stereos, as well as some light bulb boxes. Find the rate at which each appliance uses energy in watts. Have students make a list of these ranging from high to low users of electric power.

▶ Using the list suggested above, estimate the usage time of each appliance in an average day. Ask which appliances now seem to be the largest users of electrical power.

PRACTICE PROBLEM ANSWERS

1. $P = IV = (0.625 \text{ A})(120 \text{ V})$
   $P = 75 \text{ W}$

2. $P = IV$, so $I = \dfrac{P}{V}$

   $I = \dfrac{1000 \text{ W}}{120 \text{ V}} = 8.3 \text{ A}$

Connect to...
Life Science

Answer: The third prong connects the housing of the appliance to the ground, preventing shocks if there is an internal short circuit.

CHECK FOR UNDERSTANDING

Use the Mini Quiz to check for understanding.

MINI QUIZ

Use the Mini Quiz to check students' recall of chapter content.

1. **What is electrical power?** *the rate at which electrical energy is changed to another form of energy*
2. **The product of electric power used and time is _____ .** *energy*
3. **The unit of electrical energy is the _____ .** *kilowatt-hour*

Connect to...
Life Science

All plugs to appliances have at least two prongs, but some (especially larger appliances) have a third to improve safety. Find out and explain what the third prong is for.

The rate at which different appliances use energy varies. Appliances are often advertised with their power rating, which depends on the amount of electrical energy each appliance needs to operate. Table 21-1 shows the power requirements of some appliances.

Electrical power is expressed in watts (W), or kilowatts, (kW). The amount of power used by an appliance can be calculated by multiplying the potential difference by the current.

$$\text{power} = \text{current} \times \text{voltage}$$
$$\text{watts} = \text{amperes} \times \text{volts}$$
$$P = I \times V$$

One watt of power is produced when one ampere of current flows through a circuit with a potential difference of one volt. Look again at Table 21-1. Which appliance requires the most electrical power to operate? You can tell by looking at the number of watts listed for that appliance under the power usage column. Now see which appliance requires the least amount of electrical power to operate. The example problem below shows you how to calculate the electrical power usage for an appliance. This can be easily done as long as you know the values of the current and voltage.

EXAMPLE PROBLEM: Calculating Power

Problem Statement:	A calculator has a 0.01-A current flowing through it. It operates with a potential difference of 9 V. How much power does it use?
Known Information: <u>Strategy Hint:</u> Remember that electrical power is measured in watts.	current, $I = 0.01$ A potential difference, $V = 9$ V
Unknown Information:	power (P)
Equation to Use:	$P = I \times V$
Solution:	$P = I \times V = (0.01 \text{ A})(9 \text{ V}) = 0.09 \text{ W}$

PRACTICE PROBLEMS

<u>Strategy Hint:</u> Be sure your decimal is correctly placed after you multiply.

<u>Strategy Hint:</u> Your answer should be in amperes.

1. A lamp operates with a current of 0.625 A and a potential difference of 120 V. How much power does the lamp use?

2. A microwave oven uses 1000 W of power. The voltage source is 120 V. What is the current flowing through the microwave?

OPTIONS

Meeting Different Ability Levels

For Section 21-5, use the following **Teacher Resource Masters** depending upon individual students' needs.

◆ **Study Guide Master** for all students.
● **Reinforcement Master** for students of average and above average ability levels.
▲ **Enrichment Master** for above average students.

Additional Teacher Resource Package masters are listed in any PROGRAM RESOURCES boxes that are in the section. The additional masters are appropriate for all students.

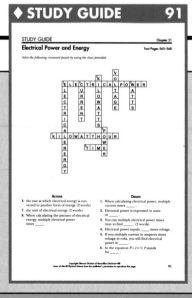

Electrical Energy

Why is it important that you not waste electricity? Most electrical energy is produced from natural resources, which are limited in supply. Electrical energy also costs you money. All the electricity you use in your home is measured by a device called an electrical meter. You may have noticed that the meter for your home has a wheel that spins quickly when you are using a great deal of electricity and is stopped when no electricity is being used. The amount of electrical energy you use depends on the power required by appliances in your home and how long they are used. For example, you can calculate the amount of energy a refrigerator uses in a day by multiplying the power required by the amount of time it uses that power.

$$\text{energy} = \text{power} \times \text{time}$$
$$\text{kWh} = \text{kW} \times \text{h}$$
$$E = P \times t$$

The unit of electrical energy is the **kilowatt-hour** (kWh). One kilowatt-hour is 1000 watts of power used for one hour. The electric utility company charges you periodically for each kilowatt-hour you use. You can figure your electric bill by multiplying the energy used by the cost per kilowatt-hour. Table 21-2 shows some sample costs of running electrical appliances.

Table 21-2

MONTHLY COSTS OF USING APPLIANCES

	APPLIANCE		
	Hair dryer	Stereo	Color television
Average power in watts	600	109	200
Hours used daily	.25	3.0	2.5
Hours used monthly	7.5	90.0	75.0
Monthly watt hours	4500	9810	15 000
kWh used a month	4.5	9.81	15.000
Rate charged	$0.09	$0.09	$0.09
Monthly cost	$0.41	$0.88	$1.35

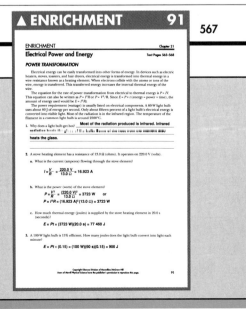

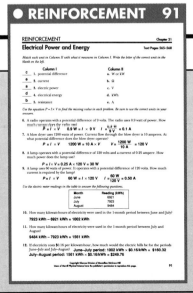

● **REINFORCEMENT** 91 ▲ **ENRICHMENT** 91

567

▶ **Home Economics:** Have students find out how to read the electric meter at their home.

PRACTICE PROBLEM ANSWERS

1. $P = 100W \times \dfrac{1 \text{ kW}}{1000 \text{ W}}$

$= 0.100 \text{ kW}$

$E = P \times t$

$= (0.100 \text{ kW})(5.5 \text{ h})$

$E = 0.55 \text{ kWh}$

2. $P = \dfrac{E}{t}$

$P = \dfrac{0.115 \text{ kWh}}{0.10 \text{ h}}$

$P = 1.5 \text{ kW}$

$P = 1500 \text{ W}$

3 CLOSE

▶ Generate a class list of ways to cut down on the amount of electrical energy used in a household.

SECTION REVIEW ANSWERS

1. the rate at which electrical energy is changed to another form of energy

2. $P = I \times V = (1.5 \text{ A})(120 \text{ V})$

$= 180 \text{ W} \times \dfrac{1 \text{ kW}}{1000W}$

$= 0.18 \text{ kW}$

$E = P \times t = (0.18 \text{ kW})(2 \text{ h})$

$= 0.36 \text{ kWh}$

3. Apply: $E = P \times t$

$= (0.11 \text{ kW})(3 \text{ h})$

$= 0.33 \text{ kWh}$

$Cost = (0.33 \text{ kWh})(9¢/\text{kWh})$

$= 2.97¢ \text{ or about 3 cents}$

4. Connect to Life Science:

$4.0006 \dfrac{\text{kWh}}{\text{day}} \times 31 \text{ days} = 0.019 \text{ kWh}$

$0.019 \text{ kWh} \times \dfrac{\$0.09}{\text{kWh}} = \$0.017$

Skill Builder
ASSESSMENT

Performance: Have students design another concept map for determining the current in a device when energy, time, and voltage are known.

EXAMPLE PROBLEM: Calculating Electrical Energy

Problem Statement: A refrigerator is one of the major users of electrical power in your home. If it uses 700 W and runs 10 hours each day, how much energy (in kWh) is used in one day?

Known Information: power, $P = 700$ W

Strategy Hint: Convert W to kW before you multiply.

time, $t = 10$ h

Unknown Information: energy (E)

Equation to Use: $E = P \times t$

Solution: Convert W to kW, 700 W/1000 W/kW = 0.7 kW

$E = P \times t = (0.7 \text{ kW})(10 \text{ h}) = 7 \text{ kWh}$

PRACTICE PROBLEMS

Strategy Hint: Remember to convert watts to kilowatts.

Strategy Hint: Use the equation $P = E/t$; convert minutes to hours.

1. A 100-W light bulb is left on for 5.5 hours. How many kilowatt-hours of energy is used?
2. How much power is used by an electric hair dryer that uses 0.15 kWh of energy during 6 minutes of use?

To get an idea of energy costs in your home, you can make a list of all the appliances you use and add together their monthly energy costs. How do you think this value would compare to your electric bill?

SECTION REVIEW

1. What is electrical power?
2. **Apply:** A television uses a current of 1.5 A at 120 V. The television is used for 2 hours. Calculate the power used in kW and the energy used in kWh.
3. **Connect to Life Science:** How many kWh of energy would be needed for brushing your teeth with an electric toothbrush daily for the month of May? How much would it cost at $0.09 per kWh?

 **Skill Builder**

✉ **Concept Mapping**

Prepare a concept map that shows the steps in calculating the energy used in operating an electrical device with known voltage and current for a known amount of time. If you need help, refer to Concept Mapping in the **Skill Handbook** on pages 684 and 685.

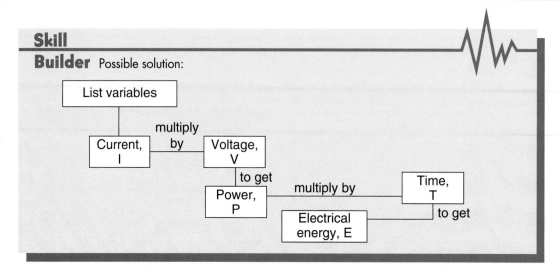

Skill Builder Possible solution:

List variables → multiply by: Current, I — multiply by — Voltage, V → to get → Power, P — multiply by — Time, T → to get → Electrical energy, E

REVIEW

SUMMARY

21-1: Electric Charge

1. Static electricity is the accumulation of electric charges on an object.

2. An electrical conductor is a material that allows electrons to move through it easily. An electrical insulator is a material that doesn't allow electrons to move through it easily.

3. An electroscope contains two suspended metal leaves in a jar that move apart when induced with an electrical charge.

21-2: Science and Society: Lightning—Its Causes and Effects

1. Clouds often contain areas of positively and negatively charged particles and can cause nearby objects to become charged by induction. A static discharge, lightning, occurs when excess electrons flow between the cloud and the charged object.

2. Some lightning-caused forest fires are allowed to burn as part of the natural processes in the forest. However, these fires also kill local plant and animal life.

21-3: Electric Current

1. The potential energy stored in an electron decreases as it moves through a circuit.

2. A dry cell creates a potential difference in a circuit, causing the electrons to flow.

3. Ohm's law states that the current in a circuit is equal to the potential difference divided by the resistance.

21-4: Electrical Circuits

1. Current only has one path along which it can travel in a series circuit, such as strings of holiday lights. Parallel circuits provide more than one path for current to follow.

2. Circuit breakers and fuses are safety devices that open a circuit if the current becomes too great.

21-5: Electrical Power and Energy

1. Electrical power is the rate at which electrical energy can be transformed into other kinds of energy.

2. A kilowatt-hour is a thousand watts of power used for one hour.

KEY SCIENCE WORDS

a. **circuit**
b. **conductor**
c. **current**
d. **dry cell**
e. **electrical power**
f. **electric field**
g. **electroscope**
h. **insulator**
i. **kilowatt-hour**
j. **lightning rod**
k. **Ohm's law**
l. **parallel circuit**
m. **potential difference**
n. **resistance**
o. **series circuit**
p. **static electricity**
q. **wet cell**

UNDERSTANDING VOCABULARY

Match each phrase with the correct term from the list of Key Science Words.

1. buildup of electric charges on an object
2. exerts a force on an electric charge
3. a material through which electrons can move easily
4. a device that is used to detect electric charges
5. any closed path through which electrons flow
6. two plates made of different metals or metallic compounds in an electrolyte solution
7. opposes the flow of electrons in a conductor
8. electric current has at least two separate paths
9. the rate at which electrical energy is converted to a different form of energy
10. relates voltage and resistance to current

SUMMARY

Have students read the summary statements to review the major concepts of the chapter.

UNDERSTANDING VOCABULARY

1. p	**6.** q
2. f	**7.** n
3. b	**8.** l
4. g	**9.** e
5. a	**10.** k

ASSESSMENT
Portfolio

Encourage students to place in their portfolios one or two items of what they consider to be their best work. For each item, ask students to explain why that item was chosen and what they learned from it. Items might be selected from the following.

• Connect to Life Science answer, p. 551
• Connect to Chemistry answer, p. 555
• Practice Problem 2 answer, p. 568

Performance

Additional performance assessments may be found in *Performance Assessment* and *Science Integration Activities* that accompany **Merrill Physical Science.** Performance Task Assessment Lists and rubrics for evaluating these activities and other products generated throughout the chapter can be found in Glencoe's *Performance Assessment in Middle School Science.*

OPTIONS

ASSESSMENT

To assess student understanding of material in this chapter, use the resources listed.

👥 COOPERATIVE LEARNING

Consider using cooperative learning in the THINK AND WRITE CRITICALLY, APPLY, and MORE SKILL BUILDERS sections of the Chapter Review.

PROGRAM RESOURCES

From the **Teacher Resource Package** use:
Chapter Review, pages 45-46.
Chapter and Unit Tests, pages 143-146, Chapter Test.

REVIEW

CHAPTER

REVIEW

CHECKING CONCEPTS

1. a	**6.** d
2. a	**7.** a
3. d	**8.** c
4. c	**9.** d
5. b	**10.** d

USING LAB SKILLS

ASSESSMENT

Use these alternate lab exercises to assess students' understanding of the skills used in this chapter.

11. Assuming a constant height, a wider diameter should decrease the resistance and increase water flow.

12. Answers will vary. One possibility would be a segment of conductor that could be lifted or taped down to complete the circuit.

THINK AND WRITE CRITICALLY

13. Both involve charged particles. In static electricity, these charges accumulate in one place. In current electricity these charges are continually flowing.

14. In the atoms of conductors, electrons are loosely held by the nucleus and are therefore more free to move. In insulators, electrons are tightly bound by atomic nuclei and are not free to move.

15. Electrons flow in a circuit because of a difference in electrical potential between two points in the circuit. Electrons flow from the point of highest potential energy (negative electrode) to the point of lowest potential energy (positive electrode). When electrons move through an appliance, they do work on the appliance, and some of their potential energy is converted to some other form of energy.

16. Lightning occurs when opposite charges build up in a cloud and Earth's surface. Lightning is actually a large static discharge.

17. According to Ohm's law, resistance and current are inversely related: as resistance increases, current decreases; as resistance decreases, current increases. Potential difference and current are directly related: as the potential difference increases, current increases, and as the potential difference decreases, the current decreases.

CHAPTER

REVIEW

CHECKING CONCEPTS

Choose the word or phrase that completes the sentence or answers the question.

1. An object becomes positively charged when it _____.
- **a.** loses electrons
- **c.** gains electrons
- **b.** loses protons
- **d.** gains neutrons

2. When two negative charges are brought close together, they will _____.
- **a.** repel
- **c.** neither attract nor repel
- **b.** attract
- **d.** ground

3. As the distance from a charged particle increases, the strength of the electric field _____.
- **a.** varies
- **c.** increases
- **b.** remains the same
- **d.** decreases

4. An example of a good insulator is _____.
- **a.** copper
- **c.** wood
- **b.** silver
- **d.** salt water

5. Connecting a charged object to Earth in order to discharge the object into Earth is called _____.
- **a.** charging
- **c.** conduction
- **b.** grounding
- **d.** induction

6. The difference in potential energy per unit charge between two electrodes is measured in _____.
- **a.** amperes
- **c.** ohms
- **b.** coulombs
- **d.** volts

7. The difference in energy carried by electrons at different points in a circuit will determine the _____.
- **a.** voltage
- **c.** current
- **b.** resistance
- **d.** power

8. Resistance in an electrical wire causes electrical energy to be converted to _____.
- **a.** chemical energy
- **c.** heat
- **b.** nuclear energy
- **d.** sound

9. Which of the following wires would tend to have the least amount of electrical resistance?
- **a.** long
- **c.** hot
- **b.** fiberglass
- **d.** thick

10. Electrical energy is measured in _____.
- **a.** volts
- **c.** kilowatts
- **b.** newtons
- **d.** kilowatt-hours

USING LAB SKILLS

11. In Activity 21-1 on page 559, you created a model of Ohm's law with a water system. How would you expect the results of this experiment to differ if you used a tube with a wide diameter? Try it and check your predictions.

12. Review your circuit designs from Activity 21-2 on page 564. How would you design a switch from the materials used in these circuits? Try it, and be sure your design is effective.

THINK AND WRITE CRITICALLY

Answer the following questions in your Journal using complete sentences.

13. Compare and contrast static electricity and current electricity.

14. How are the atoms of conductors different from the atoms of insulators?

15. What causes electrons to move through a circuit? What happens to the electrons' potential energy as they pass through an electrical appliance?

16. How does lightning occur?

17. How are resistance and potential difference related to the amount of current flowing through a circuit?

APPLY

18. Because they are higher than the roof of a building, they are struck first. They discharge the electric charges of a lightning strike into Earth.

19. To detect a negatively charged object, place a positive charge on an electroscope. Observe the electroscope's leaves as you bring the positively charged electroscope close to the object. If the object is negatively charged, the leaves will move closer together because the electrons on the object will repel electrons from the knob into the leaves, reducing the positive charge.

20. Given: $I = 1.5A$; $R = 2\ \Omega$
Unknown: $V = ?$
Equation: $I = V/R$ or $V = I \times R$
Solution: $V = (1.5A)(2\ \Omega) = 3\ V$

21. Given: $V = 120\ V$; $I = 2\ A$; $t = 4\ h$
Unknowns = P, E
Equations: $P = V \times I$; $E = P \times t$
Solutions: (1) $P = V \times I = (120\ V)(2\ A)$
$P = 240\ W = 0.240\ kW$
(2) $E = P \times t$
$= (0.240kW)(4\ h)$
$E = 0.96\ kWh$

18. Lightning rods are grounded conductors located on roofs of buildings. How do they protect buildings from lightning?
19. Explain how an electroscope could be used to detect a negatively charged object.
20. A toy car has a 1.5-A current and its internal resistance is 2 ohms. How much voltage does the car require?
21. The current flowing through an appliance connected to a 120-V source is 2 A. How many kilowatt-hours of electrical energy does the appliance use in 4 hours?
22. You are asked to connect a stereo, a television, a VCR, and a lamp in a single, complex circuit. Would you connect these appliances in parallel or in series? How would you prevent an electrical fire? Explain your answers.

MORE SKILL BUILDERS

If you need help, refer to the Skill Handbook.

1. **Making and Using Graphs:** The resistance in a 1-cm length copper wire at different temperatures is shown below.

Resistance in Microhms	Temperature in °C
2	50
3	200
5	475

Construct a line graph for the above data. Is copper a better conductor on a cold day or a hot day?

2. **Interpreting Data:** Look at the power usage of the appliances in Table 21-1 and calculate the current each appliance pulls from a 120-V source. Which appliance draws the most current?

3. **Concept Mapping:** List the events that occur when an electroscope is brought near a positively charged object and a negatively charged object. Be sure to indicate which way electrons flow and the charge and responses of the leaves.

4. **Using Variables, Constants, and Controls:** Design an experiment to test the effect on current and voltage in a circuit when two batteries of equal voltage are connected in series. What is your hypothesis? What are the variables and control?

PROJECTS

1. Research the origin and history of lightning rods. Relate your findings in a written report.
2. Obtain information from your electric company about safety rules of using electricity and make a poster to display.

4. **Using Variables, Constants, and Controls:** Answers will vary somewhat, but the conclusions of the experiment should be that connecting two batteries of equal voltage in series increases the voltage and the current.

22. The appliances should be connected in parallel so if one appliance went out, the others would still work. Either a fuse or a circuit breaker could be used to protect the circuit from excess current and therefore an electrical fire.

MORE SKILL BUILDERS

1. **Making and Using Graphs:** According to the graph, copper would be a better conductor on a cold day because its resistance decreases with temperature. Note: 1 micro ohm = 10^{-6} ohm

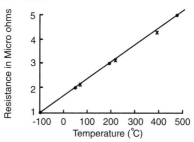

2. **Interpreting Data:** The current drawn by each appliance can be solved as follows:

$$I = \frac{P \text{ as given in table}}{120 \text{ V}}$$

The appliance drawing the highest current must have the highest power. The range oven has the highest current.

3. **Concept Mapping:**

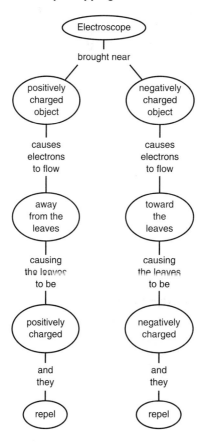

CHAPTER SECTION	OBJECTIVES	ACTIVITIES
22-1 Characteristics of Magnets (1 day)	1. **Explain** the properties of magnets. 2. **Define** the region of force around a magnet. 3. **Model** magnetic behavior using domains.	**MINI-Lab:** *What's "invisible" to a magnetic field?* p. 577
22-2 Uses of Magnetic Fields (2 days)	1. **Explain** how a coil carrying electric current can induce a magnetic field. 2. **Compare** and contrast ammeters and voltmeters. 3. **Describe** the function of an electric motor.	**Activity 22-1:** *Electric Motors,* p. 582
22-3 Producing Electric Current (2 days)	1. **Describe** how a generator produces an electric current using electromagnetic induction. 2. **Distinguish** between alternating current and direct current. 3. **Explain** how a transformer can step up or step down the voltage of an alternating current.	
22-4 Superconductivity Science & Society (1 day)	1. **Describe** the characteristics of superconductors. 2. **Consider** various applications of superconductivity.	**Activity 22-2:** *Trying Transformers,* p. 590
Chapter Review		

ACTIVITY MATERIALS

FIND OUT	ACTIVITIES		MINI-LABS
Page 573 pencil paper needle thread magnet	**22-1 Electric Motors, p. 582** paper cup or beaker nail magnet wire, 22 ga. magnet wire, 32 ga. bare copper wire, 16 ga. soda straw tape 6-volt batteries (2) sandpaper magnetic compass	**22-2 Trying Transformers, p. 590** 6-volt battery AC power supply, low voltage light, low voltage insulated wire, 32 ga. soda straw, cut to length of nail large nail knife paper clip	**What's "invisible" to a magnetic field? p. 577** ring stand utility clamp needle thread (1 meter) tape magnet selection of solids which includes iron and pure nickel

CHAPTER FEATURES	TEACHER RESOURCE PACKAGE	OTHER RESOURCES
Problem Solving: *A Magnetic Puzzle,* p. 576 **Skill Builder:** *Hypothesizing,* p. 577	**Ability Level Worksheets** ◆ *Study Guide,* p. 92 ● *Reinforcement,* p. 92 ▲ *Enrichment,* p. 92 **Activity Worksheet,** p. 182 **Technology,** pp. 19, 20	**Laboratory Manual 45,** Magnets **STVS:** Disc 7, Side 1
Technology: *Flying Trains,* p. 579 **Skill Builder:** *Comparing and Contrasting,* p. 581	**Ability Level Worksheets** ◆ *Study Guide,* p. 93 ● *Reinforcement,* p. 93 ▲ *Enrichment,* p. 93 **Activity Worksheet,** pp. 176, 177 **Concept Mapping,** pp. 49, 50 **Cross-Curricular Connections,** p. 28 **Transparency Masters,** pp. 87, 88 **Activity Worksheets,** p. 5	**Color Transparency 44,** Electric Motor-DC Generator **Laboratory Manual 46,** Electromagnets **STVS:** Disc 1, Side 2
Skill Builder: *Concept Mapping,* p. 587	**Ability Level Worksheets** ◆ *Study Guide,* p. 94 ● *Reinforcement,* p. 94 ▲ *Enrichment,* p. 94 **Critical Thinking/Problem Solving,** p. 28 **Science and Society,** p. 26 **Transparency Master,** pp. 89, 90 **Activity Worksheets,** p. 5	**Color Transparency 45,** Transformers **STVS:** Disc 2, Side 2 **Science Integration Activity 22**
You Decide! p. 589	**Ability Level Worksheets** ◆ *Study Guide,* p. 95 ● *Reinforcement,* p. 95 ▲ *Enrichment,* p. 95 **Activity Worksheet,** pp. 178, 179	
Summary Think & Write Critically Key Science Words Apply Understanding Vocabulary More Skill Builders Checking Concepts Projects Using Lab Skills	**ASSESSMENT RESOURCES** **Chapter Review,** pp. 47, 48 **Chapter Tests,** pp. 147-150 **Performance Assessment in** **Middle School Science**	**Chapter Review Software** **Test Bank** **Alternate Assessment** **Performance Assessment**

◆ **Basic**   ● **Average**   ▲ **Advanced**

ADDITIONAL MATERIALS

SOFTWARE	AUDIOVISUAL	BOOKS/MAGAZINES
Force Fields, Queue. *Magnetism,* J and S Software. *Magnets and Electromagnetism,* Queue. *Modern Theories of Magnetism,* Queue.	*Electrical Current and Magnetism,* Video, AIMS Media. *Electricity and Magnetism,* Video, Coronet. *Electromagnets and Their Uses,* Video, Coronet. *Forces,* Video, Britannica. *How to Produce Electric Currents with Magnets,* Video, Britannica. *Learning About Magnetism,* Video, Britannica.	Billings, Charlene W. *Superconductivity: From Discovery to Breakthrough.* NY: Cobblehill, 1991. Friedhoffer, Robert. *Magnetism and Electricity.* NY: Watts, 1992. Stwertka, Albert. *Superconductors: The Irresistible Future.* NY: Watts, 1991. Taylor, Barbara. *More Power to You! The Science of Batteries and Magnets.* NY: Random House, 1992.

THEME DEVELOPMENT: This chapter introduces the concept of magnetism, illustrated by several everyday applications, and develops the theme of patterns of change in magnetic materials. Emphasize the relationship between electricity and magnetism.

CHAPTER OVERVIEW

▶ **Section 22-1:** Magnetism as a property of certain materials is introduced, citing common applications of magnets. The domain model is developed to suggest a way to visualize magnetic behavior.

▶ **Section 22-2:** The formation of electromagnets by electric currents is discussed, followed by an illustration of how electromagnets are used in meters and electric motors.

▶ **Section 22-3:** Electromagnetic induction is introduced, with a focus on generators. Direct and alternating currents are contrasted. The functions of step-up and step-down transformers are also explained.

▶ **Section 22-4: Science and Society:** Finally, electricity and magnetism are tied together with a discussion of the science and applications of superconductors. The You Decide question deals with the development of superconducting trains as an alternative source of transportation.

CHAPTER VOCABULARY

magnetism	electromagnetic
magnetic poles	induction
magnetic field	generator
magnetic	direct
domains	current (DC)
electromagnet	alternating
ammeters	current (AC)
voltmeters	transformer
commutator	superconductors

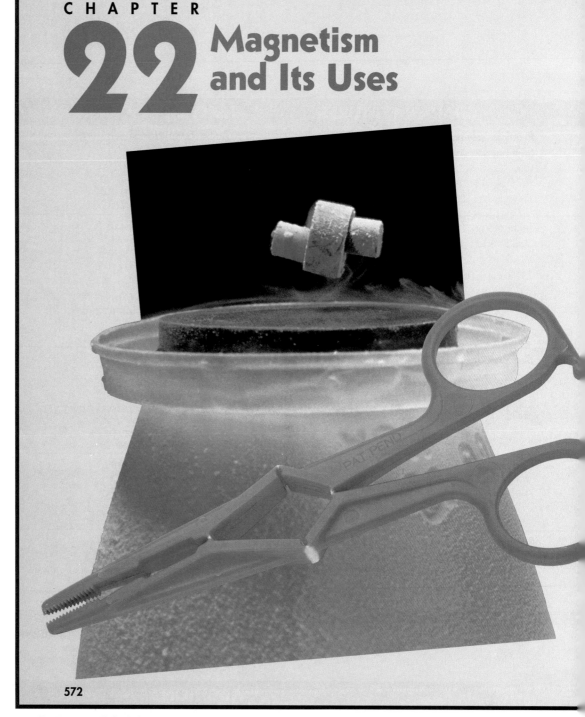

572

OPTIONS

For Your Gifted Students

Students can make a picture using a hot plate, a magnet, wax or paraffin, and an aluminum pan. They should dip sheets of paper in wax melted in the pan. After the wax has cooled, place iron filings on the paper and have students use a magnet to create a picture. Then, soften the wax using a warm hot plate until the filings sink in. Allow the wax to cool.

For Your Mainstreamed Students

As a demonstration, pass a single-wire conductor through a hole in a sheet of cardboard and connect the ends to a dry cell battery. Sprinkle iron filings on the cardboard around the wire and tap gently. Be sure you do not connect the wire to the battery for more than a few seconds. The wire will become very hot and the battery will discharge rapidly.

Did you ever get lost on your first day in a new school? Perhaps your homeroom teacher gave you a map of the building, or you had to ask an older student to help you find your way.

How do you think sailors find their way across the ocean? They have maps, but they can't stop for directions. They use a compass to show them which way is north.

FIND OUT!

Make and use a compass in this simple activity.

Magnetize a sewing needle by stroking it in one direction with a magnet. Then tie a piece of thread around the needle and let it hang. It will line up in a north-south direction. *Observe* which end points north. Use your needle compass to make a map from your science classroom to the library. Let a friend use your map and compass to find the library.

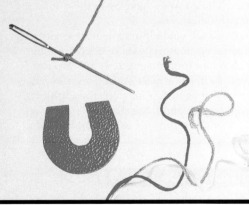

Gearing Up
Previewing the Chapter
Use this outline to help you focus on important ideas in this chapter.

Previewing Science Skills
► In the Skill Builders, you will hypothesize, compare and contrast, and make a concept map.
► In the Activities, you will observe, predict, interpret, and formulate models.
► In the MINI-Lab, you will hypothesize, observe, and interpret data.

What's next?

You have already discovered one important use of magnets. Technology has advanced by leaps and bounds since the first compass was used. We have learned how magnets work, and we have found many applications for them. As you read this chapter, think about all the ways you use magnets.

573

INTRODUCING THE CHAPTER
Use the Find Out activity to help students begin to think about places where magnetism is observed in their daily lives. Explain that they will be investigating the nature and uses of magnetism.

FIND OUT!
Preparation: Before beginning this chapter, try to have several compasses in clear view, but don't discuss them yet.
Materials: pencil and paper, needle, thread, magnet
Cooperative Learning: Arrange the class in Paired Partners for this activity. Encourage them to come up with unique maps. Have them compare their maps with others in the class.
Teaching Tips
► You may need to provide one or two examples of maps to get students started. Because the tips and the eyes are not labeled *north* or *south*, be sure students determine which ends of their needles point north.

Gearing Up
Have students study the Gearing Up feature to familiarize themselves with the chapter. Discuss the relationships of the topics in the outline.

What's Next?
Before beginning the first section, make sure students understand the connection between the Find Out activity and the topics to follow.

ASSESSMENT OPTIONS

PORTFOLIO
Refer to page 591 for suggested items that students might select for their portfolios.

PERFORMANCE ASSESSMENT
See page 591 for additional Performance Assessment options.
Process
Skill Builders, pp. 577, 587
Activities 22-1, p. 582; 22-2, p. 590
Using Lab Skills, p. 592

CONTENT ASSESSMENT
Assessment—Oral, p. 580
Skill Builder, p. 581
Section Reviews, pp. 577, 581, 587, 589
Chapter Review, pp. 591-593
Mini Quizzes, pp. 576, 580, 587
MINI-Lab, p. 577

GROUP ASSESSMENT
Opportunities for group assessment occur with Cooperative Learning Strategies and Flex Your Brain Activities.

PREPARATION

SECTION BACKGROUND

► Demonstration magnets are often made of alloys. ALNICO is a common commercial magnetic material made from *aluminum*, *nickel*, *cobalt*, and *iron*.

► Magnetic field strength is measured in terms of the magnetic flux per unit area, which is the number of magnetic field lines in a given region. It is strongest around the poles.

PREPLANNING

► Round up a selection of magnets of different sizes, shapes, and strengths. Paper clips, wire, and meters are also suggested.

1 MOTIVATE

► **Demonstration:** Anchor a tall pencil in some clay or hold it. Stack two or more ring magnets with holes in the center on the pencil with opposite poles facing each other. They will levitate. Ask students why.

TYING TO PREVIOUS KNOWLEDGE:

Ask students what kinds of attractions and repulsions they have studied this year. They should at least recall gravitation and the interaction between opposite electrical charges. Note that magnetic forces are related to electrical forces.

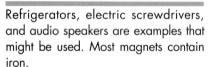

In Your JOURNAL

Refrigerators, electric screwdrivers, and audio speakers are examples that might be used. Most magnets contain iron.

Connect to...
Earth Science

Answer: Magnetite is Fe_3O_4, a compound of iron and oxygen.

22-1 Characteristics of Magnets

New Science Words

magnetism
magnetic poles
magnetic field
magnetic domains

Objectives

► Explain the properties of magnets.
► Define the region of force around a magnet.
► Model magnetic behavior using domains.

Connect to...
Earth Science

Early compasses were made of lodestone, pieces of the mineral magnetite. Find out what the chemical formula of magnetite is and identify its elements.

Figure 22-1. Magnetite is a mineral with natural magnetic properties.

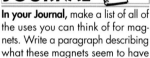

In your Journal, make a list of all of the uses you can think of for magnets. Write a paragraph describing what these magnets seem to have in common.

Magnets

Have you ever stuck two magnets together? The Greeks experimented more than 2000 years ago with a mineral that pulled iron objects toward it. This mineral always pointed north when suspended freely on a string. They described this mineral as being magnetic. Today we know that magnetism is related to electricity. Together, magnetic and electric forces can generate electricity and operate electric motors.

Magnetism is a property of matter in which there is a force of attraction or repulsion between like or unlike poles. The magnetic forces are strongest near the ends, or **magnetic poles**, of the magnets. All magnets have two magnetically opposite poles, north (N), and south (S). If a bar magnet is suspended so it turns freely, the north end will point north.

When you bring the north ends of two magnets close together, they repel. However, the north and south ends will attract. Like magnetic poles repel, and opposite magnetic poles attract. These forces decrease as the distance between the magnets increases.

Only a few materials are naturally magnetic. Permanent magnets are made from materials such as iron, cobalt, and nickel, which retain their magnetic properties for a long time. Can paper clips or nails act like magnets? By being near or rubbing against a magnet, these objects can become temporary magnets, but they lose their magnetic properties soon after they are separated from the other magnet.

574 MAGNETISM AND ITS USES

OPTIONS

Meeting Different Ability Levels

For Section 22-1, use the following **Teacher Resource Masters** depending upon individual students' needs.

◆ **Study Guide Master** for all students.
● **Reinforcement Master** for students of average and above average ability levels.
▲ **Enrichment Master** for above average students.

Additional Teacher Resource Package masters are listed in any PROGRAM RESOURCES boxes that are in the section. The additional masters are appropriate for all students.

◆ **STUDY GUIDE   92**

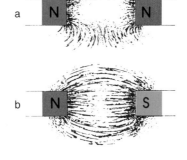

Magnetic Fields

Hold one bar magnet still and move another magnet slowly around it. What happens? Depending on the positions of the magnets, you may feel attractive forces, repulsive forces, or no force at all. The **magnetic field** is the area around the magnet where magnetic forces act. Figure 22-2 shows how you can model the magnetic field by sprinkling iron filings around a bar magnet. The filings line up along the magnetic field lines. Notice that these magnetic lines of force are most dense around the poles. Figure 22-3 shows how magnetic field lines differ when two poles repel or attract.

Have you used a compass to find out which way was north? A compass contains a magnetic needle that freely rotates in a circle and always points north. This happens because Earth is like a giant magnet surrounded by a magnetic field that extends beyond the atmosphere. The compass aligns with Earth's magnetic lines of force.

A Model for Magnetism

Many magnets are made of iron. What happens if you hold an iron nail close to a refrigerator door and let go? Why doesn't it stick to the refrigerator? Why is it that many substances don't become magnets? Because you can't see magnetism, a model, or mental picture, will help you answer these questions.

Electrons in the atoms of most materials exist in pairs and spin in opposite directions. Each spinning electron causes a magnetic field to form around it with a direction that depends on the direction of spin, so the magnetic field of one electron is cancelled by the magnetic field of the other. The atoms in materials such as

Figure 22-2. The magnetic lines of force around this bar magnet can be modeled with iron filings.

Figure 22-3. Notice the magnetic lines of force when like poles repel (a) and unlike poles attract (b).

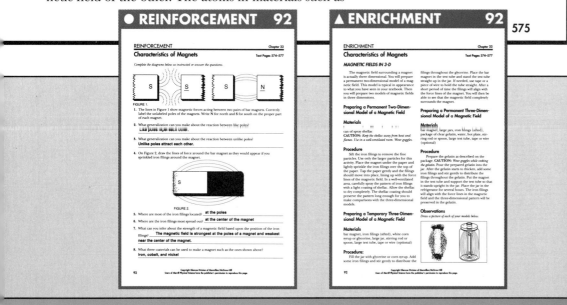
CONCEPT DEVELOPMENT

▶ Begin teaching magnetism by letting students feel the phenomenon and experiment with it. Include ring magnets on a pencil, a horseshoe magnet with some paper clips and nails, and a bar magnet with selected coins. (Canadian nickels are pure nickel and will be attracted by a magnet.)

▶ **Demonstration:** Show the areas of intensity around the ends of bar magnets by scattering iron filings around a bar magnet on an overhead projector. Be sure to put an acetate under the filings to avoid messes. By convention, magnetic field lines are said to go from the north to the south pole.

TEACHER F.Y.I.

▶ The SI unit for magnetic field strength is the tesla (T). Earth's magnetic field intensity at the surface is 10^{-4} T. Magnetic fields generated in the lab commonly reach 10 T and can be up to 100 T for a short time interval.

CROSS CURRICULUM

▶ **Language Arts:** Have students research the origin of the word *magnet*. It comes from the Greek word meaning "the stone of magnesia." This stone was lodestone, a naturally magnetic rock.

PROGRAM RESOURCES

From the **Teacher Resource Package** use:

Technology, pages 19-20, Magnetic Resonance Imaging.

VideoDisc

STVS: Detecting the Body's Magnetic Fields; Disc 7, Side 1

▶ The model of magnetic domains is abstract. Draw an analogy between inducing an electric charge with a charged object and inducing the alignment of magnetic domains with a magnet.

PROBLEM SOLVING

▶ **Answer:** They labeled the green end North and the yellow end South.
Think Critically: The blue and pink bar is not a magnet.

MINI QUIZ

Use the Mini Quiz to check students' recall of chapter content.

1 The area around a magnet where magnetic forces act is the _____ .
magnetic field

2 What will happen if you bring two north poles of magnets together?
They will repel each other.

3 Why might magnets lose their magnetic properties if they are **dropped or heated?** *Their domains become randomized due to increased kinetic energy.*

CHECK FOR UNDERSTANDING

Demonstration: Show how an ordinary paper clip can temporarily exhibit magnetic properties when a magnet is brought near it. Give students several minutes to write an explanation for this observation. *The magnet causes the domains in the paper clip to become aligned, making the paper clip a temporary magnet.*

PROBLEM SOLVING

A Magnetic Puzzle

When Shantelle came to physical science class today, Mrs. Kline placed the students in groups. She gave each group a red and silver magnet, two other metallic bars, and a long piece of string. Mrs. Kline then told the students to work in their group to determine the polarity of the three objects.

Shantelle suggested, "Because Earth has a magnetic field, we can hang the magnet from a string to make a compass. The north pole of the magnet will swing to point to the North Pole."

The group tried Shantelle's suggestion with the red and silver magnet. As a result of their findings, they labeled the red end North and the silver end South. Next, they determined the polarity of a green and yellow bar. The green end of the bar pushed the red end away, and the yellow end attracted the red end.

They tested a blue and pink bar last. The blue end attracted the red end. They were surprised when the pink end also attracted the red end.

How did Shantelle's group label the green and yellow bar?
Think Critically: What should Shantelle's group infer from the results of testing the blue and pink bar?

Figure 22-4. Atoms with paired electrons aren't magnetic, but those atoms with unpaired electrons can be magnetic.

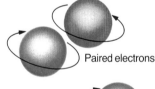

Paired electrons

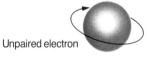

Unpaired electron

iron, cobalt, and nickel have unpaired electrons, so the electrons' magnetic fields do not cancel. As a result, each atom of these elements acts like a very small magnet.

The magnetic field created by each iron atom exerts force on the other atoms, causing groups of atoms to align their magnetic poles so that all like poles are facing the same direction. These groups of atoms are called **magnetic domains.** Figure 22-5b shows how the domains are randomly arranged in an ordinary, unmagnetized nail. If a permanent magnet strokes the nail or comes near it, the domains rearrange to orient themselves in the direction of the nearby magnetic field, as in Figure 22-5a. The nail now acts as a magnet itself. When the external magnetic field is removed, the magnetic domains in the nail soon return to their random arrangement. For this

OPTIONS

INQUIRY QUESTION

▶ **Use the model of magnetic domains to explain how a steel paper clip becomes magnetized.** *The magnetic fields of unpaired electrons in the paper clip align in random clusters, called magnetic domains, throughout the paper clip. When a magnet is brought close, its magnetic field causes the domains in the clip to align, forming a magnet.*

PROGRAM RESOURCES

From the **Teacher Resource Package** use:

Activity Worksheets, page 182, MINI-Lab: What's invisible to a magnetic field?

Use **Laboratory Manual 45,** Magnets.

reason, the nail is a temporary magnet. Even permanent magnets can lose some of their magnetic properties if they are dropped or heated. Their magnetic domains would no longer be aligned due to increased kinetic energy of the particles.

What happens when a magnet is broken in two? Would you expect one piece to be a north pole and one piece to be a south pole? Look again at the domain model in Figure 22-5. Because each magnet is actually made of many aligned smaller magnets, even the smallest pieces have both a north and south pole.

Although people have been observing magnets since the Greeks first discovered them, and the magnetic domain model explains many observations about magnets, some questions are still unanswered. For example, one of the most puzzling questions involves Earth's own magnetic field. We know Earth's magnetic poles have reversed, or flip-flopped north and south, more than 170 times during Earth's history. Scientists are unable to explain why the magnetic field reverses. They have, however, found many uses and applications for magnetism. As you read the next section, you will find out more about these applications.

SECTION REVIEW

1. Describe what happens when you bring two magnetic poles together.
2. What is a magnetic field and where is it strongest?
3. **Apply:** Explain two ways you could use another magnet to rotate the suspended magnet without touching it.
4. **Connect to Earth Science:** When free to rotate, the north pole of a bar magnet will point very close to the geographic North Pole of Earth in the Arctic Circle. Explain why the north pole of the magnet does not point exactly to the geographic North Pole.

☑ Hypothesizing

Suppose you allowed your younger brother or sister to play with a strong bar magnet. When you got it back, it was barely magnetic. Write a hypothesis to explain what might have happened to your magnet. How could you fix it? If you need help, refer to Hypothesizing in the **Skill Handbook** on page 682.

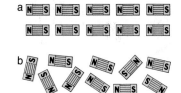

Figure 22-5. Magnetic domains are magnetized (a) and unmagnetized (b).

MINI-Lab

What interferes with a magnetic field?
Clamp a magnet to a ring stand. Thread a needle. Stick the needle on the magnet and tape one end of the thread to the table. Pull the thread until the needle is suspended below the magnet. Slip some paper between the needle and magnet. The needle doesn't fall; therefore, the paper does not interfere with the magnetic field. *Experiment* with materials such as aluminum foil, coins, and other solids. If the needle falls, the substance interferes with the field.

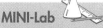

Skill Builder

ENRICHMENT
▶ Give a short lesson in using compasses in orienteering. Have students learn to orient themselves and find hidden markers using only a compass. In nice weather, this makes a good outside activity.
▶ Have students find out what ferromagnetic, paramagnetic, and diamagnetic substances are. They can give oral presentations of their findings.

Skill Builder
A reasonable hypothesis might be that your sibling dropped or heated the magnet. This could scatter the domains and reduce the magnetic properties. To fix it, you could try bringing a strong magnet near it to help realign the domains.

---

3 CLOSE

▶ Ask questions 1-2 and the **Apply** and **Connect to Earth Science** questions in the Section Review.

MINI-Lab
CAUTION: *The needle is a sharp object.*
▶**Materials:** ring stand, utility clamp, needle, thread (one meter), tape, magnet, selection of solids that includes iron and pure nickel
▶The thread can be used to pull the needle about in the field. If the field is very strong, the needle will tend to follow the direction of the field.

MINI-Lab
ASSESSMENT
Oral: Ask students what their conclusions would be about a material that pulled the needle toward it instead of making it fall or having no effect.

SECTION REVIEW ANSWERS
1. Like poles repel; unlike poles attract.
2. a space around a magnet where magnetic forces act; at the poles
3. Apply: Pull the magnet in a circle by bringing opposite poles near each other, or push the magnet around by bringing like poles together.
4. Connect to Earth Science: The north pole of the magnet must be attracted to Earth's magnetic, not the geographic, pole.

PREPARATION

SECTION BACKGROUND
▶ Interestingly, Oersted's discovery was accidental, as many discoveries are. While doing a demonstration, he observed that moving a current through a wire produced a response in a nearby compass. Oersted was a high school teacher!

PREPLANNING
▶ Try to gather some examples of electromagnets, meters, and electric motors for students to experiment with.

1 MOTIVATE

▶ **Demonstration:** Begin with Oersted's experiment. Make about 30 loops of wire and connect it to the positive and negative ends of a battery. Set it near a compass. Then reverse the connections—show how the magnetic field reverses.

▶ Have a fan blowing toward the class when they come in. Ask them what makes the blades of the fan rotate. Note that electrical energy is changed to mechanical energy. See page 580 for an explanation.

TYING TO PREVIOUS
KNOWLEDGE: Tell students that whenever they ring a doorbell, listen to music from loudspeakers, or use an electric motor, they are making use of a connection between electricity and magnetism. This connection will be explored in this section.

New Science Words

electromagnet
ammeters
voltmeters
commutator

Objectives

▶ Explain how a coil carrying electric current can induce a magnetic field.
▶ Compare and contrast ammeters and voltmeters.
▶ Describe the function of an electric motor.

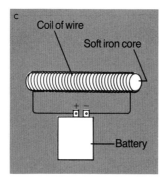

Figure 22-6. Magnetic fields form around any wire that is conducting current (a) and (b). This is the principle behind the electromagnet (c).

Electromagnets

In 1820, Hans Christian Oersted, a Danish physics teacher, observed that a current moving through a wire moved the needle on a nearby compass. When the current was reversed, the compass needle was deflected in the opposite direction. These magnetic effects ceased when the current in the wire stopped. Therefore, Oersted hypothesized, the electric current must produce a magnetic field around the wire, the direction of which changed with the direction of the current.

Figure 22-6a shows magnetic field lines around wires with current in them. Figure 22-6c shows that adding turns of the wire to make a coil causes more overlapping of the magnetic field lines, and, as a result, the magnetic field grows stronger. When a current is passed through such a coil, a strong temporary magnet called an **electromagnet** is formed. One end of the coil acts as the north pole and the other end as the south pole. The strength of the magnetic field can be increased by adding more turns to the wire coil and by increasing the amount of current passing through the wire. The electromagnet can also be made stronger by inserting an iron core inside the coil. The iron core becomes a magnet and its magnetic field is aligned with that of the electromagnet.

Electromagnets operate doorbells and loudspeakers and lift large metal objects in construction machines. They change electrical energy to mechanical energy to

---

OPTIONS

Meeting Different Ability Levels
For Section 22-2, use the following **Teacher Resource Masters** depending upon individual students' needs.
◆ **Study Guide Master** for all students.
● **Reinforcement Master** for students of average and above average ability levels.
▲ **Enrichment Master** for above average students.
Additional Teacher Resource Package masters are listed in any PROGRAM RESOURCES boxes that are in the section. The additional masters are appropriate for all students.

TECHNOLOGY

Flying Trains

Can you imagine flying over the ground at speeds of more than 500 kilometers per hour without an airplane? German and Japanese firms are currently developing high-speed trains that ride on magnets instead of rails.

One such magnetically levitated train, called a maglev, is being built by a German company and will run from the airport to downtown in Las Vegas, Nevada. The undercarriage of this train is lined with strong permanent magnets. These magnets are attracted to steel guide tracks above them, thus providing lift. Electric current is delivered at just the right time to devices mounted on the guide track so they will produce magnetic fields that pull and push the train along at speeds up to 90 km/h.

A high-speed prototype in Japan uses superconductive magnets mounted on the underside of the vehicle. These magnets interact with nonelectric coils in the guide track to produce lift and with electric coils in the guide track to produce the push and pull. This maglev will travel between cities at speeds of 500 km/h.

Think Critically: Compare the advantages and disadvantages of magnetically levitated trains versus standard rail transportation.

do work and can be turned on and off by controlling the flow of current through the coil. What would happen if the magnetic field in the doorbell were permanent instead of temporary?

Meters

Because electromagnets are sensitive to electrical currents, they can detect electric current. An instrument used to detect currents is called a galvanometer. It is made of a coil of wire connected to a circuit and suspended so it can rotate in the magnetic field of a permanent magnet. When current flows through the coil, the magnetic force causes the coil to rotate against a spring. A needle attached to the coil turns with it to provide a reading on a scale.

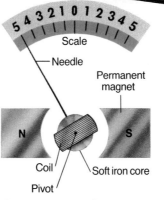

Figure 22-7. A galvanometer uses an electromagnet to detect electric currents.

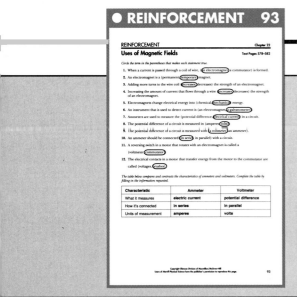

►Use a "perpetual motion" toy (often found in museum stores) to demonstrate how a magnetic field and an electric coil interact to produce motion.

►To find out more about maglevs, refer to "310-mph Flying Trains—in the '90s—in the U.S." by David Scott and John Free, *Popular Science*, May 1989, pp. 132-135.

►**Think Critically:** Magnetically levitated trains may be quieter and cheaper to operate than current trains because of the reduced friction. Maglev trains would be faster, but this might increase the accident potential.

2 TEACH

Key Concepts are highlighted.

CONCEPT DEVELOPMENT

►Use the right-hand rule to determine the direction of a magnetic field or current. Place the right thumb in the direction of the current through the wire. The fingers of the right hand then curl in the direction of the magnetic field.

►A coil of wire with many turns placed close together is called a solenoid.

Cooperative Learning: Divide the class into Science Investigation Teams. Have each team build an electromagnet by coiling wire around a large iron nail. Then have them select items they would like to try to pick up (paper clips, staples, etc.).

►There are situations where a magnetic field around a wire is not desired. Ask students if they have any idea how this problem could be avoided. An insulated wire with current traveling in the opposite direction can be placed beside the original wire or wrapped around it. This causes the total current and the total magnetic field to be zero.

VideoDisc
STVS: Electric Heart; Disc 1, Side 2

CROSS CURRICULUM

▶ **Music/Acoustics:** Have students research the function of an electromagnet in a loudspeaker, write a clear explanation, and draw a scientific diagram to illustrate how it works. If possible, take a real speaker apart and identify the parts.

TEACHER F.Y.I.

▶ The resistance of an ammeter must be very low compared to the total resistance in the circuit. This prevents the meter from interfering with the current it is measuring. A voltmeter should have a huge resistance so that little current passes through it.

CHECK FOR UNDERSTANDING

Use the Mini Quiz to check for understanding.

MINI QUIZ

Use the Mini Quiz to check students' recall of chapter content.

1 **How is an electromagnet formed?** *by passing a current through a coil, usually with an iron core*

2 **Who discovered that a compass responds to current moving through a wire?** *Hans Christian Oersted*

3 **An instrument that can be used to detect current or potential difference is a(n) _____ .** *galvanometer*

4 **A(n) _____ is a reversing switch that rotates with the electromagnet.** *commutator*

Connect to...
Earth Science

Answer: Many geophones use a suspended coil of wire and a permanent magnet to generate a current in response to movement caused by explosions or earthquakes.

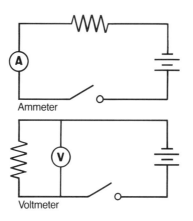

Ammeter

Voltmeter

Connect to...
Earth Science

Geologists often use electromagnetic devices called seismographs, or geophones. Find out what these devices measure and how they work.

A galvanometer can be calibrated to measure current or electrical potential depending on whether it will be used as an ammeter or a voltmeter. **Ammeters** measure the electrical current passing through a circuit in amperes and should be connected in series with the circuit.

Voltmeters measure the potential difference of a circuit in volts. Unlike ammeters, voltmeters should be placed in parallel across a part of a circuit. The reading in volts depends on the amount of current passing through the voltmeter. The higher the current, the larger the potential difference across that part of the circuit.

Electric Motors

Do you ever use an electric fan to keep cool? Your fan has an electric motor in it that changes electrical energy into mechanical energy to turn the blades. The turning blades push air toward you so your skin feels cooler.

Like galvanometers, the electric motors contain an electromagnet that is free to rotate. It rotates between opposite poles of a permanent, fixed magnet. When a current flows through the moveable electromagnet, a magnetic field is induced. This causes enough attraction and repulsion with the permanent magnet to force the coil to turn. But the rotation would stop once the magnetic fields aligned. How could you make the coil turn again?

To make the coil in the fan motor spin steadily, the direction of the current through the coil must be reversed after each half revolution. This causes the poles of the

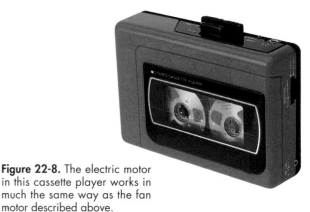

Figure 22-8. The electric motor in this cassette player works in much the same way as the fan motor described above.

OPTIONS

ASSESSMENT—ORAL

▶ **What part of a galvanometer is actually an electromagnet?** *the coil of wire that is connected to the circuit and suspended in the magnetic field*

▶ **Why does the coil in a galvanometer rotate when current passes through it?** *It becomes an electromagnet, and because it is suspended in the magnetic field of a permanent magnet, it will rotate so the magnetic fields are aligned.*

PROGRAM RESOURCES

From the **Teacher Resource Package** use:

Transparency Masters, pages 87-88, DC Generator.

Cross-Curricular Connections, page 28, Library Research.

Concept Mapping, pages 49-50.

Use **Color Transparency** number 44, DC Generator.

Use **Laboratory Manual 46,** Electromagnets.

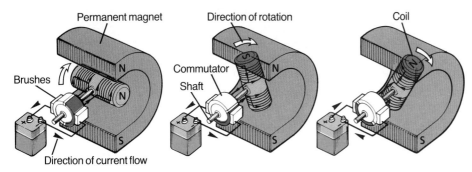

Permanent magnet   Direction of rotation   Coil

Brushes

N

N

Commutator
Shaft

S

S

Direction of current flow

rotating electromagnet to switch and turn toward the opposite pole of the permanent magnet. A stereo cassette player's electric motor operating on batteries must have a device to change the direction of the current. A **commutator** is a reversing switch that rotates with the electromagnet. Electric current reaches the commutator through fixed electrical contacts called brushes. The continual rotation of the electromagnet in your cassette player's motor keeps the cassette's motors turning. As you will learn in the next section, current supplied by the potential difference in a wall outlet reverses itself at a regular rate and many devices that operate on household current do not require a commutator.

Figure 22-9. The commutator in a motor switches the direction of the current so the coil will turn continuously.

④

Did You Know?

Lightning can magnetize objects so strongly that they are capable of lifting objects as much as three times their own weight.

SECTION REVIEW

1. Does a straight wire or a looped wire have a stronger magnetic field when both carry the same amount of current? Explain your answer.
2. What is a galvanometer?
3. **Apply:** Why does an iron core increase the magnetic field inside a coil carrying current?
4. **Connect to Earth Science:** Recycling conserves Earth's resources. How could a magnet be used in separating recyclable materials?

☑ **Comparing and Contrasting**

Compare and contrast ammeters and voltmeters. Discuss what they measure and how they are connected to the rest of the circuit. If you need help, refer to Comparing and Contrasting in the **Skill Handbook** on page 679.

Skill Builder

Skill Builder

RETEACH

Demonstration: Make three electromagnets from iron nails wrapped in wire. Wrap the first one with only a few coils, the second one with more coils, the third one with many coils. Compare the magnetic strength of the three electromagnets by attempting to pick up a number of paper clips. Discuss how increasing the number of coils causes the magnetic field lines to overlap.

EXTENSION

For students who have mastered this section, use the **Reinforcement** and **Enrichment** masters or other OPTIONS provided.

3 CLOSE

▶ Ask questions 1-2 and the **Apply** and **Connect to Earth Science** questions in the Section Review.
▶ Review the making of a magnetic field from a current traveling through a wire. Bridge to the fact that a current can also be induced by moving a wire through a magnetic field.

SECTION REVIEW ANSWERS

1. The loop has a stronger magnetic field because its magnetic field lines overlap.
2. A galvanometer is an instrument used to detect electric currents.
3. Apply: The current induces the iron to become a magnet also, increasing the magnetic field.
4. Connect to Earth Science: A magnet can be used to separate iron from other metals.

Skill Builder

Ammeters are designed to measure current and should be connected in series. Voltmeters measure potential difference and should be connected in parallel.

Skill Builder
ASSESSMENT

Oral: Ask students which device they would use to measure current in a stereo. How would they connect it?

ENRICHMENT

▶ Have students research the medical or research applications of magnetic resonance imaging. Perhaps a technician at a local hospital could visit or be interviewed about this technique.

MULTICULTURAL PERSPECTIVE

Foiled Again!
James West is an African American experimental physicist who is the coinventor of the foil electret. This device uses a paper-thin piece of plastic that is coated with metal on one side to convert sound into electrical signals. It is used in hearing aids, small microphones, and portable tape recorders. As a result of this development, all the devices mentioned above can be made much smaller and still be effective.

ACTIVITY 22-1
one class period

OBJECTIVE: Construct and **test** a working example of an electric motor.

PROCESS SKILLS applied in this activity:
▶ **Observing** in Procedure Step 3.
▶ **Formulating Models** in Procedure Steps 1, 4, and 6.
▶ **Predicting** in Conclude and Apply Questions 4 and 5.

COOPERATIVE LEARNING
Arrange the students in Expert Teams of four. Two students can build the field, and two students can build the armature.

TEACHING THE ACTIVITY

Troubleshooting: Build a working model to determine the lengths of wire needed.
▶ Make available a pair of wire cutters or strong scissors.
▶ Procedure Step 5 is critical. About 180 degrees around the wire must be scraped to allow current to flow long enough during a revolution of the armature. The *same* side of both ends must be scraped.
▶ Put your working model on display for student reference.
▶ Use the trial and error of this activity as an opportunity for students to devise solutions through careful observation and analysis.

PROGRAM RESOURCES
From the **Teacher Resource Package** use:
    Activity Worksheets, pages 176-177, Activity 22-1: Electric Motors.

Electric Motors

What examples of electric motors in your home can you think of? In this activity, you will construct a sample electric motor and analyze how it works.

Materials
- paper cup or beaker
- nail
- magnet wire, 22 ga
- magnet wire, 32 ga
- bare copper wire, 16 ga
- soda straw
- tape
- 6-volt batteries (2)
- sandpaper
- magnetic compass

Procedure
1. Construct the field coil as shown by wrapping wire around the top of the plastic cup or beaker.
2. Sandpaper the coating from 3 cm of each end of the wire.
3. Test the field coil by holding the compass inside the coil and connecting the wires to a battery. The compass should respond.
4. Construct the armature as shown. Make the direction of wrap of wire the same on both sides of the armature.
5. Scrape the coating from only one side of the ends of the armature wire that extend from each end of the straw.
6. Assemble as shown. The bare 16 ga wire should be wrapped around the beaker with a flat surface at the top on both sides to support the armature. Attach the batteries and start the motor.

Analyze
1. When testing the field coil, *infer* what the movement of the compass tells you about the field.
2. The armature is designed to turn on and off as it spins. What test could you use to see if it is working?
3. As the armature spins, what is the best position for it to turn on? At what position should it turn off?

Conclude and Apply
4. *Predict* if the motor would work if the field coil were replaced by a permanent magnet.
5. Why would the motor not work if the armature were replaced by a permanent magnet?

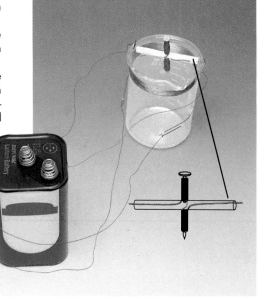

ANSWERS TO QUESTIONS
1. The response of the compass shows that the field is magnetic and that its poles are at the open ends of the coil.
2. With the field current turned off, hold a compass near the armature as it is turned by hand. Or, a light connected in series with the armature as it is turned by hand should go on and off.
3. The armature should be on when horizontal and go off when vertical.
4. Yes. The field remains constant.

5. The shape of a permanent magnet cannot be easily changed, and the field cannot be strengthened to get the motor to function.

Activity
ASSESSMENT
Performance: Ask students to predict what would happen if the coating were not scraped off one side of the armature wire. Try it.

Producing Electric Current

Objectives

▶ Describe how a generator produces an electric current using electromagnetic induction.
▶ Distinguish between alternating current and direct current.
▶ Explain how a transformer can step up or step down the voltage of an alternating current.

New Science Words

electromagnetic induction
generator
direct current (DC)
alternating current (AC)
transformer

Generators

After Oersted discovered that magnetism could be produced from electric currents, scientists tried to produce an electric current using magnets. Working independently in 1831, a British scientist, Michael Faraday, and an American scientist, Joseph Henry, found that moving a wire through a magnetic field induced an electric current in that wire. **Electromagnetic induction** is the process by which moving a wire through a magnetic field produces a current. Moving a magnet in and out of a coil of wire also produces a current. This important discovery led to numerous applications. Most of the electrical energy you use has been converted to useful electricity by electromagnetic induction.

Have you wondered what produces the electricity that comes to your home and school? Most of the electricity you use each day was electromagnetically induced in generators. A **generator** produces electric current by rotating a loop of wire in a magnetic field. The wire loop is connected to a source of mechanical energy and placed between the poles of a magnet, as shown in Figure 22-10. The design of the generator is very much like that of an electric

Figure 22-10. Electric current is produced in a generator when a loop of wire is rotated in a magnetic field.

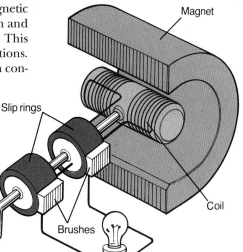

Magnet

Slip rings

Shaft

Brushes

Coil

PREPARATION

SECTION BACKGROUND

▶ Michael Faraday made many discoveries in the areas of chemistry and physics. Apprenticed to a bookseller at the age of 14, his scientific background was largely self-taught, as he had almost no formal education. He also hypothesized that light consisted of vibrations of electric and magnetic field lines, an idea later expressed in mathematical form by Maxwell.
▶ Some records indicate that Joseph Henry discovered electromagnetic induction in the United States in the same year of Faraday's work (1831).

PREPLANNING

▶ Obtain a strong magnet and a TV monitor for the demonstration below.
▶ Obtain a hand-crank generator and a small light bulb for the demonstration on page 584.

1 MOTIVATE

▶ **Demonstration:** Bring a strong magnet near an old television screen that is turned on to show what happens. Magnetic fields around a television picture tube direct the beam of electrons from the back of the tube to strike the screen at the front and produce an image. A bar magnet brought close to the face of the tube changes the magnetic field around the tube and distorts the image. The distortion is evidence that moving electrons are affected by magnetic fields. **CAUTION:** *This is not suggested for home trials. This can damage the picture tube.*

TYING TO PREVIOUS KNOWLEDGE:
Ask students to recall Oersted's discovery that an electric current produces a magnetic field. Explain that they will now learn how a changing magnetic field can produce a current in a coil.

OPTIONS

ENRICHMENT

▶ Have students work in groups to build a simple generator and then have them demonstrate how their generator works for the other students in the class.
▶ Have students find out the difference between AC (alternating current) generators and DC (direct current) generators. Have them draw a diagram of each, label the parts, and list the function of each part.

OBJECTIVES AND
SCIENCE WORDS: Have students review the objectives and science words to become familiar with this section.

2 TEACH

Key Concepts are highlighted.

CONCEPT DEVELOPMENT

▶ Emphasize that the electromagnetic induction process occurs only when the magnetic field is changing or the wire loop is moving. When both are stationary, no current is produced.

▶ Ask students where they have heard the word *generator* before. Some will probably mention the connection between electric plants and generators. **But where does the electrical energy come from?** *Mechanical energy is converted to electrical energy.*

▶ **Demonstration:** Use a hand-crank generator to produce enough electricity to light a small bulb. When you turn it faster, the bulb burns more brightly. The mechanical work is converted to electrical energy. Now disconnect the bulb and turn the crank. It is easier to turn because there is no load. The class will notice the cranking speed slow if the bulb is inserted while a student is turning the crank.

CROSS CURRICULUM

▶ **Earth Science:** Have students research the Van Allen radiation belts, composed of charged particles captured by Earth's magnetic field. Have interested students explain the Aurora Borealis (the northern lights).

Connect to...
Earth Science

Answer: Moving water rotates the turbine. Water is inexpensive and does not pollute, but dams may change ecosystems and reduce downstream water flow.

VideoDisc
STVS: Mini-Hydroelectric Power Plants; Disc 2, Side 2

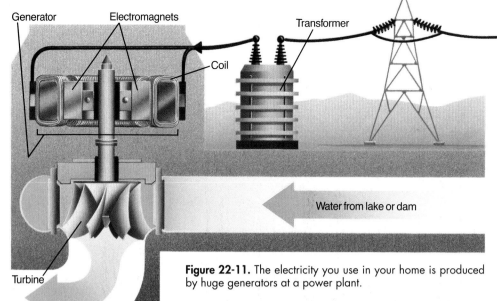

Generator   Electromagnets   Transformer

Coil

Water from lake or dam

Turbine

Connect to...
Earth Science

Study the hydroelectric generator diagrammed above. What role does water play in generating electricity? What might be some advantages and disadvantages of using water from a dam to push the turbine?

What is a turbine?

Figure 22-11. The electricity you use in your home is produced by huge generators at a power plant.

motor, except the wire loop is made to rotate by external forces. When it rotates, an electric current is produced. This is the opposite of how a motor acts. In a generator, the wire crosses through the magnetic lines of force as it rotates, causing electrons to move along the wire in one direction. After one-half revolution of the wire loop, the current changes direction. As a result, the direction of the current changes twice with each revolution. The rotation speed of generators is regulated so the current always changes direction with the same frequency.

Do you have a generator in your home that supplies all the electricity you need to watch television or wash your clothes? Probably not! You get your electricity from huge generators at a power plant. These generators are more complex than the ones discussed here. The electromagnets in these generators are made of many loops of wire wrapped around iron cores. A source of mechanical energy is needed to rotate the loop in the generator. One such source, a turbine, is a large wheel that rotates when pushed by water, wind, or steam. Potential energy released by the burning of fossil fuels or from nuclear reactions can heat water to produce steam. The thermal energy of the steam changes to mechanical energy as it pushes the turbine. The generator then changes this mechanical energy into an electric current that is easily conducted to your home.

584 MAGNETISM AND ITS USES

OPTIONS

Meeting Different Ability Levels

For Section 22-3, use the following **Teacher Resource Masters** depending upon individual students' needs.

◆ **Study Guide Master** for all students.

● **Reinforcement Master** for students of average and above average ability levels.

▲ **Enrichment Master** for above average students.

Additional Teacher Resource Package masters are listed in any PROGRAM RESOURCES boxes that are in the section. The additional masters are appropriate for all students.

◆ **STUDY GUIDE** 94

Direct and Alternating Currents

Do you have a tape player that operates either on batteries or on the electric current in your home? Is the electric current from a generator the same as the current produced by a dry cell? Both devices cause the electrons to move through a wire and can operate appliances. However, the currents produced by these electric sources are not the same.

When you use a battery to run your tape player, you are using direct current. **Direct current (DC)** flows only in one direction through a wire. Electrons always move out of the negative terminal toward the positive terminal.

❸ When you plug your tape player into the wall outlet, you are using alternating current. **Alternating current (AC)** reverses its direction in a regular pattern. In North America, generators produce alternating current at a frequency of 60 cycles per second (60 Hz). Because current in a generator changes direction twice during each rotation of the shaft, 60-Hz alternating current changes direction 120 times each second.

Are electric currents produced by a dry cell and a generator the same?

Figure 22-12. Some electrical devices, such as the tape player shown, are designed to operate on AC or DC.

Transformers

The alternating current traveling through power lines is at an extremely high voltage. Before alternating current from the power plant can enter your home, its voltage must be decreased. The current must flow

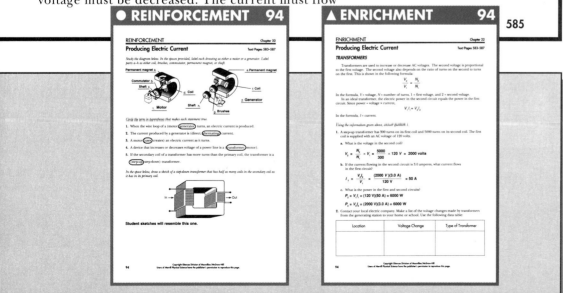
585

CONCEPT DEVELOPMENT

▶ It is advantageous to use large step-up transformers to transmit alternating current through power lines at high voltage and low current. The rate at which heat is dissipated from a resistor as a current passes through it is given by the relationship $P = I^2R$. Therefore, transmitting low current values reduces the energy lost as heat in the transmission lines.

REVEALING MISCONCEPTIONS

▶ On the surface it seems that a step-up transformer gives you "free electricity." Review the law of conservation of energy. The same energy is transferred from the primary to the secondary coil, with no gain in energy. In fact, some energy may be lost as low-temperature thermal energy to the iron core of the transformer.

Science and WRITING

Results will vary; each method has advantages and disadvantages. Students should identify these.

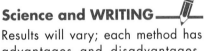

In Your JOURNAL

televisions, radios, doorbells, and so on; a step-down transformer with 13 times more primary coils than secondary coils

CHECK FOR UNDERSTANDING

Use the Mini Quiz to check for understanding.

MINI QUIZ

Use the Mini Quiz to check students' recall of chapter content.

1 **What is the process by which a current is produced by moving a wire through a magnetic field?** *electromagnetic induction*

2 **A generator operates by changing _____ energy into _____ energy.** *mechanical; electrical*

3 **Which kind of current reverses its direction in a regular pattern?** *alternating current*

4 **A device that can decrease the voltage of electricity before it enters your home is called a(n) _____ .** *step-down transformer*

In Your JOURNAL

What kinds of devices in your house are likely to use transformers? **In your Journal,** write a paragraph explaining how a transformer would convert a 120 V AC input to a 9 V output in a portable cassette player.

What is a transformer?

Science and WRITING

Write to your local electric company and find out how your electricity is generated. How does this method of generating electricity compare with others?

What kind of transformer decreases voltage?

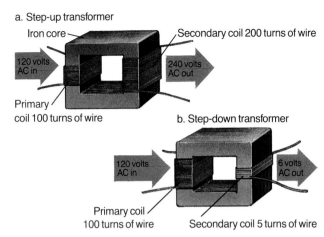

Figure 22-13. A step-up transformer increases voltage (a), and a step-down transformer decreases voltage (b).

through a device called a transformer so the voltage is lowered to a useful level. A **transformer** can increase or decrease the voltage of an alternating current. The operation of a transformer involves principles of both electromagnetism and electromagnetic induction.

A simple transformer is made of two coils of wire called the primary and secondary coils. These coils are wrapped around an iron core, as shown in Figure 22-13. As an alternating current passes through the primary coil, the iron core becomes an electromagnet. Because the current varies in direction, the magnetic field also changes its direction and induces an alternating current in the secondary coil. If the secondary coil has more turns of wire than the primary coil, then it increases, or steps up, voltage. If the secondary coil has fewer turns of wire than the primary coil, it decreases, or steps down, voltage.

A transformer reduces the voltage of the alternating current to 120 volts before it enters your home. A transformer that reduces voltage is called a step-down transformer. Figure 22-13 shows how the output voltage of a transformer will be decreased if the number of turns in the secondary coil is less than the number of turns in the primary coil. Suppose the secondary coil of a transformer has half as many turns as the primary coil. An input voltage of 120 V will yield an output voltage of 60 V. Step-down transformers allow you to operate devices such

---

OPTIONS

ENRICHMENT

▶ Have students call the local electric company and find out what a typical voltage of the power lines in your neighborhood would be. They may be able to provide diagrams or pictures of the transformers they use. Locate where the transformers around you are.

PROGRAM RESOURCES

From the **Teacher Resource Package** use:

Transparency Masters, pages 89-90, Transformers.

Science and Society, page 26, High-Voltage Power Lines.

Critical Thinking/Problem Solving, page 28, Making Electric Power Decisions.

Science Integration Activity 22

Use **Color Transparency** number 45, Transformers.

as tape players, model trains, and doorbells with 120-V household current.

Power plants commonly produce alternating current because its voltage can be increased or decreased with transformers. To transmit alternating current efficiently over long distances, power plants increase their voltages to very high values. In a step-up transformer the output voltage is greater than the input voltage because the secondary coil has more turns than the primary coil. For example, the secondary coil of a step-up transformer at a generating plant may have 100 times the number of turns as the primary coil. That means that an input voltage of 2000 V would increase to 200 000 V—high voltage indeed!

Think back over this section. Could you describe how electromagnetic induction, generators, alternating current, and transformers all affect your tape player? See if you can recall the series of steps in which AC current is produced, transported, and delivered to your home in a form that you can safely use.

SECTION REVIEW

1. How does a generator use electromagnetic induction to produce a current?
2. A transformer in a neon sign contains 20 turns in the primary coil and 80 turns in the secondary coil. Which is greater—the output voltage or the input voltage?
3. Compare and contrast alternating current and direct current.
4. **Apply:** Explain why a transformer can't be used to step up the voltage in a direct current.
5. **Connect to Life Science:** What type of fields are generated by high voltage lines? What effect do these fields have on humans?

☑ Concept Mapping

Prepare an events chain concept map to show how electricity is produced by a generator, as discussed on pages 583 and 584. If you need help, refer to Concept Mapping in the **Skill Handbook** on pages 684 and 685.

Skill Builder

Skill Builder

```
┌─────────────────────────────┐
│     Mechanical energy       │
└─────────────────────────────┘
           makes the
              ↓
┌─────────────────────────────┐
│      Wire loop rotate       │
└─────────────────────────────┘
      which cuts through the
              ↓
┌─────────────────────────────┐
│      Magnetic field         │
└─────────────────────────────┘
          inducing an
              ↓
┌─────────────────────────────┐
│    Alternating current      │
└─────────────────────────────┘
```

Skill Builder
ASSESSMENT
Performance: Have students make a concept map to show how mechanical energy is produced by an electric motor. Compare both maps.

PROGRAM RESOURCES

From the **Teacher Resource Package** use:

Activity Worksheets, page 5, Flex Your Brain.

RETEACH

▶ Do the Skill Builder activity in class to show how electricity is produced by a generator.

EXTENSION

For students who have mastered this section, use the **Reinforcement** and **Enrichment** masters or other OPTIONS provided.

3 CLOSE

❓ FLEX Your Brain

Use the Flex Your Brain activity to have students explore USES OF ALTERNATING AND DIRECT CURRENT.

ASSESSMENT
Portfolio: Use the Flex Your Brain activity to reinforce critical-thinking and problem-solving skills. In Step 2, students might list examples of appliances that use each type of current.

▶ Ask questions 1-3 and the **Apply** and **Connect to Life Science** questions in the Section Review.

SECTION REVIEW ANSWERS

1. Turning a loop of wire in a magnetic field induces a current in the loop.
2. the output voltage
3. Alternating current reverses its direction at regular intervals and is produced by a generator. Direct current travels only in one direction and is produced by systems such as dry cells.
4. **Apply:** The current in the secondary coil in a transformer is induced by the fluctuating magnetic field. DC creates a constant magnetic field. A changing magnetic field is required for electromagnetic induction.
5. **Connect to Life Science:** High voltage lines create intense magnetic fields capable of lighting fluorescent bulbs. Their effect on people is unknown, but is of increasing concern.

PREPARATION

SECTION BACKGROUND

▶ The levitation of a magnet over a superconductor can be explained by a theory called the Meissner effect. The current carried by a superconductor must move on the surface.

1 MOTIVATE

▶ Show a superconductor levitating a magnet. Demonstration kits can be purchased relatively inexpensively, or you might be able to borrow one from a nearby college.

TYING TO PREVIOUS
KNOWLEDGE: Previously, students learned that incandescent bulbs produce light as a result of passing current through a filament, which would produce heat and light because of electrical resistance. A superconductor is a material that loses all electrical resistance, so a current can actually move without energy loss for years.

Connect to...
Chemistry

Answer: Y, at. no. 39; Ba, at. no. 56; Cu, at. no. 29; O, at. no. 8. All are metals except O.

2 TEACH

Key Concepts are highlighted.

CONCEPT DEVELOPMENT

▶ As an analogy to explain the advantage of superconductors, imagine yourself on a bumpy road on roller skates. Once you are moving, you will lose energy due to friction with the ground. But if you are on frictionless ice, you cannot stop. A current in a normal conductor experiences some resistance as it moves, but it can move without resistance in a superconductor.

SCIENCE & SOCIETY **22-4** **Superconductivity**

New Science Words

superconductors

Objectives

▶ Describe the characteristics of superconductors.
▶ Consider various applications of superconductivity.

Connect to...
Chemistry

In 1987, a new compound of yttrium, barium, copper, and oxygen was discovered to be superconducting at 90 K. Find the symbols and atomic numbers of these four elements and identify each as a metal, a nonmetal, or a metalloid.

Are Superconductors Important?

What do you think about the idea of having train systems that would be levitated, or suspended over magnets, instead of running on rails? How would this be possible?

Recall that conducting materials all have some resistance to electron flow. Some of the electricity moving through the conductor is lost as heat due to this resistance. Likewise, as the temperature of a material increases, the resistance of the material increases. Ideally, the most efficient transfer of electricity would occur if conducting materials had no electrical resistance.

Superconductors are materials that have no electrical resistance. In 1911, a Dutch physicist, Heike Kamerlingh Onnes, discovered that some materials lose all electrical resistance when cooled to temperatures near absolute zero (0 K), −273°C. The temperature at which a material becomes superconducting is called the critical temperature.

One way to cool a material to superconducting temperatures is to submerge it in liquid helium. Helium is normally a gas, but it liquifies at 4.2 K. In 1986, Bednorz and Muller received a Nobel prize for making a ceramic

material that became a superconductor at 30 K. This opened a new field of research to find "high temperature" superconductors. New materials have been developed that are superconducting at more than 120 K.

Because superconductors have no electrical resistance, a current can flow indefinitely through them without losing energy. In one experiment, a current traveled through a superconducting loop for more than two years without losing energy. This characteristic of superconductors gives them potential for many different uses.

OPTIONS

Meeting Different Ability Levels

For Section 22-4, use the following **Teacher Resource Masters** depending upon individual students' needs.

◆ **Study Guide Master** for all students.
● **Reinforcement Master** for students of average and above average ability levels.
▲ **Enrichment Master** for above average students.

◆ STUDY GUIDE **95**

STUDY GUIDE   Chapter 22
Superconductivity   Text Pages 588-590

Determine whether each statement agrees with what was said in your textbook. If the statement agrees, write "agree" in the space provided. If the statement does not agree, rewrite the statement to make it agree.

1. Conducting materials have some resistance to electron flow. **agree**

2. Some electricity moving through a conductor is lost as friction. **Some electricity moving through a conductor is lost as heat.**

3. Materials that have no electrical resistance are called insulators. **Materials that have no electrical resistance are called superconductors.**

4. Some materials lose all electrical resistance when cooled to temperatures near absolute zero. **agree**

5. Absolute zero is −273 K. **Absolute zero is 0 K.**

6. One way to cool a material to superconducting temperatures is to submerge it in helium gas. **One way to cool a material to superconducting temperatures is to submerge it in liquid helium.**

7. The temperature at which a material becomes a superconductor is called the critical temperature. **agree**

8. Superconductors could make electric motors, generators, and computer parts more efficient. **agree**

9. A current that flows through a superconductor can flow indefinitely, but it loses some energy. **A current that flows through a superconductor can flow indefinitely without losing energy.**

10. A magnet moving away from a conductor induces a current in the conductor. **A magnet moving toward a conductor induces a current in the conductor.**

Copyright Glencoe Division of Macmillan/McGraw-Hill
Users of Merrill Physical Science have the publisher's permission to reproduce this page.   95

The use of superconductors could eliminate much of the electrical energy waste that we experience today. Ten percent of the energy transmitted through electrical power lines is lost as heat. For similar reasons, superconductors could make electric motors, generators, and computer parts more efficient as well. One problem to be resolved is that superconducting materials are often brittle, and therefore hard to shape into wires.

The picture at the right shows the spectacular levitation effects of magnets over superconductors. Recall that a magnet moving toward a conductor induces a current in the conductor. The current, in turn, produces a magnetic field. If the conductor is a superconductor cooled to its critical temperature, the current will move continuously through it. The magnetic forces of these currents repel the magnet and cause the magnet to float, or levitate, above the superconductor. This is the principle behind levitated trains. If a train had a powerful magnet beneath it and the rails were made of a superconducting material, the train would move above the rails. The only friction would be with the air. It would lose little energy to the environment and would not give off pollutants. What do you think it would be like to ride on a superconducting train?

SECTION REVIEW

1. How do superconductors differ from ordinary conductors?
2. Explain how a magnet levitates over a superconductor.
3. **Connect to Chemistry:** What physical property of superconducting materials currently prevents them from being used in devices such as computers or motors?

You Decide!

What would be the advantages and disadvantages of developing superconducting trains? Use information in this section to determine what the difficulties of perfecting this system might be. Do you think superconducting trains would be one part of the solution to energy shortages?

SCIENCE & SOCIETY

589

Ask students why people are so anxious to find materials that will be superconducting at higher temperatures. Ask them how they would build a train system if the superconductors had to be continually cooled with liquid helium or nitrogen.

RETEACH
Have the students calculate how cold the "high temperature" superconductors actually are. Convert 120 K to °C. 120 − 273 = −153°C. That is far below the freezing point of water! This should help students realize how inconvenient it would be to keep superconductors cool.

EXTENSION
For students who have mastered this section, use the **Reinforcement** and **Enrichment** masters or other OPTIONS provided.

3 CLOSE

▶ Ask questions 1-2 and the **Connect to Chemistry** question in the Section Review.

SECTION REVIEW ANSWERS
1. Superconductors have no resistance to electrical currents.
2. A magnet moving toward a wire loop induces a current in the loop. The magnetic force caused by these currents repels the magnets.
3. Connect to Chemistry: They are brittle, so it is hard to make wires.

YOU DECIDE!
Answers will vary. Make sure students can support their answers. Also see Technology on p. 579 for more information.

OBJECTIVE: Construct a simple transformer and compare the energy-carrying abilities of magnetic fields.
Time: one class period

PROCESS SKILLS applied in this activity are **observing** and **interpreting.**

PREPARATION
Be sure to test the batteries and bulbs ahead of time.
Cooperative Learning: Use the Science Investigation Team strategy in groups of two or three.

SAFETY
The output voltage of the AC supply should not exceed 7 volts. Remind the students that unauthorized experiments should not be performed in this activity.

THINKING CRITICALLY
Transformers are usually used to increase or decrease the voltage in a part of a circuit. Alternating current can pass through a transformer.

TEACHING THE ACTIVITY
Refer to the **Activity Worksheet** *for additional information and teaching strategies.*

• For low-voltage bulbs, cut apart a string of mini-lights for Christmas trees and strip about 1-cm of plastic coating from the ends of the wires. Bulbs rated for 1.5 V will be brighter.
• A 117 to 6.5-volt transformer, such as is used for doorbells, can be used for an AC source. Be sure students are shielded from the high voltage side of the AC source.
• Coat the coils with glue and cut the straw to separate them. They can be used in other experiments.

Activity
ASSESSMENT
Content: Ask students to explain what kind of current can transfer energy through changing magnetic fields.

DESIGNING AN EXPERIMENT
Trying Transformers

Review the design of transformers in the previous section. How does a current move between the unconnected coils of wire? Build and experiment with the transformer described below to seek an answer to this question.

Getting Started
In this activity you will construct a transformer and attempt to pass both alternating and direct current through the unconnected coils of wire. Try not to leave the circuits connected for more than a few seconds at a time to avoid overheating.

Thinking Critically
For what purpose are transformers used? What kind of current can pass through a transformer?

Materials
Your cooperative group will use:
• battery, 6 V
• AC power supply, low voltage
• light, low voltage
• insulated wire, 32 ga
• large nail
• soda straw, cut to length of nail
• knife or scissors
• paper clip

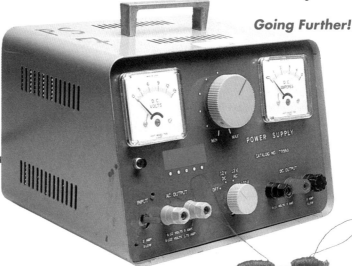

Try It!
1. Construct the transformer. Insert the nail in the straw. Wrap 300 turns of the insulated wire in a tight coil at one end of the straw. Use another piece of wire to make an identical coil at the other end. Scrape the insulation off the wire ends with the knife or scissors.
2. Connect the battery to one coil and the light to the other coil. *Observe* the bulb. Gently touch the nail with a paper clip.
3. Connect the AC source in place of the battery. *Observe* the light and notice the reaction of the paper clip when you gently touch the nail with it.

Summing Up/Sharing Results
How does the DC battery magnetism differ from the AC magnetism?

Going Further!
Observe the light as you slide the nail out of the straw. What happens? The nail is similar to a standard part in most transformers. What is the role and purpose of the nail in this design?

SUMMING UP/SHARING RESULTS
Both the DC (from the battery) and the AC (from the power supply) produce a magnetic field. Energy only reaches the light when AC moves through the primary coil. The DC from the battery produces a steady magnetic field, but the AC causes a changing magnetic field.

GOING FURTHER!
The magnetic field disappears and the bulb does not light. The nail acts as the iron core of the transformer, which becomes an electromagnet when AC passes through the primary coil.

PROGRAM RESOURCES
From the **Teacher Resource Package** use:
Activity Worksheets, pages 178-179, Activity 22-2: Trying Transformers.

SUMMARY

22-1: Characteristics of Magnets

1. Opposite poles of magnets attract; like poles repel.
2. The magnetic field is the area around the magnet where magnetic forces act.
3. Groups of atoms with aligned magnetic poles are called magnetic domains.

22-2: Uses of Magnetic Fields

1. An electric current passing through a coil of wire can produce a magnetic field around the wire. The coil becomes an electromagnet; one end of the coil forms the magnet's north pole, and the other end forms the south pole.
2. Ammeters measure electrical current in amperes and should be connected in series. Voltmeters measure the potential difference in volts and should be connected parallel.
3. An electric motor contains a rotating electromagnet that converts electrical energy to mechanical energy.

22-3: Producing Electric Current

1. A generator produces electric current by rotating a loop of wire in a magnetic field.
2. Direct current flows in one direction through a wire; alternating current reverses its direction in a regular pattern.
3. The number of turns of wire in the primary and secondary coils of a transformer determine whether it increases or decreases voltage.

22-4: Science and Society: Superconductivity

1. Superconductors are materials that have no electrical resistance.
2. The use of superconductors can eliminate electrical energy waste in the form of heat. Magnets used with superconductors could provide alternatives to current transportation methods.

KEY SCIENCE WORDS

a. **alternating current (AC)**
b. **ammeter**
c. **commutator**
d. **direct current (DC)**
e. **electromagnet**
f. **electromagnetic induction**
g. **generator**
h. **magnetic domain**
i. **magnetic field**
j. **magnetic pole**
k. **magnetism**
l. **superconductor**
m. **transformer**
n. **voltmeter**

UNDERSTANDING VOCABULARY

Match each phrase with the correct term from the list of Key Science Words.

1. area around a magnet in which a magnetic force acts
2. a property of matter in which there is a force of repulsion or attraction between like or unlike poles
3. a temporary magnet made of a wire coil through which an electric current passes
4. measures electric current
5. a device that reverses the direction of a direct current in an electric motor
6. the production of an electric current by moving a wire through a magnetic field
7. current that flows in only one direction
8. a device that changes the voltage of an alternating current
9. material with no electrical resistance
10. region of magnet where magnetic lines of force are most dense

MAGNETISM AND ITS USES **591**

SUMMARY

Have students read the summary statements to review the major concepts of the chapter.

UNDERSTANDING VOCABULARY

1. i
2. k
3. e
4. b
5. c
6. f
7. d
8. m
9. l
10. j

ASSESSMENT
Portfolio

Encourage students to place in their portfolios one or two items of what they consider to be their best work. For each item, ask students to explain why that item was chosen and what they learned from it. Items might be selected from the following.

- Technology answers, p. 579
- Cross Curriculum research and diagram, p. 580
- Activity 22-1 results and answers, p. 582

Performance

Additional performance assessments may be found in *Performance Assessment* and *Science Integration Activities* that accompany **Merrill Physical Science.** Performance Task Assessment Lists and rubrics for evaluating these activities and other products generated throughout the chapter can be found in Glencoe's *Performance Assessment in Middle School Science.*

OPTIONS

ASSESSMENT

To assess student understanding of material in this chapter, use the resources listed.

COOPERATIVE LEARNING

Consider using cooperative learning in the THINK AND WRITE CRITICALLY, APPLY, and MORE SKILL BUILDERS sections of the Chapter Review.

PROGRAM RESOURCES

From the **Teacher Resource Package** use:

Chapter Review, pages 47-48.

Chapter and Unit Tests, pages 147-150, Chapter Test.

CHECKING CONCEPTS

1. a	**6.** d
2. c	**7.** c
3. d	**8.** b
4. b	**9.** b
5. d	**10.** a

USING LAB SKILLS

ASSESSMENT

Use these alternate lab exercises to assess students' understanding of skills used in this chapter.

11. Use a bulb to check the condition of the batteries, be sure the ends are stripped and in proper contact, and check to see that the same side of both ends of the armature wire is stripped.

12. Both contain magnetic fields. In a transformer, the changing magnetic field of the primary coil induces an alternating current in the secondary coil. In a generator, a coil of wire rotating in a magnetic field has an alternating current induced in it.

THINK AND WRITE CRITICALLY

13. Spinning electrons create small magnetic fields. Paired electrons spin in opposite directions and cancel one another. The magnetic fields of unpaired electrons are not cancelled and, if aligned in a substance, make it magnetic.

14. Both have a coil of wire through which an electric current passes as it is suspended between two magnets. The coil rotates in the field produced by the fixed magnets. For the coil to keep rotating, an electric motor must also have a commutator that reverses the direction of the current in the coil.

15. A wire coil is made to rotate in a magnetic field. If a conducting loop cuts across the magnetic field, electrons in the wire loop move and produce a current.

16. It contains two coils of wire wrapped around an iron core. An alternating current passes through the first coil and produces a changing magnetic field, which induces current in the second coil. If the second coil has more turns than the primary coil, the voltage of the alternating current in

---

CHECKING CONCEPTS

Choose the word or phrase that completes the sentence or answers the question.

1. A magnet's force is strongest at its _____.
  a. north and south poles **c.** north pole
  b. south pole   **d.** center

2. As the distance between two magnetic poles decreases, the magnetic force _____.
  a. remains constant   **c.** increases
  b. changes unpredictably **d.** decreases

3. Atoms at the north pole of a bar magnet have _____.
  a. north magnetic poles only
  b. south magnetic poles only
  c. no magnetic poles
  d. both north and south magnetic poles

4. Which of the following would not change the strength of an electromagnet?
  a. increasing the amount of current
  b. changing the current's direction
  c. inserting an iron core inside the loop
  d. increasing the number of loops

5. Ammeters should be _____.
  a. designed to have high resistance
  b. designed without magnets
  c. connected in parallel
  d. calibrated in amperes

6. A device containing a wire coil suspended in a magnetic field that measures potential difference is called a(n) _____.
  a. transformer   **c.** ammeter
  b. electromagnet   **d.** voltmeter

7. The direction of the electric current in an AC circuit _____.
  a. remains constant **c.** changes regularly
  b. is direct   **d.** changes irregularly

8. Before current in power lines can enter your home, it must pass through a _____.
  a. step-up transformer   **c.** commutator
  b. step-down transformer **d.** voltmeter

9. Some materials lose all electrical resistance when they are _____.
  a. at room temperature
  b. at their critical temperatures
  c. below absolute zero
  d. heated

10. Superconductors can levitate magnets because the continuous electric current through the superconductor produces _____.
  a. a repulsive magnetic force
  b. an attractive magnetic force
  c. an anti-gravity force
  d. a mechanical force

USING LAB SKILLS

11. Review your construction of an electric motor in Activity 22-1 on page 582. Suppose you followed all directions and built another motor, but it did not rotate when you connected the battery. Describe at least two things you would check as you attempted to fix the device.

12. In Activity 22-2 on page 590, you built and experimented with a simple transformer. What do transformers have in common with AC generators?

---

the second coil is greater. This type of transformer is a step-up transformer. In a step-down transformer, the secondary coil has fewer turns than the primary coil and the voltage of the current is reduced.

17. Superconducting power lines would conduct electricity with no energy loss due to electrical resistance. Superconductors could reduce the fuel used for mass transit.

APPLY

18. The magnetic pole at Earth's North Pole must actually be a south magnetic pole, because it attracts north magnetic pole of a compass needle.

19. Magnetic domains are formed when atoms having unpaired electrons are lined up. When a magnet is dropped or heated, its atoms are forced out of position and the alignment of magnetic domains is destroyed.

20. An ammeter is connected in series to measure the total current of the circuit. A voltmeter is connected in parallel because the voltage is the same across all parallel branches.

21. 1200 V is ten times 120 V, so the secondary coil has $\frac{1}{10}$ the turns, or 10 turns.

THINK AND WRITE CRITICALLY

Answer the following questions in your Journal using complete sentences.

13. Describe the magnetic domain model.
14. Describe the basic device used in both galvanometers and DC electric motors. What additional device does an electric motor have? Why is this device necessary?
15. Explain how a generator produces an electric current.
16. Explain how a transformer works. How do step-up and step-down transformers differ?
17. How might superconductors help conserve energy resources?

APPLY

18. If a magnetic compass needle points north, what is the actual polarity of Earth's northern magnetic pole? Explain.
19. Explain why dropping or heating a permanent magnet causes its magnetic domains to shift out of alignment.
20. Why must an ammeter be connected in series with a circuit? Why must a voltmeter be connected in parallel across a circuit?
21. A step-down transformer reduces a 1200 V current to 120 V. If the primary coil has 100 turns, how many must its secondary coil have?
22. You are developing a superconducting train. On what two problems will you concentrate your research? Why?

MORE SKILL BUILDERS

If you need help, refer to the Skill Handbook.

1. **Comparing and Contrasting:** Compare and contrast electric and magnetic forces.
2. **Comparing and Contrasting:** Compare and contrast AC generators and DC motors.

3. **Recognizing Cause and Effect:** Earth's magnetic field has reversed itself many times in the past. What would be the likely effect of this switching of Earth's magnetic poles on the alignment of magnetic minerals deposited in Earth?
4. **Hypothesizing:** Some metals are strongly attracted by a magnetic field; others such as zinc are not. Propose a hypothesis about the arrangement of electrons in zinc.
5. **Concept Mapping:** Complete the following events chain map by supplying the name and function of devices used to convert the mechanical energy of a turbine at an electrical power plant into the mechanical energy of an electric fan in your home.

Initiating Step

[ ]

↓

[ ]

↓

[ ]

↓

Final Outcome

[ ]

PROJECTS

1. Research the most recent developments in superconductors. Write a brief paper stating whether or not the government should spend more money on superconductor research. Give reasons supporting your position.
2. Invent a new device that uses an electric motor. Make a poster diagram of the device.

MAGNETISM AND ITS USES **593**

22. You must find a substance that is not too brittle and exhibits superconductivity at normal temperatures. Current superconductors only work at very low temperatures and are too brittle.

MORE SKILL BUILDERS

1. **Comparing and Contrasting:** Both electric and magnetic forces are produced by electrons. Charged objects produce electric fields, and the charge itself is produced by too few or too many electrons. Magnetic fields are produced by the motion of electrons. Both types of forces become weaker as the distance from the source of the force is increased. Both forces are attractive when unlike charges or poles are brought together and repulsive when like charges or poles are brought together.
2. **Comparing and Contrasting:** Both have wire coils suspended between two fixed magnets. In a generator, the coil mechanically rotates in the magnetic field. This induces an electric current in the coil. In an electric motor, a current passes through the coil and makes it an electromagnet that rotates in the field of the fixed magnets. If an electric motor is battery-powered, then it runs off a direct current. A generator, on the other hand, always produces an alternating current.
3. **Recognizing Cause and Effect:** If Earth's magnetic field reversed its direction many times in the past, then the orientation of the magnetic field in lava would indicate the direction of the field when the lava solidified. Some layers in Earth have magnetic minerals aligned ("pointing") to the north, whereas other layers have minerals aligned to the south. Such alternating layers have been found and are themselves strong evidence that Earth's magnetic field has often reversed its polarity.
4. **Hypothesizing:** Iron is attracted by a magnetic field because it has magnetic domains, aligned atoms with unpaired electrons. A reasonable hypothesis for why zinc is unaffected might therefore be: Because electrons in zinc atoms are paired, zinc is unaffected by a magnetic field.
5. **Concept Mapping:** See the map at the left.

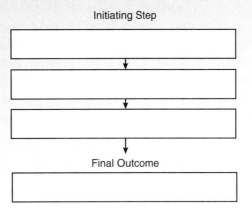

Initiating Step

Generator: converts mechanical energy of turbine into electrical current

↓

Step-up transformer: raises voltage of current to minimize energy loss in power lines

↓

Step-down transformer: lowers voltage to standard 120 V

↓

Final Outcome

Electric Motor: turns fan blades by converting electrical energy back to mechanical energy

23 Electronics and Computers

CHAPTER SECTION	OBJECTIVES	ACTIVITIES
23-1 Semiconductor Devices (2 days)	1. **Describe** how the two types of doped semiconductors conduct a current. 2. **Explain** the device that changes AC into DC. 3. **Realize** the practical benefits of an integrated circuit.	**Activity 23-1:** *Semiconductors,* p. 598
23-2 Radio and Television (1 day)	1. **Describe** how radio and television programs are transmitted. 2. **Explain** the operation of a cathode-ray tube.	**MINI-Lab:** *How do electrons make a TV picture?* p. 605
23-3 Microcomputers (2 days)	1. **Identify** the basic parts of a microcomputer. 2. **Describe** the role of the microprocessor. 3. **Distinguish** between RAM and ROM.	**MINI-Lab:** *What makes a calculator "user friendly"?* p. 609
23-4 Computer Crimes Science & Society (1 day)	1. **Discuss** the types of crimes that can be committed by computer misuse. 2. **Predict** the possible consequences of computer crimes.	**Activity 23-2:** *Magnetic Messages,* p. 614
Chapter Review		

ACTIVITY MATERIALS

FIND OUT	ACTIVITIES		MINI-LABS	
Page 595 several musical greeting cards hand lens	**23-1 Semiconductors, p. 598** diode 2 LEDs, different colors hook-up wire 1000 ohm resistor 6 volt battery AC power supply, 6 volts	**23-2 Magnetic Messages, p. 614** 12 disk magnets 2 sheets and a thin strip of card stock paper transparent tape metric ruler	**How do electrons make a TV picture? p. 605** CRT a small magnet	**What makes a calculator "user friendly"? p. 609** a pocket-sized calculator

CHAPTER FEATURES	TEACHER RESOURCE PACKAGE	OTHER RESOURCES
Skill Builder: *Interpreting Scientific Illustrations,* p. 601	**Ability Level Worksheets** ◆ *Study Guide,* p. 96 ● *Reinforcement,* p. 96 ▲ *Enrichment,* p. 196 **Activity Worksheets,** pp. 184, 185 **Transparency Masters,** pp. 91, 92	**Color Transparency 46,** Semi-conductors **STVS:** Disc 1, Side 2
Technology: *HDTV,* p. 604 **Skill Builder:** *Concept Mapping,* p. 605	**Ability Level Worksheets** ◆ *Study Guide,* p. 97 ● *Reinforcement,* p. 97 ▲ *Enrichment,* p. 97 **Activity Worksheets,** p. 190	**STVS:** Disc 1, Side 2
Problem Solving: *Computer Art,* p. 610 **Skill Builder:** *Comparing and Contrasting,* p. 611	**Ability Level Worksheets** ◆ *Study Guide,* p. 98 ● *Reinforcement,* p. 98 ▲ *Enrichment,* p. 98 **Activity Worksheets,** pp. 5, 191 **Critical Thinking/Problem Solving,** p. 29 **Concept Mapping,** pp. 51, 52 **Cross-Curricular Connections,** p. 29 **Science and Society,** p. 27	**STVS:** Disc 1, Side 2
You Decide! p. 613	**Ability Level Worksheets** ◆ *Study Guide,* p. 99 ● *Reinforcement,* p. 99 ▲ *Enrichment,* p. 99 **Activity Worksheets,** pp. 186, 187	**Science Integration Activity 23**
Summary Think & Write Critically Key Science Words Apply Understanding Vocabulary More Skill Builders Checking Concepts Projects Using Lab Skills	**ASSESSMENT RESOURCES** **Chapter Review,** pp. 49, 50 **Chapter Test,** pp. 151-154 **Performance Assessment in Middle School Science**	**Chapter Review Software** **Test Bank** **Alternate Assessment** **Performance Assessment**

◆ **Basic**   ● **Average**   ▲ **Advanced**

ADDITIONAL MATERIALS

SOFTWARE	AUDIOVISUAL	BOOKS/MAGAZINES
	Electronics and Control, Video, Journal Films. *Silicon,* Video, Britannica. *Square One: An Introduction to Computers,* Video, Modern.	Biermann, Alan W. *Great Ideas in Computer Science: A Gentle Introduction.* Cambridge: MIT Press, 1990. Bonnet, Robert L., and G. Daniel Keen. *Computers: 49 Science Fair Projects.* Blue Ridge Summit, PA: Tab, 1990. Graham, Ian. *Computers.* NY: Gloucester Press, 1992. Kaufmann, William J., III, and Larry L. Smarr. *Supercomputing and the Transformation of Science.* NY: Scientific American Library, 1993.

THEME DEVELOPMENT: In this chapter emphasize how electronic and magnetic systems interact to help us create useful devices. The previous chapter covered the connection between electricity and magnetism. Numerous applications will illustrate it here.

CHAPTER OVERVIEW

▶ **Section 23-1:** This section introduces the theory of semiconductors. Semiconductor applications including diodes, transistors, amplification, and integrated circuits are illustrated.

▶ **Section 23-2:** This section discusses radio and television transmission and shows how a cathode-ray tube produces an image on the screen.

▶ **Section 23-3:** This section identifies the components of a microcomputer, discusses the microprocessor, and presents the function of computer memory and methods of data storage.

▶ **Section 23-4: Science and Society:** This section features a discussion of computer crimes, including viruses and hacking. The You Decide question asks students to evaluate how computer crimes should be treated by our legal system.

CHAPTER VOCABULARY

rectifier	cathode-ray tube (CRT)
diode	microprocessor
transistor	RAM
amplification	ROM
integrated circuit	computer virus

CHAPTER

23 Electronics and Computers

594

OPTIONS

For Your Gifted Students

Students can test the effectiveness of various radio antennas that they design and construct from different materials. Vary the size and shape of the antenna, or connect it to available items such as pipes, phone lines, and so on. They will test the antenna's effectiveness by recording how many radio stations can be received. Predictions and results should be charted and shared.

For Your Mainstreamed Students

▶ Students can brainstorm a list of careers associated with the field of electronics. For a firsthand look at a career option, have them visit a television or radio station to observe the electronic broadcasting equipment.
▶ Invite a computer expert to visit the class to display a computer circuit board, explain recent technological advances in computers, or discuss predictions for electronics in the next decade.

Have you ever received a greeting card from a friend that made you feel especially happy? Did you ever get a card that played a song when you opened it? How can a greeting card play music? A small electronic device located inside the card actually plays the song you hear.

FIND OUT!

Observe a simple application of electronics as you do this activity.

Get a musical greeting card and examine the electronic device inside. Notice that the music plays only when the card is opened. Do you see the tiny metal disc inside the card? The disc is a type of electronic device containing a small speaker. The music is created from electric signals within the disc that are amplified and turned into sound waves by the tiny speaker. Carefully *observe* the parts inside the disc with a powerful hand lens. What do you see?

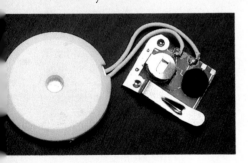

Previewing Science Skills
- ▶ In the Skill Builders, you will interpret scientific illustrations, make a concept map, and compare and contrast.
- ▶ In the Activities, you will observe, infer, classify, and communicate.
- ▶ In the MINI-Labs, you will observe, infer, and interpret.

What's next?

You've examined one type of simple electronic device. Read on to find out how this and other electronic devices are actually applications of the principles of electricity and magnetism you studied in Chapters 21 and 22.

INTRODUCING THE CHAPTER
Use the Find Out activity to help students notice the parts and details of electronic devices. Explain that they will be learning the functions of some of the parts they see in the device.

FIND OUT!
Preparation: Obtain several musical greeting cards from card shops.
Materials: musical greeting cards, hand lenses

Cooperative Learning: Form Science Investigation Teams of four to share a musical card and discuss the questions you ask together.
Teaching Tips
▶ Have students try to draw the parts of the electronic device and label them descriptively. Have them speculate where the music originates and where the sound comes out. Tell them they will be learning about some of the parts used in electronic devices.

Gearing Up
Have students study the Gearing Up feature to familiarize themselves with the chapter. Discuss the relationships of the topics in the outline.

What's Next?
Before beginning the first section, make sure students understand the connection between the Find Out activity and the topics to follow.

ASSESSMENT OPTIONS

PORTFOLIO
Refer to page 615 for suggested items that students might select for their portfolios.

PERFORMANCE ASSESSMENT
See page 615 for additional Performance Assessment options.
Process
Skill Builders, pp. 601, 605, 611
MINI-Lab, p. 609
Using Lab Skills, p. 616

CONTENT ASSESSMENT
Assessment—Oral, pp. 600, 604, 608
Section Reviews, pp. 601, 605, 611, 613
Chapter Review, pp. 615-617
Mini Quizzes, pp. 600, 603, 610
Activities 23-1, p. 598; 23-2, p. 614
MINI-Lab, p. 604

GROUP ASSESSMENT
Opportunities for group assessment occur with Cooperative Learning Strategies and Flex Your Brain Activities.

PREPARATION

SECTION BACKGROUND

▶ The science behind semiconductors is included in the vast field of solid-state physics, which is the study of the structure of solids. An explanation of the properties and behavior of semiconductors at the atomic level can be found in electron band theory, based on quantum mechanics.

▶ Pure, undoped semiconductors are said to be intrinsic.

PREPLANNING

▶ Obtain examples of transistors, diodes, resistors, and microchips from a local electronics store. They may even have some spare parts they would be willing to donate to your school.

1 MOTIVATE

▶ If possible, bring a transparent phone to class. The wiring in a phone appears complex, but is actually made of just a few kinds of electrical devices. Ask students if they can identify any of the parts.

VideoDisc

STVS: Making Integrated Circuits; Disc 1, Side 2

New Science Words

rectifier
diode
transistor
amplification
integrated circuit

Objectives

▶ Describe how the two types of doped semiconductors conduct a current.
▶ Explain the device that changes AC into DC.
▶ Realize the practical benefits of an integrated circuit.

Semiconductors

Do you use a calculator when you do your homework, average your grades, or add up the amount of money you've saved? Your calculator is only one of thousands of complex electronic devices made possible by advances in the applications of electricity and magnetism. If you carefully removed the front of your calculator, you would see tiny circuits with all sorts of unusual parts inside. You might see several kinds of semiconductor devices: a diode, a rectifier, and a transistor.

To understand what a semiconductor is and how it works, you must first think about the periodic table you studied in Chapter 10. Recall that the elements on the left side and center of the table are metals and conduct electricity. Nonmetals—poor conductors of electricity—are found on the right side of the table. They are electrical insulators. How would you classify the elements found along the staircase-shaped border between the metals and nonmetals? Would you call these conductors or insulators?

The elements located between the metals and

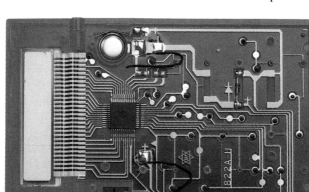

Figure 23-1. A calculator contains several different types of semiconductor devices.

OPTIONS

Meeting Different Ability Levels
For Section 23-1, use the following **Teacher Resource Masters** depending upon individual students' needs.

◆ **Study Guide Master** for all students.
● **Reinforcement Master** for students of average and above average ability levels.
▲ **Enrichment Master** for above average students.

Additional Teacher Resource Package masters are listed in any PROGRAM RESOURCES boxes that are in the section. The additional masters are appropriate for all students.

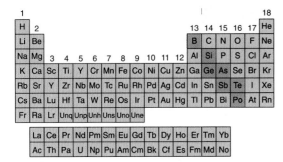

Figure 23-2. In the periodic table, the metalloids form a sort of "staircase" that separates the metals, which are to the left of the metalloids, from the nonmetals, which are on the right.

TYING TO PREVIOUS KNOWLEDGE: Ask students to distinguish between a conductor and an insulator. Explain that a semiconductor, as the prefix *semi-* implies, is in-between a conductor and an insulator. Tell them they will be finding out how semiconductors are used in common electrical devices.

OBJECTIVES AND SCIENCE WORDS: Have students review the objectives and science words to become familiar with this section.

nonmetals on the periodic table are metalloids. Some metalloids, such as silicon and germanium, are semiconductors. Semiconductors are less conductive than metals but more conductive than nonmetal insulators. Your calculator and other electronic devices in your home that use semiconductors use less current to operate than similar devices that don't use semiconductors.

The conductivity of semiconductor crystals can be increased by adding impurities. This process is called doping. Doped silicon is a commonly used semiconductor. Silicon atoms have four electrons in their outer energy level. This electron arrangement stabilizes the crystal lattice structure. If small amounts of another element with either more or fewer than four outer energy level electrons are added, a few high energy electrons will be able to move more easily through the material. So, the conductivity of the compound is higher than that of pure silicon.

Silicon is often doped with arsenic or gallium. Locate these elements on the periodic table. Arsenic atoms have five electrons in their outer energy levels. Arsenic-doped silicon has more electrons than does pure silicon, so this material is called an *n*-type (negative-type) semiconductor. Gallium atoms, however, have fewer than four electrons in their outer energy levels. Gallium-doped silicon has fewer electrons in its crystal structure than pure silicon, so it is called a *p*-type (positive-type) semiconductor. Even one other type of atom among a million silicon atoms will significantly change the conducting properties of the material. By controlling the type and amount of doping, semiconductors with a variety of conducting properties can be created.

What is doping?

Connect to... Chemistry

Germanium and silicon are commonly used semiconductors. Locate them in the periodic table. Explain why you might predict they would have similar electronic properties.

What is an *n*-type semiconductor?

What is a *p*-type semiconductor?

2 TEACH

Key Concepts are highlighted.

CONCEPT DEVELOPMENT
▶ You will need to help students conceptualize the idea behind *p*- and *n*-type semiconductors.

CROSS CURRICULUM
▶ **Chemistry:** Have students research how pure semiconductors, such as silicon or germanium, are obtained. Pure silicon crystals often have less than 1 part in 1 billion as impurities.

PROGRAM RESOURCES

From the **Teacher Resource Package** use:

Transparency Masters, pages 91-92, Semiconductors.

Use **Color Transparency** number 46, Semiconductors.

Connect to... Chemistry

Answer: Ge and Si are in the same group on the periodic table, so they would likely have the same number and arrangement of outer level electrons.

● REINFORCEMENT 96

▲ ENRICHMENT 96

OBJECTIVE: Apply observations of current flow to understanding the operation of a diode.

PROCESS SKILLS applied in this activity:
▶ **Experimenting** in Procedure Steps 1-8.
▶ **Observing** in Procedure Steps 5-8.
▶ **Inferring** in Analyze Questions 1-4.
▶ **Interpreting** in Conclude and Apply Questions 5 and 6.

COOPERATIVE LEARNING
Divide the class into Science Investigation Teams of three or four students.

TEACHING THE ACTIVITY
Troubleshooting: The resistor should be about 1000 Ω. The LEDs will burn out if a resistor is not in series with them.
▶ A 120 VAC – 6.5 VAC transformer with a 1000-Ω, 10-W resistor in series to restrict current output can provide a reasonably safe AC source.
▶ Hook-up wire can be twisted together, but alligator clips are more convenient.
▶ A demonstration of AC, DC, and pulsating DC is provided by attaching the operating LED assembly by long wires and whirling it about in a circle. In a darkened room, AC will show alternating streaks of color. DC will be a continuous streak of one color. Rectified AC will show as pulses of one color.

Have you ever passed through a turnstile as you entered a store? You and other people could only go through in one direction. Electrical devices called diodes change AC to DC current by allowing current to pass in only one direction. This experiment shows how diodes affect AC and DC circuits.

Materials
- diode
- two LEDs, different colors
- hook-up wire
- resistor, 1000 ohms
- battery, 6 volt
- AC power supply, 6 volts

Procedure
1. Attach the resistor to one of the LEDs before connecting it to the battery. Reverse battery connections until the LED lights.
2. Mark the positive side of the LED.
3. Repeat Steps 1 and 2 with the second LED.
4. Twist the positive wire of one LED with the negative wire of the other. Attach the resistor to the other two wires.
5. Connect the assembly to the poles of the battery and *observe* which LED light works. Reverse the battery connections and *observe.*

6. Connect the assembly to 6 volts AC and *observe.*
7. Attach the diode in series with the assembly and connect it to 6 volts AC.
8. Reverse the direction of the diode and reconnect to the AC current. *Observe* the response of the LEDs.

Analyze
1. A battery sends current in one direction. How does the LED assembly show this?
2. How does the LED assembly detect an alternating current?
3. What does the addition of a diode do to an alternating current?
4. What does reversing the direction of the diode accomplish?

Conclude and Apply
5. In an AC circuit, are the LEDs on all the time? How about in the DC circuit?
6. The resistance of a diode is very high in one direction and low in the other. How did this experiment show that to be true?

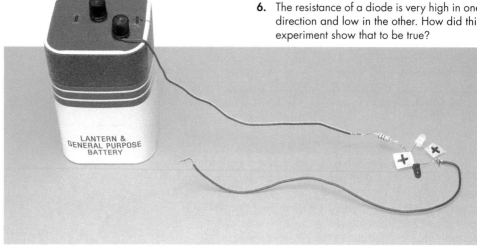

ANSWERS TO QUESTIONS
1. Only one LED at a time will light.
2. Both LEDs show light.
3. Only one LED shows light the same as DC.
4. The other LED shows light demonstrating that current has reversed.
5. An AC current reverses direction, so the LEDs must be going on and off. They would be on all the time in pure DC.
6. Current flows through diodes in one direction but is blocked if the diode is turned around.

Activity
ASSESSMENT
Oral: To assess students' understanding of this activity, see Question 11 in USING LAB SKILLS on page 616.

PROGRAM RESOURCES
From the **Teacher Resource Package** use: **Activity Worksheets,** pages 184-185, Activity 23-1: Semiconductors.

Diodes

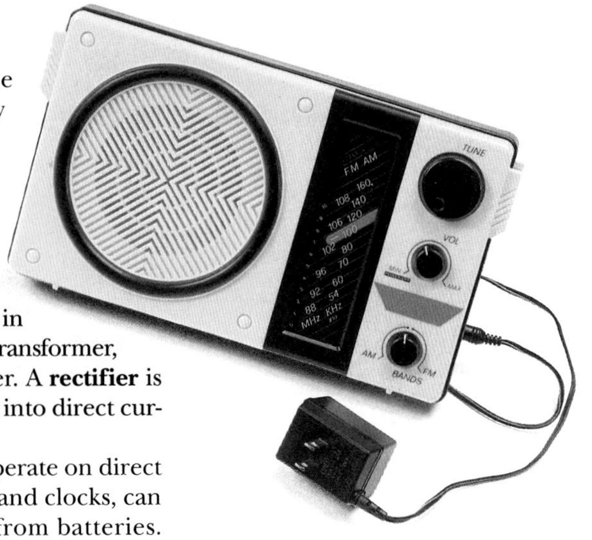

Have you noticed that some portable radios can operate on batteries, but they may have adapters that plug into wall sockets? Why do they need an adapter? Radios operate on low-voltage direct current. For the radio to operate with household alternating current, the voltage of the current must be lowered and the current must be changed to flow in one direction. A radio adapter contains a transformer,
3 which reduces the voltage, and a rectifier. A **rectifier** is a device that changes alternating current into direct current.

Many household devices are built to operate on direct current. Some, such as smoke detectors and clocks, can easily be supplied with direct current from batteries. Other appliances that use large amounts of electricity, such as your television or computer, would not be practical to operate with direct current from batteries. Therefore, transformers and rectifiers are wired into the circuits inside of radios, televisions, computers, and other similar appliances so that they can be supplied with low-voltage direct current from a source of alternating current.

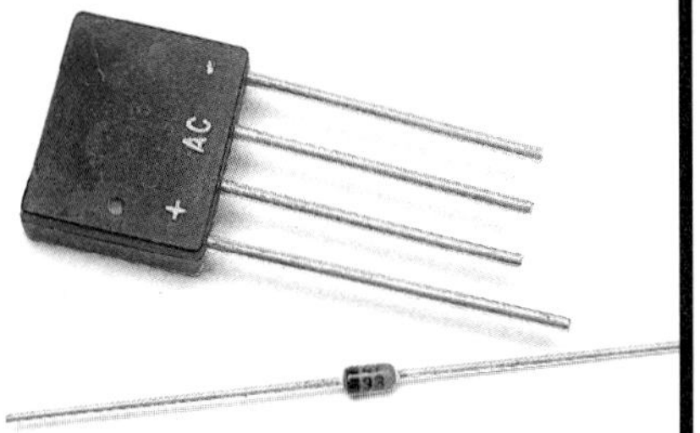

Figure 23-3. Diodes and rectifiers change alternating current into direct current.

A diode is one type of rectifier. A **diode** can be thought of as a type of "valve" or "gate" that allows current to flow only in one direction. A diode can be made by doping the ends of a crystal with different elements to make one end a *p*-type semiconductor and the other end an *n*-type semiconductor. Electrons can easily flow from the *n*-type conductor to the *p*-type conductor, but it is more difficult to make them flow in the other direction. This device is called a *pn*-diode. Your radio's adapter plug probably contains a *pn*-diode rectifier.

What is a transistor?

Transistors and Amplification

Have you wondered why some radios are called transistor radios? They contain electrical devices called
4 transistors. A **transistor** is a semiconductor that amplifies an electric signal. The signal in an electronic device is the varying electric current that represents a sound, picture, or some other piece of information. Transistors can

TEACHER F.Y.I.

▶ A zener [zā-ner] diode is a diode used to create a steady voltage in a circuit over a range of currents.

CONCEPT DEVELOPMENT

▶ A graph of current versus voltage for resistors in a circuit produces a straight line. However, a graph of current versus voltage for diodes and transistors in a circuit does not produce a straight line; they are nonlinear devices.

▶ Introduce diodes as a type of valve or gate that allows current to move in only one direction. This analogy may help students understand how a rectifier can be used to convert AC to DC.

▶ The invention of the transistor allowed electronic devices to be constructed in much smaller sizes than when using vacuum tubes. Chips, or integrated circuits, do the job of many transistors in a still smaller space.

MULTICULTURAL PERSPECTIVE

A Well-Rounded Scientist

Shirley Jackson's interest in science began with stories her mother read her about Benjamin Banneker. Although her initial curiosities as a young girl were in biology, she later demonstrated significant skills in mathematics, which led her into physics.When she entered MIT in 1964, she was one of two African American women in a group of no more than 30 to 40 women in the school—a pioneer for both women and African Americans. During her college years, she worked in the pediatric ward at Boston City Hospital. She also worked to help others by becoming a co-founder of the Black Student Union. This group was instrumental in initiating MIT's active recruitment of minority students. In 1973, she became the first African American to receive a doctoral degree in physics from MIT. Her current area, theoretical explanations for the behavior of semiconductors, makes her a member of a select group in physics. Only 20 percent of the people with doctorates in physics are working as theorists.

OPTIONS

INQUIRY QUESTIONS

▶ **Use the periodic table to determine whether a semiconductor is more or less conductive than iron or sulfur.** *A semiconductor would be less conductive than iron, a metal, and more conductive than sulfur, a nonmetal.*

▶ **What type (*n*- or *p*-type) of semiconductor would be produced by doping antimony with tin? Explain.** *Tin has fewer electrons (4) in its outer energy level than does antimony (5). A deficiency of electrons in the structure results in a p-type (positive) semiconductor.*

CONCEPT DEVELOPMENT

▶ Explaining how a transistor can amplify an electrical signal can be confusing. Emphasize that the small current received as an input signal controls the large current from the power source.

CHECK FOR UNDERSTANDING

Use the Mini Quiz to check for understanding.

MINI QUIZ

Use the Mini Quiz to check students' recall of chapter content.

1 _____ are less conductive than metals but more conductive than insulators. *Semiconductors*

2 A common method of increasing the conductivity of a semiconductor is the process of _____ . *doping*

3 An adapter in a radio that changes AC into DC probably contains a(n) _____ . *rectifier*

4 What is a major purpose of using transistors? *to amplify an electrical signal*

RETEACH

Have students interpret and explain the diagram in Figure 23-2 on page 597. Have them explain why some semiconductors are doped.

EXTENSION

For students who have mastered this section, use the **Reinforcement** and **Enrichment** masters or other OPTIONS provided.

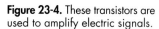

Figure 23-4. These transistors are used to amplify electric signals.

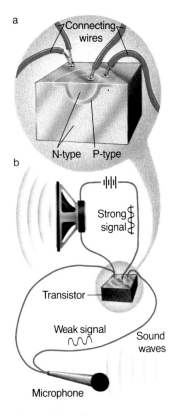

Figure 23-5. The *npn*-transistor shown above uses a weak input current to control the flow of a much larger current.

be made by doping both sides of a thin *p*-type semiconductor with arsenic. This process sandwiches a *p*-type semiconductor between the two *n*-type semiconductors producing an *npn*-transistor. An *npn*-transistor can amplify a weak electric signal until it is strong enough to be useful. **Amplification** is the process of increasing the strength of an electric signal.

Another type of transistor can be made by doping both sides of a thin *n*-type semiconductor with *p*-type semiconductors, forming a *pnp*-transistor. They differ slightly in operation, but both *pnp* and *npn* transistors can be used to amplify an input signal or current. Like diodes, these electronic components are very small and lightweight.

The signal that travels many kilometers from a broadcast station to your stereo and television receivers is too weak to reproduce the information it carries into picture or sound. In other words, it does not have a large enough amplitude to vibrate the loudspeaker and create sound that can be heard. An *npn*-transistor in the electric circuit of the stereo uses a small current from a weak incoming signal to control a large current provided by a power source. Thus, the small input signal supplied to the transistor results in a large, varying output current that can vibrate the speaker.

Your school PA (public address) system contains several transistors. When someone speaks over the system, the sound wave is converted to an electrical signal by a microphone and amplified by transistors within the circuit of the system. The amplified signal is then changed back into sound waves by a speaker. Transistors and their ability to amplify signals make it possible for you to use tape players, bullhorns, hearing aids, and televisions. They are also used in medical diagnoses to amplify tiny electrical signals given off by the heart and brain so these signals can be detected. None of these electronic devices or their applications would be possible without the transistor. It is considered to be the most fundamental part of an electronic circuit.

600 ELECTRONICS AND COMPUTERS

OPTIONS

ASSESSMENT—ORAL

▶ **What combination of devices might you use if you wanted to use a wall socket to provide electricity for a radio and you needed to amplify the signal before it reached the loudspeaker?** *Use a rectifier or diode, followed by a transistor.*

▶ **Why does a radio have to be plugged in or have batteries if there is an incoming signal (from the radio waves)?** *The radio wave does not have enough power to vibrate the speakers, so power must be added from an outside source.*

Integrated Circuits

Before transistors were invented, devices called vacuum tubes were used to amplify electric signals. These low-pressure glass or metal tubes regulated the electron flow of a circuit's current as it went through each tube. Your grandparents probably owned a television or radio that used these tubes to amplify signals. Televisions and radios today have semiconductor components instead of vacuum tubes. After the development of the transistor, integrated circuits became a reality. As a result of this electronics breakthrough, today's televisions and radios are much smaller than the older ones.

An **integrated circuit** can contain thousands of resistors, diodes, and transistors on a thin slice of silicon. These thin silicon slices, called chips, can be smaller than 1 cm on a side. The miniature circuit components in an integrated circuit are made by doping the silicon chip with small amounts of impurities. The conductors between the components are made by using photosensitive chemicals to photograph circuits on the silicon chip. Having circuit components so close together reduces the time required for a current to travel through a circuit. As a result, the integrated circuit is a very effective design for rapid information processing, which is essential in devices such as microcomputers.

Figure 23-6. Vacuum tubes, such as the one above, were used to amplify electric signals in early electronic devices.

Did You Know?

The integrated circuit concept was developed in 1952, but the actual product was not produced for 20 more years.

SECTION REVIEW

1. Describe two ways the conductivity of silicon as a semiconductor can be improved.
2. What device can you use to change AC to DC? How does it work?
3. How are integrated circuits made?
4. **Apply:** Would carbon atoms be useful in doping a silicon semiconductor? Explain.
5. **Connect to Life Science:** Why are transistors very important in medical detection devices?

☒ Interpreting Scientific Illustrations

Look at the periodic table of the elements on pages 258 and 259. List the metals, nonmetals, and metalloids. Classify each of these as a conductor, an insulator, or a semiconductor. If you need help, refer to Interpreting Scientific Illustrations in the **Skill Handbook** on page 689.

Skill Builder

PREPARATION

SECTION BACKGROUND

▶ Recall that electromagnetic waves were first used to transmit messages over long distances after the invention of the wireless telegraph in the late 1800s.

▶ The electrical signal carrying sound information is called an AF, or audio frequency, signal. The frequencies correspond to the range of hearing (20 to 20 000 Hz). The carrier waves are called RF, or radio frequency, waves. They have much higher frequencies.

1 MOTIVATE

▶ Have a television or radio on when students come into the room. Then ask them where the picture or sound comes from. They will probably say from the TV or radio station. Explain that in this section, they will study the transmission of signals and the formation of sounds and images from those signals.

▶ Bring a tape recorder to class and let each student quickly say something into it. Then play it back. Ask them how this sound differs from radio music. This helps increase their curiosity about how radio signals become audible music.

TYING TO PREVIOUS
KNOWLEDGE: Ask students what radio waves are. Remind them that radio waves make up the longest wavelengths in the electromagnetic spectrum. They are hitting each student right now. Students will find out what it takes to change these silent, invisible waves to sounds they can hear and images they can see.

Connect to...
Chemistry

Answer: The sea of mobile electrons present in metals can easily vibrate when acted on by electromagnetic waves.

23-2 Radio and Television

New Science Words

cathode-ray tube (CRT)

In Your JOURNAL

Radios and television are relatively recent inventions. **In your Journal,** write a paragraph describing how your life would be different without these technologies.

Objectives

▶ Describe how radio and television programs are transmitted.
▶ Explain the operation of a cathode-ray tube.

Radio Transmission

Now that you've studied sound, electromagnetic waves, and electricity, you should be comfortable with the concepts that explain how a radio works. Radios operate by changing transverse radio waves into vibrations that produce compressional sound waves. Recall that radio waves are the kind of electromagnetic radiation with the longest wavelength and shortest frequency. Like all electromagnetic radiation, radio waves travel at the speed of light. However, the conversion to sound waves is not possible without first converting the radio waves to electrical signals.

At the radio station, a microphone collects the compressional waves created by sounds. The microphone changes the sound waves into electrical signals. The electric current vibrations vary according to the sound vibrations. These signals are then amplified and passed through the modulator. Modulation was discussed in Chapter 19. The type of modulation varies in AM and FM radio stations. When the electrical signals are used to produce variations in the amplitude of the radio waves, they are called amplitude-modulated, or AM, waves. When the electrical signals are used to produce variations in ❶

OPTIONS

Meeting Different Ability Levels

For Section 23-2, use the following **Teacher Resource Masters** depending upon individual students' needs.

◆ **Study Guide Master** for all students.
● **Reinforcement Master** for students of average and above average ability levels.
▲ **Enrichment Master** for above average students.

Additional Teacher Resource Package masters are listed in any PROGRAM RESOURCES boxes that are in the section. The additional masters are appropriate for all students.

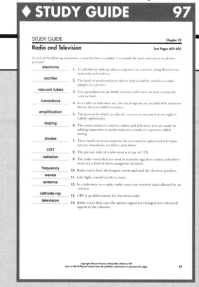

the frequency of the radio waves, they are called frequency-modulated, or FM, waves. The electric currents are amplified and sent to an antenna, where they are transformed into radio waves.

Your receiving radio has an antenna that collects these radio waves and transforms them into electric currents. If the radio is tuned to the same frequency as the radio waves, the waves will be amplified again. The carrier wave—the wave of the frequency to which the radio is tuned—is removed. This leaves only the waves that correspond to the original sound waves. The radio's loudspeaker vibrates to cause sound waves for you to hear.

Look at the radio dial shown. A set of numbers on the top of the dial corresponds to the FM frequency range and a separate set of numbers on the bottom corresponds to the AM frequency range. Every radio station, AM or FM, operates at a specific frequency and wavelength. FM stations broadcast at carrier frequencies ranging from 88 to 108 megahertz. AM stations broadcast at carrier frequencies between 540 and 1600 kilohertz (sometimes written on a scale labeled from 54 to 160 kHz × 10). Do AM or FM stations operate at a higher frequency?

Connect to...
Chemistry
What is it about the arrangement of electrons in metals that makes metals suitable to construct antennas?

Television Transmission

What do radios have in common with television sets? Both have tuners that tune the circuits to the frequency of the radio waves. Both have a loudspeaker to vibrate and produce sound and an antenna to collect radio signals. The antennas on modern radios and television sets are often hidden in the circuits of these devices. Televisions not only turn the radio waves into sound, but they also use these signals to create a visual image. Television is like a radio with pictures.

---

2 TEACH

Key Concepts are highlighted.

CONCEPT DEVELOPMENT

▶ After introducing radio transmission, but before discussing television, have students make a list of the similarities and differences between radios and television sets. This will help them think of the common parts, such as channel tuners, antennas, volume control, and loudspeakers.

▶ Discuss the function of antennas. Common antennas are made of metal rods. The radio waves produce an electric field that causes the electrons in the conductor to vibrate at the frequencies of the incoming waves.

▶ If possible, have a cathode-ray tube available to show your students. Television or electronics dealers may have picture tubes available for demonstration purposes. Point out the major parts and their functions.

STUDENT TEXT QUESTION

▶ Page 603, paragraph 3: **Do AM or FM stations operate at a higher frequency?** *FM stations.*

CHECK FOR UNDERSTANDING

Use the Mini Quiz to check for understanding.

MINI QUIZ

Use the Mini Quiz to check students' recall of chapter content.

1. **What are the two ways radio waves can be modulated?** *amplitude-modulated, frequency-modulated*

2. **What is the role of the loudspeaker in a radio?** *to vibrate in response to an electrical signal, producing sound waves*

3. **What kind of signal transmits TV video images?** *amplitude-modulated*

● REINFORCEMENT 97

REINFORCEMENT   Chapter 23
Radio and Television   Text Pages 602–605

Use the diagram below to answer questions 1–5.

Wave A

Wave B

1. Is wave A a transverse wave or a compressional wave?   transverse wave
2. What kind of wave is wave B?   compressional
3. Which wave is a radio wave?   Wave A
4. Which wave is a sound wave?   Wave B
5. How does a radio work?   by changing transverse radio waves into vibrations that produce compressional sound waves

Answer the following questions on the lines provided.

6. What does the abbreviation AM stand for?   amplitude-modulated
7. What is represented by the abbreviation FM?   frequency-modulated
8. What part of a radio or television set collects radio signals?   the antenna
9. On what part of a television set is the picture produced?   cathode-ray tube
10. How does a CRT work?   A beam of electrons is focused onto a screen that is coated with fluorescent materials. When the electrons strike the coated screen, the fluorescent materials glow to form an image.

Copyright Glencoe Division of Macmillan/McGraw-Hill
Users of Merrill Physical Science have the publisher's permission to reproduce this page.   97

▲ ENRICHMENT 97

ENRICHMENT   Chapter 23
Radio and Television   Text Pages 602–605

RADIO STATIONS

Plan a visit to a local radio station. Prepare a set of questions to ask the people who work at the station. Include at least two of the following questions.
1. What are the components that allow a radio signal to be transmitted? Draw a diagram showing how a radio signal is transmitted.

2. Why can an AM radio signal be heard farther away than an FM radio signal?   AM radio signals have frequencies that are reflected by the charged layers in the upper atmosphere. An AM signal can follow the curvature of Earth. These reflections make it possible to detect an AM radio station at a great distance. An FM radio signal has a higher frequency than an AM signal. It cannot be reflected off the ionosphere. An FM signal travels in a straight line into space.

3. The wavelengths of AM signals can be from ten to over one hundred meters long. The wavelength of FM signals are about 1 meter. Why can an FM signal be heard when a car passes under a bridge, but an AM signal is not?   An AM signal does not diffract well around obstacles such as bridges. This results in a "shadow." An FM signal has a short enough wavelength that it can reflect underneath the bridge and still be picked up by the car radio.

4. Signals from different stations should not be received at the same frequency on the radio dial. How do stations avoid transmitting at the same frequency?   Within the United States, the Federal Communications Commission (FCC) regulates radio transmission. The FCC assigns suitable frequencies to radio stations to reduce the interference of one station's signal with another. It also limits a station's power or power radiated in particular directions and may restrict hours of transmission.

Copyright Glencoe Division of Macmillan/McGraw-Hill
Users of Merrill Physical Science have the publisher's permission to reproduce this page.   97

603

Bring a radio or television into your classroom. Have students demonstrate the use of each device with proper physics explanations. They should include explanations such as how the radio waves are picked up and transformed to sound and what is happening when you change the channel.

EXTENSION

For students who have mastered this section, use the **Reinforcement** and **Enrichment** masters or other OPTIONS provided.

VideoDisc

STVS: Chroma Key; Disc 1, Side 2

PROGRAM RESOURCES

From the **Teacher Resource Package** use:

Activity Worksheets, page 190, MINI-Lab: How do electrons make a TV picture?

T E C H N O L O G Y

For more information about HDTV, see Cook, William J. "Making a Leap in TV Technology." *U.S. News and World Report*, January 23, 1989, pages 48-49.

Think Critically: Television signals are broadcast on AM and FM radio waves. Answers will vary, but make sure students can support their ideas.

The audio, or sound, signal for television programs is sent and received like an FM radio signal. The video **(3)** images are sent by AM carrier waves. Just as a microphone is used to change sound waves into varying electric currents, a television camera is used to change light into electric currents that represent the images. This electric video signal then amplitude-modulates a carrier wave. A television station simultaneously transmits the audio and video signals from its antenna.

Tuning into a television station is much like tuning a radio. When you select a channel, only a certain carrier frequency is picked up and amplified within the set. The audio portion of the television program is changed to sound by a loudspeaker. The picture you see on the screen is created by a more complex process. You may have heard that if the picture tube inside your television goes

T E C H N O L O G Y

HDTV

Would you like to have a large-screen TV with pictures as clear as a 35-millimeter photograph and the sound quality of a compact disc? This is the pledge of a new generation of television referred to as high-definition television (HDTV). HDTV sets will provide images by constructing a picture from 1125 individual horizontal lines rather than the 525 horizontal lines you have on your current TV set. This means that you can see a clear picture even if you are close to an HDTV screen that is four or five feet across.

The technology for the design and construction of the new TV sets is relatively simple to achieve. Problems arise, however, in trying to move from the United States' current broadcast system to the new broadcast system without making TV sets that aren't HDTV obsolete. Because the HDTV signals encode much more information than conventional TV signals, broadcasting HDTV

signals could interfere with conventional TV broadcasts. Japan, the United States, and some European countries are competing to set the standard for these new HDTV signals. This competition could result in the development of other forms of delivering HDTV signals such as direct broadcast satellites or fiber-optic cables.

Think Critically: How are TV signals currently broadcast? What form of broadcasting do you think would be best for HDTV signals that would not interfere with other TV signals?

OPTIONS

ASSESSMENT—ORAL

▶ **Distinguish radio waves and sound waves. Why are radio waves, not sound waves, used to send music or voices over long distances?** Radio waves are electromagnetic waves, which are transverse and travel very rapidly. Sound waves are compressional waves and travel much more slowly through air. Radio waves are faster and more efficient. If sound waves were used, we would hear all stations at the same time.

▶ **What type of modulation would exist in a radio wave with a frequency of 101.3 MHz?** *FM, or frequency-modulated*

▶ **If video signals are carried by AM carrier waves and audio signals are carried by FM carrier waves in television transmission, why do the waves arrive in your home at the same time?** *AM and FM waves are both radio waves, and all electromagnetic radiation travels at the same speed.*

out, you are faced with a major repair bill or should probably buy a new television. That's because this picture tube is the most expensive component in your TV set. The picture tube is a type of cathode-ray tube. A **cathode-ray tube (CRT)** uses electrons and fluorescent materials to produce images on a screen.

Look at the CRT in the television set at the right. A CRT is a sealed glass vacuum tube. When power is applied to the components in the tube, electrons come off a negative cathode and are focused into a beam. They move toward the screen, which is coated on the inside with materials that glow when struck by the electrons. The direction of the beam is changed by electromagnets outside of the CRT. This allows the beam of electrons to sweep the surface of the screen many times each second.

The cathode-ray tube of a color TV contains a screen lined with different materials that give off light in one of the three primary colors: red, blue, or green. The radio waves that carry the picture signal are changed into electrical signals in the television. These electrical signals control the intensity and position of the electron beams, which determine the colors and patterns of the image that forms on the screen. If you look closely at your television screen, you can see the tiny dots of red, blue, and green that make up each image. How is this process similar to the way your eye forms color images?

Figure 23-7. A television set contains a CRT.

SECTION REVIEW

1. Explain what happens inside your radio when you tune in to a particular radio station.
2. How does a cathode-ray tube produce an image?
3. **Apply:** How might a cathode-ray tube that produces a color image differ from one that produces a black and white image?
4. **Connect to Life Science:** Explain the similarities in how eyes and CRTs in televisions produce color images.

☑ Concept Mapping

Make a concept map that shows the steps involved in radio broadcasts. Begin with the voice at the microphone and end with the radio waves leaving the transmitter. If you need help, refer to Concept Mapping in the **Skill Handbook** on pages 684 and 685.

MINI-Lab

How do electrons make a TV picture?

Electrons are guided to the screen of a CRT by electrical and magnetic fields. A chemical inside the screen reacts to the electrons by flashing a color of the light. Place a small magnet on the glass surface of an operating CRT and *observe* the response. Do both poles of the magnet produce the same reaction? What happens to the colors on the screen?

MINI-Lab

Materials: a CRT, a small magnet

Teaching Tips

▶ Any small magnet will work. A stronger magnet will produce a stronger image distortion. It's best not to use too strong a magnet.

▶ A still pattern may be easier to analyze than a moving picture.

Answers

▶ The region above the magnet will show distortion downward or upward depending on the pole used.

▶ Color TVs will show a region of color change above or below the magnet.

MINI-Lab
ASSESSMENT

Content: Have students use the results of this activity to explain what controls the direction of the electron beam in a CRT.

3 CLOSE

▶ Ask questions 1 and 2 and the **Apply** and **Connect to Life Science** questions in the Section Review.

▶ Review the discussion of vision processes in Chapter 19.

SECTION REVIEW ANSWERS

1. The radio picks up and amplifies radio waves of the frequency to which the receiver is tuned.

2. Electron beams cause specific materials on the screen of the tube to fluoresce. The intensity and pattern of the beams determine the image.

3. Apply: The fluorescent materials in a color picture tube will give off red, blue, or green light. Combinations of these colors can form all other colors. But, a black and white picture tube forms images when electron beams strike a fluorescent material that glows white.

4. Connect to Life Science: Both the picture tube and the retina are sensitive to red, green, and blue. With the eye, there are red, blue, and green sensitive cones. With the TV there are red, blue, and green fluorescing materials.

Skill Builder

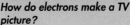

| Voice or music causes compressional waves | → | Microphone changes sound waves to electric current | → | Vibrations in current are amplified | → | Modulator creates AM or FM radio waves | → | Radio waves sent out from antenna |

Skill Builder
ASSESSMENT

Performance: Have students add the steps showing how radio waves become audible sounds.

PREPARATION

SECTION BACKGROUND
▶ Magnetic disks are made by coating the disk with a thin liquid suspension of tiny magnetized iron oxide particles. These permanent magnets are aligned by a strong magnetic field as the liquid is dried, making them resistant to reasonably rough treatment.

PREPLANNING
▶ Make sure you have at least one computer available for demonstration purposes to use with instruction in this section.

1 MOTIVATE

▶ Ask students to try to come to an agreement about whether or not computers can think. **What does a computer need to solve problems for you?** *It needs a program or set of instructions.* **How does a computer's problem-solving process differ from your own?** *A computer can only perform operations that it has been programmed to do.*

In Your JOURNAL

Students might mention video games, word processing, running programs, creating diagrams, or monitoring heart signals.

New Science Words

microprocessor
RAM
ROM

Objectives

▶ Identify the basic parts of a microcomputer.
▶ Describe the role of the microprocessor.
▶ Distinguish between RAM and ROM.

In Your JOURNAL

In your Journal, write a paragraph describing all of the tasks you have used a computer to do. How else have you seen or heard about computers being used?

What are the three main capabilities of microcomputers?

Microcomputer Components

How often do you use microcomputers? You may use them to play computer games, practice math problems, or locate a book in the library. A computer is a device you can program to carry out calculations and make logical decisions. How many simple addition problems can you do in ten seconds? Computers can store large amounts of information and perform up to several million calculations in each second. This ability makes them very efficient at processing and storing large amounts of information.

Microcomputers must have three main capabilities. First, they must be capable of storing the data or information needed to solve a problem. Next, microcomputers must be able to follow instructions to perform tasks in a logical way. Finally, microcomputers must communicate their information to the outside world. These requirements can be fulfilled with a combination of hardware and software components.

Computer hardware refers to the major permanent components of the microcomputer. When you think of a computer

---

OPTIONS

Meeting Different Ability Levels
For Section 23-3, use the following **Teacher Resource Masters** depending upon individual students' needs.
◆ **Study Guide Master** for all students.
● **Reinforcement Master** for students of average and above average ability levels.
▲ **Enrichment Master** for above average students.
Additional Teacher Resource Package masters are listed in any **PROGRAM RESOURCES** boxes that are in the section. The additional masters are appropriate for all students.

◆ STUDY GUIDE 98

STUDY GUIDE — Chapter 23
Microcomputers — Text Pages 606-611

In the blank, write the letter of the term or phrase that best completes each statement.

a 1. An integrated circuit on the main circuit board of a computer is a ____.
   a. microprocessor   b. microcomputer

a 2. RAM stands for ____.
   a. random-access memory   b. readily-available memory

b 3. ROM stands for ____.
   a. randomly-occurring memory   b. read-only memory

b 4. The group of instructions that tells a computer what to do is called ____.
   a. hardware   b. a program

b 5. The kind of memory that is permanently stored in a computer is ____.
   a. random-access memory   b. read-only memory

a 6. The temporary memory of a computer is ____.
   a. random-access memory   b. randomly-occurring memory

b 7. The major permanent components of a microcomputer are its ____.
   a. software   b. hardware

a 8. The video screen in most computers is a ____.
   a. CRT   b. CPU

a 9. Information that is lost when a computer is turned off is stored in ____.
   a. RAM   b. ROM

b 10. A hard disk drive is an example of ____.
   a. software   b. hardware

a 11. Computer programs are sometimes referred to as ____.
   a. software   b. hardware

a 12. Keyboards, joysticks, and mice are examples of ____.
   a. input devices   b. output devices

b 13. ____ disks retrieve information faster.
   a. Floppy   b. Hard

b 14. CPU is an abbreviation for ____.
   a. computer privacy unit   b. central processing unit

a 15. The brain of a computer is the ____.
   a. microprocessor   b. floppy disk

---

you probably think of the input and output devices. Output devices usually include a screen, which is part of the video display terminal, and a printer. The video screen in most computers is a cathode-ray tube similar to the one in your television set. Input devices allow you to enter data in the computer. Keyboards, joysticks, and mouses are common input devices. Disk drives are both input and output devices. The main circuit board inside the computer holds the central processing unit (CPU) and the main memory.

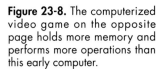

Name three output devices.

Microprocessors

The first computers were very large and slow compared to the computers you are familiar with. The United States built several of the first computers shortly after World War II, between 1946 and 1951. These early computers operated on complex circuits composed of thousands of vacuum tubes. They used a lot of energy and were large enough to fill entire rooms. The

Figure 23-8. The computerized video game on the opposite page holds more memory and performs more operations than this early computer.

607

▶ Have a computer set up in the room so students can see the various parts. Ask them what kinds of things the computer might be useful for. They may mention games, quiz questions, typing papers, or programming.

TYING TO PREVIOUS KNOWLEDGE: Take a poll: **How many students used a computer of some kind in the last week?** *Answers will vary. Most new cars, some calculators, grocery store cash registers, and even some appliances use microcomputers. In this section students will learn about the structure and function of microcomputers.*

OBJECTIVES AND SCIENCE WORDS: Have students review the objectives and science words to become familiar with this section.

Key Concepts are highlighted.

CONCEPT DEVELOPMENT

▶ To help students understand the advantage integrated circuits and microchips have over vacuum tubes, bring in a microchip and tell them how many electrical devices are on one tiny chip. Then show them the size of a vacuum tube and determine how many tubes would be needed to accomplish the same job as the microchip. In addition, the integrated circuits on microchips greatly increase the speed of processing information.

PROGRAM RESOURCES

From the **Teacher Resource Package** use:

Concept Mapping, pages 51-52.

VideoDisc
STVS: Mars Ball; Disc 1, Side 2

CONCEPT DEVELOPMENT

▶ To help distinguish between RAM and ROM, emphasize that RAM is temporary memory because information is stored electronically. Information stored in RAM can be very rapidly recalled for use. Information in ROM is retained even when the power is shut off because it is magnetically stored.

▶ Use the information found in Revealing Misconceptions below to generate a discussion about the prefix *kilo-* as used by computer designers.

REVEALING MISCONCEPTIONS

▶ Students are probably familiar with the metric prefix *kilo-*, which means one thousand of the base unit. The term has a slightly different meaning as a unit of computer memory size. One K, or a computer kilo, actually represents 1024 bytes rather than 1000 bytes.

Science and WRITING

Students have a way of simplifying things that can teach all of us something. The novice is bombarded with strange terms from the time he or she begins shopping for a computer. If a student does a particularly good job, he or she might be able to explain the information in a brochure or news article.

STUDENT TEXT QUESTION

▶ Page 608, paragraph 2: **How many bytes of information can be stored in 30 kilobytes of memory?**

30 kilobytes $\times \dfrac{1024 \text{ bytes}}{\text{kilobytes}}$

= 30 720 bytes

CONCEPT DEVELOPMENT

▶ Demonstrate the use of floppy disks and hard drives to store information. Shut the computer off after storing some information to show that RAM is lost, but you can retrieve information from floppy disks.

▶ Emphasize that hard drives are found inside most computers. Floppy disks are commonly found in 3.5- and 5.25-inch sizes. Stress that although the 3.5-inch disks are enclosed in hard plastic cases for protection, they function and are classified as "floppy" disks.

Science and WRITING

If you are "computer wise" you may be able to help novices by developing a dictionary of computer terms. Start with the terms in computer ads.

Table 23-1

BINARY CODE		
Number	Binary	Switch
0	0	○
1	1	●
2	10	● ○
3	11	● ●
4	100	● ○ ○
5	101	● ○ ●
6	110	● ● ○
7	111	● ● ●
8	1000	● ○ ○ ○
9	1001	● ○ ○ ●
10	1010	● ○ ● ○

invention of the integrated circuit rapidly improved the efficiency of computers.

A **microprocessor** serves as the brain of the computer. A microprocessor is an integrated circuit on the main circuit board. It receives electrical input from the user and tells other parts of the computer how to respond, just as your brain tells your hand to move when you touch a hot pan. It might store information using a disk drive, change a video display, or make a sound. The microprocessor contains the CPU, which is the circuitry that actually carries out the arithmetic and logical operations. CPUs are different among various kinds of microcomputers.

Computer Memory

Information is collected and stored in the memory of the computer. The memory contains thousands of tiny circuits that have switches with two positions: open (off) or closed (on). Recall that a switch must be closed for current to flow. All computer information is processed with combinations of just two numbers, zero and one, to represent these situations. This is called a binary number system. Each 0 (off) or 1 (on) represents one binary digit and is called a bit. Numbers, letters, and symbols are grouped in your computer in arrangements of eight bits called bytes. Often computer memory is expressed in terms of larger units, such as kilobytes and megabytes. One kilobyte equals 1024 bytes. How many bytes of information can be stored in 30 kilobytes of memory?

There are several kinds of memory in a microcomputer. Temporary memory stores documents and data while they are being used. The computer can send information to the memory by turning certain bits on or off. Similarly, the computer can read information from the memory by determining whether certain bits are on or off. This temporary memory is called random access memory, or **RAM**, because any bit can be used in storing information. Because information is electronically stored in RAM, the information is lost when the computer is turned off. However, using information stored in RAM is much faster than pulling it from mechanical disk drives.

When you purchase a computer, it comes with some information already stored in permanent memory. This information contains instructions required by the micro-

OPTIONS

ASSESSMENT—ORAL

▶ **Why is the memory system in a computer called a binary system?** *There are only two possible numbers, 0 or 1, that give the computer information. The prefix* bi- *means two.*

processor to operate the computer. The computer can read this memory, but information can't be added to it. For this reason, it is called read only memory, or **ROM.** Information in ROM is permanently stored inside the computer and, therefore, isn't lost when the computer is turned off. Neither RAM nor ROM is useful in helping you store your work between uses.

Data Storage

One of the main advantages of using computers is that you can save information and then come back later to make changes to it. Because RAM is lost when you turn off the computer, and you can't save information in ROM, the information must be stored in another way. Disk drives are used to record information magnetically. This process is similar to the way music is recorded on cassette tapes, but much more information can be stored on formatted computer disks. There are two main kinds of disks used for data storage.

Most computers have at least one disk drive for storing information on a floppy disk. A floppy disk is a thin, round, plastic disk coated with a magnetic material, such as iron oxide. The disk is encased in a thicker plastic case for protection. Information can be saved on the disk, and the disk can be removed from the disk drive for storage. Floppy disks can be used to transfer data or programs from one computer to another computer if the computers have compatible operating systems and disk drives.

Hard disk drives are found inside the main part of most computers. Hard disks are rigid metal disks that stay inside the computer and spin continuously when the computer is on. Hard drives are useful because they hold many times more information than floppy disks can hold. They also retrieve information much faster. A hard drive is a costly, but helpful, addition to a computer system.

Figure 23-9. A hard disk, like the one at the far right, is a permanent part of some computers. It is used to store data. Two sizes of floppy disks are shown on the left.

23-3 MICROCOMPUTERS **609**

He would lose the design if he hadn't saved it on a hard or floppy disk.

Think Critically: He could save the design on floppy disk to use later.

CHECK FOR UNDERSTANDING

Use the Mini Quiz to check for understanding.

MINI QUIZ

Use the Mini Quiz to check students' recall of chapter content.

1 **What does CPU stand for? What does the CPU do?** *Central processing unit; it is the circuitry that performs arithmetic and logical operations.*

2 **Which kind of memory can be readily accessed and used to store temporary information?** *RAM*

3 **Which holds more information, hard disks or floppy disks?** *hard disks*

4 **A(n) _____ is a set of instructions that tells a computer what to do.** *program*

RETEACH

Draw an analogy between taking an open-note exam and the RAM/ROM difference. The material you do not know is written in front of you in the notes (RAM). If you take the notes away, the information is gone. Some answers are stored permanently in your brain (ROM).

EXTENSION

For students who have mastered this section, use the **Reinforcement** and **Enrichment** masters or other OPTIONS provided.

Computer Art

Emilio spent most of his spare time drawing and painting. His teachers and friends liked his artwork and they thought it was very creative.

Emilio used the family computer to write reports for school, but he really wanted to use the computer to create artwork. He visited a computer store at the mall to see what hardware was available that he could use for this purpose.

He found a graphic tablet and a light pen that allowed him to draw on the CRT screen. First, he tried the graphic tablet. He drew on a special pad with a stylus, and his design appeared on the computer screen. To use the light pen, he drew directly on the CRT. Because the graphic tablet was less expensive and easier to use, he decided to buy it. If Emilio was creating a design and the power went off, what would happen to the design?

Think Critically: How could Emilio save a design he was working on to finish at some other time?

Uses for Computers

What is a program?

4 Computers can't complete a task without instructions for carrying out a series of operations. A program is a group of instructions that tells a computer what to do. Programs are sometimes referred to as software. Computer programmers use special languages that convert your language into instructions the CPU can understand. BASIC, Pascal, and COBOL are examples of computer languages. Whenever you play a computer game, use a word processor, or solve mathematical problems, a computer program is instructing the computer to perform in a certain way.

Microcomputers are becoming useful in more and more applications. You often use them in situations where a computer screen is not visible. For example, computers are regularly used to regulate mechanical processes in cars, to monitor heating and cooling systems in buildings,

610 ELECTRONICS AND COMPUTERS

PROGRAM RESOURCES
From the **Teacher Resource Package** use:
Cross-Curricular Connections, page 29, Using a Spreadsheet to Analyze Lab Data.
Science and Society, page 27, Junk Mail.
Activity Worksheets, page 5, Flex Your Brain.
Critical Thinking/Problem Solving, page 29, The Personal Computer.

and to enter inventory bar codes in grocery stores. Many calculators can now be programmed as well. Even some kitchen appliances contain simple, small computers to enhance their operations. Microcomputers wouldn't exist without advances in electronics, such as the transistor and the integrated circuit. Can you imagine going through one week without using a microcomputer of some sort? How do you think we'll use microcomputers of the future?

Figure 23-10. Look closely at the computer screen above and you will see a two-page spread from this book. Computers are commonly used for desktop publishing.

SECTION REVIEW

1. What are three main functions of a computer?
2. What is the difference between RAM and ROM?
3. **Apply:** How would you transfer a computer program from your computer to a friend's computer?
4. **Connect to Life Science:** How people interact with computers is a major consideration in computer design. What are some of the possible input and ouput devices on a computer?

☑ Comparing and Contrasting

Compare and contrast the advantages and disadvantages of floppy disk drives and hard disk drives. If you need help, refer to Comparing and Contrasting in the **Skill Handbook** on page 679.

Skill Builder

23-3 MICROCOMPUTERS **611**

Skill Builder
ASSESSMENT
Performance: Have students use their comparisons to explain why both hard and floppy disk drives are commonly in a computer.

---

3 CLOSE

▶ Ask questions 1-2 and the **Apply** and **Connect to Life Science** questions in the Section Review.

❓ FLEX Your Brain

Use the Flex Your Brain activity to bridge to the Science and Society topic of computer crimes by having students explore WAYS COMPUTERS MIGHT BE MISUSED.

ASSESSMENT

Portfolio: Use the Flex Your Brain activity to reinforce critical-thinking and problem-solving skills. In Step 2, students might list breaking into other computer systems or hacking, white-collar crime, or embezzling.

SECTION REVIEW ANSWERS

1. They must store data, decide what operations to perform next, and communicate with the outside world.

2. Information can be added to RAM by the user and read by the computer. Information is temporarily stored in RAM and is lost when the computer is turned off. ROM is permanent memory that the computer can only read, giving it instructions for operating the microprocessor.

3. Apply: Transfer the program to a floppy disk, or use modems or a computer network.

4. Connect to Life Science: Input devices include keyboards, joysticks, mouses, microphones, and touch sensitive screens. Output devices include screens, printers, and speakers.

Skill Builder

Floppy disk drives are useful because floppy disks can be used to transport information from one computer to another and are relatively inexpensive. However, hard disks drives can store much more information and can rapidly access information. The main disadvantage of hard disk drives is that they are very expensive.

PREPARATION

SECTION BACKGROUND

▶ A distinction is sometimes made between a computer virus and a worm program. A virus replicates itself and attaches itself to other programs to produce sometimes bizarre effects. A worm loads a system with information that replicates itself and fills the memory and files in the computer. This slows or stops the computer from functioning.

1 MOTIVATE

TYING TO PREVIOUS KNOWLEDGE:
In this chapter, you have studied microcomputers. With modems it is possible for computer systems in different places to communicate with each other through phone lines. Explain that we will learn how this is a possible problem, as it provides a door that can be broken into.

2 TEACH

Key Concepts are highlighted.

CONCEPT DEVELOPMENT

▶ Photocopy or make an overhead of a software copyright agreement. Discuss how easy it is to copy software, even with the copyright.

PROGRAM RESOURCES

From the **Teacher Resource Package** use:

Science Integration Activity 23

 **23-4** # Computer Crimes

New Science Words

computer virus

Objectives

▶ Discuss the types of crimes that can be committed by computer misuse.
▶ Predict the possible consequences of computer crimes.

In Your JOURNAL

In your Journal, discuss why music or computer programs need to be protected by copyright laws and should not be copied illegally.

How Serious Are Computer Crimes?

What do you think of when you hear the word *crime?* You probably think of stealing, vandalism, or violence. Would you believe an increasingly common type of crime is being committed by the misuse of computers?

You may have copied a friend's cassette tape onto a blank tape for your own personal use. Computer programs can also be copied from one floppy disk to another. When you purchase a program, the software company usually intends for you to make one backup copy in case the original one becomes damaged. The companies don't intend for you to copy the program to give to your friends. Cassette tapes and programs are protected by copyright laws. However, some programs are free and can be legally shared. Sharing of illegal copies of software is probably the most common of computer crimes, as well as the most difficult computer crime to safeguard against.

In recent years, computer viruses have become a problem. Some computer viruses can be deliberately planted in a computer. A **computer virus** is a type of program that can multiply inside a computer and use so much memory that it harms the system. Like a virus in your body, it can remain inactive in the computer until something causes it to spread. As a result of the virus attack, data in memory might be lost, and a strange message might appear on the screen. The infected computer might even just stop functioning. Viruses can be sent through phone lines linking computers or can spread from infected software shared between computers. Sometimes antivirus programs can find and destroy viruses before they spread or even fix the damage already done. Why do you think it is a crime to purposefully spread a computer virus?

OPTIONS

Meeting Different Ability Levels

For Section 23-4, use the following **Teacher Resource Masters** depending upon individual students' needs.

◆ **Study Guide Master** for all students.
● **Reinforcement Master** for students of average and above average ability levels.
▲ **Enrichment Master** for above average students.

Additional Teacher Resource Package masters are listed in any **PROGRAM RESOURCES** boxes that are in the section. The additional masters are appropriate for all students.

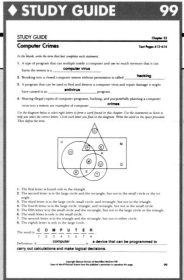

Perhaps the most controversial computer crime is "hacking." People who break into closed computer systems without permission are called hackers. They may have several motives. Some hackers may just find hacking challenging, but others are looking for specific restricted information.

Hacking is an invasion of privacy. For example, a hacker might be able to find out about your parents' financial history without permission. A hacker could break into your school's computer to alter his or her grades. Do you think this is the same type of crime as breaking into someone's house?

Make a list of the activities in your life that involve computers. How do computer crimes affect these activities? Stealing software can cause the price of software programs to go up. If a virus were to shut down a major computer system, such as the system at your bank, how would you be affected?

SECTION REVIEW

1. How does a computer virus interfere with a computer?
2. What is computer hacking?
3. **Connect to Life Science:** How does a virus in your body behave similarly to a computer virus?

You Decide!

Suppose a computer hacker broke into a secret government computer system. Should this be considered a criminal felony, such as treason, or should it be considered a misdemeanor crime, such as breaking and entering? Do you think the hacker should be punished in the same manner as someone who broke into a building and took secret files? Explain your point of view.

SCIENCE & SOCIETY

TEACHER F.Y.I.
▶ Programmers have now developed disinfectant programs that can be run on a hard drive or floppy disk to scan for signs of a viral infection.

CHECK FOR UNDERSTANDING
▶ Ask questions 1 and 2 and the **Connect to Life Science** question in the Section Review.
▶ Ask students if they can be sure their computer or a classroom computer is free of viruses. Note that the virus may be hiding in the computer waiting for a date or other signal to activate it.

RETEACH
For students who have had life science, you could draw a useful analogy between viruses that cause human diseases and computer viruses. For example, the virus that causes AIDS can be inactive for years before it spreads and attacks the body.

EXTENSION
For students who have mastered this section, use the **Reinforcement** and **Enrichment** masters or other OPTIONS provided.

3 CLOSE

▶ Use the You Decide activity to encourage students to evaluate their own point of view on computer crimes.

SECTION REVIEW ANSWERS
1. A virus multiplies and expands to fill the memory of a computer. It may cause lost data or prevent the computer from functioning.
2. Hacking is breaking into a computer system to gain information without permission.
3. Connect to Life Science: A biological virus can remain inactive in your body until something causes it to multiply, can be spread through several means, and can cause your body to act abnormally. A computer virus behaves in similar ways relative to a computer.

YOU DECIDE!

Answers will vary. Have students justify their choices.

ACTIVITY 23-2

OBJECTIVE: Invent a system of communication that stores information in magnetic fields.
Time: one class period

PROCESS SKILLS applied in this activity are **classifying, communicating,** and **defining.**

PREPARATION

Any kind or shape of magnets with poles on the faces will work, but magnets should be of equal strength.

Cooperative Learning: Divide the class into teams of two or three. You may wish to divide the tasks of labeling the magnets, designing the code, and testing the code among group members.

THINKING CRITICALLY

Opposite poles of magnets will attract each other and like poles will repel. Each letter can be represented by the numbers 0 and 1 arranged in five or fewer positions.

TEACHING THE ACTIVITY

*Refer to the **Activity Worksheets** for additional information and teaching strategies.*

• Provide each team with a thin strip and two sheets of 8″×10″ cardstock and at least 12 ceramic magnets.

• Encourage creativity in inventing the binary code for letters and the way the message sheet is structured. Students must adequately describe their own operating rules in order for the other team to read what is written.

• Follow-up discussion can further develop the lab analogy to the writing and reading of information on the magnetic material of a computer disk.

PROGRAM RESOURCES

From the **Teacher Resource Package** use:

   Activity Worksheets, pages 186-187, Activity 23-2: Magnetic Messages.

DESIGNING AN EXPERIMENT
Magnetic Messages

Floppy disks store information magnetically using a binary number system with coded combinations of the numbers zero and one to represent all entries into a computer. Can you design a method of storing a message magnetically?

Getting Started

In this activity you will *invent* a binary code to represent the letters of the alphabet. You will then use this system to magnetically encode a brief message.

Thinking Critically

How do opposite poles of magnets interact with each other? How can you represent all 26 letters of the alphabet using a code of just two numbers?

Materials

Your cooperative group will use:
• disk magnets, 12   • metric ruler
• cardstock paper, 2 sheets and a thin strip
• transparent tape

Try It!

1. Divide one sheet of the cardstock into three rows of five squares as shown.
2. Put all the magnets in a single stack. Mark the top side of each magnet with the number 1 and the bottom with the number 0.
3. *Invent* a code using only the numbers 1 and 0 to represent the letters of the alphabet.
4. Choose a three-letter word to "write" in your magnetic code. Place the code for one letter on each line and tape the magnets to the cardboard with appropriate code number side up.
5. Cover the magnets with a second sheet marked with the location of squares.
6. Tape a magnet to the end of a strip of cardboard. Holding the other end of the strip, move the magnet over each row of the top sheet and *observe* its response to the message magnets. Decode your observations of the interaction in each square to form your word.

Summing Up/Sharing Results

• How do you know what kind of magnet is underneath the suspended "reading" magnet?
• Why are there only two numbers in this magnetic code?

Going Further!

Write down your operating rules for "reading" your word. Trade your rules, letter code, and magnetic message with another team and see if they can decode your message.

SUMMING UP/SHARING RESULTS

The reading magnet will be either attracted or repelled depending on which pole of the message magnet is facing up. Each row of numbers will correspond to one letter. The magnet has only two poles so the only possible responses are attraction and repulsion.

GOING FURTHER!

Team operating rules will vary. The reader must know which way to scan, right to left, left to right, top to bottom, and so on. The reader must also know if attraction to the reader magnet means the message magnet is 1 or 0.

Activity
ASSESSMENT

Oral: Ask students if it would be possible to invent a letter code based on three digits (0, 1, 2) using this same method of magnetic decoding. Discuss the fact that there would be no way to have three possible answers if only two answers are possible: attraction and repulsion.

SUMMARY

23-1: Semiconductor Devices

1. The conductivity of semiconductors can be increased by adding impurities to them.
2. A rectifier changes alternating current into direct current.
3. Electronic devices containing integrated circuits are much smaller than those that don't contain these circuits.

23-2: Radio and Television

1. Radio and television signals are transmitted by changing electrical signals into electromagnetic radiation.
2. A cathode-ray tube uses electrons and fluorescent materials to produce pictures on a television screen.

23-3: Microcomputers

1. The basic parts of a microcomputer include the input devices, the output devices, disk drives, and the main circuit board.
2. The microprocessor receives input and tells the computer how to respond.
3. RAM is the temporary memory in a computer. ROM is memory that is permanently stored inside the computer.

23-4: Science and Society: Computer Crimes

1. Computer crimes include illegally copying software, planting computer viruses, and hacking.
2. Some computer crimes can involve stealing restricted information or altering records.

KEY SCIENCE WORDS

a. amplification
b. cathode-ray tube (CRT)
c. computer virus
d. diode
e. integrated circuit
f. microprocessor
g. RAM
h. rectifier
i. ROM
j. transistor

UNDERSTANDING VOCABULARY

Match each phrase with the correct term from the list of Key Science Words.

1. miniature components on a slice of silicon
2. any device that converts AC to DC
3. amplifies an electric signal
4. the process of making an electric current stronger
5. a TV picture tube
6. receives input and tells the computer how to respond
7. a computer's temporary memory
8. a computer program that multiplies and affects a computer's memory
9. contains stored information needed by a microprocessor to operate a computer
10. a type of rectifier

SUMMARY

Have students read the summary statements to review the major concepts of the chapter.

UNDERSTANDING VOCABULARY

1.	e	6.	f
2.	h	7.	g
3.	j	8.	c
4.	a	9.	i
5.	b	10.	d

ASSESSMENT
Portfolio

Encourage students to place in their portfolios one or two items of what they consider to be their best work. For each item, ask students to explain why that item was chosen and what they learned from it. Items might be selected from the following.

• Connect to Chemistry explanation, p. 597
• In Your Journal paragraph, p. 602
• The explanation paragraph for Activity 23-2 code and message, p. 614

Performance

Additional performance assessments may be found in *Performance Assessment* and *Science Integration Activities* that accompany **Merrill Physical Science.** Performance Task Assessment Lists and rubrics for evaluating these activities and other products generated throughout the chapter can be found in Glencoe's *Performance Assessment in Middle School Science.*

OPTIONS

ASSESSMENT

To assess student understanding of material in this chapter, use the resources listed.

COOPERATIVE LEARNING

Consider using cooperative learning in the THINK AND WRITE CRITICALLY, APPLY, and MORE SKILL BUILDERS sections of the Chapter Review.

PROGRAM RESOURCES

From the **Teacher Resource Package** use:

Chapter Review, pages 49-50.

Chapter and Unit Tests, pages 151-154, Chapter Test.

CHAPTER

REVIEW

CHECKING CONCEPTS

1. a	**6.** a
2. a	**7.** b
3. d	**8.** b
4. a	**9.** a
5. b	**10.** c

USING LAB SKILLS

ASSESSMENT

Use these alternate lab exercises to assess students' understanding of the skills used in this chapter.

11. LEDs only allow current to pass in one direction. Because AC reverses its direction and the LEDs are connected in opposite directions, both LEDs are lit.

12. Dropping a magnet can cause the magnetic domains to change alignment and reduce the magnetic effect. In this case the attraction or repulsion may be too weak to detect.

THINK AND WRITE CRITICALLY

13. In diodes, semiconductors are used to convert an alternating current into a direct current by placing an *n*-type semiconductor at one end of the diode and a *p*-type at the other so current can only flow in one direction. In transistors, semiconductors are used to amplify current.

14. The advantages of integrated circuits are that they have little electrical resistance and minimize energy loss, and a current can travel faster through the circuit. Integrated circuits cannot handle large currents, and they are too small to be easily manipulated.

15. Computers must be able to store data, perform tasks, and have some way to communicate with the outside world.

16. Computer crime includes copying and distributing copyrighted computer software, sending a computer virus to grow and wipe out a computer's memory, and breaking into closed computer systems. Answers will vary, but students should support their answers.

17. Answers to this question will vary but may include such activities as play-

---

CHECKING CONCEPTS

Choose the word or phrase that completes the sentence.

1. Elements that are semiconductors are located on the periodic table _____.
   a. between metals and nonmetals
   b. on the right side
   c. at the bottom
   d. on the left side

2. Solid-state electronic devices use _____.
   a. low current   **c.** no current
   b. high current   **d.** vacuum tubes

3. Rectifiers are used to _____.
   a. change DC to AC
   b. make sure something is right-side up
   c. amplify radio signals
   d. change AC to DC

4. The signal in an electronic device that represents sound and images is a _____.
   a. varying current   **c.** radio wave
   b. constant current **d.** sound wave

5. Transistors are used in all of the following except _____.
   a. medical diagnoses **c.** hearing aids
   b. TV vacuum tubes   **d.** tape players

6. Integrated circuits consist of _____.
   a. doped silicon chips with photographed wires
   b. generators and appliances
   c. televisions and radios
   d. vacuum tubes and transistors

7. The video images for a television program are transmitted to your home as _____.
   a. frequency-modulated radio waves
   b. amplitude-modulated radio waves
   c. cathode rays
   d. electric current

8. Computer hardware consists of all of the following except _____.
   a. video display terminal **c.** disk drives
   b. programs   **d.** keyboards

9. A computer represents information using _____.
   a. a binary number system
   b. sequences of numbers
   c. arrangements of 4 bits
   d. the numbers 1 through 10

10. Computer data and programs both can be stored permanently and transferred to other computers using _____.
   a. RAM   **c.** floppy disks
   b. ROM   **d.** hard disks

USING LAB SKILLS

11. Review the results of Activity 23-1 on page 598. Explain why both LED bulbs lit at the same time when connected to the AC power supply.

12. In Activity 23-2 on page 614, you communicated information magnetically. Explain why your "reading" magnet might no longer interact with your code magnets after being dropped.

THINK AND WRITE CRITICALLY

Answer the following questions in your Journal using complete sentences.

13. How are semiconductors used in diodes and transistors?

14. Describe the advantages and disadvantages of integrated circuits.

15. Identify three functions of a microcomputer.

16. Describe three types of computer crime. Which do you think is the most serious? Why?

17. Describe how computers affect you in everyday life.

---

ing computer games, writing papers on word processors, buying groceries, and driving a car.

APPLY

18. Diodes convert alternating current because electrons must flow from an area where there is an excess of electrons (the end with an *n*-type semiconductor) to an area where there is a deficiency of electrons (the end with a *p*-type semiconductor). If a diode had only one or the other type of semicon-

ductor, electrons could still move but not in one direction only.

19. It is not necessary to take the CD player back because the only problem is that an amplifier was never hooked up to the player. The CD player's signal is too weak to vibrate the speakers and requires a larger outside current provided by the amplifier current.

20. The loss of read only memory would be much more serious because the information stored here is absolutely necessary for the operation of the computer by the microprocessor.

18. Could a diode work properly if *both* of its ends were either *p*-type or *n*-type semiconductors? Explain your answer.

19. You have connected your new compact disc player directly to your stereo speakers, but when you turn on the CD, you hear nothing. Should you return the CD player to the store? Why or why not?

20. Which would do more harm to the operation of a computer, the loss of its random access memory or the loss of its read only memory? Explain your answer.

21. You need to store information on your computer that you can retrieve rapidly whenever you use your computer. What is the best way to store this information?

22. Why might your school keep written records even when it has computers that can store these records much more efficiently?

MORE SKILL BUILDERS

If you need help, refer to the Skill Handbook.

1. **Recognizing Cause and Effect:** Complete the table below by identifying either the cause or effect of problems associated with cathode-ray tubes.

Cause	Effect
1. Inside of tube coated with a non-fluorescent material.	1.
2.	2. Electron beam doesn't sweep the entire screen.
3. Incoming electrical signals are garbled.	3.

2. **Comparing and Contrasting:** Compare and contrast *n*-type and *p*-type semiconductors. Discuss the purpose of each semiconductor, how each functions, and what elements each uses and why.

3. **Making and Using Tables:** Construct a table to organize what you know about the parts of the microcomputer and the function of each.

4. **Interpreting Data:** Refer to the discussion of doped silicon crystals on page 597. Read the statements below and separate them into two columns. Label these columns *n*-type Semiconductor and *p*-type Semiconductor. Be sure to place the statements in each column in the correct order. Some statements can be used twice.
   a. The crystal has fewer outer energy level electrons.
   b. Conductivity of the doped crystal is increased.
   c. The extra electrons move through the crystal.
   d. A silicon crystal is doped with gallium.
   e. A silicon crystal is doped with arsenic.
   f. Voltage is applied across the crystal.
   g. The crystal has extra electrons that are free to move.

PROJECTS

1. Find out how microphones convert sound and turntable needles convert mechanical vibrations into electrical signals. Make a poster illustrating how each works.

2. Learn one of the basic computer languages and write a simple program.

21. The best way to store such information would be to store it on the computer's hard disk because this disk can hold much more information, and it can be retrieved much more rapidly than from a floppy disk.

22. Because of problems such as user error and computer viruses, computer records could be irretrievably lost. Written records are necessary for these reasons, as well as in case a hacker invades the school's computer system and changes grades.

MORE SKILL BUILDERS

1. **Recognizing Cause and Effect:**
Effect: 1. Fluorescent light is not produced. No picture.
Cause: 2. Electromagnets outside the CRT fail to function properly.
Effect: 3. Patterns and colors of image are garbled.

2. **Comparing and Contrasting:** Both types of semiconductors have been doped to increase their conductivity, and are used in devices such as diodes and transistors. They differ, however, in terms of how they allow more electrons to flow. An *n*-type semiconductor is doped with an element that has more electrons in the outer energy level than does the semiconductor. A *p*-type semiconductor is said to be a positive semiconductor because it is doped with an element that has fewer electrons in the outer electron level than does the semiconductor.

3. **Making and Using Tables:** See table at left.

4. **Interpreting Data:**
n-type Semiconductor
b, c, e, f, g
p-type Semiconductor
a, b, d, f

Component	Function
Input devices (keyboards, etc.)	Allow the user to communicate with the computer
Output devices (screen, etc)	Allow computer to communicate with the user
Microprocessor	Carries out the computer's operations; receives and translates the users commands to the computer
RAM	Temporarily stores information while the computer is being used
ROM	Stores the information needed by the microprocessor
Floppy disk	Contains information and programs to be stored and transferred to other computers
Hard disk	Contains information and programs to be stored permanently in the computer

CHAPTER
24 Radioactivity and Nuclear Reactions

CHAPTER SECTION	OBJECTIVES	ACTIVITIES
24-1 Radioactivity (1 day)	1. **Discuss** the discovery of radioactivity. 2. **Contrast** properties of radioactive versus stable nuclides.	**MINI-Lab:** *Does radiation change film?* p. 621
24-2 Nuclear Decay (2 days)	1. **Distinguish** alpha, beta, and gamma radiation. 2. **Calculate** the amount of radioactive substance remaining after a time based on its half-life. 3. **Relate** half-life to the process of radioactive dating.	**Activity 24-1:** *Half-Time—Investigating Half-Life,* p. 629
24-3 Detecting Radioactivity (1 day)	1. **Describe** how radioactivity can be detected. 2. **Explain** how a Geiger counter can determine the quantity of radiation present.	**MINI-Lab:** *What senses atomic radiation?* p. 631
24-4 Nuclear Reactions (1 day)	1. **Distinguish** nuclear fission and fusion. 2. **Explain** how nuclear fission can begin a chain reaction. 3. **Discuss** how nuclear fusion occurs in the sun.	
24-5 Nuclear Medicine Science & Society (1 day)	1. **Describe** how radioactive tracers can be used to diagnose medical problems. 2. **Discuss** how radioactive isotopes can aid in the treatment of cancers.	**Activity 24-2:** *Figuring Out Fusion,* p. 638
Chapter Review		

ACTIVITY MATERIALS

FIND OUT	ACTIVITIES		MINI-LABS	
Page 619 jar or cup marbles or other small, uniformly shaped objects stopwatch or watch with second hand	**24-1 Half-Time— Investigating Half-Life, p. 629** graph paper penny for each student	**24-2 Figuring Out Fusion, p. 638** 6 balls of green clay 6 smaller balls of white clay	**Does radiation change film? p. 621** photographic film badge or some undeveloped film a weak radioactive source, such as a small sample of uranium or pitchblende	**What senses atomic radiation? p. 631** dosimeter electroscope wool cloth plastic rod match source of beta radiation

CHAPTER FEATURES	TEACHER RESOURCE PACKAGE	OTHER RESOURCES
Technology: *Super Atom Smasher,* p. 622 **Skill Builder:** *Comparing and Contrasting,* p. 623	**Ability Level Worksheets** ◆ *Study Guide,* p. 100 ● *Reinforcement,* p. 100 ▲ *Enrichment,* p. 100 **Activity Worksheets,** p. 199	**Laboratory Manual 47,** The Effect of Radiation on Seeds
Problem Solving: *The Radioactive Clock,* p. 626 **Skill Builder:** *Interpreting Scientific Illustrations,* p. 628	**Ability Level Worksheets** ◆ *Study Guide,* p. 101 ● *Reinforcement,* p. 101 ▲ *Enrichment,* p. 101 **Activity Worksheets,** pp. 193, 194 **Concept Mapping,** pp. 53, 54 **Science and Society,** p. 28 **Transparency Masters,** pp. 93, 94	**Color Transparency 47,** Types of Radiation **Laboratory Manual 48,** Radioactive Decay—A Simulation **STVS:** Disc 2, Side 2
Skill Builder: *Observing and Inferring,* p. 632	**Ability Level Worksheets** ◆ *Study Guide,* p. 102 ● *Reinforcement,* p. 102 ▲ *Enrichment,* p. 102 **Activity Worksheets,** p. 200 **Critical Thinking/Problem Solving,** p. 30	**Science Integration Activity 24**
Skill Builder: *Concept Mapping,* p. 635	**Ability Level Worksheets** ◆ *Study Guide,* p. 103 ● *Reinforcement,* p. 103 ▲ *Enrichment,* p. 103 **Cross-Curricular Connections,** p. 30 **Transparency Masters,** pp. 95, 96	**Color Transparency 48,** Nuclear Chain Reaction **STVS:** Disc 1, Side 1
You Decide! p. 637	**Ability Level Worksheets** ◆ *Study Guide,* p. 104 ● *Reinforcement,* p. 104 ▲ *Enrichment,* p. 104 **Activity Worksheets,** pp. 195, 196	**STVS:** Disc 7, Side 1
Summary Think & Write Critically Key Science Words Apply Understanding Vocabulary More Skill Builders Checking Concepts Projects Using Lab Skills	**ASSESSMENT RESOURCES** **Chapter Review,** pp. 51, 52 **Chapter Test,** pp. 155-158 **Performance Assessment in Middle School Science**	**Chapter Review Software** **Test Bank** **Alternate Assessment** **Performance Assessment**

◆ **Basic**   ● **Average**   ▲ **Advanced**

ADDITIONAL MATERIALS		
SOFTWARE	**AUDIOVISUAL**	**BOOKS/MAGAZINES**
Nuclear Reactions, Wm. K. Bradford Publishing Co. *Radioactivity,* J and S Software.	*Atomic Energy: Inside the Atom,* Video, Britannica. *What Is Radioactivity?,* Video, Britannica. *Radioisotopes: Tools of Discovery,* Video, Britannica. *Nuclear Energy,* Video, AIT. *Radiation,* Video, Hawkhill. *How Radiation Was Discovered,* Video, Hawkhill. *Matter Into Energy,* Video, Coronet.	McCuen, Gary E. *Nuclear Waste: The Biggest Clean-up in History.* Hudson, WI: GEM, 1991. Medvedev, Grigori. *The Truth about Chernobyl.* NY: Basic, 1989. Montgomery, Mary. *Marie Curie.* Englewood Cliffs, NJ: Silver Burdett, 1990.

THEME DEVELOPMENT: Patterns of change is a theme developed in this chapter. Throughout this book, the nucleus of the atom has been modeled as essentially stable. In this chapter, students learn that the nucleus can undergo patterns of change and transformation. The identity of atoms can change when a nucleus undergoes radioactive decay. Since fission and fusion processes release tremendous amounts of energy, energy can also be brought out as a theme.

CHAPTER OVERVIEW

▶**Section 24-1:** The discovery and current applications of radioactivity illustrate the nature of radioactive elements. Characteristics of radioactive nuclides are distinguished from those of stable nuclides.

▶**Section 24-2:** The three types of radioactive decay are introduced. Nuclear half-life is presented as a useful tool for helping us date samples of once-living tissue.

▶**Section 24-3:** Cloud chambers, bubble chambers, and Geiger counters illustrate methods of detecting and counting radiation.

▶**Section 24-4:** Processes and applications of nuclear fission and chain reactions are presented and compared to those of nuclear fusion, using the fusion in the sun as an illustration.

▶**Section 24-5: Science and Society:** This section features a discussion of the use of radioisotopes in medicine. The You Decide question asks students to evaluate whether the benefits of nuclear medicine outweigh the possible risks.

618

OPTIONS

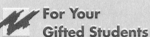

For Your Gifted Students

▶ Students can discuss what they know about radiation given off by the sun. Have them research the positive and negative aspects of the sun's rays upon humans and write a report. They may have to contact a local doctor for help.

▶ Have students survey local tanning salons for information regarding the types of rays emitted from their tanning beds. Have them compare the effect of sun versus tanning bed and make recommendations for safety.

For Your Mainstreamed Students

▶ Students can make a time line of the important discoveries and events in the area of nuclear power beginning with Henri Bequerel's discovery.

Have you ever watched a news report about the disposal of radioactive materials? Have you wondered how long these materials remain radioactive? Why are so many problems associated with radioactive materials?

FIND OUT!

Do the following activity to find out how radioactive materials decay into nonradioactive materials.

Put 32 marbles in a jar. Let these marbles represent radioactive atoms that will decay into nonradioactive atoms. Use a stopwatch or a second hand to time one-minute intervals. During the first minute, take half of the 32 marbles out of the jar and put them aside. These marbles represent atoms that have decayed into another element. During the second and third minutes, remove half of the remaining marbles from the jar. What happens to the radioactive atoms during each one-minute interval? What's the rate of decay of this radioactive element? *Predict* how many minutes would pass until only one marble is left.

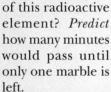

Gearing Up
Previewing the Chapter
Use this outline to help you focus on important ideas in this chapter.

Section 24-1   Radioactivity
▶ Radioactive Elements
▶ Nuclides

Section 24-2   Nuclear Decay
▶ Nuclear Radiation
▶ Half-life
▶ Radioactive Dating

Section 24-3   Detecting Radioactivity
▶ Radiation Detectors
▶ Counting Radioactivity

Section 24-4   Nuclear Reactions
▶ Nuclear Fission
▶ Nuclear Fusion

Section 24-5   Science and Society
Nuclear Medicine
▶ Are Radioactive Isotopes Useful in Medicine?

Previewing Science Skills
▶ In the Skill Builders, you will compare and contrast, interpret scientific illustrations, observe and infer, and make a concept map.
▶ In the Activities, you will predict, interpret, and formulate models.
▶ In the MINI-Labs, you will observe and compare.

What's next?

If you predicted it would take about five minutes until only one marble was left in the Find Out activity, you were correct. Some radioactive elements decay in less than one second; others take thousands of years. Some decay to form other radioactive elements. As you read this chapter, you will learn more about the many radioactive elements and how they decay.

radioactivity   cloud chamber
nuclide   bubble chamber
alpha particles   nuclear fission
beta particle   chain reaction
transmutation   nuclear fusion
gamma rays   tracers
half-life

INTRODUCING THE CHAPTER

Use the Find Out activity to help students realize that not all nuclei are stable and that some decay into other elements. Explain that we will be learning more about how this happens, as well as studying applications of radioactive decay.

FIND OUT!

Preparation: Obtain jars and place 32 marbles (paper clips, pebbles, M&M's, etc.) into each one.
Materials: jar or cup; marbles or other small, uniformly shaped objects, stopwatch or watch with second hand
Cooperative Learning: Have students work in Science Investigation Groups of three. One student should time; one should count marbles; and one should record the answers to the questions presented.
Teaching Tips
▶ Emphasize that the marbles taken out decay but do not disappear; they change into a different nucleus.

Gearing Up

Have students study the Gearing Up feature to familiarize themselves with the chapter. Discuss the relationships of the topics in the outline.

What's Next?

Before beginning the first section, make sure students understand the connection between the Find Out activity and the topics to follow.

ASSESSMENT OPTIONS

PORTFOLIO
Refer to page 639 for suggested items that students might select for their portfolios.

PERFORMANCE ASSESSMENT
See page 639 for additional Performance Assessment options.
Process
Skill Builders, pp. 623, 628, 635
MINI-Lab, pp. 621, 631
Activity 24-1, pp. 629; 24-2, p. 638
Using Lab Skills, p. 640

CONTENT ASSESSMENT
Assessment—Oral, pp. 622, 626, 628, 632
Skill Builders, p. 632
Section Reviews, pp. 623, 628, 632, 635, 637
Chapter Review, pp. 639-641
Mini Quizzes, pp. 622, 627, 631, 634

GROUP ASSESSMENT
Opportunities for group assessment occur with Cooperative Learning Strategies and Flex Your Brain Activities.

PREPARATION

SECTION BACKGROUND

▶ The elements 93 and beyond can only be produced synthetically. Glen T. Seaborg's work led to the discovery of several of these elements. He received patents for these elements and turned the rights over to the U.S. Government.

PREPLANNING

▶ For the MINI-Lab on page 621, gather some photographic film badges or some undeveloped Polaroid film and a weak source of radiation.

1 MOTIVATE

▶ Tell students they are being exposed to radiation. See how many possible sources they can list. Radiation sources may include cosmic radiation (especially while flying on airplanes), smoke detectors, radiation from soil, impurities in the brick or wood their houses are made of, radon gas in their basements, and medical/dental X rays.

TYING TO PREVIOUS KNOWLEDGE:

Remind students of their study of atomic structure. They learned that chemical reactions depend mostly on electron structures. In this chapter, the nucleus, which consists of protons and neutrons, determines the nuclear reactions.

TEACHER F.Y.I.

▶ X rays were discovered by Wilhelm Roentgen several months before the phenomenon of radioactivity was discovered in 1896 by Henri Bequerel.

24-1 Radioactivity

New Science Words

radioactivity
nuclide

Objectives

▶ Discuss the discovery of radioactivity.
▶ Contrast properties of radioactive versus stable nuclides.

Radioactive Elements

Do you have a smoke detector in your home to alert you if there's a fire? If it is an ionizing smoke detector, it probably contains a small amount of a radioactive element called americium-241.

The discovery of radioactivity about 100 years ago has led to major advances in medical diagnoses and treatments, the use of nuclear energy, and the designing of nuclear weapons. It's certainly easy to see why some uses of radiation and nuclear energy are so controversial.

Look around the room. Can you detect any evidence of radioactivity? Did you know there are small amounts of radioactive materials all around you? You can't see, hear, taste, touch, or smell the radioactivity. You even have small amounts of radioactive materials inside your body.

You may wonder how radiation was first discovered if it can't be detected by your senses. Henri Bequerel accidentally discovered radioactivity in 1896 when he left some uranium salt in a desk drawer with a photographic plate. When he later removed the plate and developed it, he found an outline of the uranium salt. He hypothesized that the uranium had given off some invisible energy and exposed the film. This process is called radiation. Marie Curie and her husband Pierre took interest in Bequerel's discovery. They began looking for other radioactive elements in a uranium ore called pitchblende. Two years after Bequerel's discovery, they discovered the elements polonium and radium. These elements are even more radioactive than uranium.

Figure 24-1. Many smoke detectors, such as this one, contain a small amount of a radioactive element.

In Your JOURNAL

In your Journal, make a list of the first things you think of when you hear the word *radiation.* Write one paragraph describing your positive thoughts about radiation and another describing your negative thoughts.

620 RADIOACTIVITY AND NUCLEAR REACTIONS

OPTIONS

Meeting Different Ability Levels

For Section 24-1, use the following **Teacher Resource Masters** depending upon individual students' needs.

◆ **Study Guide Master** for all students.
● **Reinforcement Master** for students of average and above average ability levels.
▲ **Enrichment Master** for above average students.

Additional Teacher Resource Package masters are listed in any PROGRAM RESOURCES boxes that are in the section. The additional masters are appropriate for all students.

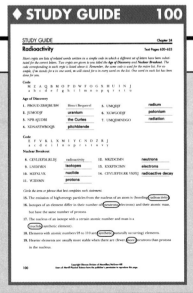

Notice where these three elements are found on the periodic table. They all have high atomic numbers and therefore are located near the bottom of the chart. Each element that has an atomic number greater than 83 is radioactive. Some other elements also have common radioactive isotopes.

You know that all elements are made of atoms, and that atoms are made up of protons, neutrons, and electrons. The protons and neutrons are held together in the nucleus by what scientists call the strong force. This force is strong enough to prevent the positive protons from pushing each other out of the nucleus of the atom; however, this force only acts across very small distances. As a result, those elements with high atomic numbers are held together less securely than, say, an oxygen atom, which has many fewer protons and neutrons in its nucleus. Particles or energy can escape from all nuclei with atomic numbers of 84 or higher. This process is called radioactive decay. These nuclei are unstable. **Radioactivity,** therefore, is the emission of high energy radiation or particles from the nucleus of a radioactive atom.

Find the elements with atomic numbers 93 to 109 on the periodic table. Elements with these atomic numbers don't exist naturally on Earth. They have been produced in labs and are called synthetic elements. These synthetic elements are very unstable. Why might these elements be difficult to study?

Nuclides

Recall that elements have isotopes. Isotopes of an element differ in their number of neutrons and in their atomic mass, but they have the same number of protons. Some isotopes are radioactive and others are not. Why is this so? The nucleus of an isotope with a certain atomic number and mass is called a **nuclide.** In many nuclides, the strong force is enough to keep the nucleus permanently together, creating a stable nuclide. However, the strong force is not sufficient to hold unstable nuclides together permanently. These unstable nuclides are radioactive because they decay to give off matter and energy.

Isotopes of elements differ in the ratio of neutrons to protons. This ratio affects the stability of the nucleus. An

Figure 24-2. Elements with low atomic numbers have stable nuclides when the numbers of protons and neutrons are close.

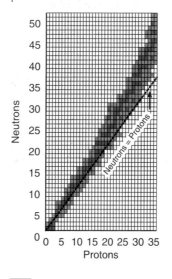

— stable nuclides

— unstable nuclides

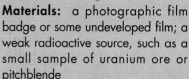
621

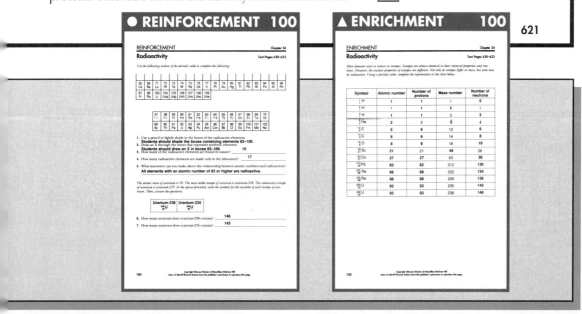

● **REINFORCEMENT** 100   ▲ **ENRICHMENT** 100

►To find out more about super atom smashers, see "The World's Biggest Machine" by Arthur Fisher, *Popular Science*, June 1987, pp. 56-57.

Think Critically: A great deal of energy is required to break up a proton and produce new particles. It will help us to learn more about the particles and forces in nature.

CONCEPT DEVELOPMENT

►Emphasize that isotopes differ in atomic mass and nuclear stability, but not in nuclear charge. Ask students why the atomic masses listed on the periodic table are not whole numbers. They may remember that the mass listed is the average of all isotopes and their respective amounts.

Connect to...
Earth Science

Answer: An ore is a natural combination of minerals in which one or more minerals exist in a concentration that makes separating it profitable.

STUDENT TEXT QUESTION

►Page 623, paragraph 2: **How many neutrons does potassium-40 have?** *21*

CHECK FOR UNDERSTANDING

Use the Mini Quiz to check for understanding.

MINI QUIZ

Use the Mini Quiz to check students' recall of chapter content.

1 **All elements that have atomic numbers greater than _____ are radioactive.** *83*

2 **What is radioactivity?** *the emission of high energy radiation or particles from the nucleus of a radioactive atom*

3 **When are isotopes of heavier elements most stable?** *when they have a neutron to proton ratio of about 3 to 2*

Super Atom Smasher

Probing the structure of the nucleus is a difficult task. As a result, construction of the largest and most expensive scientific instrument ever produced was planned. This instrument, called the superconducting super collider—or SSC—was a particle accelerator designed to smash atomic particles together to produce a shower of basic particles and provide clues to nuclear structure.

It was hoped that the SSC would be able to smash particles together in a way 20 times more powerful than that of any existing accelerator. It would have accelerated two beams of protons in opposite directions around a 53-mile racetrack-shaped vacuum chamber, guided by 10 000 superconducting magnets. As the beams approached the speed of light, they would have smashed together, creating new particles.

The SSC may have helped scientists answer questions about the structure of matter that are so fundamental that many other fields will benefit. In October 1993, however, Congress cancelled the project because of its expense.

Think Critically: Why do you think the proton beams need to be smashed at such high energies? How would this help us learn more about matter?

Connect to...
Earth Science

The Curies performed many experiments with pitchblende, an ore containing some radioactive isotopes of uranium and radium. What is the general definition of an ore?

What isotopes are unstable?

isotope of a less massive element is stable if the ratio is about 1 to 1. An isotope of one of the heaviest elements is stable when the ratio of neutrons to protons is about 3 to 2. However, the nuclei of isotopes of both lighter and heavier elements that differ much from these ratios are unstable. That is, nuclei with too many or too few neutrons are radioactive.

How can you distinguish one isotope from another of the same element? A nuclide can be represented by a symbol that gives the atomic number, mass number, and element symbol. You know the atomic number is the same as the number of protons in the element, and the mass number is the total number of protons and neutrons in the nucleus of that atom. The nucleus of the stable

622 RADIOACTIVITY AND NUCLEAR REACTIONS

OPTIONS

ASSESSMENT—ORAL

► Nucleons are particles found in the nucleus of an atom. Which of the following particles would be considered nucleons—protons, electrons, neutrons? *protons and neutrons*

PROGRAM RESOURCES

Use **Laboratory Manual 47,** The Effect of Radiation on Seeds.

INQUIRY QUESTIONS

► One isotope of uranium, uranium-238, has a half-life of 4.5 billion years. Use a periodic table to find the atomic number and calculate how many neutrons the isotope has. *238 – 92 protons = 146 neutrons*

► Explain the structural similarities and differences between uranium-238 and uranium-235. *They are both isotopes of uranium and each has 92 protons in the nucleus. uranium-238 has three more neutrons than uranium-235.*

Table 24-1

RADIOACTIVE NUCLIDES OF SOME ELEMENTS				
Element	Nuclide	Atomic mass number	Protons	Neutrons
Hydrogen	^3_1H	3	1	2
Helium	^5_2He	5	2	3
Lithium	^8_3Li	8	3	5
Carbon	$^{14}_6C$	14	6	8
Nitrogen	$^{16}_7N$	16	7	9
Potassium	$^{40}_{19}K$	40	19	21

isotope of potassium is shown below.

$$\text{mass number} \rightarrow \quad ^{39}_{19}K \leftarrow \text{element symbol}$$
$$\text{atomic number} \rightarrow$$

Now compare the stable isotope of potassium to the radioactive isotope below.

$$\text{mass number} \rightarrow \quad ^{40}_{19}K \leftarrow \text{element symbol}$$
$$\text{atomic number} \rightarrow$$

The stable isotope is called potassium-39. This isotope has 19 protons and 20 neutrons. The radioactive isotope is potassium-40. How many neutrons does potassium-40 have?

SECTION REVIEW

1. Identify the contributions of the three scientists who discovered the first radioactive elements.
2. What is the range of atomic numbers in which all isotopes are radioactive? Which of these are synthetic?
3. **Apply:** What is the ratio of neutrons to protons in lead-214? Explain whether you would expect this isotope to be radioactive or stable.
4. **Connect to Chemistry:** Use the periodic table on pages 258-259 to locate two synthetic elements that have atomic numbers less than 93.

☑ Comparing and Contrasting

Compare and contrast stable and unstable isotopes of potassium. What do they have in common? How do they differ? If you need help, refer to Comparing and Contrasting in the **Skill Handbook** on page 679.

Skill Builder

EcoTip

Radon is an odorless, colorless, radioactive gas that comes from underground rocks. Keep radon out of your house by sealing cracks in the basement floor and walls, and spaces around water pipes and drains.

RETEACH

Write each of the following nuclides on a piece of paper and have a student hold each one. Instruct them to find other nuclides that have the same atomic number. Some may be left alone. Emphasize that the groups represent different isotopes of the same element.

$^{234}_{91}Pa \quad ^{214}_{82}Pb \quad ^{214}_{83}Bi \quad ^{214}_{84}Po \quad ^{210}_{82}Pb$

$^{210}_{83}Bi \quad ^{206}_{82}Pb \quad ^{210}_{84}Po \quad ^{218}_{85}At$

EXTENSION

For students who have mastered this section, use the **Reinforcement** and **Enrichment** masters or other OPTIONS provided.

---

3 CLOSE

▶ Ask questions 1-2 and the **Apply** and **Connect to Chemistry** questions in the Section Review.

SECTION REVIEW ANSWERS

1. Bequerel found uranium salt gave off radioactivity. Marie and Pierre Curie isolated polonium and radium from pitchblende.

2. Elements 84-109 are radioactive. Elements 93-109 are synthetic.

3. Apply: 132/82 = 1.6 It is likely to be radioactive because the ratio of neutrons to protons differs from the 3 to 2 stable ratio for heavy elements.

4. Connect to Chemistry: Technetium, at. no. 43, and promethium, at. no. 61, are synthetic elements.

Skill Builder

The stable and unstable isotopes of potassium have the same number of protons and the same number of electrons. However, the unstable isotope of potassium has a higher mass number because it has one more neutron than does the stable nuclide.

Skill Builder
ASSESSMENT
Performance: Have students organize their information about potassium isotopes into a chart that shows comparisons and contrasts.

24-2 Nuclear Decay

New Science Words

alpha particles
beta particle
transmutation
gamma rays
half-life

Objectives

▶ Distinguish alpha, beta, and gamma radiation.
▶ Calculate the amount of a radioactive substance remaining after a time based on its half-life.
▶ Relate half-life to the process of radioactive dating.

Nuclear Radiation

You've heard the terms *radiocativity* and *radioactive* ever since you were a young child. Maybe you didn't know what these words meant then, but now you know they refer to unstable, radioactive nuclei that emit small particles or energy. There are three types of nuclear radiation —alpha, beta, and gamma radiation. Figure 24-3 shows the path that each type of nuclear radiation follows as it moves through a magnetic field. As you can see, each type of radiation is affected differently. Which type of radiation is most affected by a magnetic field?

Radiation in the form of **alpha particles** is given off when a nucleus releases two protons and two neutrons. Notice that the alpha particle is the same as a helium nucleus, as shown in Table 24-2. An alpha particle has a charge of +2 and an atomic mass of 4. It is the largest and slowest form of radiation, so it is also the least penetrat-

Figure 24-3. Notice how positive alpha and negative beta particles are deflected by a magnetic field.

Table 24-2

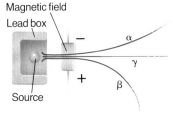

THREE TYPES OF NUCLEAR RADIATION				
Type	Symbol	Charge	Mass	Can be stopped by
alpha	${}^4_2$He, α	+2	4	Paper
beta	e, β	−1	0	Aluminum foil
gamma	γ	none	0	Lead or concrete

◆ STUDY GUIDE 101

ing. Alpha particles can be stopped by a sheet of paper, but they can be deadly if they are released by atoms inside your body.

The smoke detector mentioned earlier in this chapter gives off alpha particles that ionize the surrounding air. An electric current flows through the ionized air, but the circuit is broken when smoke particles enter the ionized air. When the circuit is broken, the alarm is set off.

Sometimes a neutron inside a nucleus decays spontaneously into a proton and an electron. The electron is emitted from the nucleus at very high speed and is called a **beta particle**. The proton formed by the decaying neutron stays in the nucleus, forming an element with an atomic number one greater than the original element. Because the total number of protons and neutrons has not changed, the atomic mass number of the new element is the same as that of the original element. A proton can also decay into a neutron and a positron. A positron is similar to an electron, but has a positive charge. Positrons are also considered to be beta particles. Beta particles are much faster and more penetrating than alpha particles. However, they can be stopped by a sheet of aluminum foil.

Isotopes that give off alpha or beta particles undergo transmutation. **Transmutation** is the process of changing one element to another through nuclear decay. The nuclear equations below show nuclear transmutations. Because two protons are lost from the nucleus in alpha decay, the new element formed has an atomic number two less than that of the original element. The atomic mass number of the new element is four less than that of the original element. In a transmutation, the atomic mass number of the decayed nuclide equals the sum of the mass numbers of the newly formed nuclide and the emitted particle.

$$^{218}_{84}\text{Po} \longrightarrow \, ^{214}_{82}\text{Pb} + \, ^{4}_{2}\text{He}$$

$$^{214}_{82}\text{Pb} \longrightarrow \, ^{214}_{83}\text{Bi} + \, ^{0}_{-1}\text{e}$$

Did You Know?

The first person whose death was attributed to radiation exposure was Marie Curie.

Connect to...
Chemistry

In the first nuclear equation shown on this page, the alpha particle is represented by the symbol $^{4}_{2}\text{He}$. Explain how an alpha particle is different from a helium atom.

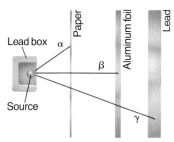

Figure 24-4. Alpha particles can be stopped by paper, beta particles by aluminum foil, and gamma rays by lead.

625

2 TEACH

Key Concepts are highlighted.

CONCEPT DEVELOPMENT

▶ Note that an isolated neutron is not stable. It spontaneously decays into a proton and an electron. Beta particles (electrons) are produced when neutrons decay in the nucleus and are not outer electrons.

▶ Following in her parents' footsteps, Irene Joliet-Curie and her husband won the Nobel prize in 1935 for discovering artificial radiation. She and her mother, Marie Curie, both died of leukemia. This disease may have resulted from high exposure to radiation. The harmful effect of radiation on human cells was not clearly understood in their time.

▶ Transmutation is difficult for many students to understand. Be sure to go through the sample equations, having them account for equal masses and equal charges on both sides of the equation.

REVEALING MISCONCEPTIONS

▶ Although a decaying neutron usually emits an electron and leaves a proton behind, the electron is not actually stored in the neutron before decay takes place. It is produced during the decay.

Connect to...
Chemistry

Answer: An alpha particle is identical to a helium nucleus, but an alpha particle has no electrons.

PROGRAM RESOURCES

From the **Teacher Resource Package** use:

Concept Mapping, pages 53-54.
Science and Society, page 28, Low-level Radiation.
Transparency Masters, pages 93-94, Types of Nuclear Radiation.
Use **Color Transparency** number 47, Types of Radiation.

● **REINFORCEMENT 101**

▲ **ENRICHMENT 101**

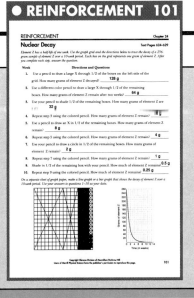

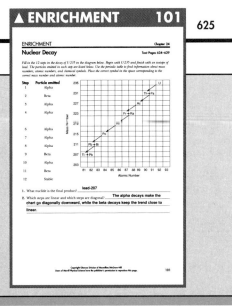

CONCEPT DEVELOPMENT

▶ In class discussions, use the Greek letters as symbols for alpha (α), beta (β), and gamma (γ) radiation.

▶ The mathematical relationship that involves half-life patterns can be used to determine the half-life by measuring the change in radioactive sample size over a known time interval.

TEACHER F.Y.I.

▶ Note that the rate of radioactive decay is nearly impossible to change. Attempts to change this rate by altering temperature and pressure conditions, other chemical reactions, or exposure to electric and magnetic fields have been unsuccessful.

▶ Radiocarbon dating was developed in the 1940s by Willard Libby. Cosmic rays from space interact with atoms in Earth's atmosphere and liberate neutrons. The presence of carbon-14 in our atmosphere results from neutron bombardment of nitrogen, which causes a proton to be emitted:

$$_{0}^{1}n + {}_{7}^{14}N \rightarrow {}_{6}^{14}C + {}_{1}^{1}H$$

Science and MATH

One percent is 0.01 or 1/100. The easiest approach is to have students write the series 1, 1/2, 1/4, 1/8, 1/16, 1/32, 1/64, 1/128 and count the number of half-lives that have passed when the fraction becomes less than 1/100. One half-life passes in the interval between fractions. Students should count 7 half-lives, 196 years.

Video Disc

STVS: Carbon-14 Dating of the Shroud of Turin; Disc 2, Side 2

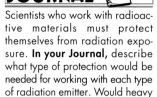

In Your JOURNAL

Scientists who work with radioactive materials must protect themselves from radiation exposure. **In your Journal,** describe what type of protection would be needed for working with each type of radiation emitter. Would heavy gloves be enough?

Science and MATH

How long does it take for a sample of strontium-90, with a half-life of 28 years, to be reduced to less than one percent of its original mass?

These two examples of transmutation confirm that the charge of the original nuclide equals the sum of the charges of the nuclide and particle formed.

The most penetrating and potentially dangerous form of radiation is not made of particles at all. **Gamma rays** are electromagnetic waves with very high frequency and energy. They have no mass, no charge, and they travel at the speed of light. They are usually released along with alpha or beta particles. Gamma rays are the most penetrating form of radiation, and thick blocks of materials with dense nuclei are required to stop them. Lead and concrete are commonly used barriers for gamma rays. Compare the symbols and the relative penetrating powers of the three kinds of radiation shown in Table 24-2.

Half-life

Safe disposal of some radioisotopes is not a problem because their nuclides decay to stable nuclides in less than a second. However, nuclides of other radioactive isotopes may require millions of years to decay. A

PROBLEM SOLVING

The Radioactive Clock

Kristine had a difficult time waking up for school. Her mother had to call to her to wake her up several times each morning.

Kristine found an old alarm clock in the attic. Now she can wake up without her mother calling her.

During the night Kristine awoke. She was startled by a greenish-white glow next to her bed. Then she realized that the glow was coming from the hands of the alarm clock. She wondered what caused the hands to glow.

The next day, she did some research in the school library and found that the hands of the clock were coated with a paint containing radium and zinc sulfide. The zinc sulfide emits little flashes of light when excited by radiation. These tiny flashes of light make the hands of the clock appear to glow. Why does the zinc sulfide in the paint appear to glow?

Think Critically: Explain why the glow of the hands will become dimmer over time.

OPTIONS

ASSESSMENT—ORAL

▶ **When thorium-230 undergoes alpha decay, what nuclide is formed?** radium-226
▶ **When lead-210 undergoes beta decay, what nuclide is formed?** bismuth-210, which has one more proton and one fewer neutron
▶ **If a beta particle is actually a particle, why does the mass number stay the same after beta decay?** The mass of the electron given off is very small compared to the mass of protons and neutrons, so the mass change can be considered insignificant.

INQUIRY QUESTIONS

▶ The half-life of radium-226 is 1620 years. Predict how much of a 10-g sample will still be radium-226 after 1620 years. After 3240 years. 5 g; 2.5 g
▶ How can we know the half-life of uranium-238 if it has a half-life of 4.5 billion years? That is the approximate age of Earth, and humans have only existed a small fraction of that time. By looking at decay rates during known amounts of time, mathematical relationships allow us to calculate the actual half-life.

measure of the time required by the nuclides of an isotope to decay is called half-life. The **half-life** of an isotope is the amount of time it takes for half the nuclides in a sample of a given radioactive isotope to decay. Half-lives vary widely among the radioactive isotopes. For example, polonium-214 has a half-life of about a thousandth of a second; but uranium-238 has a half-life of 4.5 billion years.

You can determine the amount of a radioactive sample that will remain after a given amount of time if you know the half-life of the sample. The half-lives of some radioactive elements are listed in Table 24-3. Look at the problem below to see how to calculate the amount of remaining sodium-24, which has a half-life of 15 hours.

Table 24-3

SAMPLE HALF-LIVES	
Isotope	Half-life
$^{3}_{1}H$	12.3 years
$^{14}_{6}C$	5730 years
$^{131}_{53}I$	8.07 days
$^{212}_{82}Pb$	10.6 hours
$^{194}_{84}Po$	0.7 second
$^{235}_{92}U$	7.1×10^{8} years

EXAMPLE PROBLEM: Calculating the Quantity of a Radioactive Element

Problem Statement: How much of a 20-g sample of sodium-24 would remain after decaying for 15 hours?

Known Information:
Strategy Hint: Find the half-life of sodium-24 above.

Amount of original sample of sodium-24 = 20 g
Time elapsed = 15 hours
Half-life of sodium-24 = 15 hours

Unknown Information: amount of remaining sodium-24

Equation to Use:
$$\text{amount remaining} = \frac{\text{amount of original sample}}{2^n}$$
n = number of half-lives elapsed

Solution:
$$\frac{20 \text{ g}}{2^1} = \frac{20 \text{ g}}{2} = 10 \text{ g}$$

Comment: The sample will contain 10 g of sodium-24 and 10 g of the decay product.

PRACTICE PROBLEM

Strategy Hint: Determine how many half-lives of sodium-24 elapse in 45 hours.

1. How much of a 20-g sample of sodium-24 would remain after 45 hours?

Radioactive Dating

It was mentioned earlier that you have some radioactive materials inside your body. One of these is a radioactive isotope of carbon, carbon-14. This isotope is in some of the carbon dioxide molecules plants take in as they respire. As a result, you have carbon-14 inside of you from the plants and animals you eat. Carbon-14 emits a beta particle and decays into nitrogen.

24-2 NUCLEAR DECAY **627**

MULTICULTURAL PERSPECTIVE

Hideki Yukawa

Hideki Yukawa was the first Japanese to receive the Nobel prize. He accomplished this by developing a theory about what holds the nucleus of the atom together. He reasoned that there must be a nuclear force that involves the transfer of some entity other than a proton or neutron. His theory also stated that this force must be stronger over short distances than electromagnetic forces in order to overcome the repulsion between protons.

When he published his theory in 1935, no particle had been discovered that matched the exchange particle his ideas required. It was not until 1947 that the particle Yukawa predicted was actually found. As a result of the verification of his theory, Yukawa was awarded the Nobel prize in 1949.

MINI QUIZ

Use the Mini Quiz to check students' recall of chapter content.

1 **What kind of radiation is identical to a helium nucleus?** *alpha particles*

2 **Arrange three kinds of nuclear radiation in order of increasing penetrating power.** *alpha particles, beta particles, gamma rays*

3 **What is transmutation?** *the process by which one element changes to another by nuclear decay involving alpha or beta particles*

4 **What isotope is used in radioactive dating some artifacts found in archaeological digs?** *carbon-14*

In Your JOURNAL

Gloves would stop alpha particles; thin metal strips would stop beta particles; a lead shield would stop gamma rays.

PRACTICE PROBLEM ANSWER

1. Amount of original sample = 20 g
Time Elapsed = 45 hours
Half-life of sodium-24 = 15 hours
n = number of half-lives elapsed
$n = 3$
Equation: Amount Remaining =
$$\frac{\text{Amount of Original}}{2^n}$$
Amount Remaining = $\frac{20 \text{ g}}{2^3} = 2.5 \text{ g}$

CHECK FOR UNDERSTANDING

Ask students why fallout shelters would be needed following a nuclear attack. Ask what type of radiation would pose the greatest risk to people who stayed in their own houses. Most alpha and beta particles would be stopped by the materials used to build a typical house, but gamma radiation requires a thick slab of material such as lead or concrete to stop penetration.

CHAPTER 24 **627**

RETEACH

Emphasize that the relatively big size and double positive charge of alpha particles makes them easily captured by other atoms or molecules. Beta particles, or electrons, are many times smaller, but they still have a charge. This charge causes attractions and repulsions with other particles. Gamma radiation has no mass or charge, so it is difficult to interact with and slow down.

EXTENSION

For students who have mastered this section, use the **Reinforcement** and **Enrichment** masters or other OPTIONS provided.

CROSS CURRICULUM

▶ **Archaeology:** Have students do research to learn how radioactive dating has been used to determine the ages of artifacts found in archaeological digs.

3 CLOSE

▶ Ask questions 1-3 and the **Apply** and **Connect to Life Science** questions in the Section Review.

SECTION REVIEW ANSWERS

1. Alpha particles, helium nuclei, are the least penetrating and can be stopped by paper. Beta particles are electrons and can be stopped by aluminum foil. Gamma rays are the most penetrating kind of nuclear radiation and are stopped by lead or concrete.
2. $^{222}_{86}Rn \rightarrow {}^{218}_{84}Po + {}^{4}_{2}He$; polonium
3. 20 g; 10 g; 2.5 g
4. Apply: Yes. In beta decay, a neutron decays into an electron and a proton increasing the atomic number of the element by one.
5. Connect to Life Science: Yes. Carbon-14 is radioactive and has 2 more neutrons than does carbon-12.

Skill Builder

The gamma ray has no charge and will not be affected by the magnetic field. The oppositely charged alpha and beta particles will be deflected in opposite directions.

All living things contain a somewhat constant amount of carbon-14. Decaying carbon-14 is constantly replaced in a living organism, but when an organism dies, its carbon-14 decays without replacement. The half-life of carbon-14 is 5730 years. By measuring the percentage of carbon-14 remaining in a fossil or skeleton, scientists can determine the approximate age of the material. This process is called carbon-14 dating.

Do you think carbon-14 dating could be used to determine the age of a dinosaur skeleton? No, it wouldn't work, because the last dinosaur species died out too long ago. Only remains of plants and animals that lived within the last 50 000 years contain enough carbon-14 to measure accurately. Some scientists, however, consider this dating to be accurate to only 20 000 years because of the difficulty of detecting lesser amounts of carbon-14.

SECTION REVIEW

1. Describe each of the three types of radiation and compare their penetrating power.
2. Write a nuclear equation to show how radon-222 decays to give off an alpha particle and another element. What is the other element?
3. The half-life of iodine-131 is about eight days. How much of a 40-g sample will be left after eight days? After 16 days? After 32 days?
4. **Apply:** Is it possible for an isotope to decay to an element with a higher atomic number? Explain.
5. **Connect to Life Science:** Do you have carbon-14 in your body right now? Explain at least two differences between carbon-14 and the more common isotope, carbon-12.

Skill Builder

☑ **Interpreting Scientific Illustrations**

Use Figure 24-3 on page 624 to explain why the alpha particle appears to curve up, the beta particle curves down, and the gamma ray travels straight through the magnet. If you need help, refer to Interpreting Scientific Illustrations in the **Skill Handbook** on page 689.

628 RADIOACTIVITY AND NUCLEAR REACTIONS

OPTIONS

ASSESSMENT—ORAL

▶ A new bone sample contains more carbon-14 than an old bone sample of the same size. Explain this pattern. *Because carbon-14 is radioactive, some of the carbon-14 in the old bone sample will already have decayed. This makes the level less in the old bone than in the new bone.*
▶ Could the carbon dating method be useful in dating old iron utensils? Explain why or why not. *No. The iron utensils do not contain carbon-14.*

PROGRAM RESOURCES

Use **Laboratory Manual 48,** Radioactive Decay—A Simulation.

Skill Builder
ASSESSMENT
Performance: Ask students to sketch what would happen if the magnetic field in the diagram were reversed.

ACTIVITY 24-1

DESIGNING AN EXPERIMENT
Half-Time—Investigating Half-Life

You have learned that it is possible to predict the decay rate of a sample of radioactive material. Radioactive isotopes have half-lives that vary from fractions of a second to several billion years. If the half-life of an isotope is known, you can predict the amount of a radioactive sample that will remain after a given amount of time. Can you use this information to predict when a specific atom will decay?

Getting Started

In this activity you will *model* the process of nuclear decay to *gather data* and *draw a graph* to show the decay pattern.

Thinking Critically

What happens to a radioactive sample during one half-life? Can knowing the half-life of a sample help you *predict* when one specific atom will decay?

Materials

Your cooperative group will use:
• one penny for each person
• graph paper

Try It!

1. *Construct a data table* with two columns: Half-life (tosses) and Atoms Remaining (heads up).
2. Each person in the class should have one penny. On the first line of your data table *record* your beginning data ("0" for the half-life and the number of students for the atoms remaining).
3. All students will toss their coins once, representing one half-life. All coins landing as tails have now decayed, and these students should move to the back of the room. Count the remain-

ing students and *record* this information. Repeat this process until no students remain.

———————

Summing Up/Sharing Results

• Assume each coin is an atom of a radioactive isotope. During which interval did the greatest number of "atoms" decay?
• Use the method shown on page 627 to determine how many coins should have remained after three half-lives. How close is this calculation to your actual value?

Going Further!

Plot the data from the table on a graph with half-lives on the horizontal axis and atoms remaining on the vertical axis. Connect the points with a smooth curve. According to your graph, how many half-lives did it take for half the atoms to decay? For three-fourths of the atoms to decay?

24-2   NUCLEAR DECAY   **629**

ACTIVITY 24-1

OBJECTIVE: Use a model of the half-life of an isotope to predict nuclear decay and construct a graph to show the decay pattern.
Time: one class period

PROCESS SKILLS applied in this activity are **predicting, interpreting,** and **formulating models.**

PREPARATION

Gather enough pennies for each student to have one.
Cooperative Learning: Divide the class into teams of four. After gathering the data as a class, students can work in these teams to discuss the questions and make their graphs.

THINKING CRITICALLY

During one half-life, approximately half of the unstable atoms in a sample should decay. No, the time of decay of a specific atom cannot be predicted.

TEACHING THE ACTIVITY

*Refer to the **Activity Worksheets** for additional information and teaching strategies.*
• Establish some rules for the tossing of the coins to avoid hazards of flying objects. Stress that the method of data collection should be consistent for all persons.
• This activity should statistically provide an excellent model for nuclear decay.
• Students may need assistance in setting up their graphs, plotting the points, and drawing the curve.

SUMMING UP/ SHARING RESULTS

The greatest number of atoms probably decayed in the first half-life. The calculation will vary depending on the original sample size, but the following equation should be used:

$$\frac{\text{amount (number)}}{\text{remaining}} = \frac{\text{amount (number) of original sample}}{2^n}$$

The result should be close to the actual value.

GOING FURTHER!

Student graphs will vary depending on actual results. Ideally, it should take about one half-life for half the atoms to decay and two half-lives for three-fourths of the original atoms to decay.

PROGRAM RESOURCES

From the **Teacher Resource Package** use:
Activity Worksheets, pages 193-194, Activity 24-1: Half-Time—Investigating Half-Life.

PREPARATION

SECTION BACKGROUND

▶There are several units for measuring radiation. The curie and the bequerel (the SI unit) are based on the number of disintegrations per second. The roentgen, the rad, and the gray (SI unit), measure the effect the radiation has on the absorbing material. The rem measures biological damage most effectively.

1 MOTIVATE

▶Bring in a smoke detector that uses americium-241. Light some flash paper or a candle to produce a controlled amount of smoke and use it to make the smoke detector go off.

Connect to...
Earth Science

Answer: In a cloud chamber, water or ethanol vapor condenses around ions to form visible droplets. Clouds form around dust particles in the atmosphere.

PROGRAM RESOURCES

From the **Teacher Resource Package** use:

Activity Worksheets, page 200, MINI-Lab: What senses atomic radiation?

Critical Thinking/Problem Solving, page 30, Radon.

Science Integration Activity 24

24-3 Detecting Radioactivity

New Science Words

cloud chamber
bubble chamber

Objectives

▶ Describe how radioactivity can be detected.
▶ Explain how a Geiger counter can determine the quantity of nuclear radiation present.

Connect to...
Earth Science

How is the process of forming a visible path of droplets in a cloud chamber similar to the formation of a cloud in the sky?

How does a cloud chamber detect nuclear particles?

Figure 24-5. A cloud chamber is a device used to detect particles of nuclear radiation.

Radiation Detectors

Because you can't feel a single proton or gamma ray, you must use instruments to detect their presence. Methods of detecting radioactivity use the fact that radiation forms ions by removing electrons from matter it passes through. The newly formed ions can be detected in several ways.

Have you ever seen clouds formed in a cloud chamber? A **cloud chamber** can be used to detect charged  nuclear particles as they leave cloud tracks. It contains supersaturated water or ethanol vapor. When a charged particle from a radioactive sample moves through the chamber, it leaves a path of ions behind as it knocks electrons off the atoms in the air. The vapor condenses around these ions to provide a visible path of droplets along the track of the particle. Do you think the trail of a beta particle might differ from the trail of an alpha particle? Beta particles leave long, thin trails, and alpha particles leave shorter and thicker trails.

OPTIONS

Meeting Different Ability Levels

For Section 24-3, use the following **Teacher Resource Masters** depending upon individual students' needs.

◆ **Study Guide Master** for all students.
● **Reinforcement Master** for students of average and above average ability levels.
▲ **Enrichment Master** for above average students.

Additional Teacher Resource Package masters are listed in any PROGRAM RESOURCES boxes that are in the section. The additional masters are appropriate for all students.

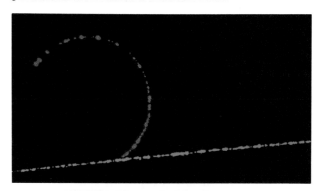
◆ **STUDY GUIDE** 102

STUDY GUIDE   Chapter 24
Detecting Radioactivity   Text Pages 630–632

Use the clues given below to identify terms related to radioactivity detection. Write each term in the space provided. Then, find and circle each term in the hidden word puzzle. The term may be written up, down, forward, backward, or diagonal.

bubble chamber
cloud chamber
electroscope
Geiger counter
gamma ray
beta particle
alpha particle
radioactivity
nuclide

Clues
1. uses lines of bubbles in a superheated liquid to track particles
2. detects charged particles by the cloud tracks they leave
3. device that detects electric charges
4. device that produces clicking sounds or flashing light by amplifying an electric current formed when radiation is present
5. radiation that travels as waves
6. a particle which leaves a long, thin trail in a cloud chamber
7. a particle which leaves a short, thick trail in a cloud chamber
8. emission of high-energy radiation or particles from the nucleus of a radioactive atom
9. nucleus of an isotope with a certain atomic mass and number

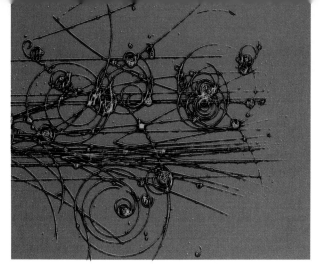

Figure 24-6. Particles of nuclear radiation can be detected as they leave trails of bubbles in a bubble chamber.

Another way to detect and monitor the paths of nuclear particles is by using a bubble chamber. A **bubble chamber** holds a superheated liquid, which doesn't boil because of increased pressure in the system. When a moving particle leaves ions behind, the liquid boils along the trail. The path shows up as tracks of bubbles.

Do you remember how an electroscope was used to detect electric charges in Chapter 21? When an electroscope is given a negative charge, the leaves repel each other and spread apart. They will remain apart until the extra electrons have somewhere to go and discharge the electroscope. A nuclear particle moving through the air will remove electrons from air molecules, leaving them positively charged. When this occurs near an electroscope, some positively charged air molecules will come in contact with the electroscope and attract the electrons from the leaves. As these negatively charged leaves lose their charges, they no longer repel and they move together.

Measuring Radiation

You constantly receive small doses of radiation from your environment. It is not known whether this radiation is harmful to your body tissues. Larger doses of radiation, however, can be harmful to living tissue. If you worked or lived in an environment that could result in exposure to high levels of radiation—a nuclear testing facility, for example—you might want to know exactly how much radiation you were being exposed to. A simple

MINI-Lab

What senses atomic radiation?
A dosimeter measures atomic radiation. It is a type of electroscope that discharges when the gases around it are ionized. Hold a lighted match so the stream of ionized air from the flame will pass near a charged electroscope. Observe the change. Bring a source of beta radiation near a charged electroscope. How does the rate at which the electroscope discharges *compare* with its distance to the radiation source?

MINI-Lab

Materials: electroscope, wool cloth and plastic rod, matches, beta source.
Teaching Tips
▶ Show students how to charge the electroscope.
▶ **CAUTION:** *Be sure the radioactive source is sealed and can be safely handled by students. If there is any doubt, do this portion as a demonstration.*
Expected Results
Both the match and the radioactive materials will discharge the electroscope faster when closer.

MINI-Lab
ASSESSMENT
Oral: Ask students if the rate of discharge is directly or inversely related to the distance.

2 TEACH

Key Concepts are highlighted.

CONCEPT DEVELOPMENT
▶ **Demonstration:** If a cloud chamber is available, place a radioactive source in it and observe the paths of the charged radioactive particles. Observe the effects of a magnet placed nearby.

CHECK FOR UNDERSTANDING
Use the Mini Quiz to check for understanding.

MINI QUIZ

Use the Mini Quiz to check students' recall of chapter content.

1. Which device for detecting radioactivity uses condensation trails? *cloud chamber*
2. A(n) _____ is a device commonly used to measure amounts of radiation. *Geiger counter*
3. Which device for detecting radioactivity produces a narrow path of boiling liquid? *bubble chamber*

RETEACH

Review the reasons that an electroscope discharges and that a Geiger counter activates in the presence of radioactivity. Have students explain the operation of a Geiger counter by interpreting the diagram in Figure 24-7.

EXTENSION

For students who have mastered this section, use the **Reinforcement** and **Enrichment** masters or other OPTIONS provided.

CROSS CURRICULUM

▶ **Occupational Safety:** Geiger counters are used at job sites to determine radiation levels. Find out how much additional radiation workers in a hospital nuclear medicine lab or nuclear power plant would be exposed to.

3 CLOSE

▶ Ask questions 1-2 and the **Apply** and **Connect to Chemistry** questions in the Section Review.

SECTION REVIEW ANSWERS

1. Geiger counter, cloud chamber, bubble chamber, electroscope, and photographic film
2. Radiation enters the tube, causing a current that is amplified and causes a speaker to click.
3. Apply: A Geiger counter if it is small and portable; it can precisely measure the intensity of the radiation.
4. Connect to Chemistry: Argon is inert so it will not react with the wire and its larger size makes it easier to ionize than helium or neon.

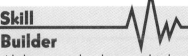

Skill Builder

Alpha particles have a higher charge and lower penetrating power and would produce the shortest trails. Beta particles are much smaller and have higher penetrating ability and would produce the long, thin trails.

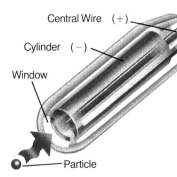

Figure 24-7. A Gieger counter can be used to measure the intensity of nuclear radiation.

method of counting radioactivity is to use a Geiger counter. A Geiger counter is a device that produces an electric current when radiation is present. ②

Figure 24-7 illustrates the parts of a Geiger counter. The tube is filled with gas at a low pressure. A positively charged wire runs through the center of a negatively charged copper cylinder. These are connected to a voltage source. Radiation enters the tube at one end, stripping electrons from the gaseous atoms. The electrons are attracted to the positive wire. They knock more electrons off the atoms in the gas and an "electron avalanche" is produced. A large number of electrons reach the wire, producing a short, intense current in the wire. This current is amplified to produce a clicking sound or flashing light. The intensity of radiation present is determined by the number of clicks in each second.

Geiger counters can be made very small and portable. They are often used to test the radioactivity at job sites where workers can be exposed to radioactive materials.

SECTION REVIEW

1. What are four ways radioactivity can be detected?
2. Briefly explain how a Geiger counter operates.
3. **Apply:** Suppose you needed to check the level of radioactivity in the laboratory of a hospital. Which method would you use? Explain your choice.
4. **Connect to Chemistry:** Geiger counter tubes are often filled with argon gas. Locate argon on the periodic table. Can you suggest why this gas would be a good choice for this purpose?

Skill Builder

☑ **Observing and Inferring**

You are observing the presence of nuclear radiation with a bubble chamber and see two kinds of trails. Some trails are short and thick and others are long and thin. What type of nuclear radiation might have caused each trail? If you need help, refer to Observing and Inferring in the **Skill Handbook** on page 678.

OPTIONS

ASSESSMENT—ORAL

▶ **Why can't a Geiger counter detect microwaves?** *Microwaves do not produce ionization.*

▶ **After uranium-235 undergoes nuclear fission, the mass of the products is less than the mass of the uranium-235 nucleus and bombarding neutron. Does this violate the law of conservation of mass? Explain.** *Yes. However, Einstein established the theory that the total amount of mass and energy in the universe was constant. This is stated as the law of conservation of mass-energy. In fis-*

sion, a small amount of mass can be changed into a huge amount of energy.

Skill Builder
ASSESSMENT
Oral: Have students explain why beta particles would likely leave longer trails.

Nuclear Reactions   24-4

Objectives

▶ Distinguish nuclear fission and fusion.
▶ Explain how nuclear fission can begin a chain reaction.
▶ Discuss how nuclear fusion occurs in the sun.

New Science Words

nuclear fission
chain reaction
nuclear fusion

Nuclear Fission

Have you ever played a game of pool? What happens when you shoot the cue ball into an area of densely packed balls? They split apart, or "break" the pack. In 1938, physicists Otto Hahn and Fritz Strassmann found that a similar result occurs when a neutron is shot into the large nucleus of a uranium-235 atom. Earlier, another physicist, Enrico Fermi, had tried to bombard large nuclei with neutrons in an effort to make nuclei that are larger than uranium. Splitting an atomic nucleus wasn't the expected outcome of this process.

Lise Meitner was the first to offer a theory to explain this process. She concluded that the neutron fired into the nucleus disturbs the already unstable nucleus and causes it to split into two nuclei of nearly equal mass. The process of splitting a nucleus into two nuclei with smaller masses is called **nuclear fission.** You may have heard of the fission that occurs in cells, or of cracks, called fissures, in Earth's surface. In all of these cases, fission means to divide. Typically, large nuclei with atomic numbers above 90 can undergo nuclear fission.

The products of a fission reaction usually include two or three individual neutrons. For example, the uranium-235 nucleus is easily split by bombarding it with a neutron and there can be many possible fission products. Sometimes, it forms a barium-141 nucleus and a krypton-92 nucleus and releases three neutrons.

$$\,^{1}_{0}n + \,^{235}_{92}U \longrightarrow \,^{141}_{56}Ba + \,^{92}_{36}Kr + 3\,^{1}_{0}n$$

Did You Know?

An estimated one million gallons of radioactive liquid will need to be disposed of daily by the year 2000.

What is nuclear fission?

Skill Builder

Answer to Skill Builder on page 635.

**Skill Builder
ASSESSMENT
Performance:** Ask students to redraw their concept maps to show how a chain reaction may be prevented.

SECTION 24-4

PREPARATION

SECTION BACKGROUND

▶ Nuclear fission is often understood by modeling a nucleus such as uranium-235 as a liquid drop. When a neutron is absorbed into the nucleus the added internal energy causes it to take on an elongated form. The strong nuclear force is weakened over this increased distance, and the repulsive electric forces dominate. When this occurs, the nucleus splits into two fission fragments and several neutrons. The fission fragments are usually close, but not equal, in mass.

1 MOTIVATE

▶ **Demonstration:** Model a chain reaction by setting up a fan of dominoes so that each domino will hit two others as it falls over. Or, fan out the matches from a fresh book of matches. Hold the matches vertically with metal tongs and ignite the match in the lower corner using another match.

TYING TO PREVIOUS KNOWLEDGE: To introduce this section, tie nuclear science to students' previous knowledge of the use of nuclear energy, especially in generating electricity and in nuclear bombs. Both processes give a hint about the tremendous amounts of energy involved in nuclear reactions.

VideoDisc

STVS: Fusion, Disc 1, Side 1

2 TEACH

Key Concepts are highlighted.

CONCEPT DEVELOPMENT

▶ Discuss the relationship between the principles of conservation of mass and conservation of energy. Recall that Einstein said that mass and energy are interchangeable, and that the total amount of mass and energy in the universe is constant.

PROGRAM RESOURCES

From the **Teacher Resource Package** use:

Cross-Curricular Connections, page 30, Survey on Nuclear Issues.

Transparency Masters, pages 95-96, Nuclear Chain Reaction.

Use **Color Transparency 48,** Nuclear Chain Reaction.

Connect to... Chemistry

Answer: The periodic table shows an atomic mass of 238.0829, representing the average of all isotopes. uranium-235 is relatively rare.

CHECK FOR UNDERSTANDING

Use the Mini Quiz to check for understanding.

MINI QUIZ

Use the Mini Quiz to check students' recall of chapter content.

① **The process used to release nuclear energy by splitting uranium-235 nuclei is called _____ .** *nuclear fission*

② **What occurs when neutrons released in fission cause other nuclei to split?** *a chain reaction*

③ **Describe the process that produces helium in the sun.** *Hydrogen nuclei fuse to become a helium nucleus by thermonuclear fusion.*

Connect to... Chemistry

Use the periodic table to find the atomic mass of uranium. Explain why this value differs from the mass number 235 given for fissionable uranium.

What is a chain reaction?

Figure 24-8. A chain reaction occurs when neutrons produced by nuclear fission bombard other nuclei, releasing more neutrons, and so on.

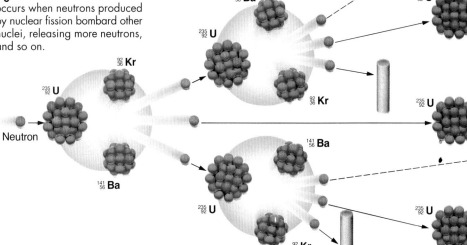

The total mass of the products is somewhat less than the mass of the uranium-235 nucleus and the neutron. Some of the mass has been converted to a tremendous amount of energy.

Do you think the energy released in the fission of a single nucleus would be dangerous? Probably, not by itself. However, the neutrons produced in the fission reaction can bombard other nuclei in the sample to split more nuclei. These reactions will each release more neutrons, and so on. If there is not some other material present to absorb these neutrons, an uncontrolled chain reaction may result. A **chain reaction** is an ongoing series of fission reactions. This can cause billions of reactions to occur in each second, resulting in the release of tremendous amounts of energy. In the next chapter, you will read about ways scientists control nuclear fission and use the energy to produce electricity.

Nuclear Fusion

You read in the last section how tremendous amounts of energy can be released in nuclear fission. In fact, splitting one uranium-235 nucleus produces several million times more energy than exploding one molecule of dynamite. Even more energy can be released in another type of nuclear reaction. This process is caused by the fusing together of nuclei, so it is the opposite of fission. **Nuclear fusion** is the combining of two nuclei with low masses to

OPTIONS

Meeting Different Ability Levels

For Section 24-4, use the following **Teacher Resource Masters** depending upon individual students' needs.

◆ **Study Guide Master** for all students.

● **Reinforcement Master** for students of average and above average ability levels.

▲ **Enrichment Master** for above average students.

Additional Teacher Resource Package masters are listed in any PROGRAM RESOURCES boxes that are in the section. The additional masters are appropriate for all students.

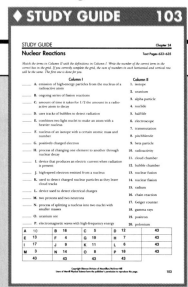

form one nucleus of larger mass. Controlled nuclear fusion is difficult to induce because extremely high temperatures are required for this process to occur.

These extremely high temperatures do exist in the stars, including the sun. The sun is a star of medium internal temperature, averaging about 20 million degrees Celsius. At these high temperatures, the atoms have so much kinetic energy that positive nuclei and electrons exist separately. Matter in this state is called plasma. This kind of fusion is called thermonuclear fusion, because such tremendous thermal conditions must exist.

When the sun first formed, most of its nuclei were hydrogen nuclei. As thermonuclear fusion occurs, four hydrogen nuclei are fused to become a helium nucleus. This process is still occurring, and about one percent of the mass of the sun's original nuclei has been changed to energy and released in the form of electromagnetic radiation. As the star ages, the percentage of helium nuclei gradually increases and the number of hydrogen nuclei decreases until there is no more for the reaction to occur. Scientists estimate that the sun has enough hydrogen to keep this reaction going for another five billion years.

Scientists are searching for a way to induce and control nuclear fusion. If they achieve this goal in the future, many of our current energy problems will be solved.

SECTION REVIEW

1. Compare and contrast nuclear fission and fusion.
2. Why does a chain reaction often occur when a uranium-235 nucleus is split?
3. **Apply:** Account for the mass of the four hydrogen nuclei that undergo fusion to form a helium nucleus within the sun.
4. **Connect to Earth Science:** Explain why the hydrogen fusion reaction that takes place in the sun can't currently produce energy for electricity on Earth.

☑ Concept Mapping

Make a concept map to show how a chain reaction occurs when U-235 is bombarded with a neutron. Show how each of the three neutrons given as products begins another fission reaction. If you need help, refer to Concept Mapping in the **Skill Handbook** on pages 684 and 685.

Science and READING
Find out what happens to the by-products of fission-produced electricity.

Skill Builder

3 CLOSE

▶ Ask the Section Review questions.

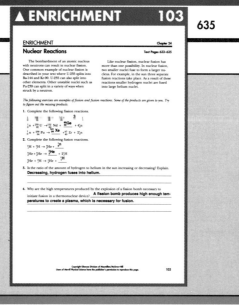

● REINFORCEMENT 103

▲ ENRICHMENT 103

PREPARATION

SECTION BACKGROUND
▶Immature or rapidly dividing cells are most susceptible to damage by radiation. For this reason, cancer cells can often be destroyed with radiotherapy. Infants and fetuses are more sensitive to ionizing radiation.

VideoDisc
STVS: PETT Scanner; Disc 7, Side 1

1 MOTIVATE

▶Take a poll. How many students in your class remember having an X ray at the dentist or doctor's office? Explain that they will learn how radiation can help diagnose medical problems in the body and even cure some cancers.

Connect to...
Life Science

Answer: Depending on the type and duration, exposure may cause a lower white blood cell count, lesions, nausea, or loss of hair. Also, leukemia, birth defects, and death.

2 TEACH

Key Concepts are highlighted.

CONCEPT DEVELOPMENT
▶ Ask students why a tracer with a half-life of several hours would be very useful. Tracers should have relatively short half-lives (several hours) so they continually emit an amount of radiation that can be detected in a short time interval. The half-life is short enough so the nuclides lose their radioactive properties rapidly.

New Science Words

tracers

Objectives

▶ Describe how radioactive tracers can be used to diagnose medical problems.
▶ Discuss how radioactive isotopes can aid in the treatment of cancers.

Connect to...
Life Science

Find out what kinds of biological effects humans can experience when exposed to abnormally large amounts of radiation.

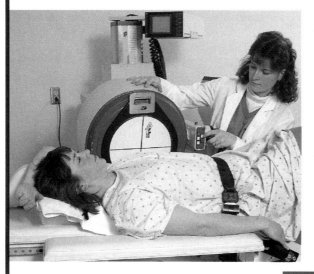

Are Radioactive Isotopes Useful in Medicine?

Did you know that radioactive isotopes can help locate and even kill cancerous tumors in the body? The rapidly growing field of nuclear medicine involves the use of radioactive isotopes in the diagnosis and treatment of many medical problems.

Just as wildlife conservationists tag animals to make them easy to follow, scientists can tag molecules with radioactive isotopes. Within the body, these radioactive isotopes behave like any other atom of the same element. However, they emit radiation as they move and can be followed with a radiation detector. Radioisotopes that are put in the body to monitor a bodily process are called **tracers.** Tracers typically have a relatively short half-life so they are constantly emitting a fair amount of radiation.

Certain parts of your body need specific elements, so the tracer is attached to a particular element that will travel to a desired location. For example, your thyroid gland, which regulates body growth and other processes, requires a certain amount of iodine to function normally. A doctor can examine the way the thyroid uses iodine by having the person drink a solution containing the radioactive isotope iodine-131. The amount of this isotope in the thyroid can be determined by a detector. A thyroid problem is detected if the rate at which iodine is used in the gland is abnormal.

636 RADIOACTIVITY AND NUCLEAR REACTIONS

OPTIONS

Meeting Different Ability Levels
For Section 24-5, use the following **Teacher Resource Masters** depending upon individual students' needs.
◆ **Study Guide Master** for all students.
● **Reinforcement Master** for students of average and above average ability levels.
▲ **Enrichment Master** for above average students.

◆ STUDY GUIDE 104

Tumors can also be found with radioactive isotopes. Cancerous cells reproduce very rapidly, so more of the radioactive isotope gathers in these cells than in those of healthy tissues. For example, technetium-99 is one element that is rapidly absorbed in brain tumors. The exact location of the tumor can be determined by using tracers, thus eliminating the need for risky exploratory surgery.

Tracing techniques help diagnose cancer, but the problem of treating the cancer remains. One treatment, therapy with ionizing radiation, often complements or replaces surgery. This radiation can be given either internally or externally. Iodine-131 is sometimes given internally to treat thyroid cancer. Cobalt-60 is often used as an external source of ionizing radiation. A beam of this radiation is aimed at the cancerous spot to destroy the cancerous cells. This treatment can shrink, and even eliminate, some cancerous tumors. Unfortunately, healthy tissue can also be damaged by radiation therapy. This treatment may produce unpleasant side effects, such as hair loss, fatigue, and nausea.

Although using radiation in medicine has some risks associated with it, the risks are often smaller than the possible complications of surgery or even medication. The decision to take any kind of medical treatment involves a certain amount of risk. Nuclear medicine is responsible for saving many lives.

SECTION REVIEW

1. How does a radioactive tracer work?
2. Describe two ways radioactive isotopes can be used in the treatment of cancerous tumors.
3. **Connect to Life Science:** Explain how a sodium chloride solution could be used to test for circulatory problems in a human leg.

You Decide!

Radioactive isotopes used in medicine produce radioactive wastes that are potentially hazardous to people and the environment for many years. Should radioactive isotopes continue to be used in medical treatments? Explain your position.

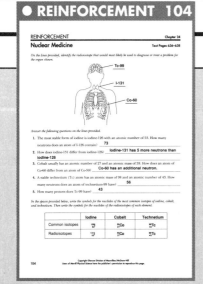
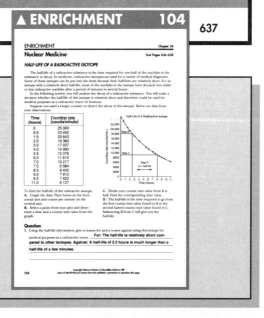
CROSS CURRICULUM
▶**Medicine:** A common use of X rays is the CAT (computer-assisted tomography or computerized axial tomography) scan. Find out how CAT scans are used in medical diagnosis.

CHECK FOR UNDERSTANDING
Ask students how iodine-131 might be useful in treating a tumor without damaging other body tissue. Because the thyroid uses iodine, most of the iodine travels to the thyroid gland.

RETEACH
Most students will have seen wildlife shows on TV. Ask how the use of radioactive tracers in the body is similar to the use of radio collars to track wild animals.

EXTENSION
For students who have mastered this section, use the **Reinforcement** and **Enrichment** masters or other OPTIONS provided.

3 CLOSE

▶Ask questions 1-2 and the **Connect to Life Science** question in the Section Review.

SECTION REVIEW ANSWERS
1. A tracer acts like any atom of the same element and can be followed with a radiation detector.
2. They can be given internally, or radiation can be projected to the site.
3. Connect to Life Science: A radioactive tracer could be added, injected, and followed.

YOU DECIDE!
Have students debate the You Decide topic in teams. Be sure that all points of view are considered.

ACTIVITY 24-2
30 minutes

OBJECTIVE: **Illustrate** the hydrogen fusion process through the use of physical models.

PROCESS SKILLS applied in this activity:
▶**Formulating Models** in Procedure Steps 1-4.
▶**Interpreting** in Analyze Questions 1-3.
▶**Inferring** in Conclude and Apply Questions 4 and 5.

COOPERATIVE LEARNING
Divide the class into Science Investigation Groups of three to six students. Provide each team with materials for making six protons. Teams can interact using the leftover protons for a second cycle of fusion.

TEACHING THE ACTIVITY

Alternate Materials: Any combination of large and small objects can be used to represent neutrons and positrons. Clay requires no pins to hold parts together.

Troubleshooting: Be sure students construct the correct nuclei at each step. If they do not, they will not be able to draw a correct conclusion.

▶The proton model shown here is useful for this activity but otherwise not representative. The released positron is a short-lived particle that reacts with an electron to become gamma radiation.

PROGRAM RESOURCES

From the **Teacher Resource Package** use:

Activity Worksheets, pages 195-196, Activity 24-2: Figuring Out Fusion.

Activity
ASSESSMENT

Oral: Ask students to explain how many other hydrogen nuclei would be needed to join the two remaining nuclei to form the next helium nucleus.

Figuring Out Fusion

The energy that warms Earth is produced in thermonuclear fusion reactions in the sun, which is about 1.5 x 10⁸ km away. We cannot do actual nuclear fusion reactions in the classroom, but we can model this process.

Materials
- 6 balls of green clay
- 6 smaller balls of white clay

Procedure
1. Make six hydrogen nuclei (protons) by sticking one small white positron to each large green neutron.
2. Refer to Step 1 of the table and make two particles of ^2_1H.
3. Refer to Step 2 of the table and make two particles of ^3_2He.
4. Refer to Step 3 of the table and make one particle of ^4_2He.

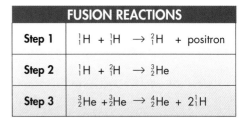

FUSION REACTIONS	
Step 1	$^1_1H + ^1_1H \rightarrow ^2_1H$ + positron
Step 2	$^1_1H + ^2_1H \rightarrow ^3_2He$
Step 3	$^3_2He + ^3_2He \rightarrow ^4_2He + 2^1_1H$

Analyze
1. Describe the steps necessary to change ^1_1H into ^4_2He.
2. In this process, what is lost and what is left over?
3. How many atoms of hydrogen does it take to make one atom of helium?

Conclude and Apply
4. What can the leftover hydrogen be used for?
5. Refer to the periodic table on pages 258-259. *Compare* the mass of one helium atom to the mass of four hydrogen atoms. If leftover mass changes to energy, where does the energy of the sun come from?

ANSWERS TO QUESTIONS

1. Two protons fuse as a positron is released, and a proton changes to a neutron. Then a normal hydrogen nucleus fuses with hydrogen-2 to make helium-3. Finally, two helium-3 nuclei fuse to make one helium-4 and two normal hydrogens.

2. Two positrons are lost. Two protons are left over.

3. It takes six hydrogen-1 to make one helium-4 nucleus. However, two hydrogen are regained in the process. Therefore, the net usage is four hydrogen-1 atoms.

4. Hydrogen that is produced in the fusion reaction can be used for the next cycle of fusion.

5. He = 4.002 602 u   4H = (4)(1.007 94 u)
                                                    = 4.031 76 u
mass loss = 4.031 76 u – 4.002 602 u
                  = 0.029 16 u

This mass is converted to energy in the fusion process. The energy of the sun comes from the conversion of mass during fusion according to the relationship $E = mc^2$.

CHAPTER REVIEW

SUMMARY

24-1: Radioactivity
1. Radioactivity was accidentally discovered by Henri Bequerel about 100 years ago.
2. Radioactive nuclides are unstable and therefore decay. Stable nuclides don't decay.

24-2: Nuclear Decay
1. The three types of radiation that can be emitted from a decaying nucleus are alpha particles, beta particles, and gamma rays.
2. The amount of a remaining radioactive substance can be determined if you know the amount of the original sample and the number of half-lives that have elapsed.
3. The age of some previously living material can be estimated by a process called carbon-14 dating.

24-3: Detecting Radioactivity
1. Radioactivity can be detected with a cloud chamber, a bubble chamber, an electroscope, or a Geiger counter.
2. A Geiger counter indicates the intensity of radiation present by producing a clicking sound or a flashing light that increases in frequency as more radiation is present.

24-4: Nuclear Reactions
1. Atomic nuclei are split during fission and combined during fusion.
2. Subatomic particles released from a nucleus during fission can split other nuclei.
3. Hydrogen atoms in the sun undergo fusion, and as a result, form helium atoms and electromagnetic radiation.

24-5: Science and Society: Nuclear Medicine
1. Radioactive tracers can go to certain areas of the body to indicate abnormalities.
2. Some radioactive isotopes can kill cancer cells.

KEY SCIENCE WORDS

a. alpha particle
b. beta particle
c. bubble chamber
d. chain reaction
e. cloud chamber
f. gamma ray
g. half-life
h. nuclear fission
i. nuclear fusion
j. nuclide
k. radioactivity
l. tracer
m. transmutation

UNDERSTANDING VOCABULARY

Match each phrase with the correct term from the list of Key Science Words.

1. emission of high-energy particles or radiation from an unstable nucleus
2. a particle of nuclear radiation with a charge of 2+ and an atomic mass of 4
3. nuclear decay that results in the formation of a new element
4. the time for one-half of a sample of a radioactive isotope to decay
5. detects nuclear particles as they leave a trail of condensed water or ethanol vapor
6. splitting a nucleus into two smaller masses
7. radioactive isotope that is used to monitor human body functions
8. the nucleus of a specific isotope
9. radiation in the form of an electromagnetic wave
10. two nuclei combining into a larger nucleus

RADIOACTIVITY AND NUCLEAR REACTIONS **639**

CHAPTER REVIEW

SUMMARY
Have students read the summary statements to review the major concepts of the chapter.

UNDERSTANDING VOCABULARY

1. k		6. h	
2. a		7. l	
3. m		8. j	
4. g		9. f	
5. e		10. i	

ASSESSMENT
Portfolio
Encourage students to place in their portfolios one or two items of what they consider to be their best work. For each item, ask students to explain why that item was chosen and what they learned from it. Items might be selected from the following.
- In Your Journal paragraph about radiation, p. 620
- Practice Problem calculations, p. 627
- Skill Builder concept map, p. 635

Performance
Additional performance assessments may be found in *Performance Assessment* and *Science Integration Activities* that accompany **Merrill Physical Science**. Performance Task Assessment Lists and rubrics for evaluating these activities and other products generated throughout the chapter can be found in Glencoe's *Performance Assessment in Middle School Science*.

OPTIONS

ASSESSMENT
To assess student understanding of material in this chapter, use the resources listed.

👥 COOPERATIVE LEARNING
Consider using cooperative learning in the THINK AND WRITE CRITICALLY, APPLY, and MORE SKILL BUILDERS sections of the Chapter Review.

PROGRAM RESOURCES
From the **Teacher Resource Package** use:
Chapter Review, pages 51-52.
Chapter and Unit Tests, pages 155-158, Chapter Test.

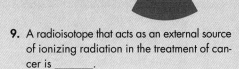

CHAPTER

REVIEW

CHECKING CONCEPTS

1. a		**6.** b	
2. a		**7.** a	
3. b		**8.** c	
4. a		**9.** a	
5. a		**10.** d	

USING LAB SKILLS

ASSESSMENT

Use these alternate lab exercises to assess students' understanding of the skills used in this chapter.

11. The curve would have the same shape, but the data points would have higher values and more half-lives would be required for the entire sample to decay.

12. The product is ^2_1H, deuterium.

THINK AND WRITE CRITICALLY

13. Radioactivity was discovered by Henri Bequerel in 1896. Marie and Pierre Curie later discovered the elements polonium and radium. Nuclear fission was produced in 1938 by Otto Hahn and Fritz Strassman and explained by Lise Meitner.

14. The strong nuclear force is less effective when the ratio of protons to neutrons in the nucleus is not a stable ratio.

15. In all living organisms there is a fixed percentage of carbon-14 while the organism is still alive. Once the organism dies, the carbon-14 that decays is not replaced. By measuring the percentage of carbon-14 in a sample of once-living material and comparing this to the percentage of carbon-14 in a living sample, scientists can approximate the age of the sample.

16. In a cloud chamber, the ions produced by the radiation cause supersaturated vapor to condense in a cloud trail. In a bubble chamber, ionized atoms of a superheated liquid boil, leaving a trail of bubbles. In an electroscope, radiation strips electrons from the air molecules, giving the molecules a positive charge. These ions cause the electroscope to discharge.

17. Because cancer cells have accelerated physiological processes, they take

---

CHECKING CONCEPTS

Choose the word or phrase that completes the sentence.

1. Radioactivity can be _____.
 a. found in your classroom **c.** seen
 b. found with a tracer **d.** smelled

2. Elements that have been produced artificially through nuclear reactions have atomic numbers _____.
 a. greater than 92 **c.** between 83 and 92
 b. greater than 83 **d.** between 93 and 109

3. When a neutron decays, the electron produced is called _____.
 a. an alpha particle **c.** gamma radiation
 b. a beta particle **d.** both a and c

4. The time for half the nuclides in a sample of a radioactive isotope to decay _____.
 a. is constant **c.** increases with time
 b. varies **d.** decreases with time

5. Carbon-14 dating could be used to date _____.
 a. an ancient Roman scroll
 b. an ancient marble column
 c. dinosaur fossils
 d. Earth's oldest rocks

6. Radiation in a nuclear laboratory could best be measured with _____.
 a. a cloud chamber **c.** an electroscope
 b. a Geiger counter **d.** a bubble chamber

7. A _____ is an ongoing series of fission reactions.
 a. chain reaction
 b. decay reaction
 c. transmutation reaction
 d. fusion reaction

8. The sun is powered by _____.
 a. nuclear decay **c.** thermonuclear fusion
 b. nuclear fission **d.** combustion

9. A radioisotope that acts as an external source of ionizing radiation in the treatment of cancer is _____.
 a. cobalt-60 **c.** iodine-131
 b. carbon-14 **d.** technetium-99

10. A major medical use of radiation is to _____.
 a. assist breathing **c.** heal broken bones
 b. ease pain **d.** treat cancers

USING LAB SKILLS

11. Review your graph of decay from Activity 24-1 on page 629. What would the half-life curve look like if your sample contained twice as many coins? Predict the new data and sketch the corresponding graph. Then try it and see.

12. Use the clay models from Activity 24-2 on page 628 to determine the product of a simple fusion reaction between a proton (^1_1H) and a neutron (^1_0n). Complete the nuclear equation:

$$^1_1H + ^1_0n \rightarrow \underline{\hspace{1cm}} + \text{gamma radiation}$$

THINK AND WRITE CRITICALLY

Answer the following questions in your Journal using complete sentences.

13. Briefly discuss the history of nuclear science.
14. Explain why certain nuclides decay.
15. Describe the basic principles of carbon-14 dating.
16. Discuss the similarities and differences in the devices that detect radioactivity.
17. Discuss the use of radioactive tracers. How do they detect cancer cells?

---

up a radioactive tracer much more rapidly than do healthy cells. Thus, most of the tracer will accumulate at the tumor and the tumor can be detected.

APPLY

18. Yes. The process depends only on electron structure. Other than being radioactive, the salt would be chemically the same as normal salt.

19. $^{66}_{29}Cu \rightarrow ^{66}_{30}Zn + ^{0}_{-1}e$

$^{226}_{88}Ra \rightarrow ^{222}_{86}Rn + ^{4}_{2}He$

20. Four half-lives elapse in 40 minutes.
remaining mass = 320 g/2^4 = 20 grams

21. The temperatures and pressures in the interior of a star are sufficiently high for atoms in the plasma state to undergo thermonuclear fusion and form successively heavier atoms as lighter nuclei collide.

22. Ionizing radiation can kill cells. Therefore, radiation can be used to kill bacteria in food and thus give it longer shelf-life. Radioisotopes such as potassium-40 can be placed in the soil of lab plants. Using radiation detectors, scientists can monitor how they are taken up by the plant.

APPLY

18. Can a radioactive isotope of sodium combine with chlorine to form table salt? If so, would its chemical and physical properties be the same as ordinary table salt? Explain your answer.
19. Copper-66 releases a beta particle as it decays, and radium-226 releases an alpha particle. Write a nuclear equation for each of these transmutations.
20. Nitrogen-13 has a half-life of about 10 minutes. How much of a 320-g sample of nitrogen-13 would remain after decaying for 40 minutes?
21. Explain the presence of relatively heavy elements such as carbon, oxygen, magnesium, and iron in stars.
22. Explain how radioisotopes are used to preserve foods and to study how plants take up nutrients from the soil.

MORE SKILL BUILDERS

If you need help, refer to the Skill Handbook.

1. **Concept Mapping:** Complete the following concept map summarizing how a Geiger counter works.

Initiating Event

Final Outcome

2. **Making and Using Tables:** Construct a table summarizing the characteristics of each of the three types of radiation.
3. **Observing and Inferring:** Another type of nuclear radiation is a positron, which has a charge of 1+ and the same mass as an electron. This particle is given off when a proton spontaneously changes into a neutron. Infer what type of radiation will be emitted from each of the following radioisotopes:
   a. Boron-8, which is unstable due to an extra proton
   b. Thorium-232, which is unstable due to its large nucleus containing too many protons and neutrons
   c. Potassium-40, which is unstable due to an extra neutron
4. **Making and Using Graphs:** Using the data below, construct a bar graph plotting the mass numbers vs. the half-lives of radioisotopes. Plot mass numbers to the nearest ten. Is it possible to use your graph to predict the half-life of a radioisotope given its mass number?

Radio Isotope	Mass Number	Half-life
Radium	222	4 days
Thorium	234	25 days
Iodine	131	8 days
Bismuth	210	5 days
Polonium	210	138 days

PROJECTS

1. Write a biography of a person who made an important contribution to nuclear science.
2. Research the causes and effects of radon pollution in the home. Report your findings to the class.

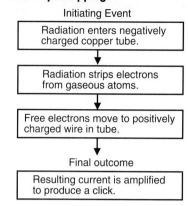

MORE SKILL BUILDERS

1. **Concept Mapping:**

Initiating Event

Radiation enters negatively charged copper tube.

Radiation strips electrons from gaseous atoms.

Free electrons move to positively charged wire in tube.

Final outcome

Resulting current is amplified to produce a click.

2. **Making and Using Tables:** See sample table below, left.
3. **Observing and Inferring:**
   a) emission of positron (extra proton is changed into neutron)
   b) emission of alpha particle (removes both neutrons and protons in very heavy nuclides)
   c) emission of beta particle (extra neutron is changed into proton)
4. **Making and Using Graphs:** Students should construct a bar graph, *not a line graph*, because the data are for discrete entities, not a continuum.

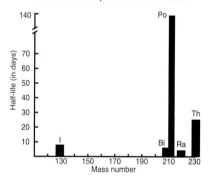

The graph shows no correlation between mass number and greatly differing half-lives.

Type of Radiation	Charge	Mass	Rel. Speed	Penetrating Power	Symbol
Alpha	+2	4	Slow	Low; Stopped by paper	$^{4}_{2}He$
Beta	−1	0	Fast	Moderate; Stopped by aluminum foil	$^{0}_{-1}e$
Gamma	0	0	Speed of light	Great; Stopped by thick lead or concrete	γ

25 Energy Sources

CHAPTER SECTION	OBJECTIVES	ACTIVITIES
25-1 Fossil Fuels (1 day)	1. **Discuss** the origin and characteristics of the three main types of fossil fuels. 2. **Describe** the need and methods for energy conservation.	**MINI-Lab:** *Can efficient use conserve fuel?* p. 646
25-2 Nuclear Energy (2 days)	1. **Outline** the operation of a nuclear reactor. 2. **Describe** the problems and methods associated with nuclear waste disposal. 3. **Discuss** nuclear fusion as a possible energy source.	**Activity 25-1:** *Nuclear Waste Disposal,* p. 653
25-3 Breeder Reactors Science & Society (1 day)	1. **Distinguish** breeder reactors and normal nuclear fission reactors. 2. **Assess** the advantages and disadvantages of operating breeder reactors.	
25-4 Alternative Energy Sources (2 days)	1. **Analyze** the need for alternative energy sources. 2. **Discuss** the methods of generating electricity with several energy sources. 3. **Describe** the advantages and disadvantages of several alternative energy sources.	**Activity 25-2:** *Energy Alternatives—A Local Plan,* p. 662
Chapter Review		

ACTIVITY MATERIALS

FIND OUT	ACTIVITIES		MINI-LABS
Page 643 microscope slides petroleum jelly microscope tong car	**25-1 Nuclear Waste Disposal, p. 653** sodium hydroxide pellets, 4 100-mL beakers, 4 phenolphthalein solution plastic food wrap aluminum foil rubber bands, 3 twist ties, 2 modeling clay forceps goggles	**25-2 Energy Alternatives—A Local Plan, p. 662** large sheet of poster paper set of colored markers miscellaneous con- struction supplies	**Can efficient use conserve fuel? p. 646** candle water aluminum foil 100-mL beaker thermometer cardboard ring stand balance graduated cylinder

CHAPTER FEATURES	TEACHER RESOURCE PACKAGE	OTHER RESOURCES
Technology: *Gas Instead of Gasoline,* p. 646 **Skill Builder:** *Comparing and Contrasting,* p. 647	**Ability Level Worksheets** ♦ *Study Guide,* p. 105 ● *Reinforcement,* p. 105 ▲ *Enrichment,* p. 105 **Activity Worksheets,** p. 208 **Transparency Masters,** pp. 97, 98	**Color Transparency 50,** Petroleum Distillation **Laboratory Manual 49,** Solar Cells **STVS:** Disc 2, Side 2
Skill Builder: *Concept Mapping,* p. 652	**Ability Level Worksheets** ♦ *Study Guide,* p. 106 ● *Reinforcement,* p. 106 ▲ *Enrichment,* p. 106 **Activity Worksheets,** pp. 202, 203 **Critical Thinking/Problem Solving,** p. 31 **Transparency Masters,** pp. 99, 100	**Color Transparency 50,** Nuclear Power Plant
You Decide! p. 655	**Ability Level Worksheets** ♦ *Study Guide,* p. 107 ● *Reinforcement,* p. 107 ▲ *Enrichment,* p. 107	
Problem Solving: *Renewable Energy Sources for Beachtown,* p. 661 **Skill Builder:** *Outlining,* p. 661	**Ability Level Worksheets** ♦ *Study Guide,* p. 108 ● *Reinforcement,* p. 108 ▲ *Enrichment,* p. 108 **Activity Worksheets,** pp. 204, 205 **Concept Mapping,** pp. 55, 56 **Cross-Curricular Connections,** p. 31 **Science and Society,** p. 29	**Laboratory Manual 50,** Using the Sun's Energy **STVS:** Disc 2, Side 2 **Science Integration Activity 25**
Summary Think & Write Critically Key Science Words Apply Understanding Vocabulary More Skill Builders Checking Concepts Projects Using Lab Skills	**ASSESSMENT RESOURCES** **Chapter Review,** pp. 53, 54 **Chapter Test,** pp. 159-162 **Unit Test,** pp. 163, 164 **Performance Assessment in Middle School Science**	**Chapter Review Software** **Test Bank** **Performance Assessment** **Alternate Assessment**

♦ Basic   ● Average   ▲ Advanced

ADDITIONAL MATERIALS

SOFTWARE	AUDIOVISUAL	BOOKS/MAGAZINES
	Energy for the Future, Video, Britannica. *Energy Watch,* Video, HRM Video. *Energy from the Sun,* Video, Guidance Associates. *LearningAbout Nuclear energy,* Video, Britannica. *Nuclear Power,* Video, Hawkhill. *Power Without End,* Video, Guidance Associates. *Renewable Energy,* Video, AIT. *Renewable Energy Resources,* Video, Guidance Associates. *The Science of Energy: From Fossil Fuels to Nuclear Reactors,* Video, Guidance Associates.	Cobb, Vicki. *Why Doesn't the Sun Burn Out? and Other Not So Dumb Questions about Energy.* NY: Lodestar, 1990. Godman, Arthur, *Energy Supply A–Z.* Hillside, NJ: Enslow, 1991. Haines, Gail B. *The Challenge of Supplying Energy.* Hillside, NJ: Enslow, 1991. Hansen, Michael C. *Coal: How It Is Found and Used.* Hillside, NJ: Enslow, 1990. Kuecken, John A. *Alternative Energy Projects for the 1990s.* Blue Ridge Summit, PA: TAB, 1991.

THEME DEVELOPMENT: Energy is an obvious theme throughout this chapter. The sections compare the use of fossil fuels, nuclear energy, solar energy, and other alternative energy sources as methods of supplying useful energy to large communities. The environmental effects of generating usable energy should also be discussed.

CHAPTER OVERVIEW

▶ **Section 25-1:** This section focuses on methods of using fossil fuels as our most common energy resource. Fossil fuels are discussed as a non-renewable resource.

▶ **Section 25-2:** The process of using nuclear reactors to generate electricity is illustrated. Nuclear waste disposal is discussed. The challenges of developing fusion power are also presented.

▶ **Section 25-3:** Science and Society: This section provides a description of the function of breeder reactors.

▶ **Section 25-4:** Alternate energy sources are compared. These include biomass, solar energy, hydroelectricity, tidal energy, wind energy, and geothermal energy.

CHAPTER VOCABULARY

petroleum	breeder reactor
fractional	photovoltaic cell
distillation	hydroelectricity
nonrenewable	tidal energy
resources	geothermal
nuclear reactor	energy
nuclear wastes	

CHAPTER

25 Energy Sources

642

OPTIONS

⚡ For Your Gifted Students

▶ Students can write a story about how they survived an imaginary week-long loss of energy sources (electric and fossil fuel), describing their daily routine. They should try to come up with ideas for an alternate energy source.

▶ Have students brainstorm ways energy is wasted and then ways to turn the waste to conservation.

⚡ For Your Mainstreamed Students

▶ Students can create mobiles illustrating different energy sources, conservation models, and examples of waste. They can make drawings or find them in other media. Illustrations should be labeled and grouped according to category.

How many times do you ride in a car or bus in one week? Is that car or bus powered by a gasoline engine? It probably is, because most automobiles are fueled by gasoline. If you live in a large city, you may often see a layer of smog all around you. Smog is a type of pollution that forms from the exhaust of thousands of cars.

FIND OUT!

Do the following activity to find out about automobile emissions.

Have an adult help you with this activity. Hold a microscope slide, upon which you have smeared a thin layer of petroleum jelly, near the opening of an automobile's exhaust pipe. Have the adult start the car and let it idle IN PARK. Be careful not to touch the exhaust pipe or breathe the vapors. Remove the slide after two minutes and *observe* it under a microscope or with a powerful hand lens. What do you see?

Previewing Science Skills

► In the **Skill Builders,** you will compare and contrast, make a concept map, and outline.
► In the **Activities,** you will diagram, research, and make observations.
► In the **MINI-Lab,** you will measure, observe, and make conclusions.

What's next?

Did you observe some dark particles on the slide in the Find Out activity? Tons of particles like these are released into the atmosphere daily when gasoline and other fossil fuels are burned for energy. Consider some of the energy alternatives mentioned as you read this chapter.

643

INTRODUCING THE CHAPTER

Use the Find Out activity to help students think about the nature of our energy resources. Point out that alternatives to fossil fuels are necessary to fulfill the energy demands of society and that they will be studying some of these options.

FIND OUT!

Preparation: You may want to make several slides ahead of time if slide presentation in class is not practical. Have students hold slides with tongs.

Materials: microscope slides, petroleum jelly, microscopes, tongs, a car

Teaching Tips
► If time is limited, make enough slides to have one slide for every two people. Have students make suggestions about the nature of the particles given off in the exhaust.
► Allow the car to run until the exhaust system heats up. A cold exhaust puts out too much condensed water vapor.

Gearing Up

Have students study the Gearing Up feature to familiarize themselves with the chapter. Discuss the relationships of the topics in the outline.

What's Next?

Before beginning the first section, make sure students understand the connection between the Find Out activity and the topics to follow.

ASSESSMENT OPTIONS

PORTFOLIO
Refer to page 663 for suggested items that students might select for their portfolios.

PERFORMANCE ASSESSMENT
See page 663 for additional Performance Assessment options.
Process
Skill Builders, pp. 647, 652, 661
Activity 25-2, p. 662
Using Lab Skills, p. 664

CONTENT ASSESSMENT
Assessment—Oral, p. 646, 651
Section Reviews, pp. 647, 652, 655, 661
Chapter Review, pp. 663-665
Mini Quizzes, pp. 646, 651, 660
Activity 24-1, p. 653
MINI-Lab, p. 647

GROUP ASSESSMENT
Opportunities for group assessment occur with Cooperative Learning Strategies and Flex Your Brain Activities.

PREPARATION

SECTION BACKGROUND
▶ The first oil well in the U.S. was drilled by Edwin Drake in Titusville, Pennsylvania, in 1859. The refineries produced mostly kerosene and heating oil until the development of gasoline-powered transportation in the 1890s.
▶ Over 50 percent of the world's oil reserves are located in the Persian Gulf region.

PREPLANNING
▶ Posters on coal mining and petroleum processing are sometimes available from state and federal departments of energy or from petroleum and coal companies.

1 MOTIVATE

▶ Have students list the ways in which they have encountered products made from petroleum. They may think of gasoline, petroleum jelly, baby oil, kerosene, or motor oil. Point out that many plastics, cosmetics, and detergents are also derived from oil.

TYING TO PREVIOUS KNOWLEDGE:
Students have studied hydrocarbons—compounds made of hydrogen and carbon—in Chapter 13. Petroleum and natural gas, both fossil fuels, are made of hydrocarbon molecules.

VideoDisc
STVS: Oil from Wood, Disc 2, Side 2

New Science Words

petroleum
fractional distillation
nonrenewable resources

Objectives

▶ Discuss the origin and characteristics of the three main types of fossil fuels.
▶ Describe the need and methods for energy conservation.

Petroleum

Do you own a sweater made of synthetic fibers such as polyester, rayon, or nylon? If so, are you aware that your sweater has something in common with the gasoline used for fuel in cars and buses? Synthetic fibers are made with chemicals that come from crude oil, and gasoline is refined from crude oil.

Crude oil, or **petroleum,** is a liquid source of energy made from the remains of plants and animals. Petroleum, along with natural gas and coal, is called a fossil fuel. 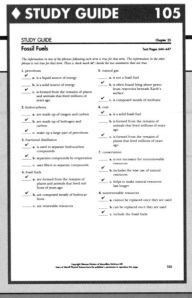 When plants and animals died, they were covered with layers of sand, mud, volcanic ash, and other matter that collected on the surface of Earth over many years. Great pressure, heat, and bacterial action acted on these buried organisms, forming fossil fuels. Petroleum and natural gas are probably made from this process acting on the remains of sea organisms.

Have you ever seen oil wells pumping in a field as you rode along a highway? Petroleum is pumped to the surface from wells drilled deep down into the ground. The crude oil that comes from these wells contains a variety of different chemicals. Because plants and animals contain large amounts of hydrogen and carbon, petroleum is composed mostly of compounds containing these elements, called hydrocarbons.

These various hydrocarbon compounds must be separated to make use of the chemical energy stored in petroleum. If you have ever seen an oil refining plant, you may have noticed several tall towers. These towers are called fractionating towers. Fractionating towers use a process called **fractional distillation** to separate hydrocarbon compounds. First, crude oil is pumped into the

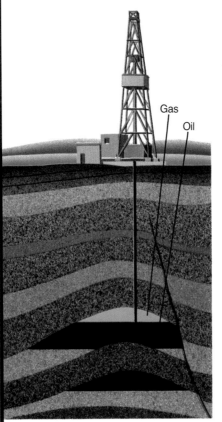

Gas

Oil

644 ENERGY SOURCES

OPTIONS

Meeting Different Ability Levels
For Section 25-1, use the following **Teacher Resource Masters** depending upon individual students' needs.
◆ **Study Guide Master** for all students.
● **Reinforcement Master** for students of average and above average ability levels.
▲ **Enrichment Master** for above average students.
Additional Teacher Resource Package masters are listed in any PROGRAM RESOURCES boxes that are in the section. The additional masters are appropriate for all students.

◆ STUDY GUIDE 105

STUDY GUIDE   Chapter 25
Fossil Fuels   Text Pages 644–647

The information in two of the phrases following each term is true for that term. The information in the other phrase is not true for that term. Place a check mark (✔) beside the two statements that are true.

1. petroleum
✔ a. is a liquid source of energy
b. is a solid source of energy
✔ c. is formed from the remains of plants and animals that lived millions of years ago

2. hydrocarbons
a. are made up of oxygen and carbon
✔ b. are made up of hydrogen and carbon
✔ c. make up a large part of petroleum

3. fractional distillation
a. is used to separate hydrocarbon compounds
✔ b. separates compounds by evaporation
c. uses filters to separate compounds

4. fossil fuels
✔ a. are formed from the remains of plants and animals that lived millions of years ago
✔ b. are composed mostly of hydrocarbons
c. are renewable resources

5. natural gas
a. is not a fossil fuel
✔ b. is often found lying above petroleum reservoirs beneath Earth's surface
✔ c. is composed mostly of methane

6. coal
✔ a. is a solid fossil fuel
b. is formed from the remains of animals that lived millions of years ago
✔ c. is formed from the remains of plants that lived millions of years ago

7. conservation
a. is not necessary for nonrenewable resources
✔ b. includes the wise use of natural resources
✔ c. helps to make natural resources last longer

8. nonrenewable resources
✔ a. cannot be replaced once they are used
b. can be replaced once they are used
✔ c. include the fossil fuels

Copyright Glencoe Division of Macmillan/McGraw-Hill.
Users of Merrill Physical Science have the publisher's permission to reproduce this page.   105

bottom of the tower and heated. The chemical compounds in the crude oil, called fractions, boil and evaporate according to their individual boiling points. Those materials with the lowest boiling points rise to the top of the column as vapor and are separated and collected. When each vapor cools below its boiling point, it again turns to a liquid. Hydrocarbons with very high boiling points may remain as liquids and be drained off through the bottom of the tower. Notice the different products made from the petroleum fractions that are shown in Figure 25-1.

Oil must travel from the oil fields to the refineries. Oil can be carried through pipelines, such as the Alaskan pipeline. It can also be carried in ship or truck fuel tankers.

You use petroleum every day for electricity and transportation, but not all the effects of petroleum usage are helpful to you or the environment. You probably know that burning petroleum has serious side effects on the environment. When petroleum is burned in cars and at electric power plants, it gives off smoke as well as carbon monoxide and other chemical compounds. These particles and compounds affect the quality of the air you breathe.

Other Fossil Fuels

Do you cook on a gas stove at home? If so, you burn natural gas to get energy to cook your food. Natural gas, like petroleum, is a fossil fuel. It is often found lying above liquid petroleum reservoirs below Earth's surface; it is extracted with the petroleum.

Natural gas is composed mostly of methane, CH_4, but it also contains smaller amounts of hydrocarbon gases such as propane, C_3H_8, and butane, C_4H_{10}. When natural gas or petroleum is burned, it combines with oxygen, and heat is given off. During this process, carbon dioxide and water are formed as chemical by-products. This is a combustion reaction. Natural gas is burned to provide energy for cooking, heating, and manufacturing.

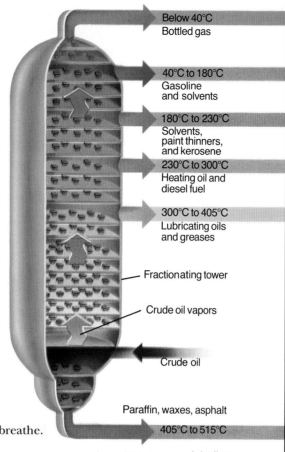

Below 40°C
Bottled gas

40°C to 180°C
Gasoline
and solvents

180°C to 230°C
Solvents,
paint thinners,
and kerosene

230°C to 300°C
Heating oil and
diesel fuel

300°C to 405°C
Lubricating oils
and greases

Fractionating tower

Crude oil vapors

Crude oil

Paraffin, waxes, asphalt
405°C to 515°C

Figure 25-1. Fractional distillation is used to separate the hydrocarbon components in petroleum.

Did You Know?

Energy consumption per household decreased in the United States by more than 25 percent between 1978 and 1987.

2 TEACH

Key Concepts are highlighted.

CONCEPT DEVELOPMENT

▶ Most fossil fuels are easily combustible, so this is a good time to caution your students about some possible dangers. Gasoline should not be used in lanterns or heaters because it is more volatile and flammable than kerosene.

▶ Many of your students may have outdoor grills or camping stoves that use propane gas. Propane is a by-product of both natural gas and petroleum processing. It is also used in transportation, especially in vehicles that run indoors, because it burns much more cleanly than other fossil fuels.

TEACHER F.Y.I.

▶ At times, the U.S. imports over 4 million barrels of oil daily. One barrel contains 42 gallons of oil.

CROSS CURRICULUM

▶ **History:** Investigate the political situation that led to the oil embargo in 1973. Another oil shortage also occurred in the late 1970s. How did these shortages affect consumers and our approach to energy resources?

REVEALING MISCONCEPTIONS

▶ Ask students in your class how many of them have a gas stove. Turn on a gas jet in your room for a few moments and let students smell the characteristic odor. Contrary to popular belief, this odor is not the odor of methane or propane. Natural gas is odorless, colorless, and tasteless. Gas companies add the odorant to the gas for safety reasons so gas leaks can be detected.

PROGRAM RESOURCES

From the **Teacher Resource Package** use:

Transparency Masters, pages 97-98, Petroleum Distillation.

Use **Color Transparency** 50, Petroleum Distillation.

MINI-Lab

Materials: candle, water, aluminum foil, 100-mL beaker, thermometer, ring stand and ring, balance, wire gauze, graduated cylinder

Teaching Tips

► Encourage experimentation in chimney size, shape, and location.
► Students may discover that candle soot on the beaker improves heat capture.

MINI-Lab
ASSESSMENT

Oral: Ask students how the results would differ if the water were heated 30°C in each case.

TECHNOLOGY

To find out more about NGVs, refer to "The Wonder Fuel for the 1990s" by Kenneth R. Sheets, *U.S. News & World Report,* July 31, 1989, pp. 38-39.

Think Critically: refueling problems in areas without natural gas refueling stations; finding automobile mechanics who can work on these fuel systems

---

CHECK FOR UNDERSTANDING

Use the Mini Quiz to check for understanding.

MINI QUIZ

Use the Mini Quiz to check students' recall of chapter content.

1 **Petroleum, natural gas, and coal are all _____.** *fossil fuels*
2 **What is fractional distillation?** *a process used to separate hydrocarbons into usable forms*
3 **_____ is a solid fossil fuel made from the remains of plants.** *Coal*
4 **All fossil fuels are _____ resources.** *nonrenewable*

MINI-Lab

Can efficient use conserve fuel?
Use a candle to increase the temperature of 50 mL of water 10 degrees Celsius. *Measure* the mass of the candle before and after so you know how much was used. Then design a chimney out of aluminum foil that will help transfer the heat of the candle to the water. Repeat the experiment to find out how much fuel you can save while heating the water the same amount.

Connect to...
Earth Science

Geologists classify coal as a biogenic sedimentary rock. What do sedimentary rocks have in common? Also, find out what the term *biogenic* means.

TECHNOLOGY

Gas Instead of Gasoline

One fuel that is an alternative to gasoline is natural gas. Cars, buses, and other vehicles that currently run on gasoline can be modified to use natural gas instead. Natural gas vehicles (NGVs) appear to contribute less than gasoline to the problems of pollution and global warming. That's because NGVs don't release as much carbon monoxide, carbon dioxide, and other pollutants as gasoline releases. It is estimated that 30 000 NGVs are already in use on our nation's highways.

Think Critically: The cost of converting a vehicle that runs on gasoline to an NGV can be offset by fuel cost savings. What other problems might NGV owners encounter?

When natural gas is used properly, it doesn't pollute the environment with the compounds that result from burning petroleum. However, the carbon dioxide that it produces can cause Earth's atmospheric temperature to rise. Natural gas is like petroleum, in that it can be transported long distances by large underground pipelines.

Coal is a solid fossil fuel made from the remains of plants. About one-fourth of the world's supply of coal is in the United States. It is sometimes mined near the surface but is more commonly mined several hundred feet underground. The quality of a coal sample depends on its age and on the type of plant life from which it formed.

When used as a fuel, coal should be cleaned to remove sulfur and other impurities that would be released into the air when the coal is burned. Sulfur compounds can be removed from unburned coal or from the smoke from burning coal to prevent the formation of compounds in the air that cause acid rain. Harmful nitrogen oxides often form when coal is burned at high temperatures. Therefore, it is desirable to find ways to burn coal at lower temperatures.

Because coal is mined from Earth, digging coal mines can disturb the natural environment. Today, laws exist to require that the environment is returned to something close to its original state when a coal mine is closed.

OPTIONS

ASSESSMENT—ORAL

► **How does carbon dioxide given off in the combustion of fossil fuels cause the temperature of Earth to rise?** *It causes the atmosphere to reflect radiation trying to escape Earth. This locks more heat within our atmosphere.*
► **If coal is made of dead plants, why is it considered a nonrenewable resource?** *It takes undisturbed conditions for millions of years to form coal. We are using it in several hundred years.*

PROGRAM RESOURCES

From the **Teacher Resource Package** use:
Activity Worksheets, page 208, MINI-Lab: Can efficient use conserve fuel?
Use **Laboratory Manual 49,** Solar Cells.

Fuel Conservation

Think of how many times you ride in a car, turn on a light, or use an electric appliance. Each time you do one of these things, you probably use some type of fossil fuel as a source of energy. Fossil fuel reserves are decreasing as our population and industrial demands are increasing. At our current rate of consumption, the United States may be out of oil in less than one century. Coal is more plentiful, but like petroleum, it is a nonrenewable resource. All fossil fuels are **nonrenewable resources—** they cannot be replaced after they are used.

We must conserve the nonrenewable energy resources we do have. Conservation can be as simple as turning off a light when you leave a room, avoiding excessive speeds when driving a car, or riding a bike instead of driving a car at all. Using energy-efficient appliances can reduce energy use in your home. Trees around your home can keep it cooler in summer and reduce the use of air conditioning. We need to develop some alternative energy sources to help us conserve now and to prepare for the time when fossil fuels may not be readily available.

Figure 25-2. Find ways to conserve energy at home, such as caulking around windows.

SECTION REVIEW

1. Describe the three main types of fossil fuels.
2. Which type of fossil fuel is the most abundant in the United States? What are the advantages and disadvantages of using this fuel?
3. **Apply:** As the plants and animals living on Earth today die, they will decay and be buried to form the fossils of tomorrow. If the formation of fossil fuels is a continuous cycle, why are they considered to be *nonrenewable* resources?
4. **Connect to Chemistry:** When hydrocarbons, such as gasoline and natural gas, are burned in the presence of oxygen, a combustion reaction takes place. What two products are formed in a combustion reaction?

☑ Comparing and Contrasting

Compare and contrast the different fossil fuels. Include the advantages and disadvantages of using each as a source of energy. If you need help, refer to Comparing and Contrasting in the **Skill Handbook** on page 679.

Skill Builder

Skill
Builder

Students should compare them based on the points discussed in this section.

Skill Builder
ASSESSMENT
Performance: Have students organize the advantages and disadvantages into a table.

Connect to...
Earth Science

Answer: Sedimentary rocks form when sediment accumulates and hardens. *Biogenic* sediments are produced by living organisms.

3 CLOSE

▶ Ask questions 1-2 and the **Apply** and **Connect to Chemistry** questions in the Section Review.

SECTION REVIEW ANSWERS
1. Petroleum is a liquid composed mostly of hydrocarbons. Natural gas is composed mostly of methane. Coal is a solid fossil fuel.
2. Coal has the advantage of being the most abundant fossil fuel and it gives off large amounts of energy. Burning impure coal pollutes the air; mining deforms natural environments; it is a nonrenewable resource.
3. Apply: We use up fossil fuels faster than they are replaced.
4. Connect to Chemistry: water and carbon dioxide

25-2 Nuclear Energy

PREPARATION

SECTION BACKGROUND
▶ Compared to fossil fuels, nuclear energy has only recently been developed as an energy resource. The atom was first split in 1939.

▶ Countries differ widely in their opinion on the use of nuclear energy. France is aiming to eventually produce up to 90 percent of its electricity from nuclear energy, while Sweden and some other nations have decided to decrease or omit reliance on nuclear energy.

PREPLANNING
▶ A number of items are needed for Activity 25-1 on page 653. Begin assembling these materials.

1 MOTIVATE

▶ Write the following question on the chalkboard: "If this community were facing an energy shortage, would you want to have a nuclear power plant supply electricity?" Take a secret vote (to avoid peer pressure) in your class before beginning this section. Ask volunteers to suggest other ways the community can provide energy or reduce consumption or suggest how nuclear waste should be disposed of.

TYING TO PREVIOUS
KNOWLEDGE: In the last chapter students learned that nuclear fission and fusion release huge amounts of energy. In this section, they will study how this energy can be used to generate electricity.

In Your JOURNAL

Encourage students to explain and support their opinions with specific facts.

New Science Words
nuclear reactor
nuclear wastes

Objectives
▶ Outline the operation of a nuclear reactor.
▶ Describe the problems and methods associated with nuclear waste disposal.
▶ Discuss nuclear fusion as a possible energy source.

Nuclear Reactors

In the last chapter you learned that nuclear fission chain reactions give off a great deal of energy. A **nuclear reactor** uses the energy from a controlled nuclear fission chain reaction to generate electricity. Nuclear reactors can vary in design. Most fission reactors have several parts in common, including fuel, control rods, and cooling systems. The actual fission of the radioactive fuel occurs in a relatively small part of the reactor, the core.

Once the core of the reactor contains fuel, uranium oxide, a chain reaction starts from a single uranium atom that spontaneously splits into two parts, releasing two or more neutrons. If two of these neutrons reached U-235 atoms and made them split, releasing two neutrons each, there would now be four neutrons. These four could produce eight, then sixteen. This happens so fast that in one millisecond there could be 1000 neutrons. Each of those would produce 1000 more in the next millisecond, make one thousand thousand (or one million neutrons) in two milliseconds, then one thousand million (one billion) in three milliseconds. The reactor would be out of control.

To control the reaction, rods containing boron or cadmium are used to absorb some of the neutrons. Moving these control rods deeper into the reactor allows them to capture more neutrons and slow down the chain reaction. Eventually only one neutron per fission is able to react with a U-235 atom to produce another fission, and energy is released at a constant rate.

The nuclear fission reaction inside the core generates tremendous amounts of thermal energy. The core is surrounded by water that cools it. The water also carries

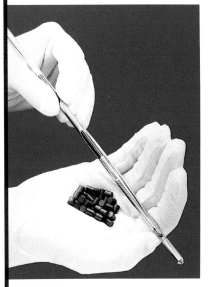
Figure 25-3. Uranium oxide pellets are used to fuel nuclear reactors.

OPTIONS

Meeting Different Ability Levels
For Section 25-2, use the following **Teacher Resource Masters** depending upon individual students' needs.

◆ **Study Guide Master** for all students.

● **Reinforcement Master** for students of average and above average ability levels.

▲ **Enrichment Master** for above average students.

Additional Teacher Resource Package masters are listed in any **PROGRAM RESOURCES** boxes that are in the section. The additional masters are appropriate for all students.

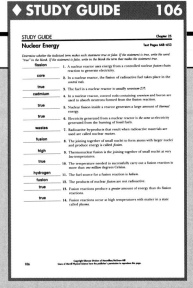

thermal energy away from the core. The heated water is pumped through a heat exchanger, where the thermal energy released boils a separate system of water to produce steam. The core and cooling system are surrounded by a barrier of thick concrete. The entire building is also built with steel-lined concrete to prevent the escape of radiation from the reactor.

Nuclear Generation of Electricity

Nuclear fission reactors currently supply over 20 percent of our nation's electricity. One advantage of using nuclear energy is that it's less harmful to the environment than the use of fossil fuels. The fission process produces no air pollution, whereas the burning of coal and petroleum creates nearly 20 000 metric tons of pollutants each day. Nuclear fission doesn't produce carbon dioxide that will escape into the atmosphere and contribute to the problem of global warming. On the other hand, the mining of uranium and extraction of U-235 does cause environmental damage.

Using nuclear fission to generate electricity also has other disadvantages. The water that circulates around the core of the reactor must cool before it goes back into streams and rivers. If it is released into those waterways while still warm, the excess heat could harm fish and other plants and animals in the water. The most serious risk of nuclear fission is the escape of harmful radiation from the power plant. Nuclear reactors have elaborate systems of safeguards to ensure that this doesn't happen. Strict safety precautions and highly trained workers can prevent most accidents.

After the chain reaction has occurred, however, the fuel rods contain fission products that are highly radioactive. These products must be contained in heavily shielded surroundings while they decay

Figure 25-4. Many safeguards are taken to prevent accidents in nuclear fission reactors.

How much of our nation's energy is supplied by fission reactors?

In your Journal, write one paragraph describing the advantages and another describing the disadvantages of generating electricity using nuclear power. Explain your opinions about whether the United States should pursue developing more nuclear power plants.

649

CONCEPT DEVELOPMENT

▶Students may be familiar with nuclear accidents that have occurred, especially at the Three Mile Island plant in 1979 in Pennsylvania and the Russian Chernobyl accident in 1986. The background of these should be discussed.

In the Three Mile Island plant, a hydrogen bubble developed above the core and was in danger of exploding. Workers accidentally turned off several safeguards against a meltdown, so the building was flooded with water to avoid a total meltdown and the bubble was slowly released into the atmosphere. The containment building was sealed off, but steam carried low-level radiation into the environment. The long-term effects of this accident are still being studied.

The Chernobyl accident was much more severe. The water coolant was lost and the core melted. The graphite moderators burned, allowing clouds of radioactive smoke to escape into the atmosphere. More than 30 people had died after a few months and many more suffer long-term effects. Most U.S. reactors use water as a moderator.

TEACHER F.Y.I.

▶Some sources estimate that accessible uranium reserves will last around 100 years. The fissionable U-235 isotope makes up less than one percent of uranium ore. Uranium must be enriched so that fuel pellets contain about three percent U-235 to sustain a chain reaction.

▶ To convey the idea of how mass-efficient nuclear energy is, tell students that in an average person's lifetime, over 1.5 million kilograms of coal versus 2.5 uranium fuel pellets will be needed to supply the person's energy needs.

▶ In addition to being an important scientific issue, the use of nuclear energy is a subject of political debate because it affects public safety.

▶ Have interested students compose a clearly written formal letter to the congressional representatives of their choice giving informed views on the use of nuclear energy. Students should consider not only the problems of nuclear energy use, but also the problems of burning fossil fuels to generate energy and the decreased standard of living that would result from energy shortage. You might provide them with a list of names and addresses of senators and representatives.

Answer: The location must have an extensive, stable rock structure that would protect the wastes from forces of erosion and earthquakes and other forms of earth movement.

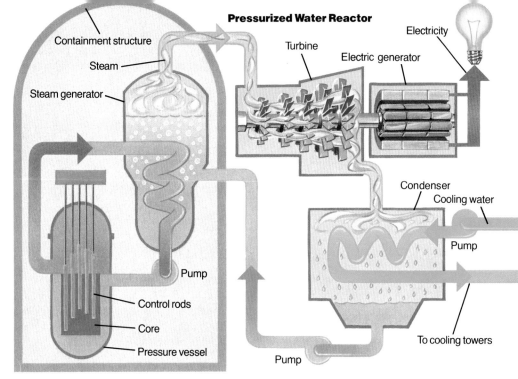

Pressurized Water Reactor

Figure 25-5. The coolant water and the water used to produce the steam that turns the turbines are not the same in a water-cooled nuclear power plant.

In 1987, Congress voted to build the first national permanent nuclear repository site at Yucca Mountain, Nevada. Burial of waste is scheduled to start in 2003, although the plan has changed several times. Find out what kind of geological features this location has that make it suitable for a nuclear repository.

so no radiation will escape into the environment. Because these fission products have long half-lives, they must be stored in containers that will last the duration of the period of radioactive decay, which can be as long as tens of thousands of years.

Another problem is the disposal of the reactor itself when it no longer runs as it should. Every nuclear reactor has a limited useful life span of a few decades. After that time, the reactor's efficiency is severely reduced by the presence of large amounts of fission products that can't be cleaned up. The reactor is then shut down or "decommissioned."

Nuclear Waste Disposal

Has your watch ever run down because the battery was too old? The battery wasn't able to produce enough energy to allow your watch to keep correct time. Once you replaced the battery, your watch worked. A similar thing happens to the fuel source in a nuclear reactor. After about three years, there is not enough fissionable U-235 left in the fuel pellets to sustain the chain reaction. These

650 ENERGY SOURCES

OPTIONS

INQUIRY QUESTIONS

▶ **Why is decommissioning a nuclear reactor not an easy task?** *Many parts of the reactor are contaminated with low-level radioactive waste and must be cared for as nuclear waste.*

▶ **If spent fuel contains reduced amounts of fissionable U-235, why must it be treated as radioactive waste?** *It contains radioactive fission products, as well as remaining uranium.*

PROGRAM RESOURCES

From the **Teacher Resource Package** use:

Critical Thinking/Problem Solving, page 31, Zimmer Power Plant Conversion.

Transparency Masters, pages 99-100, Nuclear Power Plant.

Use **Color Transparency** 49, Nuclear Power Plants.

③ used fuel pellets are called "spent" fuel. The spent fuel contains the radioactive fission products in addition to the remaining uranium. This is an example of nuclear waste. **Nuclear wastes** are radioactive by-products that result when radioactive materials are used. They are usually classified as high-level and low-level wastes for disposal.

Radiation is around you all the time. Low-level nuclear waste usually contains a small amount of radioactive material diluted by a large amount of nonradioactive material. Products of some medical and industrial processes are low-level wastes. They may include items such as protective gloves that are used in handling radioactive materials. These low-level wastes are usually buried in sealed containers in locations licensed by the federal government. When dilute enough, they are sometimes released into the air or water.

High-level nuclear waste is generated in nuclear power plants and by defense research. After spent fuel is removed from a reactor, it is stored in a deep, heavily insulated pool of water. Many of the radioactive materials in high-level nuclear waste have short half-lives. Almost half of the radiation will have been emitted in several months. But the spent fuel also contains materials that will continue to decay for thousands of years. For this reason, the waste must be disposed of in extremely durable and stable containers.

Fusion Power

Imagine the amount of energy the sun must give off to heat Earth 93 million miles away. In Chapter 24, thermonuclear fusion was explained as the process that releases this energy. Recall that thermonuclear fusion is the joining together of small nuclei at high temperatures. Fusing the nuclei in one gram of heavy hydrogen gives off about the same amount of energy as burning more than eight million grams of coal. If we could make thermonuclear fusion happen in a laboratory, we would likely have the answer to Earth's energy problems.

Figure 25-7. Two nuclei fuse to form a larger nucleus in this experimental fusion reactor.

Figure 25-6. A solid capsule of nuclear waste can be made by mixing the wastes with molten glass. These capsules are buried in sealed containers.

Science and READING

The technology to turn sunlight into usable energy is inefficient and expensive at the present time.

3 CLOSE

▶ Ask questions 1-3 and the **Apply** and **Connect to Chemistry** questions in the Section Review.

▶ Emphasize the difference between science and technology. Knowing how to split an atom is not harmful, but humans can choose to create harmful devices with it.

▶ Have students write a short essay commenting on the following quote by Albert Einstein. "The discovery of the nuclear chain reaction need not bring about the destruction of mankind any more than did the discovery of matches."

SECTION REVIEW ANSWERS

1. Control rods inserted among the fuel rods and circulating water absorb excess neutrons.

2. Both processes are used to produce steam, which is used to generate electricity.

3. It is difficult to maintain the high temperatures required for nuclear fusion. At these temperatures, materials cannot be used to contain the fusion.

4. Apply: It should initially be allowed to cool and decay in water. Then it should be sealed in an insulated container and buried deep in the ground in a repository.

5. Connect to Chemistry: The atomic mass is 238.0289 indicating U-235 is an uncommon isotope.

Skill Builder
ASSESSMENT

Performance: Have students complete the concept map beyond where smaller nuclei and free neutrons are shown.

Science and READING

The energy that reaches us from the sun is 50 000 times as much as the whole world uses. In light of this fact, why do you think we continually have energy shortages?

What is the source of energy for nuclear fusion?

The challenge lies in creating and containing nuclear fusion. The temperature needed to carry out a nuclear fusion reaction is over one million degrees Celsius. The plasma containing the hydrogen nuclei can't be contained by any material at this temperature. However, it can be contained for a short time in a "magnetic bottle" that uses a magnetic field to keep the particles in a small volume. At the present time, the energy required to maintain the high temperatures needed for the fusion reaction is greater than the energy output from the fusion of the nuclei.

Let's examine the benefits of nuclear fusion as a source of energy. Hydrogen nuclei are the source of energy for nuclear fusion. Hydrogen is the most abundant element in the universe. Unlike those in nuclear fission, the products of nuclear fusion are not radioactive. Helium is the main product of hydrogen fusion. Someday nuclear fusion may provide a permanent and economical way to generate electricity.

SECTION REVIEW

1. How is the rate of fission in a nuclear reactor controlled?
2. What do the nuclear generation of electricity and the burning of fossil fuels to generate electricity have in common?
3. Explain the major obstacles in controlling nuclear fusion.
4. **Apply:** Suppose that in a research project, you have generated a 10-gram sample of nuclear waste. Some of the materials have a fast half-life and some will decay for thousands of years. How would you classify it and how will it likely be disposed of?
5. **Connect to Chemistry:** Look up the atomic mass of uranium on the periodic table on page 258. Explain why this value differs from the mass of U-235, which is used as a fuel in nuclear reactors.

Skill Builder

☑ Concept Mapping

Design an events chain concept map for the generation of electricity in a nuclear fission reactor. Begin with the bombarding neutron and end with electricity in overhead lines. If you need help, refer to Concept Mapping in the **Skill Handbook** on pages 684 and 685.

Skill Builder

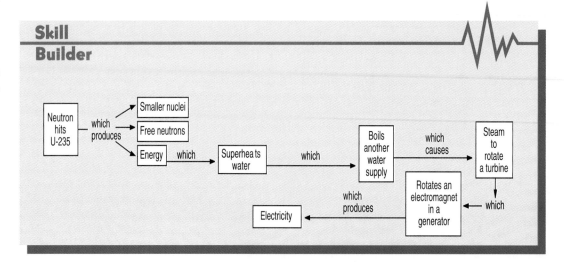

25-1 Nuclear Waste Disposal

Because many radioactive wastes will continue to decay for hundreds of years, it is important to test containment procedures that will prevent leakage into the environment. What kinds of materials do you think could effectively hold radioactive wastes while they decay? In this activity, you will model this process by determining how a pellet of sodium hydroxide can be contained most effectively.

Materials

- sodium hydroxide pellets (4)
- 100-mL beakers (4)
- phenolphthalein solution
- plastic food wrap
- aluminum foil
- rubber bands (3)
- twist ties (2)
- modeling clay
- forceps
- goggles

Procedure

1. Copy the data table.
2. Let the sodium hydroxide pellets represent pellets of nuclear waste. Your job is to *test* materials that may be able to keep unwanted chemicals from leaking into the environment. **CAUTION:** *Do not touch the sodium hydroxide pellets or solution with your hands. Always wear goggles when handling sodium hydroxide. Wipe up all spills.*
3. Fill all four beakers with water and add 3 or 4 drops of phenolphthalein to each.
4. Using the forceps, place one pellet in one of the beakers. *Record* your observations.
5. Wrap each of the remaining pellets; one in aluminum foil, one in plastic wrap, and one in clay. Secure the plastic with twist ties.
6. Drop the wrapped pellets into the remaining three beakers and cover them with food wrap.
7. *Make observations* each day for three days to determine if there is leakage from the containers. *Record* your observations in the data table.
8. After the last observations, pour the solutions into a container provided by your teacher.

Data and Observations   Sample Data

Beaker Containing Pellets	Observations		
	Day 1	Day 2	Day 3
Unwrapped	Red color	indicates	leakage
Wrapped in aluminum foil	Leakage	Leakage	Leakage
Wrapped in plastic wrap	No leakage	Leakage	Leakage
Embedded in clay	No leakage	No leakage	No leakage

Analyze

1. Was red color seen in any of the beakers after the first day?
2. After three days, which, if any, of the beakers show no red color?

Conclude and Apply

3. What kind of wrapping appears to be the most leakproof?
4. Why do you think storing and disposing nuclear wastes is a major concern of society?

ANSWERS TO QUESTIONS

1. All of the beakers containing aluminum samples will corrode, leak, and turn red. Some of the plastic containers may show leakage and turn red.
2. Clay, if properly applied, will continue to contain the chemical and the solution will remain clear.
3. the clay
4. Nuclear generation of electricity is a reliable energy source if plant safety can be maintained and a secure method of disposal can be found. Some nuclear waste will be radioactive for thousands of years.

Activity
ASSESSMENT

Oral: Have students discuss how this model fails to reflect some of the problems associated with nuclear waste disposal.

OBJECTIVE: Simulate the problems of nuclear waste disposal.

PROCESS SKILLS applied in this activity:
▶ **Observe** in Procedure Steps 5 and 8.
▶ **Record Data** in Procedure Steps 5 and 8.

COOPERATIVE LEARNING
Form Science Investigation Teams of three to six students. Have only one person on each team manipulate the pellets.

TEACHING THE ACTIVITY

Troubleshooting: When sealing the pellet in clay, start with a patty of clay about 0.5 cm thick, pull the clay up around the pellet, seal very well, and roll the material *gently* into a smooth ball.

▶ **CAUTION:** *This activity would work well as a demonstration. Sodium hydroxide is very caustic. It must not come in contact with skin or other tissues. Do not attempt this activity with students unless you emphasize safety at every step. Eye safety is essential and goggles must be worn. Make eye wash equipment available. Keep track of every pellet. Sodium hydroxide can absorb water from the air until it becomes a puddle of caustic solution. Wipe up all spills. Skin will feel slippery if contaminated. Have students wash their hands if they come in contact with the pellets and before they leave the lab.*

▶ The need for following strict handling precautions helps make the point of the activity.

▶ Discuss the idea that each pellet represents a pellet of radioactive waste and that good containment must resist contamination of the environment.

▶ Provide small squares (5 cm × 5 cm) of aluminum foil and plastic. Provide enough modeling clay to enclose a pellet.

▶ Before disposing of solutions, neutralize them by adding just enough dilute hydrochloric acid to make the red color disappear.

PREPARATION

SECTION BACKGROUND
▶ Natural uranium is only 0.7 percent fissionable U-235. Breeder reactors can multiply the amount of fissionable fuel available.

1 MOTIVATE

▶ Table tennis balls and spring mousetraps can be used to demonstrate breeder reactors. Imagine that among the "fissionable" mousetraps there are mixed in several that were almost set, but needed the spring compressed only one more millimeter. Now suppose a way could be found to harness a portion of the energy of the snapping traps to complete arming of these other traps. This is comparable to what takes place in a breeder reactor.

2 TEACH

Key Concepts are highlighted.

CONCEPT DEVELOPMENT
▶ Share this idea with your students. Imagine that by using lights in your home you could actually send out more electricity than you started with. Of course this is not possible, but it may help students understand the advantage of a breeder reactor.

CROSS CURRICULUM
▶ **History:** Research the Manhattan Project, which led to the making of the nuclear bombs.

 **25-3 Breeder Reactors**

New Science Words
breeder reactor

Objectives
▶ Distinguish breeder reactors and normal nuclear fission reactors.
▶ Assess the advantages and disadvantages of operating breeder reactors.

Are Breeder Reactors a Good Idea?

You read about using nuclear fission as a way of generating electricity in the last section. Do you remember the isotope that is commonly used as a fuel source in a fission reactor? The fuel rods are made of a small amount of U-235 in a larger sample of unfissionable U-238. The fissionable U-235 isotope is not plentiful in nature. It is a nonrenewable resource that may be depleted in less than 100 years. If nuclear energy is to be a long-lasting energy source, other nuclear fuels must be developed.

A **breeder reactor** is a nuclear reactor that produces, or "breeds," new fuel as it operates. In a breeder reactor, some of the neutrons produced by the fission of U-235 are absorbed by the U-238 nuclei while other neutrons cause fission of U-235. This requires that more neutrons be captured in the fuel rods, and it leads to difficulties in the reactor design. The new U-239 nuclei decay in several days to form Pu-239, as illustrated in the picture equation shown below.

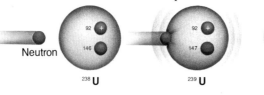 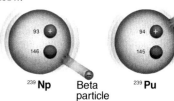

Neutron ^{238}U ^{239}U ^{239}Np   Beta particle ^{239}Pu

This isotope of plutonium is fissionable. Thus, a large supply of new Pu-239 fuel can be produced from the otherwise useless U-238 nuclei. As a result, more fuel is present after fission has occurred in the reactor than

---

OPTIONS

Meeting Different Ability Levels
For Section 25-3, use the following **Teacher Resource Masters** depending upon individual students' needs.
◆ **Study Guide Master** for all students.
● **Reinforcement Master** for students of average and above average ability levels.
▲ **Enrichment Master** for above average students.
Additional Teacher Resource Package masters are listed in any **PROGRAM RESOURCES** boxes that are in the section. The additional masters are appropriate for all students.

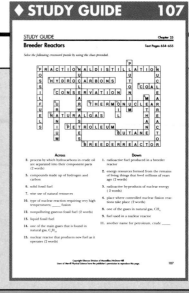

was present before the fission occurred. After operating for several years, a breeder reactor can produce twice as much fissionable fuel as it started with.

Breeder reactors have obvious efficiency advantages. The Pu-239 can be chemically separated from the remaining uranium and used in another reactor. Breeder reactors can prolong the life of nuclear energy as an energy resource, decreasing our burning of fossil fuels.

Breeder reactors can cause several hazards for society. As with nuclear fission reactors, safe radioactive waste disposal is still a problem. There is a risk of releasing low-level radioactive materials into the air and water. The plutonium fuel produced in a breeder reactor has a half-life of 24 000 years. Elemental plutonium is toxic in addition to being radioactive, and significant exposure can cause damage to the nervous system and death.

Connect to... Chemistry

Locate the element plutonium on the periodic table. Explain why plutonium cannot be mined as a natural resource in the same way uranium can.

SECTION REVIEW

1. How does a breeder reactor differ from the conventional type of nuclear fission reactor?
2. List the advantages and disadvantages of using breeder reactors.
3. **Connect to Life Science:** Explain why the Pu-239 produced in breeder reactors should be handled with exceptional care. How does it affect human health?

You Decide!

Breeder reactors produce Pu-239. This is an important component of nuclear fission weapons. How do you think breeder reactors should be regulated? Explain your point of view.

SCIENCE & SOCIETY

655

CHECK FOR UNDERSTANDING

Ask questions 1-2 and the **Connect to Life Science** question in the Section Review.

RETEACH

Place 99 colored marbles in a jar to represent U-238 and one marble of a different color to represent fissionable U-235. Explain that breeder reactors can turn the other U-238 atoms into fissionable plutonium.

EXTENSION

For students who have mastered this section, use the **Reinforcement** and **Enrichment** masters or other OPTIONS provided.

Connect to... Chemistry

Answer: Elements with atomic numbers greater than 92 are synthetically made.

3 CLOSE

▶ Use the You Decide question to facilitate discussion of the advantages and disadvantages of breeder reactors.

SECTION REVIEW ANSWERS

1. A breeder reactor produces more fissionable material as it operates; a conventional fission reactor does not.
2. They produce plutonium-239, which is toxic, has a very long half-life, and can be used to make nuclear weapons. They produce usable fuel as they operate.
3. Connect to Life Science: Plutonium-239 is radioactive and toxic.

YOU DECIDE!

You may want to guide students to discuss the depletion of uranium by ordinary reactors as well as the safety and security problems with breeder reactors.

25-4 Alternative Energy Sources

PREPARATION

SECTION BACKGROUND

▶During the Arab Oil Embargo of 1973, President Nixon declared that the U.S. would meet its own energy needs by the end of the decade. His program was called Project Independence. Years later, we still rely on imported energy to meet much of our energy needs.

▶Biomass is waste material that can be burned to produce steam. In Hawaii, the sugar industry produces a lot of bagasse, dry fiber similar to wood. Over one-third of the energy needed on two Hawaiian islands is supplied by this biomass.

▶Solar energy actually originates in thermonuclear fusion of hydrogen to helium in the sun. It travels to Earth as electromagnetic radiation.

PREPLANNING

▶Gather materials needed for Activity 25-2. The earlier students begin to prepare for this activity, the better.

1 MOTIVATE

▶Have the following items displayed on a table: a toy windmill or pinwheel, a beaker of water, a pan of wood scraps or other organic waste, and a photovoltaic cell. Have students tell how each of the items could be used to do work. Mention that these are small-scale versions of the energy sources discussed in this chapter.

TYING TO PREVIOUS KNOWLEDGE:
Mention that students have learned about fossil fuels and nuclear fission, which supply the majority of our energy requirements. But those are nonrenewable resources and they will run out.

25-4 Alternative Energy Sources

New Science Words

photovoltaic cell
hydroelectricity
tidal energy
geothermal energy

Objectives

▶ Analyze the need for alternative energy sources.
▶ Discuss the methods of generating electricity with several energy sources.
▶ Describe the advantages and disadvantages of several alternative energy sources.

The Need for Alternatives

Can you name any sources of energy other than fossil fuels and nuclear energy? Although we have enough of these energy sources to fill our energy demands today, there is a great need to develop alternative sources of energy for the future. As you have already discovered, using fossil fuels and nuclear fission for our energy needs has many disadvantages.

Nuclear fission and the burning of fossil fuels are both processes used to boil water to produce steam. Other materials can be burned to give off energy as well. Biomass is renewable organic matter, such as wood, sugar cane fibers, rice hulls, and animal manure. It can be burned in the presence of oxygen to convert the stored chemical energy to thermal energy. Biomass burning is probably the oldest use of natural resources for human needs.

Have you ever seen gasohol advertised at a gas station? How does this fuel differ from normal gasoline? Corn and other plant fibers can be fermented to convert the sugar and starch in the grain to ethanol. The ethanol is combined with gasoline to produce gasohol for use in your car engine.

Biomass and gasohol are just two examples of many energy alternatives that reduce our consumption of nonrenewable fuels. The energy alternatives discussed in this section make use of processes that occur naturally on Earth. What natural processes do you see around you that could be used to generate electricity or provide heat?

EcoTip
Make sure the tires on your family car are properly inflated. This will increase gas mileage and help to conserve gasoline.

Connect to...
Chemistry
The ethanol used in gasohol has the chemical formula C_2H_5OH.

$$H - \underset{\underset{H}{|}}{\overset{\overset{H}{|}}{C}} - \underset{\underset{H}{|}}{\overset{\overset{H}{|}}{C}} - OH$$

Determine the molecular mass of this compound.

OPTIONS

Meeting Different Ability Levels

For Section 25-4, use the following **Teacher Resource Masters** depending upon individual students' needs.

◆ **Study Guide Master** for all students.
● **Reinforcement Master** for students of average and above average ability levels.
▲ **Enrichment Master** for above average students.

Additional Teacher Resource Package masters are listed in any **PROGRAM RESOURCES** boxes that are in the section. The additional masters are appropriate for all students.

◆ **STUDY GUIDE** 108

STUDY GUIDE   Chapter 25
Alternative Energy Sources   Text Pages 656–662

Solve the puzzle below by writing the words in the diagram that fit the descriptions given. You will find another word spelled vertically in the black box.

```
1.              T I D A L  E N E R G Y
2.        G A S O H O L
3.                  E T H A N O L
4.          N U C L E A R  E N E R G Y
5.      G E O T H E R M A L  E N E R G Y
6.              W I N D
7.              S O L A R  E N E R G Y
8.  H Y D R O E L E C T R I C I T Y
9.                W I N D M I L L
10.        P H O T O V O L T A I C
11.              I C E L A N D
12.      B I O M A S S
```

1. energy produced from the movement of ocean waters (2 words)
2. fuel made from petroleum and alcohol
3. type of alcohol used in gasohol
4. energy produced from radioactive materials (2 words)
5. energy produced from thermal energy deep inside Earth (2 words)
6. moving air
7. energy from the sun (2 words)
8. electricity produced by harnessing the kinetic energy in moving water
9. device that produces electricity from moving air
10. device that converts solar energy into electricity; ____ cell
11. country where all power plants use geothermal energy
12. type of fuel produced from renewable organic materials

108

Solar Energy

The sun is Earth's only source of new energy. Have you ever seen an automobile powered by sunlight? The solar panels on the car collect and use solar energy to power the car. Methods of collecting and using solar energy are usually divided into two categories, passive and active solar energy.

Passive solar heating is the direct use of the sun's energy in maintaining comfortable indoor temperatures. Passive solar heating was used centuries ago by the Romans to heat their bath houses. Efforts in energy conservation have renewed interest in this method of heating. Buildings constructed with strategically placed windows can be heated by the sun. On warm days, these windows can be covered with blinds to prevent excessive heating.

In active solar heating, solar panels collect and store solar energy. Solar panels are made of large, darkly colored trays covered with transparent glass or plastic. Large mirrors are sometimes used to focus the sun's radiation into these solar collectors. The panels absorb the sun's energy and use it to heat water. The heated water can be used directly, or it can be stored to give off thermal energy. Solar energy can even be used to drive electric power generators in solar thermal power plants.

A device used to convert solar energy into electricity is the **photovoltaic cell,** also called the solar cell. Do you own a solar-powered calculator? It contains a solar cell. Photovoltaic cells are made of a semiconductor lined on both surfaces with a conducting metal. As light strikes the surface of the cell, electrons flow between the two metal layers, creating a current. Many cells connected in a circuit can provide significant amounts of electricity. In order to be a useful technology, photovoltaic cells must be capable of producing in their lifetime more energy than is used in producing the cells. The cells must also be economical and practical to manufacture.

What is passive solar heating?

Figure 25-8. Solar cells can be used to supply the electricity to operate an automobile.

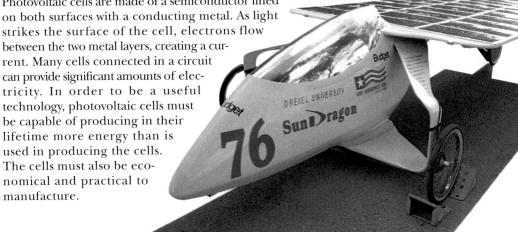

657

2 TEACH

Key Concepts are highlighted.

CONCEPT DEVELOPMENT
▶ Some students may have solar-powered calculators. Show students what a photovoltaic cell looks like. Emphasize that they are made of doped silicon semiconductors.

▶ Discuss the fact that solar energy is actually responsible for the existence of other energy resources. Wood, fossil fuels, wind, and the water cycle are all examples of stored solar energy.

CROSS CURRICULUM
▶ **Engineering:** Have students build small solar water heaters. Students should analyze and compare various designs and build several types of models to test them for effectiveness. Have them time how long it takes each model to heat a constant amount of water on the same day, so weather conditions are equal.

▶ A great many books on homemade solar heaters were published in the 1970s and 1980s. Most libraries have several.

V i d e o D i s c
STVS: Wind Power, Disc 2, Side 2

Connect to...
Chemistry

2 C atoms: 2 × 12.0110 = 24.0220
1 O atom: = 15.9994
6 H atoms: 6 × 1.00794 = 6.04764
                         46.06904

► Water wheels probably first provided mechanical energy around 200 B.C. They have been used to turn levers and run machines, such as sawmills and grain grinders. Falling water was first harnessed for the purpose of providing electricity at Niagara Falls in 1879.

CONCEPT DEVELOPMENT

► U.S. electric utility companies have also devised ways of storing hydropower to meet times of emergency or peak demand. An upper and lower reservoir are constructed near a power plant. When extra electricity is needed, water is allowed to flow from the upper to the lower reservoir. During off-peak times, electricity is used to pump water back to the upper reservoir.

► Water is a free and renewable resource. Ask your students why hydroelectricity does not supply more of our energy needs. Point out that most sites suitable for developing hydroelectric power are already in use. Many locations do not have the required water resources. Also, hydroelectric plants cannot be built in many locations because they disrupt the natural ecosystem.

► One of the biggest drawbacks to wind energy is the fact that the wind doesn't always blow. Energy from the wind is stored in several ways. Large banks of batteries are used to store electrical energy until it is needed. Sometimes, windmills can be connected into electric power lines to sell extra electricity to utility companies. In times of no wind, electricity is returned by the company.

This method of producing electricity is more expensive on a large scale than the use of nonrenewable fuels, but it can be less expensive in isolated areas, when the cost of building transmission lines to those areas is considered. Solar energy is a pollution-free resource that is becoming more economical as our solar technology develops.

Hydroelectricity

One way to produce electricity is with water. Water flowing in rivers carries tremendous amounts of kinetic and potential energy. Dams are built to store vast amounts of

water. Behind a dam, the water is very deep. Near the base of a hydroelectric dam, water is allowed to rush out through tunnels. The rushing water spins a turbine, rotating the shaft of an electric generator to produce electricity.

Hydroelectricity is electricity produced by the energy of moving water. Hydroelectric power plants are a very efficient way to produce electricity. They produce almost no pollution. The bodies of water held back by dams can provide lakes for recreational uses and irrigation. The ongoing natural water cycle makes hydroelectric power a permanent resource. After the initial cost of building a dam and power plant, the electricity is relatively cheap. However, artificial dams can disturb the balance of natural ecosystems.

Tidal Energy

The gravitational forces of the moon and the sun cause bulges in Earth's oceans. As Earth rotates, the two bulges of ocean water move westward. Each day the level of the ocean on a coast rises and falls continually. A kind of hydroelectric power can be generated by these ocean tides. The moving water can be trapped at high tide by building a dam at the opening of a river or bay. The flowing water at low tide spins a turbine, which operates an electric generator. Energy generated by tidal motion is called **tidal energy.**

658 ENERGY SOURCES

OPTIONS

ENRICHMENT

► Research the possible ecological hazards of building tidal power facilities. Some shallow-water organisms depend on unrestricted cycles of tides to bring food and remove waste.

► Have interested students research wave power, a form of hydroelectric power which uses the kinetic energy of waves and converts it to electricity.

PROGRAM RESOURCES

From the **Teacher Resource Package** use:
Science and Society, page 29, Hydroelectric Power: Past or Future?
Science Integration Activity 25
Use **Laboratory Manual 50,** Using the Sun's Energy.

Like producing hydroelectric power, generating electricity from tidal motion is nearly pollution-free. But, there are only a few places on Earth where the difference between high and low tide is large enough to be an efficient source of energy. In the United States, the use of tidal energy is being explored in the Cook Inlet in Alaska and Passamaquoddy Bay in Maine. The only functioning tidal power station in North America is at Annapolis Royal, Nova Scotia. The ocean environment will possibly make construction and maintenance of these plants difficult. Tidal energy probably will be a limited, but useful, source of energy in the future.

Wind Energy

You may have seen a windmill on a farm. Or, in a windy region, you may have seen several hundred windmills. A windmill is a turbine that is turned by the wind instead of steam or water. The windmill spins and rotates an electric generator to produce electricity.

Only a few places on Earth consistently have enough wind to rely on wind power to meet energy needs. Improved design of wind generators can increase their efficiency, so new methods of using the wind's energy are being researched. Wind generators do not actually use up any resources. They do not pollute the atmosphere or water. However, they do change the appearance of a landscape.

25-4 ALTERNATIVE ENERGY SOURCES **659**

INQUIRY QUESTIONS

▶ **Why must most windmills be facing the wind to function?** *The blades are at angles and have a slight dent in them. They must catch the wind from the top of the blades for the windmill to turn.*

TEACHER F.Y.I.

▶ There are two general types of wind machines: horizontal and vertical. Horizontal wind machines are by far the most common, and the blades must generally be facing into the wind to be effective. Vertical wind machines are relatively new. They look like giant eggbeaters, and they catch the wind from any direction.

MULTICULTURAL PERSPECTIVE

The Cost Of Electricity

What would life be like without electric lights, television, radios, or video games? Would you choose to live without them? There is a group of people in several states in the United States who have chosen to do so—the Amish. They approach what we consider modern necessities based on very strongly held beliefs about the value of family, church, and community. To their way of thinking it isn't really all that inconvenient to sacrifice chances to work together as neighbors. Machines that make it possible for one person to do a job that would otherwise take several people change the ways families and communities relate to each other. The same is true of entertainment technologies, such as television and radio, that take the place of doing things together as families or promote values to which they object. So, the Amish are very careful about what new technology they allow into their lives. For example, they don't allow individual ownership of cars because they believe cars can be destructive to the family, church, and community. Car owners are away from home too much, and cars make communities more scattered and less cohesive. However, they do allow use of public transportation, and they also make use of battery-powered lights for their buggies. These are not contradictory positions, but a reflection of their strong stance to protect and preserve their families. The basic question they ask about any change is "What is the true cost to us to use this?" If the potential cost to the family is too high, they would rather do without it.

660 CHAPTER 25

CHECK FOR UNDERSTANDING

Use the Mini Quiz to check for understanding.

MINI QUIZ

Use the Mini Quiz to check students' recall of chapter content.

1 A device that is used to convert solar energy into electricity is called a(n) _____ . *photovoltaic cell*

2 Renewable organic matter that can be used as an energy resource is called _____ . *biomass*

3 How do windmills produce electricity? *They spin and rotate an electric generator.*

4 Where does geothermal energy come from? *the hot gases and molten rock beneath the surface of Earth*

RETEACH

Ask students to list the six energy sources discussed in this section. These are biomass, solar, hydroelectricity, tidal, wind, and geothermal. Once you have established that students have a complete list, ask them to write a sentence for each source, describing how we can obtain usable energy.

EXTENSION

For students who have mastered this section, use the **Reinforcement** and **Enrichment** masters or other OPTIONS provided.

In Your JOURNAL

Accept all supported, well-thought-out answers.

Where is most of Earth's geothermal energy found?

In Your JOURNAL

Review the energy alternatives presented in this section. **In your Journal,** describe which ones you think might be useful in your area. Support your ideas with specific facts about these sources of energy.

Figure 25-9. Geothermal power plants, such as the one below, supply Iceland with most of its energy.

Geothermal Energy

Look down at the ground. What do you see and feel underneath your feet? Although you may think of the Earth as a solid sphere, hot gases and molten rock lie far beneath the surface. The inner parts of Earth contain a great deal of thermal energy, called **geothermal energy.** You do not usually notice this energy because most of it is far below Earth's crust.

In some places, Earth's crust has cracks or thin spots in it. These areas allow some of the geothermal energy to rise up near the surface of Earth. Active volcanoes permit hot gases and molten lava from deep within Earth to escape. Perhaps you have seen a geyser shoot steam and hot water from Earth. Have you ever visited or seen pictures of the famous geyser, Old Faithful, in Yellowstone National Park? This water was heated by geothermal energy. Wells can be drilled deep within Earth to pump out this hot water that ranges in temperature from 150°C to 350°C. The steam can be used to rotate turbines and turn electric generators. Use of geothermal energy can release some sulfur compounds from gases within Earth. This pollution can be controlled by pumping the water and steam back into Earth.

As with wind and tidal energy, there are only certain places on Earth where geothermal energy is accessible as an economical energy resource. For example, in Iceland, many power plants are run by geothermal energy.

What similarities can you identify between all of the alternative energy sources discussed in this chapter? Which ones do you think would be the most useful in your area?

OPTIONS

ENRICHMENT

▶Have students locate on a United States map the areas that use nuclear, tidal, solar, wind, hydroelectric, geothermal, and fossil fuels as sources of energy.

PROGRAM RESOURCES

From the **Teacher Resource Package** use:
Concept Mapping, page 55-60.
Cross-Curricular Connections, page 31, Decision Making: Voting on Scientific Issues.

 # PROBLEM SOLVING

Renewable Energy Sources for Beachtown

Rosa and her family live on the coast in Beachtown. Rosa enjoys the recreation opportunities offered by living on an ocean coast. During the hot, sunny summer, Rosa enjoys cool swims in the ocean and the strong breezes blowing on the beach. She also enjoys fishing at an inlet close to her house.

Like Rosa, many other people think Beachtown is a great place to live and are moving there. Lots of new businesses are being built all over town. The mayor and city council are concerned because the growth of the city is exceeding the production capability of the old fossil-fueled power plant.

Think Critically: What alternative energy sources could the power company consider when planning to increase its output? How do these renewable resources compare with using fossil fuels for energy?

SECTION REVIEW

1. Why is there a need for developing and using alternative energy sources?
2. Describe three main ways to use direct solar energy.
3. Identify some advantages and limitations of using hydroelectric and tidal energy.
4. **Apply:** What single resource do most of the energy alternatives discussed in this section either directly or indirectly depend on?
5. **Connect to Earth Science:** What is the source of geothermal energy? Explain how it is used to generate electricity.

☑ Outlining

Make an outline of the energy alternatives discussed in this section. List at least one advantage and one disadvantage of each. If you need help, refer to Outlining in the **Skill Handbook** on page 677.

 **Skill Builder**

Skill Builder

Answers will vary; they should be similar to the outline below.

I. Biomass
  A. Uses waste as an energy source.
  B. Produces air pollution.
II. Solar Energy
  A. Causes no pollution.
  B. Initial building is costly.
III. Hydroelectricity
  A. Inexpensive, almost no pollution.
  B. Damages the ecosystem.
C. Useful only in limited areas.
IV. Tidal Energy
  A. Almost pollution free.
  B. Only a few places are suitable.
V. Wind Energy
  A. Almost pollution free.
  B. The wind is not consistent.
VI. Geothermal
  A. The water and steam can be returned to their environment.
  B. It is not feasible in many places.

 PROBLEM SOLVING

Think Critically: Solar, wind, and tidal energy are renewable and do not pollute the air. Fossil fuels cannot be replaced and cause air pollution. The renewable energy sources are expensive to use and provide limited amounts of energy. Fossil fuels are less expensive and produce more energy when burned.

3 CLOSE

▶ Ask questions 1-3 and the **Apply** and **Connect to Earth Science** questions in the Section Review.

▶ Have students evaluate what alternative energy sources might be available in your geographical area. What advantages and disadvantages do you see in developing these sources?

SECTION REVIEW ANSWERS

1. Fossil fuels and fissionable materials are both nonrenewable resources. Fossil fuels especially are in limited supply. Burning of fossil fuels causes pollution, and nuclear waste disposal is an unsolved problem.

2. Passive solar heating: Put windows and buildings in places where the sun warms and lights the rooms. Active solar heating: Use solar panels and mirrors to focus the sun's energy for heating water or air. Photovoltaic cells: Produce an electric current from the sun's energy.

3. Both hydroelectric and tidal energy use the natural motion of water, are inexpensive, and are relatively nonpolluting. Only certain locations have the resource of moving water, and artificial dams can damage the balance of an ecosystem.

4. Apply: the sun

5. Connect to Earth Science: The source of geothermal energy is hot gases and molten rock beneath Earth. Water heated by this energy produces steam that can be used to generate electricity.

Skill Builder
ASSESSMENT

Performance: Have students use their outline to produce a collage of the energy alternatives in this section.

ACTIVITY 25-2

OBJECTIVE: Research and **present** arguments for decision making regarding the use of various sources of energy.

Time: several class periods

PROCESS SKILLS applied in this activity are **communicating, researching,** and **diagramming.**

PREPARATION

Provide butcher paper, markers, cardboard, tape, scissors, and other items that can be used to make posters and construct models. Be sure to have good written resources on energy alternatives available to the students.

Cooperative Learning: Divide the class into Problem Solving Teams, one for each energy source. Students will serve dual roles—as members of study teams and as members of the legislature.

THINKING CRITICALLY

Answers will vary with the energy source and location.

TEACHING THE ACTIVITY

*Refer to the **Activity Worksheets** for additional information and teaching strategies.*

• Assign each team an energy source—coal, petroleum, nuclear, solar, wind, hydro, tidal, or geothermal. Not all of these energy sources are feasible for all states.

• If a team wishes to take the position that no plant is necessary, they must provide ways of reducing energy needs and defend the possibility of a reduced standard of living.

• Allow one period for research, planning, and poster making, one day for model making and report preparation, and one day for reporting and voting.

PROGRAM RESOURCES

From the **Teacher Resource Package** use:

Activity Worksheets, pages 204-205, Activity 25-2: Energy Alternatives—A Local Plan.

DESIGNING AN EXPERIMENT
Energy Alternatives—A Local Plan

The design and location of a new power plant can bring forth many controversial issues. What kinds of things should be considered in planning a new power plant?

Getting Started

Your class has been appointed to *prepare* a recommendation for the construction of a new power plant in your community. Your team will *research* the problem and prepare an illustrated oral report on the energy source assigned to you by the governor (your teacher).

Thinking Critically

Does the energy source assigned to your team seem practical to use in your community? Who would be affected by this new power plant? What might be some of the advantages and disadvantages of building this new plant in your community?

Materials

Your cooperative group will use:
• large sheet of poster paper
• set of colored markers
• miscellaneous construction supplies

Try It!

1. *Research* and *describe* the energy source. How does it work? What are its strengths and limitations? Your report should include an illustration, collage, or diagram showing at least one important idea about the construction or operation of the power plant.

2. Listen carefully to the points being made in each report. Consider the appropriateness of each power source for your area. When all reports have been presented, the class will become the state legislature and vote on the type of power plant that should be constructed in your state.

Summing Up/Sharing Results

Explain why you voted as you did. Are the environmental issues acceptable? Are pollution problems involved? Is there a suitable place for construction? Will the power plant be a primary power source for an expanding population or a supplementary source for an existing population?

Going Further!

Work with your team to *construct a model* to demonstrate how some important part of your power plant works.

SUMMING UP/SHARING RESULTS

Accept all reasonable answers if they are well-explained and supported.

GOING FURTHER!

Encourage creativity. You might want to have some small solar cells available.

Activity
ASSESSMENT

Performance: Have each student summarize their team's report, in paragraph or outline form, and sketch a diagram that represents some aspect of the construction or operation of their power plant. A photo of the model could also be included as a portfolio item.

SUMMARY

25-1: Fossil Fuels

1. The three types of fossil fuels are petroleum, natural gas, and coal. They formed from the buried remains of plants and animals.

2. All fossil fuels are nonrenewable energy resources. Supplies will run out soon if they aren't used wisely.

25-2: Nuclear Energy

1. A nuclear reactor uses the energy from a controlled nuclear chain fission reaction to generate electricity.

2. Nuclear wastes must be carefully contained and disposed of so radiation from nuclear decay will not leak into the environment.

3. Nuclear fusion releases greater amounts of energy than does nuclear fission, but fusion must occur at temperatures that are too high to be contained in a laboratory.

25-3: Science and Society: Breeder Reactors

1. Breeder reactors make a continuous source of nuclear fuel as a by-product of the chain reaction.

2. Breeder reactors produce plutonium, a fissionable fuel that can be used in nuclear fission reactors or to make nuclear weapons.

25-4: Alternative Energy Sources

1. Alternate energy resources are needed to supplement or replace nonrenewable energy resources.

2. Other sources of energy for generating electricity include hydroelectricity, and solar, wind, tidal, and geothermal energy.

3. Although some alternative energy sources don't pollute the environment and are renewable, their use is often limited to the regions where the energy source is available.

KEY SCIENCE WORDS

a. **breeder reactor**
b. **fractional distillation**
c. **geothermal energy**
d. **hydroelectricity**
e. **nonrenewable resource**
f. **nuclear reactor**
g. **nuclear waste**
h. **petroleum**
i. **photovoltaic cell**
j. **tidal energy**

UNDERSTANDING VOCABULARY

Match each phrase with the correct term from the list of Key Science Words.

1. separates the hydrocarbons in crude oil
2. liquid remains of dead organisms
3. generates electricity from a controlled fission reaction
4. thermal energy inside Earth
5. source of energy that can't be replaced
6. converts solar energy directly into electricity
7. electricity produced by the energy of moving water
8. energy produced by the rise and fall of ocean levels
9. a fission reactor that produces new reactor fuel
10. by-product of fission reactions

ENERGY SOURCES **663**

SUMMARY

Have students read the summary statements to review the major concepts of the chapter.

UNDERSTANDING VOCABULARY

1. b	**6.** i
2. h	**7.** d
3. f	**8.** j
4. c	**9.** a
5. e	**10.** g

ASSESSMENT
Portfolio

Encourage students to place in their portfolios one or two items of what they consider to be their best work. For each item, ask students to explain why that item was chosen and what they learned from it. Items might be selected from the following.

• In Your Journal entry, p. 649
• Connect to Chemistry answer, p. 655
• Activity 25-2 results and answers, p. 662

Performance

Additional performance assessments may be found in *Performance Assessment* and *Science Integration Activities* that accompany **Merrill Physical Science**. Performance Task Assessment Lists and rubrics for evaluating these activities and other products generated throughout the chapter can be found in Glencoe's *Performance Assessment in Middle School Science*.

OPTIONS

ASSESSMENT

To assess student understanding of material in this chapter, use the resources listed.

👥 COOPERATIVE LEARNING

Consider using cooperative learning in the THINK AND WRITE CRITICALLY, APPLY, and MORE SKILL BUILDERS sections of the Chapter Review.

PROGRAM RESOURCES

From the **Teacher Resource Package** use:

Chapter Review, pages 53-54.

Chapter and Unit Tests, pages 159-162, Chapter Test.

Chapter and Unit Tests, pages 163-164, Unit Test.

CHAPTER
REVIEW

CHECKING CONCEPTS

1. d	**6.** d
2. c	**7.** b
3. a	**8.** b
4. a	**9.** c
5. c	**10.** d

USING LAB SKILLS

ASSESSMENT

Use these alternate lab exercises to assess students' understanding of the skills used in this chapter.

11. Materials such as plastic bags, Silly Putty, and peanut butter may be used. Good containers are usually water resistant and seal well.

12. Questions might deal with topics such as safety, environmental effects, pollution control, location, or financial concerns.

THINK AND WRITE CRITICALLY

13. Fossil fuels and biomass are burned to boil water and produce steam. Steam is produced naturally by geothermal energy. Nuclear reactors produce steam with heat from fission reactions. The steam produced by these sources turns a turbine. Hydroelectric and tidal energy use moving water to turn a turbine. Wind turns a turbine-like device. Turbines turn generators, which produce electricity.

14. Our current major energy resource—fossil fuels—is nonrenewable and will soon be depleted. Energy is conserved by turning off lights, adjusting the thermostat, and so on.

15. It is not possible because the concentration of fissionable U-235 in the reactor fuel rods is far below that needed for a nuclear explosion.

16. We do not possess the technology to build fusion reactors that can maintain the high temperatures required.

17. It has been created by the problems of our current primary energy resources. Fossil fuels are nonrenewable and produce pollutants. Nuclear reactors produce radioactive wastes

---

CHAPTER
REVIEW
CHECKING CONCEPTS

Choose the word or phrase that completes the sentence.

1. Plant and animal remains that are buried under sediments are **not** acted upon by _____ to form fossil fuels.
 a. bacteria   **c.** heat
 b. pressure   **d.** radiation

2. Hydrocarbons react with _____ during the combustion of fossil fuels.
 a. carbon dioxide   **c.** oxygen
 b. carbon monoxide   **d.** water

3. Fossil fuels are becoming more scarce as industrial demands increase and _____.
 a. the population increases
 b. the population decreases
 c. the number of nuclear reactors increases
 d. fewer plants and animals die

4. Both burning fossil fuels and nuclear fission must first be used to produce _____ in order to produce electricity.
 a. steam
 b. carbon dioxide
 c. plutonium
 d. water

5. A major disadvantage of using nuclear fusion reactors is that they _____.
 a. use hydrogen from water as fuel
 b. produce less radioactivity
 c. require extremely high temperatures
 d. use only small nuclei

6. Nuclear wastes include _____.
 a. products of fission reactors
 b. materials with very short half-lives
 c. products from medical and industrial processes
 d. all of these

7. High-level nuclear wastes are currently disposed of by _____.
 a. releasing them into water
 b. storing them in a deep, insulated pool of water
 c. burying them in unstable areas
 d. releasing them into the air

8. All of Earth's energy resources can ultimately be traced back to _____.
 a. plants   **c.** geothermal resources
 b. the sun   **d.** fossil fuels

9. Photovoltaic cells must be made _____ before they can be more widely used to produce electricity.
 a. pollution-free   **c.** less expensive
 b. nonrenewable   **d.** larger

10. _____ is an alternate source of energy that uses water heated naturally by Earth's internal heat.
 a. Hydroelectricity   **c.** Tidal energy
 b. Nuclear fission   **d.** Geothermal energy

USING LAB SKILLS

11. Use the procedure suggested in Activity 25-1 on page 653 to analyze the containment abilities of at least two other materials. Explain what properties might make a material effectively contain sodium hydroxide.

12. Review the process your class followed in Activity 25-2 on page 662. Suppose you are a state representative. Write a list of questions you would want answered for your community if a new power plant were proposed for your area.

---

that aren't easily disposed of. Alternative energy resources are not used because the necessary technology does not yet exist, is too expensive, or has limited applicability.

THINK AND WRITE CRITICALLY

Answer the following questions in your Journal using complete sentences.

13. Most of the energy resources discussed in this chapter produce electricity by means of an electric generator. Briefly discuss how each resource is used to do this.

14. Why is energy conservation important? What are some ways to conserve energy?

15. How great is the possibility of a nuclear explosion in a nuclear reactor?

16. Why isn't fusion being used today as a source of energy?

17. What specific problems have created the need for alternative energy resources? Why aren't these resources more widely used today?

APPLY

18. Which fossil fuel do you think we should use to generate electricity? What are the pros and cons of using this fossil fuel?

19. Match each of the energy resources described in the chapter with the proper type of energy conversion listed below:
    a. kinetic energy to electricity
    b. thermal energy to electricity
    c. nuclear energy to electricity
    d. chemical energy to electricity
    e. light energy to electricity

20. Evaluate the following disposal methods of high-level nuclear wastes:
    a. Bury the wastes in an area of high earthquake and volcanic activity.
    b. Place the wastes on the ocean floor.
    c. Rocket the wastes into space.

21. Classify the energy resources discussed in this chapter as renewable or nonrenewable.

22. Suppose that new reserves of petroleum were discovered and that a nonpolluting way to burn them for energy were found. Why would it still be a good idea to decrease our use of petroleum as a source of energy? (HINT: Consider fractional distillation.)

MORE SKILL BUILDERS

If you need help, refer to the Skill Handbook.

1. **Sequencing:** The ultimate source of energy for cooking food on an electric stove is the sun. List in order the steps that must occur before you can use the sun's energy in this way.

2. **Recognizing Cause and Effect:** Complete the following table that describes changes in the normal operation of a nuclear reactor and the possible effects of these changes.

Cause	Effect
1. Uranium oxide pellets containing only U-238	1.
2. Control rods are removed	2.
3.	3. Reactor core overheats; "meltdown"

3. **Making and Using Tables:** Construct a table to summarize the advantages and disadvantages of each of the energy resources discussed in this chapter.

PROJECTS

1. Research the ways in which scientists are currently trying to contain and control fusion. Write a report and present it to your classmates.

2. Design a campaign to raise public awareness of current energy problems and solutions.

ENERGY SOURCES **665**

APPLY

18. Answers will vary; however, coal might be a logical choice since its supplies are still relatively abundant, but sulfur and nitrogen oxide impurities must be removed from it.

19. (a) wind energy, hydroelectricity, tidal energy; (b) geothermal energy; (c) nuclear fission and fusion; (d) fossil fuels, biomass; (e) photovoltaic cells (solar energy)

20. (a) Not a good way because containment canisters might rupture in geologically unstable areas and release radiation. (b) This removes wastes from human populations; but corrosion by ocean water, pressure, and geological activity could result in leakage. (c) The possibility of an accidental rocket explosion should be considered.

21. renewable: solar energy, hydroelectricity, tidal energy, geothermal energy, wind energy; nonrenewable: fossil fuels, nuclear fusion, fission reactors.

22. The burning of oil as a source of energy should be curtailed so that more of it could be used to produce important chemicals, plastics, and medicines.

MORE SKILL BUILDERS

1. Sequencing: Solar energy is: (1) stored as chemical energy in the molecules of plants and animals; (2) released as thermal energy when organic remains (fossil fuels) are combusted; (3) converted to the kinetic energy of steam in a conventional power plant; (4) converted to the mechanical energy of a turbine; (5) converted to electricity by a generator; (6) converted to thermal energy for cooking by a stove.

2. Recognizing Cause and Effect: (1) The reaction will not occur because only U-235 is fissionable. (2) The reaction will continue on, uncontrolled and will overheat the reactor core. (3) The reactor's cooling system fails or the control rods fail.

3. Making and Using Tables: See left for sample table.

RESOURCE	ADVANTAGES	DISADVANTAGES
Fossil fuels	Easily transported	Nonrenewable, cause air pollution
Nuclear fission	Nonpolluting, much energy from little fuel	Produce dangerous nuclear wastes
Nuclear fusion	Inexhaustible, nonpolluting, no radioactive wastes	Needed technology does not yet exist
Biomass	Cheap, renewable	CO_2 contributes to global warming
Photovoltaic cells	Clean, inexhaustible	Too expensive
Hydroelectricity, tidal energy, wind energy, geothermal	Clean, renewable	Limited applicability

Objective

In this unit-ending feature, the unit topic, "Electricity and Energy Resources," is extended to other disciplines. Students will see how electricity and energy sources are related to events occurring around the planet.

Motivate

Cooperative Learning: Assign one Connection to each group of students. Using the Expert Teams strategy, have each group find out more about the geographic location of the Connection—its climate, culture, flora and fauna, and ecological issues.

Teaching Tips

▶ Tell students to keep in mind the connection between energy resources and the technology described in each area as they are reading this feature.

▶ Ask students to predict how each technology could be used elsewhere in the world.

Wrap-Up

Conclude this lesson by having students explain how each of the Connections relates to the unit.

HISTORY

Background: During World War I, radio communication had been restricted to use by the military. The call letters, KDKA, were assigned from a roster of letters that had previously been assigned only to ships and marine stations.

Discussion: Discuss the importance of commercial radio. Ask students to discuss how the instant communication of radio changed people's lives.

Answer to Question: It is an AM station because it broadcasts between 540 and 1600 kilohertz.

Extension: Have students interview older adults about their memories of early radio. Let students share the information with the class.

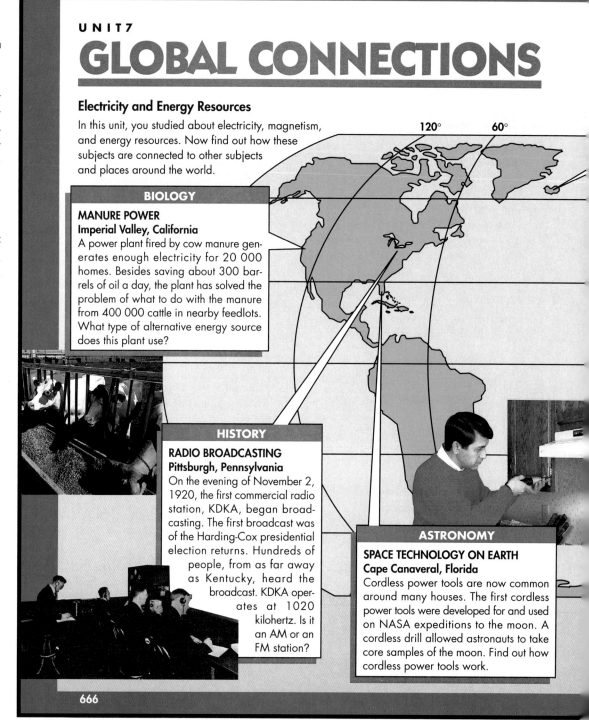

UNIT 7
GLOBAL CONNECTIONS

Electricity and Energy Resources

In this unit, you studied about electricity, magnetism, and energy resources. Now find out how these subjects are connected to other subjects and places around the world.

120°   60°

BIOLOGY

MANURE POWER
Imperial Valley, California
A power plant fired by cow manure generates enough electricity for 20 000 homes. Besides saving about 300 barrels of oil a day, the plant has solved the problem of what to do with the manure from 400 000 cattle in nearby feedlots. What type of alternative energy source does this plant use?

HISTORY

RADIO BROADCASTING
Pittsburgh, Pennsylvania
On the evening of November 2, 1920, the first commercial radio station, KDKA, began broadcasting. The first broadcast was of the Harding-Cox presidential election returns. Hundreds of people, from as far away as Kentucky, heard the broadcast. KDKA operates at 1020 kilohertz. Is it an AM or an FM station?

ASTRONOMY

SPACE TECHNOLOGY ON EARTH
Cape Canaveral, Florida
Cordless power tools are now common around many houses. The first cordless power tools were developed for and used on NASA expeditions to the moon. A cordless drill allowed astronauts to take core samples of the moon. Find out how cordless power tools work.

666

BIOLOGY

Background: The Mesquite Lake Resource Recovery Project burns about 900 tons of manure each day. Ash from the plant is sold as a concrete additive and as an absorbent for toxic wastes.

Discussion: Discuss other possible sources of biomass that could be used to generate electricity in areas that might not have access to cow manure.

Answers to Question: Cow manure is classified as biomass because it is renewable organic matter.

Extension: Have students research heating stoves and furnaces for homes that burn corn as fuel. What are their advantages and disadvantages?

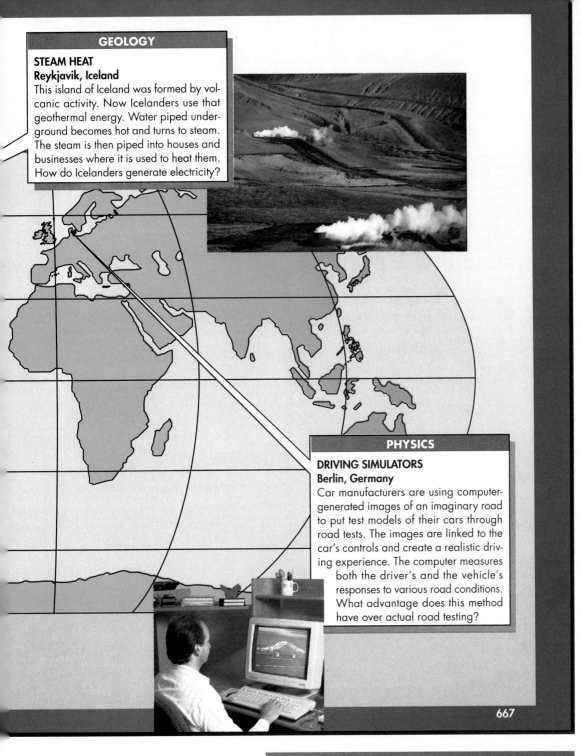

GEOLOGY

STEAM HEAT
Reykjavik, Iceland
This island of Iceland was formed by volcanic activity. Now Icelanders use that geothermal energy. Water piped underground becomes hot and turns to steam. The steam is then piped into houses and businesses where it is used to heat them. How do Icelanders generate electricity?

PHYSICS

DRIVING SIMULATORS
Berlin, Germany
Car manufacturers are using computer-generated images of an imaginary road to put test models of their cars through road tests. The images are linked to the car's controls and create a realistic driving experience. The computer measures both the driver's and the vehicle's responses to various road conditions. What advantage does this method have over actual road testing?

667

ASTRONOMY

Background: In addition to being used for jobs around the house, cordless power tools are also used in industry and medicine.

Discussion: Discuss the reason cordless power tools were needed on lunar expeditions. Ask students to cite examples of where they might use cordless power tools.

Answer to Question: Cordless power tools contain rechargeable batteries. They must be plugged into an outlet periodically to recharge the battery. After the battery is recharged, they can be used for several hours.

Extension: Have students research the kinds of batteries that are used in cordless power tools.

GEOLOGY

Background: Iceland is located near the Arctic Circle in the cold waters of the North Atlantic. In Iceland, active volcanoes are common. The island was formed by volcanoes along the Mid-Atlantic Ridge. Along the ridge, lava seeps up through deep rifts in the ocean floor.

Discussion: Discuss the advantages and disadvantages of living in an area rich in geothermal energy. Point out to students that steam-heated greenhouses also provide Icelanders with fresh produce all year long.

Answer to Question: They use the steam to rotate turbines, which then turn electric generators.

Extension: Have students research other locations where geothermal energy is used.

PHYSICS

Background: Computer programs used in airplane flight simulators are so realistic that experienced copilots can be certified by the FAA as pilots based only on simulator training and testing.

Discussion: Discuss other uses for this kind of computer program. Ask students if they think it might be useful in driver education classes.

Answer to Question: The car can be tested in situations and conditions that would be dangerous in real circumstances, such as testing the response of the car's brakes on icy roads.

Extension: Have students research how computers are used in both automobile design (CAD) and manufacturing (CAM).

CAREERS

BROADCAST ENGINEER

Background: Generally, the larger the station, the more specialized the job a broadcast engineer has. They often work odd hours and on weekends and holidays.

Related Career	Education
Field technician	technical school
Transmitter technician	technical school
Set decorator	college degree
Copywriter	college degree

Career Issue: On live call-in radio broadcasts, engineers set up a time delay so that offensive language can be "bleeped" and not broadcast.

What do you think? Lead students in a discussion about their own attitudes toward "bleeping." Do they think this practice should be stopped or continued?

COMPUTER PROGRAMMER

Background: Programmers may work in such business applications as accounting or inventory control, or in such scientific applications as research and development. Some programmers work for computer manufacturers or system software developers.

Related Career	Education
Hardware specialist	college degree
Systems analyst	college degree
Data entry operator	high school
Computer maintenance technician	technical school

Career Issue: Some people feel that we are too computerized and that too much personal information is available to too many people because of computer access.

What do you think? Lead students in a discussion of their own attitudes toward computerization. Can computers be used to invade people's privacy?

CAREERS

BROADCAST ENGINEER

Broadcast engineers are responsible for a wide variety of electronic equipment used in radio or television transmission. In small stations, they usually set up and operate equipment, as well as keep it working. In larger stations, the jobs are more specialized.

Engineers operate equipment such as microphones, lights, recording equipment, projectors, and cameras. In the control room, engineers also run the equipment that controls the quality of sound and pictures.

If you're interested in becoming a broadcast engineer, you must be flexible and be able to keep a cool head under pressure. High school classes in math and science are helpful. Broadcast engineers must have a license issued by the Federal Communications Commission. Technical schools offer course work designed specifically for preparing you to pass the tests for FCC licensing.

For Additional Information
Contact the Federal Communications Commission, 1919 M Street NW, Washington, DC 20554.

UNIT READINGS

▶McGowen, Tom. *Radioactivity: From the Curies to the Atomic Age.* Danbury, CT: Watts, 1986.
▶Vogt, Gregory. *Electricity and Magnetism.* Danbury, CT: Watts, 1985.

COMPUTER PROGRAMMER

A *computer programmer* writes programs that enable a computer to perform particular tasks or functions. The programmer takes a specific problem, studies and analyzes various ways to solve it, then devises a step-by-step procedure in terms that a computer can understand.

Programmers must be problem solvers who have the ability to think logically, yet creatively. They must also learn to use new programming languages as they are needed.

If you're interested in becoming a computer programmer you should take classes in science, mathematics, and computer science. Most computer programmers have college degrees in computer science or mathematics.

For Additional Information
Contact the Electronics Industries Association, 2001 Pennsylvania Avenue NW, Washington, DC 20006.

UNIT READINGS

Background
▶ *Radioactivity: From the Curies to the Atomic Age* traces the history of radioactivity.
▶ *Electricity and Magnetism* tells how one scientist uses the discoveries of others in the understanding of electricity and magnetism.

More Readings
1. Satry, Laurence. *Magnets.* Mahwah, NJ: Troll, 1985. Discusses the history of discoveries about magnetism.
2. Markle, Sandra. *Power Up: Experiments, Puzzles, and Games Exploring Electricity.* New York, NY: Atheneum, 1989. A fresh approach to understanding how electricity works.

Earthships: Environmental Architecture

The passage that follows describes a house design that solves a number of environmental problems.

A rchitecture is the art and profession of designing buildings. Architecture is one of the oldest art forms and dates from prehistoric times. It has been said that a society's architecture reflects the values and ideals of its people.

In that context, environmental architecture reflects the growing concern of people for the future of planet Earth with its fragile ecology and disappearing resources. Architect Michael Reynolds' concern for the environment led him to design houses he calls "Earthships."

Reynolds' earthships help solve a number of environmental problems simultaneously. First, they use discarded tires as building materials. The Environmental Protection Agency says that tires are discarded at a rate of 240 million per year in the United States. The interior and exterior walls of the earthships are constructed of tires filled with dirt and laid like concrete blocks. The walls are then covered with a coat of plaster or adobe.

Using tires provides a house with walls that are about one meter thick and gives it a very large mass. Because of this "thermal mass," the house utilizes little or no energy for cooling and heating. The base of the house is built below the frost line, meaning that the temperature of the walls will stay at approximately the temperature of Earth below that point — about 15°C. If a house gets no sun at all, but has this amount of mass, it will never get below 15°C.

Earthships in the Southwest have been built in the mountains where temperatures reach −34°C in winter and +38°C in summer. These houses are able to maintain a temperature that varies only a few degrees year round with no energy used for heating or cooling. Asked if earthships would work anywhere in the country, Reynolds said yes—even if you put them where there is no sun and you are heating with gas, you will reduce your heating costs by 90 percent.

Some earthships also generate their own electricity with solar panels mounted on the roof. They also are able to grow food year-round in the greenhouse that Reynolds incorporated in the earthship design. Even the design of the plumbing system was given environmental consideration. "Black water" from toilets goes into a septic system, but "gray water" from sinks, bathtubs, and the washing machine goes into holding tanks to be used in greenhouse irrigation.

Reynolds stresses that earthships are easy and comparatively inexpensive to build. But more importantly these are buildings that take care of people. That is why he calls them earthships.

In Your Own Words
▶ Would you like to live in an earthship? Write an essay explaining why or why not.

669

Classics
▶ Clark, Wilson. *Energy for Survival.* New York, NY: Anchor Books, 1974. Explores the energy basis of our civilization and the energy alternatives for the future.

Other Works
▶ Other articles on energy conservation and environmental concerns include: Lewis, Thomas A. "The Heat Is On!" *National Wildlife.* April-May, 1990, pp. 38-41. Matthews, Samuel W. "Under the Sun." *National Geographic.* Oct. 1990, pp. 66-99.

Biography: Michael Reynolds currently operates Solar Survival Architecture in Taos, New Mexico. His inspiration for environmental architecture came in the early 1970s during an evening news program. Three separate reports on litter, forest depletion, and a shortage of affordable housing gave him an idea. He first constructed several houses with walls constructed from aluminum cans. Later, discarded tires became his material of choice, although cans are still incorporated into parts of his earthships.

TEACHING STRATEGY
Have students read through the article on earthships. Then have them respond to the discussion questions below.

Discussion Questions
1. **Does Michael Reynolds' architecture reflect the values and ideals of our society? Explain your answer.** *More people are becoming environmentally aware. They realize that Earth has limited resources and steps must be taken to protect what they value. In this context, Reynolds' architecture does reflect newer values of society.*
2. **What environmental problems does Reynolds' earthship design address?** *The design of earthships helps to recycle discarded tires, thus reducing the problem of what to do with them. It also reduces the use of gas, oil, or electricity for heating and cooling houses. It recycles some of the water used in the houses for greenhouse irrigation, while enabling people to grow more of their own food. And in some cases, it allows homes to generate their own electricity with solar panels.*

▶ Students can obtain more information on earthships by writing to Michael Reynolds, c/o Solar Survival Architecture, Box 1041, Taos, New Mexico 87511.

APPENDIX A

SI Units of Measurement

Table A-1

SI BASE UNITS					
Measurement	**Unit**	**Symbol**	**Measurement**	**Unit**	**Symbol**
length	meter	m	temperature	kelvin	K
mass	kilogram	kg	amount of substance	mole	mol
time	second	s	intensity of light	candela	cd
electric current	ampere	A			

Table A-2

UNITS DERIVED FROM SI BASE UNITS			
Measurement	**Unit**	**Symbol**	**Expressed in Base Units**
energy	joule	J	$kg \cdot m^2/s^2$ or $N \cdot m$
force	newton	N	$kg \cdot m/s^2$
frequency	hertz	Hz	$1/s$
potential difference	volt	V	$kg \cdot m^2/(A \cdot s^3)$ or W/A
power	watt	W	$kg \cdot m^2/s^3$ or J/s
pressure	pascal	Pa	$kg/(m \cdot s^2)$ or N/m^2
quality of electric charge	coulomb	C	$A \cdot s$

Table A-3

COMMON SI PREFIXES					
Prefix	**Symbol**	**Multiplier**	**Prefix**	**Symbol**	**Multiplier**
Greater than 1			Less than 1		
mega-	M	1 000 000	deci-	d	0.1
kilo-	k	1 000	centi-	c	0.01
hecto-	h	100	milli-	m	0.001
deka-	da	10	micro-	µ	0.000 000 1

670

Table A-4

SI/METRIC TO ENGLISH CONVERSIONS			
	When you want to convert:	**Multiply by:**	**To find:**
Length	inches	2.54	centimeters
	centimeters	0.39	inches
	feet	0.30	meters
	meters	3.28	feet
	yards	0.91	meters
	meters	1.09	yards
	miles	1.61	kilometers
	kilometers	0.62	miles
* Mass and Weight	ounces	28.35	grams
	grams	0.04	ounces
	pounds	0.45	kilograms
	kilograms	2.20	pounds
	tons	0.91	tonnes (metric tons)
	tonnes (metric tons)	1.10	tons
	pounds	4.45	newtons
	newtons	0.23	pounds
Volume	cubic inches	16.39	cubic centimeters
	cubic centimeters	0.06	cubic inches
	cubic feet	0.03	cubic meters
	cubic meters	35.31	cubic feet
	liters	1.06	quarts
	liters	0.26	gallons
	gallons	3.78	liters
Area	square inches	6.45	square centimeters
	square centimeters	0.16	square inches
	square feet	0.09	square meters
	square meters	10.76	square feet
	square miles	2.59	square kilometers
	square kilometers	0.39	square miles

*Weight as measured in standard Earth gravity

671

SI/Temperature Scale Conversions

Table A-5

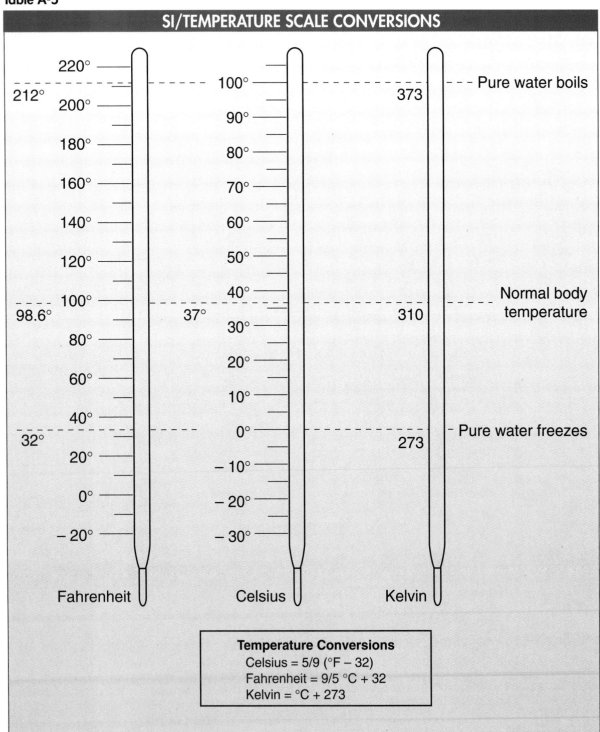

SI/TEMPERATURE SCALE CONVERSIONS

Temperature Conversions
Celsius = 5/9 (°F − 32)
Fahrenheit = 9/5 °C + 32
Kelvin = °C + 273

672

APPENDIX B

Safety in the Classroom

1. Always obtain your teacher's permission to begin an investigation.
2. Study the procedure. If you have questions, ask your teacher. Be sure you understand any safety symbols shown on the page.
3. Use the safety equipment provided for you. Goggles and a safety apron should be worn when any investigation calls for using chemicals.
4. Always slant test tubes away from yourself and others when heating them.
5. Never eat or drink in the lab, and never use lab glassware as food or drink containers. Never inhale chemicals. Do not taste any substances or draw any material into a tube with your mouth.
6. If you spill any chemical, wash it off immediately with water. Report the spill immediately to your teacher.
7. Know the location and proper use of the fire extinguisher, safety shower, fire blanket, first aid kit, and fire alarm.
8. Keep all materials away from open flames. Tie back long hair and loose clothing.
9. If a fire should break out in the classroom, or if your clothing should catch fire, smother it with the fire blanket or a coat, or get under a safety shower. NEVER RUN.
10. Report any accident or injury, no matter how small, to your teacher.

Follow these procedures as you clean up your work area.
1. Turn off the water and gas. Disconnect electrical devices.
2. Return all materials to their proper places.
3. Dispose of chemicals and other materials as directed by your teacher. Place broken glass and solid substances in the proper containers. Never discard materials in the sink.
4. Clean your work area.
5. Wash your hands thoroughly after working in the laboratory.

Table B-1

FIRST AID	
Injury	**Safe response**
Burns	Apply cold water. Call your teacher immediately.
Cuts and bruises	Stop any bleeding by applying direct pressure. Cover cuts with a clean dressing. Apply cold compresses to bruises. Call your teacher immediately.
Fainting	Leave the person lying down. Loosen any tight clothing and keep crowds away. Call your teacher immediately.
Foreign matter in eye	Flush with plenty of water. Use eyewash bottle or fountain.
Poisoning	Note the suspected poisoning agent and call your teacher immediately.
Any spills on skin	Flush with large amounts of water or use safety shower. Call your teacher immediately.

Safety Symbols

This textbook uses the safety symbols in Table B-2 below to alert you to possible laboratory dangers.

Table B-2

SAFETY SYMBOLS		
DISPOSAL ALERT This symbol appears when care must be taken to dispose of materials properly.	**ANIMAL SAFETY** This symbol appears whenever live animals are studied and the safety of the animals and the students must be ensured.
BIOLOGICAL HAZARD This symbol appears when there is danger involving bacteria, fungi, or protists.	**RADIOACTIVE SAFETY** This symbol appears when radioactive materials are used.
OPEN FLAME ALERT This symbol appears when use of an open flame could cause a fire or an explosion.	**CLOTHING PROTECTION SAFETY** This symbol appears when substances used could stain or burn clothing.
THERMAL SAFETY This symbol appears as a reminder to use caution when handling hot objects.	**FIRE SAFETY** This symbol appears when care should be taken around open flames.
SHARP OBJECT SAFETY This symbol appears when a danger of cuts or punctures caused by the use of sharp objects exists.	**EXPLOSION SAFETY** This symbol appears when the misuse of chemicals could cause an explosion.
FUME SAFETY This symbol appears when chemicals or chemical reactions could cause dangerous fumes.	**EYE SAFETY** This symbol appears when a danger to the eyes exists. Safety goggles should be worn when this symbol appears.
ELECTRICAL SAFETY This symbol appears when care should be taken when using electrical equipment.	**POISON SAFETY** This symbol appears when poisonous substances are used.
PLANT SAFETY This symbol appears when poisonous plants or plants with thorns are handled.	**CHEMICAL SAFETY** This symbol appears when chemicals used can cause burns or are poisonous if absorbed through the skin.

674

APPENDIX C

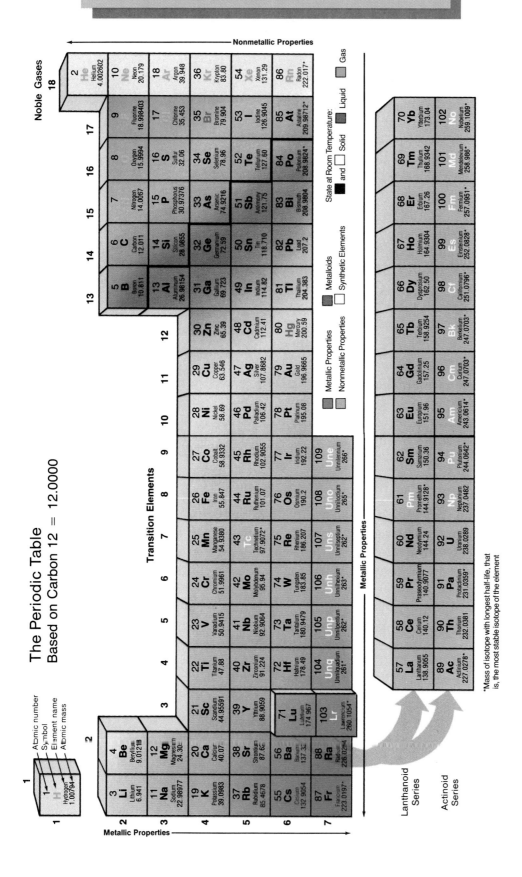

The Periodic Table
Based on Carbon 12 = 12.0000

675

Organizing Information

Sequencing

Think about going to a grocery store to purchase a loaf of bread. As you walk down the aisles, you notice that canned fruits are in one section, boxed cereals are in another, and the bread you are looking for is in yet another. What would happen if different food items were placed randomly on the shelves? It would be difficult for people to locate the food items they wanted. Just like the grocery store, much of the world around you has been put into order to make it easier to understand. Sequencing and outlining are two methods scientists use to organize information.

One method of organizing information is to create a sequence. A sequence is an arrangement of things or events in a particular order. In some of your classes, the students may have been seated in alphabetical order. By organizing students alphabetically, teachers find it easier to remember students' names and to match papers with names in their grade books.

Think about baking chocolate chip cookies. Certain steps have to be followed for the cookies to taste good. If you skip a step in order, the cookies will not turn out right. Baking chocolate chip cookies is an example of the arrangement of events in a particular order.

When you are asked to sequence things or events, you must first identify what comes first. You then decide what should come second. Continue to choose things or events until they are all accounted for and in order. Then, go back over the sequence to make sure each thing or event logically leads to the next.

Suppose you wanted to watch a movie that just came out on videotape. What sequence of events would you have to follow to watch the movie? You would first turn the television set to channel 3 or 4. You would then turn the videotape player on, insert the tape, and press the "play" button. Once the tape had started playing, you would adjust the sound and picture. Then, when the movie was over, you would rewind the tape.

Outlining

Have you ever wondered why teachers ask students to outline what they read? The purpose of outlining is to show the relationships between main ideas and information about the main ideas. Outlining can help you organize, remember, and review written material.

When you are asked to outline, you must first find a group of words that summarizes the main idea. This group of words corresponds to the Roman numerals in an outline. Next, determine what is said about the main idea. Ideas of equal importance are grouped together and are given capital letters. Ideas of equal importance are further broken down and given numbers and letters.

To get an idea how to outline, compare the following outline with Chapter 20 of your textbook.

Plane mirror

Chapter 20 Mirrors and Lenses

I. The Optics of Mirrors
   A. Plane Mirrors
      1. have flat surface
      2. reflection of
         a. left and right sides of image appear reversed
         b. image upright
         c. image same size
      3. results in virtual image
         a. light rays don't form image in front of mirror
         b. light rays meet to form image that appears like object but reversed
   B. Concave Mirrors
      1. surface curved inward
      2. reflection depends on distance of image from mirror

II. The Optics of Lenses
   A. Convex Lenses

Notice that the outline shows the pattern of organization of the written material. The boldface title is the main idea and corresponds with Roman numerals I and II. The capital letters and numbers and letters that follow divide the rest of the text into supporting ideas.

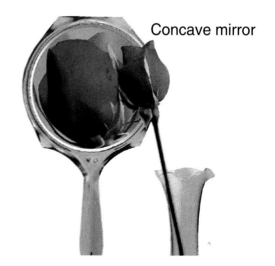

Concave mirror

Thinking Critically

Observing and Inferring

Imagine that you have just finished a volleyball game with your friends. You hurry home to get a cold drink. Opening the refrigerator, you see a jug of orange juice at the back of the top shelf. The jug feels cold as you grasp it. "Ah, just what I need," you think. You hear the tone rise as you pour the juice into a tall glass. When you quickly down the drink, you smell the oranges and enjoy the tart taste in your mouth.

As you imagined yourself in the story, you used your senses to make observations. The basis of all scientific investigation is observation. Scientists are careful to make their observations accurate. When possible they use instruments, like microscopes or telescopes, to extend their senses.

Often they use instruments to make measurements. When observations involve measurements, they are called quantitative observations. Because measurements are easy to communicate and provide a concrete means of comparing collected data, scientists use them whenever possible.

When you make observations in science, you may find it helpful to first examine the entire object or situation. Then, look carefully for details using your sense of sight. Write down everything you see before using another sense to make additional observations. Continue until you have used all five senses.

Scientists often use their observations to make inferences. An inference is an attempt to explain or interpret observations or to determine what caused what you observed. For example, if you observed a CLOSED sign in a store window around noon, you might infer the owner is taking a lunch break. But, perhaps the owner has a doctor's appointment or has taken the day off to go fishing. The only way to be sure your inference is correct is to investigate further.

When making an inference, be certain to make accurate observations and to record them carefully. Then, based on everything you know, try to explain or interpret what you observed. If possible, investigate further to determine if your inference is correct.

Comparing and Contrasting

Observations can be analyzed and then organized by noting the similarities and differences between two or more objects or situations. When you examine objects or situations to determine similarities, you are comparing. Contrasting is looking at similar objects or situations for differences.

Suppose you were asked to compare and contrast transverse and compressional waves. You start by examining your observations. You then divide a piece of paper into two columns, listing ways the waves are similar in one column and ways they are different in the other column. After completing your lists, you report your findings in a table or in a paragraph.

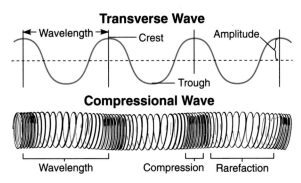

Transverse Wave

Wavelength — Crest — Amplitude — Trough

Compressional Wave

Wavelength — Compression — Rarefaction

A similarity you would point out is that both transverse and compressional waves carry energy through matter and space. A difference you might list is that matter in transverse waves moves at right angles to the direction the wave travels, but matter in compressional waves moves parallel to the direction the wave travels.

Recognizing Cause and Effect

Have you ever observed something happen and then tried to figure out why or how it might have happened? If so, you have observed an event and have inferred a reason for the event. The event or result of action is the effect, and the reason for the event is the cause.

Suppose that you had a clothesline outside your bedroom window. You look out your window every morning to determine what kind of weather the day will bring forth. You notice one warm fall day that the clothesline is sagging and make a mental note to help pull the line tighter. Another morning upon looking outside, you find the weather is quite cold, and notice the clothesline is no longer sagging. Instead, the line is taut and almost parallel to the ground.

What is the effect and what would you infer to be the cause? The effect is the change of position of the clothesline from sagging to taut. You might infer the cause to be the drop in temperature. In trying to determine cause and effect, you have made a logical inference based on observations.

Perhaps, someone in the family tightened the line while you were at school. When scientists are unsure of the cause for a certain event, they often design controlled experiments to determine what caused their observations. How could you determine what caused the tautness of the clothesline?

679

Experimentation Skills

Measuring in SI

You are probably familiar with the metric system of measurement. The metric system is a uniform system of measurement developed in 1795 by a group of scientists. The development of the metric system helped scientists avoid problems with different units of measurement by providing an international standard of comparison for measurements. A modern form of the metric system called the International System, or SI, was adopted for worldwide use in 1960.

You will find that your text uses metric units in almost all its measurements. In the activities you will be doing, you'll use the metric system of measurement.

The metric system is easy to use because it has a system for naming units and a decimal base. For example, meter is the base unit for measuring length, gram for measuring mass, and liter for measuring volume. Unit sizes vary by multiples of ten. When changing from smaller units to larger, you divide by ten. When changing from larger units to smaller, you multiply by ten. Prefixes are used to name larger and smaller units. Look at the following table for some common metric prefixes and their meanings.

METRIC PREFIXES

Prefix	Symbol	Meaning	
kilo-	k	1000	thousand
hecto-	h	100	hundred
deka-	da	10	ten
deci-	d	0.1	tenth
centi-	c	0.01	hundredth
milli-	m	0.001	thousandth

Do you see how the prefix *kilo-* attached to the unit *gram* is *kilogram,* or 1000 grams, or how the prefix *deci-* attached to the unit *meter* is *decimeter,* or one tenth (0.1) of a meter?

You have probably measured distance many times. The meter is the SI unit used to measure distance. To visualize the length of a meter, think of a baseball bat. A baseball bat is about one meter long. When measuring smaller distances, the meter is divided into smaller units called centimeters and millimeters. A centimeter is one hundredth (0.01) of a meter, which is about the size of the width of the fingernail on your little finger. A millimeter is one thousandth of a meter (0.001), about the thickness of a dime.

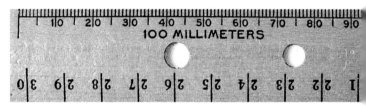

Most metersticks and metric rulers have lines indicating centimeters and millimeters. Look at the illustration. The centimeter lines are the longer numbered lines, and the shorter lines between the centimeter lines are millimeter lines.

When using a metric ruler, you must first decide on a unit of measurement. You then line up the 0-centimeter mark with the end of the object being measured and read the number of the unit where the object ends.

Units of length are also used to measure the surface area. The standard unit of area is the square meter (m²), or a square one meter long on each side. Similarly, a square centimeter (cm²) is a square one centimeter long on each side. Surface area is determined by multiplying the number of units in length times the number of units in width.

680

The volume of rectangular solids is also calculated using units of length. The cubic meter (m^3) is the standard SI unit of volume. A cubic meter is a cube one meter on a side. You can determine the volume of rectangular solids by multiplying length times width times height.

Liquid volume is measured using a unit called a liter. You are probably familiar with a two-liter soft drink bottle. One liter is about one-half of the two-liter bottle. A liter has the volume of 1000 cubic centimeters. Because the prefix *milli-* means thousandth (0.001), a milliliter would equal one cubic centimeter. One milliliter of liquid would completely fill a cube measuring one centimeter on each side.

During science activities, you will measure liquids using beakers marked in milliliters and graduated cylinders. A graduated cylinder is a tall cylindrical container marked with lines from bottom to top. Each graduation represents one milliliter.

Scientists use a balance to find the mass of an object in grams. In science class, you will likely use a beam balance similar to the one illustrated. Notice that on one side of the beam balance is a pan and on the other side is a set of beams. Each beam has an object of a known mass called a rider that slides on the beam.

You must be careful when using a balance. When carrying the balance, hold the beam support with one hand and place the other hand under the balance. Also, be careful about what you place on the pan. Never place a hot object on the pan or pour chemicals directly on it. Mass a suitable container and place dry or liquid chemicals into the container to mass.

Before you find the mass of an object, you must set the balance to zero by sliding all the riders back to the zero point. Check the pointer to make sure it swings an equal distance above and below the zero point on the scale. If the swing is unequal, find and turn the adjusting screw until you have an equal swing.

You are now ready to use the balance to mass the object. Place the object on the pan. Slide the rider with the largest mass along the beam until the pointer drops below the zero point. Then move it back one notch. Repeat the process on each beam until the pointer swings an equal distance above and below the zero point. Read the masses indicated on the beams. The sum of the masses will be the mass of the object.

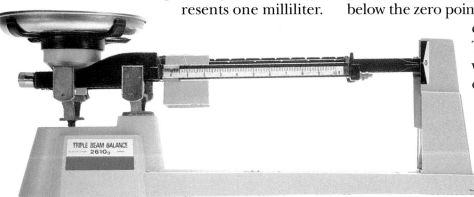

Hypothesizing

What would you do if the combination lock on your locker didn't work? Would you try the combination again? Would you check to make sure you had the right locker? You would likely try several possible solutions until you managed to open the locker.

Scientists generally use experiments to solve problems and answer questions. An experiment is a method of solving a problem in which scientists use an organized process to attempt to answer a question.

Experimentation involves defining a problem and formulating and testing a hypothesis, or testable prediction about how to solve a problem. Each prediction is tested during an experiment, which includes making careful observations and collecting data. After analysis of the collected data, a conclusion is formed and compared to the hypothesis.

Imagine it's after school, and you are changing clothes. You notice a brownish-black spot on a favorite shirt. Your problem is how to remove the stain from the shirt without damaging the shirt. You think that soap and water will remove the stain. You have made a hypothesis regarding the solution to the problem. But, making a hypothesis is not enough—the hypothesis must be tested. You try soap and water, but the stain doesn't budge.

You then observe the stain more carefully and decide that you will need to use a solvent. You have revised your hypothesis based on your observations. The new hypothesis is still only a testable prediction until you test it and examine the results. If the test removes the stain, the hypothesis is accepted. But, if the test doesn't remove the stain, you will have to revise and refine the hypothesis.

Using Variables, Constants, and Controls

When scientists do experiments, they are careful to manipulate or change only one condition and keep all other conditions in the experiment the same. The condition that is manipulated is called the independent variable. The conditions that are kept the same during an experiment are called constants. The dependent variable is any change that results from manipulating the independent variable.

Scientists can know that the independent variable caused the change in the dependent variable only if they keep all other factors constant in the experiment. Scientists also use controls to be certain that the observed changes were a result of manipulation of the independent variable. A control is a sample that is treated exactly like the experimental group, except that the independent variable is not applied to the control. After the experiment, the change in the dependent variable of the control sample is compared to the change observed in the experimental group to see the effect of the application of the independent variable.

Suppose you were asked to bring your portable compact disc player on a weekend camping trip. You put in fresh dry cell batteries so that you and your friends can play CDs all weekend. But, the player loses volume about midday Sunday and soon won't play at all. You expected the dry cell batteries to last all weekend. You played the CDs louder than you do at home, so you wonder if the volume of the player affects how long the batteries last and decide to design an experiment to find out. What would be the independent and dependent variables, the constants, and the control in your experiment?

682

This is how you might set up your experiment. You decide to compare the amount of time the player will operate at different volume settings. You purchase enough fresh dry cell batteries to operate the player at number 6, your normal listening volume, and at lower and higher volume settings. You first set the volume at number 6 and operate the player until you can no longer hear the music. You then repeat the experiment two more times using volume settings of 3 and 9. You record the amount of time the player operates at each volume setting in a data table. Your data table might look like this:

DURATION MUSIC IS HEARD	
Volume	Amount of Time
3	23 h, 46 min
6	18 h, 13 min
9	14 h, 53 min

What are the independent and dependent variables in the experiment? Because you are changing the volume setting of the compact disc player, the independent variable is the volume setting. The dependent variable is any change that results from the independent variable, so the dependent variable is the number of hours and minutes music is heard on the player.

What factors are constants in the experiment? The constants are using identical dry cell batteries, playing the same compact disc, and keeping the compact disc player in the same environment for each test. What was the purpose of playing the compact disc player at your normal setting? The normal setting of the player is the control. The duration that music is heard at the normal volume setting will be used to compare the durations at lower and higher volume settings.

Interpreting Data

After doing a controlled experiment, you must analyze and interpret the collected data, form a conclusion, and compare the conclusion to your hypothesis. Analyze and interpret the data in the table. On which volume setting did the dry cell batteries last the longest? The batteries lasted the longest on number 3, the lowest setting. On which volume setting did the dry cell batteries last the shortest duration? The batteries lasted the shortest duration on volume setting number 9. What conclusion did you form? The data indicate that as the volume increases, the dry cell batteries last for a shorter duration. How does the conclusion compare with your hypothesis for this experiment? Was it supported by the experiment or not?

Graphic Organizers

Concept Mapping

If you were taking an automobile trip, you would likely take along a road map. The road map shows your location, your destination, and other places along the way. By examining the map, you can understand where you are in relation to other locations on the map.

A concept map is similar to a road map. But, a concept map shows the relationships among ideas (or concepts) rather than places. A concept map is a diagram that visually shows how concepts are related. Because the concept map shows the relationships among ideas, it can clarify the meanings of ideas and terms and help you to understand what you are studying.

Look at the construction of a concept map called a **network tree.** Notice how some words are circled and others are written on connecting lines. The circled words are science concepts. The lines in the map show relationships between concepts, and the words written on them describe relationships between the concepts.

A network tree can also show more complex relationships between the concepts. For example, a line labeled "affected by" could be drawn from *plants* and *animals* to *chemistry,* because chemical processes occur in plants and animals. Another example of a relationship that crosses branches would be a line labeled "caused by interactions of" connecting *Earth changes* with *matter and energy.* Earth changes are caused by interactions of matter and energy.

When you are asked to construct a network tree, state the topic and select the major concepts. Find related concepts and put them in order from general to specific. Branch the related concepts from the major concept and describe the relationships on the lines. Continue to write the more specific concepts. Write the relationships between the concepts on the lines until all concepts are mapped. Examine the concept map for relationships that cross branches and add them to the concept map.

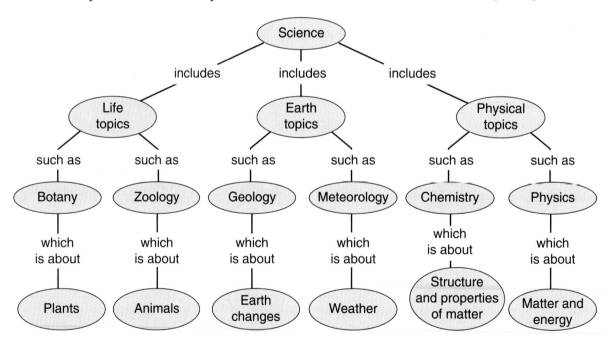

An **events chain** is another type of concept map. An events chain map is used to describe ideas in order. In science, an events chain can be used to describe a sequence of events, the steps in a procedure, or the stages of a process.

When making an events chain, you first must find the one event that starts the chain. This event is called the initiating event. You then find the next event in the chain and continue until you reach an outcome. Suppose your mother asked you to wash the dinner dishes. An events chain map might look like the one below. Notice that connecting words may not be necessary.

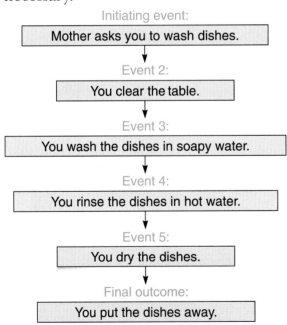

A **cycle concept map** is a special type of events chain map. In a cycle concept map, the series of events do not produce a final outcome. The last event in the chain relates back to the initiating event.

As in the events chain map, you first decide on an initiating event and then list each important event in order. Because there is no outcome and the last event relates back to the initiating event, the cycle repeats itself. Look at the cycle map of physical changes of water.

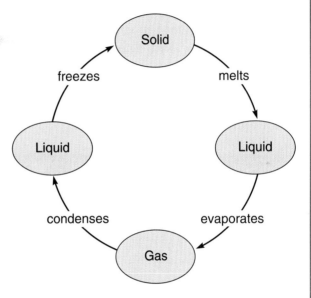

There is usually more than one correct way to create a concept map. As you are constructing a map, you may discover other ways to construct the map that show the relationships between concepts better. If you do discover what you think is a better way to create a concept map, do not hesitate to change it.

Concept maps are useful in understanding the ideas you have read about. As you construct a map, you are constructing knowledge and learning. Once concept maps are constructed, you can use them again to review and study and to test your knowledge.

Making and Using Tables

Browse through your textbook, and you will notice many tables both in the text and in the activities. The tables in the text arrange information in such a way that it is easier for you to understand. Also, many activities in your text have tables to complete as you do the activity. Activity tables will help you organize the data you collect during the activity so that they can be interpreted easily.

Most tables have a title telling you what is being presented. The table itself is divided into columns and rows. The column titles list items to be compared. The row headings list the specific characteristics being compared. Within the grid of the table, the collected data are recorded. Look at the following table:

COMMON BASES AND THEIR USES		
Name of base	**Formula**	**Uses**
Sodium hydroxide	NaOH	Drain cleaner, Soap making
Aluminum hydroxide	Al(OH)$_3$	Antacid, Deodorant
Magnesium hydroxide	Mg(OH)$_2$	Laxative, Antacid
Ammonium hydroxide	NH$_4$OH	Cleaner

What is the title of this table? The title is "Common Bases and Their Uses." What items are being compared? The uses of common bases are being compared.

What is the use of ammonium hydroxide? To find the answer, you must locate the column labeled *Uses* and the row labeled *ammonium hydroxide*. The information contained in the box where the column and row intersect is the answer. Did you answer "cleaner"? What is the formula for sodium hydroxide? The answer is NaOH. Which two bases are commonly used as antacids? If you answered aluminum hydroxide and magnesium hydroxide, you have an understanding of how to use a table.

RECYCLED MATERIALS			
Day of Week	**Paper (kg)**	**Aluminum (kg)**	**Plastic (kg)**
Mon.	4	2	0.5
Wed.	3.5	1.5	0.5
Fri.	3	1	1.5

To make a table, you simply list the items compared in columns and the characteristics compared in rows. Make a table and record the data comparing the masses of recycled materials collected by a class. On Monday, students turned in 4 kg of paper, 2 kg of aluminum, and 0.5 kg of plastic. On Wednesday, they turned in 3.5 kg of paper, 1.5 kg of aluminum, and 0.5 kg of plastic. On Friday, the totals were 3 kg of paper, 1 kg of aluminum, and 1.5 kg of plastic. If your table looks like the one shown, you should be able to make tables to organize data.

Making and Using Graphs

After scientists organize data in tables, they often display the data in graphs. A graph is a diagram that shows a comparison between variables. Because graphs show a picture of collected data, they make interpretation and analysis of the data easier. The three basic types of graphs used in science are the line graph, bar graph, and pie graph.

A line graph is used to show the relationship between two variables. The variables being compared go on the two axes of the graph. The independent variable always goes on the horizontal axis, called the *x*-axis. The dependent variable always goes on the vertical axis, or *y*-axis.

Suppose a school started a peer study program with a class of students to see how it affected their science grades.

AVERAGE GRADES OF STUDENTS IN STUDY PROGRAM	
Grading Period	Average Science Grade
First	81
Second	85
Third	86
Fourth	89

You could make a graph of the grades of students in the program over a period of time. The grading period is the independent variable and should be placed on the *x*-axis of your graph. The average grade of a student in the program is the dependent variable and would go on the *y*-axis.

After drawing your axes, you would label each axis with a scale. The *x*-axis simply lists the grading periods. To make a scale of grades on the *y*-axis, you must look at the data values. Because the lowest grade was 81 and the highest was 89, you know that you will have to start numbering at least at 81 and go through 89. You decide to start numbering at 80 and number by twos through 90.

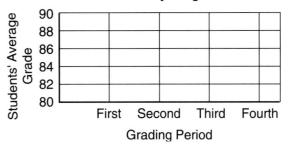

Average Grades of Students in Study Program

Next you must plot the data points. The first pair of data you want to plot is the first grading period and 81. Locate "First" on the *x*-axis and 81 on the *y*-axis. Where an imaginary vertical line from the *x*-axis and an imaginary horizontal line from the *y*-axis would meet, place the first data point. Place the other data points the same way. After all the points are plotted, connect them with a smooth line.

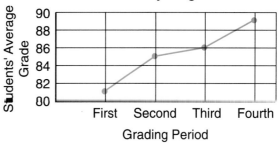

Average Grades of Students in Study Program

What if you wanted to compare the average grades of the class in the study group with the grades of another science class? The data of the other class can be plotted on the same graph to make the comparison. You must include a key with two different lines, each indicating a different set of data. Also change the title of the new graph to represent the data you are comparing.

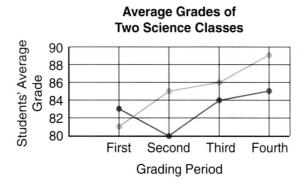

**Average Grades of
Two Science Classes**

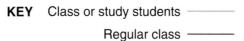

KEY Class or study students ————
Regular class ————

Bar graphs are similar to line graphs, except they are used to compare or display data that do not continuously change. In a bar graph, thick bars show the relationships among data rather than data points.

To make a bar graph, set up the *x*-axis and *y*-axis as you did for the line graph. The data is plotted by drawing thick bars from the *x*-axis up to an imaginary point where the *y*-axis would intersect the bar if it was extended.

Look at the bar graph comparing the masses lifted by an electromagnet with different numbers of dry cell batteries. The independent variable is the number of dry cell batteries, and the dependent variable is the mass lifted. The lifting power of the electromagnet as it changed with different numbers of dry cell batteries is being compared.

Mass Lifted by Electromagnets

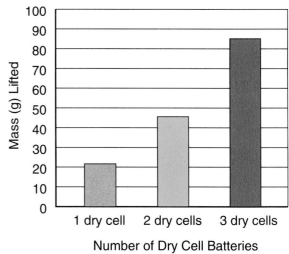

A pie graph uses a circle divided into sections to display data. Each section represents part of the whole. When all the sections are placed together, they equal 100 percent of the whole.

Suppose you wanted to make a pie graph of the periodic table to show how many elements have nonmetallic properties, how many are metalloids, and how many have metallic properties. You would have to determine the total number of elements and the number of elements of each type. Because there are 109 elements, the whole pie will represent this amount.

You count the number of elements of each type and find out there are 17 elements with nonmetallic properties, 8 metalloids, and 84 elements with metallic properties.

To find out how much of the pie each section should take, you must divide the number of elements in each group by the total number of elements. You then multiply your answer by 360, the number of degrees in a circle. Round your answer to the nearest whole number. The percentage of elements with nonmetallic properties would be determined as follows:

$$\frac{17}{109} \times 360 = 56.1, \text{ or about 56 degrees}$$

Use the formula to compute how much of the circle metalloids and elements with metallic properties would fill. Metalloids would take up 26 degrees, and metallic elements would take up 278 degrees.

To plot the groups on the pie graph, you need a compass and protractor. Use the compass to draw a circle. Then draw a straight line from the center to the edge of the circle. Place your protractor on this line and use it to mark a point on the edge of the circle at 56 degrees. Connect this point to the center of the circle with a straight line. This is the part of the circle representing elements with nonmetallic properties. Place your protractor on the line you just made and use it to mark a point on the edge of the circle at 26 degrees. Again draw a straight line from this point to the center of the circle. This part represents the metalloids. The remaining part of the circle represents the percentage of metallic elements. Complete the graph by labeling the sections of your graph and giving the graph a title.

Nonmetals, Metalloids, and Metals in the Periodic Table

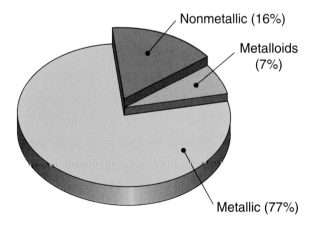

Nonmetallic (16%)

Metalloids (7%)

Metallic (77%)

Interpreting Scientific Illustrations

Your science textbook contains many scientific illustrations to help you understand, interpret, and remember what you read. When you are reading the text and encounter an illustration, examine it carefully and relate it to the text you have just read. Also read the caption for the illustration. The caption is a brief comment that explains or identifies the illustration.

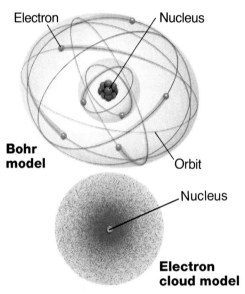

Electron   Nucleus

Bohr model

Orbit

Nucleus

Electron cloud model

Figure 10-2. The top illustration is an early model of an atom with defined paths for electrons. The lower illustration is a later model showing a region where electrons are likely to be.

Some illustrations are designed to show you how the internal parts of a structure are arranged. Look at the illustrations of atoms. The illustrations are models that, with the text, will help you understand an atom's internal parts. Notice that a caption briefly describes each illustration. Also, note that the illustrations include labels to help you understand the locations of the internal parts of an atom.

Other illustrations will help you understand how something works. The illustration of the circulation of air in a room of a house shows how a furnace works and how hot and cool air circulate within the room. The arrows indicate the flow of air within the heating system and the room to help you understand the text.

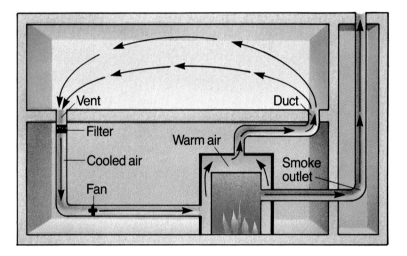

Figure 6-9. In a forced-air heating system, air heated by the furnace is used to heat the rooms of the house.

The illustrations of the house and heating system show what is called a cross section. A cross section is a section that is formed by cutting through an object. The illustration of the cross section is formed by cutting at right angles to the horizontal axis of the house and heating system.

Scientific illustrations similar to that of the heating system of a house are two-dimensional. A two-dimensional illustration has height and width. However, many of the illustrations in this text, such as the model of atoms, are three-dimensional. Three-dimensional illustrations have not only height and width but also depth. An illustration in three dimensions is similar to the way you see the world, so it is even more useful in helping you understand the science ideas you are reading about.

690

THINK LIKE A SCIENTIST

Your gym locker won't open. You can't decide what to eat for lunch. You need to explain to a friend how to get to your house. Every day you have problems that you need to solve and ideas that you need to communicate. Communicating and problem solving are not always easy to do. It is important for you to have well-developed problem-solving and communication skills. In addition to using these two types of skills, your knowledge of events that happen around you or materials that you come in contact with can be better described by using measurements dealing with that event or material. In this project, you can begin to understand some important scientific processes by combining all three types of these skills: problem solving, communicating, and measuring.

Two Languages for Temperature

At the present time, the world uses primarily two systems for measuring temperature. The Fahrenheit and Celsius systems were both named after the scientists who developed these now familiar temperature scales. Most countries around the world use the Celsius scale. Scientists also use the Celsius scale. When you hear a weather forecast in the United States, however, the temperature is reported in degrees Fahrenheit. You may also know the average body temperature for healthy humans is 98.6°F. Because two temperature scales are commonly used, it is important to be able to convert, or translate, from one to the other. How could you design an experiment or demonstration that will show conversion of temperature

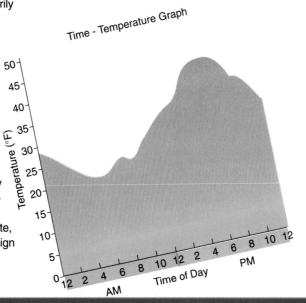

Time - Temperature Graph

REFERENCES

Asimov, Isaac. *The Measure of the Universe*. New York: Harper and Row Publishers, 1983.

Kurtz, V. Ray. *Metrics for Elementary and Middle Schools*. Washington, DC: National Education Association, 1978.

Youden, W. J. *Experimentation and Measurement*. Washington, DC: NSTA, 1989.

PROJECT 1

OVERVIEW

OBJECTIVES: Students will *investigate* the Celsius and Fahrenheit temperature scales and *measure* and *graph* their relationship. In so doing, students will develop a means of converting from one scale to the other.

SUMMARY

This project is designed to support the introductory concepts in Unit 1 that deal with problem solving, measuring, and graphing.

Students are already familiar with the Fahrenheit scale for temperature measurement. In this project they will simultaneously measure the Celsius and Fahrenheit temperatures of heated water as it cools. Students will then graph this data and use the graph to compare the two temperature scales. By analyzing the data, students will determine the relationship of the two temperature scales and develop a means of converting from one scale to the other.

In this introductory project, students will also learn the importance of clearly communicating their findings.

TIME REQUIRED

This project can be done after problem solving, graphing, and measuring have been discussed in Chapters 1-2. One class period will be required to gather the temperature data. Another period may be required to explain and demonstrate graphing techniques. Actual graphing, making posters, and collecting photos can be done outside of class. Another class period may be required for sharing of the displays.

PREPARATION

Cooperative Learning:

Divide the students into Paired Partners. If there is a shortage of materials, students can be divided into Science Investigation Groups.

• Obtain an electric hot plate, a beaker, and a Celsius and a Fahrenheit thermometer for each group. For graphs and posters, have rulers, graph paper, and poster board or butcher paper available.

- As an introduction to the project, use a term or phrase from a foreign language and ask students to translate the term into English. Explain that, for efficient communication, some study and experience are necessary. Relate this example to the study and experience needed to make temperature conversions.

- Caution students to use care not to touch any hot materials unless a thermal mit is used.

- Because this project takes place early in the year, use this opportunity to set standards for neat, organized reporting of data.

- Emphasize the need to label graph axes with units that are of proper and equal size.

- Students' graphs should indicate that a 0°C reading corresponds to 32°F and that one Celsius degree is 1.8 (9/5) times larger than a Fahrenheit degree.

measurements between the two systems? How would you communicate your findings to other people?

To start, use reference materials to find out the following information.

1. What is temperature?
2. For each of the scientists, Celsius and Fahrenheit, find out what country he was from, when he lived, and what type of science he studied.

Then perform the following experiment.

You will need to use: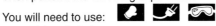

- a Fahrenheit thermometer
- a Celsius thermometer
- a beaker of water
- a hot plate

1. Use the hot plate to heat some water in a beaker.

2. When the water begins to boil, turn off the power to the hot plate.
3. Carefully place both of your thermometers near each other in the hot water.
4. As the temperature begins to drop, record the temperature readings, taken at the same time, from each of the thermometers. Be sure to label each of your paired readings as either °C or °F.
5. Collect a total of ten different paired temperature readings. You may place the beaker and thermometers in a refrigerator to make the water cool faster.

Using Your Research

From your observations, compare the size of one Celsius degree to the size of one Fahrenheit degree. This comparison can help you convert from one temperature scale to another.

To better communicate your comparison, use the same technique that scientists frequently use—prepare a graph. Set up a graph so that °C is on the vertical axis and °F is on the horizontal axis.

Going Further

Find photographs of different scenes that show people or events that are in situations of obvious temperature ranges. Examples might include a sunny beach and a snow scene. Attach these to your graph with questions about the temperature in each scene.

Another temperature scale used commonly by scientists is Kelvin. Find out how and why the Kelvin scale was developed and how it compares to the Celsius scale. Design a method to convert Celsius to Kelvin.

Even though you may not have measured it, label your vertical axis so that it includes 0°C. Make a line graph that plots each of your pairs of temperature readings. What value on the Fahrenheit axis matches the 0°C reading? This value is the amount that each Celsius degree is offset from each Fahrenheit measurement.

Next, select any ten-degree change on the Celsius axis. Use the line that you made to determine how many degrees the Fahrenheit scale would change in that interval. Using these values, determine what ratio compares one Celsius degree to one Fahrenheit degree.

Use this information to show how to change a Fahrenheit measurement to a Celsius value. Make a large poster of your graph and use your poster to explain the differences in the two systems and how to convert from one system to the other.

GOING FURTHER

• For student posters, have several old travel magazines available for students to use as sources for photos that represent extremes in temperatures.

• The Kelvin scale was developed by Lord Kelvin, an English physicist, in the 1800s. This scale uses degrees that are the same size as Celsius degrees. The zero point is the temperature where, theoretically, no molecular motion exists, and there is thus no temperature.

• 0 K equals -273°C, which is called absolute zero. Students may want to investigate the concept of absolute zero and the effects of extreme cold on matter.

• You may want to have students use their graph to convert the temperature in the daily weather forecast, in a recipe, or other source from Fahrenheit to Celsius.

PROJECT 2

OVERVIEW

OBJECTIVES: Students will *analyze* the motion and forces involved in a sport or physical activity of their choice. This process will make use of concepts studied in Unit 2, such as measuring average speed and recognizing Newton's laws of motion.

SUMMARY

Students will begin this project by researching the history of their sport. They will design and conduct an experiment to determine the average speed of a moving person or object in this sport. Students will describe examples of work being done and recognize how Newton's laws of motion are illustrated in this activity. They will share their sport's analysis in a presentation, making use of actual or videotaped demonstrations.

TIME REQUIRED

This project is designed to be worked on throughout Chapters 3-5 in Unit 2. One day is required to set up groups, explain the tasks, and select topics. Allow groups to meet in several segments of time during this unit to plan and check the progress of their project. One day is required for group presentations at the end of Chapter 5.

PREPARATION

Cooperative Learning: Establish Science Investigation Groups of three students each. Have each group assign specific roles to encourage participation by all group members.

PROJECT 2 PHYSICS IN SPORTS

In some sports, such as swimming and cross-country running, the winner of a competition is determined by who can move at the fastest average speed. Other sports, such as basketball, figure skating, and ultimate Frisbee, depend on accuracy, technique, and teamwork. You have learned that forces are used to control motion by changing the speed or the direction of an object's motion. These same forces are used to accelerate human bodies or equipment in sports.

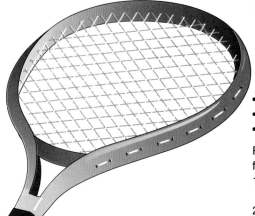

- wrestling
- football
- biking
- softball or baseball
- table tennis
- weightlifting

Analyze a Sport

Select a sport or physical activity that your group would like to study. Choose a sport you can actually play or observe. Use direct observations and measurements to explore the dynamics, or the motion and forces, involved in this sport. Suggestions for sports are listed below.

- soccer
- swimming
- volleyball
- handball
- basketball
- running
- gymnastics
- tennis

For the sport of your choice, research the following information.

1. What is the history of your sport? When and by whom was it invented?
2. Describe the objects in motion in your sport. Do people move around a lot? Do they move in straight lines or do they change directions? Is a ball or other object the focal point of the game?
3. What two things must be measured to determine the average speed of an object? Design a way to measure the average speed of a moving person or object in this sport, such as the speed of a served tennis ball. Try it! Describe how this speed is controlled by the athlete.
4. Review the definition of *work*. Try to identify and describe at least two examples of

REFERENCES

Doherty, Paul. "That's the Way the Ball Bounces." *The Exploratorium Quarterly,* Fall, 1991.

Holmes, Brian. "Spit and Dimples." *The Exploratorium Quarterly,* Fall 1991.

Miller, Mary K. "Racing the Dolphins." *The Exploratorium Quarterly,* Fall 1991.

Physics of Sports; Videodisc, Software, and Activities; Videodiscovery.

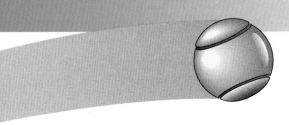

an action in which work is done in your sport. Remember, the force and the distance moved must be in the same direction. What information would you need to calculate the amount of work done?

5. Find at least one example of each of Newton's laws of motion in your sport. Describe each example as clearly as possible.

Using Your Research

After you have investigated the questions, design a presentation for the class about the physics of your sport. Your presentation should answer the questions you investigate. Use actual demonstrations of the sport as much as possible to help make your explanations clear. You might consider videotaping some motions involved in your sport if the sport itself cannot be easily demonstrated in the classroom. If possible, dress as a person would dress to participate in the sport.

Going Further

Each and every movement in each and every sport contains a great deal of physics. Make a poster that includes at least one diagram or picture of a specific action. Show an analysis of all forces and motion existing in this action by pointing to specific parts of the body or equipment that are in use. Consider the role friction plays in your sport. In what circumstances is friction desirable? Undesirable? Using your understanding of the physics involved, describe several specific things that an athlete could use to improve performance in this sport.

TEACHING NOTES

• To illustrate the concepts without leading the students toward a specific sport or activity, show an animated cartoon that contains a lot of activity to introduce this project. Ask students to identify the kinds of motion and forces involved in a particular action, such as running or striking an object. Have students describe how they would determine the average speed of a person or object moving as they do in the cartoon. Have students identify situations in the cartoon where Newton's laws are not obeyed and compare this situation to a real-life situation.

• Suggest that, in measuring the average speed of an object, students may wish to make several measures of the same event to assure consistency. Have them describe the sources of error in any measurements.

• You may wish to make up an assessment sheet for grading the presentations. Share this sheet with your students so they know exactly what they need to do to be successful in this project.

GOING FURTHER

Lead a discussion on the role of friction in sports, including air resistance and drag. Friction is necessary for people to walk and run. For example, it is undesirable for a racing swimmer to wear a baggy suit, but a runner will choose shoes that have good traction, and thus increased friction. In order to improve performance in a sport, athletes might want to know how to reduce drag, that larger forces will cause greater accelerations, and that objects moving fast have more momentum, for example.

PROJECT 3

OVERVIEW

OBJECTIVES: Students will research the contributions of various individuals to our modern understanding of atomic structure. Students will learn that scientists' conclusions are based on direct and indirect experimental evidence.

SUMMARY

The selection of two scientists starts students on a project that will lead them to an understanding and appreciation of the modern view of atomic structure. Students will place their selected scientists in the appropriate time period and explain their scientific and social environment. They will then connect the work of those scientists to any related beliefs in more modern times. By delivering a class report with props and costuming, students will bring more interest to some of their findings.

TIME REQUIRED

This project would be most effective if introduced in the latter part of Unit 3. Students will need one class period to examine the list of prospective scientists for their choices. Time outside of class will be needed for research. Another class period may be set aside for rehersal of the presentations, and one class period is needed for the actual presentation.

PREPARATION

Cooperative Learning: Divide the class into Paired Partners.

• Be aware of various resources available for student use. Advise any community or school librarian that the project is being done, and encourage them to gather possible resources.

A VIEW OF THE ATOM

Throughout history, we have records of people who wondered what made up matter. Although it is difficult for many people to visualize, all matter is made up of small pieces of material called atoms. If you asked several people to describe or diagram the general appearance of an atom, you would get many different responses. In fact, some scientists would also have varying opinions. How do we describe something we cannot see? What do you think an atom looks like?

Atomic Sleuth

Our current view of the atom is the result of historical investigations and modern experimental results. From the following list, choose two scientists to research.

• Democritus
• John Dalton
• J.J. Thomson
• Ernst Rutherford
• Marie Curie
• Anne Jump Cannon
• Max Planck
• Albert Einstein
• Neils Bohr
• Louis de Broglie
• Werner Heisenberg
• Erwin Schrödinger
• Murray Gell-Mann
• Leon Lederman

For each of your chosen scientists, answer the following questions.

696

REFERENCES

Asimov, Isaac. *Atom.* New York, NY: Truman Talley Books, 1991.

Jaffe, Bernard. *Crucibles: The Story of Chemistry.* New York, NY: Dover Publishers, Inc., 1976.

Salzberg, Hugh W. *From Caveman to Chemist.* Washington, DC: American Chemical Society, 1991.

Snow, C.P. *The Physicists.* Boston: Little, Brown and Co., 1981.

Wolf, Fred Alan. *Taking the Quantum Leap.* New York, NY: Harper and Row, 1989.

1. In what country or countries did the scientist live and work?
2. When was the scientist born? If no longer living, when did he or she die?
3. What area or areas of science did the scientist study?
4. Summarize the scientist's contributions to a view of atomic structure. How did his or her findings help our modern view of the atom?
5. What are some important or interesting facts about the scientist?

Using Your Research

With the information that you now have, make a presentation to your class. You could dress in costume to give the report. You could work with other students to make a panel of Distinguished Scientists, each student presenting and debating his or her contributions to our view of the atom. Another alternative would be to present the infor-

mation as if it were a television special. Whether you use one of these suggestions or another type of presentation, be creative.

Going Further

Even today, we still have much to learn about the structure of atoms. Investigate two of the following questions.
1. Why do many scientists believe that protons and neutrons are made of quarks?
2. How small are atoms? If placed end to end, how many oxygen atoms would form a line one centimeter long?
3. How heavy are atoms? If you had 28 g of gold, how many gold atoms would you have?
4. How does probability relate to our modern view of the atom?
5. How has the scanning tunneling microscope helped us to understand the structure of atoms?

697

TEACHING NOTES
• Before beginning this project, ask students how they could gather information about the contents of a container that they could not open. Remind students that, in a related way, this process is what scientists had to do to find out about atomic structure.
• Help students place their selected scientist in a historical setting. Ask students what political events were taking place during the scientist's lifetime, what the style of dress was, what laboratory facilities looked like, and other leading questions.
• Presentations will be more effective if they are done in chronological order.

GOING FURTHER
1. Quark theory has received support from observations of energy requirements and particle bombardment patterns of protons.
2. Assuming the diameter of an atom to be 1×10^{-10}, approximately 10^8 atoms would be required.
3. Students learned in Chapter 10 that the masses of atoms are in atomic mass units (u). If $1 \; u = 1.66 \times 10^{-24}$ g, and the mass of one atom of gold is 197 u, then

$$\frac{197 \; u}{atom} \times \frac{1.66 \times 10^{-24} \; g}{1 \; u} =$$

$$\frac{3.27 \times 10^{-22} \; g}{atom}$$

and

$$28 \; g \times \frac{1 \; atom}{3.27 \times 10^{-22} \; g} =$$

$$8.6 \times 10^{22} \; atoms.$$

4. Our present atomic view does not deal with exact positions of electrons. Rather, approximations and probabilities are how we best describe electron movement.
5. The scanning tunneling microscope has not led us to understand the interior structure of atoms, but it has been used to observe individual atoms and arrangements of atoms.

PROJECT 4

OVERVIEW

OBJECTIVES: By using the plastic container code system, students will *classify* plastics, *experiment*, and *communicate* their findings.

SUMMARY

This project directs students to apply their knowledge of carbon chemistry as they look at the practical uses of plastics and study the properties of an easily produced polymer that they make. Students will use the plastic container code to classify and identify the various plastic containers that they may encounter. Part of the project is to increase the awareness of plastic use and to possibly get involved in plastic recycling efforts.

TIME REQUIRED

This project should not be started until students begin Chapter 13. Students will need one to two class periods to find the structures of the polymers named. They will need one class period to involve other students in a plastics awareness week. One class period will be needed to synthesize the polymer. If class time is not easily available, the entire project can be done out of class.

PREPARATION

Cooperative Learning: Divide students into Expert Teams.

• Have chemistry textbooks or other references available for use by the students.

• If the polymer preparation is to be done in class, have a saturated borax solution, white school glue, paper cups, and paper towels available.

PROJECT 4 PLASTIC POLYMERS

As you got ready for school today, you may have poured the milk for your breakfast cereal from a plastic milk jug. You probably brushed your teeth using a toothbrush that has plastic bristles and a plastic handle. As you left your home, you may have grabbed your plastic-coated binder on your way out the door. Think of all the objects around you that are made of plastic. The chemicals that compose plastics typically share one common property. They can hook together to form long molecules called polymers. Polymers, including plastics, require a lot of energy to produce, and after they are formed, they can be difficult to break down. Because of these energy and disposal problems, people are now finding ways to reuse plastics by saving and recycling them.

Recycling: As Easy as 1, 2, 3

Recently, several industries have begun to imprint a classifying number on their plastic products. This number refers to a code that allows consumers to sort their plastic products based on their chemical makeup. For example, if you looked on the bottom of a plastic milk container, you may likely see the number 2 in a triangle formed from three arrows, perhaps followed by the letters *HDPE*. By examining several types of containers and using the classifying codes, you will learn more about polymer chemistry and possibly help improve our environment.

Before starting any other work on this project, use Section 14-3 of your textbook and other references to determine the general formula for the materials named in the plastic code table.

Then, use the following directions to explore plastics and to make a sample polymer.

1. Try to find examples of plastic products that are marked examples of each number.

REFERENCES

Mark, Herman F. *Giant Molecules.* New York, NY: Time, Inc., Life Science Library, 1966.

Saunders, K.J. *Organic Polymer Chemistry.* London: Chapman and Hall, 1988.

2. Prepare a display for the class that shows each number and examples of plastic products that illustrate that number.

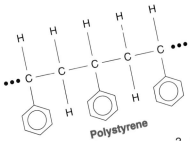
Polystyrene

3. Make a list of all the objects in the classroom that are made from plastics.

4. You may prepare your own polymer with common white school glue and a saturated solution of borax and water. Squeeze some of the glue into a cup containing the saturated borax solution. As the product forms, use your hands to pinch it together and form it into a ball. Dry the formed ball with a paper towel.

Using Your Research

Start a plastics awareness week in your class. Have students bring clean plastics from home and sort them into boxes premarked with the recycling number. At the end of a week decide what type is the most common. Contact your local landfill to determine the availability of plastic recycling operations.

Use your polymer glue ball to illustrate some of the properties of polymers. Does the glue ball bounce? Does it stretch? What caused the glue to go from a liquid to a flexible solid? Many everyday types of polymers also have a flexible nature. Some, however are more rigid.

Going Further

The use of plastic in many of our everyday objects is a relatively new development. Ask parents or older family members or friends to describe objects that are now made of plastics but were formerly made of other materials.

Contact the Plastics Institute of America in Fairfield, NJ to ask about how recycled plastics are used.

Plastic Coding System

1	PETE (polyethylene terephthalate)
2	HDPE (high density polyethylene)
3	V (vinyl)
4	LDPE (low density polyethylene)
5	PP (polypropylene)
6	PS (polystyrene)
7	Other

699

TEACHING NOTES

• Plastics make up one class of polymers that are mid-range on an extensibility scale. This scale measures how much a material can be stretched and then returned to its original dimensions. Elastomers are highest on this scale, while fibers are the least extensible.

• The plastics' identification numbers, abbreviations, general formulas, and common uses are summarized in the table below.

• If your community has an active recycling center, ask a representative to visit the class to discuss the importance and present status of plastic recycling.

• Polyethylene may be branched or linear in its structure. When it is branched, a more rigid, higher-density polymer is formed.

• In the polymer that the students make, a cross-linked molecule is responsible for making bonds between polymer chains. The borate attaches some amino acids in the casein protein of the glue to other amino acids.

GOING FURTHER

• The current address and phone number for the Plastics Institute of America is 277 Fairfield Road, Suite 100, Fairfield, NJ 07004-1932. Recycled plastics are currently being used for carpets, textiles, and clothing (PET); packaging for motor oil, household detergents, and bleach and plastic lumber (HDPE); and garbage bags (all types of retail purchase bags).

Code Number	Symbol	General Formula	Use	Code Number	Symbol	General Formula	Use
1	PETE	-O-C-C-O-C-⟨◯⟩-C- (with H, H, O, O)	Soft drink bottles	4	LDPE	-C-C-C-C- (with H H H H)	Cottage cheese containers
2	HDPE	-C-C-C-C-C- (branches, H H H H CH₂-)	Plastic milk bottles	5	PP	-C-C-C-C- (H CH₃ H CH₃)	Shampoo bottles
3	V	-C-C-C-C- (H Cl H Cl)	Garden hoses, binders	6	PS	-C-C-C-C- (H ◯ H ◯)	Foam cups and plates

PROJECT 5

OVERVIEW

OBJECTIVES: Students will *gather evidence* that catalysts have a special role in changing the rate of a reaction. They will *control variables* as they test for the presence of a catalyst and *make a model* of a generalized enzyme reaction.

SUMMARY

Enzymes are made of proteins. In the body, enzymes act as biological catalysts, each enzyme catalyzing a specific reaction. Using common food items, students will develop an investigation that shows the role the catalyst protease plays in breaking down protein. After comparing the results to a control, students will infer what has taken place. Then, students will construct a model that proposes a lock-and-key mechanism for a generalized, enzyme-catalyzed reaction.

TIME REQUIRED

This project would best be introduced when catalysts are discussed in Chapter 16. If this project is to be done in class, students will require part of one class period to prepare the gelatin dessert. An additional class period will be needed to test the gelatin with the other materials. Students will need some time to research other catalyzed reactions. One class period will be required to model the enzyme reaction.

PREPARATION

Cooperative Learning: Divide students into Science Investigation Teams.
• Obtain dry gelatin mix and materials to be tested.
• Arrange with the school cafeteria or home arts department for refrigerator access.
• Provide poster board, scissors, and markers for students to use in preparing the enzyme model.

As you read this, think of the last meal that you ate. The meal may have included some foods that are similar in makeup, such as bread and potatoes. It probably included some foods that are quite different, such as meat and vegetables. How is your body able to break down such different, complex food materials into simple, useful products that your body can use? The chemicals responsible for this relatively quick process are produced by your body and are called enzymes. Enzymes are part of a broader classification of chemicals called catalysts. In this project, you will investigate the ways in which catalysts change reaction rates. You will find out more about the importance of these interesting chemicals that bring about change without being permanently changed themselves.

A Catalyzed Reaction

Enzymes are typically named after a specific reaction and given an *-ase* ending. For example, protease refers to enzymes that break down proteins. Proteases can be found in some fresh fruits. Meat-tenderizing products also contain proteases.

Do the following activity to study how protease breaks down the protein in gelatin.

REFERENCES

Metzler, David E. *Biochemistry.* New York, NY: Academic Press Inc., 1977.

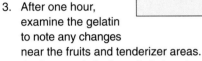

1. Using the printed instructions on the box, prepare a gelatin dessert and divide it into five samples.

2. Place a piece of freshly cut kiwi fruit on the first sample, freshly cut pineapple on the second, canned pineapple on the third, some meat tenderizer on the fourth, and use the other sample as a control.

3. After one hour, examine the gelatin to note any changes near the fruits and tenderizer areas.

4. As the protein in the gelatin breaks down, water from the gelatin is released. Make a chart showing the degree of protein breakdown in each sample.

5. Which of your samples showed the most protein breakdown in one hour? What could cause canned and fresh pineapple to have different results? What are the general breakdown products of proteins?

Using Your Research

Do other fruits contain protease enzymes? Design a testing procedure to determine the relative levels of protease in fruits.

Going Further

Just as opening a lock is most effectively done with a specific key, enzymes are able to effectively change the rate of specific reactions In fact, the fit between a lock and key is often used as a model to explain enzyme activity. You can illustrate one model for this by cutting from a piece of poster board the shapes shown.

A and B represent two molecules that will react when the two dotted areas are close. That particular positioning can happen more quickly when the enzyme molecule is present. The enzyme can easily fit A and B together in just the correct way by attaching A and B in its fitted areas. Once A and B are attached to the enzyme, the dots are aligned and A can be attached to B. The enzyme can then be removed and be free to attach to other A and B molecules.

TEACHING NOTES

• The enzyme protease, which is found in some fruits, speeds up the breakdown of proteins. Water is trapped when the proteins bond together during the gel formation. Evidence for the breakdown of the protein structure is the release of the trapped water.

• The structure and bonding within an enzyme can be changed by heating, exposure to acids and bases, or oxidation. Any of these factors could be responsible for changing the structure of the protease in canned pineapple. Without its own structure intact, an enzyme will lose its catalytic activity.

• A general reaction that involves a catalyst can be expressed as

$$X + Y \rightarrow XY$$
$$XY + Z \rightarrow XZ + Y,$$

where substance Y is the catalyst because it is regenerated. A reaction of this type can be seen in the ozone-depleting reaction shown on page 409, where chlorine atoms act to speed the breakdown of ozone.

• Other enzymes that could be studied include catalase, which will break down hydrogen peroxide into hydrogen and oxygen; amylase, the enzyme in saliva that catalyzes the conversion of starch to glucose; and papain, an enzyme found in some meat tenderizers that also breaks down proteins.

GOING FURTHER

• The lock and key model can be constructed various ways. It should be used as the group explains how the activity of a catalyst may depend on forming some attachments that more effectively align the reactants to allow them to bond more easily.

PROJECT 6

OVERVIEW

OBJECTIVES: Students will investigate the *cause* of eye problems and the *effect* that these problems have on vision. Students will also study the parts of the eye and relate them to the optics of corrective lenses.

SUMMARY

In Unit 6, students learned about the properties of light and other waves. This project will help students use these principles to understand human vision. After studying the structure of the eye, students will build a convex lens to model the lens in the human eye and find the focal length of this and other lenses. Students will contact a person employed in eye care careers in the process of researching as many vision or eye health problems as possible. They will share all this information in the form of poster presentations.

TIME REQUIRED

This project can be done while studying Chapter 20. One class period is required to establish groups and define the task. While discussing convex lenses in class, procedure Steps 2 and 3 can be done in about 30 minutes. Allow for group meeting time throughout this chapter. One class period will be required to share and discuss the posters.

PREPARATION

Cooperative Learning: Divide the class into Expert Teams of three students each.
• For each group, have available two matching watch glasses, a selection of convex and concave lenses from old eyeglasses, grafting wax or waterproof epoxy, a bowl of water, and a ruler.
• You may want to arrange for a vision care specialist to speak to the class.

PROJECT 6 VISION: MORE THAN MEETS THE EYE

How are your eyes able to focus on the words on this page? Your eye contains a lens that causes light that is reflected from objects to converge on the retina. But why do so many people wear corrective eyewear? In Chapter 20, you learned that a number of vision problems, such as farsightedness, nearsightedness, and astigmatism, can result when one or more parts of the eye do not function correctly. Eyeglasses and contact lenses are the most common ways to correct these vision problems, although laser surgery is becoming increasingly popular. If you were having trouble seeing the words on this page, whom would you see for help? Perhaps after researching some common vision problems and their methods of correction, you will see the world of vision through new eyes.

Investigating Vision

Have you ever wondered who invented and wore the first eyeglasses? What kinds of materials are used in making corrective eyewear? Who is responsible for testing and treating health of the eyes? With your group, you will be researching information in three different categories: eye and vision problems, lenses and correction of eye problems, and careers related to eye care.

Your Cooperative Learning group will use:
• a selection of convex and concave lenses
• a ruler
• two watch glasses
• grafting wax
• a bowl of water

Research the following questions and perform the suggested experiments. Be sure to record your results in as much detail as possible.

1. Sketch a diagram of the eye and label each part. Find out the role of each part in human vision.

2. Build a convex lens to model the lens in your eye. Do this by placing two watch glasses together underwater to trap water inside. Seal them together with grafting wax. How is this model lens similar to and different than the lens in your eye?

3. Find the focal length of several convex lenses, including the one you made. Hold your lens against a piece of white paper

---

REFERENCES

Ahrens, Kathleen. *Opportunities in Eye Careers.* Chicago, IL: VGM Career Horizons, 1991.

D'Alonzo, Dr. T.L. *Your Eyes!* Clifton Heights, PA: Avanti Publishing, 1991.

Falk, David, Dieter Brill and David Stork. *Seeing the Light.* New York, NY: John Wiley and Sons, 1986.

across the room from a window in a slightly darkened room. Slowly move the lens away from the paper until you see a clear image of the window blinds or an outside object on the paper. Measure the distance from the lens to the paper to find the focal length.

4. Identify as many vision or eye health problems as you can. Be sure to investigate nearsightedness, farsightedness, astigmatism, cataracts, glaucoma, and colorblindness. How are each of these problems corrected?

5. What is the difference between an optometrist and an ophthalmologist? Write a list of questions you would like to ask, and interview a person employed in the field of eye care.

Using Your Research

Design two posters to share your information with other students in the class. One poster should illustrate the human eye, including the parts and their functions. You can also describe on this poster what optometrists and ophthalmologists do. On the second poster, illustrate some of the types of eye problems you learned about. Be sure you can explain how these problems can be corrected. Present your posters to the class and encourage them to identify the problems they or someone they know have been examined or treated for.

Going Further

Think about the advances in diagnosing and treating problems of the eyes that have occurred during your lifetime. What new kinds of contact lenses and eyeglasses are available? What kinds of materials are used in corrective eyewear? What are the advantages of having glass lenses? Plastic lenses? How are lasers currently being used to treat eye problems? Will there be a time when most common eyesight problems are corrected surgically rather than with eyeglasses?

TEACHING NOTES

• You may wish to divide procedure Step 4 among the groups, giving each group a particular eye problem to focus on.

• If lenses are made with watch glasses of different sizes, have groups compare the focal lengths. Also students can experiment with the effects of filling the lenses with different clear liquids.

• If a model of the eye is available, this model may be used to reinforce the parts of the eye and their functions.

GOING FURTHER

Have students survey people younger than 18 and also adults to find out what percent wear corrective lenses. The survey can be expanded to include what type of lens is chosen. Students can investigate the benefits and drawbacks of using daily wear contacts, extended wear contacts, disposable contacts, and glass and plastic eyeglass lenses.

Lasers are commonly used to remove cataracts and can sometimes be used to correct other vision problems.

PROJECT 7

OVERVIEW

OBJECTIVES: Students will research the process and *construct a model* of how nuclear power plants produce electricity. They will *compare and contrast* the benefits and problems associated with nuclear power.

SUMMARY

In this project, students will identify the functions of the main parts of a nuclear reactor and study how the entire system works together to produce electricity. They will use common materials to build a model of a nuclear reactor. Using this scientific understanding as a base, they will analyze the benefits and problems associated with the use of nuclear power, such a the handling of nuclear waste. Their findings will be presented to the class in the form of a panel discussion or a debate.

TIME REQUIRED

This project can be worked on throughout Chapters 24 and 25. One full period should be allowed to establish groups, roles, and goals. During the study of these chapters, some time should be planned for groups to meet, build models, and answer the questions presented. At least one full period will be required for the final panel discussion or debate.

PREPARATION

Cooperative Learning:
Divide students into Paired Partners or Science Investigation Teams. Have groups assign specific roles to assure participation of all group members.
• Have some of the building materials listed in the student text available for constructing the models. Encourage students to bring other useful items, such as cereal boxes and cardboard tubes, from home.
• Write or call the United States Department of Energy to request free pamphlets and curriculum materials. Videotapes may also be available.

PROJECT 7

NUCLEAR POWER: SOLVING AND CAUSING PROBLEMS

Every day you probably depend on electrical energy to run the lights and appliances in your home or school. What is the source of this energy? When you play your stereo can you tell whether this energy comes from burning coal, harnessing energy from the wind or running water, or splitting atomic nuclei? As you learned in Chapter 25, all of these processes change energy to electrical energy that can be easily transferred to your home.

Approximately one-fifth of the electrical energy produced in the United States is generated in nuclear power plants. In this process, the nuclei of certain atoms are split, and a very small amount of mass is converted to a large amount of energy. How is this energy used to make electricity?

Nuclear Power— Constructing a Model

To understand how a nuclear power plant produces electricity, it is useful to build a three-dimensional model. You may find the description and diagram of a nuclear power plant on pages 649-650 useful in beginning this project, but you should research other

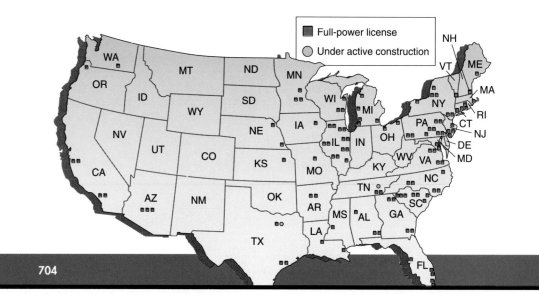

REFERENCES

Galperin, Anne L. *Nuclear Energy/Nuclear Waste*. New York, NY: Chelsea House Pub., 1992.

Kaku, Michio and Jennifer Trainer. *Nuclear Power: Both Sides*. New York, NY: W.W. Norton and Co., 1982.

Kiefer, Irene. *Nuclear Energy at the Crossroads*. New York, NY: Atheneum, 1982.

Wolfson, Richard. *Nuclear Choices: A Citizen's Guide to Nuclear Technology*. Cambridge, MA: The MIT Press, 1991.

The *Science, Society, and America's Nuclear Waste Curriculum* four-part series is available from the Department of Energy, OCRWM Information Center, Attn. Curriculum Department, P.O. Box 44375, Washington, DC 20026.

sources for more detail. Before making the actual model, do the following or answer the following questions, using several resources. Explain your findings in as much detail as possible.

1. Sketch a diagram of the main parts of a nuclear power plant. Describe the role or function of each part and how the parts work together. Be sure to clearly identify the purposes of different water systems in the plant.

2. What isotope is most commonly used as a fuel in fission reactors? How are the fuel rods prepared? Write one possible nuclear equation to show the fission of this nucleus when it is hit by a neutron.

3. Study the map of geographical distribution of nuclear plants in the United States. Where is the highest concentration of plants? State a hypothesis as to why the concentration is high in this area. Where is the nuclear power plant that is closest to your community?

4. What are the benefits and problems of using nuclear energy to generate electricity? Support your answers with concrete information.

5. Many methods of generating electricity produce some undesirable waste products. What kinds of wastes are produced in nuclear plants, and what is done to dispose of them?

6. Design a brief survey to find out people's understanding of nuclear energy and their opinions about the use of nuclear power. Give the

survey to a specific number of adults and teenagers. Tally the results.

Using Your Research

Use your understanding of the parts and operation of a reactor to design and build a scale model of a nuclear power plant. Think carefully about common objects that could be used to model a certain part, such as using straws or pencils for control rods. The following materials may be helpful:

- an assortment of cardboard or paper boxes and tubes
- construction paper
- markers
- tape or glue
- resource materials on nuclear energy from the Department of Energy

Use your model to take students on a guided tour of the plant. What types of jobs might

TEACHING NOTES

- Contact the nuclear power plant nearest your home. They may be able to provide written materials, a videotape, or a guest speaker.
- Students may need help writing a nuclear equation to show one of the possible results of splitting uranium-235. Remind them that charge (the bottom number) and mass (the top number) must be balanced in a nuclear equation. Sample equation:

$$_{0}^{1}n + _{92}^{235}U \rightarrow _{56}^{141}Ba + _{36}^{92}Kr + 3_{0}^{1}n$$

- Discuss where the energy in a nuclear reaction comes from. According to Einstein's equation, $E = mc^2$, a small amount of mass is destroyed to release a huge amount of energy. (E represents energy, m represents mass, and c represents the speed of light.)
- Facilitate a discussion of why there is a higher concentration of nuclear power plants in the eastern United States than there are in other regions. The eastern part of the country has a higher population density, and thus a greater energy demand. Also, more fossil fuels are available in some other sections of the United States.

Student answers should reflect that millions of times more energy is released from the nuclear reaction. For example, in an average person's lifetime, over 1.5 million kg of coal versus 2.5 uranium fuel pellets will be needed to supply the person's energy needs.

Breeder reactors produce uranium-239 when a uranium-238 nucleus absorbs a neutron produced in the fission of uranium-235. This uranium-239 decays in several days to produce plutonium-239, which is fissionable and can be separated and used as fuel. Plutonium-239 is also chemically toxic, and it can be used to make nuclear weapons.

be available in the field of nuclear power? Because many scientists and technicians would work in a specialized field, each group member could be responsible for explaining a specific part of the operation. Be sure to emphasize safety precautions built into the plant's design.

Stage an organized panel discussion or debate on the benefits and problems associated with the use of nuclear power. Opinions discussed must be supported with facts learned in your research. After the discussion, have the rest of the class take the survey as scientifically informed citizens.

How do these survey results compare to those of people who did not hear your discussion?

Going Further

One advantage of nuclear fission reactors is that splitting tiny amounts of uranium-235 releases tremendous amounts of energy. How does the energy per amount of mass in this process compare to the amount of energy released from burning the same mass of coal?

Although uranium-235 seems to be a more efficient source of energy, it, like coal, is a nonrenewable resource. We must have other plans to meet our long-range energy needs. Breeder reactors have been designed to extend the possibilities of nuclear energy. What are breeder reactors? What are the benefits and problems associated with breeder reactors?

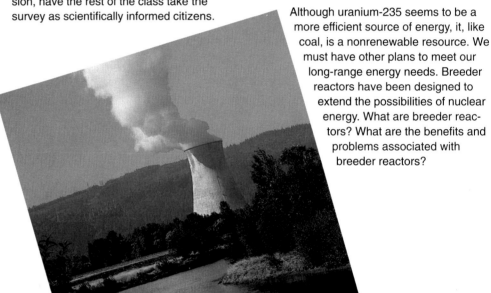

GLOSSARY

This glossary defines each key term that appears in **bold type** in the text. It also shows the page number where you can find the word used. Some other terms that you may need to look up are included, too. We also show how to pronounce some of the words that are spelled phonetically within the student text. A key to pronunciation is in the table below.

PRONUNCIATION KEY

a . . . back (bak)	oh . . . go (goh)	sh . . . shelf (shelf)
ay . . . day (day)	aw . . . soft (sawft)	ch . . . nature (nay chur)
ah . . . father (fahth ur)	or . . . orbit (or but)	g . . . gift (gihft)
ow . . . flower (flow ur)	oy . . . coin (coyn)	j . . . gem (jem)
ar . . . car (car)	oo . . . foot (foot)	ing . . . sing (sing)
e . . . less (les)	ew . . . food (fewd)	zh . . . vision (vihzh un)
ee . . . leaf (leef)	yoo . . . pure (pyoor)	k . . . cake (kayk)
ih . . . trip (trihp)	yew . . . few (fyew)	s . . . seed, cent (seed, sent)
i (i + con + e) . . . idea	uh . . . comma (cahm uh)	z . . . zone, raise (zohn, rayz)
(i dee uh), life (life)	u (+ con) . . . flower (flow ur)	

acceleration: the rate of change in velocity (speed and/or direction). (66)

acid: a substance that produces hydrogen ions (H⁺) when dissolved in water; this lowers the solution's pH below 7. (426)

acid rain: rain that is more acidic than normal because it contains dilute sulfuric acid (from coal-burning power plants) and dilute nitric acid (from car exhausts). (438)

acoustics: the study of sound. (478)

actinoid: any of the 14 radioactive elements having atomic numbers 89-102; used in nuclear power generation and nuclear weapons.

active solar heating: collecting the sun's energy with solar panels, heating water with that energy, and storing the heated water to use the energy later.

aerosol: a liquid sprayed from a pressurized container; for example, a can of insect spray.

air resistance: the frictional force air exerts on a moving object, opposite in direction to the object's motion. (88)

alchemist: a medieval version of the modern chemist; a practitioner blended primitive chemistry with magic, seeking to turn ordinary metals into gold.

alcohol: a substituted hydrocarbon in which one or more hydrogen atoms have been replaced by an –OH group; for example, ethanol. (335)

allotropes: different molecular structures of the same element; for example, some carbon molecules form soft graphite whereas others form hard diamonds. (317)

alloy: a solid solution of a metal with other metals or nonmetals; for example, brass or steel. (352)

alpha particle: a low-energy particle given off by a radioactive atomic nucleus; it is a helium nucleus (two protons and two neutrons with a positive charge). (624)

alternating current (AC): electrical current that reverses its direction many times each second; the AC in our homes reverses direction 60 times each second. (585)

amalgam: an alloy containing the element mercury; for example, dental fillings are amalgams. (355)

ammeter: a galvanometer that measures the electrical current flowing in a circuit, in amperes. (580)

amorphous: something that has no specific shape; for example, a liquid or gas.

ampere: the unit for measuring the rate of flow of electrons in a circuit; abbreviated *A*; 1 ampere = 1 coulomb of charge flowing past a point in 1 second.

amplification: the process of increasing the strength of an electric current. (600)

amplitude: in a wave, the distance from the resting position to either the crest or trough (they are the same distance). (459)

707

amplitude-modulated (AM) waves: radio waves whose amplitude is varied with voice, music, video, or data for transmission over long distances.

angle of incidence: in waves, the angle formed by the incident wave and the normal (perpendicular); labeled i.

angle of reflection: in waves, the angle formed by the reflected wave and the normal (perpendicular); labeled r.

anhydrous: a chemical compound that normally has water molecules attached to its ions, but from which the water has been removed.

antacid: an "anti-acid," or a chemical that changes an acid substance to a neutral substance.

antifreeze: a solute added to a solvent to lower the temperature at which the solvent will freeze; for example, the antifreeze added to water in a car's cooling system.

aqueous: describes a solution made with water; for example, ammonia water is an aqueous solution of ammonia gas.

Archimedes' principle: the Greek mathematician Archimedes stated that the buoyant force that pushes up on an object in a fluid is equal to the weight of the fluid displaced by the object. (210)

aromatic compounds: chemical compounds that contain the benzene ring structure; most have distinctive aromas. (334)

astigmatism: an uneven curvature of the eye's cornea, causing blurry vision.

atomic number: the number of protons in an atom's nucleus; each element has a unique number (hydrogen = 1, helium = 2, and so on). (243)

average atomic mass: the average mass of all isotopes of an element; used as a convenience, because most elements have more than one isotope and therefore more than one mass number. (253)

average speed: a rate of motion determined by dividing the distance traveled by travel time. (61)

B

balance: a device used in laboratories to measure mass; it works by balancing an "unknown" (material whose mass is to be determined) with a standard mass that is known.

balanced chemical equation: a chemical equation that has the same number of atoms of each element on both sides of the equation. (410)

balanced forces: forces that are equal in size and opposite in direction. (70)

bar graph: a type of graph used to show information collected by counting; uses vertical or horizontal bars of different lengths to help people compare quantities.

base: a substance that produces hydroxide ions (OH^-) when dissolved in water; this raises the solution's pH above 7. (430)

Bernoulli's principle: the Swiss mathematician Daniel Bernoulli stated that, as the velocity of a fluid increases, the pressure exerted by the fluid decreases. (212)

beta particle: a high-energy particle given off by a radioactive atomic nucleus; it is a negatively charged electron. (625)

BHA: a food preservative; it is a chemical inhibitor that slows the chemical reactions that spoil food (*Butylated Hydroxyanisole*).

BHT: a food preservative; it is a chemical inhibitor that slows the chemical reactions that spoil food (*Butylated Hydroxytoluene*).

binary compound: a chemical compound composed of two elements; for example, sodium chloride. (283)

biodegradable: describes a material that can be decomposed into a harmless form by the biological action of organisms such as bacteria.

biogas: gas (mostly methane) produced by plant and animal wastes that rot in the absence of air. (338)

biomass: all plant and animal material, both dead and alive; sometimes used as fuel. (338)

boiling point: the temperature at which vapor bubbles form in a liquid and rise to the surface, increasing evaporation.

Boyle's law: English physicist Robert Boyle stated that, if a container of gas is made smaller, the pressure throughout the gas increases (if the temperature stays the same). (205)

breeder reactor: a type of nuclear reactor that breeds new fuel as it operates. (654)

brittleness: a characteristic of certain materials that makes them break easily when stressed.

bubble chamber: a chamber filled with a superheated liquid; used to detect charged nuclear particles, which leave a trail of bubbles as they pass through. (631)

buoyant force: the upward force exerted on an object when it is completely immersed in a fluid. (209)

butane: a flammable gas (C_4H_{10}); a part of natural gas.

byte: a basic unit of computer memory that represents a character (number, symbol, or alphabet letter); consists of 8 bits.

C

calorimeter: an instrument used to measure changes in thermal energy.

carbohydrate: an organic compound characteristically having twice as many hydrogen atoms as oxygen atoms; for example, glucose = $C_6H_{12}O_6$ (343)

carbon-14 dating: age-determining method for carbon-containing objects up to 50 000 years old; works by calculating the half-life of the radioactive carbon-14 remaining in the object.

catalyst: a substance that speeds a chemical reaction without itself being changed. (418)

cathode-ray tube (CRT): a picture tube with an internal electron gun that fires a stream of electrons (cathode rays) at a fluorescent screen to produce pictures. (605)

central processing unit (CPU): the main circuit board inside a computer that performs the calculating and holds the main memory.

centripetal (sen TRIHP uh tuhl) acceleration: acceleration (change in speed and/or direction) toward the center of a curve. (92)

centripetal force: the force that causes an object to move toward the center of a curve. (92)

ceramic: a material made from clay or sand, usually baked at a high temperature. (357)

cermet: a synthetic material made to have the properties of both a ceramic and an alloy; for example, some magnets use cermet material (*cer*amic + *met*al). (358)

chain reaction: a continuing series of fission reactions in which neutrons from fissioning nuclei cause other nuclei to split, releasing more neutrons which split more nuclei, and so on. (634)

Charles's law: French scientist Jacques-Alexandre Charles stated that the volume of a gas increases when temperature increases (if the pressure stays the same). (205)

chemical bond: the force that holds together the atoms in a compound. (271)

chemical change: the change of one substance to another substance by changing the elements in it, or by changing their proportions. (232)

chemical formula: a precise statement of the elements in a compound and their ratio; for example, H_2O, CO_2, or $C_{12}H_{22}O_{11}$. (270)

chemically stable: describes an atom whose outermost energy level is filled with electrons, so that it does not form compounds under normal conditions; for example: helium, neon. (270)

chemically unstable: describes an atom whose outermost energy level is not filled with electrons, so it seeks electrons from other atoms and thus forms compounds; for example: sodium, chlorine.

chemical property: a characteristic of a substance that indicates whether it can undergo a certain chemical change. (233)

chemical reaction: a change in which substances are converted to different substances that have different properties. (404)

chemical symbol: a shorthand way to write the name of an element; for example: *O* for oxygen, *Fe* for iron. (242)

chloro-: prefix meaning chlorine, as in tetrachloroethylene or chlorofluorocarbon.

chlorofluorocarbon (CFC): a group of chemicals compounded of chlorine, fluorine, and carbon; used as refrigerants and spray propellants; damaging to the atmosphere's ozone layer. (409)

circuit: a closed path through which electrons (electricity) can flow. (552)

circuit breaker: a device that protects an electrical circuit. If too much current flows, the circuit breaker switches off the current flow.

cloud chamber: a chamber filled with water-saturated air; used to detect charged nuclear particles, which leave a vapor trail as they pass through. (630)

coal: a rock formed of ancient decayed plants; burned as a fossil fuel.

coefficient: in a chemical equation, a number to the left of each reactant and product that shows the relative amount of each substance involved in the reaction; for example, the *3* in $3H_2O$. (406)

coherent light: a beam of light in which all rays travel parallel to one another, so that the beam spreads out very little even over thousands of kilometers. (530)

colloid: a heterogeneous mixture containing tiny particles that do not settle; for example, milk and gelatin. (223)

combustion: rapid oxidation, or burning. (148)

commutator: a reversing switch in a direct-current electric motor that changes the polarity of the current with each half-revolution. (581)

composite: a material made by mixing other materials to combine the desirable properties of each. (367)

compound: matter that is a combination of atoms of two or more elements. (220)

compound machine: a combination of two or more simple machines. (174)

compression: in compressional waves, the dense area of the wave.

compressional wave: a wave that vibrates in the same direction in which the wave is traveling. (464)

computer: a device you can program to do calculations, make logical decisions, and manipulate data.

computer virus: a computer program designed to infect a computer and make it "sick"; it can erase data, scramble other programs, or fill up memory so the system won't work right. (612)

concave lens: a lens that is thinner in the middle and thicker at the edges and thus curves inward. (519)

concave mirror: a mirror whose surface curves inward, producing a reflected image that is enlarged. (513)

concentrated solution: a solution in which the amount of solute is near the maximum that the solvent can hold.

concentration: generally, the proportion of a solute dissolved in a solvent; specifically, the milliliters of solute, plus enough solvent to total 100 mL of solution.

condensation: the change of a substance from a gaseous state to a liquid state; for example, water vapor condensing on a cold surface. (201)

condense: to go from the gas state to the liquid state, due to a loss of heat.

conduction: the transfer of energy through matter by direct contact of particles; the movement of heat or electricity through a substance. (134)

conductor: a material that allows heat or electrons to move easily through it. (547)

constant: in an experiment, a factor that cannot change. (21)

constant speed: a rate of motion that does not vary, such as Earth's speed in orbit. (61)

contract: movement of molecules toward one another, so that they occupy a smaller space.

control: in an experiment, the standard for comparison. (20)

convection: the transfer of energy through matter by movement of the matter itself, as in air or water currents. (135)

convex lens: a lens that is thicker in the middle than at the edges and thus curves outward. (518)

convex mirror: a mirror with a surface that curves outward. (515)

cooling tower: a tower-shaped device in which water is cooled by fans or evaporation; used in factories and power plants. (147)

corrosive: describes any substance that attacks and alters metals, human tissue, or other materials; for example, battery acid, bleach, and cleaners for ovens, toilets, and drains. (274)

coulomb: the charge carried by 6.24 billion billion electrons.

covalent bond: A type of chemical bond formed by atoms when they share electrons; this force holds together molecules in gases like oxygen (O_2) and nitrogen (N_2), and in compounds like water (H_2O). (278)

crest: in waves, the highest point of a wave. (459)

critical temperature: in superconductors, the very low temperature at which a material ceases to have any electrical resistance.

critical thinking: the process of using thinking skills to solve problems. (14)

crystal: a solid having a distinctive shape because its atoms are arranged in repeating geometric patterns. (191)

current: the flow of electrons through a conductor, measured in amperes with an ammeter. (553)

deceleration: the rate of change in velocity (speed and/or direction) when velocity is decreasing; also called negative acceleration.

decibel: the unit of measure for sound intensity, abbreviated *dB*. The faintest sound most people can hear = 0 dB.

decomposition reaction: a chemical reaction in which a substance breaks down (decomposes) into two or more simpler substances. (414)

dehydrating agent: a substance that removes water from materials; for example, sulfuric acid. (428)

density: how tightly packed a substance's molecules are; expressed as the mass of a substance divided by its volume, in g/cm^3. (39)

dependent variable: in an experiment, the factor that is forced to change because the independent variable is changed. (21)

derived unit: a unit of measurement formed by combining other units of measurement; for example, density is a derived unit formed by dividing an object's mass by its volume. (38)

desalination: removing dissolved salts from seawater to produce fresh, drinkable water. (386)

desalination plant: facility for removing dissolved salts from seawater to produce fresh, drinkable water.

detergent: an organic salt similar to soap, except that detergents do not form soap scum in hard water. (444)

diatomic molecule: a molecule made up of two atoms of the same element; for example, hydrogen (H_2) or oxygen (O_2). (311)

diesel engine: an internal combustion engine that compresses a fuel-air mixture so much that it ignites from the heat of compression, without a spark.

diffraction: the bending of waves around a barrier. (503)

diffraction grating: a piece of glass or plastic with many parallel slits that acts like a prism, causing white light that passes through it to separate into its component colors (the spectrum). (505)

dilute solution: a solution in which the amount of solute is much less than the maximum the solvent can hold.

diode: a type of rectifier that allows electric current to flow only in one direction. (599)

direct current (DC): electrical current that flows in only one direction; thus direct current cells (batteries) are labeled + and – so you can install them the right way. (585)

disinfectant: a chemical that kills bacteria, such as alcohol.

dissociation: the breaking apart of an ionic compound (like salt) into positive and negative ions when dissolved in water. (396)

distillation: a water-purifying process in which water is evaporated from a solution, and the vapor is cooled to condense it to a pure liquid. (387)

DNA: *de*oxyribo*nu*cleic *a*cid, an acid in the nuclei of cells that codes and stores genetic information.

doping: adding an impurity to a semiconductor to increase its electrical conductivity.

Doppler effect: an increase or decrease in wave frequency, caused by motion of the source and/or motion of the observer; applies to all waves (including light, heat, sound, and so on).

710

dot diagram: a diagram of an atom, using the element symbol with dots to show the electrons in the outer energy level. (257)

double displacement reaction: a chemical reaction in which the positive ions in two or more substances trade places. (415)

dry cell: a power source that generates electric current by a chemical reaction; "dry" because it uses a thick, pasty electrolyte in a sealed container instead of a liquid electrolyte as in a car battery. (554)

ductile: describes metals that can be pulled into thin strands (wire). (300)

E

efficiency: the amount of work put into a machine compared to how much useful work is put out by the machine; always between 0 percent and 100 percent. (175)

effort arm: the part of a lever to which the effort force (F_e) is applied. (163)

effort force (F_e): the force applied to a machine. (159)

electrical power: the rate at which electrical energy is converted to another form of energy, such as heat; measured in kilowatt-hours. (565)

electric field: a force surrounding an electron that affects anything nearby that has an electric charge; is strongest near the electron and weakens with distance. (547)

electric motor: a device that changes electric energy into mechanical energy; for example, the motor in an electric fan.

electrolyte: a substance that forms ions in a water solution, making the water an electrical conductor; for example, sodium chloride and hydrogen chloride. (396)

electromagnet: a temporary magnet formed when an electric current is passed through a wire coil that surrounds an iron core. (578)

electromagnetic induction: electrical current induced in a wire when it is moved through a magnetic field. (583)

electromagnetic radiation: transverse energy waves that radiate in all directions from their source; vary in length from very long radio waves to extremely short X rays and gamma rays.

electromagnetic spectrum: the classification of electromagnetic waves, either by wavelength or frequency. (484)

electron: a negatively charged particle that orbits around the nucleus of an atom. (243)

electron arrangement: in an atom, how the electrons are distributed in the atom's various energy levels.

electron cloud: actually not a cloud, but the space where electrons most probably exist around the nucleus of an atom. (244)

electroscope: a device used to detect the presence of electric charges. (549)

element: matter in which all the atoms are alike; for example, zinc, chlorine, and aluminum. (220)

endothermic reaction: a chemical reaction that requires the addition of heat energy to proceed; thus the reaction absorbs heat from its surroundings. (417)

energy: the ability to cause change. (110)

energy farming: the growing of plants for use as fuel. (338)

energy transfer: the movement of energy from one object to another; for example, thermal energy flowing as heat from a stove to a skillet.

ester: a chemical compound formed by reacting an organic acid with an alcohol; some provide the scents in flowers, fruits, and candy. (444)

evaporation: the change of a substance from a liquid state to a gaseous state. (200)

exothermic reaction: a chemical reaction that releases heat energy. (418)

expand: outward movement of molecules away from one another, so that they occupy a larger space.

experiment: a controlled procedure for testing a hypothesis. (20)

external combustion engine: an engine in which the fuel is burned outside the engine, and energy from it is used to operate the engine; for example, an old-fashioned steam engine. (150)

F

factor: a condition that affects the outcome of an event.

farsighted: describes a person who sees faraway things clearly, but has trouble focusing on nearby objects.

fiberglass: hairlike strands of glass that make a good insulator when arranged in puffy layers.

filter: in working with light, a device that allows one or more colors to be transmitted while others are absorbed.

flame test: a laboratory test to identify elements by heating a substance in a flame and observing the flame color.

flammable: a chemical characteristic of a substance that allows it to oxidize rapidly; also called burnable.

flash distillation: a desalination process where seawater is pumped into a vacuum chamber so it boils quickly and at a lower temperature (because the normal air pressure is absent).

fluid: any material that can flow, such as air, water, or molten metal. (135)

fluorescence: occurs when a material absorbs ultraviolet radiation, which stimulates it to radiate visible light.

fluorescent light: light produced by phosphors when they are stimulated by ultraviolet light, as in a fluorescent light bulb. (498)

focal length: the distance from the center of a lens or mirror to its focal point. (513)

focal point: a point on the optical axis of a concave mirror or convex lens where the light rays come together. (513)

force: a push or a pull exerted by one body on another. (70)

fractional distillation: a process used in oil refineries to separate petroleum into gasoline, kerosene, and other products. (645)

fractionating towers: towers at oil refineries used for fractional distillation of petroleum.

free-fall: how an object moves in space when it is influenced only by gravity.

freeze distillation: a desalination process in which seawater is frozen to form salt-free ice.

Freon: a refrigerant gas used in refrigerators and air conditioners.

frequency: the number of waves that pass a point during one second, expressed as hertz; for example, 60 waves per second = 60 hertz. (459)

frequency-modulated (FM) waves: radio waves whose frequency is varied with voice, music, video, or data for transmission over long distances.

friction: the force that resists motion between two surfaces that are touching each other. (73)

fuel rod: a metal rod filled with uranium pellets, used as the fuel in a nuclear reactor.

fulcrum (FUL krum): the fixed point around which a lever pivots. (163)

fuse: a device that protects an electrical circuit. If too much current flows, the fuse melts, breaking the circuit to stop current flow.

galvanometer: an instrument (meter) used to detect electric currents; most electrical meters are galvanometers.

gamma rays: electromagnetic waves given off by a radioactive atomic nucleus; they have very short wavelength (high frequency), high energy, and are very penetrating. (490, 626)

gaseous solution: a homogeneous gas that is composed of two or more gases.

gasohol: a biomass fuel that is about 90 percent gasoline and 10 percent alcohol (ethanol); used in cars and trucks. (339)

gear: a wheel with teeth around its edge, designed to mesh with teeth on another gear, so as to transfer force and motion.

gelatin: a substance obtained by boiling animal bones; used in glues and foods.

generator: a device that uses electromagnetic induction to induce electrical current by rotating loops of wire through a magnetic field. (583)

geothermal energy: thermal energy from the magma underneath volcanoes. (660)

glass: a solid ceramic mixture lacking a crystal structure. (358)

graduated cylinder: a cylinder marked with a volume scale, used in laboratories for measuring liquid volumes.

granite: an igneous rock that is a mixture of crystals of several different compounds.

graph: a visual display of information or data, organized to help people interpret, understand, or quickly find information. (42)

graphite: a mineral made of carbon atoms arranged in layers that easily slide past one another, forming a dry lubricant.

gravity: the attracting force exerted by every object on every other object. The amount of force depends on the masses of the objects and their distance apart. (75)

greenhouse effect: the process by which heat radiated from Earth's surface is trapped and reflected back to Earth by carbon dioxide in the atmosphere. (18)

grounded: electrically connected to Earth (the ground), either directly or through a wire or other metal object.

groundwater: water in the ground that comes from rain and melting snow. Although often pure enough to drink, it is easily polluted by dumps, sewers, and chemical spills.

group: one of the 18 vertical columns in the periodic table. All elements in a group have similar properties. (257)

hacker: a person who uses a computer to break into other computer systems without permission.

half-life: the time required for half of the atoms in a radioactive substance to decay. (627)

halogens: highly active elements in periodic table Group 17 (fluorine, chlorine, bromine, iodine, astatine); halogens have seven electrons in their outer shells and readily combine with Group 1 elements such as sodium.

heat: the type of energy that moves from anything having a higher temperature to anything having a lower temperature. (121)

heat engine: a device that converts thermal energy into mechanical energy; for example, an automobile engine. (148)

heat mover: a device that removes thermal energy from one location and transfers it to another location having a different temperature; for example, a refrigerator, air conditioner, or heat pump. (151)

heat of fusion: the amount of energy needed to change a material from the solid state to the liquid state. (201)

heat of vaporization: the amount of energy needed to change a material from the liquid state to the gaseous (vapor) state. (202)

heat pump: a two-way heat mover that pumps heat out of a building in warm weather and into a building in cold weather. (151)

herbicide: a chemical poison that kills undesirable plants.

hertz: the unit of measure for frequency, abbreviated Hz; for example, 440 waves per second = 440 Hz.

heterogeneous mixture: a mixture in which different materials are distributed unevenly, so at any place in the mixture different combinations of materials occur. (222)

high-speed photography: a photographic method that takes clear (not blurred) pictures of fast-moving objects.

homogeneous mixture: a mixture in which different materials are blended evenly, so that the mixture is the same throughout; also called a solution. (222)

horizontal: a direction parallel to Earth's surface.

hydrate: a compound that has water molecules chemically attached to its ions. (287)

hydraulic: describes a system operated by applying pressure to a liquid.

hydrocarbon: a chemical compound containing only carbon and hydrogen atoms; for example, methane gas (CH_4). (329)

hydroelectricity: electricity produced by the energy of moving water. (658)

hydronium ion: the ion (H_3O^+) that makes a solution acidic; formed by the bonding of a hydrogen ion (H^+) to a water molecule (H_2O). (432)

hypothesis: a proposed solution to a problem or explanation of how something works; a hypothesis can be tested to see if it is correct. (16)

ideal machine: a machine in which work input equals work output; such a machine would be frictionless and 100 percent efficient. (160)

incandescent light: light produced by heat, as from a hot filament in an incandescent light bulb. (498)

inclined plane: a simple machine consisting of a sloping surface (ramp) used to raise objects; it changes the amount of force. (169)

incoherent light: light rays that are nearly parallel, but spread out. (530)

independent variable: in an experiment, the factor changed to see what effect it will have on the dependent variable. (21)

indicator: an organic compound that changes color when in an acid solution or a basic solution; for example, phenolphthalein. (426)

induction. electrically charging an object or creating an electrical current in it, without physically touching it.

inertia (ihn UR shuh): the tendency of an object to resist any change in motion; if motionless, it remains still; if moving, it keeps moving. (71)

infrared radiation: electromagnetic waves that have a wavelength slightly longer (lower frequency) than visible light; commonly known as heat; abbreviated *IR*. (487)

infrasonic waves: waves at frequencies below the limit of human hearing (below 20 Hz).

inhibitor: a substance that slows a chemical reaction. (418)

instantaneous speed: the rate of motion at any given instant, such as that given on a speedometer. (60)

insulator: a material through which heat or electricity cannot move easily. (137, 548)

integrated circuit: a thin slice of silicon, often less than 1 cm on a side, which may contain thousands of resistors, diodes, and transistors, and can perform several electronic functions at once; used in computers and electronic equipment; also called a chip. (601)

intensity: in sound waves, the amount of energy in each wave. (468)

interference: the mixing of two or more waves, which combine to form a new wave. (476)

internal combustion engine: an engine in which fuel is burned inside chambers (cylinders); for example, an automobile engine. (148)

ion: an atom having an electrical charge, either positive or negative; for example, Na^+, Cl^-. (277)

ionic bond: A type of chemical bond that holds together compounds of oppositely charged ions; for example, ionic bonding holds together Na^+ and Cl^- to make salt, NaCl. (277)

ionization: the breaking apart of a molecular polar substance (such as hydrogen chloride) to form ions when dissolved in water. (396)

isomers: compounds that have identical chemical formulas but different molecular structures and shapes. (333)

isometric exercise: exercise in which muscles push against other muscles, instead of pushing or pulling against gravity. (97)

isotopes: atoms of the same element that have different numbers of neutrons; for example, uranium-235 and uranium-238. (251)

joule (JEWL): the basic unit of energy and work, named for English scientist James Prescott Joule; 1 joule (J) = a force of 1 newton moving through 1 meter.

kelvin: the SI unit of temperature; 0 K = absolute zero (the coldest possible temperature) = $-273°C$. (41)

kilogram: the SI unit of mass; 1000 grams. (39)

kilowatt-hour: the unit of electrical power; 1 kilowatt-hour = 1000 watts of power used for 1 hour. (567)

kinetic energy: energy that causes change in the form of motion, as in a rolling ball. (111)

kinetic theory of matter: the theory that all matter is made up of tiny particles that are in constant motion. (191)

lanthanoid: any of the 14 metallic elements having atomic numbers 57-70; used in magnets, ceramics, and television picture tubes.

laser: a device that generates a beam of coherent light. (530)

law of conservation of energy: a law stating that energy can change form (for example, from potential to kinetic), but it cannot be created or destroyed under ordinary conditions. (115)

law of conservation of mass: a law stating that the mass of all substances involved in a chemical change will be the same after the change; matter is neither created nor destroyed during a chemical change. (234)

law of conservation of momentum: a law stating that the total momentum of a group of objects does not change unless outside forces act on the objects. (102)

lever: a simple machine consisting of a bar that is free to pivot (rotate) around a fixed point (fulcrum); it changes the direction or amount of force. (163)

lightning rod: a metal rod mounted atop a structure and connected to Earth (grounded) to leak off electric charges between the clouds and Earth before they grow strong enough to cause lightning. (551)

line graph: a type of graph used to show trends or continuous change by drawing a line that connects data points.

lipid: an organic compound containing more hydrogen atoms and fewer oxygen atoms than carbohydrates; for example, fats and oils. (344)

liquid solution: a liquid solvent that has dissolved in it a gas, liquid, or solid.

liter: the unit of liquid volume (L). (38)

loudness: the human perception of sound intensity. (468)

lubricant: a substance used to reduce the friction between two surfaces that move together; for example, oil, grease, or graphite.

machine: a device that makes work easier by changing the speed, direction, or amount of a force. (158)

magma (MAG muh): hot melted rock originating beneath Earth's surface; it is a potential source of energy for heating and generating electricity. (122)

magnetic: a physical property of matter that causes it to be attracted to a magnet.

magnetic bottle: a powerful magnetic field that creates a container ("bottle") to hold the hydrogen plasma needed for a nuclear fusion reaction.

magnetic domain: a group of aligned atoms in a magnetic material such as iron, caused by the magnetic field around each atom exerting a force on nearby atoms. (576)

magnetic field: the area of magnetic force around a magnet. (575)

magnetic poles: the two ends of a piece of magnetic material where the magnetic forces are strongest, labeled north pole (N) and south pole (S). (574)

magnetism: a property of matter that creates forces of attraction and repulsion between certain substances. (574)

magnifier: a device that makes things appear larger so that more detail can be seen; for example, a magnifying glass or microscope.

malleable: describes metals that can be hammered or rolled into thin sheets, like foil. (300)

mass: the amount of matter in an object; its SI unit is the kilogram (kg). (39)

mass number: total particles in an atom's nucleus; mass number = protons + neutrons; also called atomic mass. (251)

mechanical advantage (MA): the number of times a machine multiplies the effort force (the force applied to it). (160)

mechanical energy: the total kinetic energy and potential energy in a system. (115)

medium: a material (solid, liquid, or gas) through which a mechanical wave can transfer energy. (458)

melt: the changing of a substance from a solid state to a liquid state when heated above the substance's freezing/melting point.

melting point: the temperature at which a solid changes to a liquid.

metal: an element usually having these characteristics: shiny, ductile (can be drawn into wire), and a good conductor of heat and electricity. (260)

metallic bonding: the type of chemical bond that holds metals together; loose electrons and metal ions attract one another, holding the metal atoms together. (301)

metalloid: an element having some properties of both a metal and a nonmetal; for example, boron and silicon. (262)

meter: the SI unit of length (m). (34)

methane: a flammable gas (CH_4); the main gas in natural gas.

microprocessor: an integrated circuit on the main circuit board of a computer; the computer's "brain." (608)

714

microscope: an optical instrument that uses two convex lenses with relatively short focal lengths to magnify objects that are very small and up close. (524)

microwaves: electromagnetic waves that are very short (very high frequency) and have high energy. (486)

mixture: a substance made of elements or compounds stirred together but not combined chemically.

model: a representation of an idea or process to make it understandable, using a diagram, formula, or physical structure; for example, Ping-Pong balls to model a molecule or a mathematical formula to model a river's flow. (12)

modulation: the process of adding voice, music, video, or other data to radio waves, by varying either their amplitude or frequency. (486)

momentum: a property of any moving object; equals the object's mass times its velocity. (100)

monomers: organic molecules that are strung together to form polymers.

music: sound created using specific pitches, sound quality, and patterns. (474)

nearsighted: describes a person who sees nearby things clearly, but has trouble focusing on distant objects.

net force: the resulting velocity of an object when multiple forces are applied to it. (71)

neutral: (1) electrically neutral: a compound having no overall electrical charge because the total positive charge equals the total negative charge; (2) chemically neutral: a solution that is neither acidic nor basic.

neutralization: a chemical reaction between an acid and a base; the acid's hydronium ions (H_3O^+) combine with the base's hydroxide ions (OH^-) to produce water (H_2O), and the acid's negative ions combine with the base's positive ions to produce a salt. (440)

neutralize: to change an acidic solution or a basic solution so that it is neutral.

neutron: one of the two types of particles (protons and neutrons) that occur in an atom's nucleus; a neutron is neutral and has no electrical charge (neither negative nor positive). (243)

Newton's first law: English physicist Sir Isaac Newton stated that an object moving at a constant velocity keeps moving at that velocity unless a net force acts on it. (72)

Newton's second law of motion. English physicist Sir Isaac Newton stated that an object accelerates in the direction of the net force applied to it. (85)

Newton's third law of motion: English physicist Sir Isaac Newton stated that for every action, there is an equal and opposite reaction. (98)

noise: sound that has no pattern or definite pitch. (474)

noise pollution: sound that is loud, annoying, or harmful to the ear. (472)

nonelectrolyte: a substance that does not form ions in a water solution, so the water does not become an electrical conductor; for example, sugar or alcohol. (396)

nonmetal: an element that usually lacks the characteristics of a metal (shiny, can be drawn into wire, and a good conductor of heat and electricity). (261)

nonpolar molecule: a molecule in which the atoms have an equal attraction for electrons, so the molecule is not polarized into positive and negative ends. (280)

nonrenewable resources: resources such as coal, oil, and natural gas that we are using up faster than natural processes can replace. (647)

normal: in the study of light, an imaginary line drawn perpendicular to a reflecting surface or perpendicular to a medium that light is entering.

nuclear fission: the splitting of an atom's nucleus into two nuclei having smaller masses, with a simultaneous release of particles and energy. (633)

nuclear fusion: the fusing together of two atomic nuclei into a single nucleus of larger mass. (634)

nuclear reactor: a device in which uranium atoms fission to release energy; the energy is used to generate electricity. (648)

nuclear waste: waste products from nuclear power generation, nuclear weapons manufacture, nuclear medicine, and industrial use of radioactive materials. (651)

nucleic acid: an organic polymer that controls the activities and reproduction of cells. (342)

nucleus: the positively charged center of an atom. (243)

nuclide: an isotope having a specific atomic number and atomic mass. (621)

observation: using your senses to gather information; in science we use instruments to help our senses make more accurate and more detailed observations. (16)

ohm: the unit for measuring resistance; symbol Ω.

Ohm's law: German physicist Georg Ohm stated that electric current (I) equals the potential difference or voltage (V) divided by the resistance to current flow (R). (557)

opaque materials: materials you can't see through because they absorb or reflect nearly all light. (492)

optical axis: a line perpendicular to the center of a mirror or lens.

optical fibers: transparent glass fibers that can pipe light from one place to another. (532)

ore: a mineral or rock containing a useful substance that can be mined at a profit; for example, iron ore or silver ore. (356)

organic compound: a chemical compound containing the element carbon; about 90 percent of all compounds are organic. (328)

oxidation number: a positive or negative number that indicates an element's ability to form a compound. (283)

ozone layer: a layer of Earth's atmosphere that contains plentiful ozone, which absorbs ultraviolet radiation from the sun. (18)

parallel circuit: an electrical circuit where the current flows in several separate branches. If one branch is interrupted, current still flows through the other branches. (561)

pascal: the international unit of pressure; 1 pascal = 1 newton/square meter. (204)

Pascal's principle: French scientist Blaise Pascal stated that pressure applied to a fluid is transmitted equally throughout the fluid. (211)

passive solar heating: direct use of the sun's energy to heat something, without storing the energy.

petroleum: crude oil, formed by decay of ancient plants and animals; a fossil fuel that is burned and used to make lubricants and plastics. (644)

period: a horizontal row of elements in the periodic table; increasing from left to right is the number of electrons in the atoms' outer shells. (260)

periodic table: a table of the elements, in order by increasing atomic mass, arranged in rows and columns to show their repeated (periodic) properties. (255)

pH: a measure of hydronium ion (H_3O^+) concentration in a water solution, expressed on the pH scale from 0 to 14. From 7 down to 0, a solution is increasingly acidic; at 7 it is neutral (pure water); from 7 up to 14, a solution is increasingly basic. (pH = *p*otential of *H*ydrogen) (435)

phenolphthalein (feen ul THAYL een): a chemical used as a color indicator in titration; colorless in an acidic solution, but turns pink in a basic solution.

photon: a particle of light. (485)

photovoltaic cell: a solar cell; a semiconductor that converts light energy into electrical energy. (657)

physical change: a change in a substance's size, shape, color, or state (solid, liquid, gas). (230)

physical property: any characteristic of a material that you can observe, such as state, shape, size, or color. (228)

physical science: the study of matter and energy. (7)

pickling: a process that removes oxides and other impurities from steel and other metal surfaces by dipping them in hydrochloric acid. (429)

pitch: the highness or lowness of a sound, which is determined by the frequency (wavelength) of the sound. (466)

plane mirror: a mirror with a flat surface. (512)

plankton: tiny plants and animals that live in water and are food for small fish; they are easily killed by acid rain. (439)

plasma: a gaslike mixture of positively and negatively charged particles; it is the commonest state of matter in the universe. (194)

plastic: a material made from synthetic organic polymers that can be easily molded; nylon and polyethylene are examples. (362)

polarized light: light in which the waves vibrate only in one plane. (528)

polarizing filter: a filter made of chains of molecules in parallel rows that will transmit only light waves vibrating in the same direction as the molecular chains.

polar molecule: a molecule in which one atom has a stronger attraction for electrons than the other, giving the molecule a positive end and a negative end. (278)

polluted water: water that is contaminated with substances that may be harmful to living things. (199)

polyatomic ion: a group of covalently bonded atoms in which the whole group has a positive or negative charge, like NH_4^+ or CO_3^{2-} (286)

polymer: a huge molecule made of many smaller organic molecules (monomers) linked together; examples are proteins and plastics. (340)

positron: a positively charged electron.

potential difference: the difference in electric potential energy between two different points. (552)

potential energy: energy that is not causing change right now but is stored for potential use, as in a battery or a wound-up spring. (111)

power: the rate at which work is done; power = work ÷ time. (177)

precipitate: an insoluble solid that settles out of a chemical reaction occurring in a liquid. (414)

pressure: the amount of force exerted per unit of area; pressure = force ÷ area. (204)

principle: a basic rule or law describing how something always works in the natural world; for example, "gravity always pulls objects toward each other."

products: in a chemical reaction, the substances formed by the reaction. (404)

projectile: any object shot or thrown through the air. (90)

propane: a flammable gas (C_3H_8); a part of natural gas.

protein: an organic polymer formed from amino acids; various proteins make up many body tissues. (340)

proton: one of the two types of particles (protons and neutrons) that occur in the nucleus of an atom; a proton has a positive charge. (243)

pulley: a simple machine consisting of a grooved wheel with a rope or a chain running along the groove; it changes the direction and/or amount of force. (166)

716

Q

quality: in sound, the differences among sounds that have the same pitch and loudness. (475)

quark: a very small particle of matter that makes up protons and neutrons; five or six different quark types may exist. (248)

R

radiation: the transfer of energy through matter or space by electromagnetic waves such as heat, light, radio waves, X rays and gamma rays. (136, 484)

radiator: a device with a large surface area that transfers heat to surrounding air by conduction. (142)

radioactive element: an unstable element (like uranium) that naturally decays to form other elements by radiation (expelling an alpha particle, beta particle, or gamma ray from the atom's nucleus). (302)

radioactivity: the emission of particles or gamma rays from the nucleus of an atom that is unstable and radioactive. (621)

radio waves: electromagnetic waves that have long wavelengths (low frequencies). (485)

radius: the distance from the center of a circle to its circumference.

RAM: *r*andom-*a*ccess *m*emory in a computer; the temporary electronic memory in a chip that "forgets" as soon as the power is turned off. (608)

rarefaction: in compressional waves, the less dense area of the wave.

reactants: in a chemical reaction, the substances you start with before the reaction. (404)

real image: an image produced where light rays converge, as with a concave mirror or convex lens; a real image can be projected on a screen. (514)

rectifier: a device that changes alternating current into direct current. (599)

recycling: reprocessing of waste products into new products; for example, aluminum cans are recycled to make other aluminum cans or foil. (360)

reflecting telescope: an optical instrument that uses a concave mirror and a convex lens to magnify distant objects. (523)

reflection: bouncing of a wave off an object; this includes all types of waves—light, sound, radio, ocean, and so on. (500)

refraction: the bending of waves, caused by changing their speed. (501)

resistance: the opposition to the flow of electrons through a conductor, measured in ohms with an ohmmeter. (555)

resistance arm: the part of a lever that exerts the resistance force (F_r). (163)

resistance force (F_r): the force exerted by a machine to overcome resistance to gravity or friction. (159)

resonance: the tendency of an object to vibrate at the same frequency as a sound source. (475)

reverberation: the echoing effect produced by multiple reflections of sound. (477)

RNA: *r*ibo*n*ucleic *a*cid, a nucleic acid that controls production of proteins that make new cells.

ROM: *r*ead-*o*nly *m*emory in a computer; it is permanent memory stored inside the computer, even when the power is turned off. (609)

S

salt: a compound containing negative ions from an acid combined with positive ions from a base; forms during a neutralization reaction. (440)

saponification: the process of making soap. (443)

saturated hydrocarbon: a hydrocarbon compound in which each carbon atom is joined to four other atoms by single covalent bonds; an example is methane gas (CH_4). (331)

saturated solution: a solution that has dissolved all the solute it can hold at a specific temperature. (390)

scientific law: a rule that describes a pattern in nature and predicts what will happen under specific conditions. (16)

screw: a simple machine consisting of an inclined plane wrapped in a spiral around a cylindrical post; it changes the amount of force. (169)

second: the SI unit of time. (40)

semiconductor: an element that conducts electricity under certain conditions; in the periodic table, semiconductors are between metals and nonmetals. (317)

series circuit: an electrical circuit where the current flows only in one path. If the path is interrupted at any point, it stops current flow in the entire circuit. (561)

SI: International System of Units, the standard worldwide system of measurement used by all scientists; a modern version of the metric system. (31)

simple machine: a device that performs work with only one movement. Simple machines include the lever, pulley, wheel and axle, inclined plane, screw, and wedge. (158)

single displacement reaction: a chemical reaction in which one element replaces another element in a compound. (414)

smog: a form of air pollution; a colloid in which invisible solid particles mix with the air gases that we breathe. (226)

soap: an organic salt made by reacting fats or oils with a strong base such as sodium hydroxide. (443)

solar collector: a device that absorbs radiant energy from the sun. (144)

solar energy: energy from the sun, which includes heat, light, radio, ultraviolet, gamma, and other waves. (144)

solubility: the amount of a substance (solute) that will dissolve in a solvent; scientifically it is how many grams of solute will dissolve in 100 g of a solvent, at a specific temperature. (388)

solute: the substance being dissolved in a solvent; for example, in a sweet drink sugar is the solute and water is the solvent. (381)

solution: a homogeneous mixture containing tiny particles that don't settle and don't scatter light. (222)

solvent: the substance that dissolves a solute; for example, in a sweet drink sugar is the solute and water is the solvent. (381)

specific heat: the amount of energy needed to raise the temperature of 1 kilogram of a material 1 degree Celsius. (124)

speed: the rate of motion, or the rate of change in position. (60)

standard: in measurement, an exact quantity that everyone agrees to use for comparison; for example, a meter, kilogram, liter, kelvin, joule, and so on. (30)

state of matter: any of the four conditions in which matter can exist: solid, liquid, gas, or plasma. (190)

static electricity: the accumulation of electric charges on an object. No current flows because the electricity is static (motionless). (546)

step-down transformer: an electrical transformer that decreases (steps down) the voltage of a power line.

step-up transformer: an electrical transformer that increases (steps up) the voltage of a power line.

strong acid: an acid that ionizes almost completely in water solution, thus containing large numbers of hydronium ions (H_3O^+); for example, hydrochloric acid. (434)

strong base: a base that dissociates almost completely in water solution, thus containing a large number of hydroxide ions (OH^-); for example, sodium hydroxide. (435)

sublimation: a type of evaporation in which a solid changes directly to a gas without going through a liquid state. (313)

submerge: to fully immerse (completely cover) something in a fluid.

substance: matter that is an element or a compound. (221)

substituted hydrocarbon: a hydrocarbon in which one or more hydrogen atoms have been replaced by atoms of other elements. (335)

supercollider: a device to make protons collide at high speed so they break apart into quarks.

superconductor: a supercooled material that has no electrical resistance and so is a "super" conductor of electricity. (588)

supersaturated solution: an unstable solution that contains more solute than the solvent can dissolve at a specific temperature. (392)

suspension: a heterogeneous mixture containing larger particles that eventually settle out. (224)

synthesis reaction: a chemical reaction in which two or more substances combine to form a different substance. (413)

synthetic fiber: a strand of a synthetic polymer; examples are nylon, rayon, and Kevlar fibers. (365)

technology: the application of scientific knowledge to improve the quality of human life. (7)

telephoto lens: a lens having a long focal length and producing an enlarged, closeup image of an object. (525)

temperature: a measure of the average kinetic energy of the particles in matter; expressed in degrees kelvin or Celsius. (118)

terminal velocity: the greatest velocity reached by a falling object. (89)

theory: a solution to a problem; a former hypothesis that has been tested with repeated experiments and observations and found always to work. (16)

thermal energy: the total energy of particles in a material, including both kinetic and potential energy. (119)

thermal expansion: a characteristic of matter causing it to expand when heated and contract when cooled. (195)

thermal pollution: pollution caused when waste thermal energy raises the temperature of the environment. (146)

thermonuclear fusion: nuclear fusion that occurs under conditions of enormous heat (millions of degrees), as in a star or our sun.

tidal energy: electricity generated by the ocean tides. (658)

time: the interval between two events; the SI unit is the second. (40)

titration: a method for finding the concentration of an acidic or basic solution, using a solution of known concentration. (442)

total internal reflection: occurs when all the light entering an object is reflected internally, maintaining the intensity of the light. (531)

toxic: describes any substance that can injure living tissue; a poison. (274)

tracer: a radioactive isotope used for medical diagnosis; it allows a doctor to trace the location of tumors and fluid movements in the body. (636)

transformer: a device that transforms electrical current to a higher voltage or a lower voltage. (586)

transistor: a semiconductor that amplifies an electrical signal. (599)

transition element: an element in Groups 3-12 of the periodic table; each is metallic, with one or two electrons in its outer energy level. (304)

translucent materials: materials that can be partially seen through because they allow some light to pass, but not enough for a clear image. (492)

718

transmutation: changing one element to another through radioactive decay; for example, uranium-238 is transmuted into lead-206 after enough particles and rays have been emitted from its nucleus. (625)

transparent materials: materials that can be seen through because they allow nearly all light to pass through them. (492)

transuranium element: any element beyond uranium in the periodic table (having a higher atomic number than 92); these radioactive synthetic elements are made in laboratories or nuclear reactors. (309)

transverse wave: a wave that vibrates at right angles to the direction the wave is traveling. (458)

trough: in waves, the lowest point of a wave. (459)

Tyndall effect: the scattering of light by particles in a mixture, as occurs with a flashlight beam in the night sky. (226)

ultraviolet radiation: electromagnetic waves that have a wavelength slightly shorter (higher frequency) than visible light; abbreviated *UV*. (489)

unsaturated hydrocarbon: a hydrocarbon compound in which each carbon atom is joined to other atoms by double or triple covalent bonds; an example is acetylene. (331)

unsaturated solution: a solution that is capable of dissolving more solute at a specific temperature. (391)

velocity: the rate of motion in a specific direction. (65)

virtual image: an image formed of diverging light rays, as in a flat or convex mirror, or seen through a concave lens. A virtual image isn't "real" and can't be projected. (513)

visible radiation: electromagnetic waves in the only part of the electromagnetic spectrum we can see—light. (488)

volt: the unit for measuring electrical potential energy, abbreviated *V*.

voltage: a difference in electrical potential, measured in volts with a voltmeter.

voltmeter: a galvanometer that measures electrical potential differences in a circuit, in volts. (580)

volume: the amount of space occupied by an object; its SI unit is the cubic meter (m^3). (37)

watt (W): the unit of power, one joule per second. (177)

wave: a rhythmic disturbance that carries energy through matter or space. Mechanical waves require a medium to travel in; electromagnetic waves can travel either through a medium or space. (458)

wavelength: the distance between a point on one wave and the identical point on the next wave; for example, the distance between two crests or two troughs. (459)

weak acid: an acid that ionizes only partially in water solution, thus creating a small number of hydronium ions (H_3O^+); for example, acetic acid. (434)

weak base: a base that dissociates only partially in water solution, thus creating a small number of hydroxide ions (OH^-); for example, magnesium hydroxide. (435)

wedge: a simple machine consisting of an inclined plane with one or two sloping sides; examples are a chisel, knife, and axe. It changes the amount of force. (170)

weight: the measure of the force of gravity on an object, usually the force between Earth and an object at its surface. (75)

wet cell: a power source that generates electric current by a chemical reaction; "wet" because it uses a liquid electrolyte, as in an automobile battery. (555)

wheel and axle: a simple machine consisting of two wheels of different sizes that are connected so they rotate together, such as a doorknob or wheel-handled faucet; it changes the amount of force. (167)

wide-angle lens: a lens having a short focal length and producing a relatively small image of an object, but including much of the object's surroundings. (525)

work: the transfer of energy through motion; work = force × distance. (112)

X rays: electromagnetic waves having a wavelength shorter (higher frequency) than ultraviolet radiation; often used in medical photography because they can penetrate human tissue. (490)

GLOSSARY/GLOSARIO

This glossary defines each key term that appears in **bold type** in the text. It also shows the page number where you can find the word used. Some other terms that you may need to look up are included, too.

acceleration/aceleración: La razón del cambio en velocidad (rapidez y/o dirección). (Pág. 66)

acid/ácido: Sustancia que produce iones de hidrógeno (H+) cuando se disuelve en agua, lo cual reduce el pH de la solución a menos de 7. (Pág. 426)

acid rain/lluvia ácida: Lluvia más ácida de lo normal ya que contiene ácido sulfúrico diluido (de las plantas de energía que queman carbón) y ácido nítrico diluido (de los gases de escape de los automóviles). (Pág. 438)

acoustics/acústica: El estudio del sonido. (Pág. 476)

air resistance/resistencia del aire: La fuerza de fricción que el aire ejerce sobre un objeto en movimiento, esta fuerza actúa en dirección opuesta a la dirección en que se mueve el objeto. (Pág. 87)

alcohol/alcohol: Hidrocarburo de sustitución en el cual uno o más átomos de hidrógeno han sido reemplazados por un grupo -OH; por ejemplo, el etanol. (Pág. 335)

alfa particle/partícula alfa: Partícula de baja energía emitida por un núcleo atómico radiactivo; es un núcleo de helio (dos protones y dos neutrones con una carga positiva). (Pág. 624)

allotrope/alotropo: Forma molecular diferente del mismo elemento; por ejemplo, algunas moléculas del carbono forman el grafito que es blando, mientras otras forman los diamantes que son muy duros. (Pág. 317)

alloy/aleación: Solución sólida de un metal con otros metales o no metales; por ejemplo, el bronce o el acero. (Pág. 352)

alternating current (AC)/corriente alterna (CA): Corriente eléctrica que cambia de dirección muchas veces por segundo; la CA en nuestros hogares cambia de dirección 60 veces por segundo. (Pág. 585)

amalgam/amalgama: Aleación que contiene el elemento mercurio; por ejemplo, algunos empastes dentales se hacen con amalgamas. (Pág. 355)

ammeter/amperímetro: Galvanómetro que mide, en amperes, la corriente eléctrica que fluye por un circuito. (Pág. 580)

amplification/amplificación: Proceso que consiste en aumentar la fuerza de una corriente eléctrica. (Pág. 600)

amplitude/amplitud: Distancia desde la posición de equilibrio hasta la cresta o el valle de una onda (tienen la misma distancia). (Pág. 459)

Archimedes' principle/principio de Arquímedes: El matemático griego Arquímedes expuso que la fuerza boyante que empuja un objeto hacia arriba en un fluido es igual al peso del fluido desplazado por el objeto. (Pág. 210)

aromatic compound/compuesto aromático: Compuesto químico que contiene la estructura de anillo del benceno: la mayoría tiene un aroma distintivo. (Pág. 334)

atomic number/número atómico: El número de protones en el núcleo de un átomo; cada elemento tiene un número específico (hidrógeno = 1; helio = 2, etc.). (Pág. 243)

average atomic mass/masa atómica promedio: La masa promedio de todos los isótopos de un elemento; se usa como una conveniencia, puesto que la mayoría de los elementos tienen más de un isótopo y por consiguiente más de un número de masa. (Pág. 252)

average speed/rapidez media: La razón del movimiento que se determina dividiendo la distancia por el tiempo. (Pág. 61)

B

balanced chemical equation/ecuación química equilibrada: Ecuación química que tiene el mismo número de átomos de cada elemento en ambos lados de la ecuación. (Pág. 410)

balanced forces/fuerzas equilibradas: Fuerzas iguales en tamaño, pero opuestas en dirección. (Pág. 70)

Base/base: Sustancia que produce iones de hidróxido (OH⁻) cuando se disuelve en agua. Esto aumenta a más de 7 el pH de la solución. (Pág. 430)

Bernoulli's principle/principio de Bernoulli: El matemático suizo Daniel Bernoulli expuso que, cuando la velocidad de un fluido aumenta, la presión ejercida por el fluido disminuye. (Pág. 212)

beta particle/partícula beta: Partícula de alta energía emitida por un núcleo atómico radiactivo; es un electrón que está cargado negativamente. (Pág. 625)

binary compound/compuesto binario: Compuesto químico que se compone de dos elementos; por ejemplo, el cloruro de sodio. (Pág. 283)

biogas/gas metano: Gas (mayormente metano) producido por los desperdicios vegetales y animales que se descomponen en la ausencia del aire. (Pág. 338)

biomass/biomasa: Todo material vegetal y animal tanto vivo como muerto que algunas veces se usa como combustible. (Págs. 338, 656)

Boyle's law/ley de Boyle: El físico inglés Robert Boyle enunció que si se achica un recipiente de gas, la presión por todo el gas aumenta (si la temperatura permanece constante). (Pág. 205)

breeder reactor/reactor generador: Tipo de reactor nuclear que produce combustible nuevo a medida que funciona. (Pág. 654)

bubble chamber/cámara de burbujas: Cámara llena con un líquido supercalentado; se usa para detectar partículas nucleares cargadas y que dejan un rastro de burbujas al pasar. (Pág. 631)

buoyant force/fuerza boyante: Fuerza de empuje hacia arriba que se ejerce sobre un objeto cuando está completamente sumergido en un fluido. (Pág. 209)

C

carbohydrate/carbohidrato: Compuesto orgánico que se caracteriza por tener dos veces más átomos de hidrógeno que de oxígeno; por ejemplo, la glucosa = $C_6H_{12}O_6$. (Pág. 343)

catalyst/catalizador: Sustancia que acelera una reacción química sin cambiar en sí su propia composición (Pág. 418)

cathode-ray tube (CRT)/tubo de rayos catódicos: Un dispositivo con una especie de revolver interno que dispara un flujo de electrones (rayos catódicos) hacia una pantalla fluorescente para producir imágenes. (Pág. 605)

centripetal acceleration/aceleración centrípeta: Aceleración (cambio de rapidez y/o de dirección) hacia el centro de una curva. (Pág. 92)

centripetal force/fuerza centrípeta: Fuerza que causa que un objeto se mueva hacia el centro de una curva. (Pág. 92)

ceramic/cerámica: Material hecho de arcilla o arena que, generalmente, se hornea a temperaturas altas. (Pág. 357)

cermet/cermet: Material sintético que se fabrica para que tenga tanto las propiedades de la cerámica como de la aleación; por ejemplo, algunos imanes usan el cermet (*cerá*mica y *met*al). (Pág. 358)

chain reaction/reacción en cadena: Serie continua de reacciones de fisión en las cuales los neutrones de los núcleos que se fisionan causan que otros núcleos se dividan, emitiendo más neutrones que dividen más núcleos y así sucesivamente. (Pág. 634)

Charles's law/ley de Charles: El científico francés Jacques-Alexandre Charles enunció que el volumen de un gas aumenta a medida que la temperatura aumenta, si la presión permanece constante. (Pág. 205)

chemical bond/enlace químico: En un compuesto, la fuerza que mantiene sujetos a los átomos. (Pág. 271)

chemical change/cambio químico: Cambio de una sustancia a otra al cambiar los elementos que la componen o al cambiar las proporciones de dichos elementos. (Pág. 232)

chemical formula/fórmula química: Presentación precisa de los elementos en un compuesto y de sus proporciones; por ejemplo, H_2O, CO_2, ó $C_{12}H_{22}O_{11}$. (Pág. 270)

chemical property/propiedad química: Característica de una sustancia que indica si ésta puede ser sometida a cierto cambio químico. (Pág. 233)

chemical reaction/reacción química: Cambio en el cual las sustancias se convierten en diferentes sustancias que tienen diferentes propiedades. (Pág. 404)

chemical symbol/símbolo químico: Manera abreviada de escribir el nombre de un elemento; por ejemplo: *O* para oxígeno, *Fe* para el hierro. (Pág. 242)

chemically stable/químicamente estable: Descripción de un átomo cuyo nivel de energía más externo está lleno de electrones, de manera que no forma compuestos bajo condiciones normales; por ejemplo, helio, neón. (Pág. 270)

chlorofluorocarbons (CFCs)/clorofluorocarbonos: Grupo de sustancias químicas compuestas de cloro, flúor y carbono que se usan como refrigerantes y en atomizadores, las cuales dañan la capa de ozono de la atmósfera. (Pág. 409)

circuit/circuito: Camino cerrado por el cual pueden fluir los electrones (electricidad). (Pág. 552)

cloud chamber/cámara de nube: Cámara llena de aire saturado con agua; se usa para rastrear partículas nucleares cargadas, que dejan un rastro de vapor al pasar. (Pág. 630)

coefficient/coeficiente: En una ecuación química, el número a la izquierda de cada reactivo y producto que muestra la cantidad relativa de cada sustancia involucrada en la reacción; por ejemplo, el 3 en la ecuación $3H_2O$. (Pág. 406)

coherent light/luz coherente: Rayo de luz en el cual todos los rayos se mueven paralelos unos a los otros, de forma que el rayo se dispersa muy poco, aún en una trayectoria de miles de kilómetros. (Pág. 529)

colloid/coloide: Mezcla heterogénea que contiene pequeñas partículas que no se asientan; por ejemplo, la leche y la gelatina. (Pág. 223)

combustion/combustión: Oxidación rápida o fuego. (Pág. 148)

commutator/conmutador: Interruptor reversible en un motor eléctrico de corriente directa que cambia la polaridad de la corriente con cada media revolución. (Pág. 581)

composite/compuesto: Material que se hace de la mezcla de dos materiales, incrustando el primero de estos materiales en el segunda material. (Pág. 367)

compound/compuesto: Materia que es la combinación de los átomos de dos o más elementos. (Pág. 220)

compound machine/máquina compuesta: La combinación de dos o más máquinas simples. (Pág. 174)

compressional wave/onda de compresión: Es una onda que vibra en la misma dirección en la cual se mueve la onda. (Pág. 464)

computer virus/virus de computadora: Un programa de computadora diseñado para "infectar" una computadora y "enfermarla"; puede borrar datos, revolver otros programas o sobrecargar la memoria de tal manera que el sistema no funcione bien. (Pág. 612)

concave lens/lente cóncava: Lente que es más delgada en el centro y más gruesa en las orillas y por lo tanto su curva es hacia adentro. (Pág. 519)

concave mirror/espejo cóncavo: Espejo cuya superficie se curva hacia adentro, produciendo una imagen reflejada que es más grande. (Pág. 513)

condensation/condensación: Cambio del estado gaseoso al líquido; por ejemplo, vapor de agua que se condensa en una superficie fría. (Pág. 201)

conduction/conducción: Transferencia de energía a través de la materia por contacto directo de las partículas; movimiento de calor o electricidad a través de una sustancia. (Pág. 134)

conductor/conductor: Material que permite que el calor o los electrones se muevan fácilmente a través del mismo. (Pág. 547)

constant/constante: En un experimento, el factor que no se cambia. (Pág. 21)

constant speed/rapidez constante: La razón del movimiento que no cambia, tal como la velocidad de la Tierra en órbita. (Pág. 61)

control/control: En un experimento, el estándar de comparación. (Pág. 20)

convection/convección: La transferencia de energía a través de la materia por el movimiento de la materia misma, como por ejemplo en las corrientes de aire o de agua. (Pág. 135)

convex lens/lente convexa: Lente que es más gruesa en el centro que en las orillas y por lo tanto su curva es hacia afuera. (Pág. 518)

convex mirror/espejo convexo: Espejo cuya superficie se curva hacia afuera. (Pág. 515)

723

cooling tower/torre de enfriamiento: Aparato en forma de torre en el cual el agua se enfría por medio de abanicos o de evaporación. Se usa en fábricas y en centrales eléctricas o nucleares. (Pág. 147)

corrosive/corrosivo: Describe cualquier sustancia que ataca y cambia los metales, el tejido viviente o cualquier otro material; por ejemplo, el ácido de las baterías, la lejía y los limpiadores para horno, inodoros y tuberías. (Pág. 274)

covalent bond/enlace covalente: Tipo de enlace químico que forman los átomos cuando comparten electrones; esta fueréza mantiene unidas las moléculas en gases como el oxígeno (O_2), el nitrógeno (N_2) y en los compuestos como el agua (H_2O). (Pág. 278)

crest/cresta: Punto más alto de una onda. (Pág. 459)

critical thinking/pensamiento crítico: El proceso de usar la habilidad mental para resolver problemas. (Pág. 14)

crystal/cristal: Sólido que tiene una forma distintiva porque sus átomos están ordenados en formas geométricas que se repiten. (Pág. 191)

current/corriente: Movimiento de electrones a través de un conductor; se mide en amperes con un amperímetro. (Pág. 553)

D

decomposition reaction/reacción de descomposición: Reacción química en la cual una sustancia se descompone en dos o más sustancias simples. (Pág. 414)

dehydrating agent/agente deshidratador: Sustancia que elimina el agua de los materiales; por ejemplo, el ácido sulfúrico. (Pág. 428)

density/densidad: Cuan apretadas están las moléculas de una sustancia; se expresa como la masa de una sustancia dividida entre su volumen, en g/cm^3. (Pág. 39)

dependent variable/variable dependiente: En un experimento, el factor que se tiene que cambiar porque la variable independiente se cambia. (Pág. 21)

derived unit/unidad derivada: La unidad de medida formada combinando otras unidades de medidas; por ejemplo, la densidad es una unidad derivada que se forma dividiendo la masa de un objeto entre su volumen. (Pág. 38)

desalination/desalinización: Proceso por el cual se extrae la sal del agua de mar para producir agua fresca potable. (Pág. 386)

detergent/detergente: Sal orgánica parecida al jabón, excepto que los detergentes no hacen espuma en agua mineral. (Pág. 444)

diatomic molecule/molécula diatómica: Molécula compuesta de dos átomos del mismo elemento; por ejemplo, hidrógeno (H_2) o el oxígeno (O_2). (Pág. 311)

diffraction/difracción: Doblez de las ondas alrededor de una barrera. (Pág. 503)

diffraction grating/retícula de difracción: Pedazo de vidrio o de plástico que tiene muchas hendiduras paralelas que funcionan como un prisma, causando que la luz blanca que pasa por ésta se separe en sus colores componentes (el espectro). (Pág. 505)

diode/diodo: Tipo de rectificador que permite que la corriente eléctrica fluya en solo una dirección. (Pág. 599)

direct current (DC)/corriente directa (CD): Corriente eléctrica que fluye en una sola dirección y así las pilas de corriente directa (baterías) se denominan + y - para que se puedan instalar correctamente. (Pág. 585)

dissociation/disociación: Separación de un compuesto iónico (como la sal) en iones positivos y negativos, cuando se disuelve en agua. (Pág. 396)

distillation/destilación: Proceso de purificación del agua, en el cual el agua se evapora de una solución y el vapor se enfría y se condensa en un líquido puro. (Pág. 387)

dot diagram/diagrama de puntos: Diagrama de un átomo, usando el símbolo del elemento con puntos para mostrar los electrones en el nivel de energía más externo. (Pág. 257)

double displacement reaction/reacción de desplazamiento doble: Reacción química en la cual los iones positivos en dos o más sustancias cambian de lugar. (Pág. 415)

dry cell/pila seca: Fuente de potencia que genera una corriente eléctrica por medio de una reacción química; se dice que es "seca" porque usa un electrólito pastoso y grueso en un envase sellado, en vez de un electrólito líquido como el de una batería de automóvil. (Pág. 554)

ductile/dúctil: Describe los metales que se pueden moldear en alambres delgados. (Pág. 300)

E

efficiency/eficiencia: La cantidad de trabajo que se invierte en una máquina comparado con la cantidad de trabajo útil producido por la máquina; es siempre entre 0 y 100%. (Pág. 175)

effort arm/brazo de esfuerzo: Parte de la palanca a la cual se aplica la fuerza de esfuerzo. (Pág. 163)

effort force (Fe)/fuerza de esfuerzo: Fuerza aplicada a una máquina. (Pág. 159)

electric field/campo eléctrico: Fuerza que rodea un electrón y que afecta a todos los objetos cercanos y con una carga eléctrica. Es más fuerte cuando está cerca del electrón y disminuye a medida que se aleja. (Pág. 547)

electrical power/potencia eléctrica: Razón a la cual la energía eléctrica se convierte en otra forma de energía; como por ejemplo, en calor; se mide en kilovatios-horas. (Pág. 565)

electrolyte/electrolítica: Sustancia que forma iones en una solución de agua, convirtiendo el agua en un conductor eléctrico; por ejemplo, el cloruro de sodio y el cloruro de hidrógeno. (Pág. 396)

electromagnet/electroimán: Imán temporal que se forma pasando una corriente eléctrica por una espiral de metal que rodea un centro de hierro. (Pág. 578)

electromagnetic induction/inducción electromagnética: Corriente eléctrica inducida en un alambre cuando se mueve por un campo magnético. (Pág. 583)

electromagnetic spectrum/espectro electromagnético: La clasificación de las ondas electromagnéticas ya sea por longitud de onda o por frecuencia. (Pág. 484)

electron/electrón: Partícula del átomo que tiene carga negativa y que se encuentra alrededor del núcleo. (Pág. 243)

electron cloud/nube de electrones: En realidad no es una nube, sino el espacio donde probablemente existen los electrones alrededor del núcleo de un átomo. (Pág. 244)

electroscope/electroscopio: Dispositivo que se usa para detectar la presencia de las cargas eléctricas. (Pág. 549)

element/elemento: Materia compuesta de átomos iguales; por ejemplo, el zinc el cloro y el aluminio. (Pág. 220)

endothermic reaction/reacción endotérmica: Reacción química que requiere la adición de energía calórica para ocurrir; de modo que la reacción absorbe calor del medio ambiente. (Pág. 417)

energy/energía: La habilidad de causar un cambio. (Pág. 110)

energy farming/cultivo de energía: Cultivo de plantas para usar como combustible. (Pág. 338)

ester/éster: Compuesto químico que se forma por la reacción de un ácido orgánico con un alcohol. Algunos nos proveen con los olores de las flores, de las frutas y de los dulces. (Pág. 444)

evaporation/evaporación: Cambio del estado líquido al gaseoso. (Pág. 200)

exothermic reaction/reacción exotérmica: Reacción química que libera energía calórica. (Pág. 418)

experiment/experimento: Proceso controlado para comprobar una hipótesis. (Pág. 20)

external combustion engine/motor de combustión externa: Motor en el cual el combustible se quema fuera del motor y esta energía se usa para hacer funcionar el motor: por ejemplo, las antiguas locomotoras de vapor. (Pág. 150)

fluid/fluido: Cualquier materia que fluye, como el aire, el agua o el metal fundido. (Pág. 135)

fluorescent light/luz fluorescente: Luz producida por sustancias fosfóricas cuando se las estimula con luz ultravioleta, como en una bombilla de luz fluorescente. (Pág. 498)

focal length/distancia focal: Distancia del centro de una lente o de un espejo a su punto focal. (Pág. 513)

focal point/punto focal: Un punto en el eje óptico de un espejo cóncavo o de una lente convexa donde los rayos de luz se encuentran. (Pág. 513)

force/fuerza: El empujar o tirar de un cuerpo sobre otro. (Pág. 70)

fractional distillation/destilación fraccional: Proceso que se usa en la refinación del petróleo para separar el petróleo en gasolina, keroseno y otros productos. (Pág. 644)

frequency/frecuencia: Número de ondas que pasan por un punto durante un segundo, expresado en hertz; por ejemplo, 60 ondas por segundo = 60 hertz. (Pág. 459)

friction/fricción: La fuerza que resiste el movimiento entre dos superficies que se tocan. (Pág. 73)

fulcrum/fulcro: Punto fijo sobre el cual da vuelta la palanca. (Pág. 163)

725

G

gamma rays/rayos gamma: Ondas electromagnéticas emitidas por un núcleo atómico radioactivo; tienen una longitud de onda muy corta (frecuencia alta), energía alta y son muy penetrantes. (Págs. 490, 626)

gasohol/gasohol: Combustible que se hace de la biomasa, es 90% gasolina y 10% alcohol (etanol); se usa para carros y camiones. (Pág. 339)

generator/generador: Dispositivo que usa inducción electromagnética para inducir una corriente eléctrica por medio de la rotación de bobinas de alambre por un campo magnético. (Pág. 583)

geothermal energy/energía geotérmica: Energía térmica del magma debajo de los volcanes. (Pág. 660)

glass/vidrio: Mezcla sólida de cerámica que carece de estructura cristalina. (Pág. 358)

graph/gráfica: Manera visual de exhibir datos e información, que se utiliza para ayudar a las personas a interpretar, entender o encontrar información rápidamente. (Pág. 42)

gravity/gravedad: La fuerza de atracción que ejerce todo objeto hacia otros objetos. La cantidad de fuerza depende de la masa de los objetos y de la distancia entre ellos. (Pág. 75)

greenhouse effect/efecto de invernadero: El proceso por el cual el calor emitido por la superficie de la Tierra queda atrapado en la atmósfera y es reflejado otra vez a la Tierra por el dióxido de carbono en la atmósfera. (Pág. 18)

groups/grupos: Columnas verticales en la tabla periódica; los elementos dentro de un grupo tienen propiedades parecidas. (Pág. 257)

H

half-life/período de vida media: Es el tiempo necesario para que la mitad de los átomos en una sustancia radiactiva se desintegren. (Pág. 627)

heat/calor: Tipo de energía que se mueve desde algo que tiene una temperatura más alta hasta algo que tiene una temperatura más baja. (Pág. 121)

heat engine/máquina de calentamiento: Aparato que convierte la energía térmica en energía mecánica; por ejemplo, el motor de un automóvil. (Pág. 148)

heat mover/aparato que mueve el calor: Aparato que transfiere la energía térmica a otro lugar que tiene una temperatura diferente, por ejemplo, un refrigerador, un acondicionador de aire, una bomba de calentamiento. (Pág. 151)

heat of fusion/calor de fusión: Cantidad de energía requerida para cambiar un material del estado sólido al estado líquido. (Pág. 201)

heat of vaporization/calor de vaporización: Cantidad de energía que se necesita para cambiar un material del estado líquido al estado gaseoso (vapor). (Pág. 202)

heat pump/bomba de calentamiento: Bomba que mueve el calor de dos maneras: saca el calor de un edificio en tiempo caluroso, y mueve el calor hacia dentro del edificio en tiempo frío. (Pág. 151)

heterogeneous mixture/mezcla heterogénea: Mezcla en la cual los diferentes materiales están distribuidos desigualmente, así, en cualquier lugar de la mezcla pueden ocurrir diferentes combinaciones de los materiales. (Pág. 222)

homogeneous mixture/mezcla homogénea: Mezcla con igual distribución de los diferentes materiales, de manera que la mezcla es la misma por toda su extensión. También llamada una solución. (Pág. 222)

hydrate/hidrato: Compuesto que tiene moléculas de agua unidas químicamente a sus iones. (Pág. 287)

hydrocarbon/hidrocarburo: Compuesto químico que solo contiene átomos de carbono y de hidrógeno; por ejemplo, el gas metano (CH_4). (Pág. 329)

hydroelectricity/hidroelectricidad: Electricidad producida por la energía del agua en movimiento. (Pág. 658)

hydronium ion/ion de hidronio: El ion (H_3O^+) que hace que una solución sea acídica, se forma por el enlace de un ion de hidrógeno (H^+) con una molécula de agua (H_2O). (Pág. 432)

hypothesis/hipótesis: La solución propuesta a un problema o la explicación de como funciona algo; una hipótesis puede ser comprobada para ver si está correcta. (Pág. 16)

I

ideal machine/máquina ideal: Máquina en la cual el trabajo que se hace es igual al trabajo de entrada; dicha máquina no tendría fricción y sería 100% eficiente. (Pág. 160)

incandescent light/luz incandescente: Luz producida por el calor, como el de un filamento caliente en una bombilla de luz incandescente. (Pág. 498)

inclined plane/plano inclinado: Máquina simple que consiste en una superficie inclinada como una rampa usada para levantar objetos; cambia la cantidad de la fuerza (Pág. 169)

incoherent light/luz incoherente: Rayos de luz que son casi paralelos, pero que se dispersan. (Pág. 530)

independent variable/variable independiente: En un experimento, el factor que se cambia para ver qué efecto tiene sobre la variable dependiente. (Pág. 21)

indicator/indicador: Compuesto orgánico que cambia de color cuando está en una solución ácida, o en una solución básica; por ejemplo, la fenolftaleína. (Pág. 426)

inertia/inercia: Tendencia de un objeto a resistir cualquier cambio en movimiento: si está inmóvil, permanece inmóvil, si se mueve, permanece en movimiento. (Pág. 71)

infrared radiation/radiación infrarroja: Ondas electromagnéticas que tienen una longitud de onda un poco más larga (frecuencia más baja) que la luz visible. Comúnmente, se conocen como calor. (Pág. 487)

inhibitor/inhibidor: Sustancia que decelera una reacción química. (Pág. 418)

instantaneous speed/rapidez instantánea: La razón del movimiento en un instante dado, tal como la velocidad en un velocímetro. (Pág. 60)

insulator/aislante: Material por el cual ni el calor ni la electricidad pueden moverse fácilmente. (Págs. 137, 548)

insulators/aislantes: Material a través del cual el calor o la electricidad no pueden fluir fácilmente. (Págs. 137, 548)

integrated circuit/circuito integrado: Lámina delgada de silicio, a menudo, de menos de 1 cm de lado pero que puede contener miles de resistores, diodos y transistores y puede ejecutar varias funciones electrónicas a la vez; se usa en computadoras y en equipo electrónico; también, se llama pastilla de silicio. (Pág. 601)

intensity/intensidad: Cantidad de energía en cada onda sonora. (Pág. 468)

interference/interferencia: Mezcla de dos o más ondas que se combinan para formar una nueva onda. (Pág. 475)

internal combustion engine/motor de combustión interna: Motor en el cual el combustible se quema en cámaras internas (cilindros); por ejemplo, el motor de un automóvil. (Pág. 148)

ion/ion: Átomo que adquiere carga eléctrica, ya sea positiva o negativa; por ejemplo, Na$^+$, Cl$^-$. (Pág. 277)

ionic bond/enlace iónico: Tipo de enlace químico que mantiene unidos a los compuestos, por la fuerza de atracción de sus cargas opuestas; por ejemplo, el enlace iónico sujeta a Na$^+$ y al Cl$^-$ para formar la sal, NaCl. (Pág. 277)

ionization/ionización: Separación de una sustancia polar molecular (como el cloruro de hidrógeno) para formar iones cuando se disuelve en agua. (Pág. 396)

isomers/isómeros: Compuestos que tienen fórmulas químicas idénticas, pero diferentes estructuras y formas moleculares. (Pág. 333)

isometric exercises/ejercicios isométricos: Ejercicios en los cuales los músculos empujan unos contra otros, en vez de empujar o halar contra la gravedad. (Pág. 97)

isotopes/isótopos: Átomos del mismo elemento con diferentes números de neutrones; por ejemplo, uranio-235 y uranio-238. (Pág. 251)

kelvin/kelvin: La unidad de temperatura del SI; 0 K = cero absoluto (la temperatura más fría posible) = −273°C. (Pág. 41)

kilogram/kilogramo: La unidad de masa del SI; equivale a 1000 gramos. (Pág. 39)

kilowatt-hour/kilovatio-hora: Unidad de potencia eléctrica; 1 kilovatio-hora = 1000 vatios de potencia usados en una hora. (Pág. 567)

kinetic energy/energía cinética: Energía que causa cambios en la forma del movimiento, por ejemplo, una bola que rueda. (Pág. 111)

kinetic theory of matter/teoría cinética de la materia: Teoría que especifica que toda materia está hecha de pequeñas partículas que están en movimiento constante. (Pág. 191)

laser/láser: Dispositivo que produce un rayo de luz coherente. (Pág. 530)

law of conservation of energy/ley de la conservación de la energía: Ley que expone que la energía puede cambiar de forma (por ejemplo, de potencial a cinética), pero no puede ser creada ni destruida bajo condiciones ordinarias. (Pág. 115)

law of conservation of mass/ley de la conservación de la masa: Ley que enuncia que la masa de todas las sustancias involucradas en un cambio químico, permanecerá igual después del cambio; la materia ni se crea ni se destruye durante un cambio químico. (Pág. 234)

law of conservation of momentum/ley de la conservación del momento: Ley que enuncia que el momento total de un grupo de objetos no cambia a menos que fuerzas externas actúen sobre ellos. (Pág. 102)

lever/palanca: Máquina simple que consiste de una barra que da vuelta sobre un punto fijo llamado fulcro; cambia la dirección o la cantidad de la fuerza. (Pág. 163)

lightning rod/pararrayos: Varilla de metal instalada sobre una estructura o edificio y conectada a la Tierra para atrapar las cargas eléctricas, entre las nubes y la Tierra, antes de que éstas se vuelvan demasiado fuertes como para causar rayos. (Pág. 551)

lipid/lípido: Compuesto orgánico que contiene más átomos de hidrógeno y menos átomos de oxígeno que los carbohidratos; por ejemplo, la grasa y los aceites. (Pág. 344)

liter/litro: La unidad de volumen líquido (L). (Pág. 38)

loudness/volumen: La percepción humana de la intensidad de un sonido. (Pág. 468)

machine/máquina: Aparato que facilita el trabajo cambiando la rapidez, la dirección o la cantidad de una fuerza. (Pág. 158)

magma/magma: Roca ígnea, derretida, de origen subterráneo, es una fuente potencial de energía para generar calor y electricidad. (Pág. 122)

magnetic domain/dominio magnético: En un material magnético como el hierro, grupo de átomos alineados debido al campo magnético que rodea a cada átomo y que ejerce una fuerza sobre los átomos cercanos. (Pág. 576)

magnetic field/campo magnético: Área de fuerza magnética alrededor de un imán. (Pág. 575)

magnetic poles/polos magnéticos: Los dos extremos de un pedazo de material magnético donde las fuerzas magnéticas son más fuertes, se denominan polo norte (N) y polo sur (S). (Pág. 574)

magnetism/magnetismo: Propiedad de la materia que crea fuerzas de atracción y de repulsión entre ciertas sustancias. (Pág. 574)

malleable/maleable: Describe los metales que pueden ser martillados o aplanados en hojas delgadas, como laminilla o chapa de oro. (Pág. 300)

mass/masa: Cantidad de materia en un objeto; su unidad en el SI es el kilogramo (kg). (Pág. 39)

mass number/número de masa: Total de las partículas en el núcleo de un átomo; el número de masa = protones + neutrones; también se le llama masa atómica. (Pág. 251)

mechanical advantage (MA)/ventaja mecánica (VM): Es el número de veces que una máquina multiplica la fuerza de esfuerzo (la fuerza que se le aplica). (Pág. 160)

mechanical energy/energía mecánica: El total de la energía cinética, más la energía potencial en un sistema. (Pág. 115)

medium/medio: Un material ya sea sólido, líquido o gaseoso, por el cual una onda mecánica puede transferir energía. (Pág. 458)

metal/metal: Elemento que, por lo general, exhibe las siguientes características: brillantez, ductibilidad (se puede moldear en forma de alambre) y buen conductor de calor y de electricidad. (Pág. 260)

metallic bonding/enlace metálico: Tipo de enlace químico que sujeta a los metales; los electrones sueltos y los iones metálicos se atraen mutuamente para sujetar a los átomos metálicos. (Pág. 301)

metalloid/metaloide: Cualquier elemento que posee propiedades tanto de los metales como de los no metales; como por ejemplo, el boro y el silicio. (Pág. 262)

meter/metro: La unidad de longitud del SI (m). (Pág. 34)

microprocessor/microprocesador: Un circuito integrado en el circuito principal de una computadora. El cerebro de la computadora. (Pág. 608)

microscope/microscopio: Instrumento óptico que utiliza dos lentes convexas, con una distancia focal relativamente corta, para aumentar el tamaño de objetos que son muy pequeños y están cerca. (Pág. 524)

microwaves/microondas: Ondas electromagnéticas muy cortas (de muy alta frecuencia) que tienen energía alta. (Pág. 486)

model/modelo: La representación de una idea o de un proceso para ser comprendido, usando diagramas,

fórmulas o estructuras físicas; por ejemplo, usando bolas de ping-pong para hacer un modelo de una molécula, o una fórmula matemática para demostrar el curso de un río. (Pág. 12)

modulation/modulación: Proceso por el cual se agrega voz, música, video, u otros datos a las ondas de radio, ya sea variando su amplitud o su frecuencia. (Pág. 486)

momentum/momento: Una propiedad de cualquier objeto en movimiento; equivale a la masa del objeto multiplicada por su velocidad. (Pág. 100)

music/música: Sonido que se crea usando tonos específicos, calidad sonora y patrones agradables. (Pág. 473)

net force/fuerza neta: Velocidad que resulta de un objeto cuando se le aplican fuerzas múltiples al mismo objeto. (Pág. 71)

neutralization/neutralización: Reacción química entre un ácido y una base; los iones de hidronio del ácido (H_3O^+) se combinan con los iones de hidróxido de la base (OH^-) para producir agua (H_2O), y los iones negativos del ácido se combinan con los iones positivos de la base para producir una sal. (Pág. 440)

neutron/neutrón: Uno de los dos tipos de partículas (protones y neutrones) que se encuentran en el núcleo de un átomo; es neutro y no tiene carga eléctrica (ni negativa ni positiva). (Pág. 243)

Newton's first law/primera ley de Newton: El físico inglés Isaac Newton enunció que un objeto que se mueve a una velocidad constante, continúa moviéndose a esa velocidad, a menos que una fuerza neta actúe sobre el mismo. (Pág. 72)

Newton's second law of motion/segunda ley del movimiento de Newton: El físico inglés Isaac Newton, enunció que un objeto acelera en la dirección de la fuerza neta que se le aplica. (Pág. 85)

Newton's third law of motion/tercera ley del movimiento de Newton: El físico inglés Isaac Newton, enunció que por cada acción hay una reacción igual y opuesta. (Pág. 98)

noise/ruido: Sonido que no tiene patrón ni tono definido (y es generalmente desagradable). (Pág. 473)

noise pollution/contaminación por ruido: Cualquier sonido que es muy fuerte, que molesta o que es perjudicial para el oído. (Pág. 471)

nonelectrolyte/no electrolítica: Sustancia que no forma iones en una solución de agua, de manera que el agua no se transforma en conductor de electricidad; por ejemplo, el azúcar o el alcohol. (Pág. 396)

nonmetal/no-metal: Elemento que, generalmente, carece de las características de los metales. (Pág. 261)

nonpolar molecule/molécula no polar: Molécula en la cual los átomos tienen igual atracción hacia los electrones, de modo que la molécula no está polarizada o no tiene un polo positivo y otro negativo. (Pág. 280)

nonrenewable resources/recursos no renovables: Recursos tales como el carbón, el petróleo y el gas natural que estamos consumiendo a un ritmo más acelerado del que la naturaleza puede reemplazar. (Pág. 647)

nuclear fission/fisión nuclear: Un cambio nuclear en el cual el núcleo de un átomo se divide en dos núcleos que tienen masas más pequeñas y que emiten, simultáneamente, más partículas y más energía. (Pág. 633)

nuclear fusion/fusión nuclear: Es la fusión o unión de dos núcleos atómicos en un solo núcleo de mayor masa. (Pág. 634)

nuclear reactor/reactor nuclear: Un aparato en el cual los átomos de uranio se dividen para producir energía; la energía se usa para generar electricidad. (Pág. 648)

nuclear wastes/desperdicios nucleares: Los productos de desecho de la generación de energía en las plantas de energía nuclear, de la manufactura de armas nucleares, de la medicina nuclear y del uso industrial de materiales radioactivos. (Pág. 651)

nucleic acid/ácido nucleico: Polímero orgánico que controla las actividades y lo reproducción de las células. (Pág. 342)

nucleus/núcleo: La región central de un átomo que contiene cargas positivas. (Pág. 243)

nuclide/nucleido: Un isótopo que tiene un número atómico y un número de masa atómica específicos. (Pág. 621)

observation/observación: Usar los sentidos para recoger información; en la ciencia usamos instrumentos para ayudar a nuestros sentidos a hacer observaciones más exactas y detalladas. (Pág. 16)

Ohm's law/ley de Ohm: El físico alemán Georg Ohm declaró que la corriente eléctrica es igual a la diferencia de potencia o voltaje dividida entre la resistencia al flujo de la corriente. (Pág. 557)

opaque materials/materiales opacos: Materiales a través de los cuales no se puede ver porque absorben o reflejan casi toda la luz. (Pág. 492)

optical fibers/fibras ópticas: Fibras de vidrio transparente que pueden llevar la luz de un lugar a otro. (Pág. 532)

ore/mena: Mineral o roca que contiene una sustancia útil que puede ser minada lucrativamente; por ejemplo, la mena de hierro o de plata. (Pág. 356)

organic compound/compuesto orgánica: Compuesto químico que contiene el elemento carbono; aproximadamente 90 por ciento de todos los compuestos son orgánicos. (Pág. 328)

oxidation number/número de oxidación: Número positivo o negativo que indica la habilidad de un elemento para formar un compuesto. (Pág. 283)

ozone layer/capa de ozono: La capa, en la atmósfera de la Tierra, que contiene una abundancia de ozono, el cual absorbe los rayos ultravioletas del Sol. (Pág. 18)

P

parallel circuit/circuito paralelo: Circuito eléctrico donde la corriente fluye por varias ramas separadas; si se interrumpe la corriente en una de las ramas, la corriente todavía fluye por las otras ramas. (Pág. 561)

pascal/pascal: La unidad internacional de presión; 1 pascal = 1 newton/metro cuadrado. (Pág. 204)

Pascal's principle/principio de Pascal: El científico francés Blaise Pascal expuso que la presión aplicada al fluido se transmite igualmente por todo el líquido. (Pág. 211)

period/período: Hilera horizontal de elementos en la tabla periódica; el número de electrones en el nivel de energía más externo aumenta de izquierda a derecha. (Pág. 260)

periodic table/tabla periódica: Tabla en que los elementos se clasifican en orden de acuerdo al número de masa creciente, se encuentra organizada en hileras y columnas para mostrar las propiedades repetidas (periódicas) de los elementos. (Pág. 255)

petroleum/petróleo: Petróleo crudo, formado por la descomposición de plantas y de animales prehistóricos; es un combustible fósil que se quema y se usa para hacer lubricantes y plásticos. (Pág. 644)

pH/pH: Es la medida de la concentración del ion hidronio (H_3O^+) en una solución de agua, se expresa en las escala de pH de 0 a 14. De 0 al 7, una solución es, ascendentemente, acídica; el 7 indica que la solución es neutra (agua pura); y del 7 hasta el 14, la solución es ascendentemente básica. (Pág. 435)

photon/fotón: Una partícula de luz. (Pág. 485)

photovoltaic cell/célula fotovoltaica: Una pila solar o semiconductor que convierte le energía luminosa en energía eléctrica. (Pág. 657)

physical change/cambio físico: Cambio en el tamaño, forma, color o estado de una sustancia. (Pág. 230)

physical property/propiedad física: Cualquier característica observable de un material, tal como el estado (sólido, líquido, gas), la forma, el tamaño o el color. (Pág. 228)

physical science/ciencia física: El estudio de la materia y de la energía. (Pág. 7)

pickling/limpiar con baño químico: Proceso de bañar, en ácido hidroclórico, el acero y otras superficies metálicas para eliminar los óxidos y otras impurezas. (Pág. 429)

pitch/tono: La agudeza o gravedad de un sonido, determinado por la frecuencia (longitud de onda) del sonido. (Pág. 466)

plane mirror/espejo plano: Espejo con una superficie plana (Pág. 512)

plankton/plancton: Plantas y animales acuáticos pequeñísimos que sirven de alimento a los peces; el plancton muere, fácilmente, con la lluvia ácida. (Pág. 439)

plasma/plasma: Mezcla semejante a un gas, cuyas partículas tienen cargas positivas y negativas; es el estado más común de la materia en el universo. (Pág. 194)

plastic/plástico: Material hecho de polímeros orgánicos sintéticos que se pueden moldear fácilmente; por ejemplo, el nylon y el polietileno. (Pág. 362)

polarized light/luz polarizada: Luz en la cual las ondas vibran solamente en un plano. (Pág. 528)

polar molecule/molécula polar: Molécula en la que un átomo atrae más electrones que el otro, lo cual hace que la molécula tenga un polo positivo y otro negativo. (Pág. 278)

polluted water/agua contaminada: Agua contaminada con sustancias que pueden ser nocivas para los seres vivientes. (Pág. 199)

polyatomic ion/ion poliatómico: Grupo de átomos unidos covalentemente cuyas cargas son todas o positivas o negativas; como por ejemplo, NH_4^+ o CO_3^{2-}. (Pág. 286)

polymer/polímero: Molécula enorme formada por muchas moléculas orgánicas pequeñas (monómeros); por ejemplo, las proteínas y los plásticos. (Pág. 340)

potential difference/diferencia de potencial: Diferencia en energía eléctrica potencial entre dos puntos. (Pág. 552)

potential energy/energía potencial: Energía que no causa un cambio ahora mismo, pero que se almacena para uso potencial, por ejemplo, en una batería o en un resorte. (Pág. 111)

power/potencia: Razón a la cual se hace trabajo; potencia = trabajo/tiempo. (Pág. 177)

precipitate/precipitado: Sólido insoluble que se asienta en una reacción química que ocurre en un líquido. (Pág. 415)

pressure/presión: Cantidad de fuerza aplicada por unidad de área; presión = fuerza/área. (Pág. 204)

products/productos: En una reacción química, las sustancias que se forman por la reacción. (Pág. 404)

projectile/proyectil: Cualquier objeto disparado o tirado en el aire. (Pág. 90)

protein/proteína: Polímero orgánico formado de aminoácidos; diversas proteínas componen los tejidos del cuerpo. (Pág. 340)

proton/protón: Uno de los dos tipos de partículas (protones y neutrones) que se encuentran en el núcleo del átomo; tiene carga positiva. (Pág. 243)

pulley/polea: Máquina sencilla que consiste de una rueda acanalada por la que corre una cuerda o cadena; cambia la dirección y/o la cantidad de fuerza. (Pág. 166)

Q

quality/calidad: Diferencia entre sonidos que tienen el mismo tono y volumen. (Pág. 474)

quarks/quarks: Partícula diminuta de materia, de la cual están hechos los protones y los neutrones; puede que existan hasta 5 ó 6 tipos diferentes de quarks. (Pág. 248)

R

radiation/radiación: La transferencia de energía a través de la materia o del espacio por ondas electromagnéticas; tales como el calor, la luz, las ondas de radio, los rayos X y los gama. (Págs. 136, 484)

radiator/radiador: Dispositivo con un área grande de superficie que transfiere el calor al aire que lo radea por medio de conducción. (Pág. 142)

radioactive element/elemento radiactivo: Elemento inestable (como el uranio) que se desintegra, naturalmente, y forma otros elementos por medio de la radiación, tales como la expulsión del núcleo atómico de las partículas alfa o beta o de los rayos gama. (Pág. 302)

radioactivity/radiactividad: La emisión de partículas o de rayos gamma del núcleo de un átomo que es inestable y radiactivo. (Pág. 621)

radio waves/ondas de radio: Ondas electromagnéticas que tienen longitud de onda larga (baja frecuencia). (Pág. 485)

RAM/RAM: **R**andom **a**ccess **m**emory-la memoria en una pastilla de una computadora; la memoria electrónica temporal que "borra" la información tan pronto se interrumpe la corriente eléctrica. (Pág. 608)

reactants/reactantes: En una reacción química, las sustancias con las cuales se empieza antes de la reacción. (Pág. 404)

real image/imagen real: Imagen que se produce en el lugar en donde convergen los rayos de luz, como en un espejo cóncavo o en una lente convexa; una imagen real se puede proyectar sobre una pantalla. (Pág. 513)

rectifier/rectificador: Dispositivo que cambia una corriente alterna en corriente directa. (Pág. 599)

recycling/reciclaje: Reprocesamiento de los desperdicios en nuevos productos; por ejemplo, las latas de aluminio pueden ser recicladas en nuevas latas o en laminilla de aluminio. (Pág. 360)

reflecting telescope/telescopio reflector: Instrumento óptico que utiliza un espejo cóncavo, un espejo plano y una lente convexa para aumentar el tamaño de los objetos lejanos. (Pág. 523)

reflection/reflexión: Onda que rebota de un objeto; esto incluye todo tipo de ondas: de luz, de sonido, de radio, del océano, etc. (Pág. 500)

refracting telescope/telescopio refractor: Telescopio en el cual se utilizan dos lentes convexas para recoger y enfocar la luz de objetos distantes. (Pág. 523)

refraction/refracción: Doblez de las ondas causado por el cambio en su velocidad. (Pág. 501)

resistance/resistencia: Oposición al movimiento de electrones por un conductor; se mide en ohmios con un ohmiómetro. (Pág. 555)

resistance arm/brazo de resistencia: Parte de la palanca sobre la cual ejerce la fuerza de resistencia. (Pág. 163)

resistance force (F_r)/fuerza de resistencia: Fuerza hecha por una máquina para vencer la gravedad o la fricción. (Pág. 159)

resonance/resonancia: Es la tendencia que tiene un objeto de vibrar a la misma frecuencia que la fuente del sonido. (Pág. 473)

reverberation/reverberación: Efecto de eco producido por múltiples sonidos reflejados. (Pág. 476)

ROM/ROM: **R**ead **o**nly **m**emory-la memoria permanente almacenada en la computadora inclusive después de que se interrumpe la corriente eléctrica. (Pág. 609)

S

salt/sal: Compuesto que contiene iones negativos de un ácido combinados con iones positivos de una base; se forma durante una reacción de neutralización. (Pág. 440)

saponification/saponificación: Proceso de hacer jabón. (Pág. 443)

saturated hydrocarbon/hidrocarburo saturado: Compuesto hidrocarburo en el cual cada átomo de carbono tiene enlaces covalentes sencillos con otros cuatro átomos; por ejemplo, el gas metano (CH_4). (Pág. 331)

saturated solution/solución saturada: Solución que ha disuelto el máximo de soluto una temperatura específica. (Pág. 390)

scientific law/ley científica: Una regla que describe un patrón en la naturaleza y que predice lo que passará bajo ciertas condiciones específicas. (Pág. 16)

screw/tornillo: Máquina simple que consiste en un plano inclinado envuelto en espiral alrededor de un poste cilíndrico; cambia la cantidad de la fuerza. (Pág. 169)

second/segundo: La unidad de tiempo del SI. (Pág. 40)

semiconductors/semiconductores: Elementos que conducen electricidad bajo ciertas condiciones; se encuentran en la tabla periódica entre los metales y los no metales. (Pág. 316)

series circuit/circuito en serie: Circuito eléctrico cuya corriente fluye, solamente, en una dirección; si esa dirección es interrumpida en cualquier punto, el movimiento de la corriente se para en todo el circuito. (Pág. 561)

SI/SI: El Sistema Internacional de Unidades, el sistema de medidas estándares que usan los científicos en todo el mundo; la versión moderna del sistema métrico. (Pág. 31)

simple machine/máquina simple: Aparato que produce trabajo con solo un movimiento. Incluyen la palanca, la polea, la rueda y el eje, el plano inclinado y la cuña. (Pág. 158)

single displacement reaction/reacción de desplazamiento simple: Reacción química en la cual un elemento reemplaza a otro elemento en un compuesto. (Pág. 414)

smog/smog: Una forma de contaminante del aire, un coloide en el cual partículas sólidas invisibles se mezclan con los gases del aire que respiramos. (Pág. 226)

soap/jabón: Sal orgánica que se forma de la reacción de grasas o aceites con una base fuerte, como el hidróxido de sodio. (Pág. 443)

solar collector/colector solar: Dispositivo que absorbe la energía radiante del Sol. (Pág. 144)

solar energy/energía solar: Energía del Sol que incluye las ondas de calor, luz, radio, ondas ultravioletas, gama y otras ondas. (Pág. 144)

solubility/solubilidad: Científicamente, es la cantidad de gramos de soluto que se puede disolver en 100 gramos de disolvente a una temperatura específica. (Pág. 388)

solute/soluto: Sustancia que se disuelve en un disolvente; por ejemplo, el azúcar es el soluto y el agua es el disolvente en una bebida dulce. (Pág. 381)

solution/solución: Mezcla homogénea que contiene pequeñas partículas que no se asientan y que no esparcen luz. (Pág. 222)

solvent/disolvente: Sustancia que disuelve un soluto; por ejemplo, el azúcar es el soluto y el agua es el disolvente en una bebida dulce. (Pág. 381)

specific heat/calor específico: Cantidad de energía que se necesita para subir la temperatura de un kilogramo de materia, un (1) grado celsios. (Pág. 124)

speed/rapidez: La razón del movimiento, o la razón del cambio de posición. (Pág. 60)

standard/estándar: En las medidas, una cantidad exacta con la cual todos están de acuerdo, para usar como comparación; por ejemplo, el metro, el kilogramo, el litro, el kelvin, el julio, etc. (Pág. 30)

states of matter/estados de la materia: Cualquiera de las cuatro estados en los cuales puede existir la materia: sólido, líquido, gaseoso o plasma. (Pág. 190)

static electricity/electricidad estática: Acumulación de cargas eléctricas en un objeto. La corriente nu fluye porque la electricidad es estática (es decir, no se mueve). (Pág. 546)

strong acid/ácido fuerte: Ácido que se ioniza casi por completo en una solución de agua; conteniendo así, gran cantidad de iones de hidronio (H_3O^+); por ejemplo, el ácido hidroclórico (Pág. 434)

strong base/base fuerte: Base que se separa casi completamente en una solución de agua, conteniendo así un gran número de iones de hidróxido (OH^-); por ejemplo, el hidróxido de sodio (Pág. 435)

sublimation/sublimación: Tipo de evaporación en la cual un sólido cambia directamente a un gas sin pasar por el estado líquido. (Pág. 313)

substance/sustancia: Materia que compone un elemento o un compuesto. (Pág. 221)

substituted hydrocarbon/hidrocarburo de sustitución: Hidrocarburo en el cual uno o más átomos de hidrógeno han sido reemplazados por átomos de otros elementos. (Pág. 335)

superconductor/superconductor: Material que se ha sometido a un proceso de sobreenfriamiento que lo libra de toda resistencia eléctrica y, que por lo tanto, sirve de "súper" conductor de electricidad. (Pág. 588)

supersaturated solution/solución supersaturada: Solución inestable que contiene más soluto del que, normalmente, puede disolver el disolvente, a una temperatura dada. (Pág. 392)

suspension/suspensión: Mezcla heterogénea que contiene partículas grandes que, eventualmente, se asientan. (Pág. 224)

synthesis reaction/reacción de síntesis: Reacción química en la cual dos o más sustancias se combinan para formar una sustancia diferente. (Pág. 413)

synthetic fiber/fibra sintética: Hebra de polímero sintético; como por ejemplo, el nylon, el rayón y las fibras Kevlar. (Pág. 365)

T

technology/tecnología: La aplicación del conocimiento científico para mejorar la calidad de la vida humana. (Pág. 7)

telephoto lens/lente telefoto: Lente que tiene una distancia focal larga, la cual produce una imagen aumentada y un primer plano del objeto. (Pág. 525)

temperature/temperatura: Medida de la energía cinética de las partículas en la materia; se expresa en grados kelvin o celsios. (Pág. 118)

terminal velocity/velocidad terminal o final: La velocidad máxima alcanzada por un objeto que cae. (Pág. 89)

theory/teoría: La solución a un problema; una hipótesis anterior que ha sido comprobada con experimentos repetidos y observaciones, y que se ha comprobado que siempre funciona. (Pág. 16)

thermal energy/energía térmica: La energía total de las partículas en un material, incluyendo la energía cinética y la potencial. (Pág. 119)

thermal expansion/expansión térmica: Característica de la materia que causa que se expanda al calentarse y que se contraiga al enfriarse. (Pág. 195)

thermal pollution/contaminación térmica: Contaminación que resulta cuando la energía térmica de desecho aumenta la temperatura del medio ambiente. (Pág. 146)

tidal energy/energía de las mareas: Energía producida por las mareas del mar. (Pág. 658)

time/tiempo: El intervalo entre dos sucesos; la unidad de tiempo del SI es el segundo. (Pág. 40)

titration/titulación: Proceso cuantitativo en el cual se utiliza una solución estándar para determinar la concentración de otra solución ya sea acídica o básica. (Pág. 442)

total internal reflection/reflexión interna total: Ocurre cuando toda la luz que penetra un objeto es reflejada interiormente, manteniendo así la intensidad de la luz. (Pág. 531)

toxic/tóxico: Describe cualquier sustancia que puede dañar el tejido viviente; un veneno. (Pág. 274)

tracers/indicadores radiactivos: Isótopos radiactivos que se usan en los diagnósticos médicos; permiten a los médicos delinear el lugar de los tumores y de los movimientos de los fluidos en el cuerpo. (Pág. 636)

transformer/transformador: Dispositivo que transforma la corriente eléctrica a un voltaje más alto o a uno más bajo. (Pág. 586)

transistor/transistor: Semiconductor que amplifica una señal eléctrica. (Pág. 599)

transition element/elemento de transición: Elementos en los grupos 3-12 de la tabla periódica; todos son metálicos con uno o dos electrones en su nivel de energía externo. (Pág. 304)

translucent materials/materiales translúcidos: Materiales a través de los cuales se puede ver parcialmente porque permiten el paso de un poco de luz, pero no lo suficiente para ver una imagen clara. (Pág. 492)

transmutation/transmutación: Cambiar un elemento a otro por medio de la desintegración radiactiva; por ejemplo, el uranio-238 cambia (se trasmuta en) a plomo-206 después de que suficientes partículas y rayos han sido emitidos de su núcleo. (Pág. 625)

transparent materials/materiales transparentes: Materiales a través de los cuales se puede ver porque permiten el paso de casi toda la luz. (Pág. 492)

transuranium element/elemento transuránico: En la tabla periódica, cualquier elemento más allá del uranio (con un número atómico mayor de 92); estos elementos radiactivos sintéticos se hacen en laboratorios o en reactores nucleares. (Pág. 309)

transverse wave/onda transversal: Onda en que la perturbación es perpendicular a la dirección de su propagación. (Pág. 458)

trough/valle: Punto más bajo de una onda. (Pág. 459)

Tyndall effect/efecto de Tyndall: Es la dispersión de la luz por las partículas en una mezcla, como sucede con un rayo de luz de linterna en el cielo nocturno. (Pág. 226)

ultraviolet radiation/radiación ultravioleta: Ondas electromagnéticas que tienen una longitud de onda más corta (frecuencia más alta) que la luz visible. (Pág. 489)

unsaturated hydrocarbon/hidrocarburo no saturado: Compuesto hidrocarburo en el cual cada átomo de carbono está unido a otros átomos por enlaces covalentes dobles o triples; por ejemplo, el acetileno. (Pág. 331)

unsaturated solution/solución no saturada: Solución que contiene menos soluto del que puede disolver a una temperatura dada. (Pág. 391)

velocity/velocidad: La razón de movimiento en una dirección específica. (Pág. 65)

virtual image/imagen virtual: Imagen que se forma por los rayos de luz divergentes, como en un espejo plano o uno convexo; o una imagen que se ve a través de una lente cóncava. Una imagen virtual no es "real" y no se puede proyectar. (Pág. 512)

visible radiation/radiación visible: Ondas electromagnéticas en la única parte del espectro electromagnético que podemos ver: luz. (Pág. 488)

voltmeter/voltímetro: Galvanómetro que mide, en voltios, la diferencia de potencial eléctrico de un circuito. (Pág. 580)

volume/volumen: La cantidad de espacio ocupada por un objeto; su unidad en el SI es el metro cúbico (m^3). (Pág. 37)

watt/vatio(W): La unidad de potencia, un julio por segundo. (Pág. 177)

wavelength/longitud de onda: Distancia entre un punto de una onda y un punto idéntico en la siguiente onda; por ejemplo, la distancia entre dos crestas o entre dos valles. (Pág. 459)

waves/ondas: Perturbación periódica que acarrea energía a través de la materia o del espacio. Las ondas mecánicas requieren un medio por el cual moverse. Las ondas electromagnéticas pueden moverse o por un medio como el agua, o por el espacio. (Pág. 458)

weak acid/ácido débil: Ácido que se ioniza, parcialmente, en una solución de agua, y así crea un pequeño número de iones de hidronio (H_3O^+); por ejemplo, el ácido acético. (Pág. 434)

weak base/base débil: Base que se separa, parcialmente, en una solución de agua, creando así un pequeño número de iones de hidróxido (OH^-); por ejemplo, el hidróxido de magnesio. (Pág. 435)

wedge/cuña: Máquina simple compuesta de un plano inclinado con uno o dos lados inclinados, como por ejemplo el cincel, el cuchillo y el hacha, los cuales cambian la cantidad de fuerza. (Pág. 170)

weight/peso: La medida de la fuerza de gravedad sobre un objeto, generalmente, la fuerza entre la Tierra y un objeto sobre su superficie. (Pág. 75)

wet cell/pila húmeda: Fuente de potencia que genera una corriente eléctrica por una reacción química; se dice que es "húmeda" porque usa un electrólito líquido, como por ejemplo, la batería de automóvil. (Pág. 555)

wheel and axle/rueda y eje: Máquina simple que consiste de dos ruedas de diferentes tamaños que están conectadas para que giren juntas, tal como la perilla de una puerta; cambia la cantidad de fuerza. (Pág. 167)

wide-angle lens/lente de ángulo ancho: Lente que tiene una distancia focal corta, el cual produce una imagen relativamente pequeña del objeto, pero que incluye mucho de lo que rodea al objeto. (Pág. 525)

work/trabajo: Traspaso de energía por medio del movimiento; trabajo = fuerza × distancia. (Pág. 112)

X rays/rayos X: Ondas electromagnéticas que tienen una longitud de onda más corta (frecuencia más alta) que la radiación ultravioleta; se usan, a menudo, en la fotografía médica porque pueden penetrar el tejido humano. (Pág. 490)

735

INDEX

The Index for *Merrill Physical Science* will help you locate major topics in the book quickly and easily. Each entry in the Index is followed by the numbers of the pages on which the entry is discussed. A page number given in **boldface type** indicates the page on which that entry is defined. A page number given in *italic type* indicates a page on which the entry is used in an illustration or photograph. The abbreviation *act.* indicates a page on which the entry is used in an activity.

736

737

740

PHOTO CREDITS

Cover, Roger Ressmeyer/Starlight; **iv**, (1)BLT Productions, (r)StudiOhio; **v**, Bud Fowle; **vi**, Ken Frick; **vii**, (t)Doug Martin, (b)Ken Frick; **viii, ix**, Doug Martin; **x**, T. J. Florian/Rainbow; **xi**, Hickson & Associates; **xii**, Mike Brown/Gamma Liaison; **xiv**, Keith Kent/Peter Arnold Inc.; **xv**, Ken Frick; **xviii**, StudiOhio; **xix**, Doug Martin; **xx**, StudiOhio; **2-3**, Ed Degginger; **3**, Tim Courlas; **4**, BLT Productions; **5**, Doug Martin; **6**, (t)Phil Degginger, (b)National Radio Astronomy Observatory; **7**, Ken Frick; **8**, KS Studios; **9**, NOAA/NESDIS/Satellite Applications Laboratory; **10**, (t)The Bettmann Archive, (b)Lloyd Lemmerman; **11**, Tim Courlas; **12**, (t)Ken Frick, (b)Bruce Frisch/Photo Researchers; **13**, James H. Karales/Peter Arnold Inc.; **14**, Ken Frick; **16**, (tl)Ken Frick, (tr)William E. Ferguson, (b)Tim Courlas; **18**, Dan McCoy/Rainbow; **19**, Will McIntyre/Photo Researchers; **20**, Hickson & Associates; **21**, Doug Martin; **22**, Hickson & Associates; **24**, Doug Martin; **25**, Latent Images; **26**, First Image; **28**, Hickson & Associates, (inset)Ken Frick; **29**, Doug Martin; **30**, StudiOhio; **31**, National Standard of Mass; **32**, Doug Martin; **33**, KS Studios; **35**, Ken Frick; **37**, NASA; **39**, Doug Martin; **40**, (l)Ken Frick, (r)Courtesy of National Institute of Standards & Technology; **41**, Doug Martin; **46**, (t)Tom McGuire; (b)Al Tielemans/DUOMO; **47,48**, Doug Martin; **49**, Tim Courlas; **51**, File Photo; **52**, (t)Atomic Energy Commission, (b)Phil Degginger; **53**, (t)TSW, (c)Susan McCartney/Photo Researchers, (b)NASA; **54**, (tl)Pictures Unlimited, (tr)Cobalt Productions, (bl)Doug Martin, (br)Ken Frick; **55**, Michael Holford; **56-57**, Geisser/H. Armstrong Roberts; **57**, Robert Daemmrich/TSW; **58, 59** © Matt Meadows; **60**, © 1986 Steven Dahlgren/The Stock Market; **61**, (t)Bud Fowle, (b)StudiOhio; **64**, StudiOhio; **65**, (t)Scott Camazine/Photo Researchers, (b)Ed Pritchard/TSW; **68**, Doug Martin; **69**, Bud Fowle; **70**, Focus on Sports; **71**, StudiOhio; **72,73**, Doug Martin; **74**, Bud/Fowle/Sonja Welker and the BalletMet Dance Academy of Columbus, Ohio; **75**, Dan Hems/DUOMO; **76**, NASA; **77**, StudiOhio; **78**, Doug Martin; **82**, Cyril Isy-Schwart/The Image Bank; **83**, StudiOhio; **86**, Peticolas/Megna/Fundamental Photographs; **88**, (t)StudiOhio, (b)Chris Hackett/The Image Bank, (br)Runk/Schoenberger from Grant Heilman; **89**, Craig Aurness/Westlight; **90**, © 1987 Paul J. Sutton/Duomo; **91** (t), StudiOhio, (b)Richard Magna/Fundamental Photographs; **92**, © 1988 Duomo; **93**, Courtesy of Daniel L. Feicht/Cedar Point; **94**, NASA; **95**, Doug Martin; **97**, NASA; **99**, (t)Bill Ross/Westlight, (b)StudiOhio; **100**, NASA; **101** (t)Bud Fowle, (c)StudiOhio, (b)Lou Jones/The Image Bank; **102**, Ed Degginger; **103**, Gianalberto Cigowni/The Image Bank; **104**, Doug Martin; **106**, TSW; **108**, BLT Productions; **109**, StudiOhio; **110**, Latent Images; **111**, David Dennis; **112**, (t)(c)StudiOhio, (b)Cobalt Productions; **114**, Bud Fowle; **116**, Alan D. Carey; **117**, Doug Martin; **119**, StudiOhio; **120**, Bud Fowle; **122**, Aaron Haupt; **125**, NOAA/NESDIS/Satellite Applications Laboratory; **127**, David Travers/The Stock Market; **128**, Latent Images; **130**, Pictures Unlimited; **132**, BLT Productions; **133**, StudiOhio; **137**, Johnny Johnson; **138**, H. Armstrong Roberts; **139**, Ken Frick; **141**, Doug Martin; **142**, Cobalt Productions; **144**, (l)Paolo Koch/Photo Researchers, (r)John Keating/Photo Researchers; **146**, Grant Heilman; **147**, Phil Degginger/H. Armstrong Roberts; **148**, Hickson & Associates; **150**, (t)Hughes Aircraft Company, (b)Ed Degginger; **152**, Doug Martin; **154**, Ken Frick; **156** Murray Alcosser/The Image Bank; **157**, Ken Frick; **158**, (t)Jim Franck Photography, (bl)Ken Frick, (bc)StudiOhio, (br)Lloyd Lemmerman; **161**, Hickson & Associates; **162,163**, Doug Martin; **165**, (tl)Steve Lissau, (tc)Ken Frick, (tr)(b)StudiOhio; **166**, (t)Doug Martin, (b)BLT Productions; **167**, Hickson & Associates; **169**, (tl)StudiOhio, (tr)W. Geiersperger/The Stock Market, (b)Doug Martin; **170**, (l)Ken Frick, (r)Aaron Haupt; **171**, Doug Martin; **172**, John Barr/Gamma Liaison; **174**, StudiOhio; **175**, Doug Martin; **176**, Tim Courlas; **177**, © University of CA, Berkeley/Peter Arnold Inc.; **182**, (t)Culver Pictures, (b)William E. Ferguson; **183**, (t)Roger Burnard, (bl)Andrea Pistolesi/The Image Bank, (br)Marvin E. Newman/The Image Bank; **184**, (tl)(bl)Hickson & Associates, (tr)Bruno de Hogues/TSW, (br)Pictures Unlimited; **185**, S. J. Krasemann/Peter Arnold Inc.; **186-187**, Josquin Carrillo/Photo Researchers; **187**, StudiOhio; **188**, Doug Martin; **189**, StudiOhio; **190**, Dan McCoy/Rainbow; **191**, Philip A. Harrington/The Image Bank; **192**, (t)Barry Seidman/The Stock Market, (b)StudiOhio; **193**, Chip Clark; **194**, (l)Hansen Planetarium, (r)File Photo; **195**, Cobalt Productions; **196**, StudiOhio; **197,198**, Doug Martin; **199**, (l)Mark Lewis/TSW, (r)Grant Heilman; **200**, (l)Doug Martin, (r)StudiOhio; **201**, StudiOhio; **203**, Doug Martin; **204**, StudiOhio; **206**, NASA; **207**, Pictures Unlimited; **208,209**, Doug Martin; **211,212**, StudiOhio; **213**, Doug Martin; **214,216**, StudiOhio; **218**, Steve Strickland/Westlight; **219**, Doug Martin; **220**, StudiOhio; **221**, (t)StudiOhio, (c)Doug Martin, (b)KS Studios; **222**, (tl)Ed Degginger, (tr)Latent Image, (b)StudiOhio; **223**, (t)StudiOhio, (b)Doug Martin; **224**, StudiOhio; **225**, Doug Martin; **226**, Dan McCoy/Rainbow; **227,228**, StudiOhio; **229**, (t)Ken Frick, (b)Doug Martin; **230**, Doug Wilson/TSW; **231**, © Jon Brennis/Discover Publications 8/90; **232**, (t)James Westwater; (l)NASA, (r)Ed Degginger; **233**, (l,c)Ken Frick, (r)Ken Frick; **234**, (l)Colin Bell/TSW, (r)Doug Martin; **235,236**, Doug Martin; **237**, Alexander Lowry/Photo Researchers; **238-239**, Pete Saloutos/The Stock Market; **240**, File Photo, (inset)Jet Propulsion Laboratory; **241**, First Image, **242**, (t)StudiOhio; (b)Doug Martin; **243**, (t)Ken Frick, (b)The Smithsonian Institution; **244**, (t)StudiOhio, (b)Doug Martin, (b inset)First Image; **245**, William E. Ferguson; **247**, Doug Martin; **250**, (l)First Image, (r)Doug Martin; **251,252**, Doug Martin; **254**, (t)Ken Frick, (b)First Image; **255**, Stamp from the Collection of Prof. C. M. Lang, Photography by Gary Shulfer, Univ. of Wisconsin-Stevens Point: Russia 3608 (1969); **256**, Ed Degginger; **257**, (t)Doug Martin, (b)First Image; **260**, Lawrence Migdale/Science Source/Photo Researchers; **261**, Courtesy of IBM; **262**, Bill Pierce/Rainbow; **263,264**, Doug Martin; **266**, StudiOhio; **267**, Doug Martin; **268**, StudiOhio; **269**, Doug Martin; **270,273,274,275**, StudiOhio; **276,278**, Doug Martin; **279**, Franklin Bailey and Keith Stormo/© 1990 DISCOVER PUBLICATIONS; **280**, (l)StudiOhio, (r)K. G. Vock/Okapia 1989/Photo Researcher; **281**, Doug Martin; **282**, (l)W. W. Winter Ltd./The Derby Museum, (r)Doug Martin; **285,287**, Doug Martin; **288**, Bud Fowle; **290**, Pictures Unlimited; **292**, (t)Howard Bluestein/Photo Researchers, (b)FPG International; **293**, (t)Culver Pictures, (bl)Ed Degginger, (br)© The Cousteau Society; **294**, Doug Martin; **295**, Culver Pictures; **296-297**, Tim Courlas; **297**, Doug Martin; **298**, Toyofumi Mori/The Image Bank; **299**, Doug Martin; **300**, (t)FPG International, (tc)Light Source, (c)Tom Tracy Photography, (r)Ed Degginger; **301**, Charles Thatcher/TSW; **302**, Doug Martin; **303**, (l)ZEFA-U.K./H. Armstrong Roberts, (c)Doug Martin, (r)KS Studios; **304**, Doug Martin; **305**, (t)Doug Martin, (b)NASA; **306**, (l)Ken Frick, (r)Doug Martin; **307**, Mark Thayer; **308**, Ken Frick; **309**, Martin Bond/Photo Researchers; **311**, Annie Griffiths/Westlight; **312**, (t)Ken Frick, (b)Doug Martin; **313**, (t)Ken Frick, (b)Ben Simmons/The Stock Market; **314**, Dan McCoy/Rainbow; **315**, © Matt Meadows; **317**, (t)StudiOhio, (c)(r)Doug Martin; **318**, Ken Frick; **319**, Doug Martin; **320**, Manfred Kage/Peter Arnold Inc.;

321, Ken Frick; 322, KS Studios; 324, Ken Frick; 326, Doug Martin; 327, © Matt Meadows; 328, Doug Martin; 329, (t)R. Krubner/H. Armstrong Roberts, (c)Phil Degginger, (b)Doug Martin; 330, Ken Frick; 331, (t)Doug Martin, (b)Steve Strickland/Westlight; 332, (t)StudiOhio, (b)Ken Frick; 334, (l)Skinnet-Veron/Fig. Mag/Gamma Liaison, (r)Ken Frick; 335, (t)Ken Frick, (b)Doug Martin; 337, Doug Martin; 338, Mark N. Boulton/Photo Researchers; 339, Bruce Sampsel; 340, (t)Ken Frick, (l)CNRI/Science Photo Library/Photo Researchers, (r)Lab. of Molecular Biology, MCR/Science Photo Library/Photo Researchers; 341, (t)© Aaron Haupt, (b)Doug Martin; 342, Nelson Max/CCNL/Photo Researchers; 343, Ken Frick; 344, (t)Courtesy of the Simplesse Company, (b)Ken Frick; 345, Ken Frick; 346, Doug Martin; 348, Ken Frick; 350, ©Terry O'Neill/Woodfin Camp & Associates, (l&r)Ken Frick; 351, StudiOhio; 352, FPG International; 353, Ken Frick; 354, (t)Ed Degginger, (tr)(c)(br)Doug Martin; 355, (t)Tim Courlas, (b)Mike Devlin/Science Photo Library/Photo Researchers; 356, Bill Tronca/Tom Stack & Assoc.; 357, (t)The Smithsonian Institution, (bl)(br)Ken Frick, (c)BLT Productions; 358,359, Doug Martin; 360, William E. Ferguson; 361, Randall L. Schieber; 362, Ken Frick; 365, (t)StereoLithography is a proprietary product of 3D Systems, Inc., (b)Doug Martin; 366, Doug Martin; 367, (l)Dan McCoy, (r)Ken Frick; 368,369, Doug Martin; 370, Ken Frick; 372, (t)Michael Doolittle/Rainbow, (b)Carl Frank/Photo Researchers; 373, (t)Blaine Harrington III/The Stock Market, (c)Courtesy of General Motors, (b)The Bettmann Archive; 374, (tl)Doug Martin, (tr)Bill Weems/Woodfin Camp & Associates, (bl)Aaron Haupt, (br)Pictures Unlimited; 375, Photo from the Collection of Michele Tofoya; 376-377, Hans Pfletschinger/Peter Arnold Inc.; 377, Jeffrey M. Spielman/Stockphotos; 378, Steven Burr Williams/The Image Bank; 379, StudiOhio; 380, Ken Frick; 381, (t)Doug Martin, (tc)Ken Frick, (b)Doug Martin; 384, Bud Fowle; 385, Ken Frick; 386, Bill Ross/Westlight; 388, Doug Martin; 389, Latent Images; 392,393,394, Doug Martin; 395, Ken Frick; 398,399, Doug Martin; 401, Bud Fowle; 402, Guido Alberto Rossi/The Image Bank; 403, Ken Frick; 404, Culver Pictures; 405, Doug Martin; 407, ZEFZ-U.K./H. Armstrong Roberts; 408, NASA; 409, StudiOhio; 412, Doug Martin; 414, (t)Ken Frick, (b)Doug Martin; 416, Doug Martin; 417, Lawrence Hughes/The Image Bank; 418, (t)© Dawson Jones/Tony Stone Images, (b)Grant Heilman Photography; 420, Doug Martin; 422, Ted Rice; 424, Ron Watts/Westlight; 425, Doug Martin; 426, (t)StudiOhio, (b)Doug Martin; 428, Doug Martin; 429, (t)First Image, (b)Aaron Haupt; 430,431, Ken Frick; 434,435,437, Doug Martin; 438, Tom McHugh/Photo Researchers; 439, Runk/Schoenberger from Grant Heilman; 441, Doug Martin; 442, (t)Tim Courlas, (b)Doug Martin; 446, Doug Martin; 448, Tim Courlas; 449, Panographics/L. S. Stepanowicz; 450, (t)Tom Bean/The Stock Market, (b)Phil Degginger; 451, (t)The Bettman Archive, (c)Culver Pictures, (b)Francis Current/Photo Researchers; 452, (tl)Doug Martin, (tr)Roger Tully/TSW, (bl)Doug Martin, (br)Steve Weber/TSW; 453, The Salt Institute; 454-455, Courtesy of Dr. Otis Brown, Rosentiel School of Marine and Atmospheric Science, University of Miami; 455, NASA; 456, Doug Martin; 457, StudiOhio; 458, Steve Lissau; 463, KS Studios; 465, Ed Degginger; 467, Burton McNeely/The Image Bank; 469, Doug Martin; 471,472, StudiOhio; 473, John C. Beatty; 475,478(t), Doug Martin; 478(inset),480, StudiOhio; 482, Pete Saloutos/The Stock Market; 483, Shay/Gerard; 484, File Photo; 486, (tl)StudiOhio, (t)Tim Courlas, (b)StudiOhio; 487, (l) courtesy Owens Corning Fiberglass, (r)© Howard Sochurek/The Stock Market; 488, Bud Fowle; 489, StudiOhio; 490, Science Photo Library/Photo Researchers; 491, Doug Martin; 492,493,494, StudiOhio; 497, Doug Martin;

498,499,500, StudiOhio; 501, (t)E.R. Degginger/Earth Scenes, (b)Pictures Unlimited; 502, (l)Ed Degginger, (r)Kodak; 503, Vance A. Tucker; 504,505, Dan McCoy/Rainbow; 506, Doug Martin; 508, Allen Zak; 510, Cobalt Productions; 511,513, StudiOhio; 514, (t)Aaron Haupt, (b)Latent Images; 515, Doug Martin; 516,517, © Matt Meadows; 522, (l)Kurt Thorson, (r)Johnny Johnson; 525, Doug Martin; 526, NASA; 528, Cobalt Productions; 529, (t)StudiOhio, (b)Doug Martin; 531, (t)Lou Jones/The Image Bank, (b)Doug Martin; 532, John Feingersh 1988/The Stock Market; 533, Tom Tracy Photography; 534, Doug Martin; 536, StudiOhio; 538, (t)Garry Gay/The Image Bank, (b)Michael Parfit; 539, (t)Chuck O'Rear/Westlight, (c)The Bettmann Archive, (b)William E. Ferguson; 540, (tl)Ted Kawalerski/The Image Bank, (cl)Ken Frick, (tr)StudiOhio, (br)Ken Frick; 541, (l)Mike Fischer/National Museum of American Art, Washington, D.C./Art Resource, (r)National Museum of American Art, Washington, D.C./Art Resource; 542-543, D. W. Hamilton/The Image Bank; 543, Jean Marc Giboux/Gamma Liaison; 544, Hank Morgan/Rainbow; 545,547, StudiOhio; 548, Steven Burr Williams/The Image Bank; 550, © Thomas Ives/The Stock Market; 551, 1986 © Mark Gibson/The Stock Market; 555, (t)T. J. Florian/Rainbow, (b)StudiOhio; 556, Sheffield University/Science Photo Library/Photo Researchers; 557, StudiOhio; 559, Doug Martin; 560,561, Tim Courlas; 562, StudiOhio; 563, (t)Elaine Comer-Shay, (b)Doug Martin; 564, Doug Martin; 567, Mark Burnett; 570, Ken Frick; 572, Larry Hamill; 572(inset), Doug Martin; 573, Ken Frick; 574,575,576, Doug Martin; 579, P&G Bowater/The Image Bank; 580, StudioOhio; 582, Doug Martin; 585, Ken Frick; 587, Joe Bator/The Stock Market; 588, Lou Jones/The Image Bank; 589, © 1989 Makoto Iwafuji/The Stock Market; 590, Doug Martin; 592, StudiOhio; 594,595, Doug Martin; 596, StudiOhio; 598, Doug Martin; 599, (t)Ken Frick, (b)Doug Martin; 600, Doug Martin; 601, StudiOhio; 604, Hank Morgan/Rainbow; 605,606, StudiOhio; 607, The Bettmann Archive; 609, Hickson & Associates; 610,611, Doug Martin; 612, Hickson & Associates; 613, Doug Martin; 614, © Matt Meadows; 615, StudiOhio; 618, TSW; 619, Ken Frick; 620, Doug Martin; 622, Hank Morgan/Photo Researchers; 626, Ken Frick; 628, Ed Degginger; 629, StudioOhio; 630, Science Photo Library/Photo Researchers; 631, Patrice Loiez, CERN/Science Photo Library/Photo Researchers; 636,637,638, Doug Martin; 642, Steve Dunwell/The Image Bank; 643, Doug Martin; 646, Randall L. Schieber; 647, Doug Martin; 648, D.O.E./Science Source/Photo Researchers; 649, Light Source; 651, (t)© D.O.E./Science Source/Photo Researchers Inc., (b)Gordon Gahar/Lawrence Livermore Laboratory; 653, Doug Martin; 654, Dan McCoy/Rainbow; 655, Ed Degginger; 657, Mike Brown/Gamma Liaison; 658, Coco McCoy/Rainbow; 659, (b)Spencer Swanger/Tom Stack & Assoc., (r)Ed Degginger; 660, Barry Griffiths/Photo Researchers; 661, David W. Hamilton/The Image Bank; 662,664, Doug Martin; 666, (tl)David Sailors/The Stock Market, (bl)Courtesy of Westinghouse Electric Corporation, (r)Hickson & Associates; 667, (t)Blaine Harrington/The Stock Market, (b)First Image; 668, (tl)Doug Martin, (tr)(br)Hickson & Associates, (bl)Doug Martin; 669, Coco McCoy/Rainbow; 676, (t)file, (b)Ken Frick; 677, file; 678, (t)Ken Fick, (b)Lloyd Lemmerman; 679, file; 680, Ken Frick; 681, Doug Martin; 682,683,685,686, Ken Frick; 692, KS Studios; 693, (t)KS Studios, (b)© Aaron Haupt; 695, KS Studios; 697, (l)KS Studios, (r)©1993 Aaron Haupt; 698, ©Aaron Haupt; 700, KS Studios; 701, file photo; 702, ©Aaron Haupt; 703, (t)©Aaron Haupt, (b)©Will & Deni McIntyre/Photo Researchers Inc.; 705, KS Studios; 706, ©1982 Calvin Larsen/Photo Researchers Inc.